States economy provides a background for answers to these and other vital questions of fact and policy. Part I is a thoroughgoing analytical history of the more than a century in which fuel dominance shifted from wood to coal and from coal to oil and gas, and which saw the rise of electrification. Part II is an assessment of future demands for energy, built up from a detailed analysis of consumption within sectors and activities, such as households, transportation and industry, presented in full with voluminous appendix tables. Part III assesses future energy supply and presents the estimates against the background of a comprehensive survey of all recent estimates of the reserves and resources of the specific energy sources, coal, oil, gas and hydropower. This treatment provides a basis for evaluating future prospects for atomic and solar energy and other possible new sources on which explicit data are either scanty or nonexistent.

Sam H. Schurr is Director of the Energy and Mineral Resources Program at Resources for the Future, Inc. Bruce C. Netschert, Vera F. Eliasberg and Hans H. Landsberg are Research Associates, Resources for the Future, Inc., and Joseph Lerner is Industrial Specialist, Fuel and Energy Office, Office of Civil and Defense Mobilization.

Energy in the American economy, 1850—1975

Energy in the

1850

by Sam H. Schurr and
Bruce C. Netschert
with
Vera F. Eliasberg
Joseph Lerner
Hans H. Landsberg

1975

American economy, 1850-1975

an economic study of its history
and prospects

published for Resources for the Future, Inc.
by The Johns Hopkins Press, Baltimore

RESOURCES FOR THE FUTURE, INC., WASHINGTON, D.C.

Resources for the Future is a nonprofit corporation for research and education in the
development, conservation, and use of natural resources. It was established in 1952 with the
co-operation of The Ford Foundation and its activities since then have been financed by
grants from that Foundation. Part of the work of Resources for the Future is carried out
by its resident staff, part supported by grants to universities and other nonprofit organizations. Unless otherwise stated, interpretations and conclusions in RFF publications are
those of the authors; the organization takes responsibility for the selection of significant
subjects for study, the competence of the researchers, and their freedom of inquiry.

This book is one of RFF's studies in energy and minerals, which are directed by Sam
H. Schurr. Bruce C. Netschert, Vera F. Eliasberg, and Hans H. Landsberg are research
associates, as also was Joseph Lerner in the early stages of manuscript preparation. The
manuscript was edited by Virginia D. Parker.

STAFF EDITORS, Henry Jarrett and Vera W. Dodds

Preface and acknowledgements

This book is the product of a collaborative effort. Sam H. Schurr directed the entire work, wrote the Introduction and Summary (Chapter 1), and joined with Vera F. Eliasberg in writing Part I, and with Hans H. Landsberg in the writing of Part II. Joseph Lerner is the author of the projections made in Part II, and performed the underlying research. Bruce C. Netschert is the author of Part III and in addition served as editorial supervisor of the entire manuscript.

During the time this study was in progress we became indebted to many individuals and organizations. The following list of names, although extensive, does not begin to include all to whom we are grateful for advice, criticism, and other types of assistance.

Persons to whom we are indebted for supplying information or for reviewing drafts of Part I include: Moses Abramovitz, Stanford University and National Bureau of Economic Research; Jack Alterman, Bureau of Labor Statistics; Paul Boschan, consultant; Solomon Fabricant, New York University and National Bureau of Economic Research; Wilbert G. Fritz, Office of Civil and Defense Mobilization; Nathaniel B. Guyol, Standard Oil Co. of California; Richard C. Henshaw, Jr., Michigan State University; John Kendrick, George Washington University and National Bureau of Economic Research; William Parker, University of North Carolina; Robert Sadove, International Bank for Reconstruction and Development; Sidney Sonenblum, National Planning Association; Vivian E. Spencer, Bureau of the Census; Alan M. Strout, Harvard University; John A. Waring, consultant; Harold F. Williamson, Northwestern University.

For Part II the following individuals furnished information or reviewed drafts: Paul L. Ambelang, Interstate Commerce Commission; I. F. Avery, Bureau of Mines; Gertrude Bancroft, Bureau of the Census; R. H. L. Becker, Oil-Heat Institute of America; H. H. Blohm, R. L. Polk & Co.; F. S. Burroughs, *Oil Heating Marketing Reports*; W. L. Byrne, Ebasco Services, Inc.; John B. Campbell,

v

General Motors Corp.; M. B. Christensen, Bureau of Public Roads; D. S. Colby, Bureau of Mines; Marguerite E. Cook, McGraw-Hill Publishing Co.; J. A. Corgan, Bureau of Mines; A. T. Coumbe, Bureau of Mines; Larry H. Gall, Independent Natural Gas Association of America; Abraham Gerber, American Electric Power Corp.; Robert Gray, *Fueloil and Oil Heat;* Marvin Hoffenberg, Committee for Economic Development; D. H. Hottrill, Oil-Heat Institute of America; Lawrence D. Jennings, Federal Power Commission; Robert Johnson, United Air Lines; D. O. Kennedy, Bureau of Mines; J. G. Kirby, Bureau of Mines; Stanley V. Malcuit, Aluminum Company of America; Edward R. Martin, Gas Appliance Manufacturers Association, Inc.; Charles A. Mayer, The Asphalt Institute; Eugene B. McCaul, American Transit Association; Albert J. McIntosh, Socony Mobil Oil Co.; Charles E. Primoff, Office of the Assistant Secretary of Defense; Malcolm R. Rodger, Middle West Service Co.; E. L. Stern, Bureau of Public Roads; Mary B. Thornton, Federal Aviation Agency; J. A. Vaughan, Bureau of Mines; A. W. Winston, Dow Chemical Co.; and Meyer Zitter, Bureau of the Census.

We wish to thank in addition with respect to Part II those individuals and organizations who gave advice on topics not covered in this study but which were considered in the course of the research.

The list of those who furnished information for or reviewed Part III repeats the acknowledgements made in *The Future Supply of Oil and Gas,* the separate publication, in book form, of the oil and gas chapters. It also includes those whose helpful comments on that book were taken into account in subsequent revision of the oil and gas chapters, in addition to those who gave help on the other chapters of Part III. Individuals to whom we are indebted in Part III are: Paul Averitt, Geological Survey; Warren L. Baker, *World Oil;* Austin Cadle, Standard Oil Co. of California; N. K. Chaney, American Gas Association; Ira H. Cram, Continental Oil Co.; William E. Dean, Jr., Tennessee Valley Authority; Joel Dirlam, University of Connecticut; M. W. A. Edwards, Bituminous Coal Operators Association; Arno C. Fieldner, former Chief Fuels Technologist, Bureau of Mines; M. King Hubbert, Shell Development Co.; Robert G. James, Socony Mobil Oil Co.; Alfred E. Kahn, Cornell University; George A. Lamb, Pittsburgh Consolidation Coal Co.; S. G. Lasky, Department of the Interior; Walter J. Levy, W. J. Levy, Inc.; Harold Lubell, The RAND Corporation; Paul W. McGann, Bureau of Mines; H. M. McIntyre, Bonneville Power Administration; H. A. Montag, Joy Manufacturing Co.; Eger V. Murphree, Esso Research and Engineering Co.; Harry Perry, Bureau of Mines; C. J. Potter, Rochester and Pittsburgh Coal Co.; Wallace E. Pratt, consultant; Myles E. Robinson, National Coal Association; W. C. Schroeder, University of Maryland; P. R. Schultz, Blackwell Oil and Gas Co.; Philip Sporn, American Electric Power Corp.; Lyon F. Terry, Lehman Brothers; W. B. Tippy, Commonwealth Services, Ínc.; Paul D. Torrey, petroleum engineer; Lewis G. Weeks, Standard Oil Co. (New Jersey); Robert E. Wilson, Atomic Energy Commission; and V. M. Yevdjevich, Institute of Hydraulic Engineering, Belgrade.

Several individuals provided information or reviewed drafts of more than one of the parts: Richard J. Gonzalez, Humble Oil and Refining Co. (Parts I and III); Milton Lipton, W. J. Levy, Inc. (Parts I and II); Philip Mullenbach, Growth Industry Shares, Inc. (Parts I and II); Daniel Parson, American Gas Association (Parts I, II and III); Milton F. Searl, Atomic Energy Commission (Parts I and II); R. H. Smith, Pennsylvania Railroad Co. (Parts II and III); and Perry D. Teitelbaum, International Atomic Energy Agency (Parts I and II).

Credit to persons outside our organization would be incomplete without mention of the editing and graphics. We are indebted to Virginia Parker for the preparation of the entire manuscript for publication. The bringing of stylistic order to the work of several authors and to a very large mass of data was an editing task of more than ordinary difficulty. We also thank Jack Anglin and Russell Armentrout for their contributions in the graphics accompanying many of the tables.

Thanks are due also to our associates at Resources for the Future who have helped in many ways. We benefited from the comments of Orris C. Herfindahl who reviewed many sections of the manuscript. John Krutilla and Irving Fox gave helpful comments on the chapter dealing with hydropower. Selma Rein and Elizabeth K. Vogely assisted in numerous statistical aspects. Finally, we owe much to our secretary, Sally Nishiyama. Her meticulous attention to detail, and her unfailing good cheer in the face of what must have seemed to be an endless series of revisions contributed greatly to the satisfactory completion of the study.

It should, of course, be understood that the listing of an organization or individual does not necessarily imply agreement with or approval of the opinions and conclusions presented herein. The authors assume the entire responsibility for all statements and for possible inaccuracies in data and text.

Sam H. Schurr
April 15, 1960

Table of contents

TEXT TABLES

FIGURES

Energy in the American economy, 1850–1975

CHAPTER 1

Introduction and summary

The abundant use of energy, mainly from mineral fuels, is fundamental to the economic circumstances of mid-century America. With a population accounting for slightly more than 5 per cent of the world's total, the United States in the 1950's was consuming more than one-third of the world's energy supply. Thus, annual per capita consumption of energy in the United States—about nine tons of coal equivalent per person—was about six times the world's average.

Energy consumption in large amounts is typical of many different aspects of American life. As would be expected of the world's pre-eminent industrial nation, the United States uses much of its energy consumption to provide heat and power for mills and factories; indeed, industry is foremost among the energy-consuming sectors, accounting for some two-fifths of total energy consumption. We are also a nation on wheels; the transportation of goods and persons accounts for about one-fifth of all energy consumed, or about one-half as much as the amounts consumed by industry. That ubiquitous feature of present-day America—the private automobile—alone uses about one-half of all energy consumed in transportation, and 10 per cent of the country's grand total. The modern household with its energy requirements for heating, cooking, and numerous other household tasks consumes about one-fifth of the nation's energy total; counting private automobiles, households use about three-tenths of the nation's total energy consumption. Industry, transportation, and households together use almost four-fifths of all energy consumed, with the remainder accounted for mainly by commercial establishments, the government, and agriculture.

Today, as in the past, the United States draws on several primary sources to satisfy its heavy energy demands. In 1958, the most recent year for which complete data are available, 45 per cent of total consumption was supplied by oil (and natural gas liquids—NGL), somewhat more than 25 per cent by natural gas, slightly less than 25 per cent by coal, and just under 5 per cent by hydroelectric power. The heavy predominance of oil and gas in the energy total is

1

a relatively new development. As recently as the years just following World War II, coal accounted for about one-half the nation's total energy consumption, oil for about one-third, and natural gas for not much more than one-tenth. And going back even earlier, to the period after World War I, coal's share of the total stood at close to three-quarters, and oil and natural gas together at not much more than 15 per cent, with hydropower and fuel wood making up the remainder.

The transformation of the American economy from its earlier coal basis has involved the consumption in recent years of enormous amounts of oil and gas. In the single decade 1945-54, the consumption of oil and gas nearly equaled the total amounts of these commodities consumed in the United States up to that decade. The magnitude of these demands is often viewed as a matter of public concern because oil and gas reserves, as ordinarily measured, are short-lived when compared with annual rates of use. The reserves of oil, as usually measured, are only about twelve times the annual rate of production; those for natural gas are about twenty times its yearly output. As commonly measured, reserves of coal—the declining component of total energy consumption—are thousands of times greater than the annual rate of production. The United States is showing a decided preference for those energy commodities of which its natural resources are, by the usual measurements, most seriously limited.

Those who see in these facts the seeds of future problems point to postwar developments in energy prices and in the country's foreign trade position in energy materials. Between 1947 and 1955, the average value of crude oil and natural gas at the well (in constant dollar terms) rose 25 per cent and 50 per cent, respectively. During the same period, the average value of bituminous coal at the mine remained relatively stable. This is in sharp contrast to the record since the first years of the century, which shows coal prices rising appreciably while natural gas declined, and the price level in oil, despite fluctuations in the intervening years, remained virtually unchanged. (All prices are expressed in unit values at the mine or well, deflated by the index number of wholesale prices.)

The nation's changing foreign trade position in oil is popularly considered as an even stronger indicator of the fact that energy demands in the United States are running into resource limitations. The American oil industry during most of its history was the world's leading source of exports. Since World War II, it has come to rely increasingly on imports to satisfy the domestic market. By 1955, consumption of oil in this country exceeded domestic output by almost 15 per cent, and the relationship has been artificially maintained at approximately this level by governmental policy restricting oil imports. In terms of energy content, net imports of oil exceeded net exports of coal. Thus, the United States, which had been self-sufficient in energy for more than a century—ever since entering the mineral fuels age—had shifted by the mid-1950's to a net import basis for mineral fuels in the aggregate.

It is against this background of an apparent weakening in the domestic energy position of the United States that the present study was undertaken.[1] Its purpose

[1] Throughout this study the United States is defined to exclude Alaska and Hawaii, both of which achieved statehood after most of the computations had been completed.

was to provide a better understanding of the country's energy position: by study-ing the past to gain perspective on present circumstances, and by analyzing future prospects to see where the United States may be heading and the supply problems, if any, which may be encountered.

The historical part of the analysis, beginning with 1850, covers more than a century of the country's energy history, a period which has seen two almost complete transformations of the country's energy base, first from wood to coal, then from coal to oil and natural gas. This time span is long enough to include, for all practical purposes, the nation's entire history as a consumer of mineral fuels—the energy basis of our modern industrial civilization.

In selecting a target year for the assessment of future developments, the authors were strongly influenced by the fact that the uncertainties involved in such an exercise argue in favor of not looking too far ahead. Ideally, the nation's energy position and its prospects for the future should be subjected to periodic review, and it is our hope that the present study will provide the groundwork for updat-ing and reappraisal as the future unfolds.

Yet in planning this study, we felt it necessary to look ahead far enough so that there would be ample time to adopt those policy measures, in industry and government, which might be necessary to cope with supply problems that the future could bring. For example, it would be shortsighted to look ahead only five years, if the steps which would have to be taken to forestall a future prob-lem would take ten years to become effective. The selection of 1975—fifteen years beyond the publication of the book—as the date toward which this study looks, reflects our judgment that impending problems in energy supply, if any were to be disclosed, could be readily met through actions taken in the interven-ing fifteen years. With such potential sources as oil shale and nuclear energy waiting in the wings, each with a well-developed, although precommercial, tech-nology, it is even doubtful that as many as fifteen years would be needed to carry out such action programs as might be required.

In the sections which follow, some of the broad findings of the historical analysis made in Part I and the assessment of the future made in Parts II and III are summarized and evaluated. Reversing the sequence of these sections in the book, the projections of the future are considered first.

ENERGY CONSUMPTION AND AVAILABILITY IN 1975

The Broad Findings and Their Implications

Parts II and III of this volume evaluate the future energy position of the United States, both in terms of the country's growing needs and its ability to satisfy them from domestic resources. The over-all conclusion which follows from the analysis is this:

Viewed strictly from the standpoint of its natural resource position and with due allowance for technological advance, the United States in 1975 or thereabouts could satisfy its demands for all energy, and for each of the energy materials of which the total is composed, from domestic sources of supply at no significant increases in costs, except for those which might be brought about by a rise in the general price level.

This is not a forecast that the United States will satisfy its energy demands domestically—it is not even doing so at present—nor is it a recommendation that this country should choose to do so. Neither is it a forecast that energy prices (in constant dollar terms) will not rise. Policy decisions in industry and government, lying beyond the scope of this analysis, will be important in determining the actual course of events in these matters. We do not attempt to predict what these decisions will be, or to judge what they should be. Rather, our purpose is to provide basic information about energy consumption and availability which will be helpful in public debate and in guiding those responsible for reaching policy decisions.

Although this study undertakes no direct examination of policy issues, the broad conclusion—that energy demands between now and 1975 could be met from domestic resources at no significant increase in constant dollar costs—has a definite bearing on questions of national energy policy. Concern about the adequacy of domestic energy resources has played a major part in many important and highly controversial questions: to cite only two—the pace and scope of the national program for developing commercial atomic power, and the policy of restricting oil imports into the United States. Proponents of a larger and more determined effort to advance nuclear power technology have sometimes argued that such an effort is needed to obviate an impending energy supply problem in this country, or to forestall rising energy costs. Likewise, advocates of greater, or even unrestricted, freedom in the importation of crude oil and oil products into the United States have sometimes argued that such a policy is essential because of the inadequacy of the domestic resource position and the rapidly rising costs which would result from relying on native crude oil. The broad conclusion reached in this study, if substantially correct, greatly weakens the force of these arguments.

However, it would be dangerously incorrect to conclude that the broad finding of this study about the ability of domestic resources to meet demands over the next fifteen years provides all the information required for answering either of the policy questions mentioned, or others in which resource adequacy is a factor. Policy problems generally are too complex to allow a solution based on a single factor, even though it be an important one.

For example, in the matter of oil imports, even though United States oil resources could satisfy future needs at relatively constant costs, foreign oil is even today far cheaper than domestic oil, and the gap in comparative costs might widen in the future. Is it not, therefore, advantageous to obtain oil from the lower cost foreign sources of supply? If so, how, if at all, should foreign and domestic sources be balanced in order best to satisfy the political and security factors which must be considered in connection with so vital a commodity? Similarly, in respect to atomic development policy, decisions as to the speed and scope of the American program must consider the energy needs of other countries, and the international political implications of achieving and maintaining scientific and technical leadership in this field. Even in respect to domestic needs, a more determined research and development program might, in time, provide a cheaper source of energy than those now available. So with every question of policy, choosing among the alternatives involves the consideration of many different factors.

If the analysis of the future made in this study is near the mark, however, fears about the adequacy of domestic energy resources should be relegated to a secondary position in public discussion and eventual policy decision in energy matters. The number of remaining factors to be taken into account would still cover a broad field, but they could be considered calmly in an atmosphere which is not charged with apprehension about the country's ability to meet its future energy demands. The United States is *not* compelled to adopt particular policies because of impending resource exhaustion in any of the mineral fuels, or the threat of steeply rising costs. By virtue of the abundance of its remaining resources and the vitality of its technology, this country will continue to enjoy great flexibility in choosing among alternative energy policies.

.   .   .

Estimated Energy Consumption in 1975

Turning now to the particulars, total energy consumption is estimated in Part II of this study to rise by 88 per cent between 1955 and 1975. For the individual energy sources, estimated consumption in 1975 compares as follows with their consumption in 1955:

Energy source	Quantities		Percentage change 1955–75
	1955	1975	
Bituminous coal (million tons)	431	754	+ 74.9%
Anthracite (million tons)	20	14	− 30.0
Crude oil (million barrels)	2,774	5,154	+ 85.8
Natural gas liquids (million barrels)	260	769	+195.8
Natural gas (billion cubic feet)	9,614	19,881	+106.8
Hydropower (billion kilowatt hours)	120	265	+120.8
Consumed as electricity (billion kilowatt hours)	633	1,966	+210.6

The techniques and assumptions which were used in making these projections of future energy requirements are described in full detail in Part II; at this point a summary will help in evaluating the results yielded. The historical record of energy consumption in the United States, as analyzed in Part I and summarized later in this introduction, reveals that the growth in total energy use has not proceeded with regularity. It has not moved regularly either in terms of growth at a regular rate through time, or growth which bears a systematic relationship to the growth of population or the growth in gross national product (GNP). Therefore, the future was not estimated by projecting past trends in the growth of total energy, or in its relationship to population or GNP. The historical record has also been characterized by sharp shifts in the relative importance of different energy sources as components of the total. Diverse movements of the kind which have characterized the past history of energy are really impossible to explain except through a study, in some detail, of the pattern of energy use through time; in other words, an examination of the impact on energy consumption of the changing structure of the national product, of changes in consumer preference, of changes in technology, of changes in the thermal efficiency of energy use, etc.

Study of the past led, therefore, to selection of an estimating procedure which relates specific fuels to detailed changes within particular segments of the national economy. It was considered equally important, however, that the estimates for a particular fuel be made within the context of estimates for all other fuels so that the parts might ultimately yield a balanced picture of future developments. The estimates were therefore made using a procedure summarized in the following four steps:

1) For a base period (in our case 1955) information was assembled on the consumption of the various fuels and electricity in different activities and consuming sectors. This provided a detailed picture of the current pattern of energy use in the United States.

2) For the major energy-using categories, projections were made of their likely growth over the subsequent twenty years. To do this, information was assembled on their past trends and estimates from many sources as to their future prospects. All of this was done within an over-all framework provided by estimates of GNP, population, and a few other broad characteristics of the economy for the year 1975.

3) From the 1975 projections of levels of activity in the major energy-using categories, their energy consumption in 1975 was estimated in terms of specific fuels and electricity, with due regard to likely changes in efficiency of energy use and in their preferences as among the different fuels.

4) This yielded estimates of the 1975 consumption of the various fuels and electricity in the major consuming sectors, which were then aggregated to derive totals for each fuel and electricity, and a grand total for all energy. In addition to the totals shown above, Part II thus contains information on the estimated patterns of consumption, by energy-using sectors, for each fuel and electricity.

Two major assumptions underlying the consumption projections are essential to their understanding. In accord with the basic question to which the analysis of the future is directed—will energy supplies from domestic resources be adequate to meet demands consistent with a high rate of economic growth?—the 1975 energy consumption estimates are made for an economy that experiences a high rate of growth between 1955 and 1975. Both 1975 population, assumed at 233 million, and GNP, assumed at $857 billion (in 1955 prices, implying a 4 per cent annual average rate of growth between 1955 and 1975) are meant to be at the high end of the range of reasonable possibilities.

In addition, in estimating demand no significant relative price increases have been assumed for any of the energy sources. This assumption, as noted below, is a matter of methodology; it was not intended as a forecast. Actual prices in 1975, of course, will be determined by the interplay of supply and demand forces, as shaped by institutional factors, including governmental and business policies. As already indicated, the supply analysis leads to the conclusion that the several energy commodities could be made available in 1975 in sufficient amounts to meet estimated consumption at no significant increase in (constant dollar) costs; prices for any of them could, however, turn out to be higher or lower than in 1955 (in constant dollar terms) as a result of the policies adopted on oil imports, the regulation of natural gas prices, and other such factors.

Although Part II had as a main purpose the derivation of demand estimates meant to test the adequacy of supplies, it was designed to serve another purpose as well. A detailed approach was used not only to increase confidence in the results, but also in order to explore with care and in some depth the relationship between energy consumption and the levels of output and activity in the consuming categories. The latter aspect, which accounts for the size of the Appendix to Part II, was intended as a contribution to the study of energy economics whose value extends beyond supporting the specific estimates derived.

It should be noted that nuclear fuels have been excluded from the consumption estimates. Although there is every indication that nuclear energy will eventually become an important element in the energy position of the country, the uncertainties concerning the timing of this development are still very great. At present, there is little more than conjecture on the place of nuclear energy in 1975, although it is quite clear that its role will not be important by that time. Thus, estimates have been made only for the conventional energy sources. These are used later in this introduction as background against which the possible impact of nuclear energy, as projected by others, on the energy position in 1975 is examined.

.   .   .

Estimated Energy Availability in 1975

In analyzing the future availability of the several energy sources, Part III asked the following question: Given the nature and stock of natural resources, and the future level of technology which might be expected to exist, how much of each of the energy sources could be made available in 1975 from domestic resources at costs (in constant dollars) substantially the same as those in 1955? The research on this question and the analysis of future consumption, just described, went on simultaneously, but the subjects were studied separately by different members of our group. As a matter of methodology, we wanted consumption estimates which were made without regard to the findings on future availabilities, and availability estimates without regard to the findings on future consumption. Methodologically, the two sets of estimates were, however, linked by their parallel assumptions in respect to prices and costs: no significant relative increase in prices was assumed in deriving the consumption estimates, and the estimates of availability were limited to those supplies which could be produced at or near present-day costs.

How, then, does the availability of the several energy sources in 1975 compare with their estimated consumption? For every energy source, availability in 1975, as estimated in Part III, is large enough to satisfy consumption, as estimated in Part II. The compatibility between the independently derived estimates on the demand and supply side of the equation—one in terms of relatively constant prices, the other in relatively constant costs—lies behind the broad conclusion about the future presented above.

Information about natural resources and technology is basic to our analysis of the supply prospects for 1975, but the development of new information on either resources or technology was beyond the capacity of this study. Hence, it was necessary to rely on existing information on both subjects. What is new is the framework within which the information was analyzed; the treatment of technology as a dynamic variable in evaluating resources; and the inferences which are drawn in respect to supply prospects. These are summarized below for oil, natural gas, and coal, the three major energy sources. The results of a similar analysis of hydropower are not included in this summary because of the small place of hydropower in the total energy scene.

The research materials and approaches used to analyze future availability are significant by themselves, apart from the general conclusions they support. Because a major determinant of future domestic production is the natural resource position of the United States, Part III presents a systematic review of existing estimates of reserves and resources, the techniques used in making the estimates, and the assumptions and definitions of terms upon which they are based. An attempt is made to achieve greater comparability among the estimates by adjusting them in accord with a set of uniform concepts and definitions which are relevant to the problem of studying long-run supply prospects. This conceptual framework is set forth in Chapter 7. The accomplishments include the achievement of some terminological standardization where there has heretofore been much vagueness and ambiguity; but further progress and agreement along these lines are sorely needed.

The inadequacy of some of the fundamental information on which the analysis of future supply must rest is regrettable. This is particularly true of the basic information on the country's natural wealth in oil and gas. Current data on this score are subject to the most severe limitations, for they provide a measure only of "proved reserves," or discovered resources which can be recovered by currently utilized methods at current costs and prices. The nation's resource base of oil and gas includes much more than these proved reserves, but there is no systematic body of knowledge about these "unproved" resources and the costs at which they might be produced. No amount of careful sifting of existing information, nor of wisdom in determining the proper weight to be given to various factors likely to affect the situation in the future, can make up for this basic deficiency. Efforts to find feasible methods of learning more about the nation's energy resources deserve the earnest attention of both industry and government.

OIL AND NATURAL GAS

The most recent figures on the reserves of oil and gas in the United States are 31.7 billion barrels and 263 trillion cubic feet, respectively, as of the end of 1959. Expressed in relationship to production, these reserves amount to roughly twelve and a half years of production at the 1959 rate for oil and about twenty-one years of production for natural gas.

Reserve-production relationships of this type are often referred to in public discussions of the U.S. oil and gas position and sometimes lead to concern about the future. It is therefore important to understand exactly what the reserve figures measure. These reserve estimates are developed by the American Petroleum Institute and the American Gas Association and are not official U.S. government figures. They refer, as has been said, to discovered resources which can be recovered by currently utilized methods at current costs and prices. Thus, to begin with, they reflect the current state of discovery and production technology and the current economic setting. With improvements in technology or with changes in cost-price conditions, materials which do not qualify as reserves today—even materials already discovered but not considered recoverable—could constitute reserves in the future.

However, even within the limitations of current technology and present cost-price relations, the figures do not begin to represent a full accounting of resources because they refer only to those reserves which have been proved. Since the proving of reserves involves the drilling of wells—a costly process—enterprises in the oil and gas business do not engage in reserve-proving for its own sake, but only to the extent that this is required in connection with the growth of production. Hence, proved reserves, in a sense, are a working inventory of natural stocks, rather than a measure of the country's natural endowment of materials. That proved reserves are essentially a working inventory is seen also in the fact that the relationship between production and reserves tends to remain about the same year after year, at least in oil. As production drains off old proved reserves, and as more is needed, more oil is proved. Since production has been growing continuously, proved reserves of oil, in general, have also grown to keep pace with production increases.

If proved reserves figures do not tell very much about the future availability of oil and gas, what information can be used to throw light on this question? For the relevant information it is necessary to turn to estimates of the total amount of oil and gas which the underground resources of the United States (including the Continental Shelf) are expected to yield. Such estimates have been made by individual students of the subject, and their quality is not generally such as to inspire a high degree of confidence.

In contrast to reserves which have been proved, the estimates of the ultimate content of U.S. underground oil and gas reservoirs are inferred from geological evidence. This involves, first, a selection of areas of the United States which, by virtue of their geology, are considered favorable to the presence of oil and gas; and, second, the estimation of the oil and gas recoverable from these areas through the application of ratios between earth area or volume and oil and gas recoverability which have been derived from the experience of generally comparable geological areas already producing oil and gas. Even though this is an oversimplified description, it indicates how rough and unreliable the estimating process is; consequently, as might be expected, the conclusions reached by different students of the subject vary widely.

The eventual recovery of the quantities of oil and gas thus estimated implies two conditions: First, that through new discovery efforts the inferred oil and gas will be found. And, second, that, if found, the amount recovered from the underground reservoirs would bear the same relationship to the amount the reservoirs contain as has been the case in oil and gas fields already producing—in other words, that recovery efficiency and, therefore, recovery technology will not change significantly. The latter point is important because at present only one-third of the oil contained in reservoirs, on the average, is recovered.

The various estimates which others have made of the "ultimate reserves" of oil and gas in the United States are critically reviewed in Part III. From these estimates, and disregarding technological limits, a resource-base figure for future oil recovery is derived which is substantially higher than any of the existing estimates of ultimate reserves. Crude oil available for future recovery in the United States (including present proved reserves, the currently unrecoverable content of known reservoirs, and the total content of undiscovered reservoirs) is estimated to be on the order of 500 billion barrels. On a similar basis, natural gas available for future recovery is estimated to be on the order of 1,200 trillion cubic feet. Taken together with expected technological improvements in discovery and production, which are discussed in detail, Part III concludes that crude oil availability in 1975 could be on the order of 6 billion barrels and natural gas availability on the order of 22.5 trillion cubic feet. (The 1975 consumption estimates, derived in Part II, are 5.2 billion barrels and 19.9 trillion cubic feet, respectively.)

A word of warning is in order. The undiscovered resources included in the total resource base are very great. Whether they will be found depends, in part, on advances in technology, but also on the incentives which will exist for searching for oil in the United States. The latter condition depends, in turn, upon such matters as the oil import policy of the United States. Oil, even now, can be produced more cheaply abroad than in this country, and though the United States could produce all it needs domestically (according to these estimates) the policy on imports will, in fact, determine how much is produced domestically. If domestic exploration and development efforts are not maintained at a high enough level between now and 1975 to build up the necessary productive capacity, it would be impossible in that year to achieve the availability figure estimated in Part III, even if the United States should, at that time, want to do so.

It should be noted, though, that only part of the gap between proved reserves of oil and the resource-base estimate consists of resources which have yet to be discovered. About 175 billion barrels of the difference (which is almost six times the proved reserves of oil in 1959) consist of discovered resources which cannot be economically recovered by current techniques, hence are not included in proved reserve figures. The 1975 availability estimate assumes that so-called secondary recovery technology and practice, involving the restoration or augmentation of reservoir pressure through various techniques, will undergo important advances during this period and play a large part in facilitating increases in domestic oil production drawn from these previously unrecoverable resources.

Alternative domestic resources, available for both oil and gas, are not included in the foregoing estimates. Technical processes for deriving substitutes for crude oil from shale and substitutes for natural gas from coal are relatively far advanced. Investigations by private companies of the production of oil from shale, following through on work originally undertaken by the U.S. Bureau of Mines, have progressed through the operation of pilot plants. The costs at which these substitute sources can be produced is still in doubt, more so for synthetic gas than for shale oil, and the time at which they might become commercially feasible on a broad scale cannot be estimated. Nevertheless, they add an enormous potential to U.S. oil and gas resources. Rocks that can be termed oil shale occur in great quantity in this country, and although their total oil content has not been estimated, the U.S. Geological Survey has estimated that the shale oil resources of Colorado alone total about 900 billion barrels (almost twice the estimated resource base of crude oil), of which about 100 billion barrels seem recoverable with current technology and could even be made available in the form of gas. As for gas from coal, the coal deposits in the United States are so extensive that they constitute an even larger substitute gas resource.

COAL

For coal the estimates of resources are official figures of the U.S. Geological Survey. Unlike oil and natural gas, for which the most widely quoted figures refer to proved reserves, these estimates go well beyond current economic and technical limits. Not that they measure the total coal content of the earth's crust, but they do include so much more coal than has actually been "proved" that they are far along toward being a measure of the total resource base.

The most recent estimates released by the U.S. Geological Survey, as summarized in Part III, place the total coal resources of the United States at almost 2 trillion tons, of which the Survey considers almost 1 trillion tons to be recoverable. The Survey indicates that only about 5 per cent of these resources consists of "measured" amounts, by which they mean reserves for which sufficient information is available to render the error of estimate 20 per cent or less. The remaining 95 per cent is what the Survey calls "indicated" and "inferred" reserves, based partly on measurement, but largely on more general geologic information.

In comparison with the estimated recoverable figure of 1 trillion tons, the 1959 production rate would last for more than 2,000 years. Or, looked at another way, estimated cumulative production between 1955 and 1975 would come to about 12 billion tons, an amount easily supported by this vast resource figure. Such resources are clearly enormous, and in terms of quantity only there is no question about the ability of the coal industry to meet any conceivable demand for many decades. What portion of these resources could, however, be made available at current costs? This problem is approached in Part III from the direction of technology.

One area of rapid recent technological advance is strip mining, in which productivity per man-day currently averages about twenty-two tons, versus nine tons in underground mining. For most of the postwar period, strip mining has accounted for one-quarter, or slightly less, of total annual coal production. The recent development of so-called "supergiant" shovels, together with such refinements as the bucket-wheel excavator, points toward an increase in strip mine output as a percentage of the total, hence toward an increase in over-all productivity. (Some observers voice concern over the adequacy of "strippable reserves." But the new technology itself demonstrates how open-ended these "reserves" are. Current equipment can handle overburden up to 120 feet in thickness; only a few years ago, eighty feet was the maximum feasible thickness.)

But the greatest opportunities for improved productivity lie underground. Here a fundamental change in technology is under way in the form of the continuous mining machine. This change consists in the substitution of a single continuous process for extracting coal from the seam in place of a process involving several steps repeated in sequence. Introduced around 1950, the continuous miner now accounts for approximately 20 per cent of total underground production. The reduction in manpower with the continuous miners and the consequent rise in labor productivity have been dramatic. At present, however, the use of the machine is still in the early commercial stage; it is being used in mines and with auxiliary equipment, such as haulage, that were not designed to take advantage of it. When, in a few years, mines designed for the continuous miner are producing an appreciable percentage of total underground coal output, the really large increases in efficiency should be obtained. The most optimistic in the industry speak of a doubling or tripling in the productivity level.

"Preparation," the other area in which technology promises important gains, consists in the utilization of various methods to reduce the proportion of impurities in the mined coal and thus provide a delivered product of higher quality. Advances in preparation have made it possible, for example, to supply coke ovens with a satisfactory raw material produced from coal resources of lower and lower quality (higher sulfur and ash). Some 60 per cent of all bituminous coal mined is now treated in preparation plants, and the technique is thus available on a large scale to deal with the problem of declining resource quality.

Unlike the conclusions reached for oil and natural gas, those for coal in Part III do not include a quantitative estimate of availability in 1975. The vast physical extent of the coal resource base combined with the promising outlook for technology lead to the conclusion that availability to meet any foreseeable demands between now and 1975 should be possible with negligible increases, if any, in cost, or perhaps even at a slightly lower cost than at present.

ENERGY CONSUMPTION AND NATIONAL GROWTH: PAST AND PROSPECTIVE

The estimates, just summarized, carry into the future the historical process which in this study has been traced back to the middle of the nineteenth century. The future of energy consumption, as projected in Part II, therefore can be examined against the broad historical perspective provided in Part I. As already mentioned, study of the past has engendered a lack of confidence—reflected in the methodology of Part II—in the extrapolation of broad trends relating over-all energy consumption to the passage of time, the growth of population, or the increase in GNP. The behavior of such relationships in the past, therefore, is summarized from Part I, in order to explain this mistrust in their suitability for predictive purposes. In addition, the projections of the future given in Part II are compared with what has happened to total energy consumption and its components in the past.

.   .   .

The Past Growth of Energy Consumption, Population, and Gross National Product

TOTAL ENERGY CONSUMPTION

In Chapter 4, which sets forth in much detail the relationship between energy consumption and economic growth over a 105-year period, alternative statistical series are employed to measure total energy consumption in the United States. Two energy totals are required for much of the analysis: one including the mineral fuels, hydropower, and fuel wood; the other covering the mineral fuels and hydropower, but excluding fuel wood. In addition, for certain aspects of the analysis it was also necessary to introduce measures of direct waterpower and windpower. However, the more restricted purposes of this summary are adequately served by using a shorter time period than the 105 years covered in Part I, and by concentrating attention on one of the energy totals employed—that excluding fuel wood, but covering mineral fuels and hydropower, the energy sources of a modern industrial society.

Total energy use, thus defined, was in 1955 about five and a quarter times as large as it had been in 1900 (see Figure 1), which is equivalent to an average

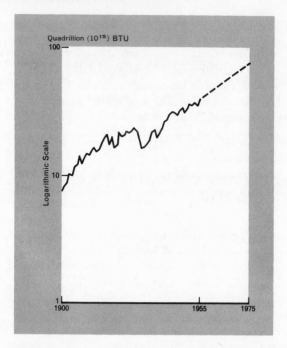

Figure 1. Energy consumption (mineral fuels and hydropower), 1900–1955 and estimated 1975.

annual growth rate of 3.1 per cent. Has this long-period increase been reached through a relatively steady growth through time? If this were the case, there would be support for the view that the average rate of growth which has characterized the past would be appropriate for estimating total energy consumption for future time periods.

The following figures, dealing with changes in the growth of total energy consumption within shorter time periods (decades, except for 1950–55), shed light on this question of regularity in growth:

Period	Per cent change	Average annual rate of change
1900–10.	+95.5%	+6.9%
1910–20.	+33.6	+2.9
1920–30.	+12.6	+1.2
1930–40.	+ 7.3	+0.7
1940–50.	+42.3	+3.6
1950–55.	+16.9	+3.2

A wide dispersion is evident, ranging from a 0.7 per cent average annual rate of increase in the decade 1930–40 to 6.9 per cent in 1900–10. Not only is the range among decade changes considerable, but there is no evidence of a clustering around any particular rate of change. On the basis of this and similar statistical evidence, we concluded that the simple extrapolation of over-all growth rates derived from past experience would be unwarranted in the projection of future energy consumption.

TOTAL ENERGY CONSUMPTION PER CAPITA

What degree of regularity do historical changes in total energy consumption exhibit when they are converted to a per capita basis? Is the growth in energy consumption systematically related to the increase in the country's population? The amount of energy consumed per person in the United States in 1955 was almost two and a half times that in 1900 (see Figure 2). But again, shorter period changes in per capita energy consumption are instructive in showing that the United States has not followed a steady path in achieving the change:

Period	Per cent change	Average annual rate of change
1900–10	+61.0%	+4.9%
1910–20	+15.9	+1.5
1920–30	− 2.7	a
1930–40	a	a
1940–50	+24.0	+2.2
1950–55	+ 7.3	+1.4

a Negligible.

Energy consumption per capita grew by 61 per cent in the decade 1900–10, rose less than a quarter as much in the following decade, changed scarcely at all between 1920 and 1940, grew again between 1940 and 1955, but at quite different rates in the subperiods within the fifteen-year period.

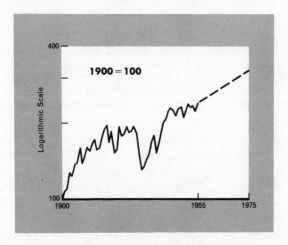

Figure 2. Index of per capita energy consumption, 1900–1955 and estimated 1975.

Here, too, we concluded that the extrapolation of growth rates in total energy consumption per capita, drawn from past experience, would be unjustified in projecting future energy consumption in relation to an assumed growth in population.

TOTAL ENERGY CONSUMPTION PER UNIT OF GNP

On a common-sense basis, one might expect that the relationship between the growth in energy use and the growth in the country's total output of goods and services (the GNP) would show a high order of regularity. Energy is so pervasive an ingredient in the production of all goods that it seems reasonable to expect that energy use should move in unison with over-all production.

To test this belief, energy consumption for every fifth year between 1880 and 1955 was divided by a series measuring GNP in constant (1929) dollars. The results, converted to index number form (1900 = 100) and shown in **Figure 3**,

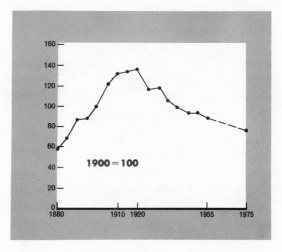

Figure 3. Energy consumptian (mineral fuels and hydropower) per unit of gross national product, five-year intervals, 1880–1955 and estimated 1975.

do not show regularity in this relationship, but instead reveal the existence of two diverse long-period movements divided by the 1910–20 decade. The period from 1880 to 1910 is characterized by persistent increases in the input of energy per unit of GNP; between 1920 and 1955, the record tends to be one of persistent decline in the ratio of energy to GNP. The decade 1910–20 appears to be transitional between these two distinct periods. Beginning with 1880, when the long upward swing of energy relative to GNP started, the increase to 1910 was 133 per cent, equivalent to an average rate of increase of 2.9 per cent per year. Between 1920 and 1955, the decline in the input of energy relative to

GNP has been on the order of 35 per cent, equivalent to an average rate of decrease of about 1.2 per cent per year.

The existence of two distinct movements in the relationship between energy consumption and the total output of the national economy is one of the most interesting aspects of the entire historical record. Accordingly, much attention is devoted in Chapter 4 to an analysis of the underlying factors. The hypotheses which are there advanced do not constitute a complete or total explanation of the long upswing and subsequent downswing in energy consumption relative to GNP. However, the combination of factors which appears to account for the downswing since the first World War—changes in the structure of national output, improvements in the over-all productive efficiency of the economy, increases in the thermal efficiency of energy use, and the growth of electrification—seems to point also to a future continuation of the declining trend.

However, this knowledge is still far from telling us how much slower the growth rate of energy consumption might be than that of GNP. As the following figures indicate, the pattern of five-year declines between 1920 and 1955 is quite erratic, and although the direction is persistently downward, there are still brief spurts in which energy consumption relative to GNP rises:

Period	Per cent change	Average annual rate of change
1920–25	−14.5%	−3.1%
1925–30	+ 1.5	+0.3
1930–35	−10.8	−2.3
1935–40	− 5.4	−1.1
1940–45	−11.9	−2.5
1945–50	+ 4.3	+0.9
1950–55	− 4.0	−0.8

It may be concluded, therefore, that in projecting the future a simple extrapolation of total energy use declining at a fixed rate relative to GNP also would not be justified on the basis of the historical evidence.

Future Estimates Compared with Past Developments

TOTAL ENERGY

Findings such as those just summarized played an important part in the choice of the approach used in Part II in which estimates of future energy consumption are made in relation to projected changes in energy-using sectors and activities, instead of by extrapolating broad trends. As indicated earlier, however, estimates of 1975 population and GNP provided the broad framework within which the detailed estimates were derived. It is of interest, therefore, to compare the resultant estimate of future total energy consumption with the assumed increases in population and GNP with which the estimating procedure began.

When the various energy commodities which have been separately estimated are added together in terms of British thermal units (Btu's) contained, total consumption is found to grow by 88 per cent between 1955 and 1975. (See Figure 1 for a comparison of past growth with estimated future growth.) Thus, the growth in energy consumption between the two years turns out to be more than twice as great as the assumed 41 per cent increase in population (from 165 million in 1955 to 233 million in 1975), but falls short of the 119 per cent increase assumed for GNP (from $391 billion in 1955 to $857 billion in 1975, both in 1955 prices). Thus, as in the past, percentage changes in total energy consumption do not move in unison with changes in population or GNP. The one persistent trend that was noted in the historical record since the end of World War I—for energy consumption to grow at a less rapid rate than the total national output—will continue in the future, according to these estimates. Between 1955 and 1975, the quantity of energy consumed per unit of GNP is estimated to fall by 15 per cent.

The average annual rates of change between 1955 and 1975 implied in the energy total estimated for the latter year are:

Total energy consumption ....+ 3.2 per cent
Per capita energy consumption ....+ 1.4 per cent
Energy consumption per unit of GNP ....— 0.8 per cent

Although the estimates were not made by extrapolating past over-all trends, these three rates turn out to be the same as those which obtained during the period 1950–55. This could be taken as an indication that the rates for 1950–55 could have been applied in the first place, thus saving much effort in estimation. But this would be a judgment made after the fact; it would not be possible to know in advance that the average annual rates for the 1950–55 period were to be preferred to other rates that could have been selected from other past time periods. The analysis, moreover, was primarily concerned with the individual energy sources and, as explained in the following section, extrapolation of their 1950–55 rates of change would have yielded estimates of 1975 consumption significantly different from those obtained with the methodology employed.

THE INDIVIDUAL ENERGY SOURCES

The consumption estimates for the individual energy sources were shown earlier. Among the fuels, the highest rate of growth is estimated for natural gas—an increase of more than 100 per cent between 1955 and 1975, from 9.5 trillion cubic feet to almost 20 trillion cubic feet. The next highest rate of growth—95 per cent—is for the liquid hydrocarbons taken together: oil with an 86 per cent increase between 1955 and 1975—the absolute change being from 3 billion barrels in 1955 to almost 6 billion in 1975; and NGL with a 196 per cent increase, from 260 to 279 million barrels. Bituminous coal is next in order, increasing by almost 75 per cent in the twenty-year period from 1955 to 1975, with tonnage estimated to increase from 431 to 754 million short tons.

Anthracite is the only one of the primary energy sources estimated to suffer an absolute decline—from 20 million tons in 1955 to 14 million tons in 1975, a decline of 30 per cent. By far the fastest rate of growth is that estimated, not for any one of the primary energy sources, but for electricity, which shows a growth from 633 billion kilowatt hours in 1955 to almost 2,000 billion in 1975— more than a 200 per cent increase. Hydropower, a component of the electricity total, is estimated to grow by 120 per cent. These estimates of future growth in the individual components of total energy consumption are compared with the past record in Figures 4 through 8.

The future patterns of growth, according to these estimates, are in sharp contrast with those of the past in that the estimated future growth rates for oil, natural gas, and bituminous coal are not nearly as far apart as in the past. This change is clearly visible in the following figures, which compare percentage changes in the consumption of coal, oil (including NGL), and natural gas for selected years between 1920 and 1955, and between 1955 and the estimates for 1975:

Energy source	1920–55	1935–55	1940–55	1955–75
Bituminous coal	− 17%	+ 19%	− 2%	+ 75%
Oil (including NGL)	+ 565	+209	+129	+ 95
Natural gas	+1,008	+369	+238	+107

The wide differences among the three in their percentage changes for 1940–55, 1935–55, and 1920–55, when coal either fell or, at best, rose slightly, while oil and gas experienced large percentage gains, are in sharp contrast to the estimated percentage changes for 1955–75.

A complete explanation of the factors accounting for the abrupt change in trends can be had only through a detailed examination of the data analyzed in Parts I and II. However, it is possible to identify one set of circumstances which provides much of the explanation for the reversal in the bituminous coal trend and for what, by the standards of recent history, must be called a remarkable closeness in the expected rates of growth of bituminous coal, oil, and natural gas. One important element in this outcome is the high rate of growth estimated for electricity between 1955 and 1975. This produces a substantial effect on the coal estimate because much of the growth in electricity generation is expected to be fueled by bituminous coal in the future, as it has been in the past.

In the recent past, though, the growing use of coal by electric utilities could not offset the great tonnage losses experienced by coal in railroad locomotive power and in space heating, as the following figures on coal consumption show:

Year	Railroads	Space heating	Electric utilities	Total of these uses
		(million tons)		
1940	85	124	49	258
1950	61	114	88	263
1955	15	68	141	224

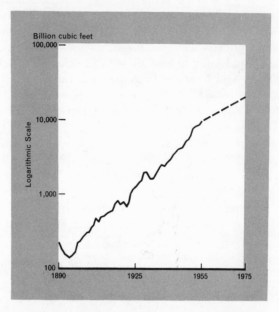

Figure 4.   Marketed production of natural gas, 1890–1955 and estimated 1975.

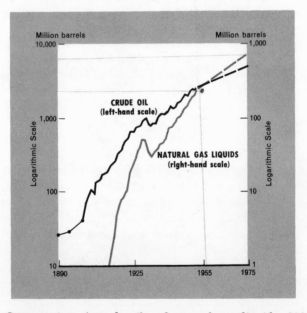

Figure 5.   Consumption of crude oil and natural gas liquids, 1890–1955 and estimated 1975.

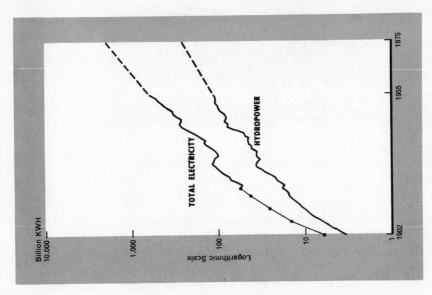

Figure 7. Electricity and hydropower, 1902–1955 and estimated 1975.

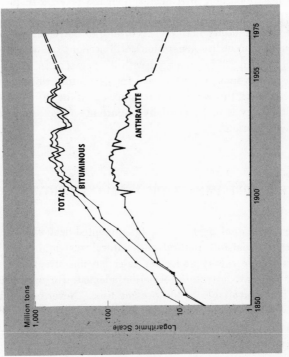

Figure 6. Coal consumption, 1850–1955 and estimated 1975.

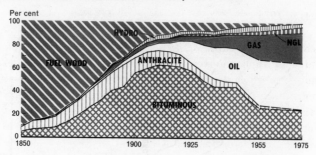

Figure 8. Specific energy sources as percentages of aggregate energy consumption, five-year intervals, 1850–1955 and estimated 1975.

The analysis in Parts I and II shows, however, that the major inroads of gas and oil into coal's railroad and residential markets have already been made, and that their future gains in these markets will no longer be large enough to offset coal's estimated greatly expanded use in connection with the growth of electric power generation. This explains the estimated substantial increase for bituminous coal compared with its decreases in the past. As for oil and natural gas, these fuels will no longer benefit as much as they have in the past from coal's loss of customers in railroading and household use, and consequently their growth in the future is expected to be less rapid than in the past.

Yet it is important to remember that the reversal in the trend for bituminous coal depends, in the final analysis, on its ability to hold on to a very large share of the electric utility market. According to our estimates, electricity production (including non-utility generation) will account for 60 per cent of the consumption of coal in 1975, compared with 37 per cent in 1955. Thus, anything that seriously cuts into the use of coal for generating electricity could, according to these estimates, throw the industry once again into its previous pattern of decline. Atomic energy is one potentially important source of competition to coal in the electricity market.

THE POSSIBLE IMPACT OF ATOMIC ENERGY

The estimates of the future so far presented deal with the conventional sources of energy—coal, oil, natural gas, natural gas liquids, and hydropower. They neglect atomic energy and other so-called unconventional energy sources, such as solar energy, because information adequate for appraising their future prospects is not available at the present time. Nevertheless, in view of the great promise which atomic energy, in particular, is said to hold for the future, it is useful to engage in some speculation as to its possible effects on the picture of the future which this study presents.

Use Prospects in 1975

Atomic energy can be utilized for peaceful purposes in a number of ways. One wide area of application, relatively well advanced, is the non-energy use of radioisotopes, in which the radioactivity can be utilized for counting, measuring, and controlling; for radiography; for sterilization and, perhaps, food preservation; and for tracing processes in industry, agriculture, and research. Such uses are, however, irrelevant to the present study, for by and large they have insignificant effects on the use of conventional energy sources. It is also possible to use radioisotopes as a source of heat or as a small-scale source of electricity, as in the "atomic battery." But these uses also can be disregarded here, since there is no evidence that they will become sufficiently large by 1975 to permit any significant energy input into the economy from this source.

The nuclear reactor can therefore be taken as the only bulk source of atomic energy that warrants consideration. In a reactor, the energy becomes available in two forms—heat and radiation. It is theoretically possible to use such radiation in many industrial processes, especially in the chemical industry, to supplant operations currently carried out with the use of heat. But again, there is no evidence at present that such use will be established as practicable and economic on a significant scale by 1975, hence the consideration of the impact of nuclear energy on the energy use pattern described in Part II can be restricted to applications of reactor heat.

Theoretically, heat generated in the nuclear reactor could be applied in all the uses to which heat is now put: electricity generation, transportation, process heat in industry, space heating, etc. However, the practical opportunities, as currently envisaged, are more limited. To evaluate these, it is necessary to devote a few paragraphs to the essential characteristics of atomic power and how they differ from those of the conventional fuels.

The heart of the difference is contained in a simple comparison: one pound of nuclear fuel is the equivalent of about 1,300 tons of coal. The release of nuclear energy means the advent of fuels with an energy concentration so enormous that in economic terms it may be said to usher in the era of weightless fuels. Hence the often expressed view that the use of atomic energy will tend to minimize geographic differences in energy cost that are so pronounced with present-day energy sources, for which transportation charges from source to consuming site are often much greater than the mine price of the fuel.

There is, however, an important offsetting factor to this mobility of the fuel. Whereas coal, oil, and gas can be burned in a furnace that occupies a corner of a home basement, and gasoline can be burned in a small engine that fits into a lawn mower or under the hood of an automobile, the controlled release of atomic energy for heat and/or power requires large installations. Large dimensions are to a considerable degree dictated by the need for shielding to contain the lethal radiation emanating from the reactor. From an economic standpoint, moreover, installations must be large in order to achieve low unit operating costs.

Thus, atomic energy combines a uniquely mobile fuel source and a cumbersome and costly apparatus in which to obtain and use it. The size of the apparatus immediately limits the uses to which atomic energy can be put, particularly in transportation, where mobility creates a need for compactness. Trucks and automobiles must be ruled out on size limitations and also on safety grounds. Locomotives are a borderline case, as yet not promising enough to have attracted much research and development attention. These applications, which are the major fuel users within transportation, are unlikely to meet competition from nuclear energy within the period covered by this study. A major segment of the market for liquid fuels, therefore, is free of the threat of competitive inroads from atomic energy.

The use of atomic power in maritime transportation, on the other hand, cannot be dismissed. An all-nuclear navy by 1975 (all combat ships, that is) has been an announced policy goal, and the enormous military advantages of such vessels have been convincingly demonstrated by the first atomic submarines. Consequently, the estimate of fuel oil consumption in 1975, made in Part II, reflects the assumption that the U.S. Navy in that year will be largely nuclear as far as combat ships are concerned. This constitutes the sole exception to our decision to make no allowance for atomic energy in 1975.

Atomic-powered merchant vessels—especially tankers and ore carriers—also offer attractive possibilities in theory, but unlike the military applications, where cost considerations are of secondary importance, these applications have yet to be proved through a period of trial and development. In any case, total marine fuel use is not important enough (less than 2 per cent of estimated energy consumption in 1975) to make much of a dent in the energy consumption patterns estimated for 1975—even in the unlikely event that atomic power were to be widely adopted.

Most attention and hope for atomic energy centers on its use for central electric power stations, in which the nuclear reactor merely replaces the furnace in the conventional thermal plant. This is the application to which most of the research and development on peaceful uses of atomic energy is being directed, and the one that has the greatest potential for affecting the future level of demand of the conventional energy sources within the time period covered in this study. Speculations here about the quantitative impact of atomic energy on the 1975 energy consumption estimates therefore will be confined to nuclear fuels as a source of electric power.

Although several large central stations generating nuclear power are now in existence—including, in the United States, the Shippingport installation near Pittsburgh—and additional ones are being built, these plants are all part of research and development programs for achieving competitive atomic power. The attainment of costs that are low enough to be competitive with those in conventionally fired electric power stations is still an objective, not a reality.

The forecasting of nuclear energy use in central power stations is, therefore, essentially a matter of guessing how many years it will take for these research and development programs to reduce nuclear costs to a competitive level. The time period depends, of course, on such factors as the vigor with which the development programs are pursued, the magnitude of the technological difficulties to be overcome, the costs of the competitive sources, etc.; and various estimators differ in their evaluation of these factors. The consensus, if any, which emerges is that competitive power—and only in regions with high energy costs, at that—is not likely to be achieved in the United States before the late 1960's.

The estimates also have been examined in order to form an idea as to the most reasonable expectation for the level of nuclear power production in the United States in 1975. It is, of course, difficult to strike a balance on a question such as this, in which some of the essential facts do not yet exist and the climate of opinion is so changeable. In our judgment, however, the most reasonable guess to be drawn from the available estimates is that atomic power might, in 1975, account for some 10 to 15 per cent of total electricity production, as estimated in this study. From present indications, this guess is, if anything, on the optimistic side, but the outlook could change as development proceeds.

Assessment of the impact of this level of atomic energy production on our estimates for the conventional sources is a matter of simple arithmetic. In Part II, electricity production is estimated to account for almost 25 per cent of all primary energy sources consumed in 1975. Thus, atomic fuels would, on this basis, replace between 2.5 and 3.75 per cent of the total of conventional energy sources estimated to be used in that year.

However, its effects would fall unevenly on the different fuels, with coal absorbing the major impact because coal, according to our estimates, will account for almost two-thirds of all the primary energy sources consumed for electricity generation in 1975. Assuming that nuclear energy's use were entirely at the expense of coal—thereby getting a measure of its maximum possible impact on the fuel which is so closely tied to the expected growth of electric energy—the quantity of coal replaced in 1975 would be between 75 million and 110 million tons. If this were to happen, the estimated bituminous coal consumption in 1975 would be between 645 million and 680 million tons, instead of the 754 million tons estimated in Part II, and the percentage increase between 1955 and 1975 in bituminous coal would be between 50 per cent and 58 per cent, instead of the estimated increase of 74 per cent.

This is an impact of some magnitude. It is not nearly enough to upset the estimated upward trend in bituminous coal between 1955 and 1975—a reversal in movement which, as already noted, provides the outstanding contrast between the future estimates and past energy trends. But it is enough, surely, to constitute an ominous portent for bituminous coal in the years between 1975 and the end of the century.

· · ·

The Broader Economic and Social Impact of Atomic Power

While the spectacular harnessing of atomic power has already revolutionized military strategy, and thereby fundamentally altered concepts of war and the conditions of peace, the effects to date of the peaceful applications of atomic energy are of small significance. Partly this is because the development of the peaceful applications of atomic power has lagged well behind its military uses. Yet, looking toward the day when competitive nuclear power will be achieved, how significant will its economic impact then be?

The direct economic impact will be slight, in all likelihood, during the time period covered in this study. Coal may begin to feel significant effects by 1975 and far greater effects in the years following. Other fuels, too, may experience market losses after 1975 as a consequence of the development of economic methods for using nuclear heat in industrial processes and in certain large-scale transportation applications. At the moment, it is fruitless to speculate about quantitative prospects along these lines because the horizons are too distant.

Yet the temptation to speculate about the economic impact of atomic power is too strong to be set aside completely by the absence of adequate information for making quantitative assessments. And enough is known about earlier energy innovations to permit at least one line of theorizing which may be helpful in achieving perspective on the broader economic impact of atomic power.

The history of energy consumption, examined in Part I, covers in its 105-year span numerous developments in the energy field that have had a profound economic and social impact on life in the United States. These include such changes as the transformation of the energy base from wood to coal in the nineteenth century; the development of improved methods of illumination and lubrication in the late nineteenth century; the tremendous growth of liquid fuels after the first World War; and the growth of electrification throughout the twentieth century.

It is probably fair to say that today none of these changes appears to have been as dramatic as the harnessing of atomic power. Yet developments such as these have completely transformed the mode and standard of life in the United States. Thus, the change in the energy base from wood, a limited resource, to coal, which was available in apparently endless amounts, opened the way to the large-scale, unimpeded growth of iron and steel production. Adequate supplies of iron and steel, in turn, made it possible to revolutionize transportation by building a railroad network which crisscrossed the country. The way was also opened to the ever-expanding production of machines constructed of metal which have provided the foundation for the modern industrial system. Not only did coal support the necessary growth in metals production, it also supplied the large amounts of fuel needed to power locomotives and the machines of industry. The growth of the system of machine production depended, too, on adequate lubrication and illumination, both made available in the latter part of the nineteenth century in sufficient amounts, at low costs, and in greatly improved quality when mineral sources, mainly oil, replaced animal and vegetable products. On another front, adequate illumination based on kerosine and also on gas manufactured from coal multiplied the effects of public education by making it easier to utilize the newly learned skills in reading and study at home in the evening hours.

In the twentieth century, the impact of liquid fuels and electricity has been critically important in facilitating further changes. Liquid fuels have been fundamental to the growth of automotive transportation, whose influence on the American way of life is obvious beyond any need for description. As for electricity, its impact is without parallel among energy developments in the present century. By virtue of the unique form in which electric energy is made available, it has made possible numerous developments in the field of communications and automatic controls which otherwise would be inconceivable. Less apparent perhaps, is the impact electricity has had on industrial plants, where the substitution of electric motors mounted on machines for the older system in which mechanical energy was transmitted by belts powered by a single prime mover has made possible a complete reorganization of production practices. The analysis in Chapter 4 provides a basis for believing that improvements in production practices, resulting from electrification, are an important element in explaining the remarkable acceleration in labor and capital productivity in the period following the first World War, which has been disclosed in historical studies of the efficiency of the American economy.

What are the unique characteristics of these significant changes in energy use? In every instance they have made possible essentially new, or enormously improved, ways of performing important social or economic functions. They have not accomplished this alone, but always in combination with other changes—railroads, automobiles, electric motors, etc.—themselves often made feasible by changes in energy sources or their form.

Conceiving of atomic energy only as a cheaper fuel for generating electric energy strips it of any possibility for having an economic impact as significant as these earlier energy innovations have had. To be sure, electricity might be somewhat cheaper than it would otherwise be, and would be generated from different raw materials, but it would still be performing the same functions that electric energy from any other source could perform just as well. The same may be said of atomic energy in any application in which it would merely substitute for another energy source which today performs exactly the same function.

Of course, if atomic energy should ultimately turn out to be very much cheaper than energy from conventional sources, profound changes could follow as a result of the new techniques of production, and new locations of productive activity which would become possible. "Making the deserts bloom" is an extreme example along this line, but there may be other, less remote, possibilities such as the economic development of regions well endowed with population and/or natural resources, but now at a severe disadvantage because of their great distance from conventional energy sources. Alternatively, if other energy sources should in the course of time become very much more expensive while atomic energy remained relatively cheap, it would make possible the continuation of existing production techniques and levels of living, which might otherwise be threatened.

Nevertheless, against the perspective provided by the history of energy use, it seems likely that even if atomic energy were to become an important element in the total energy picture, it would not have a revolutionary economic or social impact unless new and important ways of employing it were to be found, for which other energy sources are unfit. Radiation chemistry, and the use of radio-active materials as research and production tools and in medicine seem to offer very promising possibilities along this line. Another, but more remote field of opportunity, is the constructive use of nuclear explosives in such diverse applications as large-scale excavations and the underground release of otherwise un-obtainable oil and gas. Even more speculative are the potentialities of nuclear fuels, by reason of their unusual compactness, as the energy source for powering space vehicles. In view of the crucial part played by mineral fuels in the past in making possible significant changes in transportation—coal in the rise of the railroads, oil in the development of automotive transport—it may be that at some date in the distant future nuclear fuels will be looked back upon as the energy source without which the revolutionary transportation system of the space age would have been impossible.

PART I

A century of energy use: 1850–1955

CHAPTER 2

The changing level and pattern of energy use

The statistical record of energy supply and demand in the United States over the past hundred years displays two prominent characteristics: First is a large increase in the total amount of energy consumed. Second is a remarkable flexibility in the availability of the primary energy sources such as wood, coal, oil, and gas, which resulted in large shifts in supplying the growing total energy needs. This chapter centers on these aspects to provide a broad basis for more detailed analysis, in succeeding chapters, of the production and consumption records of individual energy sources and of the relation between energy use and economic growth.

SCOPE OF THE STATISTICS

In tracing the historical growth of energy consumption in the leading industrial countries it is customary to include only the so-called commercial or industrial energy sources—mineral fuels and hydropower. Coal is so intimately associated with the process of industrialization that there is a tendency to overlook the fact that as late as 1870 three-quarters of the total fuel supply in the United States was in the form of wood, that well into the second half of the nineteenth century falling water was an important source of mechanical power for industry, and that windpower was important in water transportation and agriculture. In the pre-Civil War era, waterwheels, not coal, turned the machinery of the manufacturing plants. These plants were not concentrated in the coalfields of Pennsylvania, but along the streams and by the waterfalls of New England.

31

Among the fuels, wood was not only the principal domestic heating material, it was also widely used in steamboats and railroads, and to a lesser extent in manufacturing. And even as late as the beginning of the twentieth century harbors still contained forests of sailing vessel masts and the dominant feature of many rural landscapes was the windmill.

Treatment of these other energy sources—wood, wind, and water—is made difficult, however, by a paucity or complete absence of statistics on their utilization over significant portions of the historical record of the 1850–1955 period. The present analysis faces the problem in the aggregate energy data in the following fashion: *Fuel wood* is included, despite the availability of only the barest data series, because it is vital to the long-run record. Direct *waterpower*[1] and *windpower* are excluded, with full recognition of their significance in the nineteenth century, due to the absence of statistical data useful for historical series. The scattered figures that do exist are referred to in the discussion of wood in Chapter 3. *Hydropower* is included beginning with its emergence as an energy source in 1890. The mineral fuels, for which statistics in the hundred-year period are generally adequate, are included as appropriate: *coal* for the entire period, *oil, natural gas,* and *natural gas liquids* from the dates of their commercial emergence.

This study is restricted to inanimate energy sources. Animate energy, supplied by human workers and work animals, is excluded because of the lack of sub-stantiated statistical data and the conceptual difficulties involved in converting it into inanimate energy equivalents which would permit their inclusion in an aggregate energy consumption figure.

The statistical framework for this discussion is given in detail in the Appendix to Part I. In building up an aggregate energy consumption figure it was not possible to achieve uniformity in the treatment of the various energy sources. The consumption statistics for hydropower and the mineral fuels used for this pur-pose are for "apparent consumption," that is, production minus exports plus imports, and, since 1920, including net stock changes in the mineral fuels.[2] But fuel wood is represented by direct consumption estimates.

The basic consumption statistics for the energy sources are in terms of physical quantities—tons (all references in this book are to short tons unless otherwise specified), cords, cubic feet, barrels, etc. These data are converted to the common denominator of British thermal units (Btu's) by applying a conversion factor representing the inherent Btu content of the physical unit. This procedure is discussed in the Appendix Note on Problems of Measurement. The conversion factors used in this part of the study are given in Appendix Table II. It should be observed here that one of the chief drawbacks of the conversion to inherent Btu

---

[1] Throughout this book the term "waterpower" denotes the direct use of the mechanical energy of turning waterwheels; "hydropower" refers to the generation of electricity with waterwheels.

[2] The apparent consumption of oil reflects, in addition, the net foreign trade position in refinery products.

values for common units is that they do not reflect the different thermal efficiencies of the various fuels. This shortcoming is most serious with respect to wood, the use of which involved an especially low thermal efficiency. In the early part of the 100-year period, when wood was the chief fuel, this results in overstatement of total energy "utilization" as distinguished from input.[3]

Hydropower presents a special conversion problem. Here the conversion is accomplished on the basis of the Btu equivalent of the fuel which would have been required to generate the same amount of electricity. The Btu fuel equivalent is calculated for each year by using the prevailing average central station efficiency rate (that is, the amount of fuel required to generate a kilowatt hour—kwh—of electricity). Since there have been great and continuous improvements in the efficiency of converting fuel to electricity (a sevenfold multiplication in efficiency between 1900 and 1955), the conversion rate has changed considerably over time.

It is, of course, possible to use as the conversion factor the absolute energy equivalent of kwh and Btu's. One kwh equals 3,412 Btu, and both measure the same amount of energy. To use this arithmetic equivalence, however, would be to understate the relative importance of hydropower. Since the energy aggregate in the United States consists essentially of fuels, and since the fuels used to produce electricity are represented in the statistics by their Btu contents, it is considered better to include hydropower on a fuel basis (that is, by the equivalent of fuel that would produce the same number of kwh).

THE LEVEL AND COMPOSITION OF ENERGY USE

Much of the significance of the level of total energy use by an economy, and of changes in that level over time, lies not in the level itself but in its relationship to such indicators of the development of the economy as population and gross national product (GNP). Some aspects of energy use from this point of view are discussed in Chapter 4, which deals with energy consumption and economic growth. The discussion here has a simpler purpose. It is to describe long term changes in the level and composition of energy use as a background against which to discuss the record of the individual energy sources in Chapter 3.

The record of energy use in the United States in the period 1850–1955 is given in Table 1 and Figure 9. Since it is difficult to visualize trillions of Btu's the Btu figures are accompanied in Table 1 by the equivalent tons of coal which

[3] The low efficiency with which wood was used is not because the thermal effectiveness of wood combustion is inherently much lower than that of coal. In terms of the proportion of contained Btu's to Btu's converted into heat, the difference between coal and wood is minor. But at the time when wood was the dominant fuel, the equipment in which it was burned was such that a large portion of the heat was lost.

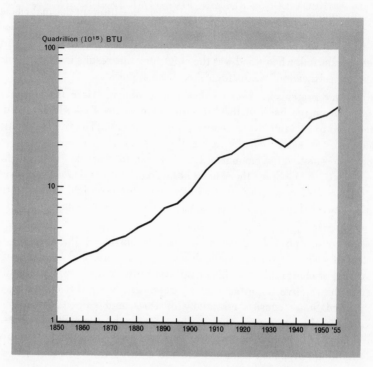

Figure 9.   Energy consumption, five-year intervals, 1850–1955.

contain the given Btu quantity. Even in 1850, the total fuel consumption was already a large absolute figure, equivalent to 90 million tons of bituminous coal. By 1905, energy consumption was the equivalent of one-half billion tons, and during World War II it passed the level equivalent to a billion tons. In 1955, at the end of the period under review, total energy consumption was the equivalent of more than 1.5 billion tons of bituminous coal, seventeen times that of 1850. Over the 105-year period, energy consumption demonstrated a sustained growth which, although varying in pace for different periods (see Chapter 4), was interrupted only once, by the depression of the 1930's.

The continuous long-term growth in total energy use has been accompanied by very great changes in the composition of energy supply. The choice among wood, coal, oil, natural gas, and hydropower at different times has depended on shifts in their availability, movements in their comparative prices, advances in technology, changes in the structure of the nation's output of goods and services, and shifts in consumer preference. Dramatic shifts in the relative importance of the individual sources are revealed in the historical record as shown in Table 2 and Figure 10.

TABLE 1. ENERGY CONSUMPTION, FIVE-YEAR INTERVALS, 1850–1955

Year	Energy consumption[a] (trillion Btu)	Bituminous coal equivalent[b] (million tons)
1850	2,357	90
1855	2,810	107
1860	3,162	121
1865	3,409	130
1870	3,952	151
1875	4,323	165
1880	5,001	191
1885	5,645	215
1890	7,012	268
1895	7,661	292
1900	9,587	366
1905	13,212	504
1910	16,565	632
1915	17,764	678
1920	21,378	816
1925	22,411	855
1930	23,708	905
1935	20,456	781
1940	25,235	963
1945	32,700	1,248
1950	35,136	1,341
1955	40,796	1,557

[a] Includes fuel wood, mineral fuels, and hydropower.
[b] Equivalence factor: 26.2 million Btu per ton.

SOURCE: Appendix Table VII.

At the beginning of the period covered, the energy basis of the economy was almost wholly fuel wood, with 90 per cent of total fuels obtained from this source. As late as 1870, about three-quarters of all energy used was still coming from fuel wood. By the mid-1880's, however, coal had become the principal source of energy, supplying approximately half the total. Coal achieved its peak share in the over-all energy supply during the first decade of this century, when it accounted for more than three-quarters of the total. In the post-World War I period, the position of coal declined and that of oil and natural gas rose so that, by 1955, the share of the liquid and gaseous fuels in the total energy supply had risen to nearly two-thirds.

Among the individual fuel positions it will be noted that anthracite reached its peak share within total energy consumption near the end of the nineteenth century, a decade or so prior to the peak of bituminous. Both types of coal declined almost continuously as proportions of the total after reaching their

TABLE 2. SPECIFIC ENERGY SOURCES AS PERCENTAGES OF AGGREGATE ENERGY CONSUMPTION, FIVE-YEAR INTERVALS, 1850-1955

(Measured in Btu's)

Year	Bituminous coal (1)	Anthracite (2)	Total coal (3)	Oil (4)	Natural gas (5)	Natural gas liquids (6)	Total liquids and gaseous fuels (7)	Total mineral fuels (8)	Hydro-power (9)	Mineral fuels and hydro-power (10)	Fuel wood (11)
1850	4.7%	4.6%	9.3%					9.3%			90.7%
1855	7.3	7.7	15.0					15.0			85.0
1860	7.7	8.7	16.4	.1%	n.a.		n.a.	16.5			83.5
1865	9.6	8.9	18.5	.3	n.a.		n.a.	18.8			81.2
1870	13.8	12.7	26.5	.3	n.a.		n.a.	26.8			73.2
1875	19.9	13.4	33.3	.3	n.a.		n.a.	33.6			66.4
1880	26.7	14.3	41.1	1.9	n.a.		1.9%	43.0			57.0
1885	33.4	16.9	50.3	.7	1.5%		2.2	52.5			47.5
1890	41.4	16.5	57.9	2.2	3.7		5.9	63.8	.3%	64.1%	35.9
1895	45.8	18.8	64.6	2.2	1.9		4.1	68.7	1.2	69.9	30.1
1900	56.6	14.7	71.4	2.4	2.6		5.0	76.4	2.6	79.0	21.0
1905	61.2	14.5	75.7	4.6	2.8		7.4	83.1	2.9	86.1	13.9
1910	64.3	12.4	76.8	6.1	3.3		9.3	86.1	3.3	89.3	10.7
1915	62.7	12.2	74.8	7.9	3.8		11.8	86.6	3.9	90.5	9.5
1920	62.3	10.2	72.5	12.3	3.8	.2%	16.3	88.8	3.6	92.5	7.5
1925	58.4	7.3	65.6	18.5	5.3	.6	24.4	90.0	3.1	93.2	6.8
1930	50.3	7.3	57.5	23.8	8.1	1.0	33.0	90.6	3.3	93.9	6.1
1935	45.6	6.3	52.0	26.9	9.4	0.9	37.1	89.1	4.1	93.2	6.8
1940	44.7	4.9	49.7	29.6	10.6	1.1	41.3	91.0	3.6	94.6	5.4
1945	44.8	4.0	48.8	29.4	11.8	1.5	42.8	91.6	4.5	96.1	3.9
1950	33.9	2.9	36.8	36.2	17.0	2.2	55.4	92.1	4.6	96.7	3.3
1955	27.2	1.5	28.7	40.0	22.1	2.9	65.0	93.7	3.7	97.4	2.6

n.a. Not available.

SOURCE: Appendix Table VII.

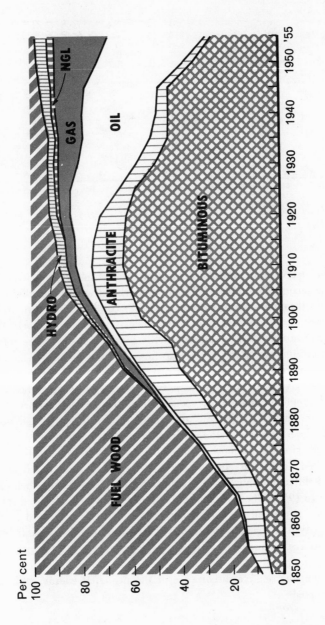

Figure 10. Specific energy sources as percentages of aggregate energy consumption, five-year intervals, 1850–1955.

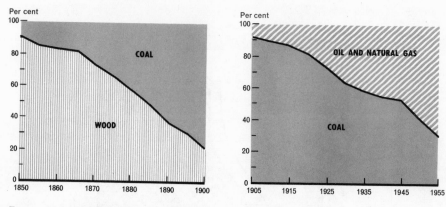

Figure 11(a) and 11(b).   Shifts among major energy sources: (a) from wood to coal; (b) from coal to oil and natural gas, 1850–1955.

peaks; the decrease in the share of bituminous was only briefly interrupted during the second World War. The hydrocarbons were of negligible or minor importance through the nineteenth century. Oil began its important rise in relative position after World War I, natural gas just prior to World War II, and natural gas liquids (NGL)—although still a minor share of the total—showed indications of increasing importance at the end of the period.[4] The mineral fuels together underwent an uninterrupted rise in importance throughout the 105-year period, and have been the dominant type of energy source since about 1885. Hydropower entered the energy scene at the turn of the century, but attained only a minor, albeit fairly constant, share of the total (as measured by the previously described conversion method).

Unlike the situation in most of the leading industrial nations, the reign of coal in the United States was comparatively short. Coal contributed more than 50 per cent of the total annual energy supply for only about half a century, roughly from 1885 to 1940. The rise of liquid and gaseous fuels and the displacement of coal roughly paralleled the rise of coal and the decline of wood in the over-all energy supply half a century earlier. The percentage shares contributed by the principal sources changed as follows (see Figure 11). Thus, within a hundred years, the composition of the U.S. fuel and power base changed twice so markedly that the relative importance of the principal energy sources was completely reversed.

Movement	Between 1850 and 1895	Between 1910 and 1955
Increased	Coal, from 9% to 65%	Oil and gas, from 9% to 65%
Declined	Wood, from 91% to 30%	Coal, from 77% to 29%

[4] Unlike the other mineral fuels, natural gas liquids are not a primary energy source but are obtained by processing natural gas. They are basically dependent on natural gas production and can never be more than a minor factor in the energy total (see Chapter 10).

TABLE 3. INDEXES OF ENERGY CONSUMED, BY SPECIFIC SOURCES, FIVE-YEAR INTERVALS, 1850–1955

(1900 = 100)

Year	Anthracite (1)	Bituminous coal (2)	Total coal (3)	Oil (4)	Oil including NGL (5)	Natural gas (6)	Total liquid and gaseous fuels a (7)	Total mineral fuels (8)	Hydro-power (9)	Fuel wood (10)	Aggregate energy consumption (11)
1850	7.7	2.0	3.2					3.0		106.1	24.6
1855	15.3	3.8	6.2					5.8		118.6	29.3
1860	19.5	4.5	7.6	1.3		n.a.	0.6	7.1		131.1	33.0
1865	21.6	6.0	9.2	4.4		n.a.	2.1	8.8		137.3	35.6
1870	35.7	10.0	15.3	4.8		n.a.	2.3	14.5		143.6	41.2
1875	41.0	15.9	21.1	4.8		n.a.	2.3	19.8		142.5	45.1
1880	50.8	24.6	30.0	41.9		n.a.	20.0	29.4		141.5	52.2
1885	67.9	34.7	41.5	17.5		32.5	25.4	40.5		133.2	58.9
1890	82.2	53.4	59.4	68.1		102.0	85.9	61.1	8.8	124.8	73.1
1895	102.2	64.6	72.4	73.4		58.3	65.5	71.9	36.0	114.4	79.9
1900	100.0	100.0	100.0	100.0		100.0	100.0	100.0	100.0	100.0	100.0
1905	135.5	149.0	146.2	266.4		147.6	204.2	150.0	154.4	91.5	137.8
1910	146.1	196.2	185.9	439.7		214.3	321.6	194.8	215.6	87.6	172.8
1915	153.2	205.0	194.3	616.2	619.2	267.1	434.7	210.1	276.4	83.8	185.3
1920	154.5	245.4	226.6	1,150.2	1,168.6	322.6	725.4	259.4	310.0	79.9	223.0
1925	115.4	240.8	215.0	1,814.8	1,869.0	472.6	1,137.4	275.6	280.4	76.1	233.8
1930	121.8	219.5	199.4	2,468.1	2,575.1	766.7	1,627.7	293.2	314.0	72.2	247.3
1935	92.0	171.9	155.5	2,401.3	2,478.2	761.5	1,578.8	248.9	332.4	69.3	213.4
1940	88.3	207.9	183.2	3,269.4	3,388.6	1,057.5	2,167.4	313.6	366.8	67.4	263.2
1945	93.0	270.0	233.5	4,200.4	4,414.8	1,536.1	2,906.7	409.1	594.4	62.6	341.1
1950	71.8	219.1	188.8	5,548.5	5,890.4	2,368.6	4,045.3	442.1	640.4	57.8	366.5
1955	42.5	204.5	171.1	7,130.1	7,652.4	3,573.4	5,515.4	522.2	598.8	53.0	425.5

n.a. Not available.

a 1860–80: oil only, data for natural gas consumption not available.

SOURCE: Appendix Table IX.

Table 2 and Figure 10 deal only with relative shares. These data reflect the profound changes in the country's pattern of energy use, but they do not supply any information about the absolute levels of energy derived from the several principal sources. These levels are shown in Table 3. For purposes of comparison, the consumption of the several energy commodities has been expressed in index form, using the year 1900—the approximate midpoint of the period under review—as the base year.[5]

The series for coal (columns 1 through 3 in Table 3) show that although the use of both anthracite and bituminous coal rose sharply between 1850 and 1900, the increase was greater in bituminous. Consumption of anthracite reached its all-time peak, some 50 per cent above the 1900 level, in the period just after World War I, and thereafter began a decline that carried it, by 1955, down to little more than two-fifths the 1900 level, or about the same as in 1875. Bituminous consumption, on the other hand, rose to almost two and one-half times its 1900 level in the imediate post-World War I period, and, although it declined thereafter, it touched a new peak slightly over two and a half times the 1900 level during World War II. A second decline set in during the post-World War II period, but bituminous use remained at least more than double the 1900 level. Because of the dominance of bituminous throughout the record, the movement of the total coal index tends to resemble the behavior of bituminous. Total coal consumption in 1900 was thirty times the 1850 figure, but at the end of the ensuing fifty-five years was only 71 per cent greater than at the turn of the century. In sum, the record for coal is one of rapid growth in the nineteenth century and first decade of the twentieth, followed by retardation and subsequent long-term stagnation, despite fluctuations caused by wars and business cycles.

The record for liquid and gaseous fuels (Table 3, columns 4 through 7) is very different, as might be expected from the fact that the great quantitative increase in their consumption has occurred in recent decades. Although the nineteenth century witnessed a substantial percentage growth in the use of these products, the absolute levels of consumption were quite small. In the twentieth century, the record is one of very rapid expansion interrupted only slightly by the depression of the 1930's. Over the fifty-five years, oil consumption multiplied about seventy times (or about seventy-five times if NGL are included) while the consumption of natural gas increased by about half as much. There is also a difference in the timing of the growth of these two energy sources. Between 1900 and 1930, oil consumption multiplied about twenty-five times, natural gas less than eight times; but, in 1955, gas use was almost five times and oil just about three times the use in 1935. Over-all the consumption of liquid and gaseous fuels in 1955 was fifty-five times the 1900 level.

The consumption of fuel wood, shown in Table 3, has striking elements. Although it is commonly considered as an obsolete energy source in the United States, the decline in actual consumption from its early peak is more modest than may be generally realized. Wood reached its absolute peak in the 1870's, at a

[5] Index numbers are based on the inherent Btu values of the individual fuels, and these values serve also as the basis for aggregating the individual commodities.

TABLE 4.   HYDROPOWER CONSUMPTION, FIVE-YEAR INTERVALS, 1890–1955

Year	Quantity (million kwh)	Index (1900=100)
1890	250	9.0
1895	1,000	35.9
1900	2,786	100.0
1905	5,054	181.4
1910	8,626	309.6
1915	13,886	498.4
1920	19,719	707.8
1925	26,753	960.3
1930	37,470	1,344.9
1935	44,064	1,581.6
1940	52,245	1,875.3
1945	87,309	3,133.8
1950	102,671	3,685.2
1955	120,304	4,318.2

SOURCE: Appendix Table VI.

level almost 50 per cent higher than that of 1900. The decline, once started, was virtually uninterrupted; nevertheless, in 1955, fuel wood consumption in absolute terms still stood at about 50 per cent of its 1900 level. Of course, the strikingly different picture conveyed by the absolute level of fuel wood, in contrast to its changing relative position in the total energy picture, underlines the great expansion in the long-period record of aggregate energy consumption. Fuel wood accounted for one-fifth of a total energy input in 1900 that was itself less than one-fourth of the total energy use in 1955. Conversely, the total energy input in 1955 was so large in absolute terms that even 2.6 per cent of it, fuel wood's share in that year, constituted a comparatively large quantity of wood.

Hydropower, although of modest relative importance in the total throughout its historical record, experienced a substantial growth in absolute terms—multiplying six times between 1900 and 1955 (Table 3, column 9). This increase was slight compared to the expansion in liquid and gaseous fuels, but somewhat greater than the growth of aggregate energy consumption and of total mineral fuels and considerably greater than the increase achieved by coal. On the other hand, the figures in Table 3 represent the use of a changing efficiency factor in converting kwh to a Btu basis (compare indexes of hydropower consumption in Table 4 and Table 3, column 9). Since the quantity of fuel needed to produce a kwh declined drastically over the period, this method of integrating hydropower into total energy consumption (although preferred for adding hydropower and fuels together) gives a misleading impression of the record of actual hydropower use. The figures in kwh are given in Table 4, which shows that by 1955 the actual consumption of hydropower was forty-three times the use in 1900. On this basis, its increase among the primary energy sources was exceeded only by crude oil. Hydro-generated electricity, in other words, underwent a very large absolute growth, even though it continued to be a minor element in the total.[6]

THE CUMULATIVE GROWTH OF MINERAL FUEL CONSUMPTION

Still another perspective on the increase in energy use is achieved by viewing consumption on a cumulative basis. As previously indicated, mineral fuels are by far the dominant source of all energy consumed in the United States, having provided upwards of 90 per cent of the total since the 1920's. For all mineral

[6] It should also be noted that the growth of hydro-generated electricity is substantially smaller than the growth in total electricity generation (hydropower plus thermal power). By 1955, the latter had multiplied the 1902 figure more than a hundred times (see Table 60) compared to about forty fold in hydropower.

TABLE 5. MINERAL FUEL CONSUMPTION IN EACH
FIVE-YEAR PERIOD BETWEEN 1850 AND 1954 AS A PERCENTAGE OF
TOTAL MINERAL FUEL CONSUMPTION OVER THE WHOLE PERIOD[a]

(Measured in Btu's)

Year	All mineral fuels		Coal		Liquid and gaseous fuels	
	Total (1)	Cumulative (2)	Total (3)	Cumulative (4)	Total (5)	Cumulative (6)
1850–54........	0.1%	0.1%	0.2%	0.2%	b	
1855–59........	0.2	0.3	0.3	0.5	b	
1860–64........	0.2	0.5	0.4	0.9	b	
1865–69........	0.4	0.9	0.5	1.4	b	
1870–74........	0.5	1.4	0.8	2.2	b	
1875–79........	0.7	2.1	1.1	3.3	b	
1880–84........	1.0	3.1	1.5	4.8	0.1%	0.1%
1885–89........	1.5	4.6	2.1	6.9	0.3	0.4
1890–94........	2.0	6.6	2.8	9.7	0.4	0.8
1895–99........	2.6	9.2	3.6	13.3	0.5	1.3
1900–04........	3.5	12.7	5.0	18.3	0.8	2.1
1905–09........	4.9	17.6	6.8	25.1	1.4	3.5
1910–14........	6.1	23.7	8.1	33.2	2.1	5.6
1915–19........	7.2	30.9	9.3	42.5	3.1	8.7
1920–24........	7.5	38.4	8.8	51.3	5.0	13.7
1925–29........	8.7	47.1	9.4	60.7	7.5	21.2
1930–34........	7.2	54.3	6.7	67.4	8.2	29.4
1935–39........	8.2	62.5	6.9	74.3	10.5	39.9
1940–44........	11.0	73.5	9.4	83.7	14.0	53.9
1945–49........	12.4	85.9	9.1	92.8	19.0	72.9
1950–54........	14.1	100.0	7.4	100.2[c]	27.1	100.0
1850–1954......	100.0%		100.0%		100.0%	

[a] For 1850–99, estimates of consumption during five-year periods obtained by averaging consumption figures for the first and last year of each period. For 1900 and subsequent years, based on annual consumption data.

[b] Less than 0.1 per cent.

[c] Does not add to 100.0 because of rounding.

SOURCE: Appendix Table VII.

fuels and for the two general subcategories—coal, and liquid and gaseous fuels—Table 5 shows how much of the total consumption over the period 1850-1954 was used in each successive five-year period, together with the cumulative percentage of the total from the initial year to the end of each period. At the turn of the century, cumulative mineral fuel consumption since 1850 was less than one-tenth of the total over the period to 1955. The enormous quantities involved in recent years mean that one-half of the total consumption occurred after the early 1930's, and one-quarter of the total occurred in the single decade 1945–54.

The course of coal consumption is reflected in the somewhat smaller influence of recent coal use within its cumulative total. Nevertheless, one-half of all the coal used in the United States between 1850 and 1955 was consumed after the early 1920's, in the period of the relative decline of coal as an element of total energy supply. This again lends emphasis to the high absolute level of coal consumption even after it had ceased to expand.

The remarkable pace of growth in oil and natural gas is also evident in Table 5. Since the beginnings of the industry fall within the period covered in this study, the data refer to total historical consumption. Three-fifths of all these fuels used in the United States through 1954 was consumed after 1940; in the single decade 1945–54, the demand for oil and natural gas was the equivalent of almost one-half of the cumulative consumption through time.

DOMESTIC AND FOREIGN SUPPLY

The recent growth in U.S. energy consumption has been accompanied by a significant change in its foreign trade position in energy: a shift from a net exporter to a net importer of mineral fuels. This change is traced in Table 6, which shows the consumption of mineral fuels, measured in Btu's, as a percentage of the energy contained in the principal mineral fuels produced in this country. In the very early part of the period under review, until about 1860, small amounts of coal were imported. But this was before the United States had entered the mineral fuel age. From that time until only a few years ago, this country was self-sufficient with regard to energy supply. Once this nation's abundant reserves of coal began to be developed, output not only kept up with the spectacular growth of domestic demand, but provided an exportable surplus for other countries, which at times—especially during and after the two World Wars—amounted to substantial quantities.

The U.S. oil industry from its very beginning was heavily oriented to exports and, in the early years, sales to foreign countries often exceeded the domestic use of petroleum products. Although in the post-World War I period net exports accounted for only a small percentage of total output, the quantities involved were large. This was especially true during World War II. Until just after the war, the United States held its position as the world's leading petroleum exporter. Then the large absolute increase in U.S. demand began to surpass domestic production.

By 1955, consumption of oil—measured in Btu's—exceeded domestic output by 13 per cent (see Table 6). This amount of net oil imports was larger (again in terms of Btu's) than net exports of coal. Thus, by the mid-1950's the United States had become a net importer of mineral fuels.

TABLE 6.   MINERAL FUEL CONSUMPTION AS A PERCENTAGE OF CORRESPONDING DOMESTIC PRODUCTION, SELECTED YEARS, 1850-1955

(Measured in Btu's)

Year	All mineral fuels (1)	All coal (2)	All liquid and gaseous fuels (3)	Crude oil plus net imports of petroleum products [a] (4)
1850...............	101.4%	101.4%		
1855...............	101.0	101.0		
1860...............	100.4	100.4	100.0%	
1865...............	99.5	100.2	71.4	
1870...............	98.8	100.5	37.9	
1875...............	97.3	99.8	22.4	
1880...............	97.5	99.8	65.8	
1885...............	96.9	99.5	60.1	
1890...............	97.1	99.2	80.2	
1895...............	96.4	98.7	70.6	
1900...............	95.8	97.5	77.2	
1905...............	96.5	97.8	84.8	
1910...............	96.1	97.2	87.8	
1915...............	95.2	95.9	90.7	
1920...............	92.1	90.3	101.1	
1925...............	96.4	96.8	95.2	
1930...............	100.5	97.3	106.4 [b]	
1935...............	96.0	96.0	95.9	
1940...............	94.8	93.7	96.3	
1941...............	97.7	95.5	100.5	
1942...............	94.2	92.8	96.4	
1943...............	98.1	100.0	95.5	
1944...............	95.5	95.0	96.2	
1945...............	97.0	96.6	97.3	96.8%
1946...............	96.0	93.3	99.0	99.3
1947...............	92.7	86.4	99.8	100.3
1948...............	93.8	86.8	100.7	101.9
1949...............	102.6	100.6 [c]	104.0	107.3
1950...............	98.3	88.2	106.4	111.0
1951...............	97.0	87.8	103.6	107.2
1952...............	98.6	89.5	104.1	108.3
1953...............	101.0	93.2	105.3	110.4
1954...............	102.2	92.7	106.8	112.4
1955...............	102.1	91.2	107.8	113.3

[a] Shown separately only for post-World War II period of change to net import basis.

[b] Anomaly representing excess consumption over production through large withdrawals from stocks at the beginning of the depression of the 1930's.

[c] Anomaly representing excess consumption over production (through drawdown of stocks) because of large production loss due to strikes.

SOURCES: Appendix Tables II and VII.

CHAPTER 3

The record of
the major energy sources

The development of energy production and consumption in the United States is described in this chapter through the record of the major primary energy sources. Accordingly, the chapter consists of sections on wood, coal, oil, and natural gas. By thus focusing the survey, a simple and useful chronological scheme may be used. One can distinguish three successive "eras," or periods during which wood, coal, and oil and gas were the dominant energy source. These three periods are traced as a convenient means of emphasizing the changes over time, but the reader should be warned that, as in any artificial breakdown or categorizing, there is overlapping among the periods and consequent unavoidable repetition between the sections.[1]

FUEL WOOD

Only a century ago, the main energy sources utilized in the United States were wood, waterpower, and windpower. These were the same sources the first settlers used when they arrived on the shores of the New World, indeed, the same that had been used since ancient times. Wood was the principal fuel for domestic as well as industrial purposes; wind and falling water furnished the greater part of

[1] Windpower and direct waterpower, which were important primary energy sources during the nineteenth century, are considered briefly in the section on wood. Electricity, which is not a primary energy source except as it is hydro-generated, is treated in this chapter only as one of the consumers of primary energy. The production and use of electricity as such is discussed briefly in Chapter 4. Hydroelectric power, which is a primary energy source, has been of minor importance in the national scene and is therefore not considered in this chapter, but has been covered in Chapter 2.

all inanimate mechanical energy. This was an economically rational energy-supply pattern for a society with more than four-fifths of its population living in rural areas. Yet it is surprising to find that not only was the total energy input in this country during the early stages of development already quite large, but these ancient resources, utilized on a large scale, constituted the energy basis for the beginnings of an industrial society that within a few decades was to become the leading industrial nation in the world.

Among the traditional energy sources, wood was by far the most important. All evidence indicates that it was used lavishly, although the actual quantities can be estimated only very roughly. Data on the use of fuel wood a century ago must be taken to represent orders of magnitude rather than precise quantities. Statistical information in general is scanty for those times, and reliable data for non-commercial commodities are practically nonexistent. "Cordwood was about as plentiful as air. But nobody wrote about air—why write about firewood, or even record statistics about it?"[2]

The fragmentary information on consumption of fuel wood in the mid-nineteenth century available today represents crude estimates based mainly on the size and distribution of the population, the climate, the housing conditions, and the availability of wood in the various regions of the United States. These estimates make allowance for the slow shift from open fireplaces to stoves and for the gradual replacement of wood by coal, and show a rapid decline in the annual per capita use of fuel wood from the peak reached by the middle of the nineteenth century.

·   ·   ·

The Statistical Record

In view of the special difficulties posed in dealing quantitatively with water-power and wind energy, together with the fact that wood and coal dominated the energy picture in the second half of the nineteenth century, the changing position of wood during that period is traced by comparing it with that of coal.

The extent to which wood maintained its initial dominant position in the energy economy of the United States throughout most of the nineteenth century is shown in Table 7 and Figure 11. In 1850, the "fuel basket" consisted of more than nine-tenths wood and less than one-tenth coal. Twenty years later, the share of wood was still about three-quarters of the total. The physical quantity of wood burned has been estimated at approximately 100 million cords in 1850. In absolute terms, consumption was rising during the following decades, reaching a peak of nearly 140 million cords in 1870. In 1850, about 12 cords and, in 1870, 3.5 cords of wood were used as fuel for every ton of coal consumed. During the 1870's, a gradual decline in absolute consumption began. By the turn of the century, the physical quantity of fuel wood used was at approximately the same

[2] R. V. Reynolds and A. H. Pierson, *Fuel Wood Used in the United States, 1630-1930*, U.S. Department of Agriculture, Forest Service Circular No. 641, Washington, February 1942, p. 2.

TABLE 7. ESTIMATED CONSUMPTION OF FUEL WOOD COMPARED
TO COAL AND TOTAL ENERGY CONSUMPTION, FIVE-YEAR
INTERVALS, 1850-1955

Year	Physical quantities		Trillion Btu			Fuel wood as percentage of total (6)
	Fuel wood (thous. cords a) (1)	Coal (thous. net tons) (2)	Fuel wood (3)	Coal (4)	Total Energy b (5)	
1850......	102,000	8,507	2,138	219	2,357	90.7%
1855......	114,000	16,346	2,389	421	2,810	85.0
1860......	126,000	20,100	2,641	518	3,162	83.5
1865......	132,000	24,522	2,767	632	3,409	81.2
1870......	138,000	40,639	2,893	1,048	3,952	73.2
1875......	137,000	55,689	2,872	1,440	4,323	66.4
1880......	136,000	79,246	2,851	2,054	5,001	57.0
1885......	128,000	109,557	2,683	2,840	5,645	47.5
1890......	120,000	156,399	2,515	4,062	7,012	35.9
1895......	110,000	190,665	2,306	4,950	7,661	30.1
1900......	100,000	262,790	2,015	6,841	9,587	21.0
1905......	95,000	384,024	1,843	10,001	13,212	13.9
1910......	91,000	487,743	1,765	12,714	16,565	10.7
1915......	87,000	510,011	1,688	13,294	17,764	9.5
1920......	83,000	594,381	1,610	15,504	21,378	7.5
1925......	79,000	563,254	1,533	14,706	22,411	6.8
1930......	75,000	522,618	1,455	13,639	23,708	6.1
1935......	72,000	407,426	1,397	10,634	20,456	6.8
1940......	70,000	479,910	1,358	12,535	25,235	5.4
1945......	65,000	611,167	1,261	15,972	32,700	3.9
1950......	60,000	494,102	1,164	12,913	35,136	3.3
1955......	55,000	447,012	1,067	11,703	40,796	2.6

a In estimates of fuel wood consumption, especially for the early period, the term "cord"
is used not as a precise measure of volume but as the rough equivalent of the amount of
cut and stacked wood contained in a pile 4 x 4 x 8 feet.

b Includes fuel wood, mineral fuels, and hydropower.

SOURCES: Appendix Tables VI and VII.

level as around 1850. But the relative share of wood in the greatly expanded
total energy supply had declined over this period from nine-tenths to one-fifth.

Per capita consumption of fuel wood decreased continuously with only minor
fluctuations after the middle of the nineteenth century; first rather slowly—less
than 10 per cent between 1850 and 1860—then at a faster rate, varying between
20 and 30 per cent per decade. The pertinent figures, comparing the decreasing
quantities of wood used per person with the exanding coal consumption, are
shown in Table 8.

These figures do not take into account the contribution of waterpower and
windpower. The early industrial development in this country was to a high degree
dependent on waterpower, especially from the innumerable small streams in
New England, where simply constructed and easily operated waterwheels furnished the mechanical power for textile mills and other small-scale manufacturing
plants. And the roles of sailing vessels in water transport and windmills in well-

TABLE 8. ESTIMATED PER CAPITA CONSUMPTION OF FUEL WOOD
COMPARED WITH PER CAPITA COAL CONSUMPTION,
FIVE-YEAR INTERVALS, 1850-1955

Year	Fuel wood (cords) (1)	Fuel wood in bituminous coal equivalent (net tons) (2)	Actual coal consumption (net tons) (3)	Percentage decrease in fuel wood consumption per decade (4)	
1850	4.39	3.51	0.36		
1855	4.16	3.33	0.60		
1860	4.00	3.20	0.63	1850–60	9.8%
1865	3.70	2.96	0.69		
1870	3.46	2.77	1.02	1860–70	13.5
1875	3.04	2.43	1.24		
1880	2.71	2.17	1.58	1870–80	21.7
1885	2.26	1.81	1.94		
1890	1.90	1.52	2.48	1880–90	29.9
1895	1.58	1.26	2.74		
1900	1.31	1.01	3.45	1890–1900	31.0
1905	1.13	0.84	4.58		
1910	0.98	0.73	5.28	1900–10	25.2
1915	0.87	0.64	5.08		
1920	0.78	0.58	5.59	1910–20	20.4
1925	0.68	0.50	4.86		
1930	0.61	0.45	4.24	1920–30	21.8
1935	0.57	0.42	3.20		
1940	0.53	0.39	3.63	1930–40	13.1
1945	0.46	0.34	4.37		
1950	0.40	0.30	3.25	1940–50	24.5
1955	0.33	0.24	2.70		

SOURCE: Appendix Table X.

pumping are well-known. While an evaluation of the contribution of wind and
falling water to the total energy supply of the country raises intricate conversion
and measurement problems, their importance suggests that the effort be made.
One possible approach consists in starting from the simple question, how much
fuel materials—wood or coal—would have been required in order to replace the
amount of work obtained by harnessing windpower and direct waterpower? This
can be done by comparing the horsepower hours (hph) derived from falling water
and wind with the power obtained by employing coal-generated or wood-generated
steam. Then this output of mechanical work can be related to the quantities of
fuel materials—say, tons of coal—required to obtain it at the prevailing efficiency
of converting coal into mechanical energy. The scanty data available for both—
the amount of mechanical work derived from inanimate sources of energy as well
as the quantities of fuel materials necessary to produce them—of course, are no
more than crude approximations. The data are not substantiated measurements,
but only broad estimates that enable one to gain an impression of the relative
importance of different inanimate energy sources utilized a century ago in manufacturing, transportation, and agriculture.

Rough calculations using this approach indicate that around 1850 some 19 million tons of bituminous coal would have been required to replace the work obtained by harnessing falling waterpower and windpower. This is more than twice the 8.4 million tons of bituminous coal and anthracite produced in that year, and equals 23 per cent of the 82 million tons of coal that are the equivalent in British thermal units (Btu's) of the total fuel wood consumed in that year. The corresponding figures for 1860 are 25 million tons of bituminous, compared to a total coal output of 20 million tons and 100 million tons of coal equivalent consumed in the form of fuel wood. In the ensuing decade, coal production finally surpassed the fuel equivalent needed to furnish the mechanical work output generated by windpower and waterpower. By 1870, the latter may have been equivalent to an input of approximately 15 million tons of bituminous, while total coal production had risen to 40 million tons and total fuel wood consumption amounted to 110 million tons of coal equivalent.[3]

. . .

The Uses of Wood in the Nineteenth Century

HOME HEATING

Around 1850, the estimated annual consumption of firewood exceeded 100 million cords, or nearly 4.5 cords per capita. More than nine-tenths of this was used in households, including domestic manufactures such as the drying of tobacco and the smoking of meat. About three-quarters of the total was burned in open fireplaces. Conservative estimates indicate that around 1850–60 an American family used on the average some 17.5 cords of wood per year to keep comfortably warm according to their standards. This is the theoretical energy equivalent of approximately 2.5 tons of coal per person at that time.[4] What was considered "comfortably warm" by the vast majority of American families, who were living remote from the urban centers of the East Coast, is illustrated in the following quotation:

All cabin dwellers gloried in the warmth of their fireplaces, exploiting their world of surplus trees where a poor man, even a plantation slave, could burn bigger fires than most noblemen in Europe. . . .

[3] See Appendix, "Note on the Measurement of Direct Waterpower and Windpower in 1850, 1860, and 1870."

[4] In comparison, the energy used in homes in recent years is the equivalent of less than two tons of coal per capita, including all present-day home energy uses. (See Table 53 in Chapter 4.) Only one ton of coal equivalent is estimated to be used for domestic heating proper. The shift from wood to coal and then from coal to oil and natural gas, combined with the change in equipment from open fireplace to the modern central heating system, resulted in an increase in the thermal efficiency of energy utilization from about 8 per cent in 1850 to some 60 per cent in the mid-1950's. Thus, in recent years a per capita fuel input only two-fifths that of 1850 (measured by its Btu content) supplied about three times as much useful space heat.

In the dead of the winter, a family kept warm, not by buying "sich uppish notions" as blankets, but by putting more wood on the fire and sleeping in their clothes. . . . The kind of hospitable settler who burned a whole log in order to boil a kettle of tea didn't consider his fire psychologically good until he had crammed a quarter of a cord into a space eight feet wide and four feet deep and had a small-scale forest fire roaring in front of him. If the fire was too hot, he left the doors open, but fire he would have if only to brighten up the dark end of the house.[5]

While the industrially more advanced and more urbanized countries of Western Europe were confronted with growing shortages of timber, the United States was still in the process of cutting its way through virgin forests. The forests had to disappear to make room for farms; and much of the wood went up the chimneys of the newly established homes. If the amount of wood cut in clearing the homestead was not sufficient for the extravagant heating habits of that period, fuel was available for the asking—or rather, for the cutting—from the forest or woodland surrounding many of the new farms.[6]

It has been estimated that the same quantity of wood, burned in a well-constructed wood stove, would supply about four times as much heat as when used in an open fireplace. There were many reasons why in this country stoves replaced the fireplace only very gradually and at a comparatively late period, among them the high cost of manufactured equipment and the transportation difficulties prevailing around the middle of the nineteenth century. One additional important reason for the widespread and long-lasting use of a type of heating with very low thermal efficiency was the simple fact that to chop fuel wood small enough for use in stoves would have required a substantial amount of human labor. Energy in the form of fuel wood was abundant, but manpower was scarce. It made no sense to waste man-hours in order to economize in the use of a seemingly unlimited natural resource. Man's labor was the most valuable resource of all.

In the early part of the period under review, not only was wood abundant and inexpensive in most of the settled regions of the country, also it was quite adequate for most of the uses to which it was put.[7] Its chief disadvantages were

[5] R. G. Lillard, *The Great Forest* (New York: Alfred A. Knopf, 1948), p. 85.

[6] Between 1850 and 1860, some 50 million acres—an average of 5 million acres a year—were added to the area of improved farmland, not counting additions to farm pastures and farm woodland. Assuming that a substantial portion of this newly cleared cropland was gained not from forests but from brush and prairie land, and assuming, therefore, a low average yield of 15 cords of wood per acre, some 75 million cords per year became available by transforming forests into fields. The consumption of fuel wood during this decade has been estimated at 100 to 125 million cords a year. At that time, wood was not only the main source of fuel but also the most widely used structural material. Yet by far the largest portion of total wood consumption was burned as fuel. Of this more than half, possibly much more, became available automatically as the by-product of clearing and settling virgin land.

[7] However, the portents of the next fuel era were present early in U.S. history in those regions where coal was more easily accessible and less costly than wood. In the early nineteenth century, coal very gradually began to replace wood as domestic fuel in the large seaboard cities. From this period, a record has been preserved showing the quantities of fuel consumed by the city of Philadelphia during the year March 1826–March 1827. Since

weight and bulk in relation to its energy content. One cord of good hardwood has about four-fifths as much energy content as one ton of coal but weighs approximately twice as much and has considerably greater volume. Hence, irrespective of the uses to which fuel wood is put and the quality of the equipment in which it is used, much larger quantities in both weight and volume are required to supply the energy equivalent of a ton of coal.

INDUSTRY AND TRANSPORTATION

In the middle of the nineteenth century, only a small fraction of the total fuel consumption was utilized for industrial purposes. Although accurate data for this period are lacking, rough but reasonable estimates indicate that around 1850 only about one-tenth of the total fuel supply was converted into mechanical energy and, by 1870, approximately one-fifth was so utilized.[8] They imply for the period around 1870 an annual fuel input for mechanical work of about 800 trillion Btu, which is the energy equivalent of some 30 million tons of coal—in comparison

---

this is one of the few bits of information on comparative amounts and costs of different fuels at a time when wood was predominant, it is reproduced here:

Fuel	Quantity	Value	Unit Price
Wood	140,150 cords	$630,675	$4.50
Anthracite	28,610 tons	178,815	6.25
Bituminous coal.......	5,019 tons	38,553	7.68
Charcoal	3,200 tons	32,000	10.00

Calculated from data in Marcus Bull, *Experiments to Determine the Comparative Value of the Principal Varieties of Fuel* (Philadelphia: 1827), as quoted in Howard N. Eavenson, *The First Century and a Quarter of American Coal Industry* (Pittsburgh: privately printed, 1942), p. 150.

Converted into Btu's, these data yield the following information on comparative quantities and prices:

Fuel	Energy content (million Btu)	Cost (per million Btu)
Wood	2,937,544	21.5¢
Anthracite	726,694	24.6
Bituminous coal	131,498	29.3
Charcoal	77,440	41.3
Total 3,873,176	Average	22.7¢

Wood thus accounted for more than three-quarters of the total fuel supply in terms of energy content. It was still somewhat cheaper than coal, even at this large seaboard city. But here, delivery costs included, its price approached that of coal. This was at a time when total U.S. coal production amounted to only some 650,000 tons a year, with Pennsylvania the source of nearly three-quarters of the total. In terms of inherent energy, national coal output represented 17 trillion Btu—that is, not even four and one-half times the fuel consumption of one big city.

[8] This share rose from 12 per cent in 1850 to 15 per cent in 1860 and 20 per cent in 1870, according to J. F. Dewhurst and Associates, *America's Needs and Resources, A New Survey* (New York: The Twentieth Century Fund, 1955), Appendix 25-3, Tables J and K, pp. 1114-15.

with 50 million tons of coal then used for the same purposes in Great Britain. These amounts seem plausible in view of Britains' more advanced industrialization. Almost its entire energy supply was being furnished by coal. In 1869, consumption amounted to somewhat more than 100 million short tons, and of this it has been estimated that some 30 per cent was burned for space heating, about 25 per cent was used for process heat, and 45 per cent was converted into mechanical work.[9]

There exists scarcely any information on the question of when wood was first put to a "modern" use—the generation of steam power. But there is no doubt that well into the second half of the nineteenth century wood was an important source of heat and power for industrial purposes. The first engines on steamboats and the first locomotives were fired with wood. Wood remained until about 1870 the principal fuel used by railroads. Yet the total amount consumed in manufacturing and transportation was small compared to the huge quantities used in the household. Most likely it never exceeded about 10 million cords—the Btu equivalent of some 8 million tons of bituminous coal—per year out of a total annual fuel wood consumption of 100 million to 140 million cords. Some estimates[10] put the peak quantity of wood transformed into mechanical energy as low as 6 million cords in 1860. At that time, the railroads were the heaviest users, and scattered references indicate that they may have burned up to 6 million cords a year in the late 1860's. An additional 2 to 3 million cords of fuel wood may have been used for the generation of steam power in manufacturing and in water transportation.

Next to the railroads and steamboats, the largest single industrial consumer was the iron industry. Around 1850, more than half of all iron produced was still smelted with charcoal. The quantities of charcoal used in smelting and forging appear to have remained fairly stable at a level of 70 to 75 million bushels a year between the 1850's and 1870's, rising to 86 million in the early 1880's.[11] The amount of wood required for the preparation of charcoal may be estimated at approximately 1.5 million cords a year, a very small percentage of the total fuel wood consumption.[12]

---

[9] See W. S. Jevons, *The Coal Question*, ed. A. W. Flux (rev. ed.; New York: Macmillan & Co., 1906), p. 139; and Palmer Putnam, *Energy in the Future* (New York: Van Nostrand, 1953), p. 370. See also Table 21.

[10] See Dewhurst, *op. cit.*, Appendix 25-3, Table K, p. 1115.

[11] U.S. Geological Survey, *Mineral Resources of the United States, 1882* (Washington, D. C.: U.S. Government Printing Office, 1883), p. 115; and also Table 9, below.

[12] The weights and measures employed in the scanty contemporary statistics on charcoal are somewhat inconsistent and confusing. Using the common conversion factor of 20 pounds per bushel of charcoal, the above-mentioned quantities were equal to 700,000–750,000 tons. Since wood yields approximately one-half of its bulk in charcoal, but only one-quarter of its weight, the preparation of 750,000 tons of charcoal would have required some 3 million tons of wood. The weight of one cord of wood varies with different types. If one accepts the generalization that one cord of good dry hardwood weighs about 2 tons, it follows that some 1.5 million cords were converted into charcoal annually. The Btu value of charcoal is rather close to that of bituminous coal—24.2 to 26.2 million Btu per ton. Thus, the inherent heat value of 750,000 tons of charcoal is equal to that of approximately 700,000 tons

The earliest detailed record concerning the use of fuel wood refers to the decade during which total consumption reached its peak (per capita consumption had passed its peak some decades earlier). The amount of wood burned for all purposes for the decade 1870 through 1879 has been estimated at 1,407 million cords, or 140 million cords per year.[13] The Census of Manufactures for 1879 contains a breakdown (see Table 9) which shows that some 5 million cords—that is, about 3.5 per cent or, if one includes the wood used in the preparation of charcoal, some 4.5 per cent of the total consumption—were used for industrial purposes.[14]

TABLE 9. FUEL WOOD CONSUMPTION IN 1879

(Thousand cords)

Use		Cordwood	Including wood for charcoal [a]
Domestic use..		140,537	140,537
Industrial use..		5,241	6,700
Railroads.............................	1,972		
Steamboats...........................	788		
Mineral operations.....................	625		
Manufactures........................	1,856		
Total..		145,778	147,300 [b]

[a] Industrial charcoal use was 74 million bushels (of which 70 million were in iron manufacture), requiring approximately 1.5 million cords of wood.
[b] Approximate.

SOURCE: C. S. Sargent, "The Forests of the United States in Their Economic Aspects," *Census of Manufactures*, Vol. 9 (Washington, D. C.: U.S. Government Printing Office, 1879), p. 489.

By the midpoint of the nineteenth century, coal production in the United States had barely reached 8.5 million tons. Even if, as has been estimated (see section on coal later in this chapter), up to 75 per cent of this total output was consumed in the generation of steam power, the contribution of wood to the energy input

of coal. But charcoal is about four times as bulky as bituminous coal. Although the weight of a bushel (until the 1870's the most widely used measurement) varied from region to region, it seems to have averaged 80 pounds for bituminous coal, 40 pounds for coke, and 20 pounds for charcoal. Weight and volume of charcoal yield from *Forestry Handbook*, ed. R. D. Forbes (New York: Ronald Press, 1955), p. 215; Btu values from Putnam, *op. cit.*, p. 326.

[13] Reynolds and Pierson, *op. cit.*, Table 2.

[14] This share of about 4 per cent for industrial uses may have been somewhat greater in the preceding decades before coal began to replace wood in manufacturing and transportation. The 6 to 9 million cords of fuel wood which may have been used in generating steam power for railroads and other transportation and in manufacturing in the 1860's come to about 5 to 7 per cent of total fuel wood consumption in that period.

for productive purposes—as distinct from space heating and other household uses—may have been at that time about as large as, or perhaps even larger than that of coal. But the energy input for the generation of steam power and for industrial process heat from both fuels combined was still very small. It has been roughly estimated at the equivalent of 12 to 16 million tons of bituminous coal in 1850 and some 18 to 25 million tons in 1860,[15] but these amounts were substantially supplemented by wind and water to support the rapidly growing demand for power in manufacturing and transportation.

The progress in the industrialization and mechanization of this country during the second half of the nineteenth century is reflected in the growing installed horsepower (hp) of prime movers, which rose from 2,304,000 hp in 1849 to 7,764,000 hp in 1869. In the former year, manufacturing accounted for nearly one-half the total. Ten years later, it was surpassed by railroad horsepower; in 1869, its share had fallen to less than one-third.[16] The importance of falling water and windpower as a source of mechanical energy during this period is shown in the rough estimates in Table 10 which attempt to attribute total horsepower hours generated in selected years to wind and water as well as coal and wood.

TABLE 10.   ESTIMATED MECHANICAL WORK OUTPUT, 1850-70

(Billion horsepower hours)

Energy source	1850		1860		1870	
	Hph	Per cent	Hph	Per cent	Hph	Per cent
Wind....................	1.4	64%	2.1	58%	1.1	33%
Water...................	0.9		1.3		1.7	
Coal....................	0.7	36	1.8	42	4.9	67
Wood...................	0.6		0.7		0.8	
Total...............	3.6	100%	5.9	100%	8.5	100%

SOURCE: J. F. Dewhurst and Associates, *America's Needs and Resources, A New Survey* (New York: The Twentieth Century Fund, 1955), Appendix 25-3, Table L, p. 1116.

According to these estimates, the share of wind and water appears to have ranged from two-thirds of the total in 1850 to one-third in 1870. Their relative importance, although great, was on the decline, and there seems to be little doubt

[15] See Dewhurst, *op. cit.*, Appendix 25-3, Table K, p. 1115; and Putnam, *op. cit.*, p. 89. The lower estimates by Dewhurst refer to energy input for mechanical work only. The higher figures are supposed to include input for process heat. They were calculated by applying Putnam's estimates of the relative shares of the three components of the energy system—work, process heat, and space heat—to this study's total Btu consumption data for the respective years.

[16] See Dewhurst, *op. cit.*, Appendix 25-4, p. 1117. Data for 1849 and 1869 are from C. R. Daugherty, A. H. Horton, and R. W. Davenport, *Power Capacity and Production in the United States*, U.S. Geological Survey, Water Supply Paper No. 579, Washington, 1928. Data for sailing vessels and windmills, which are included in the above totals, are based on Dewhurst, *op. cit.*, Appendix 25-3.

that during the 1860's the amount of mechanical energy, measured in terms of horsepower hours, derived from coal and wood began to exceed that furnished by windpower and direct waterpower. This shift is indicated also by other statistical information. A Census report for 1869 states that of the total installed horsepower in manufacturing industries (some 2,236,000 hp), 48.2 per cent was represented by waterwheels and 51.8 per cent by steam engines, an almost equal division. By 1879, nearly two-thirds of the installed horsepower in manufacturing was represented by steam engines and only one-third by waterwheels.[17] By that time, the horsepower in steamships was almost two and one-half times as large as the horsepower represented by the use of sailing vessels.[18] In the last decades of the nineteenth century, windpower and direct waterpower were relegated to minor positions as sources of mechanical energy.[19]

[17] U.S. Department of the Interior, Census Office, "Statistics of Power and Machinery Employed in Manufacture," *Reports on the Water-Power of the United States*, Part I (Washington, D. C.: U.S. Government Printing Office, 1885), p. XII.

[18] See Dewhurst, *op. cit.*, Appendix 25-4, p. 1117.

[19] According to Dewhurst's estimates (*ibid.*, p. 1116), wind and direct waterpower accounted for about 10 per cent of all horsepower hours (hph) of mechanical energy in 1890 and less than 5 per cent in 1900.

Although the present study is restricted to inanimate energy sources it should be mentioned here that according to estimates by the same author the work output derived from work animals exceeded that obtained from all inanimate sources until well into the second half of the nineteenth century. In absolute terms, it continued to increase until about 1910. But in the latter year inanimate sources supplied about eight times as much horsepower hours as animals. In the following decade, the spreading use of the internal combustion engine began to replace horses, mules, and oxen on the farm and in the field of transportation. By 1920, the work output obtained from animals had dropped to less than 6 per cent of the total.

To integrate animal power into the nineteenth century energy economy raises still more intricate problems than the conversion of windpower and waterpower into fuel equivalents. In the second half of the nineteenth century, falling water and wind were harnessed for purposes for which also coal-fired and wood-fired steam engines could have been and were being used—mainly to supply power for factories, well-pumping, and water transport. But prior to the introduction of motor fuel, there existed no adequate fuel source which could have replaced work and draft animals. By the time the internal combustion engine began to be more widely used on farms and in road transportation the efficiency of converting fuel into mechanical work had greatly increased. For this reason, animal power is not integrated into the nineteenth century energy supply. But because of its importance during the early part of the period under review it seems appropriate to quote the following estimates (*ibid.*, pp. 1113, 1116) which may serve as a basis for comparison with or conversion into inanimate energy equivalents by whichever method is considered preferable.

ESTIMATED WORK OUTPUT FROM ALL SOURCES EXCEPT HUMAN LABOR

	Work output (billion hph)		Average efficiency of converting fuel into mechanical work (per cent)	
Year	From work animals	From all inanimate energy sources	Coal	Oil
1850	5.4	3.6	1.1%	
1860	7.6	5.9	1.3	
1870	8.4	8.5	1.8	
1880	11.1	16.0	2.3	
1890	14.4	30.3	2.6	
1900	16.9	57.6	3.0	3.0%
1910	18.0	142.8	4.4	5.0
1920	15.2	268.1	7.0	7.0

Wood in the Twentieth Century

The data remain inadequate for tracing the course of fuel wood in the present century. Even today, information on fuel wood is scarce and it usually is not included at all in energy statistics. This seems justified for the most recent years when its relative contribution to the over-all supply was negligible, although the absolute amounts consumed (estimated at 50 to 60 million cords per year for the 1950–55 period) were still substantial.[20] It is surprising to find that well into the 1940's the share of fuel wood as a source of primary energy was greater, in Btu terms, than that of hydropower.[21] By the 1950's, as a result of the recent rapid decline of anthracite, wood's share as a source of primary energy also exceeded that of anthracite. At that time, as well as a century earlier, wood was mainly a household fuel, used for heating and cooking in rural areas. In this specific field of residential energy use, its relative importance was greater in recent decades (see Table 11) than is generally recognized.

TABLE 11. WOOD CONSUMPTION COMPARED WITH TOTAL
ENERGY CONSUMPTION FOR RESIDENTIAL AND COMMERCIAL USES,
FIVE-YEAR INTERVALS, 1935–50

(Trillion Btu)

Year	Total from all sources [a]	Wood, including mill waste	Wood as per cent of total
1935	6,166	1,258	20.4%
1940	6,864	1,017	14.8
1945	8,272	1,017	12.3
1950	9,371	1,022	10.9

[a] Totals include electric and nonelectric energy consumption by households, but only nonelectric energy use by commercial enterprises. The latter amounts to approximately 30 per cent of the quantities shown in the first column. Since wood is used mainly as a household fuel its share in residential energy consumption is larger than indicated in this table. For 1950, it may be estimated at about 15 per cent of all fuel and power used in the domestic sector.

SOURCE: A. T. Coumbe and I. F. Avery, "Fuels Consumed for Residential and Commercial Space Heating, 1935–1951," U. S. Bureau of Mines, *Information Circular 7657*, Washington, January 1953, Table 12.

[20] U.S. Department of Agriculture, *Timber Resources for America's Future*, Forest Resource Report No. 14, Washington, January 1958, p. 153, estimates the 1952 consumption at 59 million cords. A report by the Stanford Research Institute, *America's Demand for Wood, 1929–1975* (Tacoma, Wash.: Weyerhauser Timber Company, 1954), p. 69, estimates the 1950 consumption at 55 million cords.

[21] This is also true even if hydropower is converted into the equivalent of fuels that would have been required in its thermal generation.

In 1940, some 7.7 million dwelling units—that is, more than one-fifth of all residences with some sort of heating equipment—were relying on wood. By 1950, this number had declined to 4.3 million, representing about one-tenth of all heated dwelling units.[22] The rapid decrease in the number of rural homes using wood and the shift to liquid fuels, gas, coal, and electricity are expected to continue. There is only one market that has been expanding in recent years: many new modern houses feature wood-burning fireplaces. It would not be surprising if, in the near future, the greatest portion of all fuel wood used would again be burned in fireplaces—with the difference that the necessity of a hundred years ago has now become a luxury.[23]

COAL

The history of the coal industry in the United States dates back about two centuries. In 1758, the first recorded commercial shipment of 32 tons was "exported" from the James River district in Virginia, destined mainly for New York.[24] During the following century, coal mining expanded steadily but by industrial standards at a very modest scale. Until the 1830's, production was small in absolute terms, sporadic, and locally restricted. The years between 1830 and 1850 were a time of exceptionally fast growth, not only in production, which rose nearly tenfold, but also in the regional spread of the emerging industry which was introduced in newly settled territories. By 1850, the beginning of the period covered in this study, coal mining was established on a commerical level.

The rise of the coal industry to a dominant position, which began at the middle of the nineteenth century can be divided into the following subperiods: 1850 to 1885, rapid development of coal mining into a major basic industry; 1885 to World War I, continued growth in output and predominance among the energy sources; post-World War I, stagnation in output and relative decline among the energy sources. The history of coal in the United States raises a number of problems which should be viewed against the background of the industrialization of this nation and the development in other advanced countries. Some of the more

---

[22] U.S. Bureau of the Census, *Statistical Abstract of the United States, 1950* (Washington, D. C.: U.S. Government Printing Office, 1951), p. 742; *ibid.*, 1957, p. 776; and Stanford Research Institute, *op. cit.*, p. 69.

[23] Stanford Research Institute (*ibid.*, p. 69) includes the following estimates of recent and future U. S. consumption of fuel wood (in millions of cords):

Year	Heat, rural farm	Heat, rural nonfarm	Heat, urban	Fireplace	Other	Total
1950.......	20.6	13.0	5.8	14.0	1.6	55.0
1975.......	2.3	3.7	2.4	17.0	0.2	25.6

One paradoxical reason for the increasing use of wood in fireplaces is the decline in the consumption of coal in homes. Many no longer have either coal or coal grates, so wood is substituted where only occasional heating is required.

[24] Eavenson, *op. cit.*, pp. 32-34, 419, 441.

important questions are: Why did coal production and use on a large scale develop so late? What were the main developments outside the energy field that stimulated the rise of the coal industry? What has been its role in the fuel and power economy of the country? Why has coal become a stagnating industry within a growing economy?

· · ·

The Period before 1850

The knowledge of coal mining which the early settlers brought with them went back in West European countries to the thirteenth or even twelfth century. Around 1600, coal mining was well established in England, Germany, Belgium, and France; output in Britain amounted to about a million tons a year. By 1700, the city of London consumed nearly 500,000 tons annually; and at the beginning of the American Revolution, some 850,000 tons.[25] Yet the immigrants who settled the original colonies made almost no attempt to exploit the rich coal resources within their territory.[26]

The towns along the Eastern Seaboard imported small quantities of coal from England and Nova Scotia. From the few records that have been preserved it appears that during the colonial period these imports did not exceed 9,000 tons a year.[27]

COAL—AN UNUSED RESOURCE

The pioneers who moved into the river valleys beyond the Appalachians actually seemed to have forgotten the existence and uses of coal. As late as the 1840's, the introduction of this unknown and untried fuel encountered strong prejudices along the rivers of the Midwest, where steamboats had become the chief means of transportation. A report to the State Board of Agriculture, dated May 1857, by the manager of the first coal mining enterprise in Indiana, includes the following description of the struggle of the new industry:[28]

"The Company which I represent are now acting under the first charter granted by the Legislature of Indiana for the mining of coals. This was obtained in the

[25] Jevons, *op. cit.*, p. 263.

[26] Coal was used in the United States long before its colonization. Small amounts from outcroppings were used by the Indians as paints and ornaments, rather than as fuel. But one Indian tribe, the Hopis, in what is now Arizona, mined coal as early as 1000 A.D. to heat their houses and to fire pottery. This was before coal came into general use as a fuel in Europe. About 100,000 tons or more were mined before the Spaniards came to Arizona. (Eavenson, *op.cit.*, pp. 353-55.) Coal was known to exist in Virginia, Pennsylvania and what is now Illinois almost as soon as these regions were settled. But during most of the colonial period there was little need to touch the rich deposits of the country. Small amounts of coal taken from outcroppings were used locally and sporadically, but there were hardly any attempts to start systematic coal-mining operations.

[27] *Ibid.*, p. 3.

[28] *Ibid.*, pp. 277–79.

year 1837, by a few New England capitalists, who immediately commenced operations under its very liberal provisions. With every promise of brilliant success, they expended a large amount of money in lands (then perfectly wild), buildings, drifts, shafts, boats, engineering, etc., and, when they were ready to deliver coals to the passing steamboats, they ascertained, to their cost: *that the steamboat engineers were of the opinion that such fuel would not make steam.* (Italics added.) After eight years of exertion, the Company were unable to extend their sales over two hundred thousand bushels [about 8,000 tons] a year, although they had the only coal mines opened below the Falls of the Ohio. . . .
"The early efforts to introduce the use of these coals to markets below us, on the Ohio and Mississippi Rivers, were attended with uninterrupted loss. . . . After the operations of nearly twenty years, and an investment of something over six hundred thousand dollars, reckoning interest at six per cent, we are now just beginning to make both ends meet, and to rely with reasonable certainty on satisfactory dividends in the future. . . .
"The rapidly increasing demand for heat and power in our manufactories and on our steam boats and railroads; the cutting down of our forests for purposes of agriculture, and the increasing cost of obtaining coals from the Appalachian field, are now bringing our own coal deposits into prominent notice."

A similar report, supposedly dated 1840, has been preserved from Mobile, Alabama, a seaport already settled for more than a hundred years.[29]

"David Handy purchased some lands near the Blount County line. On this land there was coal in the bed of the Warrior River. He built two flat-boats in the fall and loaded them with coal and floated them to Mobile. In Mobile nobody would buy the coal. He had to give it away and send a negro along with every bucketful to show the people how to light and burn it."

With such attitudes prevailing, an observer of that period would have felt justified in believing the prediction made more than a century earlier by a visitor to America who wrote: [30]

". . . And as for Coals, it is not likely they should ever be used there in anything, but Forges and great Towns, if ever they happen to have any; for, in their Country Plantations, the Wood grows at every Man's Door so fast, that after it has been cut down, it will in seven Years time, grow up again from seed to substantial Fire Wood."

In the 1850's a coal expert from England reported that the actual consumption in what he called the "Western and Southern district" (stretching from Cincinnati to New Orleans) was less than one-third of what he termed "the natural demand" of the region. He found that steamboats, locomotives, and households were almost entirely supplied with wood; many of the towns were not lighted with gas; manufacturers were unable to obtain the quantities of coal they would willingly take; there were insufficient depots and no certainty of a continuous supply so that steamboats and railroads "must obtain fuel at whatever costs from the forests, on which alone they can depend."[31]

[29] *Ibid.,* p. 294.
[30] *Ibid.,* p. 30.
[31] *Ibid.,* pp. 258–60.

These statements from contemporary observers touch upon the main reasons why coal was so slow in coming to play a role in the American economy: The abundance of wood, the lack of transportation facilities, and a conservatism that engendered mistrust of a "new" source of energy.

THE EMERGING USES OF COAL

The close interdependence between coal mining, on the one hand, and the rise of the iron industry, the spreading use of steam power, and the expansion of rail transportation, on the other, had been established in Britain during the second half of the eighteenth and early part of the nineteenth centuries. By the middle of the eighteenth century, timber supplies had become so scarce and charcoal so prohibitively costly that the English iron industry was said to be unable to produce more than some 20,000 tons of pig iron a year.[32] The invention of coke making and the successful use of coke for smelting, which began on a larger scale around 1760, opened the way for the use of coal as metallurgical fuel and the rapid expansion of the modern iron industry. As coal mines grew deeper, steam pumps took over the tedious task of draining water from the mines. Then, steam engines began to be employed to power hoists for raising the coal to the surface. The early use of steam power for draining and lifting was soon supplemented by the use of steam engines as motive power in railroad transportation, first employed principally as connecting links between mines and water transport at rivers and ports.

While in Great Britain the use of coal was a *sine qua non* of industrialization, the United States with its ample forests was able to achieve a fair degree of industrial development using wood and waterpower, not coal, as the main energy source. In the field of transportation, an extensive railway network had been built long before coal overtook wood as the principal locomotive fuel. Locomotives fired with coal were first introduced on a large scale after the Civil War, although railroad mileage was already extensive, having reached 30,600 miles by 1860. (By 1870, it had grown to 52,900 miles.) The modernization of iron manufacture in the United States did not begin with the substitution of mineral coal for charcoal in the blast furnace, but with other types of innovations which, in effect, reversed the order of technological change experienced earlier in Great Britain. Because the primary impulse for change in the United States came from the scarcity of labor rather than of wood, a labor-saving device—the rolling of iron to replace trip hammers, first introduced in 1817—was the earliest step in the process of industrializing the manufacture of iron. Improved methods for producing refined iron from pig iron, involving the substitution of puddling in a reverberatory furnace for refining in an open forge, followed next. This change did involve the substitution of mineral coal for charcoal. However, the most

---

[32] See J. D. Weeks, "Report on the Manufacture of Coke," *Tenth Census of the United States*, Vol. X, Department of the Interior, Census Office (Washington, D. C.: U.S. Government Printing Office, 1884), p. 27. See also T. S. Ashton, *Iron and Steel in the Industrial Revolution* (Manchester, England: Manchester University Press, 1924), p. 13.

voracious consumer of fuel, the blast furnace in which iron ore is reduced to pig iron (which during the second half of the eighteenth century had been converted from charcoal to mineral coal in Great Britain), did not undergo a similar transformation in the United States until the middle of the nineteenth century. The substitution of mineral coal for charcoal in the blast furnace was thus the last of the major steps in the early modernization of iron manufacture in the United States.[33]

Despite the many prejudices, the use of coal for raising steam slowly made its way. By the middle of the nineteenth century, it was recognized in most if not all regions of the country as a fuel well suited for the generation of steam. In 1838, a committee appointed by the Kentucky legislature "to investigate the present state of the Coal Trade and Iron business" reported that:[34]

> "Several experiments were made during the last year, by steamboats, to ascertain the difference between cord wood and coal for fuel, and the result has been, as the committee are informed, that the daily expense of fuel, when Coal is used is less than one half the expense of cord wood. These experiments were generally made at a disadvantage, as the firebeds were constructed for wood and not Coal, and it is therefore reasonable to conclude that, in a few years, Coal will supersede wood as a steamboat fuel. This much is certain, that the price of wood will increase as the timber on the river bottoms is cut down and consumed, while the cost of Coal will diminish, because the Coal trade is evidently on the increase, and the competition among sellers is already reducing prices on the river."

This prediction was not immediately fulfilled, as is clear from the contemporary observation cited earlier. On the other hand, there exist contemporary reports suggesting the acceptance of coal in river transportation in the early 1840's. For example, in 1844, according to the report of a Kentucky coal-mining company, 10 to 12 bushels of coal were recognized as equal to a cord of wood for generating steam, and few steamboats passed without taking some of this "very valuable fuel," which was sold for 7 cents a bushel ($1.75 per ton) at the landing.[35]

The prices of both coal and wood varied considerably from one location to another, depending largely on transportation costs, and these examples from Kentucky may not have been typical for other regions. Information on comparative quantities and costs of different fuels used for specific purposes during this early period is scanty, but it can be inferred from these examples that about one-half ton of coal could replace some two tons of wood at half the cost. Once these conditions prevailed and were recognized—which happened at different times in different regions—the spread of steam power and the use of coal developed hand in hand.

A parallel development was occurring in the home-heating field. In the first decade of the nineteenth century, it was demonstrated that anthracite could be

---

[33] Louis C. Hunter, "The Heavy Industries Before 1860," *The Growth of the American Economy*, ed. H. F. Williamson (2nd ed.; New York: Prentice-Hall, 1955), pp. 175 ff.

[34] Eavenson, *op. cit.*, p. 305.

[35] *Ibid.*, p. 310.

burned in a grate in a fireplace without an artificial draft (where used in forges and furnaces it had always been with a forced draft), and being comparatively clean and smokeless, it gradually became the preferred domestic coal in the cities. The rich anthracite district was not too far from the population centers along the Atlantic coast, and shipments by river (and somewhat later by canals and improved waterways) increased rapidly from about 1820 on. By 1840, output had passed the million-ton mark; during the following decade anthracite production quadrupled.

Until about 1850, more than half of all the bituminous coal produced in the United States was mined in Pennsylvania, and of this more than half came from the great Pittsburgh seam. Natural conditions—the thickness of the seam, its almost horizontal attitude, and its location along rivers—facilitated mining operations and transportation. Yet until the middle of the nineteenth century the bituminous coal industry expanded somewhat more slowly than anthracite mining, due partly to the lesser popularity of bituminous as a domestic fuel and partly to the more remote location of the main field from the large urban centers. For a long period, the city of Pittsburgh was the principal market; its growth as an industrial center was from the very beginning based on the ample and cheap supply of coal. Only after the use of coal for steam generation began to spread, and bituminous coal was adopted as a metallurgical fuel, did this less costly and more widely available type of coal assume the leadership.

. . .

The Statistical Record of Output and Consumption, 1850–1955

In 1850, coal production stood at 8.4 million tons—having risen from 900,000 tons in 1830 and only 100,000 tons in 1800. In the following decades, output grew by enormous strides. In 1870, 40 million tons were mined; around the turn of the century, 270 million tons; and at the temporary peak in 1918, some 680 million (see Table 12 and Appendix Table I). During its period of rapid growth from the midpoint of the nineteenth century to the end of World War I, coal production rose about eighty fold. Up to 1890, it roughly doubled every ten years; in the following decades, its advance was somewhat slower in relative terms but huge in absolute quantities.

This upward trend was interrupted in the post-World War I period. Even in the prosperous late 1920's, coal production barely reached 600 million tons a year. During the depression of the 1930's output fell rapidly; at its lowest point in 1932 it was 360 million tons. Then a gradual recovery began but, at the eve of World War II, coal mining had not regained the level of the 1920's. In the upsurge during and immediately after the war, coal production reached its second peak in 1947, when output was about the same as during the first peak some thirty years earlier. By the mid-1950's, coal production fluctuated around 500 million tons—it had returned to the level of the years prior to World War I.

This is an unusual growth pattern for a basic industry. For a long period the development of coal mining followed the classical growth curve of an expand-

TABLE 12. PRODUCTION OF COAL, FIVE-YEAR INTERVALS, 1850-1955

Year	Coal (thousand net tons)			Percentage increase or decrease per decade (4)	
	Bituminous (1)	Anthracite (2)	Total (3)		
1850........	4,029	4,327	8,356		
1855........	7,543	8,607	16,150	1850-60	+139.8%
1860........	9,057	10,984	20,041		
1865........	12,349	12,077	24,426	1860-70	+101.7
1870........	20,471	19,958	40,429		
1875........	32,657	23,121	55,778	1870-80	+96.4
1880........	50,757	28,650	79,407		
1885........	71,773	38,336	110,109	1880-90	+98.7
1890........	111,302	46,469	157,771		
1895........	135,118	57,999	193,117	1890-1900	+70.9
1900........	212,316	57,368	269,684		
1905........	315,063	77,660	392,723	1900-10	+86.0
1910........	417,111	84,485	501,596		
1915........	442,624	88,995	531,619	1910-20	+31.2
1920........	568,667	89,598	658,265		
1925........	520,053	61,817	581,870	1920-30	−18.4
1930........	467,526	69,385	536,911		
1935........	372,373	52,159	424,532	1930-40	−4.6
1940........	460,772	51,485	512,257		
1945........	577,617	54,934	632,551	1940-50	+9.4
1950........	516,311	44,077	560,388	1950-55	−12.4 [a]
1955........	464,634	26,200	490,834	1945-55	−22.4

[a] Refers to five-year period.

SOURCE: Appendix Table I.

ing industry: a high rate of growth during the early phase (which lasted until about 1910), and a retardation of growth in the next decade. This was followed, however, not by a gradual flattening out of the growth rate, but by a reversal of the trend. In the period since World War I, disregarding the effect of business cycles and of the second World War, the over-all trend shows a decrease in absolute terms and hence, of course, a substantial decline in the position of coal relative to other sources of energy and to general economic development.

. . .

1850-85: The Rise of Coal

By 1850, the coal industry had established a secure, though still rather modest place for itself in the economy of the country. The 8.4 million tons produced in the United States was at that time virtually identical with consumption (see Tables 12 and 13 and Figure 12). Net imports accounted for some 150,000 tons, less than 2 per cent of domestic output. Slightly more than half of the total production was anthracite, mined in northeastern Pennsylvania; the rest was bituminous coal, the bulk of which was produced in western Pennsylvania. More than three-quarters of the total coal output of the country was concentrated in this one state, followed by Ohio with 600,000 tons; the counties that later

TABLE 13.   CONSUMPTION OF COAL, FIVE-YEAR INTERVALS, 1850-1955

Year	Coal (thousand net tons)			Per capita consumption of total coal (net tons) (4)	Percentage increase or decrease per decade	
	Bituminous (1)	Anthracite (2)	Total (3)		Total coal consumption (5)	Per capita coal consumption (6)
1850............	4,215	4,292	8,507	0.36	1850-60	
1855............	7,823	8,523	16,346	0.60	+136.3%	+75.0%
1860............	9,258	10,842	20,100	0.63	1860-70	
1865............	12,534	11,988	24,522	0.69	+102.2	+61.9
1870............	20,817	19,822	40,639	1.02	1870-80	
1875............	32,919	22,770	55,689	1.24	+95.0	+54.9
1880............	51,036	28,210	79,246	1.58	1880-90	
1885............	71,868	37,689	109,557	1.94	+97.4	+57.0
1890............	110,785	45,614	156,399	2.48	1890-1900	
1895............	133,998	56,667	190,665	2.74	+68.0	+39.1
1900............	207,275	55,515	262,790	3.45	1900-10	
1905............	308,823	75,201	384,024	4.58	+85.6	+53.0
1910............	406,633	81,110	487,743	5.28	1910-20	
1915............	424,978	85,033	510,011	5.08	+21.9	+5.9
1920............	508,595	85,786	594,381	5.59	1920-30	
1925............	499,193	64,061	563,254	4.86	-12.1	-24.2
1930............	454,990	67,628	522,618	4.24	1930-40	
1935............	356,326	51,100	407,426	3.20	-8.2	-14.4
1940............	430,910	49,000	479,910	3.63	1940-50	
1945............	559,567	51,600	611,167	4.37	+3.0	-10.5
					1950-55	
1950............	454,202	39,900	494,102	3.25	-9.5[a]	-16.9[a]
					1945-55	
1955............	423,412	23,600	447,012	2.70	-26.9	-38.2

[a] Refers to five-year period.

SOURCES: Appendix Tables VI and X.

became West Virginia, with 350,000 tons; and Illinois and Maryland, which each produced some 250,000 tons.

For this period, a breakdown of total coal consumption does not exist, hence its distribution between household and industrial use is unknown. One of the few estimates available assumes that around 1850 three-quarters of all coal used was transformed into steampower and mechanical work. This would leave only a negligible quantity for industrial process heat, such as the smelting of ore, and domestic use combined.[36]

---

[36] Dewhurst (op. cit., p. 1115), in his table entitled "Energy Input for Work Performance," estimates coal consumption by steamboats, railroads, and steam-power generation in manufacturing for 1850 as follows:

Bituminous coal	3,380,000 tons
Anthracite	3,000,000 tons
Total	6,380,000 tons

This leaves a residual of 2,120,000 tons from the estimated total consumption in that year (see Table 13) for both industrial process heat and household use. This would seem rather small (see 1851 Census report quoted below) and suggests that the above estimate of mechanical work is correspondingly too high.

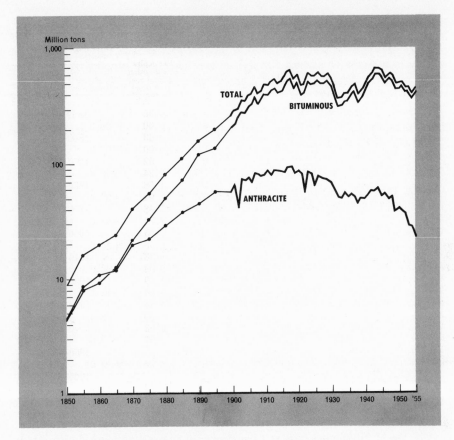

Figure 12. Coal consumption, 1850–1955.

There exists, however, a Census record of the consumption by the leading manufacturing industries, which indicates the beginning of the rapidly growing use of coal in industry. In 1851, when coal production amounted to 10.5 million tons, some 1.7 million were used by the iron and textile industries. The bulk of this (1.5 million tons) went into pig iron, castings, and wrought iron manufacture. In addition, the iron industry consumed some 71 million bushels of charcoal, mainly for smelting.[37]

After the 1850's, it was the growing demand for iron in railroad construction and maintenance which led to the shift from charcoal to mineral coal as metallurgical fuel. Although in the country as a whole wood continued to be abundant and low-cost, this no longer held true for the local timber supplies in the vicinity

[37] *Report of the U.S. Commissioner of Patents,* based on a report of the Superintendent of the Census, Executive Document 102, 32nd Congress, 1st Session (Washington, D. C.: Government Printing Office, 1852), pp. 576–93.

of the old iron works. When these were exhausted the furnaces were usually abandoned and new ones built closer to the timber source in order to reduce fuel transportation costs.[38] The shift to mineral coal as blast furnace fuel began in the iron works of eastern Pennsylvania, where large supplies of anthracite were readily available. By 1842, Pennsylvania had twelve anthracite furnaces which produced 15,000 tons of pig iron; nearly 100,000 tons were smelted in 210 charcoal furnaces.[39] In 1855, about one-half, and a few years later nearly two-thirds, of the country's total iron output was produced with anthracite (see Table 14 and Figure 13).

TABLE 14.   PER CENT OF ANNUAL PIG IRON PRODUCTION SMELTED WITH DIFFERENT FUELS, SELECTED YEARS, 1854-90

Year	Anthracite	Bituminous coal and coke	Charcoal
1854	46.1%	7.4%	46.5%
1855	48.7	8.0	43.3
1860	56.5	13.3	30.3
1865	51.5	20.4	28.2
1870	49.9	30.6	19.6
1875	40.1	41.8	18.1
1880	42.1	45.4	12.5
1885	32.1	59.1	8.8
1890	23.8	69.4	6.8

SOURCE: *The Mineral Industry, Its Statistics, Technology and Trade*, ed. R. P. Rothwell, Vol. I (New York: Scientific Publishing Company, 1892), p. 278.

The use of bituminous coal as a metallurgical fuel spread more slowly, partly because pig iron smelted with raw or coked bituminous coal was not suited as well for the manufacture of tools, farm implements, and household goods as charcoal iron.[40] Although coke had been used experimentally in iron works since 1835, twenty years later only some 55,000 tons of bituminous coal were consumed in making coke for the blast furnaces in the Pittsburgh region. The

---

[38] Actually, charcoal is an efficient smelting fuel and, measured by weight, the amount required is not much larger than the amount of coke and less than the coal needed to prepare the coke. Measured by volume, however, nearly three times as much charcoal as coke is needed to make one ton of iron. The fuel needed to produce one ton of pig iron in 1838 was:

Charcoal .... 200 bushels (2 tons)
Coke .... 75 bushels (1.7 tons)
Coal .... 2.8 tons (assuming 60 per cent coke yield)

But to obtain two tons of charcoal some eight tons of wood were needed. *Report on the Manufacture of Coke*, Bureau of the Census (Washington, D. C.: U.S. Government Printing Office, 1883), p. 25. See also footnote 12 above. The *Report on the Manufacture of Coke* gives forty-five pounds as the weight of one bushel of coke.

[39] Eavenson, *op. cit.*, p. 151.

[40] Hunter, *op. cit.*, p. 178.

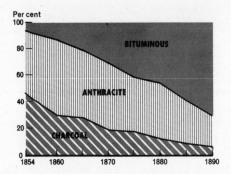

Figure 13. Percentage of annual pig iron production smelted with different fuels, selected years, 1854–90.

railroads opened a new market; pig iron smelted with coke was first used in large amounts in the manufacture of rails. By 1870, when iron output had grown to nearly 2 million tons, about one-half was produced with anthracite, some 30 per cent with coke (including small amounts of raw bituminous coal), and about 20 per cent still with charcoal. From 1875 on, iron made with bituminous fuel exceeded that smelted with anthracite (see Table 14 and Figure 13).

With the introduction of the Bessemer process in the late 1860's, large-scale and low-cost steel production became possible, and steel rails soon proved their superior strength and durability. The fast-growing demand for this product gave a powerful impetus to the coal industry. Coke production on a larger scale got under way in the 1870's and, by 1880, 5.2 million tons of bituminous coal were consumed in the production of 3.3 million tons of coke. Of the 1.4 million tons of steel manufactured in that year, more than half was rolled into rails. By that time, the railroad network had expanded to 90,000 miles and the indirect demand of the railroads for coal via the iron and steel industry was overshadowed by the much larger requirements for coal as locomotive fuel.

Between 1850 and 1890, coal production approximately doubled every decade, and by the latter year amounted to nearly 160 million tons (see Table 12). Net exports were still insignificant—approximately a million tons. In 1890, bituminous accounted for more than two-thirds of all coal mined, and its share continued to increase. The role of anthracite in industrial production had begun to decline when coke from bituminous coal became the principal metallurgical fuel; the bulk of anthracite was used for space heating. By contrast, the larger share of the bituminous coal output was utilized in manufacturing and transportation.

·   ·   ·

1885–World War I: The Dominance of Coal

The year 1885, when coal consumption—110 million tons—began to overtake wood, may be taken as a turning point in the composition of the American fuel basket. Of the 70 million tons of bituminous coal consumed, 42 per cent was burned as locomotive fuel, the railroad having become by far the most important single customer. The production of coke took 13 per cent, and the remaining 45 per cent was distributed among all other industries and domestic use.[41]

Wood continued to supply a substantial portion of all energy consumed, especially in domestic heating, thus leaving a larger share of the total mineral fuels to be utilized in manufacturing and transportation. This explains, at least in part, how the United States was able to overtake its leading industrial competitor, the United Kingdom, in iron and steel output before it matched it in coal consumption. In 1880, U.S. iron production was only half as large as Britain's; ten years later it had surpassed the British, and steel output was larger by nearly one-fifth (see Table 15). In 1890, this country accounted for 34 per cent of the world's pig iron output and 36 per cent of the steel production, but only 28 per cent of the world's coal output. Not until the turn of the century did the production of coal in the United States exceed that of Britain (see Table 16).

Another indication of this lag is per capita coal consumption. This measure of the intensity of coal use reveals that it was only during the first decade of the twentieth century that the United States also became the leading coal consumer

TABLE 15. PIG IRON AND STEEL PRODUCTION IN THE
UNITED STATES AND THE UNITED KINGDOM, TEN YEAR
INTERVALS, 1850–1910

(Million net tons)

Year	United States		United Kingdom	
	Pig iron	Steel	Pig iron	Steel
1850	0.63		2.58	
1860	0.92		4.29	
1870	1.87	0.08	6.68	0.32
1880	4.30	1.40	8.68	1.46
1890	10.31	4.79	8.85	4.12
1900	15.44	11.41	10.03	5.66
1910	30.58	29.23	11.21	7.13

SOURCES: Figures for United States from U.S. Bureau of the Census, *Historical Statistics of the United States, 1789–1945* (Washington, D. C: U.S. Government Printing Office, 1949), Series G 96–97 and J 165; those for the United Kingdom, see, *The Mineral Industry, Its Statistics, Technology and Trade*, ed. R. P. Rothwell, Vol. I (New York: Scientific Publishing Company, 1892), p. 282, and U.S. Geological Survey, *Mineral Resources of the United States, 1889–90* (Washington, D. C.: U.S. Government Printing Office), pp. 18, 21; *ibid.* for *1900*, p. 91; *ibid.* for *1915*, Part II, p. 331.

[41] H. S. Fleming, *A Report to the Bituminous Coal Trade Association on the Present and Future of the Bituminous Coal Trade* (New York: The Bituminous Coal Trade Association, 1908), p. 10.

TABLE 16. PRODUCTION OF COAL IN VARIOUS COUNTRIES AND
WORLD PRODUCTION, FIVE-YEAR INTERVALS, 1850–1910

(Million net tons)

Year	United States (1)	United Kingdom (2)	Germany (3)	France (4)	Belgium (5)	World (6)	U.S. production as a percentage of world production (7)
1850..	8.4	60.5 ᵃ	6.0 ᵇ	5.0	6.4	n.a.	n.a.
1855..	16.1	72.2	11.3 ᵇ	8.2	9.3	n.a.	n.a.
1860..	20.0	94.1	15.2 ᵇ	9.2	10.6	n.a.	n.a.
1865..	24.4	110.0	31.2	13.1	13.1	200.7	12.2%
1870..	40.4	123.7	37.5	14.5	15.1	234.9	17.2
1875..	55.8	149.3	52.7	18.7	16.5	308.5	18.1
1880..	79.4	164.6	65.2	21.3	18.6	364.7	21.8
1885..	110.1	178.5	81.2	21.5	19.2	447.8	24.6
1890..	157.8	203.4	98.4	28.8	22.4	563.7	28.0
1895..	193.1	212.3	114.6	30.9	22.5	644.2	30.0
1900..	269.7	252.2	164.8	36.8	25.9	846.0	31.9
1905..	392.7	264.5	191.6	39.0	24.1	1,036.5	37.9
1910..	501.6	296.0	245.0	42.5	26.4	1,278.6	39.2

n.a. Not available.
ᵃ Figure refers to 1851.
ᵇ Figures refer to Prussia only; all figures for Germany include lignite.

SOURCES: Figures for the United States, 1850–85, from H. N. Eavenson, *The First Century and a Quarter of American Coal Industry* (Pittsburgh: privately printed, 1942), pp. 433–34, Table 20; and for 1890–1901, from U. S. Bureau of Mines. Other countries for 1850–65 from *The Mineral Industry, Its Statistics, Technology and Trade,* ed. R. P. Rothwell, Vol. II (New York: Scientific Publishing Company, 1892), pp. 220–21; and for 1870–1910 from U.S. Geological Survey, *Mineral Resources of the United States, 1910,* Part II (Washington, D. C.: U.S. Government Printing Office), pp. 60–61.

in per capita terms (see Table 17). At the turn of the century, coal consumption in the United States amounted to 260 million tons (see Table 13). Compared with this huge quantity, exports were small. Wood had been relegated to an insignificant position, except as a household fuel; but the new sources of energy—oil, natural gas, and hydropower—were still of relatively minor importance. Coal already supplied nearly three-quarters of the greatly increased total energy input, and its dominant position appeared unchallenged. For practical purposes, the supply of coal had become identical with total energy supply.

At the same time, the future demand for coal appeared headed for much higher levels. Despite fluctuations and temporary setbacks, such as those associated with the depression of 1907–08, the rapid growth of the economy as a whole that characterized the last quarter of the nineteenth century continued until World War I. In the decade 1899–1909, gross national product (GNP) expanded by one-half, and in per capita terms by nearly one-quarter. The output of the manufacturing industries rose by 58 per cent; production of basic materials such as pig iron and steel increased even faster—by 89 and 125 per cent. The power equipment in manufacturing nearly doubled, from 9.8 to 18.1

TABLE 17. TOTAL AND PER CAPITA CONSUMPTION OF COAL IN THE
UNITED STATES AND THE UNITED KINGDOM, SELECTED YEARS, 1850-1910

| | United States | | | United Kingdom | |
Year	Total (million net tons)	Per capita (net tons)	Year	Total (million net tons)	Per capita (net tons)
1850........	8.5	0.4	1853........	56.3	2.5
1860........	20.1	0.6	1861........	87.0	3.5
1870........	40.6	1.0	1871........	113.8	4.1
1880........	79.2	1.6	1881........	144.6	4.7
1890........	156.4	2.5	1891........	162.8	4.8
1900........	262.8	3.4	1901........	180.6	4.7
1905........	384.0	4.6	1905........	189.2	4.7
1910........	487.7	5.3	1910........	207.0	4.9

SOURCES: United States: Table 13 and Appendix Table X. United Kingdom: Based on
The Mineral Industry, Its Statistics, Technology and Trade, ed. R. P. Rothwell, Vol. II
(New York: Scientific Publishing Company, 1892), p. 221; W. S. Jevons, *The Coal
Question*, ed. A. W. Flux (rev. ed., New York: MacMillan & Co., 1906), p. 139; H. S.
Fleming, *A Report to the Bituminous Coal Trade Association on the Present and Future
of the Bituminous Coal Trade* (New York: Bituminous Coal Trade Association, 1908),
p. 63; and Palmer Putnam, *Energy in the Future* (New York: Van Nostrand, 1953),
p. 363. Coal consumption in the United Kingdom calculated from production minus
exports of coal, coke, packaged fuel, and bunker coal for ships engaged in foreign trade.

million hp. Railroad mileage continued to expand; railroad horsepower increased from 21.8 to 48.5 million.[42] Electric power production, after a slow
start around 1880, grew rapidly after 1900. The rise of a specialized electric
utility industry and the expanding share of purchased energy in the convenient
form of electricity greatly accelerated the trend toward mechanization and mass
production. Around the turn of the century the term "labor-saving device" was
coined in the United States.

All of these industrial and technological developments pointed to an increasing demand for energy that in the prevailing opinion of that period would be
met mainly by the ever-increasing use of coal. Although there was little substantiated information on available coal reserves, coal resources were known to
be so huge that they would last hundreds of years (see Chapter 8). But the
doubling of consumption during every decade between 1850 and 1900 seemed
to indicate also an enormous increase in the demand for a nonrenewable raw
material. Observers concerned with the future were well aware that a large
share of the existing coal was not accessible or was not easily mined, that the
best and most easily accessible deposits were generally exploited first, that

[42] GNP—Appendix Table XIII. GNP per capita—Appendix Table XII. Manufacturing—
Solomon Fabricant, *The Output of Manufacturing Industries, 1899–1937* (New York: National
Bureau of Economic Research, 1940), p. 44, Table 1. Pig iron and steel—U.S. Bureau of the
Census, *Historical Statistics of the United States, 1789–1945* (Washington, D. C.: U.S.
Government Printing Office, 1949), Series G 96 and J 165. Horsepower in manufacturing—
Ibid., Series J 11 and J 12. Railroad horsepower—C. R. Daugherty, A. H. Horton and R. W.
Davenport, *op. cit.*

recovery was much less than the total coal in place and, most important, that only a small portion of the inherent energy of coal was utilized in the form of heat or power, but that every ton of coal burned was irrevocably lost.

There was at that time an awareness of the great progress that had been made in coal utilization—from more efficient space heating equipment to greatly improved boilers and engines. It was pointed out that some thirty years earlier at least five pounds of coal had to be burned in a steam boiler in order to produce one horsepower hour of mechanical work, whereas the most modern internal combustion engines run with coal gas could produce one horsepower hour with as little as one pound of coal.[43] These improvements were praised not only because they decreased the cost of coal per unit of power, but also because they meant a saving of an irreproducible natural resource for use by future generations in this and other industrially advanced countries. The American coal experts were convinced that the United States, which had incomparably larger coal reserves than any other developed country, would sooner or later have to meet the greatly increased import needs of other nations. For this country, they anticipated a slower future rate of growth of coal consumption because of a continued increase in the efficiency of use, but they were convinced that per capita consumption would continue to expand as a result of the decreasing cost per unit of heat and power derived from coal and that this in turn would accelerate the mechanization in nearly all sectors of the economy.[44]

On the basis of these ideas, estimates of future coal demand were developed that make fascinating reading today. One such forecast which is of considerable interest is that made by H. S. Fleming of the probable coal consumption, in the aggregate and by main uses, for the period 1905 to 1950, based on experience during the period 1885–1905.[45] It is presented in Table 18 and Figure 14. As a forecast of future coal demand, this estimate was far off the mark (Table 18, columns 3 through 8). The actual 1950 coal demand was only about one-third as large as the predicted consumption; the use of coal by railroads and the export level were overestimated by seven times; coal input for coke production was expected to be nearly two and one-third times as large as the actual requirements turned out to be.

Even so, the predicted coal demand in 1950—which, under the author's assumptions, may be taken to represent the equivalent of total energy demand in that year—is only 1.5 per cent higher than the actual total energy consumption in that year (Table 18, columns 10 and 11). It is rare, indeed, to find an economic estimate covering nearly half a century that comes as close to the mark as this one did with respect to total energy demand. It is even more remarkable to find that the estimate was substantially correct not only in its

[43] Fleming, *op. cit.*, p. 2.

[44] *Ibid.*, and H. A. Kuhn, *Substantial Prosperity* (Pittsburgh: Westmoreland Coal Company, 1907).

[45] Fleming, *op. cit.*, pp. 6–8, 10 (Fleming was secretary-treasurer of the Bituminous Coal Association).

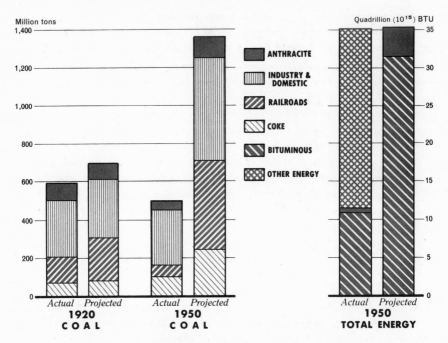

Figure 14.   Fleming's projected coal consumption versus actual coal and energy consumption.

terminal level but also in the changing rates of growth on which that level was based. The estimated increase in coal demand was, for example, 79 per cent over the decade 1900–10 and 44 per cent for the 1930–50 period (taking twenty years to smooth out the effects of the unforeseeable depression and World War II). The actual increase in total energy consumption during those two periods was 73 per cent and 52 per cent. The contradiction between the essential correctness of the forecast as an estimate of total energy demand and its incorrectness as an estimate of coal demand is striking. Although Fleming was remarkably accurate (whether or not for the right reasons) in his appraisal of the economy's future needs for energy, he failed to foresee the changes which would take place in the combination of energy sources which would be used to satisfy these needs.[46]

In a sense, this forecast reflects a typical weakness of many studies in the field of energy—the tendency to consider an energy commodity separately rather than as a component of a combination of energy sources whose composition will depend on changes in the structure of the economy, technological innovations, comparative price movements, shifts in consumer preference, etc. It shows also

[46] A very similar forecast was made in the same year by Edward W. Parker in "Past and Future Coal Production," *Mines and Minerals*, Vol. 28 (May 1908), p. 463. He predicted for the decade 1946–55 a coal production of 1,371 million tons. Actual output during this period amounted to 546 million tons, or 39.8 per cent of the expected production.

TABLE 18. FLEMING'S COAL PROJECTION VERSUS ACTUAL CONSUMPTION OF COAL AND OF ALL ENERGY

(Thousand net tons)

Energy source	Coal								All energy		
	Actual consumption		Projected consumption		Actual consumption		Actual as per cent of projected		Projected 1950 consumption (trillion Btu)	Actual 1950 consumption (trillion Btu)	Actual as per cent of projected $\{\frac{(10)}{(9)} \times 100\}$
	1885	1905	1920	1950	1920	1950	$\{\frac{(5)}{(3)} \times 100\}$ 1920	$\{\frac{(6)}{(4)} \times 100\}$ 1950			
	(1)	(2)	(3)	(4)	(5)	(6)	(7)	(8)	(9)	(10)	(11)
Coke..................	8,071	49,531	82,188	242,204	76,191	103,845	92.7%	42.9%			
Railroads.............	29,350	109,267	222,568	468,214	135,414	64,010	60.8	13.7			
Industrial and domestic	31,131	131,655	304,581	547,538	296,990	286,347	97.5	52.3			
Total bituminous......	68,552	290,453	609,337	1,257,956	508,595	454,202	83.5	36.1	32,958	11,900	36.1%
Bituminous exports....	(766)	(7,794)	(31,713)	(175,991)	(38,517)	(25,468)	121.5	14.5			
Total anthracite.......	37,682	75,200	85,566	106,505	85,786	39,900	100.3	37.5	2,705	1,013	37.4
Total coal	106,234	365,653	694,903	1,364,461	594,381	494,102	85.5	36.2	35,663	12,913	36.2
Energy consumption other than coal......										22,223	
Aggregate energy consumption									(35,663)	35,136	98.5

SOURCES: Columns 1 through 4, H. S. Fleming, *A Report to the Bituminous Coal Trade Association on the Present and Future of the Bituminous Coal Trade* (New York: Bituminous Coal Trade Association, 1908), pp. 8, 10; columns 5 and 6, U.S. Bureau of Mines, *Minerals Yearbook*, various issues (Washington, D. C.: U.S. Government Printing Office); and column 10, Appendix Table VII.

how much estimates of future demand for raw materials are influenced by the state of knowledge about the availability of resources. At the beginning of the century and for many years thereafter, oil resources were so grossly under-estimated that their exhaustion was expected in the near future; hence it was thought that oil could be disregarded in any long-range projections of energy use. The following remarks, although written much later, typify this shortcoming:

> Oil, natural gas, water power, and wood are all in use for one or another of the purposes served by coal. . . . Our own supply of petroleum, at the present rate of consumption and waste, could not be expected to last more than fifteen or twenty years. . . . Our petroleum wells might be empty by 1940. . . . Natural gas has even less promise for the future. . . . Water power . . . is limited in amount. . . . Wood also is replaceable, though not always replaced. . . . To get an amount of wood sufficient to take the place of a year's supply of coal we would have to devote all our arable land to scientific forestry. . . . Of all the fuels now in use, therefore, coal is the only one which seems to have much of a future.[47]

The Fleming forecast was worked out in the very year that coal accounted for the greatest share it was ever to reach in the total energy supply: nearly 78 per cent in 1907 (see Figure 10). Unnoticed, the peak of its relative importance passed. Absolute consumption of coal continued to increase, though at a slower rate, for another decade until 1918. In that year, total coal consumption, stimulated by the war demand, amounted to 651 million tons, of which bituminous accounted for about 90 per cent. The year 1918 not only marked the end of the virtually uninterrupted absolute rise in the demand for coal, it was also the last year in which coal contributed more than three-quarters of the total energy consumption. And it was the only year in which per capita consumption exceeded six tons.

. . .

Post-World War I: A Period of Relative Decline

After World War I, a decline in coal production and consumption began that lasted until 1932. Even in prosperous 1929, the demand for coal remained under 600 million tons. At the lowest point during the depression, coal consumption amounted to 357 million tons, barely 55 per cent of the quantity used in 1918. The gradual recovery that started in 1933 culminated in the war year of 1943 in exactly the same record consumption reached in the war year of 1918— 651 million tons. During that quarter century, the population of the country had increased by 31 per cent; GNP had risen by 130 per cent, and the output of manufacturing industries by 225 per cent; the gross consumption of energy, measured in Btu's, had increased by nearly one-half.

Stimulated by the serious coal shortage overseas following the end of World War II, production in this country continued to increase for a short period, and reached its all-time high in 1947, when 688 million tons of coal were mined,

---

[47] E. T. Devine, *Coal, Economic Problems of the Mining, Marketing and Consumption of Anthracite and Soft Coal in the United States* (Bloomington, Ill.: American Review Service Press, 1925), pp. 20–22.

slightly more than production in 1918 (678 million tons). Bituminous coal output was nearly 9 per cent larger and anthracite production 42 per cent smaller than at the previous peak. In 1947, coal exports reached 77 million tons, almost twice the amount of the largest export level after World War I.

From its second consumption peak in 1943, coal declined through 1955 by nearly one-third, or slightly more than 200 million tons. In those twelve years, the demand for bituminous coal fell by 29 per cent, that for anthracite by more than one-half. During the mid-1950's, annual demand for coal fluctuated around 450 million tons (see Table 13 and Figure 12). In absolute terms this is still huge, but it is low on the coal industry's barometric scale.

The statistical record of coal consumption by class of use is shown in Table 19 and Figure 15. Examination of these data reveals some of the factors under-

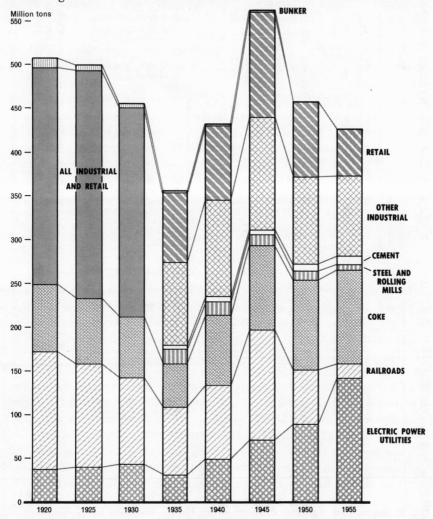

Figure 15. Coal consumption by consumer class, 1920–55.

TABLE 19. COAL CONSUMPTION BY CONSUMER CLASS, FIVE-YEAR INTERVALS, 1920-55

Year	Bituminous coal									Anthracite			All coal
	Electric power utilities (1)	Class I railroads (2)	Coke (3)	Cement mills (4)	Steel and rolling mills (5)	Other industrial (6)	Retail deliveries (7)	Bunker, foreign[a] (8)	Total (9)	Households and commercial (10)	All other[b] (11)	Total (12)	Grand total (13)
Thousand net tons													
1920	37,124	135,414	76,191		249,380			10,486	508,595			85,786	594,383
1925	40,222	117,714	74,533		261,858			4,866	499,193			64,061	563,254
1930	42,898	98,400	69,805		240,390			3,497	454,990			67,628	522,618
1935	30,936	77,109	50,515	3,456	16,585	95,705	80,444	1,576	356,326	42,200[c]	8,900	51,100	407,426
1940	49,126	85,130	81,386	5,559	14,169	109,427	84,687	1,426	430,910	39,300[c]	9,700	49,000	479,910
1945	71,603	125,120	95,349	4,203	14,241	127,969	119,297	1,785	559,567	38,900[c]	12,700	51,600	611,167
1950	88,262	60,969	103,845	7,923	10,877	97,187	84,422	717	454,202	29,600[c]	10,300	39,900	494,102
1955	140,550	15,473	107,377	8,529	7,353	90,665	53,020	445	423,412	15,100[d]	8,500	23,600	447,012
Percentage distribution													
1920	7.3%	26.6%	15.0%		49.0%			2.1%	100.0%				
1925	8.0	23.6	14.9		52.5			1.0	100.0				
1930	9.4	21.6	15.3		52.8			0.8	100.0				
1935	8.7	21.6	14.2	1.0%	4.7%	26.9%	22.6%	0.4	100.0				
1940	11.4	19.8	18.9	1.3	3.3	25.4	19.7	0.3	100.0				
1945	12.8	22.4	17.0	0.8	2.5	22.9	21.3	0.3	100.0				
1950	19.4	13.4	22.9	1.7	2.4	21.4	18.6	0.2	100.0				
1955	33.2	3.7	25.4	2.0	1.7	21.4	12.5	0.1	100.0				

[a] This series has been revised by the U.S. Bureau of Mines to include consumption by Lake vessels back to 1933. In order to keep it comparable with earlier years the old series is shown above and the series "other industrial" has been adjusted accordingly.

[b] By subtraction from column 12. Consists of anthracite used in electric and gas utilities, in railroads, and a variety of industrial uses.

[c] A. T. Coumbe and I. F. Avery, "Fuels Consumed for Residential and Commercial Space Heating, 1935-1951," U.S. Bureau of Mines, *Information Circular 7657*, Washington, January 1953.

[d] Appendix Table A-6.

SOURCE: U.S. Bureau of Mines, *Minerals Yearbook*, various issues (Washington, D. C.: U.S. Government Printing Office), except where other-

lying the drop in the absolute and relative levels of coal consumption. Among the many and varied reasons for the decline of coal, the most frequently cited and doubtless the most important is the substitution of liquid and gaseous fuels. In addition there have been increases in the thermal efficiency of coal utilization. The most significant expanding market for coal—electric power generation— probably would have consumed even greater quantities if the gains in conversion efficiency had not been as large as those actually experienced.

The railroads were the most important single stimulus in the early rise of the coal industry; they were also the most important single factor in its decline. The course of events in this market, where coal suffered its most severe loss, is complex, involving both the level of rail traffic and the fuel consumption pattern of the railroads. After their very great expansion during the early stages of U.S. industrial development, the railroads did not continue to grow in propor- tion to the economy as a whole. Not only did the network cease large-scale expansion after World War I, but more important, the growth in freight ton- miles declined from a nearly threefold increase in the first quarter of the cen- tury to only 40 per cent in the following twenty-five years. Passenger-miles more than doubled between 1900 and 1925; they declined by more than 10 per cent in the period 1925–50.[48]

At its peak just after World War I, the railroad market absorbed about 135 million tons of bituminous coal, nearly one-quarter of total consumption. It has been estimated that if the railroads had used no other fuel in the early 1950's, their consumption at the time would have been about 150 million tons.[49] Al- though this is several times the actual consumption in those years, it is significant that the railroad market for coal would not have expanded much even under the most favorable circumstances. The greater part of the expansion of trans- portation since the end of World War I occurred outside the railroad system and was taken over by means of transportation that used oil, not coal, as a source of energy.

However, on top of the declining relative importance of railroads within total transportation, there occurred an actual falling off in the use of coal for railroad fuel as compared to other fuels. Thus, the sharp decline in the use of coal, particularly in the years following the second World War, is the direct result of oil's invasion of the railroad fuel market. Diesel engines proved so much more efficient and cheaper to maintain than coal-burning steam locomotives that the change to oil proved more economical despite the fact that its cost per Btu is higher than coal. After the end of World War II, steam locomotives fired with coal were replaced by diesel-electric engines at such a rate that by 1952, 68 per cent of all energy used for motive power was furnished by diesel oil. Together with the 7 per cent supplied by fuel oil and the 3 per cent from elec-

---

[48] *Historical Statistics of the United States, 1789–1945, op. cit.,* and U.S. Bureau of the Census, *Continuation to 1952 of Historical Statistics of the United States, 1789–1945 (Wash- ington, D. C.: U.S. Government Printing Office, 1954),* Series K 31, 41, 45.

[49] Bituminous Coal Institute, *1953 Bituminous Coal Annual* (Washington, D. C.: 1953), p. 108.

tricity, this reduced coal to a mere 22 per cent of all energy used by locomotives.[50] In that year, the railroad system consumed 38 million tons of bituminous coal. By 1955, this had been reduced to 15 million tons, not much more than one-tenth of the 135 million tons after World War I. (Three years later, in 1958, just over 4 million tons were consumed, and, of these, only one-quarter for motive purposes.)

Another change in transportation, but of far smaller quantitative importance than those in the railroad market, was the replacement of coal by oil in maritime transport. In 1920, more than 10 million tons of bituminous coal were consumed in overseas transportation. By the mid-1950's, this amount had been reduced to a half million tons—a decline of 95 per cent.

A factor of considerable importance in the decline in coal consumption was coal's replacement, mainly by liquid and gaseous fuels, in the residential and commercial market. According to the figures in Table 19, coal consumption in this market was somewhat over 125 million tons in 1935 and 1940, rose to more than 160 million tons during World War II, then declined sharply in the postwar decade to about 115 million tons in 1950, and less than 70 million tons in 1955.[51] In contrast to coal, the consumption of oil and gas in this market experienced an almost uninterrupted growth between 1935 and 1955. As a result of these two disparate movements, the percentage importance of coal and of oil and gas in the household and commercial field changed radically. In 1935, coal accounted for 78 per cent of all mineral fuels consumed in this market, and liquid and gaseous fuels for 22 per cent; by 1955, coal's share had dropped to 23 per cent and that of liquid and gaseous fuels had risen to 77 per cent—a total reversal of proportions.[52]

In the industrial market, coal has fared much better than in railroads and in the household and commercial sectors. Table 19 shows that in the four categories constituting industrial consumption of bituminous coal (shown separately in columns 3 through 6), total industrial consumption rose between 1935 and 1955, although there was a decline from the peak levels experienced during World War II. Even though coal's performance in industry was better than in transportation and the household and commercial market, it still involved a sharp relative decline measured against the great increases in the level of industrial output since the mid-1930's.

For the manufacturing sector, this decline can be traced back over nearly fifty years. The record of coal in this sector (see Table 20) is of special interest

[50] *Ibid.* It should be noted that these percentage figures are based on the amount of coal—about 150 million tons—that would have been required if there had been only steam locomotives using no other fuel than coal. This particular approach was used in order to measure the displacement of coal which had actually taken place.

[51] Derived by adding retail deliveries of bituminous coal, which approximates household and commercial consumption, to the household and commercial figures for anthracite (Table 19, columns 7 and 10).

[52] Figures for 1935 derived from A. T. Coumbe and I. F. Avery, *op. cit.*, Table 12. Figures for 1955 from Tables 81 and 83. Proportions based on figures excluding fuel equivalents of electric energy consumed.

because during the entire period for which data are available the manufacturing industries have been the largest coal consumer. Between 1909 and 1947, their share in coal consumption by the economy as a whole remained fairly stable, fluctuating between 34 and 38 per cent. The increase to 45 per cent of the total by 1954 was brought about mainly by the rapid decline in coal use by railroads and households during the postwar period. In absolute terms, consumption of coal by manufacturing industries declined by one-fifth between 1947 and 1954. In the latter year, it was only 7 per cent larger than it had been in 1909. Over this period, manufacturing production expanded fivefold. Thus, per unit of output, coal consumption declined by about four-fifths during forty-five years. Although coal still is, by far, the leading fuel used in manufacturing (see Table 79), its relative importance has been declining continuously. Fuel oil consumption, on the other hand, in 1954 was more than twelve times its 1909 level, and the use of natural and manufactured gas was nearly twenty-three times greater.[53] Per unit of output in manufacturing, fuel oil consumption rose to two and a half times and gas consumption to four and a half times the previous level.

The decline of coal as a source of heat and power in the manufacturing sector is even greater than Table 20 indicates, since these data include the coal consumed in coke making. The amount of coal so utilized rose from 59.4 million tons in 1909 to 85.4 million in 1954,[54] leaving 106.2 million tons and 91.3 million

TABLE 20. COAL CONSUMED BY MANUFACTURING INDUSTRIES, SELECTED YEARS, 1909–54

Year	Coal[a] (thousand net tons)			Per cent of total coal consumption (4)	Index of coal consumed by manufacturing (1909 = 100) (5)	Index of output of manufactures (1909 = 100) (6)	Index of coal consumed per unit of output (1909 = 100) (7)
	Bituminous (1)	Anthracite (2)	Total (3)				
1909..	151,123	14,470	165,593	37.0%	100.0	100.0	100.0
1919..	188,838	13,740	202,578	38.3	122.3	149.8	81.6
1929..	196,780	9,452	206,232	34.9	124.5	228.6	54.5
1939..	138,182	5,168	143,350	33.7	86.6	224.7	38.5
1947..	210,141	8,781	218,922	36.8	132.2	394.1	33.5
1954..	172,716	4,000	176,716	45.3	106.7	500.6	21.3

[a] Represents coal used by manufacturing industries for heat, power, and as a raw material for further manufacture—such as making coke.

SOURCES: Columns 1 through 3, U.S. Bureau of the Census, *U.S. Census of Manufactures: 1954*, Vol. I (Washington, D. C.: U.S. Government Printing Office, 1957), p. 208–3, except for anthracite consumption in 1954 which is an estimate based on Appendix Table A-6. Column 4, from column 3 and Appendix Table VI. Column 6, 1909, from Solomon Fabricant, *The Output of Manufacturing Industries, 1899–1937* (New York: National Bureau of Economic Research, 1940), p. 44; 1919–54, from Federal Reserve Board Index of Manufacturing Production, linked and shifted to 1909 base.

[53] U.S. Bureau of the Census, *U.S. Census of Manufactures: 1954*, Vol. I (Washington, D. C.: U.S. Government Printing Office, 1957), p. 208–3.

[54] U.S. Bureau of Mines, *Minerals Yearbook*, various issues (Washington, D. C.: U.S. Government Printing Office).

tons, respectively, for other purposes. The consumption of coal by the coke industry for the period 1920–55 is shown in Table 19, column 3. While total use of bituminous coal dropped by 17 per cent, the quantity used in coke making expanded by 40 per cent. Coal's favorable performance in this field reflects the fact that in this important market it could not be threatened by competitive energy sources, since there has been no feasible substitute for coke as a metal-lurgical fuel. However, even in this market, factors have been at work to reduce the amount of coal consumed in relation to the output of steel.

From 1900 to 1950, the quantity of coal used for coking increased 225 per cent, but output of coke rose slightly more, by 255 per cent; thus there was a moderate saving in the required coal input. Output of pig iron increased by an even greater amount, 328 per cent. These figures are not wholly conclusive, since not all coke output goes into the iron and steel industry. In earlier years, a substantial share was used in residential and commercial heating. Neverthe-less, the amount of coal required to produce a ton of pig iron has clearly been declining. In 1918, the iron and steel industries consumed 3,194 pounds of coking coal per net ton of pig iron; in 1946, only 2,706 pounds.[55] A far greater change occurred in the relationship between pig iron and steel output. By 1950, steel production was 8.4 times the 1909 level—nearly twice as much as the pig iron increase. This was made possible by the long-term growth in the use of scrap in making steel (since the 1930's scrap has accounted for about one-half of the furnace charge). This, in turn, has had an adverse effect on the demand of the steel industry for coal. The scrap charged to the steel furnace does not, like pig iron, require the use of coal (as coke in the blast furnace) to produce it. Thus, between 1900 and 1950, steel output rose more than two and one-half times as much as coal used in coke making. By far the most important reason for this disparity is to be found in changes in steel production methods quite independent of developments in the energy field.

In one sense, some of the foregoing data are misleading, since they fail to reflect the fact that a substantial portion of the market which coal has lost as a primary fuel has been regained in the form of electricity. For example, the amount of electric power purchased by manufacturing industries has greatly expanded in recent decades, from 36.4 billion kilowatt hours (kwh) in 1929 to 102.8 billion kwh in 1947 and 187 billion kwh in 1954.[56]

As can be seen from Table 19, electric power utilities have provided the only market in which coal consumption has expanded rapidly. To be sure, coal's relative importance as a fuel to electric utilities has declined from nearly nine-tenths of all fuels consumed by thermal power plants in the early 1920's, to seven-tenths in 1955.[57] But, over the same period, generation of electric power

[55] *Minerals Yearbook, 1947, op. cit.,* p. 266.

[56] *U.S. Census of Manufactures: 1947,* Report MC 203, *op. cit.* (1949), p. 3; and *ibid.* for *1954* (1957), p. 208–3.

[57] Federal Power Commission, annual reports, *Consumption of Fuel for Production of Electric Energy,* as quoted in *Historical Statistics of the United States, 1789–1945, op. cit.,* Series G 194–99, and Edison Electric Institute, "Electric Utility Industry in the United States," *Statistical Bulletin for the Year 1957* (New York: 1958), p. 47.

by such plants rose from 24 billion to 434 billion kwh. Consumption of coal for this purpose increased from 37 million tons in 1920 to 140 million in 1955. With the sole exception of the depression years of the 1930's this market expanded steadily and at a fast rate. In the single decade 1945–55, the amount of coal consumed by electric utilities just about doubled. The expanding market in this field is the more impressive if one considers the great advance in the efficiency of transforming fuel into electric power. At the beginning of this century, nearly 7 pounds of coal were required to generate 1 kilowatt hour. By 1920, this had decreased to 3 pounds; in 1950, it was 1.19 pounds; and in 1954, for the first time, slightly less than 1 pound.

In Figure 16, the foregoing data on bituminous coal consumption are presented in terms of the changing percentages of the total accounted for by each of the different consumer classes. Between 1920 and 1955, the relative importance of coke and electric power in total consumption grew; coke from 15 per cent of

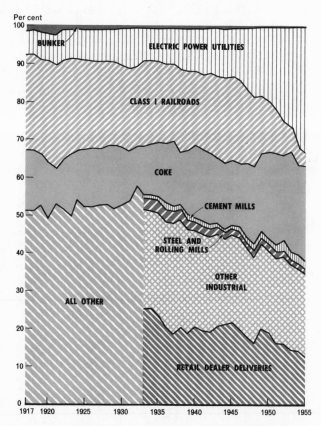

Figure 16. Use pattern of bituminous coal and lignite, 1917–55.

TABLE 21. COAL CONSUMPTION IN GREAT BRITAIN AND IN THE UNITED STATES, SELECTED YEARS, 1869-1955

(Million net tons)

Consumer class	Great Britain[a]				United States					
	1869	1903	1938	1955	1870	1885	1905	1920	1940	1955
Total bituminous coal[b]	105.9	187.0	175.6	212.2	20.8	68.6	290.5	498.1	429.4	423.1
Railways	2.2	14.6	13.2	12.2		29.4	109.3	135.4	85.1	15.5
Electricity		n.a.	14.9	42.9			n.a.	37.1	49.1	140.6
Coke	} 36.4	} 31.4	19.1	} 33.5		} 8.1	49.5	76.2	81.4	107.4
Iron and steel industry			10.0[c]						} 129.1	} 106.6
Other industry	39.3	88.5	67.3	50.1		} 31.1	} 131.7	} 249.4		
Gas works	7.3	16.8	19.1	27.9					84.7	53.0
Domestic use[d]	20.7	35.8	32.0[c]	31.8					n.a.	n.a.
Miscellaneous	n.a.	n.a.	n.a.	13.8						
Total anthracite[e]	n.a.	n.a.	n.a.	n.a.	19.8	37.7	75.2	85.8	49.0	23.6
Total coal consumption	105.9	187.0	175.6	212.2	40.6	106.3	365.7	583.9	478.4	446.7
Per capita consumption (net tons)	3.9	4.8	3.8	4.3	1.0	1.9	4.6	5.6	3.6	2.7

n.a. Not available.

[a] Data for 1869 and 1903 refer to United Kingdom.

[b] Excluding exports and bunkers, foreign trade. Totals for the United States are the sums of the use categories shown and vary slightly from "apparent consumption" shown in Table 13.

[c] Estimated.

[d] For Great Britain includes small amounts of anthracite and nonresidential consumers with an annual consumption of less than 100 tons of coal. For the United States, covers retail deliveries, including nonresidential consumers.

[e] Anthracite is of negligible importance in Great Britain.

SOURCES: Figures for Great Britain in 1869 and 1903 based on W. S. Jevons, The Coal Question, ed. A. W. Flux (rev. ed., New York: Macmillan & Co., 1906), p. 139; those for 1938 and 1955, Central Statistical Office, Annual Abstract of Statistics, No. 95 (London: Her Majesty's Stationery Office, 1958), Table 150. Figures for United States in 1870 from Table 13; for 1885 and 1905 based on H. S. Fleming, A Report to the Bituminous Coal Trade Association on the Present and Future of the Bituminous Coal Trade (New York: Bituminous Coal Trade Association, 1908), pp. 8, 10; and for 1920, 1940, and 1955: Table 19.

the total in 1920 to 25 per cent in 1955, electric power from about 7 per cent to 33 per cent. Railroads, on the other hand, which accounted for more than one-quarter of the total in 1920, consumed less than 4 per cent in 1955. Detailed annual data for the other use classes began in the mid-1930's. Between 1935 and 1955, the relative importance of retail deliveries declined by about one-half, from approximately one-quarter of the total to just over 12 per cent. Over the same period, industrial uses other than coke declined from about 33 per cent to 25 per cent of the total.

·   ·   ·

Coal in the United States and Great Britain: Rapid Change vs. Relative Stability

In concluding this brief survey of the rise and decline of coal, it is of interest to compare the history of coal consumption in the United States with that in Great Britain, the classical country of industrial development. This is done in broad outline in Table 21.

It will be observed that the breakdown of total coal consumption shown in the table goes back to 1869 for Great Britain but only to 1885 for the United States. These were two years in which the production of pig iron, an important indicator of industrial development, was roughly equal. Table 21 reveals the contrast between the slowness and relative stability of the development in Britain, especially since the beginning of the twentieth century, and the dynamic changes in this country. Over a period of eighty-five years, per capita consumption of coal in Britain remained, with only slight fluctuations, between 3.8 and 4.8 tons per year. During the same period, the per capita use of coal in the United States increased from one to nearly six tons and then fell to less than half the latter figure. In one of the main fields of use, the British iron and steel industry, including coke production, consumed approximately the same amount of coal at the beginning of the century as at the end of the period. In this country, coal used for coking more than doubled during the present century. The British railroads used in 1955 just about the same amount of coal as around 1900. In the United States, this market in 1955 had shrunk to about one-seventh of its size in 1905.

Among these contrasting figures one similarity stands out: since the last pre-war year (1938 in Britain and 1940 in the United States), the use of coal for electricity generation has nearly tripled. For Britain, with its rapidly deteriorating coal reserves, this development has led to plans and programs for supplementing coal with other sources of energy, including nuclear power. In the United States, with its very large coal resources, the growing demand for electric power poses no problem for coal but instead points to an expanding market which coal could readily satisfy.[58]

---

[58] Although this chapter traces long-run trends in energy use rather than changes in the production of energy materials, it should be mentioned here that during the post-World War II period there have been great improvements in production methods and productivity in coal mining (see Chapter 8).

OIL

The Beginnings of the Industry

A century ago, the successful completion of the first well purposely drilled to obtain petroleum marked the beginning of the oil industry. Many separate developments came together to set the stage for the spectacular entrance of the new industry, which was destined to play a leading role.

By the middle of the nineteenth century, the need for efficient and cheap illuminants and lubricants to replace scarce and costly animal and vegetable oils had become a pressing technological problem. Petroleum had been known to exist in oil springs, seepages in the earth, and salt wells for many decades; it had been chemically analyzed and found to be an excellent raw material for illuminating and lubricating oils. In the coal oil and camphene industries,[59] crude distillation processes to produce oil for lighting had been devised. In the salt well industry, adequate methods of drilling had been developed. A seemingly unlimited market existed and the capital to launch a new industry to meet this market was available. The only thing lacking was, in fact, petroleum—at least petroleum in sufficient quantities. Then, in 1854, a petroleum company was founded and some of the land around the springs on Oil Creek in Pennsylvania was bought up. After a few futile attempts at digging for oil, the ingeniously simple idea of drilling a well, in a way similar to that by which salt wells had been drilled for years, proved a success.[60]

On August 27, 1859, oil was struck at a depth of 69.5 feet at Titusville, Pennsylvania, and the rush for the "liquid gold" was on. Within the first ten years, the new industry expanded its production from 500,000 to 4,215,000 barrels (equivalent in energy content to nearly a million tons of coal).

It is difficult to imagine two rising industries whose early phases were so dissimilar as those of coal and petroleum. Coal mining developed; the oil industry was created. With coal, more than eighty years elapsed between the first recorded commercial shipment and a production level of one million tons. With petroleum, a corresponding expansion was compressed into one decade. The coal industry was for a long time hampered by the lack of transportation facilities; the oil industry created its own transportation system within a few years. The slow growth of coal mining, spread over a wide area, attracted hardly any attention and few records of its early progress have been preserved. The petroleum industry was concentrated in one narrow region which during the first two decades produced 95 per cent of the total output. Its history is well documented; many of its early steps—from the monthly production of the main wells to monthly prices, from exports to the yield of the principal petroleum products—can be traced back to a fairly early phase, if not to the very beginning. Coal mining

[59] Camphene, a lamp oil distilled from turpentine and alcohol, was introduced in the 1830's. It could be burned alone or mixed with alcohol.

[60] Drake's innovation in the technique of drilling consisted in driving a pipe into the earth and drilling from the surface to cope with water seepage and cave-ins instead of digging down to bedrock and then starting to drill, as was the practice in salt wells.

in its early phases was a rather pedestrian industry in which scarcely anything spectacular happened. The oil industry was from its very beginning—and especially in its beginning—a feverish business, subject to violent fluctuations between sudden overproduction and the eager and highly speculative search for new wells.[61]

The price of a barrel of crude oil at the well dropped from $19.25 in January 1860 to 10 cents in January 1862, only to rise again to $11.00 in December 1864.[62] Sizable fortunes were made and ruinous failures were suffered. Some of the earliest wells turned out to be gushers, which poured out 2,000 to 4,000 barrels a day initially, only to cease production suddenly and completely. Output could not be checked or regulated. Thousands of barrels of the inflammable liquid ran upon the ground or into creeks. The machinery of collecting, transporting, processing, and marketing the new and little known material at the beginning was crude or nonexistent, but it was developed in an incredibly short time.[63]

In the simple refining process of the early period, up to 70 per cent of the crude petroleum could be converted into illuminating oil at a processing cost of only 4 cents to 10 cents a gallon. One year after the drilling of the first well, fifteen refinery plants had been established in the neighborhood. Soon Pittsburgh became a refining center; by 1863, it had sixty plants having a capacity of 26,000 barrels weekly. And in only a few more years, stills had been erected in several cities of the East Coast. During this period, storage and marketing problems were being solved. Large wooden reservoirs were constructed; barge and rail lines were extended into the oil fields. In 1862, the first wooden pipeline conveyed oil from the well to a refinery 1,000 feet away. Only a few years later, wrought iron pipelines began to form connecting links with local railroads and, by 1866, hundreds of wooden tank cars were in use. With these developments, the new illuminant soon could be sold not only all over the United States, but also abroad.

. . .

The Statistical Record of Crude Oil and its Products, 1860–1955

PRODUCTION, CONSUMPTION, AND FOREIGN TRADE

The record of oil production and consumption in the United States over the past century is shown in Tables 22 and 23 and Figure 17. From the very beginning

[61] Many of the dissimilarities between the early history of coal mining and the beginnings of the oil industry are, of course, largely a function of the development of the economy as a whole. Undoubtedly, the coal industry would have fared differently if its commercial development had started later.

[62] U.S. Department of the Interior, *Mineral Resources of the United States, 1882, op. cit.*, p. 203.

[63] See Paul H. Giddens, *The Birth of the Oil Industry* (New York: Macmillan, 1938), pp. 93–94, 142–47, 151; and also Harold F. Williamson and Arnold R. Daum, *The American Petroleum Industry, 1859–1899, The Age of Illumination* (Evanston, Ill.: Northwestern University Press, 1959), pp. 228–31.

TABLE 22.   PRODUCTION AND CONSUMPTION OF OIL, FIVE-YEAR INTERVALS, 1860–1955

(Thousand barrels)

Year	Crude production (1)	Net exports (E) or imports (I) of crude (2)	Apparent consumption of crude (1) ± (2) (3)	Net exports (E) or imports (I) of products (4)	Apparent consumption[a] incl. net trade in products[b] (3) ± (4) (5)	Net exports (E) or imports (I) of crude plus products[b] (2) ± (4) (6)	Net exports (E) or imports (I) as per cent of crude production (6) ÷ (1) (7)	Net exports (E) or imports (I) as per cent of apparent consumption (6) ÷ (5) (8)	Per capita consumption (barrels) (9)
1860	500		500		500				0.02
1865	2,498	E 293	2,205	E 314	1,770	E 728	E 29.1%	E 41.1%	0.05
1870	5,261	E 248	5,013	E 2,460	2,011	E 3,250	E 61.8	E 161.6	0.05
1875	8,788	E 394	8,394	E 5,262	2,002	E 6,786	E 77.2	E 339.0	0.04
1880 c	26,286	E 875	25,411	E 7,383	17,203 c	E 9,083	E 34.6 c	E 52.8	0.34 c
1885	21,859	E 1,939	19,920	E 11,412	7,172	E 14,687	E 67.2	E 204.8	0.13
1890 c	45,824	E 2,299	43,525	E 14,221	27,652 c	E 18,172	E 39.7 c	E 65.7	0.44 c
1895	52,892	E 2,650	50,242	E 18,409	29,726	E 23,166	E 43.8	E 77.9	0.43
1900	63,621	E 3,274	60,347	E 19,944	39,564	E 24,057	E 37.8	E 60.8	0.52
1905	134,717	E 3,004	131,713	E 26,056	105,119	E 29,598	E 22.0	E 28.2	1.25
1910	209,557	E 3,717	205,840	E 31,486	173,559	E 35,998	E 17.2	E 20.7	1.88
1915	281,104	I 14,371	295,475	E 51,372	243,230	E 37,874	E 13.5	E 15.6	2.42
1920	442,929	I 96,880	521,876	E 67,634	454,242	I 29,246	I 6.6	I 6.4	4.27
1925	763,743	I 48,487	800,217	E 84,121	716,096	E 35,634	E 4.7	E 5.0	6.18
1930 d	898,011	E 38,424	1,060,067 d	E 89,305	970,762 d	E 50,881	E 5.7	E 5.2	7.88
1935	996,596	E 19,191	999,804	E 53,947	945,857	E 73,138	E 7.3	E 7.7	7.43
1940	1,353,214	E 8,834	1,321,073	E 36,119	1,284,954	E 44,953	E 3.3	E 3.5	9.73
1945	1,713,655	I 41,339	1,758,505	E 109,346	1,661,487	E 68,007	E 4.0	E 4.1	11.87
1950	1,973,574	I 142,891	2,121,358	I 58,933	2,180,291	I 201,824	I 10.2	I 9.3	14.37
1955	2,484,428	I 273,850	2,751,053	I 51,803	2,802,856	I 325,653	I 13.1	I 11.6	16.96

(Footnotes to table on next page.)

of the petroleum industry to the present, the record is one of almost uninterrupted increase. Production expanded tenfold within the first decade of the industry's existence, from a small output of about a half million barrels in 1860 to over 5 million in 1870. The next tenfold increase took twenty years to achieve; by 1890 output was close to 50 million barrels. Some thirty years later, in 1922, another tenfold increase had taken place, raising production to more than 500 million barrels. By 1929 the billion-barrel mark was passed. The only significant interruption in the growth record was the short-lived decline during the depression of the 1930's, when output dropped to 785 million barrels. Between 1935 (when the previous level was regained) and 1955, crude oil production expanded more slowly in relative terms. During those twenty years, the average annual growth rate was 4.5 per cent; in the period 1909–29, it had been an average of 9 per cent. But the expansion after 1935 involved huge quantities, raising output from a billion to 2.5 billion barrels, while that from 1909 to 1929 involved an absolute increase of about 800,000 barrels.

The record of oil consumption can be traced for present purposes through the statistics of apparent domestic consumption, which are calculated from production of crude oil minus exports plus imports of petroleum and petroleum products and, for the period since 1920, changes in stock.[64] A comparison of the series on petroleum production and apparent consumption (see Table 22, columns 1 and 5) over the past century shows that the relationship between the domestic

---

[64] As shown in the notes to Table 22, stock changes were of great significance for some years during the early period.

(*Footnotes to Table 22.*)

ᵃ Figures for 1920 and subsequent years are adjusted for net changes in stocks of crude.

ᵇ Product figures for 1865–1915 are adjusted to approximate crude oil equivalent, allowing for losses ranging from 20 per cent in 1865 to 2.4 per cent in 1915. For 1920 and subsequent years, refinery losses are considered sufficiently small to require no adjustment of data.

ᶜ Since the data for the early period are not adjusted for stock changes, the apparent consumption and per capita consumption figures for 1880 and, to a lesser degree, 1890, are excessive. In these years, production of crude was exceptionally large, 32 and 30 per cent, respectively, above the preceding year. Exports as a percentage of crude output were comparatively low. Inventories increased from less than 4 million barrels in 1875 to about 18 million in 1880 and 34 million in 1885. But in 1885 output had declined, the share of exports was two-thirds of domestic production of crude, inventories began to decrease. By 1890, they had dropped to less than 10 million barrels. In the meantime, however, beginning in 1886, the newly discovered Ohio-Indiana oil fields were developed and by 1890 stocks of crude in that region had risen to over 20 million barrels. Together with the stocks from the Appalachian fields total inventories in 1890 were about 30 million barrels. See Harold F. Williamson and Arnold R. Daum, *The American Petroleum Industry, 1859–1899, The Age of Illumination* (Evanston, Ill.: Northwestern University Press, 1959), pp. 373, 566, 601.

ᵈ In 1930, difference between production and consumption was made up mainly by exceptionally large withdrawals from stocks, amounting to 123,632,000 barrels.

sources: Column 1, Appendix Table I; columns 2 and 4, U.S. Geological Survey and U.S. Bureau of Mines, *Mineral Resources of the United States*, various issues, and *Minerals Yearbook*, various issues (Washington, D. C.: U.S. Government Printing Office); column 5, Appendix Table VI; and column 9, Appendix Table X.

TABLE 23.   INDEXES OF PRODUCTION AND CONSUMPTION OF OIL,
FIVE-YEAR INTERVALS, 1860-1955

(1900 = 100)

Year	Crude production (1)	Percentage increase per decade (2)	Apparent consumption[a] (3)	Percentage increase per decade (4)	Apparent per capita consumption (5)	Percentage increase per decade (6)
1860........	0.8		1.3		3.8	
1865........	3.9	1860-70	4.5	1860-70	9.6	1860-70
1870........	8.3	937.5%	5.1	292.3%	9.6	152.6%
1875........	13.8	1870-80	5.1	1870-80	7.7	1870-80
1880[b].......	41.3	397.6	43.5	752.9	65.4	581.3
1885........	34.4	1880-90	18.1	1880-90	25.0	1880-90
1890[b].......	72.0	74.3	69.9	60.7	84.6	29.4
1895........	83.1	1890-1900	75.1	1890-1900	82.7	1890-1900
1900........	100.0	38.9	100.0	43.1	100.0	18.2
1905........	211.7	1900-1910	265.7	1900-1910	240.4	1900-1910
1910........	329.4	229.4	438.7	338.7	361.5	261.5
1915........	441.8	1910-20	614.8	1910-20	465.4	1910-20
1920........	696.2	111.4	1,148.1	161.7	821.2	127.2
1925........	1,200.5	1920-30	1,810.0	1920-30	1,188.5	1920-30
1930........	1,411.5	102.7	2,453.6	113.7	1,515.4	84.5
1935........	1,566.4	1930-40	2,390.7	1930-40	1,428.8	1930-40
1940........	2,127.0	50.7	3,247.8	32.4	1,871.1	23.5
1945........	2,693.5	1940-50	4,199.5	1940-50	2,282.7	1940-50
1950........	3,102.1	45.8	5,510.8	69.7	2,763.5	47.7
1955[c]........	3,905.0	25.9[d] 45.0[e]	7,084.4	28.6[d] 68.7[e]	3,261.5	18.0[d] 42.9[e]

[a] Includes net trade in petroleum products.

[b] See footnote [c], Table 22.

[c] If the base were moved by only one decade to 1910, the discrepancy between the index numbers of production and consumption would be far smaller; the production index for 1955 would be 1,185.6, the apparent consumption index, 1,614.9.

[d] Percentage increase over five-year period, 1950-55.

[e] Percentage increase over ten-year period, 1945-55.

NOTE: The above indexes are based on physical quantities (barrels) and differ slightly from those in Appendix Tables V and XI, which are based on Btu values. (See notes to Appendix Table II on Btu values of Pennsylvania grade and other crude oil.)

SOURCE: Table 22.

output of crude oil and the consumption of oil and its products was subject to wide change.

Prior to 1900, taking the first forty years of the petroleum industry as a whole and disregarding short-term deviations, production grew at a faster rate than apparent domestic consumption, roughly in the ratio of 1.0 to 0.6. Between 1900 and 1955, this relationship was reversed. Apparent demand for petroleum and its products increased considerably faster than domestic crude oil output; consumption expanded to seventy times, production to forty times the 1900 level (see Table 23).[65]

[65] It should be noted that this vast difference between the growth of production and that of consumption is to a large extent due to the selection of 1900 as the base year. See footnote c, Table 23.

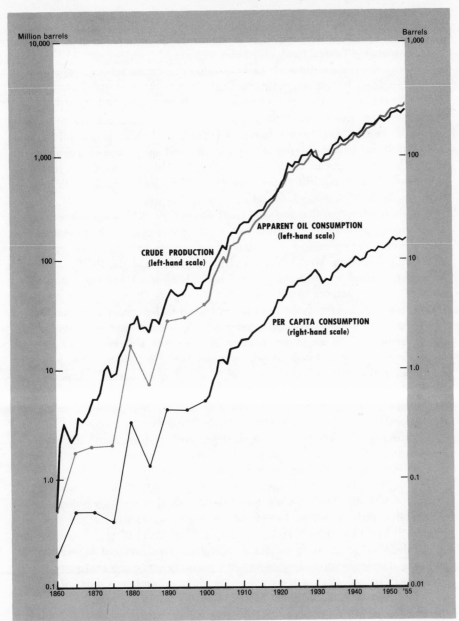

Figure 17. Production and consumption of oil, 1860–1955.

The great disparity between the growth of production and of consumption between 1900 and 1955 reflects the remarkable transformation in the country's net foreign trade position in oil and its products during this period. In 1900, the United States was a net exporter of oil and its products in an amount exceeding one-third of domestic crude production; in 1955, the U.S. position had changed to one of net importer in an amount exceeding 13 per cent of domestic crude output (see Table 22, columns 7 and 8).

Although the present status of the United States as a net importer of crude oil and oil products did not materialize until after World War II, the statistics show important changes in the U.S. foreign trade position in oil well before that time. Net exports relative to domestic production declined continuously for a long period, as can be seen from column 7 of Table 22. Thus, between 1900 and 1915, while net exports of petroleum and its products increased by about 14 million barrels, output of crude oil grew by 217 million barrels, resulting in a decline of almost two-thirds in the importance of net exports relative to production (see Table 22, columns 1, 6, and 7).

It is significant, too, that the net export position in 1915 was compounded of a net import position in crude oil and a net export position in products—the latter being large enough to more than offset the net imports of crude. Much of the period between World War I and the depression of the 1930's was similarly characterized: a net import position in crude oil which was more than offset by a net export balance of oil products. During the 1930's and most of the 1940's, the U.S. foreign trade position continued to be one of net exporter, in some years consisting of an export balance both in crude and products, and in others, as in 1945, of an import balance in crude and a larger export balance in products. Taking oil and oil products together, the United States generally ran a net export balance until the post-World War II period. However, the decline in the relative importance of exports compared to crude production and to domestic consumption continued, with fluctuations, throughout the history of the petroleum industry (see Table 22, columns 7 and 8).

Following World War II, the U.S. foreign trade position in oil underwent a basic change: the net export balance which had characterized U.S. oil history to that time was replaced by large and growing net imports. In the 1947–55 period, during which consumption rose by 50 per cent, crude oil output grew by only one-third. The absolute quantities involved were huge; demand increased by nearly a billion barrels within eight years; production of crude petroleum by 630 million barrels. But during this period of most intensive use of oil, the average annual growth rate of consumption was not higher than it had been during the preceding twenty-five years; actually it was slightly lower. Between 1921 and 1947, apparent consumption, as well as crude oil output, grew at an average rate of about 5.5 per cent per annum. From 1947 to 1955 the average growth rate of consumption was 5.3 per cent; but that of crude oil production had declined to 3.7 per cent. The result was that late in 1947 petroleum imports began to exceed exports. By 1950, net imports amounted to 200 million barrels; in 1955, they had risen to 325 million. More than one-tenth of the domestic consumption in 1955 was being met by supplies from abroad. The shift in the foreign trade position from the largest net exporter to the largest net importer occurred during the late 1940's in a period during which the United States continued to produce more than one-half of the world's crude oil output. It was only in 1955 that the production of all other countries combined exceeded that of the United States by a slight margin. In that year the U.S. share in world production amounted to 48.5 per cent.[66]

Per capita consumption of petroleum increased virtually without interruption from the beginning of the oil industry. Between 1900 and 1955, it rose from half a barrel to seventeen barrels per person annually. The rate of increase in per capita consumption was, of course, more rapid in the early years than in the more recent period; from 1945 to 1955 per capita consumption rose by 43 per cent, while during the first decade of this century it increased by about 260 per cent. But at the beginning of this century this spectacular annual growth rate of 13.7 per cent meant a jump from one-half to barely two barrels per person per year. In the first post-World War II decade, the modest average growth rate of 3.6 per cent a year resulted in an absolute increase in per capita consumption from twelve to seventeen barrels a year (see Table 22, column 9, and Table 23, columns 5 and 6).

THE SHIFTING COMPOSITION OF REFINERY PRODUCTS

The use of crude oil as a fuel without processing was more extensive during the earlier history of the petroleum industry than is usually realized. But direct crude oil use has, on the whole, been of minor and steadily decreasing importance compared to the role of refined products. Accordingly, the story of petroleum in the U.S. energy economy can best be told in terms of its refined products. For present purposes, these can be divided into five major categories:[67]

Gasoline. A mixture of liquid hydrocarbons distinguished by their low specific gravity and high volatility (that is, low boiling point).

Kerosine. Liquid hydrocarbons of somewhat higher specific gravity and lower volatility.

Distillates and residual oil. The first category comprises liquid hydrocarbons still higher in specific gravity and lower in volatility. The latter category consists of those liquid constituents of crude oil with the highest boiling point, hence "residual" after the more volatile components have been distilled off.

Lubricating oils. Liquid hydrocarbons with the properties of lubrication (that is, the ability to reduce friction by forming a thin film between surfaces that will persist under pressure and motion).

Other products. Miscellaneous products ranging from wax and asphalt to liquefied refinery gases (LRG) and the so-called petrochemicals.

The uses of some of these product groups overlap considerably and the dividing line between various products has shifted over time. Gasoline is, and gen-

---

[66] *Minerals Yearbook, 1956, op. cit.*, p. 433.

[67] It should be mentioned here that crudes from different fields are individualistic and do not have the same yield of the various refined products. Some may have a low gasoline yield with heavy distillate and/or residual yields, while others may have very high gasoline yields. Most crudes are not particularly satisfactory for production of lubricating oil while certain Pennsylvania and Gulf Coast crudes are prized for their lubricating oil properties.

erally has been used, almost exclusively as a motor fuel.[68] Kerosine, on the other hand, has had a changing use pattern, beginning as an illuminant, later used predominantly as a fuel for heating and cooking (range oil). It has also been used as a motor fuel in tractors and other agricultural equipment and most recently in jet engines. Distillate oils proper are used chiefly for space heating, but also in the generation of steam and steam power in manufacturing and transportation. Included in this category is diesel fuel for internal combustion engines of the diesel type. Residual fuel oils are industrial fuels used for both process and space heat in the mining, smelting, and manufacturing industries, and as boiler fuel in the generation of steam power in manufacturing and in water and railway transportation and the production of electricity. (More recently, residual has begun to be used in diesel engines properly equipped for this purpose.)

The historical record of the major refined petroleum products is shown in Table 24. Estimates of refinery output by product are available from the mid-1870's. At that time, an annual production of some 6.5 million barrels of illuminating oils accounted for 85 per cent of the total refinery output. Kerosine remained the leading product of oil refineries into the first decade of the twentieth century. Throughout the late nineteenth century output rose at a fast rate, increasing 4.5 times within twenty-five years. Then its growth slowed down and not quite doubled during the first quarter of this century. It doubled again between the mid-1930's and 1955, when it stood at 117 million barrels. Another old product of petroleum refining—lubricating oils—although of small importance in absolute quantity terms, increased at a still faster rate in the early period of the industry, from 200,000 barrels in the mid-1870's to 12 million in 1914 and 25 million in 1920. It fluctuated with only minor increases until about 1935, then doubled in the following two decades. In 1955, output of lubricating oils was 56 million barrels.

Quite a different growth pattern is shown by gasoline and refined fuel oils. Throughout the nineteenth century, they were of minor importance compared to kerosine. In the first quarter of this century, their production expanded rapidly, reaching large absolute quantities. Refinery output of fuel oils rose from 7.3 million barrels in 1899 to 365 million in 1925; gasoline from 6.7 million to 260 million barrels. Gasoline overtook the fuel oil group for the first time in 1930 and, by 1935, gasoline output was 27 per cent larger than that of fuel oils. (The latter group caught up with gasoline output during some World War II years; for example, in 1943 it even outstripped it by 6 per cent.) In the postwar decade 1945–55, gasoline production rose much faster, by 72 per cent as compared to a 42 per cent increase in fuel oil output. This, however, was a period during which domestic production was supplemented by net imports which, by 1955, had risen to 10 per cent of U.S. refinery output of fuel oils. Taking the

[68] Except in the early period when it was used in air-gas machines for gas light in buildings removed from gas utility systems and as a heating fuel in gasoline stoves. See Williamson and Daum, op. cit., pp. 235, 683.

TABLE 24. OUTPUT OF PRINCIPAL REFINED PETROLEUM PRODUCTS, SELECTED YEARS, 1865–1955

(Million barrels)

Year	Gasoline[a] (1)	Kerosine[b] (2)	Fuel oils[c] (3)	Lubricating oils (4)	Other finished products[d] (5)	Total[e] (6)
1865........						1.3
1870........						3.9
1873–75 [f].....	0.9	6.5		0.2	n.a.	7.6
1879........	1.5	11.0	0.5	0.4	n.a.	13.4
1889........	3.9	20.2	1.4	1.8	n.a.	27.3
1899........	6.7	30.0	7.3	4.0	n.a.	48.0
1904........	6.9	32.4	8.6	7.5	n.a.	55.4
1909........	12.9	39.8	40.5	12.8	n.a.	106.0
1914........	34.8	46.2	88.8	12.3	n.a.	182.1
1920........	116.3	55.2	211.0	24.9	35.5	442.9
1925........	259.6	59.7	365.0	31.1	42.2	757.6
1930........	432.2	49.2	372.5	34.2	76.9	965.0
1935........	457.8	55.8	360.1	27.9	85.1	986.7
1940........	597.4	73.9	499.5	36.8	122.6	1,330.1
1945........	774.5	81.0	718.7	41.9	177.5	1,793.5
1950........	998.1	118.5	824.1	51.7	204.4	2,196.9
1955........	1,331.5	117.1	1,022.9	55.8	352.8	2,880.2

n.a. Not available.

[a] Includes naphtha, benzine, and, in later period, aviation gasoline and natural gas liquids (NGL) blended in gasoline at refineries. Excludes jet fuel which is included in "other finished products."

[b] Until 1914, "illuminating oils" which are not necessarily identical with what is today called "kerosine."

[c] In 1879 and 1889, "residuum"; in later years, gas oil, distillates (including diesel), and residual fuel oils.

[d] Prior to 1920, omitted because of fragmentary data and conversion difficulties.

[e] Prior to 1920, excluding "other finished products"; 1920–55 excluding unfinished oils and losses and transfers of liquefied petroleum gases (LPG) from natural gas liquid plants to refineries. Figure for 1955 includes 56.6 million barrels of jet fuel produced from 43.2 million barrels gasoline, 9.9 million barrels kerosine, and 3.5 million barrels distillate oil.

[f] Annual average.

SOURCES: Figures for 1865, 1870, 1873–75, and 1889 from Harold F. Williamson and Arnold R. Daum, *The American Petroleum Industry, 1859–1899, The Age of Illumination* (Evanston, Ill.: Northwestern University Press, 1959), pp. 485, 615, and Appendix A. Figures for 1879 from S. F. Peckham, *Production, Technology and Uses of Petroleum and its Products*, Tenth Census of the United States, Vol. X (Washington, D. C.: U. S. Government Printing Office, 1884), p. 270. Figures for 1899–1914 from U. S. Bureau of the Census, *Historical Statistics of the United States, 1789–1945* (Washington, D. C.: U. S. Government Printing Office, 1949), Series J 158–61. Figures for 1920–55 from U. S. Geological Survey and U. S. Bureau of Mines, *Mineral Resources of the United States*, various issues, and *Minerals Yearbook*, various issues (Washington, D. C.: U. S. Government Printing Office).

period since 1935 as a whole, both groups, gasoline and fuel oils, expanded at nearly identical rates. Output of gasoline rose from 458 million barrels in 1935 to 1,332 million in 1955, or 2.9 times; that of fuel oil, from 360 million to 1,023 million barrels, or 2.8 times. Production of both groups was then measured in billions of barrels, that is, in quantities ten or twenty times as large as kerosine and lubricating oils, formerly the leading products.

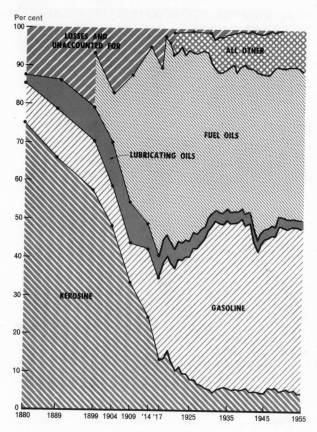

Figure 18.   Petroleum products as percentage of refinery crude input, selected years, 1880–1955.

Such differential growth among the main product groups is, of course, a reflection of the dramatic changes in the use pattern of petroleum products over the history of the oil industry. These changes in use are clearly portrayed in the shifting pattern of refinery product output, as measured by the product yield per barrel of crude oil input, shown in Table 25 and Figure 18. The most notable feature of the long-run historical record is the preponderant role of kerosine in the early decades of oil refining, and its uninterrupted decline in relative importance until the years of the depression. From a level of 75 per cent of total petroleum products in 1880, kerosine (or rather "illuminating oils" which are not necessarily identical with what is today called "kerosine") decreased to 58 per cent in 1899, then plummeted to 13 per cent by 1918. In recent decades, it hovered around 5 per cent of the total (including the kerosine component of jet fuel). The share of lubricating oils has been comparatively stable (except for two decades at the turn of the century), but minor. At the turn of the century,

TABLE 25. PETROLEUM PRODUCTS AS PERCENTAGE OF REFINERY
CRUDE INPUT,ª SELECTED YEARS, 1880–1955

Year	Gasolineᵇ (1)	Kerosineᶜ (2)	Fuel oilsᵈ (3)	Lubricating oils (4)	All other finished products (5)	Losses and unaccounted forᵉ (6)
1880	10.3%	75.2%	n.a.	2.1%	f	12.4%
1889	12.8	65.9	n.a.	7.7	f	13.6
1899	12.9	57.6	14.0%	9.1	f	6.4
1904	10.3	48.3	12.8	11.6	f	17.0
1909	10.7	33.0	33.6	10.7	f	12.0
1914	18.2	24.1	46.5	6.6	f	4.6
1918	25.3	13.3	53.5	6.1	f	1.8
1920	26.1	12.7	48.6	5.7	6.1%	0.8
1925	32.4	8.1	49.3	4.2	5.7	0.3
1930	42.0	5.3	40.2	3.7	8.3	0.5
1935	44.3	5.8	37.3	2.9	8.5	1.2
1940	43.2	5.7	38.6	2.8	9.2	0.5
1945	40.7	4.7	41.8	2.4	9.9	0.5
1950	43.0	5.6	39.2	2.5	9.7	0
1955	44.0	4.3	37.3	2.0	12.4	0

n.a. Not available.

ª Gallons of product as percentage of 42-gallon barrel of crude oil input; excluding input of natural gas liquids.

ᵇ Including naphtha, benzine, and aviation gasoline; excluding jet fuel, which is included in "other finished products."

ᶜ Prior to 1920, "illuminating oils."

ᵈ Includes gas oil, distillates, and residual.

ᵉ Column 6 is derived as the residual of 100 per cent. However, in practice, the concept of refinery losses is rather complex since there are volumetric gains as well as losses in a refinery. In recent years, it is not unusual for a refinery's actual output to exceed its input in volume. The gain arises from cracking and other processes which by breaking up large complex molecules produce resultant molecules occupying more space than the original.

f Included in "losses and unaccounted for."

SOURCES: Figures for 1880–1945 from American Petroleum Institute, *Petroleum Facts and Figures, 1950* (9th ed., New York), pp. 217–19, 251; for 1950 and 1955 from U. S. Bureau of Mines, *Minerals Yearbook, 1956*, Vol. II (Washington, D. C.: U. S. Government Printing Office), p. 377.

fuel oils accounted for 14 per cent of the total refinery output. After slight fluctuations during the first years of this century, distillate and residual fuels rose rapidly to one-third of the total petroleum product output by 1909, and continued to rise until the end of World War I, when they reached the historical peak of 53.5 per cent. This was followed by a decline to 40 per cent by 1930, and the fuel oil group has fluctuated near this level since that time. Gasoline (including naphtha, benzene, and other light products of distillation) accounted for 10 per cent of the total refinery yield in 1880 and this level was more or less maintained until a few years before World War I, when gasoline began to represent an increasing share in refinery output. From 18 per cent in 1914, it rose to 42 per cent in 1930 (gasoline reached its peak of 45 per cent in 1939), and accounted for two-fifths or more of the total thereafter.

Over the past three decades, the heterogeneous group of quantitatively less important commodities—which frequently are lumped under the label "all other finished products"—expanded considerably, not only as a share in total refinery output, but also in the number of products involved. In 1925, this group—comprising wax, petroleum coke, asphalt, road oil, still gas, and "other" products—accounted for about 6 per cent of the total refinery output. By 1955, it had risen to over 12 per cent. In the former year, "old" products of petroleum refining, such as asphalt and wax, constituted more than one-half of this group; in the mid-1950's, they had declined to one-quarter, while new products—jet fuel and an increasing number of petrochemicals—had correspondingly risen in relative importance.

This statistical record provides the basis for a more detailed examination of the history of the major product groups. For convenience, one can distinguish three periods, roughly determined by the dominance[69] of one specific product group: the kerosine period, the period of distillate-residual dominance, and the gasoline period. These periods do not, of course, have clearly defined limiting dates and all of the product groups have a continuing history throughout the several periods. It is believed, however, that despite a somewhat arbitrary character this chronological division provides a useful framework for an examination of the underlying causes in the shifting consumption pattern of oil products. In order to emphasize the use rather than the product, the three periods are labeled somewhat differently. The first is termed "the period of illuminants," the second is considered "the fuel oil period," and the third is labeled "the internal combustion fuel period."

.   .   .

The Illuminants Period

THE DOMINANT ROLE OF ILLUMINANTS

Petroleum arrived on the scene in answer to a world-wide quest for a new source of artificial light. In the United States, at the middle of the nineteenth century, the main illuminants were camphene, lard oil, and candles made from tallow and stearin. The great period of offshore whaling had ended, and the superior sperm oil and sperm candles were too expensive for widespread use. Whale oil had become so scarce that it sold for $2.50 a gallon and this prohibitive price was expected to rise. Lard and tallow, too, were scarce and in great demand, not only as illuminants but also as lubricants. Domestic supplies had to be supplemented by imports of some 225,000 barrels of tallow and about an equal quantity of lard oil a year.[70] Camphene, the first distilled oil illuminant used in this country, was highly explosive and bad-smelling, but it provided a bright white light and was available in large quantities. During the 1840's, it

[69] Measured in physical quantities, not monetary values.
[70] Giddens, *op. cit.*, p. 18.

became the most widely used lamp oil. Although less costly than other illuminants, its retail price rose as high as $2.00 per gallon in the following decade.[71]

The growing demand for illuminants was abetted by a combination of circumstances, among which was the spread of public education and literacy. In the decade 1850–60, the free public school system had been established in principle, at least in the northern states. More and more people were learning to read and wanted to make use of this new skill. The semidarkness of a home lighted by tallow candles or a single oil lamp might have sufficed for household tasks and simple handicraft. But reading required superior illumination which might have been satisfied by the use of several lamps per home, were it not for the high cost of illuminating oils. Another major factor was the spread of the factory system which demanded large-scale illumination, especially in the winter months. In addition, many aspects of the progressing urbanization contributed to the need for artificial light.

These demands could have been met to a certain extent by lighting based on the large-scale use of gas manufactured from coal, as had occurred in Britain. Around 1860 Britain had largely solved the problem of illuminating streets, factories, and, partly also, private residences in her cities through the use of manufactured gas. Actually, manufactured gas from coal had been used as an illuminant in the United States almost as early as in Great Britain. It was first employed in that country in the last years of the eighteenth century; the very first use in the United States appears to have been in a cotton mill in Rhode Island in 1813.[72] In 1816, the Baltimore Gas Light Company was established; by the mid-nineteenth century some fifty gas plants were in operation. But the circumstances were not ripe for widespread use of coal as a gas source in the United States.[73]

Chief among the reasons why gas lighting based on coal did not develop on a larger scale in the United States was the largely rural character of this country and the great distances separating small towns and isolated farms from the urban centers where gas utilities could be established.[74] A contributing factor, rarely mentioned, was the slowness with which coal use in general emerged. Until well into the 1850's, the gas works in the large cities of the East Coast were dependent on coal imported from England. In later decades when coal production began to expand rapidly, and when coke with its potential gas by-product

---

[71] Williamson and Daum, *op. cit.*, pp. 33–34. They quote the following wholesale prices per gallon for various lamp oils in Philadelphia at the end of 1858: sperm oil, $1.32; lard oil, $0.895; turpentine, $0.505; alcohol, $0.519.

[72] Eavenson, *op. cit.*, p. 612.

[73] Manufactured gas nevertheless did gain an early place as the illuminant for street lighting, business establishments, and upper class residences in the cities. By 1875, there were more than 400 gas companies. See H. C. Passer, *The Electrical Manufacturers, 1875–1900* (Cambridge: Harvard University Press, 1953), p. 12.

[74] It was not until the 1920's that bottled gas (liquefied petroleum gases—LPG) for lighting, cooking, and heating could conveniently and profitably be transported to isolated farms and country homes.

became an important fuel for iron ore reduction, the petroleum industry was already fully established. And, by the time manufactured gas began to become available in sufficiently large amounts to meet a substantial share of the growing demand for illuminants, it was in severe competition with the other sources of artificial light—oil, natural gas, and, finally electricity. Coal in the United States never had a chance to play a dominant role (indirectly) in the light market until electricity took over and coal was transformed into a more modern and convenient form of energy.[75]

Important as gas works and gas lighting were in Britain by the middle of the nineteenth century, they were largely restricted to cities. As in the United States, the rural areas suffered from a scarcity of illuminants. The 1840's and 1850's were therefore a period of intensive experiments with new sources of light in both countries. It was in England that, in 1847, petroleum from a spring in a coal mine in Derbyshire producing a few barrels daily was first refined into illuminating and lubricating oils. When, after a few years, this spring gave out, its owner invented a process for obtaining a similar oil by the distillation of coal.[76] Coal oil proved a satisfactory and cheap lighting fluid and soon its production was taken up in the United States. The name "kerosene," by which only a few years later the new petroleum illuminant was to become known all over the world, was actually first used for coal oil. By 1859, some fifty to sixty plants in the Pittsburgh area and on the East Coast were manufacturing this kerosene, which was well on its way to replacing all other more costly or more dangerous illuminating fluids.

Simultaneously, however, some isolated experiments were made with petroleum obtained from springs and salt wells in Pennsylvania. This substance resembled coal oil and seemed to have possibilities as an illuminant. About 1850, a crude distillation process was devised and small amounts of the refined oil were sold under the name "carbon oil." It proved safer and cheaper than other oils and was soon introduced in western Pennsylvania and New York. Within a few years it had become so popular that the small quantities of petroleum available from springs and salt wells could no longer meet the demand. The price of "carbon oil" rose from 75 cents to $2 a gallon.[77] As a result, petroleum, which up to that time had been considered a nuisance when encountered in salt mining, was suddenly transformed into a valuable substance.

[75] This combination of factors explains in part why the coke industry in this country was so slow to change from beehive to by-product ovens. It was only after World War I that the amount of by-product coke exceeded that from beehive ovens. The latter consumed at the peak, in 1910, 53 million tons of coal which, at the rate of 10,000 cubic feet of gas per ton, would have yielded 530 billion cubic feet of gas for lighting or heating—an amount which was allowed to go to waste—together with some 400 million gallons of coal tar, close to 150 million gallons of light oils, and 600,000 tons of ammonium sulfate. See *1950 Bituminous Coal Annual, op. cit.,* p. 115, and Eavenson, *op. cit.,* pp. 581–84.

[76] Giddens, *op. cit.,* p. 19; and Leonard M. Fanning, *The Rise of American Oil* (New York: Harper Bros., 1936), p. 91.

[77] Giddens, *op. cit.,* p. 28.

With the emergence of the petroleum industry, the flourishing coal oil industry by the end of 1860 was on the decline and its distilleries were replaced or converted into petroleum refineries. Coal oil had paved the way for the replacement of animal and vegetable oils by a mineral oil. Now, in turn, it was replaced by a mineral illuminant that immediately proved superior. The blaze from "rock oil," as petroleum was first called, was larger and the light brighter; it was not only cheaper but one gallon burned twice as long as any other illuminating fluid.[78] The new refined product took over the trade name "kerosene,"[79] and, for use in lamps and stoves, for nearly half a century remained the leading product of the petroleum industry.

Its importance as a source of artificial light may be gauged from a detailed report for the Census year June 1879–May 1880, the twentieth anniversary of the oil industry. In that year, production of illuminating oils amounted to 11,002,249 barrels, of which 7,346,516 were exported, leaving 3,655,733 for domestic consumption—that is, an average 10,000 barrels or 420,000 gallons per day, just about enough to fill 70 modern tank trucks. Depending on the type of lamps and wicks used, one gallon of illuminating oil furnished 100 to 190 hours of light in lamps of 5 to 10 candlepower, or on the average, roughly 1,000 candlepower hours. Thus, the comparatively modest quantity consumed could supply 420 million candlepower hours per day. For a population of 50 million, this amounted to an average 8.4 candlepower hours, or one hour of lamplight equivalent in illuminating power to that formerly supplied by eight candles, for every person every day of the year.[80]

THE GROWING NEED FOR LUBRICANTS

Although much less in the public mind, the need for new sources of lubricants was as pressing as that for more artificial light. By the middle of the nineteenth century, the rapid growth of the factory system, the invention of new machines, and the expansion of steamship and railroad transportation had reached the point where the scarcity of efficient lubricants had become a serious bottleneck:

> The whale oils which hitherto have been much relied on in this country to furnish light, are yearly becoming more scarce, and may in time almost entirely fail, while the rapid increase of machinery demands a large portion of the purest of these oils for lubricating.[81]

The further spread of mechanization, as reflected in the rising level of installed horsepower in industry and transportation (from 1.9 million hp in 1849 to 7.4

[78] The wholesale price for coal oil early in 1860 was 75 cents per gallon. That for illuminating oil from petroleum was 36 cents in 1862, rose during the Civil War when it was heavily taxed to 72 cents, then dropped to 26 cents per gallon in 1870. (Williamson and Daum, *op. cit.*, pp. 59, 326.)

[79] The commonly accepted spelling has since become "kerosine."

[80] S. F. Peckham, *op. cit.*, pp. 238, 270.

[81] *Scientific American*, Vol. XII (June 27, 1857), p. 239, as quoted in Louis C. Hunter, "Products of the Earth, 1866–1918," in *The Growth of the American Economy*, ed. Harold F. Williamson (2nd ed., New York: Prentice Hall, 1951), p. 46.

million in 1869 and 24.8 million in 1889),[82] required an ever-increasing supply of good lubricants to keep the wheels turning. Technological advances pointed towards more power and higher speeds. But increasing friction, insufficiently counteracted by tallow and lard fats and whale or vegetable oils, stood in the way of making use of more efficient machinery.

The refining process for kerosine necessarily yielded a number of other products, especially naphtha and gasoline, for which there was little use. Some was sold in adulterated illuminating oil; other uses were as a solvent, as a source of gas in air-gas installations, and as an enricher of coal gas. The remaining heavy oil in the bottom of the still could be made into lubricants and wax, but these products encountered strong prejudice and were difficult to sell because of their offensive smell and poor lubricating properties. In the first years of the industry, most lubricants were produced not by refining, but directly from heavy crude oil filtered through bone black. They frequently were used as additives to animal and vegetable fats and oils. Only after the development in 1869 of a process of slow distillation, which deodorized the paraffin oils and greatly improved their lubricating qualities, were they more widely accepted.

Around 1870, although little was known about the science of lubrication, production of refined petroleum lubricants was begun on a larger scale. During the 1880's and 1890's the testing of lubricating materials was put on a scientific basis, the connection between friction and viscosity was recognized, and bath lubrication of bearings was developed. Once mineral oils could be adapted to specific lubricating tasks, they proved greatly superior to animal and vegetable oils and fats.

FOREIGN TRADE

The new oil industry from the very beginning was oriented to exports. By the end of the Civil War, the value of petroleum products exported was already $15.7 million, and the oil industry ranked sixth in the United States export trade.[83] Between the late 1860's and 1900, net exports of crude and products were the equivalent of at least one-third of domestic crude production, and at times amounted to more than three-quarters of the total, a remarkably high level (see Table 22, column 7). Refined products quickly came to account for the bulk of the export trade, and among them illuminating oil was by far the most important. Thus, kerosine during this period dominated the oil scene in both production and foreign trade. The fast growing volume of exports during the first forty years of the oil industry is shown in Table 26.

The bulk of these exports—some 90 per cent in the 1860's and the 1870's and about 70 per cent in the following decade—went to Europe. In the first years, Great Britain was the principal customer, after a futile fight waged by its coal oil industry against the new product. In 1868, it was superseded by Germany, which

[82] Daugherty et al., op. cit.
[83] Giddens, op. cit., p. 100.

TABLE 26. PRODUCTION OF CRUDE OIL AND EXPORTS OF CRUDE
AND REFINED PRODUCTS, TEN-YEAR INTERVALS, 1869–99

(Thousand barrels)

Item	1869	1879	1889	1899
Production of crude oil............	4,215	19,914	35,164	57,071
Exports, total...................	2,317	8,972	14,672	22,612
Crude.......................	307	616	1,738	2,693
Naphtha.....................		358	338	387
Illuminating oils..............	2,010	7,895	11,959	17,197
Lubricants...................		59	599	1,605
Residuum...................		44	40	730

SOURCES: Production of crude, U. S. Geological Survey, *Mineral Resources of the United States*, various issues (Washington, D. C.: U. S. Government Printing Office); exports, Harold F. Williamson and Arnold L. Daum, *The American Petroleum Industry, 1859–1899, The Age of Illumination* (Evanston, Ill.: Northwestern University Press, 1959); p. 334 and Appendix B.

remained the largest importer of U.S. illuminating oils until 1890, when Britain again took first place. The role of U.S. illuminants in the European lighting market (excluding Russia, which was an oil-producing country) may be gauged from the fact that in the mid-1880's they accounted for an average per capita consumption of nine-tenths of a gallon which supplied about 125 lamplight hours per person per year in Europe.

Although much less important in quantitative terms, U.S. exports of lubricating oils were of great significance in supporting the fast-growing industrialization and mechanization of West European countries towards the end of the nineteenth century. In the twenty-year period between 1879 and 1899, during which production of refined lubricants increased ten times (see Table 24), the share of exports rose from 15 to 40 per cent of the U.S. output. The bulk of the foreign shipments—between 40 and 55 per cent—went to Great Britain. Germany, which absorbed 12 to 18 per cent of the exports, was the second largest foreign consumer of the U.S. lubricating oils.[84]

THE DEVELOPMENT OF PETROLEUM TRANSPORTATION

The rapid expansion of both domestic and foreign markets was dependent on the development of a new transportation system suited to the special requirements of the new industry. At first, oil was shipped in wooden barrels by horse-drawn wagons. The price of the scarce barrels—$2 and, occasionally, even $4 each—sometimes exceeded the value of a barrel of crude oil. And on top of that cost was the teamsters' charge of $2 to $3 for hauling one barrel from the well to the nearest railroad. In 1865 the first wooden railroad tank car with a capacity of 90 barrels was introduced. It was followed in 1869 by iron tank cars and in

[84] See Williamson and Daum, *op. cit.*, p. 496 and Appendix D.

1893 by steel tank cars with far greater capacity. Also in 1865 it was demonstrated that petroleum could be pumped through pipelines; a five-mile-long wrought iron line moved oil to the railroad station at a charge of $1.00 per barrel. In 1874, many of the gathering lines were merged in a Standard Oil subsidiary, United Pipe Lines. Five years later, the first big pipeline—the six-inch Tide-Water line, 110 miles long—was built across the Appalachians. Within another few years, more than 75 per cent of all crude oil produced was carried by pipelines to railroad stations or refineries. When rich new oil fields were discovered in Ohio and Indiana in the late 1880's and in Texas, California and Oklahoma during the first decade of this century, larger pipelines were laid. By 1910 there were nearly 20,000 miles of trunk lines and over 24,000 miles of gathering lines.

The first full cargo of oil crossed the Atlantic in 1861. It was shipped in barrels in the hold of a wooden sailing ship from Philadelphia to London. Two years later, the British, in an iron sailing vessel, transported oil in a subdivided cargo space using the hull of the ship as container and doing away with expensive barrels or tins. This vessel may be considered the forerunner of the modern tanker. The first steam tanker was a Russian ship, built in Sweden in 1878; it was important in the development of the oil industry, not only as the first steam tank ship but also because it burned oil as fuel. The prototype of the modern tanker was a German vessel launched in England in 1886. Two years later the first U.S. steam tanker was built by the Standard Oil Company. In 1900, there were 109 ocean-going tankers of more than 2,000 gross tons in operation, three under the U.S. flag. Ten years later, the world tanker fleet had doubled, the number of U.S. tankers had risen to 31 and accounted for 109,000 out of a total of 845,000 gross tons.[85]

·   ·   ·

The Fuel Oil Period

THE EMERGING USE OF FUEL OIL

Oil, although pre-eminent during its "kerosine period" in the illuminating market, was faced with competition from other forms of artificial light. In the 1870's, new processes of gas manufacturing were introduced which produced

[85] The expansion of petroleum transport facilities is indicated in the following data: By 1920, total pipeline mileage was about 70,000. In 1930, pipeline transportation was adapted to the shipment of refined oil products. On the eve of World War II, total mileage had increased to 127,000 and by the mid-1950's to about 190,000. In 1955 there were also some 125,000 railroad tank cars in petroleum service, the largest with a capacity of 450 barrels. As for international transportation, in 1920, the world tanker fleet consisted of 540 ocean-going vessels, with the United States accounting for nearly one-half. By 1940, it comprised 1,637 ships, including 383 American vessels. The main improvement between the two World Wars was the conversion from geared turbine propulsion to diesel-electric drive; since World War II, the main changes have been in size and speed. In 1955, there were 2,681 tankers with a gross tonnage of 27,338,000 in operation; 490 American vessels accounted for 5,094,900 gross tons, exceeded only by the British tanker fleet of 535 ships with a gross tonnage of 5,121,800. See American Petroleum Institute, *Petroleum Facts and Figures, 1950* (9th ed.: New York),

cheaper and better gas,[86] and electric lighting in the form of the arc light made its commercial appearance. In 1882, Edison's first commercial incandescent electric lighting system went into operation. During the 1880's, manufactured and natural gas, and especially the developing electric power industry, made great inroads into the lighting market in urban areas. Only a few years later, the first gasoline-powered motor vehicle was to be built in the United States, but the age of the automobile was still a long time in the future. Perhaps the growth of the petroleum industry would have faltered by the end of the nineteenth century but for the emergence of a new market, the use of oil and oil products as industrial and, to a lesser extent, household fuel.

Petroleum was not readily accepted as fuel at first, partly because the equipment best suited for its use had not been developed, but mainly because the price of oil was higher than that of coal or wood, except at times in the Oil Creek region. There, crude oil was ocasionally used as boiler fuel in refineries. During the Civil War, the Navy began a series of experiments with the use of fuel oil in vessels. They proved that oil could be burned in steamships, that the gains in speed were considerable, that fires could be started and extinguished much faster, and that the ships could be kept at sea without refueling two to three times as long as with the use of coal. But the danger of explosion (a ship could be destroyed by a single shot) was considered too great, there were high losses through volatilization, and the smell and high temperature in the fuel room were unbearable. In 1867 the Secretary of the Navy reported:

> It appears that the use of petroleum as fuel for steamers is hopeless; convenience is against it, comfort is against it, health is against it, economy is against it, and safety is against it. Opposed to these the advantages of the probably not very important reduction in bulk and weight, with their attending economies, cannot prevail.[87]

Perhaps the Navy was being overcautious, for oil was already occasionally burned in steamships on the California run, in which coal had to be transported over great distances. Greater power and speed, and savings in storage space and labor costs for fueling made the use of oil attractive. Throughout the 1870's, experiments to burn oil in steam vessels, locomotives and also in manufacturing plants, continued, but in most instances petroleum proved too costly compared to coal.[88]

---

pp. 274, 297, 304; *ibid., 1956* (12th ed.), pp. 241, 248, 250, 268; and *American Petroleum Institute Quarterly*, Centennial Issue (New York, 1959), pp. 52-53, 55-56, 59-60.

[86] Passer, *op. cit.*, pp. 195-96.

[87] Peckham, *op. cit.*, p. 248; Giddens, *op. cit.*, p. 194.

[88] In the late 1880's, oil began to be employed on a small scale as locomotive fuel on the West Coast and in the Southwest, the regions farthest removed from the coal fields. This was not, incidentally, wholly a matter of using local oil supplies, for California became an important oil-producing state only in the very first years of the twentieth century. In 1880, one of the foremost experts of the petroleum industry warned that all reports and rumors about the occurrence of oil in the Santa Barbara and Los Angeles area were unsubstantiated. In that year, output in California amounted to only 41,000 barrels of a total U.S. production of more than 26 million barrels. California was an oil-importing state. The San Francisco market was supplied with Pennsylvania oil that had to be transported via Cape Horn.

Against the advantages of oil as a cleaner, more convenient, more efficient and more concentrated fuel than coal (one ton of fuel oil has the Btu content of nearly one and one-half tons of coal) was the important drawback of its higher cost. Until the beginning of the twentieth century, the Appalachian region—where coal mining was concentrated—was the largest oil producer. The fact that petroleum first became available in large quantities close to the centers of the coal industry is one of the reasons why oil was not immediately accepted as fuel.

The use of crude oil in transportation and manufacturing received its first great impetus after the discovery of the Lima, Ohio-Indiana fields in the mid-1880's. In contrast to the crude of Pennsylvania, the Lima-Indiana crude originally was not suitable for refining into illuminants. Nevertheless, while there was little use for it, production in the new rich fields skyrocketed; shipments amounted to only a fraction of output, inventories were growing, storage facilities were lacking, some outlet had to be found. An intensive campaign to popularize the qualities of oil as fuel for steam generation and heating combined with the low price of Lima crude (15 cents a barrel at the well, 60 cents a barrel delivered in Chicago)[89] proved at least partly successful. By 1889, the potentialities of petroleum for use as a fuel had been demonstrated and recognized. A Census report for the year 1889, which classified the total crude petroleum production according to the main uses for which the different types of oil were intended, estimated the share of fuel oils at 35 per cent (see Table 27).[90]

Around the same time, experiments to remove the sulfur and to refine Lima crude into an acceptable illuminating oil proved successful. In the late 1890's, almost the entire output was absorbed by newly established Standard Oil refineries. Lima crude yielded some 35 to 45 per cent of illuminating oil, the

TABLE 27. PRODUCTION OF CRUDE PETROLEUM BY TYPE OF OIL, 1889

Category [a]	Quantity (thousand barrels)	Per cent of total
Illuminating oils	22,650	64.4%
Lubricating oils	121	0.4
Fuel oils	12,393	35.2
Total crude production	35,164	100.0%

[a] The classification in this table by types of oil is based on the characteristics of the crude oils. The actual refinery products yielded by the crude oils show quite a different pattern of relative importance, as comparison with Table 25 indicates, because crudes generally yield a variety of products.

SOURCE: U. S. Geological Survey, *Mineral Resources of the United States, 1889–90* (Washington, D. C.: U. S. Government Printing Office), p. 292.

[89] Williamson and Daum, *op. cit.*, pp. 600–601.

[90] Of the total quantity officially classified as fuel oil, 12,153,000 barrels, or 34.6 per cent of the U.S. output, was Lima crude. Shipments from the Lima-Indiana fields in the same year amounted to 5,800,000 barrels.

remainder was sold as refined fuel oil or further processed into lubricants or other products. Refinery output of fuel oils, which had only doubled from half a million barrels to little over a million between 1879 and 1889, expanded to over 7 million barrels in 1899 (see Table 24). By that time, the Lima-Indiana fields had already passed their peak. But they were important on the national oil scene—apart from their decisive role in the development of Standard Oil—because their cheap and otherwise not marketable product had paved the way for the acceptance of petroleum as a source of heat and power that could compete with coal.

EXPANSION OF FUEL OIL USE

By 1904, considerably larger quantities of oil were already burned as fuels than is indicated by their modest share—13 per cent (see Table 25)—in the total refinery output, if allowance is made for the consumption of crude as fuel. As late as 1909, more than one-quarter of the total deliveries of crude oil did not enter the refineries but was sold directly as fuel. Actually, the official statistics of that period distinguish between "refinery oil" and "fuel oil" or "burning oil." A breakdown based on this classification conveys a rather different picture of the relative importance of fuel oils than shown by refinery statistics. On this basis, 51 million barrels out of total crude oil deliveries of 196 million barrels, or 26 per cent of total crude went directly to fuel use.[91] For the same year, the reported output of petroleum refineries (see Tables 24 and 25) showed 40.5 million barrels, or 34 per cent of the total ouptut of 106 million barrels, as fuel oils.

Thus, in 1909, the total quantity of fuel oils, both produced in refineries and delivered directly from the fields, amounted to 91 million barrels, nearly one-half the crude oil production of that year. By that time, the great centers of oil production had shifted to Texas, California, and Oklahoma. In 1909, California was the leading petroleum-producing state and accounted for about four-fifths of the crude oil delivered for fuel. In the West, where the price of coal was high but oil could be obtained cheaply from fields and refineries, it had proved to be a less costly, more efficient, and cleaner railroad fuel. Consumption of oil by railroads, especially those of the West and Southwest, increased steadily; by 1909, it had reached 20 million barrels, nearly one-quarter of the total quantity of fuel oils supplied in that year. An equally large amount—19.7 million barrels—was consumed by the manufacturing industries. Still another market was opened by the changed attitude of the Navy toward the new fuel:

> The introduction of fuel oil into the United States Navy has been quite rapid and with fully as good results as were anticipated. . . . The engineering and military advantages of the use of fuel oil are clearly recognized by the Navy Department, as a result of experiment and experience. In the new construction fuel oil is being more and more extensively used.[92]

[91] *Mineral Resources of the United States, 1910*, Part II, *op. cit.*, p. 334.
[92] *Mineral Resources of the United States, 1909*, Part II, *op. cit.*, p. 310; *ibid.*, *1910*, Part II, p. 353.

Complete statistics on the consumption of fuel oils during the period before World War I are not available. In 1916, when output of distillate and residual oils by refineries appears to have exceeded 100 million barrels, an additional 37 million barrels of domestic crude petroleum for fuel use were delivered by pipe-line companies, some 3 million were consumed in drilling and pumping operations, and a large portion of the 20 million barrels of crude oil imported was burned as fuel.[93] Deducting exports (which in 1916 amounted to 23 million

TABLE 28. INDICATED CONSUMPTION OF FUEL OILS, INCLUDING CRUDE OIL USED AS FUEL, 1918–22

Item	1918	1919	1920	1921	1922
Crude and refined oil for fuel (million barrels):					
Indicated total consumption of crude.......	408	423	522	521	585
Less crude runs to stills.................	326	362	434	443	501
Indicated other consumption of crude (chiefly for fuel, but incl. losses)................	82	61	88	78	84
Plus indicated consumption of refined fuel oils	143	164	186	196	240
Total consumption of crude and refined oils for fuel......................	225	225	274	274	324
Energy equivalent (trillion Btu)...........	1,379	1,383	1,681	1,683	1,992
Coal equivalent (million net tons).........	53	53	64	64	76
Coal equivalent as percentage of U. S. coal production...........................	8%	10%	10%	13%	16%

SOURCE: U. S. Geological Survey, *Mineral Resources of the United States, 1923*, Part II (Washington, D. C.: U. S. Government Printing Office), p. 410.

TABLE 29. CONSUMPTION OF FUEL OILS, INCLUDING CRUDE OIL, BY USE, 1919

(Thousand barrels)

Railroads (Class I)..	37,763
Vessels (bunker oil)...	26,531
Navy...	5,845
Gas manufacture..	22,700
Utility generation of electricity...	11,050
Refineries..	23,717
Crude used in field...	5,600
Subtotal...	133,206
Manufacturing (excl. oil refineries)......................................	69,636
Mining (excl. crude used in field).......................................	4,147
Total...	206,989

SOURCE: U. S. Bureau of Mines, *Mineral Resources of the United States, 1925*, Part II (Washington, D. C.: U. S. Government Printing Office), p. 355.

[93] *Ibid., 1916*, Part II, p. 700.

barrels of "residuum"), from this total of 160 million barrels, the consumption of oil as fuel can be estimated at about 140 million barrels—again nearly one-half of the domestic production of 300 million barrels of crude.

For the period immediately following World War I, which marks the beginning of the gradually increasing displacement of coal by fuel oils, there is available an estimate of the aggregate consumption of refinery and crude oil burned as fuel and of the quantity of coal replaced by this use of oil (see Table 28). Complete Census data, available for 1919, support the general validity of these estimates (see Table 29).

THE STATISTICAL RECORD OF THE FUEL OILS

Table 30 represents an effort to assemble a long period record of fuel oils and their relative importance as a portion of the total output of petroleum. It is pieced together from different statistical sources, some of them fragmentary, and it reflects a number of arbitrary choices. In column 2 of Table 30, the record of refined fuel oils is traced. It is a record of almost uninterrupted growth. Production expanded more than fivefold in the first decade of the twentieth century, more than doubled between 1909 and 1914 and again between 1914 and 1920. Thereafter, the growth was at a slower pace; output in 1955 was four times that of 1920, but the absolute amounts involved in this period of slower growth were huge compared to the quantities at the beginning of this century. The figures in column 6, which include the estimated amounts of crude oil used as fuel, differ markedly in the earlier years from the quantities of refined products. Although they might be somewhat overstated they provide a more correct measure of the amounts of oil actually used as fuel.

Viewing the position of fuel oils in the over-all petroleum picture, it is evident that they reached the peak of their relative importance in the early 1920's. The rapid quantitative rise of refined fuel oil output during World War I is reflected in the increase of their share within total refinery output (column 4 of Table 30). From one-eighth of the total in 1904, fuel oils rose to one-third in 1909, and one-half in the 1920's. From this peak, their share declined to about 40 per cent of the refinery yield in the 1930's and to one-third in 1955, approximately the same relative level as in 1909.

The inclusion of "fuel crude" gives somewhat different results. Output of refined fuel oils and the estimated quantities of crude used as fuel combined already equaled nearly one-fifth of the total crude oil production in 1889, rose to two-fifths in 1904, and apparently amounted to about two-thirds in the early 1920's (see Table 30, column 7).[94] In later years, the quantities of crude used as fuel were negligible, so that the declining share of fuel oils in the over-all petroleum picture is hardly affected by the exclusion of this category.

[94] As indicated in the Note to Table 30, these quantities shown for 1920 and 1925 are known to be too large.

TABLE 30. PRODUCTION OF REFINED FUEL OILS AND ESTIMATED
CONSUMPTION OF CRUDE AS FUEL, SELECTED YEARS, 1889-1955

(Quantities in thousand barrels)

Year	Kerosine (sales of range oil only) [a] (1)	Production of refined fuel oils (gas oil, distillate, and residual) [b] (2)	Refined fuel oils including kerosine used as range oil (1) + (2) (3)	Refined fuel oils as percentage of crude oil refinery input [c] (4)	Estimated consumption of crude oil as fuel (5)	Refined fuel oil plus crude used as fuel (3) + (5) (6)	Refined plus crude fuel oil as percentage of total crude oil production (7)
1889...		1,400	1,400	n.a.	5,000 [d]	6,400	18.2%
1899...		7,262	7,262	14.0%	n.a.	n.a.	n.a.
1904...		8,571	8,571	12.8	41,138 [e]	49,709	42.5
1909...		40,476	40,476	33.6	50,720 [f]	91,196	34.3
1914...		88,810	88,810	46.5	n.a.	n.a.	n.a.
1920...	4,000	210,987	214,987	49.5	88,000 [g]	302,987	68.4
1925...	6,000	364,991	370,991	50.1	90,145 [h]	461,136	60.4
1930...	8,000	372,498	380,498	41.0	[i]		
1935...	20,000	344,887	364,887	37.8	[i]		
1940...	40,715	474,856	515,571	39.8	[i]		
1945...	43,540	652,304	695,844	40.5	[i]		
1950...	79,869	719,407	799,276	38.2	[i]		
1955...	84,331	850,173	934,504	34.2	[i]		

n.a. Not available.

[a] By and large, kerosine was used as an illuminant prior to 1920, therefore it is not included. Use as range oil for 1920–35 estimated; 1940–55 from U. S. Bureau of Mines, *Minerals Yearbook*, various issues (Washington, D. C.: U. S. Government Printing Office).

[b] Diesel oil excluded for 1935–55.

[c] Barrels of product as a percentage of crude oil refinery input. 1920–55: including kerosine sold as range oil.

[d] Estimate based on Harold F. Williamson and Arnold L. Daum, *The American Petroleum Industry, 1859–1899, The Age of Illumination* (Evanston, Ill.: Northwestern University Press, 1959), pp. 601, 610, 614.

[e] Estimated at 75 per cent of crude oil production in California, Texas, and Louisiana. See U. S. Geological Survey, *Mineral Resources of the United States, 1905* (Washington, D. C.: U. S. Government Printing Office), pp. 813, 818, 819.

[f] *Ibid., 1910*, Part II, p. 334.

[g] *Ibid., 1923*, Part II, p. 410.

[h] *Minerals Yearbook, 1934, op. cit.*, Statistical Appendix, p. 230. Figures for 1920 and 1925 include an undetermined amount of losses and stock changes, and thus overstate the quantities used as fuel oil.

[i] In 1930 and subsequent years, crude oil used as fuel and losses combined were negligible, ranging from 27 million barrels in 1930 to 14 million barrels in 1955. Information on crude oil used as fuel is incomplete, therefore it is not included in totals.

NOTE: Because this table is meant to include all types of fuel oil, as distinct from illuminating and internal combustion oils, it includes two items not referred to as fuel oil in the long-run statistics presented in Tables 24 and 25. For the period 1889–1925, statistics are included, wherever possible, on the amount of crude oil used directly as fuel (column 5). Since crude oil used as fuel was particularly important in the earlier period of the industry, the table attempts to provide a measure of the amounts so used. The quantities so classified for 1920 and 1925 are known to be too large because they include an unknown but probably relatively small amount of crude not used for fuel and because they do not make allowance for changes in stocks. However, crude oil used for fuel is wholly excluded in subsequent years when it was of relatively small and rapidly declining importance. Kerosine is treated in reverse fashion. For the years 1889–1914, when it was used mainly as an illuminant, it is excluded even though an indeterminate quantity was used as a fuel oil. In later years, range oil for stoves and

THE USE PATTERN OF FUEL OIL IN RECENT DECADES

The consumption pattern of the two main categories constituting the refined fuel oils—distillates and residual fuel oil—for the 1940–55 period is shown in Tables 31 and 32. The sales of distillate fuel oils (excluding diesel) to main consuming categories are given in Table 31. The heating use of distillates, mainly in homes and commercial establishments, is by far the most important, tending to account for more than four-fifths of the total consumption in 1940 and 1955. (The 1945 and 1950 figures reflect the wartime restriction in such civilian use, and the subsequent recovery.) Each of the other uses is a relatively insignificant part of the total. The largest is in the industrial sector (mining and manufacturing), which rose in relative importance from 4 to 6.5 per cent of the total between 1940 and 1955, and underwent a five-fold increase in absolute amounts. Only use by electric power and gas plants showed an absolute decline—by about 16 per cent.

The consumption pattern of residual fuel oil over the same period, unlike that of distillates, shows no dominant use. Indeed, no single consuming group accounted for as much as one-third of total sales of residual oils in any year shown in Table 32. Commercial and residential use accounted for only 8 to 15 per cent of total residual sales. During the fifteen-year period, manufacturing and mining, vessels, and electric power stations are far more important as consumers of residual than of distillates. Among the users of residual, utilities grew most rapidly—an increase of about 170 per cent. This reflects to some extent the inroads of oil into electricity generation, but principally the rapid growth of electricity production, itself.[95] As a result, this category increased its importance among all residual fuel oil uses by nearly one-half. Sales to the commercial and residential sectors just about doubled in absolute amounts, while consumption in manufacturing and mining increased about two and a half times. The most spectacular change, however, was the absolute decline of more than three-quarters in railroad use and its corresponding fall from one-fifth of the total sales of residual oil to one-fortieth.

In summarizing developments in the consumption of fuel oils in the 1940–55 period, it is worth noting that sales of distillates tripled—mainly because of the fast expansion of the residential market—while consumption of residual oil rose only by two-thirds. The great increase in the demand for distillate was fully met by domestic refinery output. In 1955, net exports of distillate amounted to 20

[95] The decline in absolute consumption by this group between 1950 and 1955 is due mainly to decreasing sales for the manufacture of gas.

(*Note to Table 30, continued.*)

     space heaters was of increasing importance, although during the 1920's and early 1930's the greater portion was still consumed as an illuminant. By 1940, however, more than half of all kerosine produced was sold for use as range oil; and, in 1955, this share had risen to over 70 per cent. The rest was consumed in such miscellaneous uses as weed-killing and tobacco-curing, as tractor fuel, in small amounts still in its oldest use as an illuminant, and in increasing quantities in its most modern use—in the production of jet fuel. These miscellaneous uses are excluded in this table.

TABLE 31. SALES OF DISTILLATE FUEL OIL[a] BY USES, FIVE-YEAR INTERVALS, 1940-55

(Quantities in thousand barrels)

Use	1940		1945		1950		1955		1955 index (1940=100)
	Quantity	Per cent	Quantity	Per cent	Quantity	Per cent	Quantity	Per cent	
Residential and commercial heating[b]	115,533	85.0%	121,342	73.4%	220,947	76.0%	339,714	82.5%	294.0
Mining and manufacturing	5,373	4.0	13,046	7.9	22,853	7.9	26,853	6.5	500.0
Oil company use	841	0.6	899	0.5	4,988	1.7	7,485	1.8	890.0
Electric power and gas plants[c]	2,930	2.2	3,757	2.3	6,643	2.3	2,454	0.6	83.8
Railroads	1,356	1.0	2,422	1.5	3,619	1.2	4,604	1.1	339.5
Vessels	270	0.2	756	0.5	753	0.3	806	0.2	298.5
Armed forces	}9,680	7.1	7,416	4.5	1,903	0.7	3,182	0.8	}310.0
Miscellaneous uses[d]			15,575	9.4	28,878	9.9	26,823	6.5	
Total	135,983	100.0%	165,213	100.0%	290,584	100.0%	411,921	100.0%	302.9

[a] Including gas oil but excluding diesel oil and kerosine sold as range oil.

[b] This category is referred to as "heating oils" in Bureau of Mines statistics. It consists mainly of fuel oils consumed in homes and commercial establishments, but presumably includes also such miscellaneous uses as government and institutional consumers.

[c] Use by manufactured-gas companies amounted to 2,100,000 barrels in 1955.

[d] Including distillate sold as range oil: 1940—3,977,000 barrels; 1945—7,481,000; 1950—14,793,000; 1955—17,374,000.

SOURCE: U. S. Bureau of Mines, *Minerals Yearbook*, various issues (Washington, D. C.: U. S. Government Printing Office).

TABLE 32. SALES OF RESIDUAL FUEL OIL^a BY USES, FIVE-YEAR INTERVALS, 1940-55

(Quantities in thousand barrels)

Use	1940		1945		1950		1955		1955 index (1940 =100)
	Quantity	Per cent	Quantity	Per cent	Quantity	Per cent	Quantity	Per cent	
Residential and commercial heating^b	44,846	13.3%	43,874	8.1%	72,716	13.1%	86,282	15.5%	192.4
Mining and manufacturing	66,610	19.7	91,176	16.8	148,111	26.7	173,030	31.1	259.8
Oil company use	50,864	15.0	57,336	10.6	53,263	9.6	53,387	9.6	105.0
Electric power and gas plants^c	28,234	8.4	34,532	6.4	93,062	16.8	75,966	13.6	269.1
Railroads	64,904	19.2	112,297	20.7	60,878	11.0	15,018	2.7	23.1
Vessels	61,554	18.2	100,365	18.5	92,947	16.8	115,128	20.7	187.0
Armed forces	}21,094	6.2	97,485	18.0	28,333	5.1	28,368	5.1	}181.0
Miscellaneous uses			5,200	1.0	4,898	0.9	9,804	1.8	
Total	338,106	100.0%	542,265	100.0%	554,208	100.0%	556,983	100.0%	164.7

^a Includes a small amount of crude oil burned as fuel in oilfields and by industrial plants, representing about 1.0 per cent of the total supply of residual in 1955 (*Minerals Yearbook, 1955*, p. 405).

^b See footnote b in Table 31. Residual fuel oils are consumed mainly by commercial establishments, larger apartment houses, etc., rather than in private homes.

^c Consumption by electric power plants amounted to 70,900,000 barrels in 1955.

SOURCE: U. S. Bureau of Mines, *Minerals Yearbook*, various issues (Washington, D. C.: U. S. Government Printing Office).

million barrels, slightly more than 3 per cent of domestic production. Of the much smaller increase in consumption of residual between 1940 and 1955, more than one-half—some 120 million barrels—was supplied by net imports in the latter year. The imports of heavy fuel oils, mainly from Venezuela and the Netherlands Antilles, amounted to 28 per cent of domestic refinery output.

The consumption statistics for distillates and residual fuel oil are combined in Table 33 in order to show the relative importance of the main use groups in total fuel oil sales and to provide a statistical record over a longer period. Over the thirty-year period, 1926–55, total fuel oil consumption more than tripled. Residential and commercial heating is shown to be the most dynamic element in the growth of total fuel oil use over the past thirty years—increasing from 7 per cent of the total in 1926 to 44 per cent in 1955. Manufacturing and mining accounted for one-fifth of total fuel oil consumption in 1955, the same relative importance as thirty years earlier. Railroad use was the only consumption category to undergo an absolute decline over the thirty-year period—to one-fourth its earlier level. Both marine and oil company uses declined relative to the total over the thirty-year period, although both increased in absolute terms. Electric power and gas plants more than doubled in the absolute amounts of fuel oil consumed, but declined somewhat in relative importance in the total due to decreasing use of oil in gas manufacture.

To what extent has this group of petroleum products, which by and large is directly competitive with coal, actually supplied the energy that could also have been derived from coal? The problem of interfuel competition and substitution is exceedingly complex and may be approached by different methods and on different levels. Thus, the displacement of coal by residual oil for use in steamships and steam locomotives represents a form of substitution which is different from the replacement of steam engines by diesel locomotives. While steam power can be generated by very different energy materials, internal combustion requires specific fuels.[96] Another intricate problem in defining and measuring substitution arises from the fact that different fuel materials can be used for the same purposes with different degrees of efficiency. Despite these complicating factors, it is worth comparing the inherent energy in fuel oils consumed (in Btu terms) with the quantities of coal containing the equivalent amount of inherent energy, which, in turn, can be compared with actual coal consumption. This is done in Table 34 for the 1935–55 period.

The fuel oils included in this comparison are limited to those types which, in the above definition, are interchangeable with coal. Diesel oil is excluded and of the total kerosine consumption only the share used as range oil is included. As seen from item 3, fuel oil consumption, first converted into Btu's and then into tons of coal, was the equivalent of 87 million tons of bituminous coal in 1935 and 244 million tons in 1955. In terms of inherent energy, fuel oils were the equivalent

---

[96] With technological advances which permit the conversion of coal into liquid fuels, interchangeability—although absent at the level of fuel use—could be achieved at the ultimate resources level. However, although this degree of flexibility may be reached in the future, it is not feasible under present conditions of costs and technology.

TABLE 33. SALES OF FUEL OILS[a] BY USES, SELECTED YEARS, 1926–55

(Quantities in thousand barrels)

Use	1926 (1)	1930 (2)	1935 (3)	1940 (4)	1945 (5)	1950 (6)	1955 (7)	Percentage distribution 1926 (8)	1955 (9)	1955 index (1926=100) (10)
Residential and commercial heating[b]	22,779	42,703	76,853	160,379	165,216	293,663	425,996	6.7%	44.0%	1,870.1
Mining and manufacturing	69,336	59,379	63,576	71,983	104,222	170,964	199,883	20.4	20.6	288.3
Oil company use	48,701	53,437	48,116	51,705	58,235	58,251	60,872	14.3	6.3	125.0
Electric power and gas plants	33,652	26,749	23,647	31,164	38,289	99,705	78,420	9.9	8.1	233.0
Railroads	72,218	67,900	55,651	66,260	114,719	64,497	19,622	21.2	2.0	27.2
Vessels	79,288	94,131	74,581	61,824	101,121	93,700	115,934	23.3	12.0	146.2
Armed forces[c]	}14,056	19,869	23,561	30,774	104,901	30,236	31,550	4.1	}3.2	}485.0
Miscellaneous uses[c]					20,775	33,776	36,627		}3.8	
Total	340,030	364,168	349,811	474,089	707,478	844,792	968,904	100.0	100.0	284.9
Total, including diesel[d]			(365,985)	(498,758)	(773,890)	(949,514)	(1,138,110)			(334.7)

[a] Including residual oil, distillate, and gas oil, but excluding diesel oil and kerosine sold as range oil.
[b] See footnotes b in Tables 31 and 32.
[c] Including distillate sold as range oil.
[d] Diesel oil consumption not available separately for 1926 or 1930, but was negligible. For 1935, diesel oil is excluded from totals, but not from the individual use groups. For comparison with earlier years, fuel oil consumption including diesel is shown in parentheses.

SOURCES: U. S. Bureau of Mines, *Minerals Yearbook*, various issues (Washington, D. C.: U. S. Government Printing Office), except diesel oil consumption, which is from American Petroleum Institute, *Petroleum Facts and Figures, 1950* (9th ed.: New York), p. 28; and *ibid., 1956*, p. 34.

TABLE 34. FUEL OIL CONSUMPTION COMPARED WITH ACTUAL
COAL CONSUMPTION, 1935 AND 1955

(Measured in barrels, Btu equivalents, and coal equivalents)

Item	Residual fuel oils (1)	Distillate and gas oils (excluding diesel oil) (2)	Kerosine (range oil only) (3)	Total (4)
1. Consumption (thous. bbl.):				
1935................	279,596	70,215	20,000	369,811
1955................	556,983	411,921	84,331	1,053,235
2. Btu values of fuel oil consumption (trillion Btu):[a]				
1935................	1,759	409	113	2,281
1955................	3,502	2,399	478	6,379
3. Bituminous coal equivalents of fuel oil consumption (mill. net tons):				
1935................	67.1	15.6	4.3	87.1
1955................	133.7	91.6	18.2	243.5
4. Actual coal (bituminous and anthracite combined) consumption (mill. net tons):				
1935................				407.4[b]
1955................				447.0[b]
5. Btu values of coal consumption (trillion Btu):[a]				
1935................				10,634
1955................				11,703
6. Fuel oil consumption (measured in Btu) as percentage of actual coal consumption:				
1935................				21.5%
1955................				54.5%

7. Actual coal consumption plus fuel oil consumption, measured in bituminous coal equivalents (mill. net tons):	Coal	Fuel oil	Total
1935................	405.8[b]	87.1	492.9
1955................	446.7[b]	243.5	690.2

[a] Conversion factors (from U. S. Bureau of Mines, *Monthly Petroleum Statement*, No. 402):
  Residual oil...........................one barrel   =   6,287,000 Btu
  Distillate oil..........................one barrel   =   5,825,000 Btu
  Kerosine..............................one barrel   =   5,670,000 Btu
  Bituminous coal.......................one net ton = 26,200,000 Btu
  Anthracite............................one net ton = 25,400,000 Btu

[b] The sets of figures in items 4 and 7 are not identical because in item 7 anthracite is converted into bituminous coal equivalents. This results in a slightly different quantity figure.

SOURCE: U. S. Bureau of Mines, *Minerals Yearbook, 1937* (Washington, D. C.: U. S. Government Printing Office), pp. 1040–45; *ibid., 1956*, Vol. II, pp. 402–12.

of one-fifth of all coal used in 1935; twenty years later their share had risen to more than one-half of the total coal consumption (see item 6). One might speculate that, in the absence of those fuel oils which are interchangeable with coal, the demand for coal would have grown by about 200 million tons (see item 7), instead of the 40-million-ton increase actually realized.

.   .   .

The Internal Combustion Fuel Period

THE DEVELOPMENT OF MOTOR VEHICLE TRANSPORTATION

Today it is almost forgotten that some fifty years ago three types of automobiles—steam cars, electric cars, and internal combustion engine cars—were competing in races which attracted great interest and made people automotive minded. For some time it seemed that in the field of automotive transportation the steam engine would win over its rivals. Steam carriages were as old as the Watt steam engine, but public prejudice against horseless vehicles kept them off the roads for more than a century. In 1769 a Frenchman was jailed for frightening people and horses by riding around in a steam carriage. In 1836 the British Parliament passed the "red flag law" which provided that a man carrying a red flag by day and a lantern by night must walk in front of every steam carriage to warn people. This law remained in force until 1896. Towards the end of the nineteenth century, the early steam vehicles, which had been clumsy, heavy, and noisy, were greatly improved, and slowly the prejudice against them began to fade. By 1890, electric automobiles had been developed and were in use in the United States. But they were expensive and had to be recharged frequently.

Gas engines, the forerunner of all present-day internal combustion engines, had been developed in principle as early as the seventeenth century. That no results of practical value were achieved for about 200 years was largely due to the lack of a suitable fuel. Before gasoline became available, benzene from coal, illuminating gas, and, earlier, even gunpowder were used in the attempts to develop motive power in an "explosion" engine. The idea that an air-gas mixture might be compressed before ignition was developed at the close of the eighteenth century. The following decades were a period of experimentation. About 1870—a decade after the birth of the oil industry—the new fuel, gasoline, began to be used experimentally; and, in 1876, the first gasoline-fueled, four-stroke cycle engine, in which the gas is compressed before ignition, was constructed in Germany. First developed as a stationary engine, it was adapted shortly for use in vehicles. Ten years after this invention, the first Benz motor car was patented. It was a light, gasoline-fueled car which operated on the four-stroke cycle. During the following few years, the most important features of present-day automobile engines were added, and in the early 1890's motor cars were developed which proved so efficient and successful that to the present day there have been no fundamental changes in the basic principles of the ordinary automobile engine.

In the United States, which was still in the midst of the railroad boom, roads were bad or nonexistent in large parts of the country. Thus, at that time, the tremendous distances worked against the automobile. Nevertheless, by 1900, some 4,200 automobiles had been built in the United States. Most were still steam driven, with electric cars next in favor, and only about one-quarter using internal combustion engines. But these proportions were soon to change. The rising petroleum industry furnished not only a suitable fuel, but also the lubricants needed for the new internal combustion engines.

The rivalry between steam, electric, and internal combustion engines continued, but the scales began to tip in favor of the gasoline-driven cars. In this country, Olds switched from steam to internal combustion cars in 1900. Ford, after constructing a gasoline-driven racing car that won contest after contest, founded his motor company in 1903. In that year, the American automobile industry began to adopt the principle of interchangeability of parts and thereby laid the foundation for mass production. By 1909, the Ford Model T was standardized. Around that time, steam carriages and electric cars began disappearing into the background as the motorization of the United States progressed.

The number of registered motor vehicles jumped from 8,000 in 1900 to over a million in 1913, exceeded the 10-million mark in 1921, and stood at 20 million in 1925. This meteoric rise was slowed down during the 1930's, and at the bottom of the depression there was an absolute decline of about one-tenth from the previous peak. In the last year before World War II, motor vehicle registration amounted to 32.5 million. Between 1940 and 1955, it again nearly doubled and in the latter year stood at 62.8 million. Of this total, passenger cars, including taxis, accounted for 52 million, trucks for 10.4 million, and buses for one-quarter million.[97]

THE GROWTH IN GASOLINE USE

For nearly fifty years, because there was little use for gasoline, the refining plants had allowed large amounts of this product to go to waste. It could have been used had there been a market because, through an accidental discovery it had been known almost since the beginning of the petroleum industry that under high temperatures crude oil could be made to yield a greater share of gasoline. When the rise of the automobile industry opened a new rapidly expanding market for this product, the petroleum industry adapted its output to a changing pattern of demand.

Around 1900, a 42-gallon barrel of crude oil when refined yielded, on the average, some 24 gallons of kerosine, 6 gallons of fuel oils, and 5 gallons of gasoline—or 58 per cent, 14 per cent, and 13 per cent, respectively (see Table 25 and Figure 18). In 1913, the cracking method was introduced, and this new

[97] U.S. Department of Commerce, Bureau of Public Roads, *Highway Statistics, 1955* (Washington, D. C.: U.S. Government Printing Office, 1957), p. 42.

refining process greatly increased the gasoline yield per barrel of crude. By 1918, the yield per barrel had changed to 22.5 gallons of distillate and residual fuel oils, 10.6 gallons of gasoline, and only 5.6 gallons of kerosine. It was not until 1930, however, that the turning point was reached and gasoline became the most important refinery product in quantitative terms. At that time the refinery yield was gasoline, 42 per cent, distillates and residual, 40 per cent, and kerosine, 5 per cent.

While demand for motor fuel multiplied six times between 1925 and 1955— from 224 million barrels to 1,334 million barrels (see Table 35)—the number of motor vehicles in use increased only a little over three times—from 17,895,000 to 58,861,000 (see Table 36). This disparity can be attributed to two unrelated trends. One is the increasing proportion of total motor fuel going to non-highway use. In 1925, highway use accounted for 90 per cent of the total; in 1955, only 83 per cent (see Table 35). The second, and more important, trend is the increase in fuel consumption per vehicle. As shown in Table 36, average annual gasoline consumption per motor vehicle increased from 473 gallons in 1925 to 790 gallons

TABLE 35. DOMESTIC CONSUMPTION OF GASOLINE, INCLUDING AVIATION GAS AND NAPHTHA, SELECTED YEARS, 1918-55

(Quantities in thousand barrels)

| Year | Total estimated consumption [a] (1) | Highway use by motor vehicles | | Tractors and other farm machinery | | Aviation use | | | |
		Quantity (2)	Per cent of total (3)	Quantity (4)	Per cent of total (5)	Civilian and military (6)	Per cent of total (7)	Civilian only (8)	Per cent of total (9)
1918..	74,506								
1920..	101,208								
1925..	223,865	201,429	90.0%						
1930..	394,800	351,381	89.0						
1935..	434,810	386,976	89.0			1,754	0.4%	1,056	0.2%
1940..	589,490	524,643	89.0	22,976	3.9%	n.a.	n.a.	2,308	0.4
1945..	696,333	467,310	67.1	41,667	6.0	116,990	16.8	6,154	0.9
1950..	994,290	833,810	83.9	73,095	7.4	39,517	4.0	16,749	1.7
1955..	1,334,205	1,107,405	83.0	87,278	6.5	70,141	5.3	31,677	2.4

n.a. Not available.

[a] Including losses from evaporation and handling.

SOURCES: Column 1 from U. S. Geological Survey, *Mineral Resources of the United States*, various issues, and U. S. Bureau of Mines, *Minerals Yearbook*, various issues (Washington, D. C.: U. S. Government Printing Office). Column 2 from Table 36, gallons converted into barrels. Columns 4, 6, and 8 for 1935-50 from American Petroleum Institute, *Petroleum Facts and Figures, 1950* (9th ed., New York), pp. 95-96, 229; *ibid., 1956* (12th ed.), pp. 85, 203. Column 4, 1955 from Appendix Table F-3. Column 6, 1955 from *Minerals Yearbook, 1956*, Vol. II, *op. cit.*, p. 387. Column 8, 1955 from U. S. Bureau of the Census, *Statistical Abstract of the United States, 1957* (Washington, D. C.: U. S. Government Printing Office), p. 578.

in 1955, a rise of 67 per cent. The increase in consumption per vehicle was concentrated in the earlier part of the thirty-year period as shown in Table 36. From 1925 to 1940, the number of motor vehicles in use increased by almost 70 per cent, the amount of gasoline they consumed, by 160 per cent. In the following fifteen years, both vehicles in use and fuel consumption approximately doubled (with increases of about 95 per cent and 110 per cent). Taking passenger cars, trucks, and buses together, annual gasoline consumption per vehicle averaged 473 gallons in 1925, rose almost uninterruptedly to 733 gallons in 1940, declined during the war, then leveled off at close to 800 gallons in the postwar period.

The non-highway use of motor fuels represents, in the main, two rapidly expanding groups: farm equipment and aviation. Over three-quarters of total fuel consumption by agricultural machinery consists of gasoline, which in 1950 amounted to 7.4 per cent of total gasoline consumption (see Table 35). Tractors in use on farms numbered 827,000 in 1929; rose from 1.5 million in 1940 to 3.6 million in 1950, and to over 4.5 million in 1955.[98] Despite the tremendous expansion of commercial and private aviation over the past twenty years, fuel consumption by civilian aircraft accounted for only a small share (somewhat over 2 per cent) of total motor fuel demand in the mid-1950's. Over the period 1935–55, revenue passenger-miles flown by scheduled domestic airlines expanded approximately sixty-three times and ton-miles in domestic express and freight service (excluding mail) rose 207 times (see Appendix Table XXVI). In contrast, fuel consumption by civil aircraft rose only thirty times (see Table 35). Including military aircraft, the demand for aviation gasoline in 1955 was 70,141,000 barrels, forty times the level twenty years earlier. Yet even this figure represents only 5.3 per cent of total motor fuel consumption in 1955. After jet-propelled aircraft began to replace the conventional piston engine planes in military aviation, jet fuel—a blend of lower grade gasoline, kerosine, and distillate fuel—furnished a rapidly increasing share of the total aviation fuel. Between 1952 and 1955, the demand for this new type of fuel nearly tripled, rising from 20 million to over 56 million barrels,[99] about 80 per cent of the consumption of aviation gasoline.

From the start, the rapidly growing requirements for gasoline not only were fully met by U.S. refinery output, but in every year from 1918 to 1955 there was a net export balance, although of widely varying amounts. Net exports of motor fuel reached their peak in 1944 when nearly 100 million barrels, or 13.2 per cent of domestic production, were shipped abroad. (Incidentally, this percentage share was similar to that during World War I, when the peak export in 1918 amounted to 14.7 per cent of domestic output of motor fuel.) By the mid-1950's, net exports of gasoline ranged from 30 million to 35 million barrels a year. In 1955, they represented only 2.2 per cent of the domestic production of 1,374 million barrels. But gasoline still held the first place among the net exports of various refined petroleum products. Of the total input of crude into refineries, however, 283 million or 11.6 per cent was supplied by foreign crude oil.

[98] *Petroleum Facts and Figures, 1950, op. cit.,* p. 95; *ibid., 1956,* p. 85.
[99] *Minerals Yearbook, 1956,* Vol. II, *op. cit.,* p. 374.

TABLE 36. MOTOR VEHICLES AND GASOLINE CONSUMPTION, FIVE-YEAR INTERVALS, 1925-55

Year	Total motor vehicles [a]			Passenger cars			Motor trucks			Buses [b]		
	Average number in use (thous.) (1)	Gasoline consumption (mill. gal.) (2)	Average consumption per vehicle (gal.) (3)	Average number in use (thous.) (4)	Gasoline consumption (mill. gal.) (5)	Average consumption per vehicle (gal.) (6)	Average number in use (thous.) (7)	Gasoline consumption (mill. gal.) (8)	Average consumption per vehicle (gal.) (9)	Average number in use (thous.) (10)	Gasoline consumption (mill. gal.) (11)	Average consumption per vehicle (gal.) (12)
1925...	17,895	8,460	473	15,453	6,507	421	2,372	1,810	763	70	142	2,035
1930...	24,647	14,758	599	21,306	11,355	533	3,241	2,946	909	100	457	4,572
1935...	24,344	16,253	668	20,760	12,290	592	3,471	3,553	1,024	113	410	3,624
1940...	30,057	22,035	733	25,386	15,818	623	4,532	5,646	1,246	139	571	4,109
1945...	30,638	19,627	641	25,641	12,901	503	4,834	5,926	1,226	163	800	4,908
1950...	45,607	35,020	768	37,453	25,131	671	7,990	9,300	1,164	164	589	3,596
1955...	58,861	46,511	790	48,949	34,215	699	9,729	11,791	1,212	183	505	2,764

[a] Since figures represent average number in use, not number of registered vehicles, and refer to gasoline-using vehicles only, excluding diesel and liquefied petroleum gas, the numbers are lower than those given in Appendix Table XXV, and in Appendix to Part II, Section D, which refer to all motor vehicles. The discrepancy is especially large in the case of commercial buses, of which by 1955 about one-half used diesel.

[b] The breakdown as between school buses and commercial buses for 1950 and 1955 is: Commercial buses, 1950, column 10, 63; column 11, 508; column 12, 8,073; and for 1955, column 10, 46, column 11, 390, column 12, 8,410. School buses, 1950, column 10, 101; column 11, 81; column 12, 807; and for 1955, column 10, 136, column 11, 114, column 12, 840.

SOURCES: American Petroleum Institute, *Petroleum Facts and Figures, 1950* (9th ed.; New York), p. 92; *ibid., 1956* (12th ed.), p. 82.

DIESEL FUEL

In 1892, the design principles of the diesel engine were patented in Germany. The basic feature of the engine is the high compression of air within the cylinder and its consequent heating to such a degree that it spontaneously ignites fuel which is injected into the compressed air. It differs from the spark-ignition gasoline engine mainly in the nature of the fuel charge. In the latter, fuel and air are mixed in a definite proportion, while in the diesel engine the air-to-fuel ratio is varied with load conditions. The high air-to-fuel ratio and the high compression thus make the diesel engine not only more efficient than the gasoline engine in its use of fuel, but permits the use of a less costly fuel.

Commercial diesel engines were built in the United States as early as 1898. Only after the 1930's, however, when an improved fuel-injection system became predominant, did diesel engines begin to be widely used. They were used chiefly in vessels, and to a lesser extent in trucks and buses; in stationary and automotive equipment in road building, mining, and manufacturing; and in the generation of electricity. Just before World War II, the diesel engine gave evidence that it was about to come into its own in railroad use in this country. This development was delayed, however, by the war, and it was not until the postwar period that it took place on a grand scale. The fast-expanding use of diesel engines in the past two decades is evidenced by the fact that consumption of diesel oil increased tenfold, from 16 million barrels in 1935 to 169 million in 1955. This compares, over the same period, with the tripled use of gasoline and the increase by nearly three times of sales of fuel oils (excluding diesel). Of the total demand for gasoline and diesel oil combined, diesel accounted for some 3.5 per cent in 1935. By 1955, its share had risen to more than one-tenth.

The consumption pattern of diesel fuel since 1940 is given in Table 37. The growth rates of different uses have varied widely, with consequent shifts in the relative importance of the main consumer categories. The most striking change occurred in railroad use—in 1945, it was only 18 per cent of the total sales of diesel oil; by 1955, it was almost one-half of the total. This rapid growth reflects a technological change of exceptional thoroughness and swiftness; the American railroad system became almost totally dieselized in less than ten years. This phenomenon is, of course, well known, as is its effect on coal. What is less widely realized, however, is the similar effect on residual fuel oil. Residual was an important steam locomotive fuel, and the advent of the diesel locomotive was responsible for the absolute decline of more than three-quarters in this use between 1940 and 1955 (see Table 32). Diesel locomotives proved so much more efficient that the total demand for oil by railroads—residual and distillate, including diesel which had grown by more than forty times—increased by less than one-half during this fifteen-year period.

In contrast to use by railroads, the consumption of diesel oil by marine vessels rose only slightly. From the leading use, accounting for more than one-half the total in 1940, consumption by vessels declined to one-fifth in 1945 and to less than one-tenth in 1955.

TABLE 37. SALES OF DIESEL OIL BY USES, FIVE-YEAR INTERVALS, 1940–55

(Quantities in thousand barrels)

Use	1940 Quantity	1940 Per cent	1945 Quantity	1945 Per cent	1950 Quantity	1950 Per cent	1955 Quantity	1955 Per cent	1955 index (1940=100)
Mining and manufacturing	1,957	7.9%	6,025	9.1%	14,268	13.6%	16,753	9.9%	856.1
Oil company use	223	0.9	229	0.3	704	0.7	1,112	0.7	498.7
Electric power plants a	1,631	6.6	3,067	4.6	6,564	6.3	3,430	2.0	210.3
Railroads	1,838	7.5	12,036	18.1	45,084	43.1	80,064	47.3	4,356.0
Vessels	12,979	52.6	13,374	20.1	12,119	11.6	15,869	9.4	122.3
Armed forces	1,115	4.5	22,950	34.6	4,650	4.4	7,763	4.6	696.2
Miscellaneous uses b	4,926	20.0	8,731	13.1	21,333	20.4	44,215	26.1	897.6
Total	24,669	100.0%	66,412	100.0%	104,722	100.0%	169,206	100.0%	685.9

a Including negligible amounts sold to manufactured-gas plants.
b Including highway use. In 1955, trucks and buses consumed more than 24 million barrels of diesel oil. (U.S. Bureau of Mines, *Mineral Market Report*, No. MMS 2681.)

SOURCES: American Petroleum Institute, *Petroleum Facts and Figures, 1950* (9th ed., New York), pp. 28–36; *ibid., 1956* (12th ed.), pp. 34–41.

TABLE 38.   THE CONSUMPTION PATTERN OF OIL AND OIL PRODUCTS,ᵃ FIVE-YEAR INTERVALS, 1920-55

(Quantities in thousand barrels)

Year	Internal combustion fuels			Kerosine ᶜ (4)	Fuel oils			Other finished products (8)	Not identified and losses ᵉ (9)	Grand total ᶠ (10)
	Gasoline ᵇ (1)	Diesel (2)	Total (3)		Distillate ᵈ (5)	Residual (6)	Total (7)			
Quantities:										
1920	101,208	n.a.	101,208	33,082	185,972		219,054	25,064	110,478	455,804
1925	223,865	n.a.	223,865	39,969	307,004		346,973	52,393	103,751	726,982
1930	394,800	n.a.	394,800	34,736	368,531		403,267	87,404	40,979	926,450
1935	434,810	16,174	450,984	47,645	69,854	280,695	398,194	102,068	32,440	983,686
1940	589,490	24,669	614,159	68,776	136,182	340,163	545,121	147,391	19,949	1,326,620
1945	696,333	66,412	762,745	75,573	159,672	523,423	758,668	229,121	22,151	1,772,685
1950	994,290	104,722	1,099,012	117,844	290,163	553,793	961,800	296,328	17,917	2,375,057
1955	1,334,205	169,206	1,503,411	116,808	411,922	557,057	1,085,787	497,004	1,573	3,087,775
Percentage of total:										
1920	22.2%	n.a.	22.2%	7.3%	40.8%		48.1%	5.5%	24.2%	100.0%
1925	30.8	n.a.	30.8	5.5	42.2		47.7	7.2	14.3	100.0
1930	42.6	n.a.	42.6	3.7	39.8		43.5	9.4	4.4	100.0
1935	44.2	1.6%	45.8	4.9	7.1%	28.5%	40.5	10.4	3.3	100.0
1940	44.4	1.9	46.3	5.2	10.3	25.6	41.1	11.1	1.5	100.0
1945	39.3	3.7	43.0	4.3	9.0	29.5	42.8	12.9	1.3	100.0
1950	41.9	4.4	46.3	5.0	12.2	23.3	40.5	12.5	0.7	100.0
1955	43.2	5.5	48.7	3.8	13.3	18.1	35.2	16.1	0.05	100.0

n.a. Not available.

ᵃ The above data represent apparent consumption, which is a derived figure representing the total new supply (that is, production plus imports) of crude petroleum, natural gas liquids, and their derivatives minus exports and plus decreases or minus increases in reported stocks. Because there are substantial secondary and consumers' stocks that are not reported to the Bureau of Mines, this figure varies from consumption or sales figures (*Minerals Yearbook, 1956*, Vol. II, p. 321).

ᵇ Includes gasoline and naphtha from crude oil and NGL; excludes jet fuel which is included in "other finished products" (column 8).

ᶜ Represents total apparent consumption for kerosine, including the amounts used as illuminant.

ᵈ Excludes diesel oil which is included in "internal combustion fuels." Figures and percentages for 1920-30 include residual.

ᵉ Includes crude oil used as fuel in earlier years.

ᶠ These figures differ from those for apparent consumption of crude oil, including net trade in products shown in Table 22, column 5, because natural gas liquids are included and they are derived by adding the apparent consumption of finished oil and NGL products. If apparent consumption of NGL is taken into account, the discrepancies between the two sets of figures are minor, as shown below:

Apparent consumption (thous. bbl.)	*1945*	*1950*	*1955*
Total from Table 22	1,661,487	2,180,291	2,802,856
Total from Table 38	1,772,685	2,375,057	3,087,775
Discrepancy	111,198	194,766	284,919
Apparent consumption of NGL from Table 47 . .	110,762	178,883	277,500

SOURCES: U.S. Geological Survey, *Minerals Resources of the United States*, various issues, and U.S. Bureau of Mines, *Minerals Yearbook*, various issues (Washington, D. C.: U.S. Government Printing Office).

The growth of diesel power in automotive use affected the categories with the second and third highest growth rates. An increase of eight and a half times in sales to the mining and manufacturing category reflects mainly the widespread adoption of heavy diesel-powered equipment, although it also covers the use of "packaged" diesel-powered plants for electricity generation. A ninefold expansion in the miscellaneous category is largely a reflection of the growth in diesel-powered highway transport and diesel equipment in road building and construction.

By the mid-1950's domestic demand for all internal combustion fuels—gasoline and diesel combined—amounted to 1.5 billion barrels, having doubled in the single decade 1945–55. With the exception of a few years during World War II, their share in the consumption of all petroleum products increased continuously; in 1955, this group accounted for nearly one-half of the total.

The changing pattern of oil products since the end of World War I is shown in Table 38 and Figure 19, which for completeness include products derived from natural gas liquids (NGL)[100] as well as from crude oil. While NGL were of relatively small importance in the total—equivalent to about one-tenth of crude oil in 1955—they are complementary to and competitive with refined oil products. Thus, their inclusion in the product pattern of all liquid fuels shown in Table 38 provides a summary look at the oil sector of the U.S. energy economy by tracing the consumption pattern for all liquid hydrocarbons over a thirty-five year period.

[100] The NGL are treated separately in the following section on natural gas.

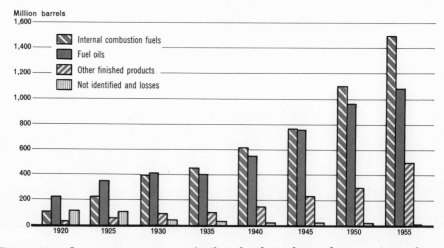

Figure 19. Consumption pattern of oil and oil products, five-year intervals, 1920–55.

NATURAL GAS

Unlike the oil industry, natural gas entered the American scene so incon-spicuously that it remained almost unnoticed for many decades. The occurrence of "burning springs" in various parts of the country had been known to the earliest settlers. Natural gas was encountered frequently in the drilling of water and salt wells where it was considered a nuisance and was allowed to escape. The earliest recorded commercial use of natural gas was in 1821 in Fredonia, New York, where it was consumed mainly as lighting fuel. The first natural gas com-pany in the United States was the Fredonia Gas Light and Waterworks, founded in 1865. But this was an isolated instance, as was the use of natural gas on a small scale in Sacramento, California, as early as in the mid-1850's.

In 1878, a large gas well was discovered near Murrysville, Pennsylvania, and the year 1883, during which a pipeline from this well to the city of Pittsburgh was opened, may be considered the beginning of the natural gas industry.[101] Prior to this time, as a result of the development of the oil industry, rich natural gas deposits were discovered in the search for petroleum. Since petroleum had its beginnings in Pennsylvania, there was little demand for gas—either as a heating or lighting fuel—because coal and fuel wood were available for heating purposes and kerosine for lighting. For many years, gas was considered a waste product, or at best a cheap illuminant or fuel to be used only in the oil fields or in their immediate vicinity. In the late 1860's and 1870's, there were isolated experiments of natural gas being burned by iron and steel works near Pittsburgh for heating, puddling, steam generation, and reverberatory furnace fuel. About the same time, natural gas was used on a small scale for burning fire-bricks and as a source of lampblack for printers ink.[102]

Through the 1880's, the utilization of this fuel, as a by-product of the oil industry, was confined to the Appalachian region, with one noteworthy exception: in northwestern Ohio explorations were begun with the purpose of discovering gas. The search for gas resulted in 1884 in the discovery of vast gas reservoirs which were tapped with the main purpose of supplying industrial plants with cheap fuel. One year later, the rich oil fields near Lima, Ohio, where discovered in the course of drilling for gas.[103] During the westward march of the oil industry, the prolific gas fields of the midcontinent and Gulf Coast regions and of California were discovered. But the utilization of gas in the huge amounts that became available depended on the development of efficient methods for its trans-portation.

[101] *Mineral Resources of the United States, 1916*, Part II, *op. cit.*, pp. 600 ff.; see also S. F. Peckham, *op. cit.*, pp. 242, 249; and U.S. Bureau of Mines, *Mineral Facts and Problems*, Bulletin 556 (Washington, D. C.: U.S. Government Printing Office, 1956), p. 652.

[102] Peckham, *op. cit.*, pp. 242, 244.

[103] Williamson and Daum, *op. cit.*, pp. 590–91.

The Development of Pipeline Transportation

In contrast to coal and oil which can be transported in various ways and which can be easily stored, natural gas must either be used at the point of production or moved through pipelines (at least thus far); and it cannot be stored above ground in large quantities.

The very first natural gas pipeline, made of wood, was used in Fredonia. The first "long" iron line—5.5 miles long—was built in 1872, leading into Titusville, Pennsylvania,[104] although the pipeline serving the city of Pittsburgh after 1883 was the first of major importance. Pipeline mileage grew thereafter and by 1889, for example, the total length of the lines used in natural gas distribution was 7,149 miles.[105] These early pipes were narrow in diameter, at the most eight inches, and could not withstand a pressure of more than eighty pounds per square inch, and most were very short for local distribution. The first high-pressure pipeline, 525 pounds per square inch, was laid in 1891 to pump gas over a distance of 120 miles from the fields in northern Indiana to Chicago; but the large-scale development of the modern natural gas transmission system came much later.

In the first years of the twentieth century, when the rich oil fields of Oklahoma, Texas, and California were developed, as much as 90 per cent of all natural gas[106] produced in the oil fields was still being lost or wasted. When attempts were made to transport some of the gas, it was put in the pipelines just as it was produced by the oil wells, without first removing the volatile liquids contained in the gas. The liquids condensed in the lines and caused great trouble until "drips" or "scrubbers" were installed at the beginning of the lines to remove them. This "drip gasoline" was a waste product until the fast growing demand for regular and aviation gasoline during the first World War made it a valuable addition to crude oil gasoline.

Prior to the late 1920's, the transportation of natural gas over a distance of 250 or at the most 300 miles was considered an outstanding accomplishment. But toward the end of the 1920's, the use of conventional screw couplings in connecting the pipe were replaced by welded pipe joints. Seamless pipes of larger diameter began to be manufactured from steel of great tensile strength which permitted high transmission pressures. Thus greater use could be made of the high natural pressure existing in some gas fields. Through improvements in compressor stations, which restore the pressure as the gas moves along, long-distance lines could transport several times the volume of gas piped without recompression. These improvements and the use of heavy power equipment for the laying of pipe extended the range over which natural gas could be transported easily and eco-

---

[104] Federal Power Commission, *Natural Gas Investigation* (Washington, D. C.: *Report of Commissioner Nelson Lee Smith and Commissioner Harrington Wimberly*, Docket No. G-580, U.S. Government Printing Office, 1949), pp. 237–38.

[105] *Mineral Resources of the United States, 1889–90, op cit.*, pp. 366, 368.

[106] Natural gas as found in the earth occurs in two ways: as " dry" gas which contains only a small quantity of liquid or volatile hydrocarbons and as "wet" gas in association with crude liquid petroleum. Wet gas contains appreciable amounts of liquid hydrocarbons which are removed and are the source of useful products.

nomically to 1,000 miles by the mid-1930's (see Figure 20). The technological advances, which made possible long-distance interstate pipelines, became the foundation for the spectacular increase in the use of natural gas.

It was not until after World War II that the longest and largest lines connected the Southwest, the center of natural gas production, to the Northeast. The so-called "Big Inch" (diameter 24 inches, length 1,250 miles) and "Little Big Inch" (diameter 20 inches, length 1,475 miles) pipelines, were constructed during World War II by the federal government to facilitate the movement of crude oil and products from Texas to the Middle Atlantic Coast region. These subsequently were purchased by the natural gas industry. In the twenty-year period between 1935 and 1955, the total mileage of pipelines (excluding those used to transport manufactured, mixed, and liquefied petroleum gas) increased from 167,400 miles to 448,770 miles. Of the latter, 260,600 miles were distribution lines, 142,490 miles transmission lines, and 45,680 miles were field and gathering lines.[107]

As a result of greatly extending the pipelines, the consumption of gas became much less concentrated in the producing regions. This is illustrated by the increase in the volume that went into interstate transmission. In 1921, the first year for which such information is available, 150 billion cubic feet, representing 22.5 per cent of the marketed production, were transported in interstate commerce. In 1945, the volume exceeded a trillion cubic feet, but this was only little more than one-fourth of the total marketed production. By the mid-1950's, some 5 trillion cubic feet, more than one-half of the marketed production, went into interstate transmission.[108] By 1955, only two states in New England (Maine and Vermont) and three in the Northwest (Washington, Oregon, and Idaho) were not connected with the pipeline network.[109] In the following year, natural gas supply was extended to the Northwestern states; only Maine and Vermont remained outside the network (see Figure 20).

The variable demands upon the capacity of long transmission lines, caused mainly by the sharp peaks during the heating season, present a basic problem of economical gas distribution. To meet this problem, progress has been made in the development of underground storage facilities. In 1940, there were only nineteen underground storage pools in operation. With the great expansion of the use of natural gas for domestic and commercial heating in the post-World War II period the need to assure seasonal peak deliveries grew correspondingly. By the mid-1950's, the number of storage pools had increased to nearly 200, distributed over twenty states. In 1955, some 500 billion cubic feet of natural gas were put into underground storage, over 200 billion of this total in Pennsylvania and West Virginia. In the same year more than 400 billion cubic feet were withdrawn for distribution.[110]

[107] See American Gas Association, *Historical Statistics of the Gas Industry* (New York: 1956), Tables 49, 50; and *1958 Gas Facts* (New York), Table 47.

[108] Various issues of *Mineral Resources of the United States, op. cit.,* and *Minerals Yearbook, op. cit.*

[109] *Minerals Yearbook, 1956,* Vol. II, *op. cit.,* pp. 286–89.

[110] *Minerals Yearbook, 1955,* Vol. II, *op. cit.,* p. 283; American Gas Association, *Gas Requirements and Supplies of the Gas Utility and Pipeline Industry, Annual 1956 to 1960* (New York: 1957), p. 15.

Figure. 20. Major natural gas pipelines, 1930 (above) and 1958 (below). (Data for 1930 furnished through courtesy of Ebasco Services, Inc.; data for 1958 through courtesy of Federal Power Commission.)

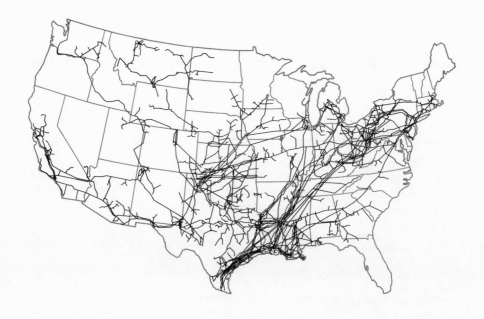

The Statistical Record of Natural Gas Production and Consumption

The historical record of natural gas production and consumption is given in Tables 39 and 40 and Figure 21. The production series which is available for the longest period refers to "marketed production," which consists essentially of that portion of total withdrawals from reservoirs which was put to commercial use. Beginning in 1920, when marketed production was redefined, the term refers to gas utilized, plus the volume added to storage and pipelines and that lost in transmission. Only for the years since 1920 is there a series available on "gross production" (or withdrawals), which includes marketed production plus the

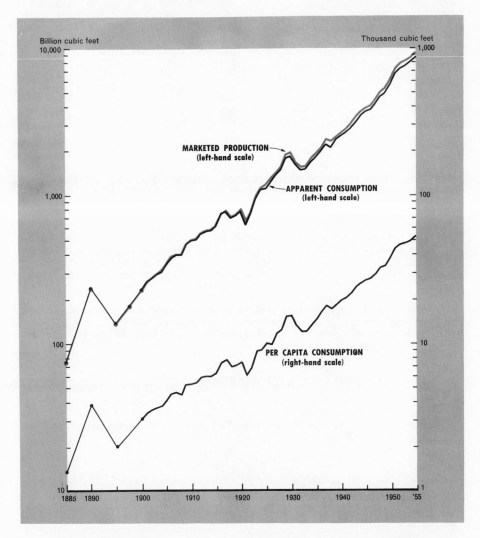

Figure 21.   Production and consumption of natural gas, 1885–1955.

TABLE 39. PRODUCTION AND CONSUMPTION OF NATURAL GAS,
FIVE-YEAR INTERVALS, 1885-1955

(Billion cubic feet; except per capita consumption in thousands)

Year	Production Gross[a] (1)	Production Net[b] (2)	Marketed[c] (3)	Apparent consumption Excluding transmission losses[d] (4)	Apparent consumption Including transmission losses[e] (5)	Per capita consumption (thous. cu. ft.) (6)
1885.........	n.a.		76	76		1.35
1890.........	n.a.		239	239		3.79
1895.........	n.a.		137	137		1.97
1900.........	n.a.		236	235		3.09
1905.........	n.a.		351	346		4.13
1910.........	n.a.		509	502		5.43
1915.........	n.a.		629	626		6.22
1920.........	1,051		812	785	799	7.37
1925.........	1,566		1,210	1,150	1,171	9.93
1930.........	2,498		1,979	1,867	1,902	15.15
1935.........	2,450	2,396	1,969	1,854	1,907	14.56
1940.........	3,753	3,316	2,734	2,575	2,634	19.49
1945.........	6,000	4,840	4,042	3,740	3,839	26.73
1950.........	8,480	7,083	6,282	5,767	5,942	38.02
1955.........	11,720	10,179	9,405	8,700	8,920	52.65

n.a. Not available.

[a] Gross production equals marketed production of wet and dry gas plus the quantities repressured, vented, and wasted. Estimates of gross production, but on a somewhat different basis, were first made in 1935. These estimates were revised and extended back to 1920 to conform with the above definition adopted in 1947.

[b] Gross production minus the quantities of gas returned to the reservoir for pressure maintenance.

[c] Marketed production of gas as measured prior to extraction of natural gas liquids (see footnote d below): 1885-1905, calculated on the basis of contemporary estimates of the quantity of coal and wood displaced by gas or the value of gas sold (hence the strong possibility of spurious results); 1910-15, amount of natural gas that was commercially utilized; 1920 and subsequent years, gas utilized plus volume added to storage and pipeline fill and lost in transmission.

[d] Apparent consumption of gas: 1885-95 equals estimated marketed production of untreated gas; 1900-15, marketed production minus exports; 1920-55, marketed production minus net exports, net stored, lost in transmission, and volume loss due to extraction of natural gas liquids.

[e] Column 4 plus transmission losses.

SOURCES: Columns 1 and 2 from U.S. Geological Survey, *Mineral Resources of the United States*, various issues, and U.S. Bureau of Mines, *Minerals Yearbook*, various issues (Washington, ·D. C.: U.S. Government Printing Office). Column 3 from Appendix Table I. Column 4 from Appendix Table VI. Column 5 from U. S. Bureau of Mines, *Mineral Industry Surveys*, Weekly Coal Report No. 2061, Washington, March 15, 1957, Table 24. Column 6 from Appendix Table X.

amounts repressured, vented, and wasted. For the period 1935-55, Table 39 also shows "net production"—that is, gross production less the quantities of gas returned to the earth for pressure maintenance in oil reservoirs. With increasing knowledge of the function of gas in the production of oil and with improved techniques for applying this knowledge, the quantities so reinjected increased from

TABLE 40. INDEXES OF PRODUCTION AND CONSUMPTION
OF NATURAL GAS, FIVE-YEAR INTERVALS, 1900-1955

(1900 = 100)

Year	Marketed production		Apparent consumption (excluding transmission losses)		Per capita consumption	
	Index (1)	Percentage increase per decade (2)	Index ᵃ (3)	Percentage increase per decade (4)	Index (5)	Percentage increase per decade (6)
1900.........	100.0		100.0		100.0	
1905.........	148.7	1900–1910	147.2	1900–1910	133.7	1900–1910
1910.........	215.7	115.7%	213.6	113.6%	175.7	75.7%
1915.........	266.5	1910–20	266.4	1910–20	201.3	1910–20
1920.........	344.1	59.5	334.0	56.4	238.5	35.7
1925.........	512.7	1920–30	489.4	1920–30	321.4	1920–30
1930.........	838.6	143.7	794.5	137.9	490.3	105.6
1935.........	834.3	1930–40	788.9	1930–40	471.2	1930–40
1940.........	1,158.5	38.1	1,095.7	37.9	630.7	28.6
1945.........	1,712.7	1940–50	1,591.5	1940–50	865.0	1940–50
1950.........	2,661.9	129.8	2,454.0	124.0	1,230.4	95.1
1955.........	3,985.2	132.7 ᵇ	3,702.1	132.6 ᵇ	1,703.9	97.0 ᵇ

ᵃ These index numbers are based on physical quantities (cubic feet) consumed, and differ slightly from those shown in the Appendix Table IX, which are based on Btu values of 1,075 Btu per cubic foot of wet gas in the early period and 1,035 Btu per cubic foot of dry gas for 1920 and subsequent years.

ᵇ Refers to the decade 1945–55.

2 per cent of the gross production in 1935 to 18 per cent in 1945, and were 13 per cent of the greatly expanded gross withdrawals in 1955. Thus, net production is a measure of output which represents the amount of gas actually removed from the reservoir. "Apparent consumption," prior to 1920, was just about the same as marketed production. Subsequently, apparent consumption has been derived by subtracting from marketed production not just exports, as in earlier years, but also net amounts stored, losses in transmission, and the volume losses connected with the extraction of natural gas liquids from natural gas.

Measured in terms of marketed production, a level of output in the neighborhood of 235 billion cubic feet of natural gas had been reached by the turn of the century. During the ensuing decade, marketed production more than doubled. Between 1910 and 1920, the rate of growth slackened, with an increase of 60 per cent, but during the 1920's it again picked up, increasing about two and a half times. In the following decade, the effect of the depression years held the increase down to 38 per cent. After 1940, the natural gas industry expanded again at an accelerated pace and with greatly increased volume. In the first postwar decade, 1945–55, an increase of 133 per cent brought the marketed production to 9,405 billion cubic feet. In terms of inherent energy, this quantity is equivalent to 390 million tons of bituminous coal. Per capita consumption rose from 3,000 cubic feet in 1900 to nearly 53,000 in 1955, or the energy equivalent of slightly more than two tons of coal.

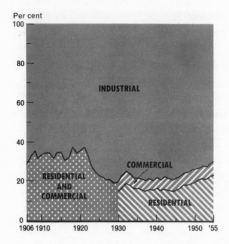

Figure 22. Natural gas consumption pattern, selected years, 1906–55.

A comparison of the growth of natural gas production with that of crude oil output (see Appendix Table V, columns 4 and 5) reveals that in 1955 the production of each was about forty times as large as at the beginning of this century.[111] To a certain extent this reflects the close interdependence of the two industries, but it is noteworthy that the two reached their 1955 levels by quite different growth patterns. Until the beginning of World War II, the oil industry expanded nearly twice as fast as natural gas production. Since then this relationship has been reversed. Between 1940 and 1955, while crude oil output nearly doubled, production of natural gas reached a level three and a half times that of 1940. During this period, the increase in natural gas was nearly three times as large as that in crude oil output. It was actually through the compensating disparities in the expansion of the two industries at different times rather than by a parallel movement through time that the virtual identity in the fifty-five year growth of petroleum and natural gas production came about.

Unlike the flexibility of oil in meeting a wide variety of consumer requirements with a variety of different products, natural gas is essentially a single product. Nevertheless, it has many advantages over other fuels. It requires only a minimum of processing and is clean and convenient to use. The amount of heat derived from natural gas can be easily controlled, it imposes no storage problem on the consumer, and it has been, on the average, less expensive than other fuels at the point of production. A disadvantage lies in the fact that transportation is limited to pipelines, which pose special problems in that they are fixed facilities and need assured near-capacity throughput between given points of origin and destination for economic operation.

Natural gas consumption statistics by uses are shown in Tables 41 and 42, and Figures 22 and 23. Statistics by two broad classes of use—"residential and commercial" and "industrial"—are available for a fifty-year period, with a further

---

[111] The comparative growth in consumption of the two fuels is discussed in Chapter 2.

breakdown between residential and commercial since 1930 (Table 41); while the breakdown of industrial into more detailed use classes is available since 1920 (Table 42). Over the past fifty years, industrial consumption of natural gas has fluctuated from about two-thirds to four-fifths of the total natural gas use.[112] But viewing the fifty-year period as a whole, the shares of industrial use and residential and commercial consumption have remained about the same. From 1906 to 1955, residential and commercial consumption moved from 28 per cent to 30 per cent of the total use; industrial consumption, from 72 per cent to 70 per cent of the greatly expanded total. However, their growth rates have not followed the same pattern. During the first two decades of this century, the use of natural

TABLE 41. CONSUMPTION OF NATURAL GAS, SELECTED YEARS, 1906-55 [a]

(Quantities in billion cubic feet)

Year	Residential [b] (quantity) (1)	Commercial (quantity) (2)	Residential and commercial (percentage of total) (3)	Industrial Quantity (4)	Industrial Percentage of total (5)	Total consumption (quantity) (6)
1906........		111	28.5%	278	71.5%	389
1910........		170	33.4	339	66.6	509
1915........		217	34.6	411	65.4	629
1920........		286	35.8	512	64.2	798
1925........		272	22.9	916	77.1	1,188
1930........	296	81	19.4	1,565	80.6	1,942
1935........	313	100	21.7	1,496	78.3	1,910
1940........	444	135	21.8	2,076	78.2	2,655
1945........	607	230	21.5	3,063	78.5	3,900
1950........	1,198	388	26.3	4,440	73.7	6,026
1955........	2,124	629	30.4	6,317	69.6	9,070

[a] A small amount of natural gas here included was consumed in the form of a mixture of manufactured and natural gas.
[b] Commercial consumption included in residential figures until 1930.

SOURCES: U.S. Geological Survey, *Mineral Resources of the United States*, various issues, and U.S. Bureau of Mines, *Minerals Yearbook*, various issues (Washington, D. C.: U.S. Government Printing Office).

[112] For the period since 1920, the figures in column 6 of Table 41 differ slightly from those in Table 39, columns 4 and 5. The former represent reported consumption and include small amounts of natural gas mixed with manufactured gas; the latter represent "apparent consumption," calculated as described in the footnotes to Table 39.

A breakdown which divides energy consumption into "residential and commercial" and only one other class called "industrial," would for every fuel show the industrial sector as dominant. Such a broad classification would in the case of oil include under "industrial" the huge amounts used in transportation and in the case of coal the great quantities which are used by electric utilities and which until recently were consumed by railroads. In natural gas, on the other hand, minerals and manufacturing industries and electric power generation account for some four-fifths of the industrial total (see Appendix Table XXVII).

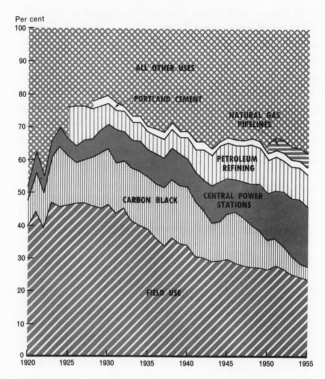

Figure 23. Industrial use pattern of natural gas, 1920–55.

gas in the residential and commercial sector expanded faster than industrial consumption; and, in the 1920's, this trend was reversed. Then, while residential and commercial use increased by one-third, industrial consumption tripled within ten years and reached its peak proportion (80 per cent in 1930) in the total. It maintained its share of nearly four-fifths until the end of World War II. In the 1945–55 decade, however, domestic and commercial use again rose at a faster rate than industrial consumption.

In 1955, the amount of energy inherent in the 2,753 billion cubic feet of natural gas used in the residential and commercial sector was the equivalent of 109 million tons of bituminous coal. Household use amounted to 2,124 billion cubic feet, of which it has been estimated that some 1,375 billion cubic feet were consumed for space heating and the remainder for cooking, water heating, and various other household uses.[113] The natural gas consumed in households for space heating in 1955 contained an amount of energy equivalent to that in some

[113] See Table 41 and Appendix Tables C-1 and C-6. The figure of 1,375 billion cubic feet of gas includes a small amount of manufactured gas and liquefied petroleum gases distributed through mains.

TABLE 42. INDUSTRIAL USES OF NATURAL GAS, FIVE-YEAR INTERVALS, 1920-55 [a]

(Quantities in billion cubic feet)

Year	Field use		Carbon black		Petroleum refineries		Natural gas pipelines		Portland cement		Central power stations		Other uses [b]		Total
	Quantity (1)	Percentage of total (2)	Quantity (3)	Percentage of total (4)	Quantity (5)	Percentage of total (6)	Quantity (7)	Percentage of total (8)	Quantity (9)	Percentage of total (10)	Quantity (11)	Percentage of total (12)	Quantity (13)	Percentage of total (14)	Total (15)
1920	202	39.5%	41	8.0%	n.a.		n.a.		n.a.		22	4.3%	247	48.2%	512
1925	424	46.3	140	15.3	88	9.6%	n.a.		n.a.		46	5.0	218	23.8	916
1930	723	46.2	267	17.1	99	6.3	n.a.		41	2.6%	120	7.7	315	20.1	1,565
1935	580	38.8	242	16.2	80	5.3	n.a.		27	1.8	125	8.4	442	29.5	1,496
1940	712	34.3	369	17.8	128	6.2	n.a.		42	2.0	183	8.8	642	30.9	2,076
1945	917	29.9	432	14.1	338	11.0	n.a.		38	1.2	326	10.6	1,011	33.0	3,063
1950	1,187	26.7	411	9.3	455	10.2	126	2.8%	97	2.2	629	14.2	1,535	34.6	4,440
1955	1,508	23.9	245	3.9	625	9.9	245	3.9	131	2.1	1,153	18.3	2,410	38.1	6,317

n.a. Not available.

[a] A small amount of natural gas here included was consumed in the form of a mixture of manufactured and natural gas.

[b] Comparison with data from U.S. Bureau of the Census, *U.S. Census of Manufactures: 1939*, and *ibid., 1947* (Washington, D. C.: U.S. Government Printing Office), indicates that in these years between 75 per cent and 80 per cent of this class of use is accounted for by manufacturing industries. See Table 43.

SOURCES: U.S. Geological Survey, *Mineral Resources of the United States*, various issues, and U.S. Bureau of Mines, *Minerals Yearbook*, various issues (Washington, D. C.: U.S. Government Printing Office).

54 million tons of coal. These data should not be taken to imply that all residential space heating by natural gas actually displaced an amount of coal with the same energy content. In some areas of the United States, especially in the South and Southwest, natural gas and oil contributed to the heating of dwellings which otherwise would not have been heated at all. However, natural gas has a higher degree of thermal efficiency in space heating than coal, so that the quantity of coal actually displaced by gas in the residential and commercial sector is larger than a comparison of inherent Btu values indicates. It is particularly in this use sector that the convenience of natural gas has constituted an important advantage.

Analysis of the factors underlying the development of the industrial uses of natural gas depends on the data shown in Table 42, supplemented by more detailed information from Census reports. The usefulness of the data in Table 42 is seriously impaired by the presence of the omnibus category "other uses" which in some years is the largest class. From data of the *Census of Manufactures* for 1939 and 1947 it is possible to determine that, in those years, more than three-quarters of "other uses" was consumption of natural gas by manufacturing industries. (The *Census of Manufactures* for 1954 does not distinguish between consumption of natural and manufactured or mixed gas.) In 1939, the quantity of natural gas consumed in "other uses," which corresponds to the data shown in column 13 of Table 42, was 607 billion cubic feet; in 1947 it was 1,123 billion, or 30.9 per cent and 33.6 per cent, respectively, of the total industrial uses of natural gas in those years. The share of manufacturing industries in these "other uses" is shown in Table 43. The growth in "other uses" as shown in Table 42 represents, at least in recent years, the increasing consumption of natural gas by the manufacturing sector. Ruling out the high percentage figure for 1920, which is in a way misleading,[114] the relative importance of this sector within total natural gas consumption has risen almost continuously.

Among the industrial uses identified in Table 42, the largest class is "field use," which represents the natural gas used in drilling and pumping gas and oil wells, and in the operation of natural gasoline plants. Generally, all gas used for productive purposes in oil and gas fields, excluding the amounts repressured and the gas consumed in the manufacture of carbon black, is considered as field use. Although this use increased in absolute quantities without interruption, except during the depression, and in 1955 was seven and a half times as large as in 1920, it has declined as a proportion of total industrial consumption. From 46 per cent in 1925, its share dropped to 24 per cent in 1955. In part, this signifies the growing availability of markets outside the gas fields, acting as an incentive to economizing in the use of gas in the field. But for many field uses natural gas performs an essential function for which no feasible alternative fuel use exists, which accounts for the large absolute increase in this use category.

---

[114] The high percentage accounted for by "other uses" in 1920 is in part misleading because it includes certain uses which are separately identified in later years, and also because it reflects the fact that gas consumed in the manufacture of carbon black was relatively unimportant in 1920 compared with most of the subsequent years shown in the table.

TABLE 43. CONSUMPTION OF NATURAL GAS IN
MANUFACTURING INDUSTRIES, 1939 AND 1947

(Billion cubic feet)

Industry	1939	1947
Food and kindred products.....................................	81	110
Paper and allied products.......................................	30	69
Chemical and allied products....................................	58	171
Stone, clay, and allied products[a]...............................	108	164
Primary ferrous metals...	117	148
Primary nonferrous..	34	70
Fabricated metal products......................................	12	21
Miscellaneous manufactures....................................	44	92
Total..	484	845
Consumption by manufacturing industries as a percentage of total "other uses"..	79.7%	75.2%

[a] Excluding Portland cement which is separately listed in Table 42.

SOURCES: Appendix Tables XXVII and XXVIII.

The manufacture of carbon black, in which natural gas is used as a raw material rather than as a fuel, absorbed until the late 1940's a greater share of the total industrial consumption than any other identified use except field operations. Since natural gas was available in large quantities as a by-product of oil operations, and could not be transported to distant markets for lack of adequate pipeline facilities, it constituted an easy source, available at minimal cost, to carbon black plants located in the oil and gas fields. The advent of the automobile age and the expansion of the rubber tire industry—which uses over 90 per cent of carbon black—caused the fast growth of this use of natural gas, which was interrupted only by the depression. In the post-World War II period, however, the rapidly increasing value of natural gas in other uses, technological developments which greatly increased the yield of carbon black from natural gas, and a shift to petroleum as a raw material brought about an absolute decline in natural gas consumption for carbon black manufacture. In the 1945–55 decade, it dropped from 432 billion cubic feet to 245 billion; its share in the total industrial use decreased from 14 per cent to 4 per cent. Over the longer period, 1920–55, output of carbon black increased thirty-four times (from 51 million to 1,744 million pounds), but the use of natural gas for this purpose increased only six times. By 1955, natural gas furnished the raw material for only about one-half of the total carbon black production; the remainder was obtained from liquid hydrocarbons.[115]

[115] *Mineral Resources of the United States*, Part II, *op. cit.*, pp. 145 ff., and *Minerals Yearbook, 1955*, Vol. II, *op. cit.*, pp. 268 ff.

Consumption of natural gas by petroleum refineries, shown in Table 42, refers to its input as fuel, not as feedstock. Despite a doubling in the quantity thus used over the 1945–55 decade, its role in total industrial consumption declined slightly; by the mid-1950's, it accounted for one-tenth, about the same proportion as thirty years earlier. However, from 1925 to 1955, while the input of oil for fuel use by petroleum refineries declined from 50 million to 44 million barrels and the use of coal from 6 million to less than a million tons, consumption of natural gas expanded from 88 billion to 625 billion cubic feet. The share of natural gas in total fuel use by refineries (measured by the Btu content of the various fuels) rose from 8 per cent to 35 per cent.[116]

The category "natural gas pipelines" refers to the use of gas as fuel for the compressors that move the gas through the pipelines. Although minor, the doubling of the quantity consumed for this purpose in the five-year interval 1950–55 raised its share from 2.8 to 3.9 per cent of the total. This rapid growth is, of course, a reflection of the fast pace of pipeline construction over that period.

The use of natural gas as fuel for electric utility plants increased more than fifty times between 1920 and 1955, much faster than for any other identified industrial category. Its share rose uninterruptedly from 4 per cent to nearly one-fifth of the total. In the 1945–55 decade, the absolute quantity used for the generation of electric power expanded three and a half times; its relative importance nearly doubled. Electric utility buyers with their large demand offer attractive opportunities for interruptible sales (easily handled by those power plants which can switch from gas to oil or coal at short notice).

All in all, despite the growing relative importance of residential and commercial use noted earlier, natural gas consumption continues to be dominated by the industrial user. Partly this results from the substantial, although declining, relative importance of those industrial uses which are closely related to oil and gas production operations. Even in 1955, gas consumed in field use, in the manufacture of carbon black, as fuel for pumping gas through pipelines, and as fuel in petroleum refineries accounted for more than 40 per cent of the industrial use category, and nearly 30 per cent of all natural gas consumption. Partly, though, the continuing dominance of industrial use is related to the economics of pipeline operation, which necessitates as high and as constant a throughput of gas as is possible. This is accomplished through "interruptible" service to industrial consumers, in which the latter take large quantities of gas at low rates in the periods between seasonal peaks of household and commercial demand, subject to curtailment or total interruption during peak demand periods.[117] Thus, the relative decline in field use and the absolute decrease in consumption for carbon black manufacture was largely, though not wholly, offset by the

[116] See Appendix Tables A-14 and A-15.

[117] See Chapter 10 for further discussion of this point. In 1956, interruptible deliveries by natural gas companies amounted to 20 per cent of all sales including the companies' own use. Interruptible company use accounted for 13 per cent of the total interruptible service. See *Gas Requirements and Supplies of the Gas Utility and Pipeline Industry, op. cit.*, p. 23.

growing industrial use of pipelined gas. The rest was absorbed by the residential and commercial market which, in recent years, has expanded faster than industrial uses.

The increasing share of pipelined gas in total natural gas consumption is also reflected in the faster expansion of sales by gas utilities compared to over-all use. In the twenty-year period 1935–55, total demand rose almost five times, while utility sales increased sixfold. In the former year, they accounted for little more than one-half of all natural gas used (excluding transmission losses), in the latter, for 70 per cent (see Table 44). Over the same period, the share of natural gas in total sales by gas utilities—that is, including sales of manufactured and mixed gas—rose from 82 per cent to 95 per cent. Manufactured gas dropped from over 12 per cent to less than 1.0 per cent and, by the mid-1950's, had ceased to be a factor in the gas utility market (see Table 45).

TABLE 44. TOTAL CONSUMPTION AND UTILITY SALES OF NATURAL GAS, FIVE-YEAR INTERVALS, 1935–55

(Trillion Btu)

Year	Total consumption (1)	Utility sales (2)	Utility sales as a percentage of total consumption (3)
1935	1,919	1,063	55.4%
1940	2,665	1,468	55.1
1945	3,871	2,256	58.3
1950	5,969	3,850	64.5
1955	9,005	6,334	70.3

SOURCES: Column 1, Appendix Table VII. Column 2 from American Gas Association, *Historical Statistics of the Gas Industry* (New York: 1956), Table 88, and *1957 Gas Facts* (New York), Table 83.

. . .

Natural Gas Liquids

In the foregoing discussion of natural gas, the statistics of production relate to both wet and dry gas, while those of consumption refer (since 1920) to dry gas. The difference between the two is a measure of the volume of losses involved in the extraction of natural gas liquids (NGL) from raw gas. These liquid components, which occur in most of the raw gas produced, either spontaneously liquefy at the wellhead, or they can be liquefied and removed from the gas, if available in sufficient volume to justify the cost of extraction. Natural gas liquids are conventionally divided into three major categories: "natural gasoline," "liquefied petroleum gases" (LPG), and "condensate." (The composition and characteristics of the three NGL categories are described in Chapter 10.)

TABLE 45. GAS UTILITY SALES, BY TYPE OF GAS,
FIVE-YEAR INTERVALS, 1935–55

(Quantities in trillion Btu[a])

Year	Total (1)	Natural gas Quantity (2)	Natural gas Per cent of total (3)	Manufactured gas Quantity (4)	Manufactured gas Per cent of total (5)	Mixed gas Quantity (6)	Mixed gas Per cent of total (7)	Liquefied petroleum Quantity (8)	Liquefied petroleum Per cent of total (9)
1935...	1,292	1,063	82.3%	161	12.5%	68	5.2%		
1940...	1,724	1,468	85.2	169	9.8	87	5.0		
1945...	2,587	2,256	87.2	209	8.1	120	4.6	2	0.1%
1950...	4,209	3,850	91.5	222	5.3	128	3.0	9	0.2
1955...	6,659	6,301	94.7	46	0.7	304	4.5	8	0.1

[a] Gas sales by utilities are usually measured in millions of therms; one therm is the equivalent of 100,000 Btu. Measured in physical quantities, the proportions would be different since manufactured gas has only about half the Btu value or therm value of natural gas per cubic foot.

[b] Even for manufactured and mixed gas a significant portion of the Btu content is derived from natural gas being used either as a production fuel or for mixing. The amounts of natural gas so utilized rose from 98 trillion Btu in 1945 to 213 trillion in 1955.

SOURCE: American Gas Association, *Historical Statistics of the Gas Industry* (New York: 1956), Tables 33 and 86, and *1958 Gas Facts* (New York), Tables 38 and 84.

The first plant for extraction of natural gasoline from oil-well gas was built in 1903 in a West Virginia oil field.[118] But natural gasoline first became important during the first World War, not only because it contributed to meeting the rapidly expanding domestic and export demand for gasoline from crude oil,[119] but also because it supplied the base stock for a type of fuel required for what was at the time considered high-altitude flying. By the 1920's, natural gasoline plants began to convert into more valuable fuels gaseous compounds which were previously wasted or burned as ordinary natural gas, thus laying the foundation for the bottled gas industry. As the market for bottled gas developed, the LPG were joined by similar products obtained in oil refining, termed liquefied refinery gases (LRG).

In 1911, the first year for which statistics are available, only 0.5 per cent of all natural gas produced was treated to recover NGL; in 1915, 4 per cent. By 1920, this share had risen to 47 per cent of the gross production. Since World War II, the quantity of natural gas processed for NGL extraction fluctuated between 60 and 70 per cent. Although NGL have a relatively long history (but always as a by-product), they have been of small importance in the total energy picture for almost the entire period covered by this survey. As late as 1940, they supplied only about 1 per cent of all energy consumed in the United States (see Table 2 and Figure 10). By 1955, having undergone a great expansion since World War II, they accounted for almost 3 per cent of total energy consumption, and were the equivalent of about 11 per cent of domestic crude oil production (a

[118] Federal Power Commission, *Natural Gas Investigation*, Docket No. G-580, *op. cit.*, p. 90.
[119] In 1918, natural gasoline accounted for 7.5 per cent of the total gasoline production.

level which slightly exceeded the relative importance of net imports of crude oil in that year). In view of the small share of NGL in total energy consumption over most of the past century, no attempt is made here to cover this energy source in the same fashion as the others.[120] Instead, the discussion which follows is restricted to the decade following World War II, a statistical summary of which is given in Table 46.

TABLE 46.   NATURAL GAS LIQUIDS PRODUCTION, 1946–55

(Quantities in thousand barrels)

Year	Total NGL (1)	Natural gasoline[a] Quantity (2)	Per cent of total (3)	LPG Quantity (4)	Per cent of total (5)	Condensate and other products[b] Quantity (6)	Per cent of total (7)
1946.......	115,739	72,527	62.7%	33,556	29.0%	9,657	8.3%
1947.......	132,173	75,607	57.2	45,043	34.1	11,523	8.7
1948.......	146,721	83,532	56.9	52,597	35.8	10,592	7.2
1949.......	157,086	88,321	56.2	57,869	36.8	10,896	6.9
1950.......	181,961	97,854	53.8	72,282	39.7	11,825	6.5
1951.......	204,754	106,928	52.2	86,377	42.2	11,449	5.6
1952.......	223,515	108,716	48.6	102,033	45.6	12,766	5.7
1953.......	238,579	113,407	47.5	111,735	46.8	13,437	5.6
1954.......	252,133	115,188	45.7	123,912	49.1	13,033	5.2
1955.......	281,371	125,718	44.7	142,207	50.5	13,446	4.8

a Includes also natural gasoline mixtures, finished gasoline, and naphtha produced from natural gas.

b Includes kerosine and distillates produced from natural gas.

SOURCE: U.S. Bureau of Mines, *Minerals Yearbook*, various issues (Washington, D. C.: U.S. Government Printing Office).

The magnitude of the recent growth in NGL output is evident from Table 46. Between 1946 and 1955, total production increased two and a half times—from about 115 million barrels at the beginning of the decade to more than 280 million at the end. The fastest growing component of the total was LPG, which increased by more than 300 per cent, while natural gasoline grew about 75 per cent; the production of condensate expanded by about 40 per cent.

The result of these different growth rates is a large change in the pattern of NGL production over the decade. Whereas, in 1946, natural gasoline accounted

[120] An additional reason for not attempting to cover the total historical record of NGL here is to be found in the poor quality of the historical statistics for this group of products. For example, until 1940, LPG data represented marketed production only, even though a large percentage of total output was used at the point of production and never entered the sales statistics. Since production data for earlier years are incomplete, the historical statistics exaggerate the long-period growth of the industry.

The data for NGL which have been used in building the aggregate energy figures used elsewhere in this study (particularly in Chapter 2) are given in Appendix Table VI.

for 63 per cent of the total versus 29 per cent for LPG; in 1955, the relative positions had shifted markedly, with natural gasoline accounting for only 45 per cent and LPG dominant with one-half the total. The decline in the relative importance of natural gasoline, which had for so long dominated the NGL total, is partly due to changes in the quality of finished gasoline. The main use of natural gasoline has been as a blending agent for motor fuel. But since natural gasoline is generally paraffinic and has a low octane number, its suitability for blending has somewhat declined in recent years in the face of higher octane requirements.[121] On the other hand, LPG have been growing rapidly because of their widening use in domestic and commercial applications, which constitute almost half of total consumption, and their rapidly increasing importance as chemical feedstock. Information on the consumption pattern of NGL is shown for the first decade after World War II in Table 47.

TABLE 47. CONSUMPTION OF NATURAL GAS LIQUIDS, 1945, 1950, 1955

(Thousand barrels)

Item	1945	1950	1955
1. Total apparent consumption of all natural gas liquids (excluding liquefied refinery gases)	110,762	178,833	277,500
2. Shipments of natural gasoline, mixtures, finished gasoline, naphtha, and liquefied petroleum gases to refineries and jobbers	93,032	120,044	168,089
3. Sales of liquefied petroleum gases (including liquefied refinery gases):[a]			
Domestic and commercial[b]	12,698	48,155	66,698
Internal combustion	2,221	3,090	15,519
Chemical industry	5,340	14,869	35,552
Synthetic rubber industry	4,971	5,440	9,671
Other industrial uses	3,883	5,169	10,081
Gas manufacture	1,281	5,993	5,090
Refinery fuel	c	c	2,405
All other uses	2	205	760
Total	30,400	82,919	145,778

[a] Liquefied refinery gases (LRG) are recovered in refining crude oil, not in processing natural gas, and thus do not belong in the group of natural gas liquids as conventionally defined. But since they are identical with LPG as products, and since the sales statistics for NGL for uses other than gasoline include LRG, they are included in the above data. Since World War II, the growth in LRG consumption paralleled that of LPG, though on a smaller scale. Sales of LRG amounted to 10,421,000 barrels in 1945; 25,275,000 in 1950; and 42,113,000 in 1955.

[b] Includes irrigation pumping and tractor fuel.

[c] Prior to 1955, included in "other industrial uses."

SOURCES: Item 1 from Appendix Table VI; others from U.S. Bureau of Mines, *Minerals Yearbook*, various issues (Washington, D. C.: U.S. Government Printing Office).

[121] *Minerals Yearbook, 1956*, Vol. II, *op. cit.*, p. 319.

The recent growth in NGL production is not due solely to developments on the demand side. An important cause has been the growth of natural gas production itself, which increased the availability of NGL. This has been supplemented by the fact that the gas must be dehydrated to avoid damaging condensation during high-pressure pipeline shipment. Along with dehydration, it is profitable to strip the liquids, which have a higher Btu content than the lighter compounds of dry gas, prior to pipelining the gas, since typically there is no premium paid for excess Btu content above a guaranteed minimum. Still another factor contributing to the rapid growth of the industry has been development of the cycling process, in which NGL are removed at the plant and the gas then reinjected into the reservoir. Finally, the production and handling of greater quantities of LPG have made possible external economies, such as LPG pipelines and underground LPG storage facilities, which, in turn, have aided in meeting increases in demand.

.   .   .

The principal factors lying behind the long-run behavior of each of the various energy sources have been examined in order better to understand the similarities, and, in particular, the differences in the historical development of the various fuels. The breakdown of the energy total in this way is vital to an understanding of its changing structure through time. There remain, however, important questions about the historical behavior of the energy total in relation to the over-all growth of the national economy. The next chapter is devoted to these questions, and although it turns away from details such as those dealt with in this chapter, the analysis is fortified by the knowledge of the underlying interrelationships uncovered in the preceding pages.

CHAPTER 4

Some aspects of energy consumption in relation to U.S. economic growth

The purpose of this chapter is to relate historical changes in the growth of total energy consumption in the United States to two major aspects of the country's economic development—population growth and the expansion in the nation's output of goods and services. Accordingly, the first section deals with the increase in total energy consumption over the past hundred years. This is followed by a discussion of the relationship between energy consumption and the growth of population, i.e., the changes which have taken place in the per capita level of energy use. Finally, energy use is described in relation to the growth of gross national product (GNP), and here an effort is made to probe, in exploratory fashion, some of the factors lying behind historical changes in the relationship between the amounts of energy consumed and the nation's over-all output of goods and services.

THE RATE OF INCREASE IN ENERGY CONSUMPTION

Numerous aspects of the historical record of total energy consumption have already been considered in Chapter 2, primarily in order to provide a backdrop against which to describe in Chapter 3 the production and consumption record of the individual primary energy sources. In this section, total energy consumption will be examined from another standpoint: its rate of growth over the past century, with particular attention to fluctuations in the rate of change.

For the purpose served by Chapter 2 a total energy series consisting of the mineral fuels, hydropower, and fuel wood was presented. This total is also relevant to the analysis to be made here, but another series is also analyzed—a total which includes mineral fuels and hydropower, but excludes fuel wood. Because of the dominant role of wood until the last quarter of the nineteenth century,

144

quite different pictures of the growth of energy consumption emerge depending upon the inclusion or exclusion of wood, and it is significant to consider the record from both standpoints as is done in the historical statistics presented in Table 48 and Figure 24.[1]

TABLE 48.   ENERGY CONSUMPTION IN THE UNITED STATES, FIVE-YEAR INTERVALS, 1850–1955

Year	Mineral fuels, hydropower, and fuel wood [a]				Mineral fuels and hydropower (excluding fuel wood)			
	Trillion Btu (1)	Index (1900 = 100) (2)	Per cent change (3)	Average annual per-centage rate of growth (4)	Trillion Btu (5)	Index (1900 = 100) (6)	Per cent change (7)	Average annual per-centage rate of growth (8)
1850..	2,357	24.6		1850–60	219	2.9		1850–60
1855..	2,810	29.3	+34.2%	3.0%	421	5.6	+137.9%	9.1%
1860..	3,162	33.0		1860–70	521	6.9		1860–70
1865..	3,409	35.6	+25.0	2.3	642	8.5	+103.3	7.4
1870..	3,952	41.2		1870–80	1,059	14.0		1870–80
1875..	4,323	45.1	+26.5	2.4	1,451	19.2	+103.0	7.3
1880..	5,001	52.2		1880–90	2,150	28.4		1880–90
1885..	5,645	58.9	+40.2	3.4	2,962	39.1	+109.2	7.7
1890..	7,012	73.1		1890–1900	4,497	59.4		1890–1900
1895..	7,661	79.9	+36.7	3.2	5,355	70.7	+68.4	5.4
1900..	9,587	100.0		1900–1910	7,572	100.0		1900–1910
1905..	13,212	137.8	+72.8	5.6	11,369	150.1	+95.5	6.9
1910..	16,565	172.8		1910–20	14,800	195.5		1910–20
1915..	17,764	185.3	+29.1	2.6	16,076	212.3	+33.6	2.9
1920..	21,378	223.0		1920–30	19,768	261.1		1920–30
1925..	22,411	233.8	+10.9	1.0	20,878	275.7	+12.6	1.2
1930..	23,708	247.3		1930–40	22,253	293.9		1930–40
1935..	20,456	213.4	+6.4	0.6	19,059	251.7	+7.3	0.7
1940..	25,235	263.2		1940–50	23,877	315.3		1940–50
1945..	32,700	341.1	+39.2	3.4	31,439	415.2	+42.3	3.6
1950..	35,136	366.5		1950–55	33,972	448.7		1950–55
			+16.1	3.0			+16.9	3.2
1955..	40,796	425.5		1850–1955	39,729	524.7		1850–1955
			+1,630.8	2.8			+18,041.1	5.1

[a] Includes all the energy sources covered in the total energy series shown in Table 1.

SOURCE: Appendix Table VII.

A comparison of the two sets of statistics, as was to be expected, reveals that the long-period growth in the consumption of mineral fuels and hydropower is substantially greater than the growth of the total series which includes fuel wood. While the former multiplied 180 times in the 105-year period, the series including wood grew only about one-tenth as much, to about seventeen times its earlier

[1] Because the statistical information for wood is quite inadequate, it is necessary to rely on crude estimates. The statistical basis of the totals for mineral fuels and hydropower is much more dependable.

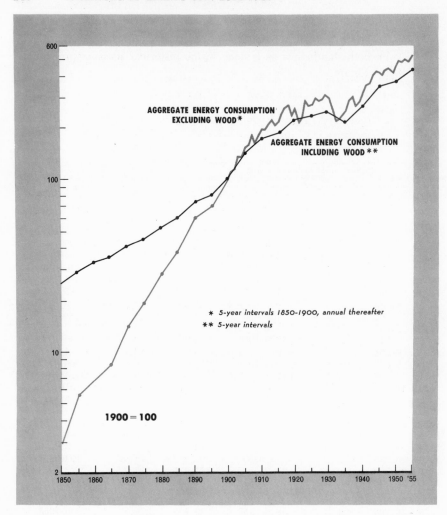

Figure 24. Index of aggregate energy consumption, 1850–1955.

level. In large part, this wide disparity in the growth record of the two is traceable to their divergent paths in the last half of the nineteenth century, when the series including wood quadrupled, while that for mineral fuels and hydropower increased about thirty-three times. During the twentieth century, the difference in growth between the two series has been more moderate, with energy including wood more than quadrupling in the fifty-five years, while the aggregate excluding wood stood at more than five times its 1900 level.

These wide differences in the growth record of the two series are, of course, a reflection of the fact that consumption of wood already stood at a high absolute level by the middle of the last century, whereas coal was just beginning to play a role in the U.S. energy economy about that time, and oil, natural gas, and hydropower had not arrived upon the scene as sources of energy.[2] Thus, the series excluding wood reflects the fast growth rates which are to be expected in the early period of industries just getting under way. From this standpoint, the series including wood provides not only a more complete picture of the long-period growth of energy consumption in the United States, but one which is more realistic in that the high early growth rate of the expanding new mineral fuels is moderated by the far slower growth and subsequent decline of the well-established use of fuel wood.

From another standpoint, however, the series excluding wood may be more significant. Although wood supplied 90 per cent of the British thermal units (Btu's) consumed in the United States in the middle of the nineteenth century, it was, at that time and through all of its subsequent history as a major energy source, predominantly a household fuel. It will be recalled, for example, that Chapter 3 and Table 9 included estimates that about 90 per cent of all wood consumed in 1850 was used in households; and the Census for 1879 shows 95 per cent of all wood consumption going into households. In contrast, the mineral fuels and hydropower from the outset were used predominantly in industry and transportation. Thus, it has been estimated that in 1850 about 75 per cent of the coal output was consumed in manufacturing and transportation.[3] Hence, the series based on mineral fuels and hydropower more accurately reflects the long-period growth of industrial fuels consumption in the United States than does the total which includes wood.

The major deficiency of the total for mineral fuels and hydropower as an indicator of the growth of industrially oriented energy consumption occurs in the early years of the historical period covered in this survey, when direct waterpower and windpower were important energy sources in manufacturing and transportation. It is well, therefore, to attempt to round out the statistical record for these early years—even though this can be done only by using estimates which are extremely rough both in concept and in measurement[4]—in order to gain some idea of the degree to which the basic statistical measures used in this chapter would be changed if waterpower and windpower were included.

For the nineteenth century, Table 49 adjusts the statistical series presented in Table 48 to include direct waterpower and windpower. Comparison of the statistics in the two tables discloses that the energy total which includes fuel wood is not seriously affected by the inclusion of direct waterpower and windpower, while the effects on the total excluding wood are quite severe. When direct water and

[2] The reader is reminded of the definitions provided in Chapter 2. Hydropower, as defined in this study, refers only to electricity generated from falling water, not its direct use as a source of mechanical power.

[3] The percentage may have been even greater, since the above estimate refers only to the use of coal for conversion into mechanical work, and excludes the amounts consumed for industrial process heat and metallurgical purposes.

[4] See Chapter 3 and the "Appendix Note on the Measurement of Direct Waterpower and Windpower," for a discussion of the concepts and statistics used in aggregating direct waterpower and windpower with the other energy sources.

TABLE 49. ENERGY CONSUMPTION, INCLUDING DIRECT WATER-POWER AND WINDPOWER, TEN-YEAR INTERVALS, 1850-1900[a]

Year	Mineral fuels, hydropower, and fuel wood plus direct waterpower and windpower				Mineral fuels and hydropower (excluding fuel wood) plus direct waterpower and windpower			
	Trillion Btu (1)	Index (1900 = 100) (2)	Per cent change (3)	Average annual percentage rate of growth (4)	Trillion Btu (5)	Index (1900 = 100) (6)	Per cent change (7)	Average annual percentage rate of growth (8)
1850..	2,866	29.1			728	9.3		
				1850-60				1850-60
1860..	3,814	38.7	33.1%	2.9%	1,173	15.0	61.1%	4.9%
				1860-70				1860-70
1870..	4,349	44.2	14.0	1.3	1,456	18.6	24.1	2.2
				1870-80				1870-80
1880..	5,344	54.3	22.9	2.1	2,493	31.8	71.2	5.5
				1880-90				1880-90
1890..	7,305	74.2	36.7	3.2	4,790	61.2	92.1	6.7
				1890-1900				1890-1900
1900[b].	9,848	100.0	34.8	3.0	7,833	100.0	63.5	5.0

[a] Windpower, direct waterpower and hydroelectric power converted into fuel equivalents at the prevailing rate of transforming coal into mechanical work or electric power.

[b] The statistics are not carried beyond 1900 because of the small relative importance of direct waterpower and windpower in the twentieth century.

SOURCES: See Chapter 3 and the "Appendix Note on the Measurement of Direct Waterpower and Windpower."

wind are ignored in the series excluding wood, the years 1850 and 1860 appear to be seriously understated, and 1870 is apparently understated by about one-third. Beginning with 1880, however, the understatement in the series excluding wood is no longer great enough to affect the totals in any significant way. By 1870, wind and water were less than half as important as coal, and by 1880 the index numbers of output for the series excluding and including direct windpower and waterpower are almost the same (28.4 and 31.8, respectively, with 1900 as 100; see column 6, Table 48, and column 6, Table 49).

In the analysis carried through in this chapter, therefore, only the two energy series shown in Table 48 are employed. The record reveals wide fluctuations in rates of growth. The series including wood grew at an annual average rate of 2.8 per cent between 1850 and 1900, and at a rate of 2.7 per cent between 1900 and 1955. The growth rates by decade, however, are by no means as stable as the similarity of these two long-period rates would suggest. On the whole, the expansion was much more steady during the second half of the nineteenth century than in the first half of the present century. In the earlier period, the average annual growth rates within calendar decades ranged from 2.3 per cent to 3.4 per cent; they reached a peak of 5.6 per cent per year during the first decade of this century, and a low of only 0.6 in the 1930's.

The fluctuations have been wider for the series covering only mineral fuels and hydropower. Its growth between 1850 and 1900 was at an average annual rate of 7.4 per cent (about two and a half times the rate of increase of the series including wood), while the increase between 1900 and 1955 amounted to an average rate of 3.1 per cent per year (only one-tenth greater than that for the series including wood). The rapid rate of growth during the nineteenth century reflects mainly the early expansion of the coal industry; in the twentieth century the rapid expansion of oil and gas is not reflected in the same way because its effect on the total was moderated by the smaller growth and subsequent decline of coal (analogous to the moderating effect of wood in the larger total in respect to the rates of growth in the nineteenth century). The average annual growth rates within decades, when wood is excluded, exhibit even wider fluctuations, particularly during the twentieth century, when they ranged from a low of 0.7 per cent in 1930–40 to a high of 6.9 per cent in 1900–10. In the nineteenth century, the annual growth was more stable: for the years 1860–90, the average annual rates of increase within decades were approximately the same, ranging from 7.4 to 7.7 per cent, whereas in 1850–60 and 1890–1900 the average annual increases amounted to 9.1 per cent and 5.4 per cent.

The record for both series is instructive in demonstrating the lack of regularity in the rate at which energy consumption has expanded in the United States. This emphasizes the danger of simple trend extrapolation as a means of projecting the future of energy use. Certainly the average annual rate of increase in recent years—some 3.5 per cent in the decade 1940–50 and somewhat over 3 per cent during the period 1950–55—is in no sense typical of the long-term historical record.

ENERGY CONSUMPTION PER CAPITA

During the period 1950–55 the consumption of energy in the United States supplied by mineral fuels, hydropower and wood averaged nearly 38,000 trillion Btu annually. This is equivalent to the inherent energy in approximately 1.5 billion tons of bituminous coal or, on a per capita basis, 9 tons of coal per year. While the U.S. population accounted for slightly over 6 per cent of the world's total in the early 1950's, the amount of energy consumed in this country represented more than one-third of the world supply from similar sources. Thus, per capita consumption of U.S. energy resources was roughly six times the world average.[5]

[5] The energy sources included in the estimates of world production, which were compiled by the United Nations (UN), are shown in the table below. In UN statistics, energy is measured not in Btu's but in electricity equivalents. Thus, column 1 below shows fuels converted into megawatt hours at their full inherent calorific value, and hydropower measured directly in megawatt hours. To permit comparison with U.S. energy statistics, these electricity equivalents have been converted in column 2 into Btu's at the rate of 1 kilowatt hour = 3,412 Btu (the latter calculation is equivalent to converting the fuels into

Long-Run Changes in Per Capita Energy Consumption

The historical path which the United States followed in reaching its present-day position in per capita energy consumption is traced in Table 50 and Figure 25. As in the preceding section, two measures of total energy consumption are shown, one including mineral fuels, hydropower, and fuel wood, the other including mineral fuels and hydropower, but excluding fuel wood. Per capita energy consumption in 1955 was thus either two and a half times including wood, or twenty-five times excluding wood, the 1850 level.

Although the relationship between changes in energy consumption and the growth of the nation's total output of goods and services—its GNP—is the subject of the next section, it is instructive to compare the long-period change in per capita energy consumption with the per capita growth of GNP. National product or income figures for the mid-nineteenth century, based on extremely rough estimates, indicate that real GNP per capita in 1955 was approximately five to five and a half times the 1850 figure.[6] Thus, it appears that over the past century,

---

their inherent Btu values, as is done throughout this study). Column 3 shows U.S. energy consumption as measured in this study, with one exception: hydropower is shown at its direct calorific equivalent, not at the prevailing central station fuel consumption rate, in order to make it comparable with the world statistics. For this reason, the figures for total and per capita consumption in the United States shown here are slightly smaller than those used elsewhere in this study.

Energy source	World production in electricity equivalent (1,000 million megawatt hours) (1)	World production in Btu equivalent (trillions) (2)	U.S. consumption in Btu equivalent (trillions) (3)	U.S. consumption as a percentage of world production (4)
Coal (including lignite and peat)...	13.3	45,380	11,868	26.2%
Petroleum (and NGL)............	7.7	26,272	15,334	58.4
Natural gas.....................	2.7	9,212	7,550	82.0
Total mineral fuels..............	23.7	80,864	34,752	43.0%
Hydropower.....................	0.4	1,365	382	28.0
Vegetable fuels.................	4.6	15,695	1,125	7.2
Total.........................	28.7	97,924	36,259	37.0%
Per capita (million Btu)ᵃ.........		38.4	230.9	

ᵃ World population (estimate) 2,550,000,000; U.S. population 157,022,000, 6.2 per cent of world. See Appendix Table X and U.S. Bureau of the Census, *Statistical Abstract of the United States, 1957* (Washington, D. C.: U.S. Government Printing Office), p. 928.

NOTE· Not all categories are strictly comparable as between UN and the authors' estimates; UN includes still gas with natural gas, lumber mill wastes with fuel wood.

SOURCES· Column 1 from United Nations, Department of Economic and Social Affairs, "World Energy Requirements in 1975 and 2000," *Proceedings of the International Conference on the Peaceful Uses of Atomic Energy*, Geneva, 1955, Vol. I (New York· 1956), p. 3. Column 3 from Appendix Tables VI, VII, X, XI.

[6] Appendix Table XII for the 1880–1955 period. Estimate of GNP for 1850–70 from Moses Abramovitz, *Resource and Output Trends in the United States Since 1870*, Occasional Paper 52 (New York: National Bureau of Economic Research, 1956), p. 6. Abramovitz writes: "... aggregate output well-nigh doubled from 1850 to 1870," and adds "These are W. I. King's figures (*The Wealth and Income of the People of the United States*, Macmillan, 1915, Table XXIII), as deflated by Simon Kuznets ("Long-Term Changes in the National Income of the United States of America Since 1870," published in *Income and Wealth of the United States*, edited by Simon Kuznets, Cambridge, Bowes and Bowes, 1952, p. 240)." The 1870 GNP has been estimated at 30 per cent of that in 1900.

TABLE 50. PER CAPITA ENERGY CONSUMPTION,
FIVE-YEAR INTERVALS, 1850–1955

Year	Index numbers of per capita energy consumption (1900 = 100)		Percentage change		Average annual percentage rate of growth	
	Mineral fuels, hydropower, and fuel wood (1)	Mineral fuels and hydropower (excl. fuel wood) (2)	Mineral fuels, hydropower, and fuel wood (3)	Mineral fuels and hydropower (excl. fuel wood) (4)	Mineral fuels, hydropower, and fuel wood (5)	Mineral fuels and hydropower (excl. fuel wood) (6)
1850...	80.4	9.4	...........1850–60...........			
1855...	81.4	15.5	− 1.0%	+76.6%	ª	5.9%
1860...	79.6	16.6	...........1860–70...........			
1865...	75.8	18.1	− 1.3	+60.2	ª	4.8
1870...	78.6	26.6	...........1870–80...........			
1875...	76.1	32.4	+ 0.5	+61.7	ª	4.9
1880...	79.0	43.0	...........1880–90...........			
1885...	79.1	52.6	+11.8	+66.7	1.1%	5.3
1890...	88.3	71.7	...........1890–1900...........			
1895...	87.4	77.3	+13.3	+39.5	1.3	3.4
1900...	100.0	100.0	...........1900–10...........			
1905...	125.1	136.3	+42.3	+61.0	3.6	4.9
1910...	142.3	161.0	...........1910–20...........			
1915...	140.2	160.7	+12.0	+15.9	1.1	1.5
1920...	159.4	186.6	...........1920–30...........			
1925...	153.6	181.1	− 4.1	− 2.7	ª	ª
1930...	152.8	181.5	...........1930–40...........			
1935...	127.5	150.4	− 0.8	ª	ª	ª
1940...	151.6	181.6	...........1940–50...........			
1945...	185.5	225.8	+21.3	+24.0	2.0	2.2
1950...	183.9	225.1	...........1950–55...........			
			+ 6.6	+ 7.3	1.3	1.4
1955...	196.0	241.6	...........1850–1955...........			
			+143.8	+2,470.2	0.9	3.1

ª Negligible.

SOURCE: Appendix Table XII.

per capita energy consumption including wood increased only about half as much as real GNP per person, while per capita consumption of fuel and power excluding wood expanded approximately four and a half to five times as much as GNP per person.

Since it is often assumed that increases in the per capita use of energy are an important factor in raising over-all productivity in modern society (as commonly measured in output per man-hour), it is surprising to find that total energy consumption (mineral fuels, hydropower, and fuel wood) has increased less than half as much per capita as GNP over the past hundred years or so. This fact becomes less puzzling, however, when it is viewed against what is known about energy consumption in this country in the mid-nineteenth century.

As indicated in Chapter 3, the lavish use of fuel wood in mid-nineteenth century America reflected the fact that it was virtually free, made available as forests were cut down to make room for farms and living space. Conservative

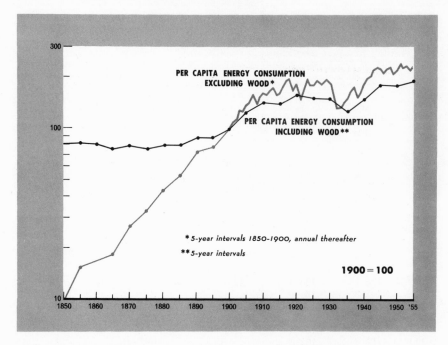

Figure 25.   Index of per capita energy consumption, 1850–1955.

estimates based on the scanty data indicate that as early as the 1850's, and possibly even earlier, the annual consumption of energy per person in this country was about 100 million Btu, the equivalent of 3.9 tons of coal.[7]

During the decade 1850–60, only one other country, the United Kingdom, had a level of energy consumption approaching that of the United States. The available information indicates that around 1860 the per capita input of energy in Great Britain was equivalent to some 92 million Btu or 3.5 tons of coal. The countries next in line—Belgium, Germany, and France—lagged far behind. In the United Kingdom, energy consumption of 100 million Btu per person per year appears to have been reached around 1865; in Germany, this level was attained only shortly before World War I.[8]

These figures, particularly those comparing the United States and Great Britain, are surprising, for one might have expected that the contrast between the relatively unindustrialized economy of the one compared to the industrialized economy of the other would have been reflected in their per capita energy consumption. The answer, of course, is to be found not in total fuel consumption but in the much higher level of coal consumption in Great Britain. In 1850, per capita

[7] See Appendix Table XI.
[8] Palmer C. Putnam, *Energy in the Future* (New York: Van Nostrand, 1953), Appendix Tables 4-10N, 4-11N, and 4-14N.

coal use in Great Britain was about five times that in the United States.[9] It can be argued, therefore, that the relatively high per capita energy consumption of the United States in 1850 is deceptive, at least as a base for comparison with energy use per person in this country a hundred years later. It is inappropriate as a base because the over-all energy total consisted predominantly of household fuels—which, moreover, were being burned at very low levels of efficiency in open fireplaces.

But does an 1850 total consisting of only mineral fuels (hydropower appeared later) provide a preferable base for measuring a century of change in per capita energy consumption? Has the per capita use of the energy sources which are predominantly industrial fuels actually increased four and a half to five times more than the per capita growth of national product? This, too, is doubtful, mainly because in the mid-nineteenth century direct waterpower and windpower were substantially more important than coal as sources of power for manufacturing and transportation and neither is included in this energy total.

The wide difference between the two series in depicting changes in per capita energy consumption between 1850 and 1955, and the failure of either to serve satisfactorily for comparison with GNP per capita for the period, underline the futility of efforts to make such direct comparisons between years separated by a century which has seen a complete transformation both in the structure of the economy and its energy base. Comparisons spanning so long a period are better made by shifting attention from the terminal years, so widely separated in time, to the intervening years. Their record is traced in this chapter mainly in five-year and ten-year comparisons. On the whole, such periods are long enough to reveal patterns of change, yet not so long that measurement is distorted by major transformations in the structure of the national economy and in the composition of the energy base, or by abrupt changes in the quality and coverage of the underlying statistics. These short-period comparisons are the links here employed in constructing the statistical chain with which the 105-year period is spanned.

·   ·   ·

Fluctuations in Per Capita Energy Consumption

A pattern in the short-period changes in energy consumption per capita can be discerned in Table 50. Between 1850 and 1885, per capita consumption of total energy including wood remained unchanged, while consumption excluding wood grew at a high and fairly constant rate. The consumption of coal expanded rapidly, from less than half a ton per capita in 1850 to nearly two tons in 1885, but this expansion was balanced, in Btu terms, by a corresponding decrease in the per capita use of fuel wood. In other words, while the coal-plus-wood total was at a virtual standstill, coal alone made rapid strides. The average annual rate of increase in per capita consumption of approximately 5 per cent which characterized this period in total mineral fuels consumption was not to be achieved

See Chapter 3 and Table 17.

again, except for the decade 1900–1910. The growth of mineral fuels (essentially coal) during this period explains the otherwise paradoxical fact of per capita total energy consumption remaining constant during decades when industrialization was advancing so rapidly. Not only were much greater quantities of fuel going into industrial uses, but coal was burned with greater efficiency than wood.[10]

Not until the decade 1880–90 does the total energy series per capita, including wood, show any increase; it was during this decade, too, that mineral fuels accounted for the first time for more than 50 per cent of all energy consumption.[11] The per capita consumption of energy excluding wood continued, nevertheless, to rise much faster. While the former series grew at an annual rate of 1.1 per cent in the decade 1880–90, and 1.3 per cent in the decade 1890–1900, the latter grew at about 5.3 per cent and 3.4 per cent in these two periods.

In the decade 1900–1910, the two series began, for the first time, to draw close together, reflecting the fact that mineral fuels and hydropower by this time accounted for between 80 and 90 per cent of all energy consumption. From 1910 to the present, the decade rates of the two series have been quite similar as mineral fuels and hydropower have come to account for upward of 90 per cent of the total (90.5 per cent in 1915; 94 per cent in 1930; 97 per cent in 1955).

Both series exhibit a rather high degree of regularity during the second half of the nineteenth century, but for different reasons: The mineral fuels series grew persistently at a high rate owing to the early expansion of coal consumption; the series including wood grew barely at all because coal's rise was essentially offset by wood's decline. Following this period of regularity, the decade growth rates tend to show a fair degree of dispersion, ranging from a high rate in the decade 1900–1910 to periods of no increase at all between 1920 and 1940.

The record since the end of World War I would justify the conclusion that the high rates experienced during the nineteenth and early twentieth century by the series on mineral fuels and hydropower have subsequently been replaced by much lower rates of growth. Since the end of World War I only one decade— that of World War II—has been characterized by an annual average rate of

[10] See Chapter 3, the section on the emerging use of coal, on the comparative efficiency of converting coal and wood into steampower in the mid-nineteenth century. If 10 to 12 bushels (800 to 960 pounds, or roughly half a ton) of coal were equal to one cord of wood, the respective inherent Btu equivalents are 13.1 million for coal versus 21 million for wood, indicating an efficiency for coal about two-fifths greater than for wood. On industrial use of wood and coal in the late nineteenth century, see Tables 9 and 18. Around 1880, only some 7 million cords of wood (the Btu equivalent of 5 to 6 million tons of coal) out of a total consumption of more than 145 million cords were used in industry and transportation. In 1885, some 37 million tons of bituminous coal, 55 per cent of the total consumption, were used by railroads and in coke manufacture; statistics are not available on coal used in other manufacturing industries, but if these were included, it is obvious that industrial uses would be well over 55 per cent of all coal. It has been estimated, as noted above, that in 1850 industrial uses accounted for about 75 per cent of total coal consumption.

[11] See Table 2; mineral fuels accounted for 52.5 per cent of all Btu's of energy consumption in 1885.

growth as high as 2 per cent. Thus, on the basis of the record, it is as hazardous to identify a "representative" growth rate of per capita consumption as it is to do so for total energy consumption. Even if attention is focused on the total for mineral fuels and hydropower in recent years, important differences exist (see Table 50).

ENERGY CONSUMPTION IN RELATION TO GROSS NATIONAL PRODUCT

So far, the data examined provide little evidence of regularity of pattern either in historical changes in total energy consumption or in per capita energy consumption. This section considers another relationship—that between changes in total energy consumption and changes in the nation's total output of goods and services. The pervasive role of energy in a modern industrial society suggests that there should be a close over-all relationship between the use of energy materials and the production of goods and services. How has this relationship behaved through time and what are the reasons for the historical changes which have taken place?

. . . .

Relative Importance of Energy Materials in the Gross National Product

This analysis of the relationship between energy consumption and the total output of goods and services relies mainly on two statistical aggregates: GNP, which is a dollar measure of the nation's total output of goods and services, and Btu's of total energy input, which represent the inherent energy values of the different primary energy sources used. To relate the two aggregates, which are added together using different common units—dollars in one case, and Btu's in the other—index numbers measuring the movement of the two relative to a common base period are compared.

However, before turning to the comparative movement of the indexes of national output and energy consumption, it is well to have some measure of the relative importance of energy as an input into total national production. For this purpose, a common unit of measurement such as monetary value is needed for both energy materials and national product. Adding together the dollar values of energy commodities yields a total which can be compared directly with the dollar total for GNP. This is done in Table 51.

Such a comparison reveals that in 1955 the value of primary energy materials consumed (measured at point of production, excluding processing and transportation costs) constituted about 3 per cent of the total value of goods and services, and that for the past fifty-five years the ratio of energy consumption to GNP has typically ranged somewhere between 2.2 per cent and 3.3 per cent,

TABLE 51.   VALUE OF ENERGY CONSUMED AS A PERCENTAGE OF
GROSS NATIONAL PRODUCT,[a] FIVE-YEAR INTERVALS, 1900–1955

Year	Energy (million current dollars)			Gross national product (billion current dollars) (4)	Energy consumption as per cent of GNP (5)
	Mineral fuels (1)	Wood and hydropower (2)	Total (3)		
1900	$ 362	$90	$ 452	$18.7	2.4%
1905	547	90	637	25.1	2.5
1910	742	98	840	33.4	2.5
1915	855	103	958	38.7	2.5
1920	3,864	341	4,205	88.9	4.7[b]
1925	2,790	174	2,964	91.3	3.2
1930	2,545	145	2,690	91.1	3.0
1935	1,931	151	2,082	72.5	2.9
1940	2,519	166	2,685	100.6	2.7
1945	4,412	321	4,733	213.6	2.2
1950	8,814	511	9,325	285.1	3.3
1955	11,365	440	11,805	390.9	3.0

[a] In comparing the value of energy consumption with that of gross national product, valuations in current dollars were used for both. Mineral fuels were valued at the original point of production of coal, petroleum, natural gas, and natural gas liquids. The value of wood and hydropower was estimated by converting their inherent Btu's (hydro in terms of the fuel which would have been required to generate the same amount of electric energy) into bituminous coal equivalents, and then multiplying the coal equivalents by the current mine price of bituminous coal. Estimates were necessary since there is no available value figure for the falling water used to generate electricity, and the available value figures for wood are of dubious validity.

[b] The year 1920 was exceptional. Coal consumption and prices rose sharply following the strike of late 1919. Contributing to high prices was an unprecedented export demand, due partly to the British coal strike. Consumption of petroleum greatly exceeded production and prices rose considerably. In 1919, the value of energy materials consumed was 3.4 per cent of GNP; in 1921, 3.8 per cent.

SOURCES: Column 1, Appendix Table XVI; column 2, footnote [a] above; column 4, 1900–25, estimates of GNP in current dollars, underlying index numbers shown in Table 52 (see sources to Table 52); 1930–55, U.S. Department of Commerce, Office of Business Economics, *Survey of Current Business*, National Income Supplements, various issues.

averaging somewhat less than 3 per cent.[12] Energy thus measured, constitutes a relatively small input into the nation's total flow of product. When in the subsequent analysis stress is placed on changes in the input of energy relative to the nation's total output, it should be borne in mind that this input-output ratio refers to the relationship between a small input and a very large—and heterogeneous—output. Under these circumstances, it would not be surprising if energy's ratio to national output were to fluctuate widely even during short periods of time. Despite this possibility, the historical record of the relationship between energy and GNP, as will be seen, appears to be characterized by rather persistent long-run tendencies whose influence is strong enough to outweigh any erratic movements in the ratio.

[12] Measured at the point of consumption rather than production, the value of energy materials consumed is about twice as large. See Edward S. Mason, *Energy Requirements and Economic Growth* (Washington, D. C.: National Planning Association, 1955), p. 31, Table 5.

Changes in the Relationship Between Energy
and Gross National Product

The relationship between energy consumption and GNP between 1880 and 1955 is shown in Table 52 and Figure 26. The table begins with 1880 rather than with the earlier years covered in the energy series because reliable GNP estimates are not available for prior years. As in the preceding sections, two aggregate energy series are used, one including fuel wood along with mineral fuels and hydropower, the other excluding fuel wood. Again the two energy series yield very different long-run pictures. Over the entire period, the series including wood declines relative to GNP by about one-third, while the series excluding wood increases by more than one-half relative to GNP. Significant differences also occur in shorter-run changes, but these are confined mainly to the late nineteenth and early twentieth century, the period during which wood declined drastically in relative importance as a source of energy. Between 1920 and 1955, the difference in movement of the two series relative to GNP is of small importance; both declined by nearly two-fifths.

The analysis presented in the remainder of this chapter is based mainly on the energy total that includes only mineral fuels and hydropower. In the period considered, the growth of the U.S. economy has been dominated by the industrialization process, hence it is appropriate that the energy input to be compared with national output consist of the fuels of industrialization. Nevertheless, it is interesting to look briefly at the energy-GNP comparisons based on the series including fuel wood to note the profound effect which wood has on the long-term behavior of this relationship.

TOTAL ENERGY, INCLUDING FUEL WOOD, RELATIVE TO GNP

Comparing historical changes in total energy consumption, including wood, with gross national product yields the apparently paradoxical finding that the highly mechanized American economy of the mid-1950's consumed about one-third less energy in relation to its national product than the still largely agricultural society around 1880. Factors previously mentioned are largely responsible for this anomaly. As late as 1880, wood accounted for more than one-half of the total fuel supply, and some 95 per cent of all the wood was consumed for household purposes, largely for space heating, but also including domestic manufactures. By contrast, the 1955 direct household use accounted for approximately 20 per cent of the total energy consumption; and, even including private automobiles, the domestic sector consumed only about 30 per cent of the total. Thus, around 1880 nearly two-thirds of the total fuel supply was consumed in households and only little more than one-third by the rest of the economy. By the mid-1950's, these shares were more than reversed.

Although energy consumption in the household sector is not without influence on the over-all performance of the economy—adequate heating, lighting, and, recently, space cooling, certainly play a part in enhancing economic productivity

TABLE 52. ENERGY CONSUMPTION PER UNIT OF GROSS NATIONAL PRODUCT, FIVE-YEAR INTERVALS, 1880-1955

Year	Index of GNP (1900 = 100; measured in 1929 dollars) (1)	Indexes of energy consumption per unit of GNP (1900 = 100)		Percentage change		Average annual percentage rate of change	
		Mineral fuels, hydropower, and fuel wood (2)	Mineral fuels and hydropower, excl. fuel wood (3)	Mineral fuels, hydropower, and fuel wood (4)	Mineral fuels and hydropower, excl. fuel wood (5)	Mineral fuels, hydropower, and fuel wood (6)	Mineral fuels and hydropower, excl. fuel wood (7)
1880....	50.0	104.4	56.8	1880-85 −1.5%	+20.1%	1880-85 −0.3%	+3.7%
1885....	57.3	102.8	68.2	1885-90 +3.8	+27.0	1885-90 +0.8	+4.9
1890....	68.6	106.6	86.6	1890-95 −7.9	+0.3	1890-95 −1.6	+0.1
1895....	81.4	98.2	86.9	1895-1900 +1.8	+15.1	1895-1900 +0.4	+2.9
1900....	100.0	100.0	100.0	1900-1905 +10.0	+19.8	1900-1905 +1.9	+3.7
1905....	125.3	110.0	119.8	1905-10 +6.2	+10.4	1905-10 +1.2	+2.0
1910....	147.9	116.8	132.2	1910-15 +0.3	+1.5	1910-15 +0.1	+0.3
1915....	158.2	117.1	134.2	1915-20 −0.8	+1.3	1915-20 −0.2	+0.3
1920....	191.9	116.2	136.0	1920-25 −15.1	−14.5	1920-25 −3.2	−3.1
1925....	237.0	98.6	116.3	1925-30 +0.7	+1.5	1925-30 +0.2	+0.3
1930....	249.1	99.3	118.0	1930-35 −10.3	−10.8	1930-35 −2.1	−2.3
1935....	239.4	89.1	105.2	1935-40 −6.7	−5.4	1935-40 −1.4	−1.1
1940....	316.8	83.1	99.5	1940-45 −13.4	−11.9	1940-45 −2.8	−2.5
1945....	473.7	72.0	87.7	1945-50 +3.8	+4.3	1945-50 +0.7	+0.9
1950....	490.6	74.7	91.5	1950-55 −4.7	−4.0	1950-55 −1.0	−0.8
1955....	597.6	71.2	87.8	1880-1920 +11.3	+139.4	1880-1920 +0.3	+2.2
				1920-1955 −38.7	−35.4	1920-1955 −1.4	−1.2

SOURCES: Appendix Tables IX and XIII. The authors thank John W. Kendrick who made available his estimates of GNP (Department of Commerce concept) which are derived from estimates of Simon Kuznets for the period prior to 1929. These will be published in the forthcoming National Bureau of Economic Research volume, Productivity Trends in the United States. Kendrick's estimates of GNP in 1929 dollars were

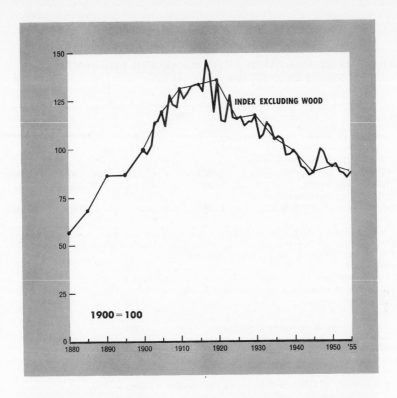

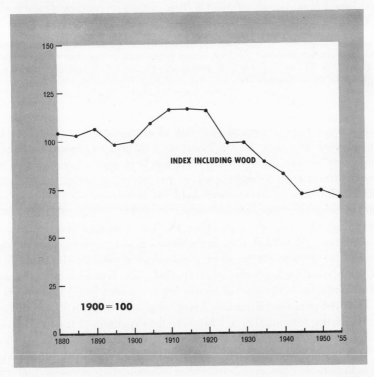

Figure 26. Energy consumption per unit of gross national product (above, excluding wood; below, including wood) five-year intervals, 1880–1955.

TABLE 53.   SOME COMPARISONS OF TOTAL AND RESIDENTIAL
ENERGY CONSUMPTION IN 1880 AND 1955

Energy consumed	1880		1955	
	Quantity (trillion Btu)	Per cent of total	Quantity (trillion Btu)	Per cent of total
1. Total energy (from wood, mineral fuels, and hydropower).....	5,000	100%	40,796	100%
2. Thereof in residences..........	3,200	64	8,456	21
3. All other (i.e., nonresidential, or used mainly in "production")..	1,800	36	32,340	79

1955 index numbers of energy consumed (1880 = 100)	Quantity in Btu's	Energy (Btu's) per unit of GNP [a]
4. Total energy (from wood, mineral fuels, and hydropower)............................	816	68
5. Thereof in residences.....................	264	22
6. All other (nonresidential or used mainly in "production")...........................	1,797	150

Per capita energy consumption in residences	1880	1955
7. In million Btu...........................	63.7	51.2
8. In tons of coal equivalent.................	2.4	1.9

[a] Index number of GNP in 1955 was 1,195 relative to 1880 = 100.

SOURCES: Item 1 from Appendix Table VII. Item 2, 1880, 95 per cent of total fuel wood consumption (see C. S. Sargent, "The Forests of the United States in Their Economic Aspects," *Census of Manufactures*, Vol. 9 [Washington, D. C.: U. S. Government Printing Office, 1879], p. 489, plus approximately one-quarter of total coal consumption (the greater part was used for steam power and in iron and steel production). Item 2, 1955, Appendix Table C-6, plus nearly the total 1955 fuel wood consumption. Excludes private automobiles.

—its effect is not to be compared with that of energy which is transformed into mechanical work to power the machinery or into heat to process the materials of an industrial society. Hence, when there has been such a great change in the relative importance of household energy, it is of interest to divide the total energy consumption into two portions—household use and consumption for all other uses, that is, essentially "production" purposes—and to compare these shares with the expanding GNP as is done in Table 53. This indicates that, between 1880 and 1955, energy input other than in residences rose by 50 per cent per unit of GNP, while the portion consumed in households dropped to about one-fifth of what it had been at the beginning of the period. The over-all result of these two divergent trends was a decrease of energy input per unit of GNP of nearly one-third. Thus the paradoxical finding has a simple explanation in the decline in residential energy consumption in relation to the expansion of the total economy.

The drastic shift in the relative importance of the household sector in total energy consumption over the past seventy-five years may be a feature which is unique to American economic development. British statistics show that over a slightly longer period the share of the domestic sector in total energy consumption remained fairly stable. In 1869, some 23 per cent of all coal (which was practically synonymous with total energy) used in the United Kingdom, was burned in households and small commercial establishments; the corresponding figures for 1903 and 1954 are 24 per cent and 27 per cent.[13] Unlike the development in this country, the long-term relationship between aggregate energy consumption and national output in Britain should have been influenced little, if at all, by changes in the weight of the household sector.

TOTAL ENERGY, EXCLUDING FUEL WOOD, RELATIVE TO GNP

Average annual rates of change in the consumption of mineral fuels and hydropower relative to gross national product for five-year periods are shown in column 7 of Table 52. A quick scanning of these figures indicates that the relationship between the input of these energy sources and the total output of the economy has varied widely—from increases of 3.7 per cent (1880–85) and 4.9 per cent (1885–90) to declines of 3.1 per cent (1920–25) and 2.5 per cent (1940–45). It is obvious, too, that these extremes are not erratic departures from an otherwise parallel movement of the two series. The record of the relationship between these two series is marked by great diversity. Apparently, just as it was not possible to find representative rates of change for energy consumption or energy consumption per capita, so it also is not possible to find typical rates of change over the long term for energy consumption per unit of GNP.

Despite this, however, the long-run record of the relationship between energy supplied by mineral fuels and hydropower and GNP reveals what appears to be a definite pattern, consisting of a long-term upswing in the energy-GNP ratio which, after a transitional period of about a decade, was followed by a distinct downswing (see Table 52 and Figure 26). The record between 1880 and 1910 is one of persistent increase in the input of energy per unit of GNP; between 1920 and 1955, the record appears to be one of persistent decline. The decade 1910–20, which separates the two long periods, appears to be transitional, with almost no change in the relationship between the input of energy and the output of the economy.[14]

[13] See W. S. Jevons, *The Coal Question*, ed. A. W. Flux (rev. ed., New York: Macmillan & Co., 1906), p. 139; and Central Statistical Office, *Annual Abstract of Statistics, 1955* (London: Her Majesty's Stationery Office, 1955), pp. 130, 138–39. The 1954 data include the coal consumed in the production of gas and electricity used in the domestic, but not in the commercial, sector.

[14] Since the total for mineral fuels and hydropower includes energy consumed in all sectors of the economy, it may be questioned how the relationship would behave if only the energy going into nonhousehold uses were included. Complete data which would permit such a comparison for the period since 1880 unfortunately are not available. In Table 53, it was estimated that in 1880 about one-quarter of coal consumption (in that year synonymous with mineral fuels) was used in households. The comparable percentage for 1955 is slightly less. For selected years of the more recent period, 1929–55, statistics presented in Section J of the Appendix to Part II show the distribution of energy consumption among broad

Although the broad picture seems clear enough, certain reservations should be noted. As already noted, in the early decades, the increase in industrially oriented energy relative to GNP is slightly overstated because direct water and wind power are not included in this series, but this was of relatively small importance following 1880 when the comparison with GNP begins. Table 52 shows two five-year intervals in the post-1920 period in which input of energy relative to the national product shows a small increase. However, the use of data for every fifth year as the basis for computing percentage changes or average annual rates of change makes the results sensitive to peculiarities which may exist in the energy-GNP relationship in particular years, due to factors such as the position which these years occupy in business cycles. Even so, overlapping five-year averages, based on annual data for the period since 1900 for which reliable data are available, confirm the two main findings: Wide disparities in annual rates of change in energy input relative to GNP and a distinct reversal of the upward trend in energy use per unit of national output in the post-World War I period (see Table 54). Such a series also eliminates the apparent slight relative increase in energy consumption between the years 1925 and 1930, which stands out in Table 52. There remains only one period, which compares the war years 1941–45 with the immediate postwar period of 1946–50, in which energy use shows a relative increase. This period must be considered as exceptional, characterized by an unusually fast expansion of GNP during the war years, which was followed by an extremely slow rise between 1946 and 1950 (there actually were three years of absolute decline, and two of increase). The fluctuations in the growth rate of energy consumption in these two periods were also unusually great, but not quite as pronounced as in the case of GNP. These unusual circumstances were sufficient to cause what is here interpreted as a temporary interruption in the long-term downward trend in the energy input-GNP ratio.

---

consuming sectors. These data indicate that the percentage of the total going to the household and commercial sector remained comparatively stable over these years; hence the movement of an energy total excluding household and commercial would be approximately the same as that of the grand total.

For the longer period, there are available estimates of the share of total energy consumption going into mechanical work and process heat. Putnam, *op. cit.*, pp. 101–05, has made one such estimate, and the percentage share as he estimates it has been applied to the energy totals utilized in the present study. Between 1880 and 1955, these estimates of energy consumed for "productive purposes" show a rising trend relative to GNP for the period 1880–1920, and a declining trend between 1920 and 1955. Another estimate, in this case for mechanical work only (that is, inanimate energy which was utilized to perform tasks which conceivably, even if inadequately, could be accomplished by muscle power), was made by J. F. Dewhurst and Associates in *America's Needs and Resources, A New Survey* (New York: The Twentieth Century Fund, 1955), Appendix 25-3, Tables J and K. Their estimates, too, when related to the total output of the economy show a rising trend for energy relative to GNP between 1880 and 1910–20, and a sharply declining trend since then.

These estimates derived from Putnam and Dewhurst are extremely rough, consequently it would not be proper to place great weight on the precise picture which they convey. It is interesting, though, that in broad outline they bear out, in their relationship to the growth in national product, the long-term upswing and downswing found in the ratio of total energy consumption to GNP.

TABLE 54. AVERAGE ANNUAL PERCENTAGE RATES OF CHANGE IN
ENERGY CONSUMPTION, GROSS NATIONAL PRODUCT, AND
ENERGY USE PER UNIT OF GNP, OVERLAPPING FIVE-
YEAR AVERAGES, 1901–55

Period	Energy consumption, excluding wood (Btu's) (1)	Gross national product (based on 1929 dollars) (2)	Energy input per unit of GNP (3)
1901–05 to 1906–10.....	+6.4%	+3.9%	+2.4%
1906–10 to 1911–15.....	+3.5	+2.3	+1.2
1911–15 to 1916–20.....	+3.9	+3.4	+0.5
1916–20 to 1921–25.....	+0.3	+2.9	−2.5
1921–25 to 1926–30.....	+3.1	+3.6	−0.5
1926–30 to 1931–35.....	−4.6	−3.5	−1.2
1931–35 to 1936–40.....	+4.2	+5.8	−1.4
1936–40 to 1941–45.....	+6.2	+8.7	−2.3
1941–45 to 1946–50.....	+1.9	+0.8	+1.1
1946–50 to 1951–55.....	+2.8	+4.3	−1.4

SOURCES: Appendix Tables IX and XIII.

If the long-term upswing and downswing in the historical record is valid, the periods are found to coincide with other significant changes that took place in the pattern of energy consumption and in the general economy. The composition of the energy mix (Table 2) reveals that in 1885, for the first time, coal accounted for more than one-half of all energy materials consumed in the United States, and around 1910 coal achieved its position of peak relative importance in the energy total (about 75 per cent). Thus, the period of rising energy consumption relative to GNP corresponds essentially to the period in which coal's dominance in the American energy picture was established and reached its peak. The period of decline in energy input relative to national output conicides with that phase of the energy consumption record in which the rise of the liquid and gaseous fuels occurred, and in which electrification grew at a rapid rate. As far as changes in the total economy are concerned, 1880 is the first year in which the percentage of the total population gainfully occupied in nonagricultural pursuits exceeded those engaged in agriculture—by the slightest of margins. Thus, the point from which these comparisons start coincides with a significant turning point in the nation's pattern of economic activities. Finally, the post-1920 period in which national output rises relative to energy input is one in which there has been a general quickening in the productivity of the economy relative to such major input factors as labor and capital. The possible influence of all the above factors—both on the side of energy and of the general economy—are referred to later in the analysis of factors which may help to explain the energy-GNP pattern.

In summary, then, the long-period statistical record of mineral fuels and hydro-power consumption relative to GNP yields the following picture:

1) From 1880 to 1955, there occurred an increase of some 55 per cent in energy consumption per unit of GNP, which is equivalent to an average rate of about 0.6 per cent per year.

2) This long-period rise of quite modest proportions is composed of the following diverse movements:

a) An increase between 1880 and 1910 of 133 per cent, equivalent to an average rate of increase of 2.9 per cent per year.

b) A comparative stability between 1910 and 1920. The decade 1910–20 marks both the culmination of the period of rise, and the transition to a new basic relationship between energy and national product.

c) A decline between 1920 and 1955 of about 35 per cent, equivalent to an average rate of decline of about 1.2 per cent per year.

.   .   .

Some Factors Involved in Long-Run Changes
in the Relationship Between Energy and GNP

An adequate explanation of the changes in the long-run relationship between the energy consumption of mineral fuels and hydropower and the development of GNP would require the examination of detailed statistics on the use of the various energy commodities in different industries and economic sectors. Both total energy consumption and GNP are heterogeneous aggregates, with a greatly changing composition over the seventy-five years under study. The national product changes involve the relative rise and decline of activities and industries some of which consume great amounts of energy per unit of output, some small quantities per unit of product. The changes in the energy aggregate involve the shifting importance of commodities which are used with varying thermal efficiencies even in the same productive activity. At the same time, technological and managerial changes have operated to increase efficiency of production relative to the various input factors, and so forth. It is not possible to explain the behavior of these aggregate relationships without uncovering in detail these underlying changes which have combined to produce the broad patterns of change.

Unfortunately, the data on energy consumption in specific industries and activities are not available in enough historical detail to permit the required detailed kind of analysis. Also, it is certain that even those data sources which are available—some of them scattered far and wide in a myriad of historical writings—have been far from exhausted in the research underlying this report. Consequently, no more is attempted in the following pages than the presentation of a set of general hypotheses, with some supporting data concerning factors which are believed to have played a major part in producing the historical pattern already described. Further research and analysis would be needed to prove or disprove these hypotheses, and to adduce other important explanatory factors.

The discussion which follows focuses on the fundamental change in the relationship between energy and GNP which occurred following the first World War, the transition from a long-run tendency for energy consumption to rise relative to GNP to a trend in which the consumption of energy fell persistently relative to national output. By concentrating attention on this basic transformation in the relationship between energy consumption and national product it is possible to uncover some of the factors which have at different times during the seventy-five years weighed heavily in producing the results already observed in the statistical measures of the energy-GNP relationships.

The analysis is presented in terms of factors falling under two broad headings:

1) Changes in the total economy, which cover those influences originating outside of the energy sector, such as changes in the structure of the economy and the over-all efficiency of its performance.

2) Changes within the energy economy, such as changes in the thermal efficiency of energy use and the shifting composition of the energy mix.

Of course, the distinction between these two classes of factors is not clear-cut. For example, improvements in the over-all efficiency of the economy's performance obviously are related to the manner and form in which energy is consumed; for example, the rise of electrification—a change within the energy economy to be discussed later—appears to be an important factor in explaining the growth of over-all productivity in the economy. Nevertheless, the distinction provides a useful framework for distinguishing between what may be viewed as essentially different classes of factors.

CHANGES IN THE TOTAL ECONOMY

Structural Changes. Since this analysis deals with the fuels of industrialization, it is to be expected that the more rapid the growth of manufacturing and mining in relation to the total economy, the greater will be the consumption of industrial fuels relative to the growth of the nation's total output of goods and services. It is therefore reasonable to begin with the hypothesis that the upward trend in consumption of mineral fuels and hydropower per unit of national product between 1880 and the 1910–20 decade and the downward trend between 1920 and 1955 are connected with differences in the rate of expansion of the industrial sector compared with that of the total economy during these periods.

This hypothesis is partly borne out by the facts. In 1920, manufacturing and mining, measured by indexes of output, were about five times greater than in 1885.[15] This expansion was considerably faster than that for the economy as a

[15] The years 1885 and 1920 have been chosen for comparison instead of 1880 and 1910, which could have been used as well. The former years were chosen because the rise in the ratio of energy input to GNP continued until 1920, although at a very slow rate after 1910; and to facilitate the comparison of index numbers covering two equally long periods of thirty-five years each.

whole, which in terms of GNP rose to three and a third times the former level (see Table 55 and Figure 27). It is not surprising that in a period of such rapid industrialization the consumption of energy per unit of national output would rise. In the second period, from 1920 to 1955, when the consumption of energy fell relative to GNP, the industrial sector again expanded faster than the economy as a whole, even though mining lagged behind. While GNP rose from 100 in 1920 to 311 in 1955, manufacturing output expanded to 359, mining output to 234, and total industrial production to 339 (see Table 55). However, during this period, the faster growth of industry was not nearly so pronounced as previously; barely 10 per cent more than total national output as compared to nearly 50 per cent more in the earlier period.

The impact on energy consumption of the comparative rates of growth of industry relative to national output in these two periods was intensified by the fact that the rate of mechanization of manufacturing, as measured by horsepower (hp) installed per unit of output, apparently was far more rapid in the pre-1920 period than in the following years. The relevant data for manufacturing, which accounted for some 95 per cent of all industry during the period under review (as measured by value of product, with mining accounting for the remaining 5 per cent), are given in Table 56.

TABLE 55. COMPARATIVE GROWTH: GROSS NATIONAL PRODUCT, INDUSTRIAL OUTPUT, AND ENERGY PER UNIT OF GNP, 1885–1920 AND 1920–55

Year	GNP (1)	Manufac-turing output (2)	Mining output (3)	Total industrial output (4)	Manufac-turing (5)	Mining (6)	Total industrial (7)	Energy (mineral fuels and hydropower) per unit of GNP (8)
		Indexes			Ratio of increase compared to GNP (GNP = 1.00)			
1885..	100	100	100	n.a.				100
1920..	335	479	540	n.a.	1.43	1.61	n.a.	199
1920..	100	100	100	100				100
1955..	311	359	234	339	1.15	0.75	1.09	65

n.a. Not available.

SOURCES: Column 1 from Appendix Table XIII. Column 2 figures for 1885–1920 from U.S. Bureau of the Census, *Historical Statistics of the United States, 1789–1945* (Washington, D. C.: U.S. Government Printing Office), Series J 13 and J 14, index of physical production of manufacturing (Warren M. Persons) linked to index of physical output of all manufacturing industries (National Bureau of Economic Research). Column 2 figures for 1920–55 from Federal Reserve Board Index of Manufacturing Production. Column 3 from Index of Physical Volume of Mineral Production, U. S. Bureau of Mines, *Minerals Yearbook, 1956*, Vol. I (Washington, D. C.: U.S. Government Printing Office), pp. 3–4. Column 4 from Federal Reserve Board Index of Industrial Production (manufactures and minerals combined). Column 8 based on Table 52.

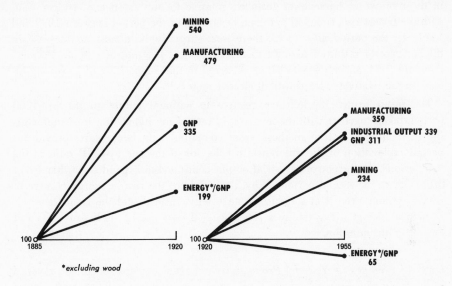

Figure 27. Comparative growth: gross national product, industrial output, and energy per unit of GNP, 1885–1920 and 1920–55.

TABLE 56. OUTPUT IN MANUFACTURING, HORSEPOWER RATING
OF INSTALLED EQUIPMENT, AND HORSEPOWER INSTALLED PER
UNIT OF OUTPUT IN MANUFACTURING, SELECTED YEARS, 1879–1954

Year	Output (1)	Horsepower installed (2)	Horsepower installed per unit of output (3)
Index numbers (1899 = 100):			
1879............................	37.1	34.8	93.8
1889............................	66.5	60.5	91.0
1899............................	100.0	100.0	100.0
1909............................	157.8	184.1	116.7
1919............................	221.8	289.4	130.5
1929............................	363.6	419.1	115.3
1939............................	372.7	508.5	136.4
1954............................	829.8	1,104.5	133.1
Percentage increases:			
1879–1919.................	498%	732%	39%
1919–54.....................	274	282	2

SOURCES: Column 1 from John W. Kendrick, *Productivity Trends in the United States* (New York: National Bureau of Economic Research, forthcoming), shifted to 1899 = 100. Column 2 from U.S. Bureau of the Census, *U.S. Census of Manufactures: 1954*, Vol. I (Washington, D. C.: U.S. Government Printing Office, 1957), p. 207–2, Table 1; represents prime movers and electric motors driven by purchased electricity.

These data show that between 1879 and 1919 there was a substantial increase in the number of horsepower installed relative to output—nearly 40 per cent, with the fastest rise, some 30 per cent, occurring in the period between 1899 and 1919. In the period after 1919, there was, surprisingly, almost no increase in the horsepower rating of manufacturing equipment per unit of output. Between then and 1954, an important change occurred in the composition of power equipment in the relatively fast growth of electric motors.[16]

The faster growth of industry relative to national output in the pre-1920 period, taken together with the more rapid rate of mechanization in manufacturing in relation to output in those years compared with later years, provides a partial explanation of the difference in behavior of the energy-GNP ratio in the two periods. But even so, industrial output continued to expand somewhat faster than GNP in the second period. Why, then, did not the rise in energy relative to GNP continue, even if at a reduced rate? Why, instead, did the trend reverse? Structural change along the lines just discussed does not by itself provide a full answer to this question.

Over-All Changes in National Productivity. Partial explanation of the reversal in the trend of energy relative to GNP which occurred after 1920 may be found in another force affecting the total economy—the efficiency with which input factors generally were transformed into the final products constituting the nation's output of goods and services. There are definite indications that the economy's efficiency in this regard, as measured by the national product relative to the input of labor and capital, underwent a change in trend at about the same time.

The detailed studies of the National Bureau of Economic Research dealing with the productivity of the U.S. economy indicate that a distinct acceleration in productivity increase began shortly after World War I. Solomon Fabricant remarks that:

> The change in trend that came after World War I is one of the most interesting facts before us. There is little question about it. It is visible not only in the indexes that (John) Kendrick has compiled for the private domestic economy. . . . It can be found also in his figures for the whole economy, including government, as well as in his estimates for the group of industries for which productivity indexes are available.[17]

These general observations refer to statistical findings that total output per unit of labor and capital combined rose by an average annual rate of 1.3 per cent between 1889 and 1919, and by 2.1 per cent between 1919 and 1957. The total was composed of increases in output per weighted man-hour of labor of 1.6 per

---

[16] This is discussed, along with the significance of the growing use of electric motors in making possible a more efficient organization of the entire production process, later in this chapter in connection with the rise of electricity.

[17] Solomon Fabricant, *Basic Facts on Productivity Change*, Occasional Paper 63 (New York: National Bureau of Economic Research, 1959), p. 11.

cent and 2.3 per cent in the two periods, and per unit of weighted tangible capital input of 0.5 per cent and 1.3 per cent.[18]

The historical course of energy relative to GNP does not parallel that of labor and capital, as disclosed in the studies of the National Bureau. The turning point in the energy-GNP relationship involved a reversal in trend, whereas that in labor and capital productivity involved not a reversal, but a marked increase in rate in what has been a single persistent direction of change. What is significant for the purposes of this analysis is that national output after 1919 grew much faster relative to the input of labor and capital than it had in the earlier period. There is no apparent reason to believe that the same broad influences which operated to accelerate the growth in national output after World War I in relation to the input of labor and capital should not also have increased, in some measure, the rate of growth of national output relative to the input of energy. In part, therefore, the reversal in trend in the energy-GNP relationship after 1920 may be explained by changes in efficiency in the national economy arising out of the growth of society's "intangible capital"—Fabricant's term for "all the improvements in basic science, technology, business administration, and education and training, that aid in production"—and other broad influences affecting the efficiency of production.

It is well known that the increasing use of inanimate energy per worker plays an important part in raising the over-all productivity of the economy, but the foregoing assumes that the factors which produced the post-1920 acceleration in the growth of national output relative to capital and labor inputs were of a sort that could also increase the "productivity" of energy inputs relative to national output. Can such an assumption be supported? A possible element in its support is found in the very nature of the factors falling within intangible capital as this term has been defined. These factors appear, in part, to be of a sort which could serve to increase the productivity of energy, although some of them (for example, basic science and technology) might also depend for their

[18] *Ibid.* In Fabricant's study, "output" represents gross physical output in the private sector of the economy, measured in constant prices. This index of output is compared to an index of labor and capital input in the private economy. Labor input is measured in terms of weighted man-hours: instead of deriving a total by simply adding together all man-hours, weights are applied to man-hours in the different industries and the man-hours are added together after they are weighted. High-pay industries are weighted more heavily than low-pay industries, thus taking into account some of the differences in skill, education, and experience among laboring groups. Capital input is measured by the constant dollar value of the stock of real capital—land, plant, equipment, and inventories—employed in the several sectors, weighted by base period rates of return. (This procedure implies that capital services move proportionally with capital stocks. Since the total volume of tangible capital seldom declines even during depressions or recessions, the input of capital per unit of output tends to rise, or to decrease at a lower rate, during business contractions than during periods of expanding output.) The combined index of input of labor and tangible capital ("total input") is derived by adding together the two separate indexes weighted according to the base-period earnings per unit of labor and capital. *Ibid.*, pp. 6–9, and John W. Kendrick, *Productivity Trends: Capital and Labor*, Occasional Paper 53 (New York: National Bureau of Economic Research, 1956), p. 6.

effectiveness on substantial increases in energy input per unit of national product. The composition of intangible capital thus leaves the question unresolved.

There is, however, some statistical indication of the fact that the post-1920 acceleration in the increase in productivity within manufacturing has not been the result of a comparable acceleration in mechanization. The relevant data, covering the period 1879–1954, comparing output per man-hour with horsepower installed per man-hour, are assembled in Table 57.

TABLE 57. MAN-HOURS, OUTPUT PER MAN-HOUR, AND HORSEPOWER RATING OF INSTALLED EQUIPMENT PER MAN-HOUR IN MANUFACTURING INDUSTRIES, SELECTED YEARS, 1879–1954

Year	Man-hours worked (1)	Output per man-hour (2)	Horsepower installed per man-hour (3)
Index numbers (1899 = 100):			
1879	54.2	68.4	64.2
1889	76.7	86.6	78.9
1899	100.0	100.0	100.0
1909	138.5	113.8	132.9
1919	173.7	127.5	166.6
1929	165.3	219.8	253.5
1939	134.7	276.5	389.1
1954	223.8	370.3	493.5
Percentage increases:			
1879–1919	220%	86%	160%
1919–54	29	190	196

SOURCES: Columns 1 and 2 from John W. Kendrick, *Productivity Trends in the United States* (New York: National Bureau of Economic Research, forthcoming), shifted to 1899 = 100. Column 3 based on horsepower figures shown in Table 56.

This table shows that between 1879 and 1954 output per man-hour (labor productivity) grew continuously. Over the same period, the number of horsepower installed per man-hour also increased uninterruptedly. However, while the number of horsepower installed per man-hour grew by about 160 per cent between 1879 and 1919, labor productivity increased only 86 per cent. The increase of 196 per cent in horsepower per man-hour in the years after 1919 went along with a growth of 190 per cent in labor productivity. Thus, the *acceleration* in the growth of labor productivity in manufacturing in the period following 1919 did not depend on a similar acceleration in the growth of horsepower installed per man-hour. Although changes in the degree of mechanization do not yield a direct measure of the input of energy, these comparisons establish a prima-facie case for the proposition that the productivity of energy, at least in manufacturing, grew at a substantially faster rate after 1920 than before. This was apparently in response to general forces increasing productivity throughout the economy, in which, as will be argued later, a change in the form of energy application —the rise of electricity—played an important part.

To summarize the effects of changes in the total economy on the energy-GNP ratio, the following hypothesis is broadly consistent with the facts examined: Prior to the 1910–20 decade, the fast growth of industrial output relative to the total national output resulted in a rising trend of energy consumption relative to gross national product. After 1920, although industrial output continued to grow faster than total national output, energy consumption per unit of GNP declined. This was (1) because the growth of industrial output relative to total national product was slower than before 1920; and (2) because general factors which resulted in a higher rate of output relative to both labor and capital inputs apparently had a similar effect in raising national product relative to the input of energy.

CHANGES IN THE ENERGY ECONOMY

Thermal and Economic Efficiency of Energy Utilization. The energy input totals basic to this analysis measure the inherent Btu values of the primary energy materials consumed in the United States. It is well known that the efficiency of converting these materials into useful heat and mechanical work has changed considerably during the historical period studied. On the whole, these changes have been in the direction of fuller utilization of the inherent energy contained in the primary materials. Indeed, the explanation most frequently advanced for the downward trend in the ratio of energy input to GNP in recent decades runs in terms of such improvements in the efficiency of energy use.

However, the increasing efficiency of energy utilization, as measured by the relationship between the economy's energy inputs and its output of goods and services, is explained by more than just the higher effective rate of converting raw energy materials into useful energy. As shown in the preceding sections, the decline in energy consumption relative to national output in the years following 1920 was caused also by changes taking place in the total economy which have affected this relationship.

The failure explicitly to recognize the two classes of factors affecting the efficiency of energy use is attested by the lack of an accepted terminology to distinguish between the two. For purposes of this analysis, such terminology is needed, and the following concepts and definitions have been adopted. "Thermal efficiency," a term which has wide currency in energy studies, is here used strictly to mean the ratio between raw energy input and useful energy output; "economic efficiency of energy use" is used to mean the ratio between raw energy input and the output of goods and services in the economy, or in one of its sectors.

Thermal efficiency, although a widely used term, requires some additional explanation. Because the overwhelming share of all energy consumed in this country was and is derived from fuel materials, the most widely accepted measure of energy is the British thermal unit. And thermal efficiency is defined as the ratio of raw Btu input to Btu output—for instance, the Btu's contained in the pounds of coal burned under a boiler to the Btu content of the steam actually utilized in the processing of industrial materials. However, one could just as well convert the inherent, latent energy in the natural resources consumed and the energy actually utilized into horsepower hours (hph)—or, as is the custom in United Nations statistics, into kilowatt hours (kwh). The input-output ratio would still be the same as if expressed in thermal units. For traditional reasons, Btu's are generally used as the energy common denominator in the United States even if mechanical energy (horsepower hours) or electrical energy (kilowatt hours), rather than thermal energy, are the units actually measured. Thus, in the case of direct steampower thermal efficiency measures the ratio of the Btu content of the coal burned in a steam engine to the Btu equivalent of the horsepower hours of mechanical work actually obtained at the point of use. In the case of electric power, thermal efficiency measures the ratio of the Btu content of the fuels burned in an electric power station to the Btu equivalent of the kilowatt hours produced (including or excluding losses in transmission to the point of use, depending on the definition of the case).

Thermal efficiency, as is apparent, measures technological or engineering efficiencies which, in themselves, are no yardstick for measuring the economic efficiency of energy use. The latter can be measured only by going beyond the energy sector proper—that is, beyond comparing energy input with energy output—and by relating, as stated above, raw energy input to the output of the economy or one of its sectors. For the entire economy, therefore, the economic efficiency of energy use may be defined as the ratio of raw energy consumption to gross national product.

Thermal efficiency and economic efficiency, so defined, obviously are interrelated. Improvements in thermal efficiency are doubtless among the factors which in recent decades greatly contributed to the decline in gross energy consumption relative to the output of the economy. But this relation is by no means a simple or straightforward one. Thermal efficiency is dependent mainly on the end uses to which energy materials are put, on the equipment in which they are used, and on the type of raw energy materials used for certain purposes. It varies widely from one application to another—possibly more in this country than in others because all types of mineral fuels are available at moderate cost. To give one extreme example for the United States: In recent years, the thermal efficiency ranged from about 75 per cent in commercial space heating using natural gas in up-to-date central heating equipment to 4 or 5 per cent in the few remaining coal-burning steam locomotives.

The foregoing example illustrates an important point—that raw energy can be transformed into heat with a much higher degree of thermal efficiency than can be achieved by converting heat into mechanical work. The highest degree of thermal efficiency thus would be achieved by an economy which used the greatest portion of its energy input for heating as the end purpose, and only a minor share for mechanical work. But this type of thermally most efficient energy utilization would exist within an economy in which over-all productivity (and presumably the economic efficiency of energy use as well) was relatively low because of the absence of mechanization.

For example, according to the best estimates available at present the over-all thermal efficiency of energy utilization in the United States in recent years was about 35 to 40 per cent (with about two-fifths of all energy consumption transformed into mechanical work) as compared with the thermal efficiency in Russia a hundred years ago (1860), which has been estimated at about 33 per cent. By contrast, the thermal efficiency of the British energy system in the late 1860's stood at some 8 to 9 per cent. In the case of Russia, the relatively high efficiency a century ago was achieved by using some nine-tenths of all fuels consumed for space heating in well constructed stoves. In Britain, at about the same time, the widespread use of coal fireplaces held the space-heating efficiency down to some 15 per cent. But only less than one-third of the total British energy consumption went into space heating; one-quarter was used for industrial heat and about two-fifths to generate steam and steam power. Since at that time coal was converted into mechanical work via steam at an average efficiency of only about 2 per cent, the large share of energy used in mechanical work kept the average thermal efficiency of energy utilization very low—at about one-third of that of the contemporary Russian energy system.[19]

One is tempted to summarize this aspect of the relation between thermal and economic efficiency of energy in the form of a paradox. The greater the share of the total energy input converted into mechanical work (directly or via generation of electricity) and, thus, the greater the contribution of energy in raising over-all productivity by replacing and multiplying human labor, the lower the over-all thermal efficiency. On the other hand, the greater the share of energy inputs going into heat, the lower the over-all productivity of the economy but the higher the thermal efficiency of its energy system.

The concept of economic efficiency of energy use is in a way analogous to that involved in relating man-hours worked to total output as a measure of the changing efficiency or productivity of labor—and subject to some of the same limitations as an index of man-hours to GNP covering a long period. An average man-hour of, say 1880, is in many respects different from an average man-hour of the 1950's; so, also, does an average million raw Btu's of 1880 differ from an average million consumed in the 1950's. Some of the reasons they differ are the same: The composition of the labor force has changed, and so has the composition of the fuel and power basket. Workers are, in general, better educated, and, similarly, certain energy commodities in use today are an improvement over those used seventy-five years ago (a kilowatt hour is, in this sense, a pound of coal with a college education), and so on. Perhaps, most important, the two measures are also alike in that both reflect improvements which are not due alone to the increasing efficiency of the input factor involved. The rise in labor productivity reflects gains growing out of factors other than the superior performance of labor, so does the increase in the economic efficiency of energy use measure improve-

[19] See Putnam, *op. cit.*, pp. 91–92. Likewise, the faster industrialization of Germany as compared to that of France and the larger share of the mechanical work component in Germany towards the end of the nineteenth century kept the over-all thermal efficiency of the German energy system below that of France *(ibid.)*.

ments resulting from forces other than the straightforward growth in thermal efficiency.[20]

Economic efficiency of energy use, as an all-inclusive measure, embodies as one of its components changes in thermal efficiency, and such improvements have played an important part in decreasing raw energy input in relation to national output. Some estimates have been made of long-run changes in the thermal efficiency of converting fuels into useful heat and mechanical work in the United States. Although the data and concepts on which they are based are very crude, the broad picture they convey is one of greater and more rapid increases in efficiency in the twentieth century than in the latter half of the nineteenth century. Putnam estimates that the average thermal efficiency of energy use for all purposes rose from 8 per cent in 1850 to 11 or 12 per cent in 1900, and to 30 per cent in 1947.[21] Dewhurst assumes a rise in the efficiency of converting fuels and hydropower (direct waterpower in 1850) into mechanical work from 1.8 to 3.2 per cent between the middle and the end of the nineteenth century, and an increase to 13.6 per cent by 1950.[22] If true, these factors would help to explain the course of the energy-GNP ratio as shown in the present study.

Changes in the Composition of Total Energy Consumption. The energy total here being compared with GNP has undergone important changes in its composition during the period under study. Among these are: (1) shifts among primary energy sources, such as the major shift in relative importance from coal to oil and natural gas; (2) the long-term trend away from the direct consumption of raw energy materials to the use of processed and converted energy products, such as the switch from coal to diesel oil as a railroad fuel and the growth of electric power generation; and (3) in the field of mechanical energy, the replacement of steam power by electricity. These shifts were dependent on and closely interconnected with changes in the equipment in which the various sources and forms of energy were utilized, as for example, the replacement of the stove by the modern central heating system, the change from steam engines to internal combustion engines in transportation, and the replacement of steam-driven machines by electric motors in the industrial sector.

How has the energy-GNP relationship been affected by these changes? To throw light on this question, total energy consumption since 1920 in Table 58 is divided into the following categories: energy used in the form of electricity, as internal combustion fuels, and in all other forms—essentially the energy used as heat, mainly for industrial purposes and in space heating. For these three categories, Table 58 shows the amounts consumed every fifth year between 1920 and 1955 and index numbers measuring the growth in consumption relating each component to the growth in GNP.

[20] The analogy is somewhat stronger with simple man-hours than with weighted man-hours, but essentially it applies to both.

[21] Putnam, *op. cit.*, pp. 89–90, 95, 416.

[22] Dewhurst, *op. cit.*, Appendix 25-3, Table I, p. 1113.

TABLE 58. CONSUMPTION OF ELECTRICITY, INTERNAL COMBUSTION FUELS, AND ALL OTHER ENERGY, FIVE-YEAR INTERVALS, 1920–55

I. *Physical Quantities*

Year	Total mineral fuels and hydropower, excl. wood (trillion Btu) (1)	Electricity [a]			Internal combustion fuels [b]		All other energy [c]	
		Kilowatt hours (million) (2)	Btu equivalent (trillion) (3)	Per cent of total (4)	Trillion Btu (5)	Per cent of total (6)	Trillion Btu (7)	Per cent of total (8)
1920..	19,768	57,499	2,268	11.5%	527	2.7%	16,973	85.8%
1925..	20,878	85,939	2,280	10.9	1,166	5.6	17,432	83.5
1930..	22,253	116,229	2,395	10.8	2,056	9.2	17,802	80.0
1935..	19,059	120,272	2.232	11.7	2,356	12.4	14,471	75.9
1940..	23,877	182,021	3,110	13.0	3,202	13.4	17,565	73.6
1945..	31,439	273,817	4,481	14.2	3,998	12.7	22,960	73.1
1950..	33,972	390,460	5,645	16.6	5,751	16.9	22,576	66.5
1955..	39,729	633,078	7,598	19.1	7,958	20.0	24,173	60.9

II. *Index Numbers (1920 = 100)*

Year	GNP [d] (based on 1929 dollars) (9)	Electricity		Internal combustion fuels (Btu's) (12)	All other energy (Btu's) (13)
		Kilowatt hours (10)	Btu equivalent (11)		
1920.........	100.0	100.0	100.0	100.0	100.0
1925.........	123.5	149.4	100.5	221.2	102.7
1930.........	129.8	202.1	105.6	390.1	104.9
1935.........	124.7	209.2	98.4	447.1	85.3
1940.........	165.1	316.5	137.1	607.6	103.5
1945.........	246.8	476.2	197.6	758.6	135.3
1950.........	255.6	679.0	248.9	1,091.3	133.0
1955.........	311.4	1,101.0	335.0	1,510.1	142.4

III. *Index Numbers of Energy Consumption Per Unit of GNP (1920 = 100)*

Year	Electricity		Internal combustion fuels (Btu's) (16)	All other energy (Btu's) (17)
	Kilowatt hours (14)	Btu equivalent (15)		
1920......................	100.0	100.0	100.0	100.0
1925......................	121.0	81.4	179.1	83.2
1930......................	155.7	81.4	300.5	80.8
1935......................	167.8	78.9	358.5	68.4
1940......................	191.7	83.0	368.0	62.7
1945......................	192.9	80.1	307.4	54.8
1950......................	265.6	97.4	427.0	52.0
1955......................	353.6	107.6	484.9	45.7

[a] Includes utility generation; generation of industrial, mine, and railway power plants; and small net imports of hydro. Btu equivalents measure the fuel required in the generation of electric energy at current conversion rates (that is, heat rates), with hydropower included in terms of the fuel which would have been required if it were thermally generated. Average heat rate (Btu per kilowatt hour) from Edison Electric Institute; declining from 37,223 Btu in 1920 to 11,699 in 1955 for utility generation; industrial generation estimated as requiring 20 per cent more Btu's per kilowatt hour than utility generation.

(*Footnotes continued on next page.*)

Turning first to the comparative growth of the three categories, the far faster growth of electricity and of internal combustion fuels than of all other energy is striking. In 1955, kilowatt hours of electric power stood at eleven times the 1920 level, internal combustion fuels at fifteen times its 1920 level, while the third category had risen by less than 50 per cent. Expressed in relation to the growth in GNP, the index number of kilowatt hours of electricity stood at 354 compared to 1920, that of internal combustion fuels at almost 500, and that of all other energy at less than 50. Thus, the decline in total energy consumption per unit of GNP between 1920 and 1955 from 100 to 65 embodies a sharp rise in internal combustion fuels and kilowatt hours of electricity per unit of GNP, and a decline in "all other energy" which is generally similar to that of total energy, although steeper.

The strong influence of the category "all other energy" on the total index of energy consumption per unit of GNP is easily explained by its relative size. Although this category declined from 86 per cent to 60 per cent of the total between 1920 and 1955, it is still, far and away, the dominant one. The increase of internal combustion fuel over the same period from less than 3 per cent to 20 per cent of the total, although impressive, still makes it only one-third as important as the "all other energy" category. As for electricity, its kilowatt hour rise per unit of GNP is hardly reflected in total energy consumption, because it is included in the total in terms of the Btu equivalent of the fuels required in its generation, and the latter amount has not grown nearly as much as kilowatt hours because of marked improvements in the thermal efficiency of electric power generation (compare columns 2 and 3, 10 and 11, and 14 and 15 of Table 58). The rise of electricity in the post-1920 period is analyzed separately in the next section because this is an outstanding case in which changes in both the thermal and economic efficiency of energy use appear to have combined to produce profound effects on the over-all energy-GNP relationship.

Since the "all other energy" category, as shown in Table 11, dominates the total, it is important to assess the factors which account for its declining movement relative to GNP in the post-1920 period. In order to understand the behavior of this large and heterogeneous category, it is necessary to divide it into principal consuming sectors.

(Footnotes to Table 58, continued)

[b] Includes gasoline and diesel oil consumption, minus diesel used by electric power plants. Conversion rate: 5,208,000 Btu per barrel of gasoline; 5,712,000 Btu per barrel of diesel oil. For 1945 to 1955, includes also liquefied petroleum gases used in internal combustion. Conversion rate: 4,011,000 Btu per barrel. From Tables 38 and 47.

[c] Total energy consumption (excluding fuel wood) from Appendix Table VII, less Btu equivalent of electric power made available (including transmission losses) and less Btu value of apparent consumption of internal combustion fuels.

[d] From Appendix Table XIII, shifted to 1920 = 100.

NOTE: For annual data on Btu's consumed in the form of gasoline, electric power, coal in coke, and all other energy, see Perry D. Teitelbaum, *Nuclear Energy and the U.S. Fuel Economy, 1955-1980* (Washington, D. C.: National Planning Association, 1958), Appendix 5, Table 2.

Fuel use by industry—for process steam and in high temperature furnace applications—was the dominant component of this category in 1955, accounting for some 12,000 trillion Btu, or almost one-half of the total.[23] Next in importance is the consumption of fuel, mainly for space heating, in households and commercial establishments, which accounted for about 8,000 trillion Btu or one-third of the entire category.[24] It is therefore relevant to inquire to what extent improvements in the thermal efficiency of fuel use in industry, households, and commercial establishments have influenced the decline in the category "all other energy" relative to GNP between 1920 and 1955. The significant shift from coal to oil and gas in the production of heat for industrial, residential, and commercial purposes, and the changes in equipment, have resulted in substantial improvements in the thermal efficiency of energy use. For example, in transforming fuel into heat for industrial process purposes, thermal efficiency has been estimated at 55 per cent for coal, 60 per cent for oil, and 80 per cent for gas.[25] Similarly, in residential and commercial space heating, it has been estimated that coal has a thermal efficiency of from 40 to 60 per cent, oil from 60 to 65 per cent, and gas 70 per cent and over.[26]

For the industrial sector, it is possible to derive a direct measure of the relationship between total energy input and physical output for selected years since 1929. These data, shown in Table 59, indicate that the output of manufacturing and mining (measured by the Federal Reserve Board index) increased from an index base of 100 in 1929 to 236 in 1955, while gross energy input (in Btu's) rose

TABLE 59. INDUSTRIAL PRODUCTION AND ENERGY CONSUMPTION IN MANUFACTURING AND MINING, SELECTED YEARS, 1929-55

Index Numbers (1929 = 100)

Year	Industrial production (1)	Energy consumption (2)	Energy consumption per unit of industrial output (3)	Energy consumption per unit of GNP (4)
1929.......	100	100.0	100.0	100.0
1939.......	99	83.7	84.5	85.4
1947.......	170	133.7	78.6	87.8
1955.......	236	168.7	71.5	76.6

SOURCES: Column 1, Federal Reserve Board Index of Industrial Production, shifted to 1929 = 100; column 2, Appendix Tables J-1 and A-37; and column 4, Appendix Table XIII.

[23] See Appendix Table A-37.

[24] See Appendix Tables B-1 and C-6.

[25] Nathaniel B. Guyol, "U.S. Energy Resources for the Future," Standard Oil Company of California, San Francisco, California, mimeographed, 1956, Appendix, p. 1.

[26] *Ibid.* and W. M. Holaday *et al.*, "Fuels—Their Present and Future Utilization," *Proceedings, Twenty-Ninth Annual Meeting, American Petroleum Institute, Section III, Refining* (Chicago: 1949), pp. 29–30.

to 168.7. This represents a decline in the ratio of energy use per unit of product from 100 (index) to 71.5 in the industrial sector—a slightly greater decrease than that in the economy as a whole during the same period. Another way of looking at these figures is this: In 1929, the industrial sector consumed 9,315 trillion Btu, thus if its energy use had expanded at the same rate as output, the 1955 consumption would have amounted to 21,984 trillion Btu. But the actual consumption was 15,712 trillion Btu, of which some 12,000 trillion consisted of energy consumed directly as heat. This saving amounts to 6,272 trillion, or 15 per cent of the aggregate 1955 energy consumption of the economy.[27]

A factor of considerable importance in the decline of the "all other energy" category, as shown in Table 58, relative to GNP between 1920 and 1955 is that coal burned by steam locomotives, which was a sizable element in the total in 1920, had by 1955 virtually disappeared as a result of the dieselization of railroads. Thus, without the coal used by railroads, this category accounted for 66 per cent of total energy consumption in 1920 instead of the 86 per cent shown in Table 58. Subtracting the coal used by railroads, the decline in the percentage share of the total accounted for by this category would be from 66 per cent in 1920 to about 60 per cent in 1955, and relative to GNP its 1955 index number would stand at 58 rather than 46.

Coal was, of course, replaced by diesel oil, which is included with internal combustion fuel in Table 58. Thus some part of the decline in "all other energy" relative to GNP is offset by an increase in the internal combustion fuels, which have risen rapidly relative to GNP. What, then, is the net effect on thermal efficiency of the replacement of coal by diesel oil? If, in 1955, the railroads had consumed no other fuel than coal, the improved efficiency in burning coal in steam locomotives would have permitted a saving in energy input per unit of freight service of 40 per cent compared to 1919–20. Still greater savings were achieved by the substitution of diesel oil for coal. In 1955, railroad freight service consumed:

8,594,000 tons of coal = 225 trillion Btu

53,428,000 barrels of diesel oil = 305 trillion Btu

Since, per unit of freight service, diesel oil was utilized about 5.8 times as

[27] Since the energy inputs in this example include not just heat used directly, but all energy consumed in manufacturing and mining, the calculations indicate that the decline in the fuels used directly for heat (including some used for direct-drive mechanical power) has not been achieved through an offsetting increase in energy consumed in other forms, for example, as electricity. However, it would be incorrect to take this over-all saving in Btu's as a measure of increases in thermal efficiency, as such. The output of industry is heterogeneous, hence a decline in the input of energy relative to industrial output gives rise, although on a reduced scale, to the same problems of interpretation as the decline in the energy-GNP relationship. The result, which in the terminology of this study measures the increase in the economic efficiency of energy use, is a composite of increases in thermal efficiency, plus changes in structure, plus changes attributable to the complex of factors which have increased production relative to various input factors, and which go under the heading of "productivity increase."

efficiently as coal,[28] the above quantity replaced 1,766 trillion coal Btu, or 67,405,000 tons of bituminous coal. The difference between 1,766 trillion and the 305 trillion actually used in the form of diesel oil, amounts to 1,461 trillion Btu, or nearly 4 per cent of the aggregate 1955 energy consumption of the economy. Similar savings, but on a much smaller scale, were achieved in passenger service and in yard-switching service.

Thus, changes in the type of fuels consumed in railroad transportation from coal to diesel oil, in addition to accounting for a substantial portion of the decline in the "all other energy" category relative to GNP have, in thermal efficiency terms, played a part in the over-all decline of energy input relative to GNP. Significant improvements in thermal efficiency, and also in the economic efficiency of energy use in industry, through changes in the energy mix and in related equipment, have, as already indicated, also characterized heat consumption in industry, households, and commercial establishments, which together account for more than four-fifths of the category "all other energy."

Turning now from the "all other energy" category to the internal combustion fuels, the picture is far less clear. With the rapid growth in automotive transportation, the use of internal combustion fuels grew almost five times as much as GNP from 1920 to 1955. As for the thermal efficiency of motor vehicles, the available data do not permit anything approaching a firm measure to be derived. Under average use and load conditions the thermal efficiency of private automobiles is rather low, although presumably higher than that of coal-burning steam locomotives around 1920 (which to a certain extent they replaced). However, the thermal efficiency of the automobile is a matter of small significance compared with the changes that automotive vehicles have wrought in the American way of life, and, through these, on national productivity and the economic efficiency of energy use.

It is obvious that the rise of the automobile has brought about a new era of mobility, with increasing flexibility in the location of industry and population which must have had an important influence on the over-all productivity of the national economy. On the farm, too, the spreading use of internal combustion engines has served to multiply the productivity of U.S. agriculture. Automobiles have also tended to equalize urban and rural ways of life in important respects: to cite one example, in making possible consolidated schools, to which children travel by bus, and which offer a higher quality of instruction than the one-room rural schoolhouse of an earlier day. In some ways similar to the introduction of adequate artificial illumination in the nineteenth century, the automobile has added useful hours to the day by reducing the time needed to overcome the increasing distances between home, place of work, of shopping, education, and recreation. This greater mobility, however, has encouraged the growth of suburbanization and the dispersion of the population of metropolitan areas and increased the distances which must be covered in the routine of everyday living. In view of the

---

[28] Based on Interstate Commerce Commission statistics, which show that in 1955 railroads consumed 101 pounds of coal (equivalent to 1,323,000 Btu) per 1,000 gross ton-miles of road freight service, and 1.68 gallons of diesel fuel (228,480 Btu) to perform the same work.

complexity of the interrelationship between the growth of automotive transportation and national output, it would be quite unrealistic to evaluate the substantial increase in consumption of internal combustion fuels for automotive purposes in terms of thermal efficiencies alone. The net influence of automotive transportation on the acceleration in national productivity following World War I would, by itself, be the subject for another book.

The foregoing materials on the relationship between shifts in the energy consumption pattern by main categories and changes in the thermal and economic efficiency of energy use are only illustrative. Without doubt, improvements in thermal efficiency have been an important factor contributing to the decline in the energy input-GNP ratio in the post-World War I period; and the acceleration in the rate of increase in thermal efficiency in the present century, as compared to the nineteenth century, doubtless contributed to the change in the trend in the energy-GNP ratio experienced after the 1910–20 decade. Unfortunately, however, the information available at present does not provide a basis for measuring the impact of changes in thermal efficiency in the innumerable different applications of energy in a precise and substantiated manner. Even if such information were available it would explain only one aspect of the interconnection between energy utilization and the development of the national economy.

The Rise of Electricity. An adequate statistical record for electricity begins in 1902, although commercial production and distribution started some twenty years earlier. Even in 1902, when the first nation-wide census was taken, the figures on total electricity generated were based largely on estimates. In any event, the industry was young at the turn of the century, and its growth as a significant force in the economy is confined essentially to the subsequent period.

The rise of electricity is important among the factors underlying the behavior of the energy-GNP relationship for two main reasons: The efficiency with which fuels have been converted to electric energy has improved considerably during the past half century; and the application of electricity in production has grown rapidly. The latter is an aspect of the shifting composition of energy consumption, and in particular of the trend away from primary to secondary energy forms referred to earlier, but it merits special consideration because of its implications for the organization of industrial production.

The growth of electricity production between 1902 and 1955 is summarized in Table 60 and Figure 28, which also include for comparative purposes the data on total energy consumption presented earlier in this chapter. Both electricity generation and total energy consumption are shown also in index numbers, with 1902 as a base to indicate the comparative growth of the two series. The fact that electricity grew much more rapidly than total energy consumption is clearly evident; between 1902 and 1955 electricity's growth was over twenty times that of the total.

This rapidly growing element within the energy total was characterized by marked advances in thermal efficiency. In the generation of electricity, the amount of fuel required by thermal utility stations to produce one kilowatt hour declined from an average of 6.85 pounds of coal or coal equivalent in 1900, to

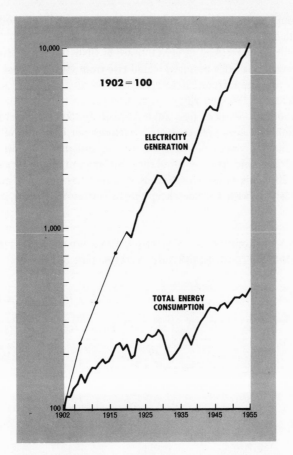

1902 = 100

ELECTRICITY
GENERATION

TOTAL ENERGY
CONSUMPTION

*Figure 28. Index of electricity generation and total energy consumption,
1902–55.*

3 pounds in 1920 and 0.95 pounds in 1955. This represents an increase in thermal
efficiency of more than seven times since 1900. What have been the effects of
this increase in efficiency on the energy-GNP relationship? Illustrative calculations
for the period 1920–55 are presented in the following paragraphs to throw light
on this question.

From 1920 to 1955, the Btu value of fuels actually burned to produce electric
power from steam (and a small amount by internal combustion) rose, expressed
in index numbers, from 100 to 412.5; the output of kilowatt hours produced from
these fuels grew from 100 to 1,357.[29] If the total U.S. electricity production were

[29] Btu's increased from 1,492 trillion to 6,155 trillion; kilowatt hours generated from fuels,
from 37,780 million to 512,774 million. (Btu's derived on the basis of the weighted average
of Btu's required per kilowatt hour in electric utilities and industrial generation: in 1920—
39,444 Btu; in 1955—12,003 Btu.)

treated as though it had all been thermally generated,[30] the corresponding data would show that by 1955 a 3.4 multiplication of the 1920 Btu's converted into electricity would have resulted in eleven times as many kilowatt hours as in 1920 (or in index numbers: Btu's required would rise from 100 in 1920 to 338 in 1955; kilowatt hours produced, from 100 to 1,112).[31]

Between 1920 and 1955, energy consumption per unit of gross national product dropped by about 35 per cent (see Table 52, column 5). Assume, however, that the consumption of energy for nonelectric purposes per unit of GNP had declined to the extent that it actually did over this period, but that the electricity actually produced in 1955 would have required the same amount of fuel Btu's per kilowatt hour as in 1920. This is the situation as it would have been if everything had developed as it did, with the one exception of no improvements in the thermal

TABLE 60. GENERATION OF ELECTRICITY COMPARED WITH TOTAL ENERGY CONSUMPTION, SELECTED YEARS, 1902-55

Year	Electricity		Total energy consumption (mineral fuels and hydropower)	
	Million kilowatt hours (1)	Index (1902 = 100) (2)	Trillion Btu (3)	Index (1902 = 100) (4)
1902.......	5,969	100	8,715	100
1907.......	14,121	237	13,831	159
1912.......	24,752	415	15,708	180
1917.......	43,429	728	19,597	225
1920.......	56,559	948	19,768	227
1925.......	84,666	1,418	20,878	240
1930.......	114,637	1,921	22,253	255
1935.......	118,935	1,993	19,059	219
1940.......	179,907	3,014	23,877	274
1945.......	271,255	4,544	31,439	361
1950.......	388,674	6,512	33,972	390
1955.......	629,010	10,538	39,729	456

SOURCES: Column 1, figures for 1902-17: *Census of Electric Light and Power Statistics* as quoted in U.S. Bureau of the Census, *Historical Statistics of the United States, 1789-1945* (Washington, D. C.: U.S. Government Printing Office), Series G 171. 1920-55 based on Federal Power Commission, *Production of Electric Energy and Capacity of Generating Plants* as quoted in Edison Electric Institute, "Electric Utility Industry in the United States," *Statistical Bulletin for the Year 1957* (New York: 1958), p. 13. Excludes small net imports of hydro, which are included in the electricity consumption shown in Table 58. Column 3 from Appendix Table VII.

[30] Hydroelectricity constituted the following percentages of total electricity generated:

1920.........33.2%		1940.........27.8%	
1925.........30.1		1945.........31.2	
1930.........31.3		1950.........26.0	
1935.........35.9		1955.........18.5	

[31] Differs from the index numbers shown in Table 58 because above figures do not include small net imports of hydro.

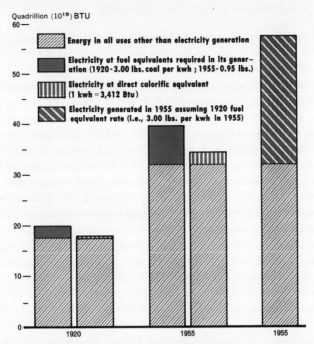

Figure 29. The effect of changes in the thermal efficiency of electricity generation on the measurement of total energy consumption, 1920 and 1955.

efficiency of converting primary energy sources into electricity.[32] Under this assumption (again treating the total electricity production, including hydro, as if it had been thermally generated) the consumption of energy in 1955 and its relation to the expansion of the economy as a whole since 1920 would have been the following (see Figure 29):

Item	1955 consumption of energy (trillion Btu)
Energy in all uses other than electricity generation, actual consumption (excl. wood)	32,179
Electricity, kilowatt hours actually produced in 1955 at 1920 fuel equivalent required per kwh	24,811 [a]
Total	56,990
Index of energy input per unit of GNP (1920 = 100)	92.6

[a] Fuel or fuel equivalents actually required for the total electricity generation in 1955 amounted to 7,550 trillion Btu.

The drop in the energy input-GNP ratio would then have been only about 7.5 per cent, instead of the actual decline of about 35 per cent. This would seem to indicate that almost all of the decline in the ratio of energy consumption to the output of the economy as a whole during the post-World War I period may be

[32] It is, of course, clear that in the absence of these improvements in thermal efficiency the cost of electricity would have been higher and, consequently, the growth of electric power consumption would not have been as great as it actually was.

explained by improvements in the thermal efficiency of generating electricity.

But there is another side to the picture. In spite of the large gains in the efficiency of transforming primary fuels into electric power, some 0.95 pounds of coal or 12,000 Btu were required in 1955 to produce one kilowatt hour which has an inherent energy content of 3,412 Btu.[33] Some 72 per cent of the raw Btu input was lost in the conversion process and never entered the economy beyond the energy sector proper. Since the electric power ultimately utilized in the production of goods and services does not consist of the changing Btu equivalents of the fuels required to generate it, but of actual kilowatt hours, it may be just as reasonable to measure the production and consumption of electricity by the constant inherent Btu value of the kilowatt hour. This is the practice in some countries, in which electricity obtained from waterpower is a significant component of total energy; it is also the approach used in the United Nations publications dealing with energy. (While production of energy is measured in UN statistics by the full, inherent Btu—or calorific—values of the primary energy materials, their consumption statistics generally count all electricity, including that generated from fuels, at its actual Btu equivalent of 3,412 Btu per kilowatt hour.) Using this basis of measurement, the aggregate energy input per unit of GNP dropped by nearly two-fifths between 1920 and 1955—which is not far from the total decline of 35 per cent derived above. The reason for this is that no matter which method of measurement is used, the Btu's of electric energy constitute a comparatively small percentage of the energy total, so that the aggregate is dominated by the movement of the Btu's of energy consumed for nonelectric purposes, as shown in the following figures:

Item	Energy consumption (trillion Btu)	
	1920	1955
1. Including electricity at direct calorific equivalent:		
Energy in all uses other than electricity generation (excl. wood)..	17,535	32,179
Electricity (kilowatt hours generated at 3,412 Btu)............	193	2,146
Total...	17,728	34,325
1955 index of Btu input per unit of GNP (1920 = 100)........		62.2
2. Including electricity at fuel equivalents required in its generation:		
Energy in all uses other than electricity generation (excl. wood).	17,535	32,179
Electricity (fuel equivalent required in its generation at the prevailing conversion rate).............................	2,233	7,550
Total...	19,768	39,729
1955 index of Btu input per unit of GNP (1920 = 100)........		64.5

[33] Electric utilities tend to burn a type of coal with a somewhat lower Btu content than the average for all coal. A comparison of Btu's (heat rate) and pounds of coal (fuel rate) required on the average by electric utilities to produce one kilowatt hour indicates a Btu content of 12,263 per pound in 1955 as compared to the average value for all coal of 13,100 Btu per pound.

Thus, one is again confronted with the phenomenon for which an explanation was attempted, namely, that the amount of energy (measured in Btu's) actually available to be utilized decreased by some 38 per cent relative to the over-all performance of the economy.[34] Consistent with the calculations just presented, the following hypothesis may be advanced to explain this phenomenon. Despite the comparatively small share of electricity in Btu terms, the relative growth of electric power may still be important in explaining the decline in the energy-GNP ratio after 1920, if (1) electricity has been substituting for other energy sources in a manner in which Btu's in the form of electricity replace substantially greater numbers of nonelectric Btu's; and (2) the use of electricity permits industrial production to be organized more efficiently, thereby increasing over-all economic productivity, which is reflected in a rising trend of national output relative to all input factors including raw energy consumed. Some data bearing on this hypothesis are presented in the following paragraphs.

The first thing to examine is the growth of electricity relative to the growth of total energy consumption. As noted earlier, over the entire period covered by the statistics, electricity has grown substantially faster than all energy. If the record is examined in terms of the periods of rise and decline in the total energy-GNP relationship, the following pattern is found:

Item	Rising energy–GNP ratio: 1920 index (1902 = 100)	Declining energy–GNP ratio: 1955 index (1920 = 100)
Consumption of all energy (Btu's).......	226.8	201.0
Electricity generated (kwh).............	947.5	1,112.1
Ratio of growth in electricity generation to growth of total energy consumption.	4.2	5.5

Thus, electricity grew faster relative to all energy in the period when the over-all ratio of energy to GNP declined than it had in the period when the ratio rose.

More significant than the general increase in the relative importance of electricity in the later period was its increasing use in manufacturing operations. Tables 61 and 62 provide the relevant data. The first of these tables deals with capital input in manufacturing and with horsepower per unit of capital. It shows a steep increase in capital input relative to manufacturing output between 1879 and 1919, and a sharp decline between 1919 and 1953. However, this up and down movement of capital in its relation to manufacturing output was connected with an opposite movement in horsepower installed per unit of capital, which declined between 1879 and 1919 and rose between 1919 and 1953, so that at the end of the period there was more than twice as much horsepower installed per unit of capital as in 1919.[35]

---

[34]It should be noted that in the above calculations energy other than for electricity generation is measured before conversion into heat or power ultimately utilized. Thus, changes in the thermal efficiency outside of the electricity sector are not taken into account.

[35] There is a striking similarity in the long-run pattern between energy consumption per unit of *national* output and capital input per unit of *manufacturing* output. At first glance, the parallel movement suggests a connection between the two based on the fact that capital

Against the background provided in Table 61, the rapid growth in the electrification of industry is striking. This is depicted in Table 62 and Figure 30, which show the horsepower of electric motors in relation to total mechanical horsepower used in manufacturing. Since 1899, there has been a rise in the relative importance of electric motors from 5 per cent of total manufacturing horsepower to between 85 per cent and 90 per cent in recent years. By 1909, electric motors constituted one-quarter of all manufacturing horsepower; between 1909 and 1919, their relative importance grew to more than one-half; and, from 1919 to 1939, the horsepower of electric motors had grown to about 90 per cent of total horsepower. Thus, the growth in the relative importance of electric motors was concentrated in the period between 1910 and 1939.

The dominant position achieved by electric motors in manufacturing is a factor of prime importance for several reasons. First, it is apparent that the relatively small share in total energy consumption of Btu's in the form of electricity is a poor guide to the importance of electrical machinery in the industrial sector of the economy.

In addition, the shift from other sources of power—mainly steam—to electric energy involves the substitution of a more efficient source of power in the sense that a larger percentage of the energy consumed in the factory is converted into mechanical work. The over-all thermal efficiency of a system of machines within a factory, belt-driven by a steam-powered prime mover, was less than 10 per cent,[36] whereas with the electric motor mounted on the machine, some 70 to 90 per cent of the power may be effectively transmitted from the plant substation to the machine.[37] Thus, in thermal efficiency terms, an "electric Btu" can be considered as worth several times as much as a Btu formerly used for steam-based mechanical power in manufacturing. But perhaps more important, with the individual electric motor drive each machine requires an energy supply only

---

equipment is the instrumentality for applying energy in production. However, the counter pattern of horsepower per unit of capital, and the movement of horsepower per unit of manufacturing output (see Table 56) indicates that the relationship between the movement of capital input in manufacturing and energy input in the total economy is far more complex.

However, it seems plausible to advance the hypothesis that the increasing efficiency in capital in the manufacturing sector in the post-World War I period was connected with the increase (and the change in composition) in energy-using equipment for mechanical work (horsepower installed) to more than twice the 1919 level per unit of capital.

[36] Assuming the efficiency of the average stationary steam engine to be in the neighborhood of 15 per cent and losses in the belt-drive system of roughly 50 per cent. For discussions of comparative efficiencies at the time of transition, see: A. D. DuBois, "Will It Pay to Electrify the Shops?" *Industrial Engineering and The Engineering Digest*, Vol. XI, No. 1 (January 1912), pp. 6–7; A. P. Haslam, *Electricity in Factories and Workshops* (London: Lockwood, 1909), p. 9; and D. C. Jackson, "The Applicability of Electrical Power to Industrial Establishments," *Transactions*, American Institute of Electrical Engineers, Vol. XXIX, Part I (February 16, 1910), pp. 111–12.

[37] Further losses between the utility central station and the plant substation would range up to 10 per cent. The figures in this whole comparison are merely illustrative. The number of variables and their wide ranges preclude the use of a statistical average as representative of the two sets of conditions.

TABLE 61. CAPITAL INPUT PER UNIT OF OUTPUT AND HORSEPOWER RATING OF INSTALLED EQUIPMENT PER UNIT OF CAPITAL IN MANUFACTURING, SELECTED YEARS, 1879–1953

Year	Capital input (1)	Capital input per unit of output (2)	Horsepower installed per unit of capital (3)
Index numbers (1899 = 100):			
1879	25.9	69.8	134.4
1889	60.1	90.3	100.7
1899	100.0	100.0	100.0
1909	185.7	117.7	99.1
1919	317.1	142.9	91.3
1929	341.3	93.9	122.8
1937	291.5	77.6	174.4
1953	524.6	59.3	210.5
Percentage changes:			
1879–1919	+1,124%	+105%	−32%
1919–53	+65	−59	+131

SOURCES: Columns 1 and 2 from John W. Kendrick, *Productivity Trends in the United States* (New York: National Bureau of Economic Research, forthcoming), shifted to 1899 = 100. Column 3 is based on horsepower figures shown in Table 56. Capital figures are available for 1937 and 1953, while horsepower figures are available for 1939 and 1954. Hence, the ratios shown for 1937 and 1953 were derived by applying the horsepower figures for 1939 and 1954 to the capital figures for 1937 and 1953.

TABLE 62. ELECTRIC MOTOR USE IN RELATION TO TOTAL MECHANICAL HORSEPOWER IN MANUFACTURING, SELECTED YEARS, 1899–1954

Year	Total horsepower (thousand) (1)	Electric motors[a] (thousand hp) (2)	Electric motors as per cent of total horsepower (3)
1899	9,811	475	4.8%
1904	13,033	1,517	11.6
1909	18,062	4,582	25.4
1914	21,565	8,392	38.9
1919	28,397	15,612	55.0
1925	34,359	25,092	73.0
1929	41,122	33,844	82.3
1939	49,893	44,827	89.8
1954	108,362	91,821	84.7

[a] Represents electric motors driven by purchased electricity and by electric power generated at the establishment.

SOURCE: U.S. Bureau of the Census, *U.S. Census of Manufactures: 1954*, Vol. I (Washington, D. C.: U.S. Government Printing Office, 1957), p. 207–2, Table 1.

when it is being used; in the old mechanical drive, shafts and belting (miles of such apparatus in a large establishment) were idling continuously between periods of use. Clearly, a large decline in "steam Btu's" could have been achieved through a much smaller increase in the use of "electric Btu's."

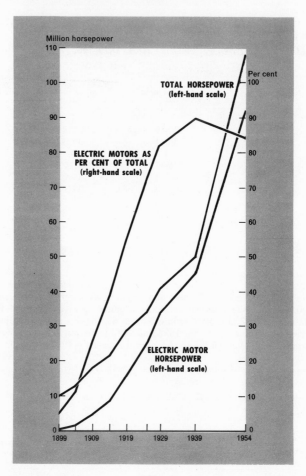

Figure 30. Electric motor use in relation to total mechanical horsepower in manufacturing, 1899–1954.

Finally, the growing use of electric motors in manufacturing and the improvements in electrical control equipment brought with them a flexibility in industrial operations previously impossible to achieve. Before the advent of the electric motor, mechanical power, where needed, had to be obtained from the single prime mover in the plant no matter how small the needs might be. Manufacturing operations thus had to be designed to accommodate the location of the machines to that of the prime mover (the larger power demands had to be established close to the prime mover) rather than to the sequence of the production process. The introduction of the unit drive, in which each machine has its own motor or motors, changed all this: power was available in completely flexible form, and could be distributed throughout the factory in accord with other criteria of efficient organization and with very little energy loss between the plant substation and the machine.

It seems probable, therefore, that the greatest impact of electricity on the efficiency of industrial operations was achieved not as a result of the replacement of Btu's which were less efficient thermally by more efficient ones, but in terms of electricity's impact on the total economics of industrial operations. The release from the restrictions of internal mechanical energy transmission systems opened up wholly new possibilities for applying modern techniques of industrial and business management. It is, therefore, not farfetched to speculate that the marked acceleration in the increase in labor and capital productivity after World War I is attributable in some degree to the new methods of organizing production made possible through the growing electrification of industrial operations.[38]

All of the foregoing seem to support the hypothesis stated earlier: that despite the comparatively small share of Btu's consumed in the form of electricity, even in recent years, the rise of electricity may be a factor of considerable importance in explaining the decline in the energy-GNP ratio since the end of World War I.

. . .

Summary

Since a good deal of ground has been traversed in the foregoing discussion of the historical relationship between energy consumption and gross national product, a summary of the findings may be useful. The statistics examined reveal a persistent increase in energy consumption relative to GNP between 1880 and 1910, comparative stability between 1910 and 1920, and a persistent decline between 1920 and 1955.

Two groups of explanatory factors were examined: changes in the total economy and changes in the energy economy. The former include structural changes in total output and over-all changes in efficiency reflected in productivity increases; the latter include changes in thermal efficiency, shifts among energy sources, and the rise of electricity.

Structural changes in the direction of the increasing importance of the industrial sector were found to be a continuing trend during the entire historical period.

[38] Tables 61 and 62 provide a direct basis for believing that the increase in capital productivity in manufacturing following the first World War is tied to the growth in the electrification of manufacturing.

As a separate point, the purchase of electricity from central stations also affects the long-term comparability of the statistics of capital in manufacturing. In the early days, there was no separation between the prime mover and the factory. The steam-generating equipment and even the early electric generator were part of the capital equipment of the manufacturing industries, and so counted. Some time in the 1920's a turning point was reached. By 1929, the power equipment consisted of 82 per cent of electric motors and, of these, only 36 per cent were driven by self-produced power. Of all installed horsepower (including prime movers), 53 per cent were powered by purchased electricity. In 1954, only one-third of the total power equipment was driven by self-produced electricity, diesel engines or other prime movers. The manufacturing plants had ceased to be their own power plants, a basic change from the early days, which contributed to the relative decline of manufacturing capital, compared to output.

However, the relative importance of industry and also its mechanization per unit of output grew faster before 1920 than after. General productivity increases in the economy yielding greater national output in relation to the input of labor and capital—which, by the same token, should increase national output relative to gross energy input—were found to be a persistent factor, but growing faster after 1920 than before. Increases in thermal efficiency of energy utilization were at work throughout the entire period examined, but were stronger in the twentieth century than in the second half of the nineteenth. The rise of electricity—which was found to involve major increases in thermal efficiency and, more important, was probably a significant factor in increasing the over-all productivity of the economy—is confined to the twentieth century, with an acceleration in the period following World War I.

Changing economic structure in the direction of greater industrialization and mechanization in terms of rated horsepower equipment compared to output, which should lead to greater energy consumption per unit of national product, was apparently a dominant factor at work in the period until about World War I. Following 1920, changing economic structure still worked in the same direction, but with greatly reduced force. The other factors examined—changing composition of the energy aggregate, faster increases in thermal efficiency of energy utilization, the impact of electrification, and the acceleration in the rise of over-all economic productivity—all of which worked on balance in the direction of less energy input per unit of national output, were dominant.

The above explanations are hypotheses which appear to fit the facts which have been examined. More research and analysis are needed on all aspects of the complex relationship between energy use and economic growth.

PART II

The future of energy consumption

CHAPTER 5

Concepts, scope, and method in estimating future energy consumption

The focus of attention now shifts from past developments to future prospects. The main purpose of Part II is to provide estimates, for the year 1975, of total energy consumption as well as of the individual energy sources which will constitute the total. These consumption estimates, with the supporting statistical materials given in the Appendix to Part II, are meant to be matched against the estimated availability of energy sources analyzed in Part III, in order to throw light on the following basic question:

Will the supply of energy pose difficulties to the realization of a high future growth rate for the American economy or any part of it?

Two factors have been instrumental in fashioning the approach taken here in estimating future consumption.

1) *The over-all economic assumptions* within which the analysis is conducted were determined by the basic objective of testing the *adequacy* of resources. Therefore, over-all economic growth rates have been assumed which are on the high side in order to test supply availability against requirements which are meant to be at the high end of a range of reasonable possibilities. In addition, the consumption estimates are based on the assumption that the *real price* of each of the energy sources will remain essentially unchanged between 1955 and 1975. This is equivalent to assuming (a) that the average price of all energy sources together does not change significantly relative to the general price level, and (b) that the price relationships among the different energy sources remain essentially unchanged. Adequacy of resources is, therefore, tested against demand conditions

193

assuming no relative price increases for any of the energy sources.[1] This approach is one of methodology; it in no way represents a forecast of either what is most likely to happen or what is most desirable. It is chosen to examine whether demand, under the assumption of constant price, will be satisfied by supply, under the parallel assumption of constant cost.

2) *The basic methodology employed* in making the consumption estimates was determined by certain lessons learned in the historical analysis of energy use; in particular, that past consumption has not been related in a simple way to over-all economic aggregates such as population or gross national product (GNP), nor has it grown at a regular rate. It was felt, moreover, that only the development of a detailed statistical statement of energy consumption would lend itself to a projection containing the explanation of the change in the aggregate, and thus one that could be regarded with a substantial measure of confidence. Hence, although the analysis begins with assumptions about the future growth of population and GNP, the heart of the projection method lies in the estimation of future energy consumption in specific energy-consuming activities—many of which, in one way or another, are of course related to either population or GNP. This methodological requirement accounts for the size of the Appendix to Part II in which the statistics bearing on particular energy-consuming activities are assembled, analyzed, and applied to the estimation of future consumption.

The consumption estimates derived for the total and for specific energy sources may be described briefly in the following terms: They are the sum of a large number of separately, though not always independently, computed partial estimates for different economic sectors and activities made against the background of what is meant to be a high, but not unreasonable, over-all rate of American economic growth.

OVER-ALL ECONOMIC ASSUMPTIONS

Gross National Product

The over-all economic assumptions here employed were selected following the examination of various projections of GNP and its determinants such as the size of the labor force, annual average hours of work, and output per man-hour. For purposes of this analysis, a growth of GNP for the period 1955–75 at the rate of 4 per cent compounded annually was deemed justifiable.

[1] As indicated later, the future consumption of energy is estimated from the past and present pattern of consumption as modified by the estimated growth of the economy as a whole, its pertinent parts, and technological change. To the extent that these estimates of the future are influenced by the examination of past trends of fuel consumption (and many of them are) they will, of course, partly mirror the effects of past price movements. Unfortunately, this cannot be avoided.

Although the rate of 4 per cent is considerably higher than growth rates that have prevailed in other twenty-year periods in the United States, it has been exceeded in the past for as long as a decade—for example, from 1940 to 1950. Of the projections of GNP to 1975 made by others, most tend to approach rates between 3.25 per cent and 4 per cent per year. The growth rate of 4 per cent chosen here thus is at the upper end of a band of growth rates within which it is difficult to select that most likely to take place, but not so difficult to select the one most appropriate for use in comparing the estimate of energy needs to that for energy availability in 1975. Such a comparison helps determine whether availability of energy sources may constitute a significant obstacle to the development of the economy at a reasonably high rate of growth. As the selection of a rate of growth of future economic development necessarily involves judgment and arbitrariness, the purpose of the study makes it appropriate to err on the high rather than on the low side. In this way, the projection, to the extent that it is linked—both directly and indirectly—to the expected change in GNP, is more likely to reveal possible stringencies in the supply of one or more sources of energy.

The 1975 GNP based on a growth rate of 4 per cent is $857 billion (in 1955 dollars), or about two and one-quarter times the size of the 1955 GNP. In absolute terms, this represents an unprecedented expansion. On the basis of the population assumption discussed below and stipulating no increase in GNP per capita, the 1975 GNP would rise to $552 billion. The difference of roughly $300 billion between the two levels of GNP constitutes the margin of progress in the two decades. It is an impressive margin, equivalent to an improvement in per capita GNP over the two decades of more than 55 per cent.

Appendix Table I-1 presents the underlying factors which could support a growth rate of 4 per cent. These figures show that the realization of a rate of 4 per cent does not require any extraordinary combinations of high labor force participation, drastic slowdown in the shortening of the work week, or an unusually high increase in the rate of output per man-hour.

However, the figures put together in Appendix Table I-1 are only one of the combinations of labor force, hours of work, and productivity which may be postulated to support a GNP growth rate of 4 per cent. Other combinations have not been shown; instead, the material has been limited to a demonstration that the combined values underlying such a development are not unreasonable. Although the estimated growth rate is designed to be on the high side, this should not be taken to mean that even higher rates of growth would be impossible to achieve.

. . .

Population

The 1975 population assumed for this study is 233 million, implying a population compound growth in the two decades following 1955 of 1.7 per cent per year. This is the same rate that prevailed between 1950 and 1955, but one that has not been sustained (disregarding immigration) for as long as twenty years since the beginning of the century.

This population estimate was made at a time when the highest 1975 population estimate of the Census Bureau[2] came to 228.5 million. Thus, the estimate of 233 million used here exceeded by 4.5 million the highest estimate which had so far been made by the Census Bureau. In 1958,[3] the Census Bureau released later population estimates in which the high estimate for 1975 was 243.9 million, which exceeds the figure used in this study by almost 11 million. The next to the highest Census estimate was 235.2 million, which exceeds the figure used here by only 2.2 million. The great majority of the calculations made in this study had been completed by the time the new estimates became available, and it therefore proved impractical to incorporate an estimate based upon these later Census projections.

Nevertheless it is worth considering the implication of the Census revisions for the estimates of energy consumption derived in this study. The Census high estimate of 1955 was revised upward by us to adjust for what were judged to be conservative life-expectancy assumptions. Thus, our revision of the earlier Census figures applied to that segment of the total population which through its participation in the labor force and through its formation of households directly affects the level of energy-consuming activities. In its 1958 revisions, the Census Bureau also revised upward its previous life-expectancy assumptions, but in its highest estimate it also assumed a considerably higher fertility rate than in its 1955 report. For its highest estimate, the Census report comments that the fertility assumption "represents a gross reproduction rate that has not been attained since the beginning of this century, and which is not expected to be sustained over any length of time."[4]

In thus describing its highest estimate, the Census Bureau would seem to be casting substantial doubt on its reasonableness as a basis for assessing probable future population developments. However, quite apart from the reasonableness of the estimates, the fact that high fertility assumptions are basic to the high estimate is reflected in the resulting age breakdown of the estimated 1975 population. A comparison of the Census Bureau's highest 1975 estimate (243.9 million) with its second highest (235.2 million) in terms of age composition reveals that for the segment of the population eighteen years of age and over the two are identical (and this segment is identical also for the lowest two of the Bureau's four population estimates for 1975); and for the segment fourteen years of age and over they differ by a little over a million. The estimate of 233 million used in this analysis of future energy consumption is close to the Census Bureau's second highest figure. Thus, it is evident from the above comparisons that the age segments of the population which most markedly affect energy consumption, through participation in the labor force and through the formation of households, would

[2] U.S. Bureau of the Census, *Current Population Report*, Series P-25, No. 123, October 20, 1955, Washington, D. C.

[3] *Ibid.*, No. 187, November 10, 1958.

[4] *Ibid.*, p. 2.

have been altered only slightly if the highest Census population estimates had been used. Also, an indication that the population estimate of 233 million is on the high side—as it is intended to be—is found in a bulletin issued subsequently to the release of the revised Census projections which states: "The population of the United States will probably reach about 226 million by 1975."[5]

Returning now to the derivation of the population estimate used in this study, the initial step was to examine the 1955 Census projections available at the time. These are shown, together with other population projections, in Appendix Table I-2. Since the 1975 life-expectancy assumption in the highest available 1955 Census projection had already been reached in 1956, to use that high would have implied no increases in life expectancy after 1956.[6] The increase of 4.5 million used in this study over the then current Census highest estimate of the 1975 population allowed only for anticipated increases in life expectancy. As noted, the existing Census assumption regarding future fertility was left untouched. Similarly, no changes were made in the Census assumptions regarding immigration in the period 1955–75, although it is entirely possible that increases in immigration above the level stipulated by the Census Bureau could occur. For either of the two reasons, the ultimate population might be higher than 233 million, although increases arising from higher fertility assumptions would barely have affected the estimates of energy consumption.

Population forecasting, needless to say, is far from being an exact science. The purpose in presenting examples of population forecasts made during the last twenty years in Appendix Table I-2 is not to point out the failings of experts. Rather, it is to illustrate the point that even in the field of demography—which

[5] U.S. Bureau of the Census, *Population and Labor Force Projections for the United States, 1960 to 1975,* Bulletin No. 1242 (Washington, D. C.: U.S. Government Printing Office, June 1959).

[6] This fact was noted by Conrad Taeuber, a leading demographer and Assistant Director of the Census Bureau. "Since the assumed ultimate levels [of life expectancy for 1975] were reached in 1956, this has the effect of continuing the 1956 levels unchanged until 1975. This may be unrealistic, and it now seems that by 1970–1975 the expectation of life may have been increased by 4 to 6 years over the level used in the published projections. It is now expected that the Bureau's next revisions of its projections will take into account further reductions in mortality. . . ." See Conrad Taeuber, "The Census Bureau Projections of the Size, and the Age and Sex Composition of the Population of the United States in 1975." Chapter 9 in *Applications of Demography; The Population Situation in the U.S. in 1975,* Donald J. Bogue, ed. (Chicago: Scripps Foundation for Research in Population Problems, Miami University, and Population Training Center, University of Chicago, 1957), p. 54.

Another leading demographer, Pascal K. Whelpton, expressed similar doubts and translated them into quantitative terms. He estimated that the increase in life expectancy would reduce deaths between 1955 and 1975 by about 5 million and that the population living at that time would be larger by slightly more than 5 million because of children born to those living longer. See Whelpton, "Census Projections: Some Areas of Doubt," *Conference Board Business Record* (published by the National Industrial Conference Board, Inc., New York), Vol. 13, No. 8 (August 1956), pp. 365-69.

works with data that have accumulated over long periods and operates in the field of biology as much as in the field of social science—projections have not in the past, even at relatively short range, been borne out by succeeding events.

. . .

Number of Households

Household numbers are important for projecting future energy consumption because they are the starting point for estimating residential consumption of energy. As in population, the projection of the number of households began with Census Bureau estimates. Here again, the highest available Census figure was selected as the point of origin.[7] This figure was adjusted upward for two reasons: First, the highest household projection made by the Census Bureau is not based on its highest population estimate. Second, the household figure had to be adjusted to conform with the higher population estimate of 233 million projected in this study for 1975. As a result, the number of households used here was raised from the top Census Bureau projection of 67,378,000 to 68,878,000 (or by 1.5 million), of which 56,162,000 would be family households and 12,716,000 primary individual households.

Substituting the top Census population projection for the one used in the Census household projections would not affect the number of households by more than 100,000 since the large difference in the two population estimates—6.9 million—is caused by different fertility assumptions. It thus affects the group up to twenty years of age which would influence the size, but hardly the number, of households. The difference of 4.5 million between the highest Census population estimate and the 233-million estimate results principally from the lower mortality assumed in this study. It thus affects the number of households. Indeed, because of age structure (including large numbers of surviving widows and widowers), the estimate used in this study must result especially in a large increase in individual households. That is why it has been assumed that of the total increase, beyond the Census projection, of 1.5 million households (one household every three persons—or slightly fewer persons per household than in the Census projection, due to the larger number of individual households), two-thirds will go to swell the number of individual households and the balance of half a million to family households. Since consumption of household energy must be assumed to be substantially smaller for individual than for family households, the distinction is important not only qualitatively, but quantitatively (see especially Appendix Tables C-17 and C-38).

Appendix Tables I-3 through I-6 furnish some background material for the household projection, limited wholly to the Census projections themselves. Table I-3 shows the important role played by individual households in the growth of all

---

[7] The Census Bureau's latest available household estimates are themselves based on the Bureau's population projection of 1955. In addition, the Census Bureau itself relied entirely on the second-highest of the four population projections contained in the 1955 report for all of its four household projections.

households by 1975 and in the degree of uncertainty surrounding this figure. Almost two-thirds of the range between the lowest and the highest estimate results from differences in the assumptions regarding individual households, and in all projections individual households increase faster than do family-type households. This tendency is brought out for the past as well as the future in Table I-4, which demonstrates the growing significance of individuals in household formation. Table I-5 shows one of the causes: the growing tendency for unrelated individuals to establish households.[8]

A smaller contribution to the growth in households is depicted in Appendix Table I-6 which shows the "undoubling" of families in the past and the increase in this development in the future. It signifies that increases in households are not caused by family formation, but rather by establishment of separate households by previously doubled-up families. According to the Census Bureau, this movement, by 1975, will have practically reached its ultimate conclusion in the elimination of all doubled-up households.

·   ·   ·

Labor Force, Work Hours, and Productivity

Census Bureau estimates also were the starting point for the estimate of labor force used in this analysis. Since the latest available Census figures are based on the Bureau's 1955 population estimates, and in addition, are related to the second highest of the four population estimates made, the Census labor-force estimates had to be adjusted to bring them into accord with the highest Census population estimate, and the upward revision of that figure used in this study.

Appendix Table I-8 is a summary guide to the basic Census materials.[9] The average of the four labor-force projections, none of which seems to have features that would make it preferable over the others, is 92.1 million. Use of the highest Census population estimate, because its increases are essentially in the low-age groups, would add no more than perhaps 600,000 people to the labor force. But the 4.5 million people added by this study's adjustment of the top Census projection would be largely in high-age brackets. For them, a labor participation rate of 45 per cent is assumed, or about one-quarter below the average (roughly 60 per cent) in both 1955 and 1975. The resulting adjusted labor force is 94.7 million.

The last missing elements among the basic economic determinants of GNP are hours of work and output per man-hours. Hours of work is one of the dimensions in which the labor market resolves the forces of supply and demand. In line with

---

[8] Individual households, in technical language termed "primary individual households," are defined as those households formed by household heads living alone or with nonrelatives only. Actually, most of these households consist of single individuals; in 1955 the 6,075,000 households of this type contained some 7 million individuals, or an average of less than 1.2 per household.

[9] Appendix Table I-7 has been included as relevant background material because it illustrates the tendency to underestimate the future labor force, even on the part of an outstanding authority.

other projections, it was assumed that hours of work would decrease, and the decrease was set at 10 per cent. By 1975, this would correspond to 1,872 hours per year for each person in the labor force. Appendix Table I-9 summarizes the underlying calculations.

Average output per man-hour has been assumed to increase at the rate of 2.75 per cent per year for the 1955–75 period. Although this rate of increase is sub-, stantially above that of some of the longer periods in the past, the general tendency has been for the rate of output per man-hour to increase more rapidly in the more recent past.[10] For example, while the output per man-hour increased at the rate of just over 2.5 per cent per year between 1910 and 1956, the rates have tended to rise in successive periods. During the 1910–19 period, output per man-hour increased at the rate of 0.7 per cent, while in the following twenty years, from 1919 to 1939, the rate of increase was fairly uniform for each of the decades, with increases at the rate of 2.5 per cent per year. In 1939–46, the rate of increase dropped to 2.2 per cent. Finally, for 1947–56, the rate of increase was at 3 per cent per year.

The way in which output per man-hour behaves is obviously a crucial question. Various important projections in the past have tended to use increases in output per man-hour at 2.5 per cent per year—for example, the report of the President's Materials Policy Commission (PMPC)[11] and the staff study for the Joint Committee on the Economic Report.[12] Nonetheless, in the light of the historical record and the purpose of this undertaking (to produce estimates of energy consumption which are on the high side in order to ascertain whether energy sources may be an important limiting factor), the 2.75 per cent rate represents a reasonable assumption. It is worth repeating at this point that other combinations of the underlying factors would equally satisfy the GNP annual growth rate of 4 per cent. A growth of only 2.5 per cent in productivity might be combined, for example, with an increase in labor input of 1.5 per cent, derived from a labor force nearer 100 million instead of 94.7 million as here assumed, or by a lesser reduction in weekly hours. None of these assumptions is beyond reasonable likelihood.

GENERAL DESCRIPTION OF SCOPE AND METHOD

Energy Sources Covered

The projection encompasses what may be termed the modern conventional sources of energy: coal, oil, natural gas, natural gas liquids, and hydropower.

---

[10] The subsequent data appear in *Productivity, Prices and Income*, materials prepared for the Joint Economic Committee, Congress of the United States, by the Committee staff. (Washington, D. C.: U.S. Government Printing Office, 1957), p. 22.

[11] President's Materials Policy Commission (PMPC), *Resources for Freedom*, Vol. II (Washington, D. C.: U.S. Government Printing Office, 1952), p. 111.

[12] *The Potential Economic Growth of U.S. During the Next Decade*, materials prepared for the Joint Committee on the Economic Report by the committee staff (Washington, D. C.: U.S. Government Printing Office, 1954), p. 21.

Because of its quantitative importance and its rapid rate of growth, electricity is treated as a separate factor, but the energy sources estimated to be used in generating electricity are also included with the particular fuels in deriving their total estimated consumption in 1975.

Since the energy sources discussed are substitutable over a wide range of uses, their projection has been undertaken on a simultaneous basis, and they are so discussed in this and subsequent chapters. This approach has the added advantage that it keeps the projection of any one of the energy sources from claiming an undue share of the expected growth in the national demand for energy, a defect that tends to afflict projections of demand for individual energy sources.

Perfect technical substitutability is realized perhaps to the greatest extent in the production of heat, both in homes and in industry, and in electric power generation in which all of the fuels, as well as falling water, can be used to generate an identical final product. (It is for this reason that hydropower can be easily fitted into the total energy picture in fuel terms, even though it is the only nonfuel source of conventional energy considered.) Elsewhere in energy consumption, substitutability is more limited, perhaps the most extreme case being the present need for liquid fuels in automotive transportation. However, the distinguishing features of each fuel which limit its usefulness in certain fields of application and enhance its usefulness in others are the continuing subjects of investigation and change, with technological progress enhancing the technical feasibility of substitution. For example, the future may see the large-scale economic conversion of solid fuels to liquid and gaseous forms, thus allowing coal to replace oil and natural gas in uses in which the latter sources are now preferred. In addition, the economic limits of substitutability may be enlarged by such developments as the use of water transportation for natural gas (see Chapter 10) and the extension of pipeline transportation—now limited to oil and gas—to coal (see Chapter 8).

Energy applications do not exhaust the uses to which fuel materials are put. Such products as petroleum coke, used in electric furnace electrodes; asphalt for road paving; carbon black for manufacturing rubber tires; and the ever-widening list of the so-called petrochemicals, comprising the plastics, cleaning agents, pharmaceuticals, and insecticides; to name only a few—all have their origin in one or the other of the hydrocarbon family of fuels. No attempt has been made to exclude these uses from the aggregates. In particular, the consuming sector referred to as "miscellaneous" (Section G in the Appendix to Part II) contains specific projections for them.

The limitation of this projection to the sources of energy now in principal use has led to the exclusion of two classes of energy source. The first—and this differentiates the scope of Part II from that of Part I—is the exclusion of wood. The analysis in Part I included wood as an energy source because of its importance in the preceding century and the early decades of the present century. For some time, however, wood has been a small element in the total energy picture and there is no evidence that this will change in the future. The 1975 consumption estimates made herein therefore ignore wood.

At the other extreme, nuclear energy, which is a recent addition to the list of energy sources, and the so-called "unconventional" energy sources—of which the sun, wind, and tides are most prominent—have been excluded. The exclusion of nuclear energy—with the single exception of allowing for decreased use of fuel oil by the Navy—in a projection looking toward 1975 is undoubtedly surprising at first glance, but there is good reason for it. Nuclear energy may eventually become an important, if not the dominant, element in the energy position of this country, but the uncertainties surrounding the timing of this development are still very great. Although there has been much discussion on the place of nuclear energy in 1975, there is little more than conjecture to go on. If there is any consensus, it is that by 1975 the impact on energy production and consumption will be very small. Accordingly, the estimates have been kept in terms of the conventional energy sources and used as background against which the possible impact of nuclear energy on the energy position in 1975 may be examined.

The exclusion of the unconventional energy sources may strike the reader as less surprising, yet they have dominated the energy scene for a very long period, being prominent among the primitive sources of energy. And they are still far more important than is generally realized. Indeed, the term "unconventional" is in a sense a misnomer. The energy sources themselves are not unusual; it is the techniques of trying to capture and utilize the energy that warrant the term "unconventional." These three elementary streams of energy—sun, wind, and tides—recently have been receiving increased engineering attention in various parts of the world. Although the possibility of eventual significant economic application of wind and tidal energy in this country cannot be excluded, there is no evidence that this is likely to occur during the period under study. This is perhaps less true of solar energy, which has already enjoyed modest success in water heating in the southernmost portions of the country and is a subject of investigation as a mode of house heating and cooling.

·   ·   ·

Estimating Methods Used

A projection of energy consumption along the lines undertaken in this study requires first that a detailed current statistical base be established from which the future estimates can be carried forward. The year 1955 was chosen for this purpose as the latest year for which necessary data were available. Under conditions of perfect availability of data, the 1955 energy-use table would distribute all of the energy commodities used in 1955 among the main types of consumers; and within these categories would further identify the use, or application, made of the energy. Thus, to a given consuming activity—for example, the iron and steel industry—there would be allocated a portion that reached the industry as electricity, another portion as metallurgical fuel, another portion for space heating, etc. The electricity component, in turn, might be further divided into the various functions within the industry such as lighting, motors, electric furnace operation, etc.

The data are, however, far from perfect, so that the above description constitutes an ideal which cannot be attained in actual practice—even with the exhaustive work involved in establishing the 1955 statistical base. A more detailed statement than is warranted by the scope of this study may be found in *Energy Consumption and Production in the United States, 1954,* by Perry D. Teitelbaum.[13] There the more intricate parts of the flow of energy are traced to the limit for the year 1954. Nevertheless, sufficient detail is available to provide a base for projecting the future pattern of energy consumption.

From the 1955 base, two steps lead to the 1975 demand pattern: First is the projection of future output levels for the specific industries and activities represented in the energy-use pattern. Second is to estimate possible future changes in the relationship between the energy these industries or activities consume and their levels of output. The first step requires the assembly and study of materials dealing with growth patterns in many different parts of the economy, with particular emphasis on those which are significant energy consumers. Care must be exercised that the levels projected for the various industries and economic sectors form part of a consistent total picture, and one which is in harmony with the general framework set by the GNP projections within which the estimates are being made. The second step requires attention to various aspects of the historical pattern and indicated future directions of the relationship between energy consumption and levels of output in specific activities arising from such factors as changes in the efficiency of energy use, movements in the relative importance of different fuels in supplying the demand for energy as a result of shifts in consumer preference, technological changes in fuel-using equipment, etc.

The detailed calculations involved in assembling the 1955 consumption pattern, and projecting the 1975 levels along the general lines just indicated, are contained in the Appendix to Part II, and are summarized in the next sections of this chapter. An attempt has been made to lay bare the relationships underlying the estimates presented in this study. Several purposes are served by so doing. It allows changes to be made in the total on the basis of differing assumptions which others might wish to introduce, affecting any part of the underlying data, or on the basis of actual developments that deviate from the assumptions here made. It permits speculation as to the effects of unanticipated developments as well as of developments that have not been fully taken into account in the projection. It permits the expert in one or another field of energy consumption readily to locate the data of interest to him, and, in line with his judgment, to substitute his own version or improve the existing structure without having to speculate as to the way in which the estimate was derived and, equally important, without disturbing the remainder. Finally, it identifies the areas in which there are major gaps in the available information or major uncertainties. Though no explicit attempt has been made to evaluate critically the types of data available in the energy field or to describe what would constitute ideal sets of data, the text

[13] U.S. Bureau of Mines, in press.

abounds with examples of situations that could benefit from improved data and constitutes an invitation to such improvement.

The size of the Appendix derives precisely from the desire to enable the reader not only to follow the step-by-step construction of the estimate but to provide the opportunity for varying the assumptions and thus deriving different estimates.

THE DERIVATION OF THE ESTIMATES

The following pages are devoted to a summary description of the data, assumptions, and methods used in making estimates of the future level of energy consumption. The general reader may find that this portion contains as much technical detail as he is willing to digest; if so, he will not need to refer to the Appendix material which takes him through the calculations themselves.

For the purpose of these projections, total energy consumption in the U.S. economy has been classified into six major consuming sectors, plus one miscellaneous category. These are shown in Table 63, which indicates also their relative importance as energy consumers in 1955. Industry is the most important of the sectors, accounting for about two-fifths of all energy consumed in 1955; transportation is next with about one-fifth; households are third with just under one-fifth; and commercial, government, and agriculture follow in that order. The category of miscellaneous uses and losses accounted for about 7 per cent in 1955, which places it close behind the commercial sector in relative importance.

Within the transportation total, the estimates carry separate figures for transportation services self-performed by households and by the civilian government. These

TABLE 63. THE RELATIVE IMPORTANCE OF ENERGY-CONSUMING SECTORS IN THE U. S. ECONOMY, 1955

Sector [a]	Percentage of total mineral fuels and hydropower consumed
Industry	39.2%
Commercial	8.5
Households	18.6
Transportation	20.2
Self-performed by households	9.3
Self-performed by government (excl. military)	0.3
General	10.6
Government	4.6
Agriculture	1.8
Miscellaneous uses and losses	7.1
Total	100.0%
Consumed in the form of electricity	19.2%

[a] The sectors listed in this table are the categories used throughout Part II.

SOURCE: Table 78.

can, if desired, be assigned to the parent consuming sectors rather than to transportation. This is particuarly significant in the case of households, for almost one-half of transportation's share of total energy consumption is accounted for by transportation self-performed by households. This is a measure of energy consumed in private automobiles in the United States. If this amount is added to the energy consumption of households, it raises the latter's share of the total to almost three-tenths, which is surpassed only by industry. Because of the great relative importance of households—and the largely unexplored nature of energy use in this consuming sector—a great deal of attention has been devoted to household consumption of energy in this study.

Also indicated in Table 63 is the relative importance of energy used in the form of electricity, generation of which, in 1955, accounted for almost one-fifth of all energy raw materials consumed in the U.S. economy. This category is set off separately in Table 1 because it is already included in the sector figures shown in the table. The relative importance of electricity is so great that in the calculations here it is identified separately in all of the consumption figures—both in 1955, and as projected to 1975. In addition, consumption of electricity for each of the sectors is translated into the fuels required in its generation and delivery, and these are added to the sector's direct fuel consumption to derive its total fuel consumption. The methods used in translating electricity consumption into fuel requirements are described in the final section of this chapter. All the other sections are concerned with describing the methods, assumptions, and data used for deriving energy consumption—in 1955 and as projected to 1975—within the particular sectors. As will become evident, these estimates are always derived in terms of subcategories within the major sectors.

. . .

Industry

OTHER THAN ELECTRICITY CONSUMPTION

The estimating procedure constitutes a middle ground between projecting fuel input for all industry and subdividing industry into a large number of components, and projecting fuel input for each. While the second alternative is theoretically the more attractive, it requires a diversified fund of information that is rarely if ever available for any one research effort. It requires not only that information be available detailing fuel consumption during the base year in a large number of individual industries; it requires also the availability of data in equal detail for a number of other years in order to establish statistical indicators of trends in the level and pattern of fuel consumption in various industries. Thus, even if 1955 had been a Census year for industry, which it was not, it is doubtful whether any more detailed breakdowns could have been used, since comparable data for enough other years are lacking.

With a half dozen or so important exceptions, only a large heterogeneous group has been projected. The exceptions suggested themselves principally on the grounds of availability of detailed annual statistics and simplicity of end product, making it feasible to study past behavior in some detail. The categories for which separate projections were made are in two broad groups: The first is composed of *iron and steel, cement, and petroleum refining*. The second, called *special industrial group*, consists of coal use by mines, natural gas use in gas fields, coal and oil for nonmotive use in railroads, and coke used outside the iron and steel industry. (The latter two, in a way, are leftovers from other statistical operations and for the sake of convenience are subsumed with mine and gas field use under this general heading.) Taken together, these two groups accounted for about two-thirds of all the energy consumed in industry (other than in the form of electricity) in 1955 (see Appendix Table A-9). A third classification—*general industrial group*—includes all the rest of industry. This conglomeration of activities, projected as a single item (essentially all mining and manufacturing not covered in the first two groups), accounted for the remainder.[14]

To establish the 1955 statistical base, showing the use of each fuel in the particular consuming industries or activities, is often complex but represents no particular problems. The operations and results are presented in Appendix Tables A-1 through A-9. The projection to 1975, taking up Appendix Tables A-10 through A-23, is accomplished separately for each of the three broad groups.

To project fuel input in iron and steel, as well as cement, the following steps were taken: The 1975 level of iron and steel and cement production was estimated in terms of an assumed relationship between the output of these products and of all industry. Next, 1975 fuel consumption per unit of output (where output is measured by the index of physical production) was estimated in iron and steel and cement. Total industrial output in the future was assumed to move at the same rate as GNP; iron and steel and cement output relative to total industrial output was estimated in terms of relationships which prevailed, on the average, during the period 1952–56; and fuel input per unit of output of cement and iron and steel was based on present-day levels adjusted for assumed future improvements in fuel efficiency. In each instance, separate estimates for self-generated electricity were made to obtain the net fuel consumption of those portions consumed in generation of electricity. These operations are presented in Appendix Tables A-10 to A-13.

The projection of fuel used in petroleum refining should properly remain undetermined until the completion of the study yields the level of petroleum refining in 1975. Yet, through its consumption of petroleum, refining constitutes a part of the projected total demand, and other estimates could not go forward without completion of this segment. This problem was resolved by projecting fuel use in refining on the basis of an approximation of total petroleum consump-

---

[14] Certain industrial uses in which oil and gas constitute a chemical feedstock are projected separately in the "miscellaneous" category described later in this chapter.

tion in 1975 as indicated by analysis at a preliminary stage of the study.[15] No changes are assumed in fuel consumption per unit of refinery output, as both the historical record and current geographical differences within the United States suggest such diverse influences at work that it seemed preferable not to tackle this very complex matter, but to carry into 1975 the fuel-output relationship that prevailed in 1955 (Appendix Tables A-14 through A-17).

Within the special industrial group, a parallel problem exists in the projection of coal use in mines and gas use in gas fields. The approach used in breaking into this circle was the same as in petroleum refining. Approximate growth in demand, as suggested at a preliminary stage of the study, was used to determine the change between 1955 and 1975, and thus to complete the estimate (Appendix Table A-19).[16]

Output in the general industrial group is assumed to increase in step with the over-all growth in industrial output which, in turn, is assumed to grow at the same rate as GNP (Appendix Table A-22). A subsidiary problem—namely, that output should in fact grow faster in this category to make up for the fact that output is assumed to grow more slowly in some of the industries treated separately (for example, iron and steel)—is recognized. However, it is not allowed for, except in a purely mechanical way by assuming a somewhat lower rate of improvement in fuel efficiency than past trends might suggest. This conservatism has the effect of boosting total fuel requirements, and thus acts in the same direction as would a faster rise in output. The distribution of the projected fuel requirements among the different fuels stipulates a further shrinkage in coal use, and allows for a relative increase in gas consumption. The latter is based upon a moderate deceleration of the apparent past trend.

ELECTRICITY CONSUMPTION

The procedure for projecting electricity consumption by industry provided for separate estimates in aluminum and magnesium production, in which use of electricity per unit of output is exceedingly high, and a single estimate for all the rest of industry. In addition, industry has been defined to exclude the consumption of electricity in Atomic Energy Commission (AEC) operations, even though the regular statistics on industrial electricity consumption do include this use.[17] In this study, AEC consumption, which in 1955 was equivalent to

[15] The estimated preliminary growth used for petroleum consumption between 1955 and 1975 was 90 per cent. At the completion of the study, the projected growth turned out to be 86 per cent.

[16] The assumed coal tonnage for 1975 was 751 million tons, as against the final projection of 768 million tons. Natural gas was assumed to grow by 110 per cent, as compared with the final projection of 107 per cent.

[17] In the Census Bureau statistics, AEC's electricity consumption is included with industry because, by and large, the AEC's electricity consumption takes place in plants which are privately operated, although federally owned; in Edison Electric Institute statistics, AEC establishments fall into the "large light and power sales" class of customers.

about 20 per cent of all industrial consumption excluding the AEC, is covered within the government sector. The relevant statistics for electricity consumption by industry are shown in Appendix Table A-24, and related information (some of it used to derive Table A-24, some showing the past development of the relevant use categories) is shown in Appendix Tables A-25, A-26, and A-30.

Aluminum and magnesium, the two use categories which are separately projected, constituted about 10 per cent of total industrial electricity consumption in 1955 (Appendix Table A-29). In estimating the future output levels of these two metals (Appendix Tables A-33 through A-36), the growth rates for aluminum (about 7.5 per cent) and for magnesium (about 8.75 per cent) constitute a kind of consensus of the producers and researchers in this particular field. In estimating future electricity consumption per unit of output, increases in efficiency have been assumed. The assumed efficiency improvements in aluminum are based on a reading of past trends; for magnesium, they are in line with past changes and certain expressions of future expectations.

The projection to 1975 for the rest of industry (Appendix Tables A-30 through A-32) is based upon the assumed general industrial growth rate of 4 per cent per year. The refinement of lowering this rate to compensate for the estimated faster growth in the excluded aluminum and magnesium sector has been avoided. The general growth rate is combined with an assumed growth in electricity consumption per unit of output. The latter is based, with a liberal degree of judgment, upon past changes in this relationship, but the rate adopted (2 per cent per year per point of the index of industrial production based upon 1947–49 = 100) appears to be in harmony with the past.

As with the estimates of nonelectricity consumption, improvements—or at least greater confidence—in these estimates would probably result from studying past relationships between output and power consumption for smaller and more homogeneous segments of industry, and then projecting on the basis of the knowledge gained in such analysis and of conjectures as to future technological as well as economic trends. Again, lack of available data is a major factor standing in the way of such detailed analysis.

·   ·   ·

Commercial

OTHER THAN ELECTRICITY CONSUMPTION

In the commercial group, the first step was to determine the amounts of energy consumed in 1955 in forms other than electricity (Appendix Table B-1). For natural gas, the quantity consumed by commercial establishments is so designated in the data sources.[18] In the case of coal and natural gas liquids (NGL)—

---

[18] There is, however, some question as to the validity of the designation since explanations of the categories of gas use—as published by the American Gas Association which is the statistical source—would suggest that the category called "commercial" is a residual which includes all gas uses other than residential, industrial, governmental, and interdepartmental sales.

or, more specifically, the liquefied petroleum gas (LPG) component of NGL—the quantity had to be estimated from totals generally interpreted to embrace household and commercial use. Finally, oil consumption was estimated on the basis of grades—the heavier ones—which are commonly considered as going into commercial uses. There are arbitrary elements in deriving the 1955 figures for coal, oil, and NGL; judgment largely based on trade sources is about the only available basis.

In projecting the future consumption of natural gas, reliance was placed on a remarkably constant historical relationship which had been found to exist between residential and commercial consumption (Appendix Table B-2). Thus, the 1975 estimate of commercial natural gas consumption (Appendix Table B-3) was derived from the projections made for residential consumption (Section C of the Appendix to Part II) through a simple assumption of a continuing close relationship between the two classes of consumption.

Owing to the complete absence of data regarding both the number of fuel customers or per-customer fuel consumption in this category, the starting point for estimating coal, oil, and NGL in 1975 (Appendix Table B-4) was the assumed increase in the number of commercial electricity customers between 1955 and 1975. Although these figures refer specifically to the commercial customers for electricity, they are taken as an index of the total number of commercial establishments in both years. The percentage increase in number of commercial customers (or establishments) was used to estimate the increase in the total of gas, coal, oil, and NGL consumption; the implied assumption as to consumption per customer in 1975 is, of course, arbitrary.

The total was then allocated to coal, oil, and NGL, after allowance for the increase in natural gas use already estimated by a different method, on the basis that 1975 coal use will decrease by one-third from 1955, and that the balance will go to oil and NGL. There is little doubt that coal will continue to diminish in importance in this sector, but the specific reduction stipulated here does not claim to be more than a rough estimate. There is a great need of factual information in this field. Fortunately, the various quantities involved are not very significant in total energy demand.

ELECTRICITY CONSUMPTION

There exists no annual series of electric power sales to commercial customers, but careful investigation demonstrates that in recent years the Edison Electric Institute's series called "small light and power sales" is, for all practical purposes, equivalent to sales to commercial customers. While this often is taken for granted, the extent to which this equivalence has prevailed over time has been carefully checked in this study, and the results of the computations summarized in Appendix Table B-8. They show that, with some exceptions, the category has been broadly representative of sales to commercial customers in the past two decades, and that this has been especially pronounced in more recent years. Therefore, the "small light and power sales" series has been used as standing in fact for commercial consumption in 1955.

In projecting commercial electricity consumption to 1975, reliance was placed on certain relationships found to exist in the past between residential and commercial use of electricity (see Appendix Tables B-5 through B-7). The number of commercial customers was estimated from projections of the number of households on the basis of a quite consistent factor found to characterize the past relationship between the two. The estimated number of customers was then multiplied by an assumed consumption per customer which, in turn, was derived by applying a factor based on the past relationship between residential and commercial consumption per customer to the 1975 projection of residential consumption per customer.

·   ·   ·

Households

OTHER THAN ELECTRICITY CONSUMPTION

Since statistics for household fuel consumption are so deficient, the determination of the amounts consumed in 1955 involved a considerable amount of estimating. These difficulties were intensified by a decision to divide household fuel consumption between uses for space heating and non-space heating. This distinction was judged important for projection purposes.

Proceeding fuel by fuel, in the order in which the Appendix material is presented, gas residential consumption in 1955 is divided into space heating and other uses by assuming that sales made in the third calendar quarter go exclusively to uses other than space heating and that this level, held constant through the rest of the year, approximates the use for non-space heating for the year, leaving the balance to be considered as space-heating consumption (Appendix Table C-1).

Undoubtedly this it not entirely accurate. On the one hand, summer vacations, less indoor cooking, and the higher entry temperature of water in the summer tend to lead to an understatement of non-space heating by this approach. On the other hand, some small amounts of space heating in the third quarter, gas air cooling, and possible seasonal factors in the level of home laundering, tend to lead to an overstatement of non-space heating. On the whole, nonetheless, the method probably has considerable virtue, especially as the factors making for inaccuracy may tend to offset one another.

In the case of oil, the estimation of the amounts going to household use in 1955 was based first on a selection of grades of oils which are ordinarily consumed in households. The distribution of the total amounts consumed between space heating and other uses was estimated by drawing on the personal judgment of trade and government experts (Appendix Tables C-2 and C-3).

For coal and LPG, the starting point is a category in the 1955 statistics which combines household and commercial sales. It was necessary to estimate the distribution of this total between household and commercial,[19] and the subsequent allocation of the household item to space heating and other uses. Both allocations are quite rough, but are based on the only judgment possible with the available information (Appendix Tables C-4 and C-5).

It is in the projection of household fuel consumption to 1975 that the importance of separating space heating from total consumption becomes apparent. Even though there remains an area of speculation, the data available on trends in space-heating installations permit this particular activity to be carried forward on a foundation that can be regarded with more confidence than could the heterogeneous total of all household uses.

In the main, the method for projecting the 1975 figures is concerned with estimating oil and gas consumption for space heating in that year. It is proper to concentrate attention on these two energy sources because together they account for more than three-quarters of all fuel consumption in residential space heating in 1955. There are two main planks which support the projection of oil and gas in space heating: First is an estimate, made available by the American Gas Association, of the current distribution of space-heating systems, distinguishing between gas and oil, and central and noncentral heating (Appendix Table C-7). The second is a special survey, with substantially the same framework, conducted by the U.S. Bureau of Labor Statistics (BLS), covering new construction in the first calendar quarter of 1956 (Appendix Table C-8).

Two suppositions were made to marry the two sets of data: First, it was assumed that the distribution as revealed by the 1956 BLS survey in essence would rule for all new construction through 1975 (Appendix Table C-9). No information found in the course of this study justifies any other guess as to the distribution of heating systems in new construction through 1975. Past trends show a continuing expansion of gas heating, with oil heating having receded from a large relative increase made during the 1940's, and electricity not in the picture to any significant degree.[20] It is assumed that the swing towards gas in new construction will not take it beyond the dominating position it had achieved by 1956.

The second supposition was that the heating pattern in households now heated by oil and gas would, through replacements during the period ending in 1975, move very gradually towards the oil and gas pattern of heating which prevailed in the new housing constructed in 1956 (see Appendix Table C-10). The pace assumed here—a one-quarter edging towards the pattern found in new housing —is largely arbitrary, but it does draw on whatever data and judgment are available concerning past replacement of one form of heating by another.

[19] This allocation is the basis of the commercial consumption of coal and LPG, referred to earlier.

[20] U.S. Department of Labor, Bureau of Labor Statistics, *New Housing and Its Materials, 1940–1956*, Bulletin No. 1231 (Washington, D. C.: U.S. Government Printing Office, August 1958).

The mechanics of making the actual space-heating projection may be followed in Appendix Tables C-9 through C-14. One of these, Table C-11, involves auxiliary assumptions regarding the number of households in 1975 that will be heated by sources of energy other than gas and oil; the footnotes to the table explain the reasoning that suggested the particular pattern shown. While there is room for debate here, the balance of the past and present is so heavily on the side of gas and oil heating that, in the absence of substantial signs of a reversal in this pattern, possible errors in the other heating fuels (see, for example, the discussion later of space heating by electricity) are not of major importance.

In projecting fuel for uses other than space heating, the most carefully developed estimate is that for natural gas (Appendix Tables C-15 through C-17). Rates of use for each of the important appliances involved—and their number is limited—have been stipulated on the basis of a great many published estimates. Most of them arise from work on the gas and electricity consumption rates of major appliances, some done by gas interests, some by electric power interests, and some by consumer-oriented research (Appendix Table C-32). The rates chosen represent the authors' best judgment in this field. So do the rates of saturation among gas customers of each gas-fueled appliance, which take into account the existence of appliances powered by competing energy sources (essentially electricity) and thus are kept within the confines of total households (Appendix Tables C-23 through C-30). As for coal, oil, and LPG used for non-space heating, fairly arbitrary assumptions had to be made as to their level of consumption in 1975 (Appendix Table C-18).

ELECTRICITY CONSUMPTION

The amount of electricity consumed by residences in 1955, as shown in Appendix Table C-19, is derived in a straightforward way from the statistics published by the Edison Electric Institute.[21] However, while total quantities consumed in 1955 (and in earlier years) are well known, much less is known about the amounts devoted to each of the diverse uses to which electricity is put in the household. Even the elementary division between lighting and appliance uses is surrounded by uncertainty. Despite this lack of information, it seems necessary to project residential consumption of electricity not as a whole, but in terms of the individual components which make up the total. Much attention, therefore, has been devoted in the Appendix to assembling and analyzing a large array of materials pertaining to the composition of household consumption of electricity, as a basis for separately projecting the constituents of total electricity use in the home. It is only when one considers individual uses that

---

[21]All rural sales are included under residential consumption, although some electricity in the rural category is undoubtedly consumed in agricultural production. Also, the commercial sector includes an indeterminate household component, consisting of electricity consumed in large multifamily buildings.

one realizes fully the limits set to electricity's expansion by competing sources of energy. The reader's attention is directed, for example, to Appendix Tables C-26 and C-29 dealing with water heaters and ranges, as an illustration of how the simultaneous consideration of competing fuels helps to give the projection a more realistic focus.

The basic approach in projecting 1975 electricity use in the home, therefore, is made along the following lines. More than a dozen individual applications of electricity in the home are identified. These include lighting, heating, cooling, etc., and various appliances such as dishwashers, ranges, refrigerators, clothes dryers. For each of the identified applications (and a miscellaneous catch-all class) the average number of kilowatt hours (kwh) of annual electricity consumption are estimated for the year 1975. These consumption factors apply, however, only to those homes in which the appliance or function will actually be employed; hence it is necessary to project the percentage of all homes in which the actual use will take place. The latter measure is known as the "per cent of saturation" or the "saturation rate," and, in this study, estimates range from 100 per cent for lighting down to about 5 per cent for electric heating. Multiplying estimated average annual consumption by the estimated saturation rates yields average consumption per residential customer (and, through certain additional assumptions, per household) for each application and, when summed, average consumption in all uses.

The steps just described are summarized in Appendix Table C-37, which draws directly or indirectly on most of the foregoing Appendix Tables C-22 through C-36. The over-all average obtained in Appendix Table C-37 is then applied in Appendix Table C-38 to the estimated number of households in 1975 to derive total estimated household electricity consumption in 1975.

Pains have been taken to develop future rates of saturation and average consumption factors. As an examination of the cited Appendix tables, and especially Table C-32 and C-36, will illustrate, there is great divergence of opinion on the underlying factors. The rates adopted do not represent a statistical average, but rather the net reflection left by a study of the literature. The cross-currents of fact, surmise, and suppliers' optimism in this field are the justification for the many details, which are to be found in the Appendix tables. In addition, brief comments are warranted here on three important components of the estimated growth between 1955 and 1975: air conditioning, space heating, and lighting. A fourth sizable use—water heating—is dealt with in Appendix Table C-26.

1) *Air Conditioning:* Central air conditioning units in particular are heavy power consumers and thus are potentially large users of residential electricity. If the assumption of 20 per cent as a saturation rate for central cooling in 1975 (Appendix Table C-37) seems relatively low, this must be judged first of all in combination with the saturation rate of individual room coolers—60 per cent. The two jointly—and they are most certainly additive—yield the very high saturation rate of 80 per cent. While for statistical purposes this is stated as

an average, it is not to be taken to indicate that 80 out of 100 connected customers will have air conditioning of one type or another, since customers will, on the average, have more than one unit (Appendix Table C-22, footnote f). Even then, however, on climatic grounds alone, the rate can hardly be expected to come closer to full saturation. Within the total, the ratio of three room conditioners for every central unit appears a feasible rate, perhaps one even weighted too heavily on the side of central cooling units. It could be attained, roughly, if half of all housing units to be constructed by 1975 were to have central air conditioning, or if about one-third of currently existing households were to be so equipped by 1975, or by some intermediate combination of the two.

2) *Space heating:* In the past, electric space heating has been held back by the competition of fuels to a greater degree than any other application, so that in 1955, it is estimated there were less than a quarter of a million electrically heated households. Precisely, however, because of the present-day low level of saturation, combined with the very high consumption per unit, space heating is one use which potentially could cause a very great increase in electricity consumption by 1975. While in public discussion this is sometimes assumed, it is not the view here adopted.

The expense involved in converting existing housing to electric heating suggests that the prime source for a substantial increase in this use of electricity must be in new construction. Given the estimated 1975 proportion of all households residing in dwellings to be constructed in the 1955–75 period, and given the low annual level of electric-heat installations in new construction at the outset of this period, it follows that even dramatic rates of increase in the proportion of new construction equipped with electric space heating will yield only a modest over-all proportion of all households with electric space heating.

This can be illustrated by two every unlikely suppositions: (a) Assume that electric-heating installations were to rise over the next two decades so that instead of practically none in 1955, by 1975 one-half of all new construction would have electric heat—an assumption utterly at variance with past and current conditions.[22] (b) Add to these installations substantial rates of conversion to electric heating in housing units existing in 1955, say 50,000 a year—again a most unlikely magnitude in view of past and current experience. The result—electrically heated households would amount to just over 11 per cent of all households in 1975.[23]

---

[22] In newly constructed nonfarm housing, the percentage of electrical heating has remained at 1 per cent of the total between 1950 and 1956. See *New Housing and Its Materials, 1940–56, op. cit.,* p. 41.

[23] New construction, 1955–75: 27,100,000

    25 per cent of new construction, 1955–75:.......... 6,775,000
        plus 50,000 per year for 20 years.............. 1,000,000
        plus 200,000 carried over from 1955........... 200,000

    Total electrically heated, 1975.................... 7,975,000
    equal to 11.6 per cent of 68,878,000 households in 1975 (compare Appendix Table C-11)

The above illustration is of course extravagant in its assumption of growing acceptance of electric heating. Even so, the resulting increase in average space-heating consumption per wired household from the 605 kwh assumed in this study (Appendix Table C-37) to some 1,210 kwh would be equivalent to an increase in total power consumption per average consumer of less than 10 per cent. Thus, it is obvious that even a most unlikely speed-up in the spread of electric space heating would not, in the twenty years 1955–75, have a revolutionary effect on household consumption of electricity. The assumption made in this study is more realistic, but still assumes a sharp increase in acceptance of electric space heating. The assumption is that 12.5 per cent of the 27.1 million dwelling units constructed in 1955–75—or 3.4 million units—will have electric space heating. The attainment of this goal for the period as a whole presupposes installations in the later years at percentage rates far higher than for the period as a whole, since the 1956 installation rate was on the order of only 1.0 per cent of new construction, and since it can reasonably be anticipated that the installation rate will increase more slowly in the beginning. Therefore, a 1975 rate considerably above 25 per cent would be required to yield the over-all rate of 12.5 per cent during 1955–75.

It is further assumed that there would be 200,000 conversions during the period and a carryover of 200,000 electrically heated units from 1955. These, together with the 3.4 million newly constructed units, add to 3.8 million units in 1975, or 5.5 per cent of all 1975 units.

3) *Lighting:* Appendix Tables C-34 through C-36 bring together various figures on consumption of residential electricity for lighting in the past, and certain projections for the future. Striking differences exist, both in the projections and, even more surprisingly, in the past.

The most thorough study of electricity consumption in lighting that has come to the authors' attention is one being performed by the Middle West Service Company. Their interim estimate shows a consumption level considerably below that estimated by others for recent years. However, there are grounds for believing that even the Middle West Service Company's estimate of 771 kwh per residential customer for lighting in 1956 (Appendix Table C-34) is too high; and that the correct figure is well below this (see Appendix Table C-35, in which estimates for lighting by the customers of particular utilities are shown). The difficulty seems to be that the figures ordinarily available for lighting are arrived at by deducting assumed rates of appliance use from total residential consumption, leaving lighting as a residual. Sometimes, too, no adjustment is made to exclude miscellaneous appliances—that is, minor appliances not separately enumerated.

It has been arbitrarily assumed in this study that the average residential consumption for lighting in 1955 was 10 per cent below the 1956 estimate made by the Middle West Service Company, which yields a 1955 figure of 700 kwh per residential customer. This figure, which is well below other estimates in Appendix Table C-34, was projected to 1975 by applying an average annual increase of 25 kwh per customer. The latter factor is derived from estimates made by the General Electric Company for the period 1955–65 of the increase in lighting use which would take place without a special promotional program (Appendix Table C-36).

The 1975 level here assumed—1,200 kwh for electricity per residential customer—concedes a rate of growth equal to that anticipated by a major electric company in the absence of special "lighting campaigns," but falls substantially short of the very optimistic targets based upon such campaigns. The estimate for 1975 has as its starting point a 1955 level that is lower than that assumed by others because it makes an allowance for the "miscellaneous" uses—which seem, especially on the basis of the pioneer work being done by the Middle West Service Company, to be lumped with lighting consumption in estimates of past and current consumption.

· · ·

Transportation

TRANSPORTATION AS A CONSUMING SECTOR

It is important to identify transportation as a consuming sector because about one-fifth of all energy is used for transportation purposes. Identifying transportation as a consuming sector, however, makes for complications within the over-all classification system because a sizable percentage of the energy used for transportation is consumed directly in other sectors, in the sense that the transportation function is self-performed within the sector. Therefore, not only has energy consumed in all transportation been measured, but also, within this total, the energy consumed in self-performed transportation in two of the other consuming sectors—households and government—has been identified separately. Of the two, self-performed transportation within the household sector is far and away the more important—a reflection of the pervasive role of privately owned automobiles in U.S. life. Energy consumed in transportation which is self-performed within other consuming sectors—industrial, agricultural, and commercial establishments—has not been separately estimated because the necessary data either are not available or provide no basis on which to separate "personal" from "productive" transportation. As for government, the energy totals shown for all transportation do not include energy materials consumed in military transportation. Nor, by the same token, does the separately identified item of energy consumed in self-performed government transportation include military transportation. All the energy materials consumed by the military, including the amounts consumed in military transportation, are covered in this study only within the government sector.

The classification system used in projecting energy consumption in transportation divides all transportation into major categories which essentially are different media: railroads, marine transport, automotive transport, aviation, and pipelines. Within the major categories, there are often subcategories which were used in making the projections of energy consumption. Some subcategories are in terms of the specific fuels consumed; others involve modes of transportation. For example, the consumption estimates for automotive transportation are composed of estimates developed separately for trucks, commercial buses, school and nonrevenue buses, passenger automobiles, etc. In addition, the automotive transportation category is the one in which self-performed transportation in households and government occurs, and for which separate estimates are made of the energy consumed in these activities.

In order to carry through the projection of future consumption, the pattern of energy use in transportation had to be established first for 1955. Although the transportation sector is marked by an abundance of source material, there is a lack of the clear definitions and distinctions needed for the categories selected in this study. A major effort, therefore, had to be devoted to evolving the current pattern of energy distribution before the projection could be attempted. The data, techniques and assumptions employed in estimating 1975 energy consumption in transportation are so voluminous that summarization is very difficult. Only the main elements supporting the estimates will be outlined here; the full account is contained in the Appendix tables.

MAJOR FREIGHT MEDIA: RAILROADS, TRUCKS, AND SHIPS

The first step was to estimate the future size of the freight market and its division among the principal transportation media. The historic pattern available over a long period (Appendix Table D-1) was used for establishing a basis for the 1975 projection. Comparison reveals that, in the past, total intercity freight volume, as defined in this particular series compiled by the Interstate Commerce Commission (ICC), has moved more or less in unison with gross national product (Appendix Table D-2). The assumption, in estimating total 1975 freight volume, was that it would continue to do so. The assumptions as to how the total freight traffic might be divided in 1975 among the different modes (Appendix Table D-3) were derived from an inspection of the historical trends. The computed increases between 1955 and 1975, applied to 1955 fuel consumption with certain adjustments for changes in fuel composition and efficiency, are utilized for railroads (Appendix Tables D-4 through D-11) and trucks (Appendix Tables D-25 through D-27), and for the cargo element of the aviation estimate (see below and Appendix Table D-50).

It should be pointed out that the freight statistics which underlie the projection do not cover all freight movements, but they have been used here for estimating the *rates* of traffic increase between 1955 and 1975, not the demand for energy itself. These rates are applied to the energy consumption figures for 1955,[24] which have been designed to represent as fully as feasible total fuel consumption in freight transport. Thus, in the case of railroads, the 1955 energy

---

[24] Where reasonable estimates can be made, the resulting projections are further adjusted for improvements in fuel efficiency (for example, trucks).

consumption is based on the annually reported actual consumption of fuels and electricity (Appendix Table D-4), and for trucks, the 1955 fuel consumption is derived from the consumption data reported by the Bureau of Public Roads (Appendix Table D-16).

The railroad fuel projection is performed with the aid of several subsidiary assumptions, such as complete replacement of coal and residual oil by diesel oil (Appendix Tables D-8 and D-11); a further reduction in passenger service based upon the slow decline evidenced in the past (Appendix Table D-10); and minor internal changes attending upon those assumptions, such as relative reduction in yard-switching service (Appendix Table D-9) and increase in electricity consumption for purposes other than locomotion. The projected decline in passenger service is perhaps less drastic than current discussion would make one suspect, but a look at Appendix Table D-10 suggests that the wartime bulge has now disappeared and the slow decline of the late 1930's, rather than the fast decline of the 1940's, appears to be setting the pace.

For waterway traffic, the rate of increase resulting from the projection for all traffic modes (Appendix Table D-3) was not used because the two principal components of marine fuel consumption—bunker (international) and nonbunker (domestic)—in the past have moved in quite different relationship to gross national product (Appendix Table D-12). Consequently, separate rates of growth were used, as shown in Appendix Table D-13. In addition, the exclusion from the ICC statistics of major classes of traffic, such as intracoastal and coastwise deep-sea shipping, makes application of the rate of increase derived from these data inadvisable.

PASSENGER AUTOMOBILES

Estimates made for passenger automobiles include fuel consumption for all automotive purposes except trucks, which have been estimated in conjunction with other freight media. Fuel consumption for passenger automobiles is by far the largest element in energy consumed in transportation in 1955, and as estimated for 1975. It accounts for about 75 per cent of the total for transportation in 1955 and almost 80 per cent of the estimated total in 1975 (Appendix Table D-60).

The estimate of automotive fuel consumption in 1975 combines two factors: the estimated number of automobiles in that year, and estimated fuel consumption per automobile (Appendix Tables D-31 to D-38). The estimated number of vehicles in 1975 was based on a modified extension of the trend in vehicles per population aged eighteen and above, as observed over the fifteen-year period 1940–55 (Appendix Table D-32). And it was assumed that there would be no change in fuel consumption per vehicle—again based upon historical trends but reinforced by other evidence (Appendix Tables D-35 through D-37).

In projecting the number of automobiles in 1975, the authors have not been unmindful of how far off the mark some previous attempts have been. The projection made in 1925 by Professor Reed provides a useful illustration. His projection of an upper limit of 5.1 persons per automobile to be attained somewhere around the year 2000, was in fact surpassed in 1939, only fourteen years after the projection had been made.[25] A more recent projection, that made by the President's Materials Policy Commission in 1950,[26] also was predicated on an upper limit in the relationship between population and vehicles. The anticipated 1975 level of one car per two to two and a half persons over thirteen years of age was in fact attained in 1956–57. It is easy to guess that the total number of automobiles projected by the PMPC for 1975—65 million cars—is almost certain to be reached and surpassed in the early sixties.

The method used in this study was developed in the context of the above and other past estimates and their common failure to have given sufficient weight to the U.S. proclivity for owning automobiles. The recent trend to multiple-car ownership (Appendix Table D-21) in itself introduces an entirely new dimension in estimating future automobile numbers. The highway construction program is another important factor, as is the possible change in attitudes towards smaller cars. Saturation, after all, is a relative concept. Given satisfactory highway and parking opportunities, quite apart from increases in national income, the saturation point in terms of the number of automobiles and their use is elusive. The ultimate limits, set by population growth and time available for driving, seem far in the distance. A leading transportation economist, Wilfred Owen, of The Brookings Institution, recently termed one car for every 2.5 persons a "conservative expectation."[27] The projection used in this study, which is equivalent to just over two persons per car, appears less formidable against this background, though, in conformity with the study's general concept to err on the high side, it certainly is not conservative.

The particular automobile population derived in Appendix Table D-32 is based on a projection which gives heavy weight to the postwar experience. It treats the period 1950–55 on a par with the period 1940–55, and derives an annual average of the two in respect to increases in automobiles relative to the population eighteen years and over. One way, partly conjectural, of evaluating this projection is to construct a hypothetical pattern of car ownership in 1975 which would result in roughly the total number of cars here estimated. This model is set up in Appendix Table D-33. Some support is provided in Appendix Table D-34, which presents factual background on recent changes in the relationship of car numbers per capita in densely populated areas and in the country as a whole.

The assumption of constant fuel consumption per automobile is less difficult to arrive at than the number of vehicles. The recent leveling off in gasoline

---

[25] Noel J. Reed, "A Form of Saturation Curve," *Journal of the American Statistical Association*, Vol. XX (new series), No. 151 (September 1925), pp. 390–96.

[26] PMPC, *op. cit.*, p. 114.

[27] W. Owen, *The Metropolitan Transportation Problem* (Washington, D. C.: The Brookings Institution, 1956), p. 40.

consumption per automobile revealed by the historical data (Appendix Tables D-35 and D-36) is one of the principal reasons for leaving consumption per vehicle unchanged between 1955 and 1975. Another is the difficulty of reconciling two different series of fuel efficiency—one compiled by the Bureau of Public Roads and one by General Motors (Appendix Table D-37). Perhaps both faster driving on turnpikes and slower stop-and-go driving in congested areas have made the General Motors test course less representative. In any event, the Bureau of Public Roads data, which derive from actual consumption, keep one from accepting the test results as suggesting a gradual and consistent increase in miles per gallon consumed.[28] Increasing addition of power-consuming accessories to automobiles is further likely to counter probable improvements in fuel efficiency. At the same time, the spread of multiple-car ownership and the probable growth in the use of smaller cars may work in the direction of lower fuel consumption per car on the road. It is difficult to see how, in the face of this array of facts and considerations, one can do other than adopt the attitude of "no change."

Projection of fuel consumption by automotive vehicles other than trucks and automobiles is covered in Appendix Tables D-18, D-29, and D-30. Allocation of the projected consumption of all types of automotive vehicles to the various consuming sectors appears in Appendix Tables D-18, D-40, and D-42. Historical relationships have been the prime consideration, as explained in the footnotes to the various tables.

AVIATION

With the separation of 1955 air traffic into various segments, such as domestic passenger, domestic cargo, international, etc. (Appendix Tables D-46 through D-48), it is feasible to project each branch according to the best evidence or forecasts available. Appendix Tables D-49 to D-58 present the basis for the 1975 estimates. To a substantial degree, they are based upon forecasts made in 1956 by the Civil Aeronautics Administration (CAA) for the years 1960, 1965, and 1970.

An auxiliary assumption concerns fuel used per mile or hour in 1975 as compared to 1955 in various types of flying. On the basis of past experience and frequently on the strength of expert judgment (as noted in the pertinent Appendix tables), no change in efficiency has been assumed in any of the branches, except that account has been taken of the different unit fuel requirements of jet planes and piston planes in identical activities. A substitution factor of jet fuel for gasoline of 1.5 gallons of jet fuel for each gallon of gasoline seems to represent a kind of informal consensus of experts, but only actual experience will provide the raw materials out of which a dependable factor can be fashioned.

[28] J. M. Campbell, the Scientific Research Director of General Motors, in a communication to Resources for the Future, expresses the belief that ". . . a tendency to offset the increased efficiency of the engine by driving faster and utilizing more of the increased power for added acceleration" is believed to be a possible explanation of the discrepancy.

Since interest centers in fuel consumption per mile of passenger-revenue service, the question of the number of seats per jet plane in itself introduces a large variable into the calculation, as does the size distribution of planes and the length of flight pattern. The substitution factor used, therefore, is quite tentative, even though based on extensive checks and discussions.

PIPELINES

Current information on energy consumed in pipeline transportation is inadequate, and projections in this study reflect these inadequacies. For oil pipelines, the statistics are too fragmentary even to attempt an estimate of future consumption. For gas pipelines, it has been assumed that shipping volume will grow as fast as the increase in natural gas production. As in the case of growth in the consumption of petroleum, coal, and natural gas, this increase had to be assumed prior to the completion of the study and it was taken as 110 per cent between 1955 and 1975. The only fuel for which consumption data for natural gas pipelines exist, however, is natural gas itself, though it is known, of course, that gas lines use substantial quantities of electricity. To cite an important instance, the Texas Eastern Transmission Company reported it had consumed about 1 billion kwh of electricity in 1955.[29] Thus, the pipeline treatment remains unsatisfactory also in the case of natural gas lines.

ALL TRANSPORTATION

Appendix Tables D-59 and D-60 pull together the over-all outcome of the numerous estimates whose derivation has been summarized in the foregoing pages and others not described in the text but which can be found in the Appendix tables. The classification scheme described at the outset of this section is employed in these tables to summarize the 1955 figures and the 1975 projections.

.   .   .

Government, Agriculture, and Miscellaneous

For various reasons, detailed below, data on the consumption of energy in the remainder of the economy—government, agriculture, and all other branches not treated separately—have to be compiled from widely scattered and often inconsistent sources. Since these sectors jointly account for less than 15 per cent of all energy consumption in 1955 and 1975, only the major assumptions utilized in the projection are here discussed. The details—and there are many of them, frequently intricate—have been incorporated in extensive footnotes to the statistical tables which are found in Sections E, F, and G of the Appendix

[29] F. P. Goertzen, "Use of Electric Power for Natural Gas Transmission," paper given before meeting of Petroleum Electric Power Association, Fort Worth, Texas, June 3-4, 1958.

to Part II. There, the reader interested in the precise derivation of the consumption pattern may follow all of the procedures used and reconstruct the estimates.

GOVERNMENT

Uncertainty of definition and coverage in the available statistics and, in some instances, inability altogether to identify and isolate energy streams entering government consumption render difficult even the determination of the 1955 pattern.

Proceeding by degree of complexity, identification of electricity consumption is relatively straightforward (Appendix Table E-1). Utility statistics carry two categories of consumption: "street and highway lighting" and "other public authorities."[30] This leaves AEC consumption to be determined separately (Appendix Table A-27) and omits government manufacturing activities which are included in industrial consumption. Some uncertainty attaches to consumption in military establishments which may not be fully covered under other public authorities. Projection to 1975 is based on past growth trends (Appendix Table E-2) supported in the instance of other public authorities by the assumption that there exists a relatively stable interrelationship between the scale of energy consumption in government activities and in commercial activity (as evidenced in past patterns—see Appendix Table E-4) and that this relationship will prevail also in the future. Projection of street and highway lighting, however, is based solely on a long and persistent growth trend of the category itself (Appendix Table E-3) without the demonstration of a fixed relationship to any other branch of the economy. As for future consumption by the AEC, we have taken our cue of stability from the fact that its power purchases have recently leveled off. An interesting symptom of this expectation is the fact that *Electrical World*, in its weekly reports, has ceased reporting separately on power purchased by the AEC, for the explicit reason that increases in AEC consumption had come to a halt.

Determination of gas consumption by government (Appendix Tables E-10 through E-12) seems simple at first glance. A statistical category called "other" includes, according to the definition supplied by the American Gas Association, sales to governmental customers as well as interdepartmental sales (the latter only when not accomplished on a rate basis as regular sales). The character of this group is somewhat uncertain. When five states—Tennessee, Texas, Kansas, New Mexico, and California—are subtracted from the total, the remainder is found to develop at a rate similar to that of commercial consumption (Appendix Table E-11, column 8). Therefore, this portion of natural gas consump-

---

[30] There is little doubt that a designation like other public authorities does not in fact coincide in coverage with all consumption by public bodies, even apart from the difficulties created by the military component. However, its broad meaning was considered sufficiently precise for the purpose of this projection.

tion by government was projected to 1975 on the assumption that it would grow at the same rate as commercial. As for the five other states, no satisfactory explanation was found for their departure from this pattern nor for their lack of a seasonal movement common to both residential and commercial consumption. It may be speculated that in these states such special aspects as sales to AEC installations (Tennessee) and to military establishments and centrally administered irrigation programs play an important role, but short of a state-by-state or company-by-company analysis this cannot be verified. Thus, the extraordinary amount of natural gas consumption in these states is considered as a special case, and this amount is assumed to remain unchanged in absolute terms to 1975.

The most serious difficulties arise with coal and oil. As for coal, only fragmentary statistics have been located; these would not permit even approximating the quantities consumed by government. Presumably, the sales of coal to government are included in retail deliveries, some perhaps in the industrial classification. In the case of petroleum, there is at least partial coverage: military consumption (Appendix Tables E-6 through E-9) and nonmilitary gasoline consumption, both on and off highways (Appendix Tables D-39 through D-42 and E-5). Past growth trends have been used as the ruling criteria for projection to 1975 of nonmilitary government consumption, with the precise nature of these assumptions stated in the footnotes to the Appendix tables cited. Statistical coverage stops short of other petroleum products (for example, fuel oil for space heating, diesel oil for construction and maintenance activity, etc.). These are covered in the commercial sector or the miscellaneous category (Appendix Table G-21)—it is not possible to state how much in each.[31]

The military segment, for obvious reasons, is difficult to handle. Here, projections of oil demand lean heavily on Department of Defense forecasts reaching to 1963 (Appendix Table E-6). In addition, the tenor of the explanations that accompanied the release of these forecasts has served as a clue to developments in the years following 1963. The ruling assumption in the military aviation field is that, after the very fast start, jet fuel will slow down in its rate of growth. At the same time, a small base quantity of aviation gasoline will remain in demand for many years to come. Fuel consumption by ground forces is projected substantially unchanged, while the principal problem in marine propulsion is the rate at which the Navy will substitute nuclear power for residual oil. One need hardly stress the conjectural nature of these projections. There are some fragmentary data available on consumption of gas and electricity in the

[31] An example of this type of difficulty is found in an advice contained in the U.S. Bureau of Mines, *Mineral Market Report*, No. MMS 2681, to the effect that all oil companies have been requested, beginning in 1956, to show as oil sales to the military the same figure as that developed by the Defense Department's Division of Petroleum Logistics, and therefore to include in the category also oil intended for heating government buildings (to the extent occupied by the Defense Department, it must be understood). Before 1956, such oil was classified as "heating oil" rather than military. Thus, it is probable that 1955 estimates of government consumption used in this study include no oil for space heating.

Army. As there is no certain way of relating tnese magnitudes, data for which were supplied by Army sources, to the sales categories set up by the trade associations reporting electric and gas sales, these data have not been used. In the main, these amounts are probably reported under government, so what is involved is the distribution of the government total between military and nonmilitary.

For the various reasons described above, the government category lacks coverage; compared to the other sectors, its consumption is somewhat, though probably not greatly, understated. Of course, the amounts omitted from the government statistics are covered, although not identified, in other consuming sectors, since all consumption in the economy is accounted for.[32]

AGRICULTURE

The coverage afforded to agricultural consumption in the standard sources as well as in this study is unsatisfactory in several respects. Even in the establishment of the 1955 consumption pattern, one encounters substantial obstacles. Conceptually, this sector should cover all energy consumed in the agricultural production process. However, while all household uses should be and are properly excluded, many uses connected with the farming process are also excluded.

This situation prevails in electricity use, as there is no satisfactory way of ascertaining consumption for any productive activity other than irrigation and pumping, which forms the subject of a broad estimate made by the Federal Power Commission (FPC). Otherwise, farm consumption is not identifiable, either *in toto* or in its constituent parts (household uses, productive uses). The customer class of "rural sales" is in no way coterminous with agricultural use, but constitutes merely a rate classification. To the extent that it covers farms, it presumably relates to the farm's total consumption; but it also covers nonfarming rural customers and, as is evident even from the small number of customers covered by the classification, is not comprehensive in its farm coverage. In this study's projections, the "rural" category as a whole has been assigned to residential consumption (Appendix Table C-19), and thus exaggerates the latter by having it include whatever farm uses (milking, cooling, incubators, etc.) might form part of rural sales.

In the petroleum field, the projector is somewhat better off.[33] Broader coverage is provided principally by a special Census Bureau report (relating to the year 1955) made in connection with the 1954 Census of Agriculture. As

---

[32] The one probable exception to this statement is the production and consumption of power generated and consumed by military establishments which, according to available evidence, is not reported in any available statistical series.

[33] It should also be noted that fuels consumed in automobile and truck transportation self-performed on farms is not separately identified as part of the agriculture sector's energy consumption. In this aspect, energy consumption in transportation in agriculture is treated no differently than in the industry and commercial sectors, but the failure to make separate identification may be more important relatively than in those sectors because of the significance of truck transportation as an element of total fuel consumption in agriculture.

is pointed out in the footnotes to Appendix Table F-1, however, the interpretation of some of the survey material presents substantial difficulties and defies satisfactory reconciliation with the standard source of fuel consumption data— the U.S. Bureau of Mines. Briefly, at the root of the dilemma is the fact that the Census carries a basket category entitled "tractor fuel" which has to be translated into specific petroleum products in order to fit into the general framework of this study. There is no entirely satisfactory method of doing this, not excepting the one used in Appendix Table F-1.

Beyond electricity and petroleum, this study provides no coverage for agricultural energy consumption. Partly, this results from the exclusion of wood, despite the fact that the consumption of wood is of some importance on farms. Partly, it is caused by the absence of usable data; such is the case for both gas and coal. Farms, as business operations (as opposed to places of living) reported consumption of natural gas in the 1954 Census of Agriculture. But the amount consumed, given only in dollars, is too small (about 1.0 per cent of the cost of all petroleum products reported to have been consumed by farms) to justify a separate volume estimate by way of average prices paid. Furthermore, as general gas statistics do not carry a farming or rural category, it would not, in any event, have been possible to make the corresponding adjustment in the gas statistics of the other user categories. Coal was not specifically reported to have been consumed in the production process, but a small amount of "non-petroleum fuel"—reported as little more in value than 0.5 per cent of all farm fuels— probably includes whatever coal was used.

The 1975 projection is based on two simple assumptions. For electricity, accepting the limitations of coverage for 1955, the projection made by the Federal Power Commission for 1980 (Appendix Table F-2) has been adopted, since the population basis underlying the FPC projection for 1980 is not far from that assumed here for 1975. For petroleum, a growth rate of 2 per cent per year has been assumed through 1975. Because of the basic difficulty of establishing the 1955 petroleum fuel pattern, no attempt has been made to use different projection rates for different types of petroleum fuels.

The rate of 2 per cent reflects the anticipation of a growth of that magnitude in farm output, based upon a 1956 U.S. Department of Agriculture study[34] but modified by the higher 1975 population base assumed in this study. Any error in this assumption on the growth rate undoubtedly is on the side of aiming the projection too high, for it is not likely that the larger requirements of food and fiber will call for a proportionate growth in the use of machinery. Anticipated cost advantages and consolidation of acreage, however, might lead to increases in machinery other than tractors. Compared to the record of the past two decades, the assumed growth rate appears miserly. According to a survey

[34] U.S. Department of Agriculture, Agricultural Research Service, *Farm Output, Past Changes and Projected Needs*, Agriculture Information Bulletin No. 162 (Washington, D. C.: U.S. Government Printing Office, August 1956).

of liquid petroleum fuel in agriculture,[35] fuel consumed by tractors increased at an annual rate of almost 7 per cent between 1940 and 1953, but the spread of machinery has recently slowed down sufficiently to make anything like this past rate appear unlikely.[36]

MISCELLANEOUS USES AND LOSSES

The activities covered under this heading represent with few exceptions uses in which the energy-generating capacity of the material is not the reason for its use. Rather, it is the physical and chemical characteristics other than combustibility that are exploited. One might therefore question whether the inclusion of these uses is not out of place in a description of current and projected energy demand. When it is recalled, however, that each of these uses represents a claim for materials that may be alternatively consumed for the generation of energy, it is obvious that they must be accounted for in any comprehensive aggregation of demand. In addition, the miscellaneous heading includes losses not accounted for elsewhere in this study.

Oil and, to a small degree, natural gas liquids, are the principal fuels considered in the miscellaneous sector. Natural gas enters the picture only in two instances. Coal is not considered at all, even though it has important uses as a chemical raw material. Gas consumption, with the sole exceptions of carbon black manufacture and waste, is exhaustively covered in the statistics of the American Gas Association whose use categories have been adhered to, sometimes with adjustments, throughout this study. Non-energy uses of gas—other than for carbon black production—are included in industrial gas consumption. Coal consumption is covered exhaustively in the various use classes employed in this study, with the industrial classification including all non-energy exploitation.

The miscellaneous uses covered fall roughly into three groups: First is the manufacture of well-defined end products, used either as such (for example, asphalt, road oil, lubricants) or in further manufacture (carbon black, wax, synthetic rubber, and the vast and growing family of petrochemicals that go into such fields as plastics, fertilizers, pharmaceuticals, insecticides, detergents, synthetic fibers, etc.). The second group is waste and losses. And the third is "odds and ends"—that is, the small amounts of major products such as distillates or kerosine, which are referred to as "miscellaneous" or "unaccounted for" and cover those instances in which exact use or application is unidentified.

[35] U.S. Department of Agriculture, Agricultural Research Service, Agricultural Marketing Service, *Liquid Petroleum Fuel Consumption for Farm Purposes*, Statistical Bulletin No. 188, July 1956, especially Table 5, p. 12.

[36] U.S. Department of Agriculture, Agricultural Research Service, Agricultural Marketing Service, *Changes in Farm Production and Efficiency, A Summary Report*, Statistical Bulletin No. 233, August 1958, especially Table 17.

The accounting for losses and other unidentified amounts is required (1) as a check on the completeness of the 1955 estimates, since all the separate uses in each energy source have been accounted for and the input into the economy as a whole is known; and (2) as a guide for the amounts that must be put into the 1975 projection to allow realistically for the miscellaneous uses and waste bound to occur in the energy economy.

There is little difficulty in putting together the 1955 consumption pattern for most of the products or uses. Most of them appear in published sources, and a few are derived as balancing amounts. For some products, however, meaningful projections to 1975 require a good deal of investigation into their relationships and uses, and in many instances the resulting projections retain a large arbitrary element.

Asphalt and carbon black (Appendix Tables G-11 through G-20) are two illustrations of this dilemma. The total quantity of asphalt consumed in 1955 is readily available in the standard sources. When the demand picture is analyzed, it turns out that there exist quite distinct use markets. Five use categories —road asphalt for new construction and for maintenance, roofing asphalt for new housing and for maintenance, and asphalt for other purposes—in the past have each followed their own course of development. Consequently, the projection is developed on the basis of distinct assumptions regarding future road building, road maintenance, and housing construction.

Similarly, the amounts projected for 1975 carbon black production are based on past trends in carbon black use in different fields: rubber manufacture, exports, and all other uses. The reader may feel that since the growth rates assumed often have a somewhat arbitrary basis, there is little point in setting up the different uses to which these rough rates are then applied. However, to identify distinctly different markets for identical products, even if projection of their growth is based on conjecture only, was deemed useful for building the detailed structure on which future estimates may be based, with a correspondingly smaller effort to be devoted in subsequent studies to disentangling the consumption structure.

Other than the sometimes intricate details of setting up the basic categories, this sector presents few major problems. Some, as the "home" category in petroleum statistics of the liquid hydrocarbons going into carbon black production, remain unresolved (Appendix Table G-16, footnote b). However, the quantitative effect of these difficulties is minor. In general, much weight has been given to past growth trends as explained in the footnotes to Appendix Table G-1.

. . .

Electricity, by Source of Energy

Unlike the preceding sectors—industry, households, transportation, etc.— electricity is not an energy-consuming sector within this study's analytic scheme.

The essential purpose of the statistical calculations performed in Appendix H is to bring together in one place the figures on electricity consumption which have already been derived in the statistical analyses for the energy-consuming sectors, and to translate these figures—for 1955 and as projected for 1975—into the fuels and waterpower (together referred to as "fuels" hereafter for simplicity's sake) required to generate the electricity. Each consuming sector can then be assigned the fuels needed to generate the electricity it consumes. In this way, it is possible to get a total for each sector which includes not only the fuels consumed directly, but also the amounts consumed indirectly via the use of electricity.

In attributing to each sector the fuels required to generate the electricity it consumes, the sector is not, of course, being charged with the equivalent in British thermal units (Btu) of the electric energy consumed, but with the Btu content of the energy required to produce and deliver the electricity consumed. The latter is several times the former owing to the sizable energy losses involved in converting the heat of fuels into electric energy, and the subsequent losses in transmission and distribution of electricity. It is because the losses in energy transformation are so large that an adequate accounting of fuel use must attribute to the consuming sector the calorific value of the fuel required rather than that of the electricity consumed. With the exceptions noted below, the energy losses are, for simplicity, allocated to the consuming sectors in direct proportion to their purchases of electricity.

THE 1955 PATTERN

Data on the purchases of electricity by the major consuming sectors are readily available; these are shown in Appendix Table H-1. The primary objective of the statistical calculations of most of the remaining tables in Section H of the Appendix to Part II dealing with 1955 (Appendix Tables H-2 through H-10) is to translate these figures on electricity consumption into the fuels required in their generation and delivery. Since the pattern and efficiency of fuel use in electricity generation and delivery is known to be different for some of the major components of total electricity consumption, these Appendix tables are devoted to identifying such components and the particular pattern of fuel use of each. The major components are utility generation, non-utility generation and its disposition, and AEC generation and consumption.

The total electricity sales, represented in Appendix Table H-1, are translated in Appendix Table H-2 into electricity generated and the fuels consumed in generation. The following components of total utility sales—each with its own fuel-input pattern—are identified: (1) utility generation, and (2) purchases by utilities from (a) industrial plants generating electricity, (b) AEC installations, and (c) imports. Another category is also identified in Appendix Table H-2: electricity purchases by AEC from utility systems. The latter is separately identified because enough is known about the utilities supplying AEC power to apply the particular fuel input pattern which is relevant to this component.

The statistics shown in Appendix Table H-2 are in good part derived from Appendix Tables H-3 through H-7, which supply the underlying data for deriving the separate patterns of fuel consumption and thermal efficiency for the AEC and for industrially generated electricity. Examination of these tables shows that statistics on fuels consumed in utility-generated electricity are obtained directly from the basic sources. But the statistics pertaining to fuel consumption for the other categories were derived in special ways. This was necessary not only because the grouping of industry chosen in the analysis of industrial fuel consumption had to be observed to complete the fuel analysis, but also because a considerable amount of estimating was required for factors connected solely with their electricity aspect.

In the first place, an assumption as to the amount sold to utilities had to be made (Appendix Table H-5). This was known for AEC and for the transit sector (where it is zero), but not for industry. Here the assumption was based mainly on some fragmentary data, not too recent in date and not too well defined in coverage.[37]

The second problem concerns the share of the different energy sources in non-utility generation. Again, this was known precisely for AEC generation (Appendix Table H-4). In the case of transit power, all of it was assumed to be coal-generated; this is probably only roughly true, but the entire amount is too small to cause concern. In the case of industry, the most important non-utility generator of electricity, resort was had to a somewhat more complex procedure. It was assumed that industrial generation in 1955 was 25 per cent less efficient than generation in utility systems. It happens that this lower efficiency is roughly equivalent to that achieved by utility systems in 1949 (Appendix Table H-7). Therefore, both the 1949 heat rate and fuel composition in utility generation have been used to estimate fuel consumption in industrial generation in 1955 (Appendix Table H-6). This is obviously a rough solution and is based on such factors as age of equipment, size of units, growth rates, and other equally general elements. There is general agreement that the thermal efficiency in non-utility generation is lower than that of utilities, but no comprehensive data or estimates in recent years have been assembled to establish the heat rate and, even less so, the fuel composition for non-utility generation and their relationship to the same factors in utility generation. Given the substantial role played by non-utility generation, research in this field would make a real contribution.

The special aspects of AEC purchases from utilities should also be noted (Appendix Table H-3). Transmission and other losses in AEC purchases from the utility system have been assumed at only 5 per cent of sales as compared with a factor of some 17 per cent of sales (or 12 per cent of generation) in the utility

---

[37] Since the completion of the study it has been found that the Federal Power Commission collects data concerning the purchase of electricity by electric utilities from non-utility sources on an individual utility basis but does not aggregate or publish these figures.

system as a whole. The rationale of this assumption is the low level of transmission losses, resulting from the proximity of the supplying utilities to the receiving AEC installations, and the absence of utility system distribution losses. Similarly, all thermal generation of AEC-supplying utilities is treated as coal burning. This is based upon what is known about the power stations involved (Appendix Table A-27).

Another assumption worth noting is the rate at which hydro-generation is converted into equivalent Btu's. This is merely a computational convention required for adding together hydro and fuels to get fuel input totals. For that purpose, as usual, the over-all heat rate of the thermal portion of utility generation has been ascribed to hydropower.

The outcome of the calculations is summarized in Appendix Tables H-8 and H-9 in accord with the energy-consuming sectors used in this study. Appendix Table H-8 deals only with utility sales (including the amounts purchased by utilities from other sources and resold) and, in effect, applies the sales pattern shown in Appendix Table H-1 to the fuel input picture shown in Appendix Table H-2. In Appendix Table H-9, electricity generated and retained by non-utilities for their own use is added to utility sales in order to show total electricity consumption and the fuels required in its generation for the several energy-consuming sectors.

THE 1975 PROJECTION

The estimation of electricity consumption in 1975 was, of course, a part of the projections for each of the energy-consuming sectors, and is described in the preceding discussions of these sectors and in the relevant Appendix sections. The purpose of the calculations here described is to translate the estimated 1975 electricity consumption of the various sectors into the particular sources of energy —fuels and water power—which will be required to produce and deliver the electricity. The steps employed in this translation differ only in detail from those just described for 1955, although facts are replaced by assumptions in the 1975 calculations. The factors of primary importance are (1) the assumed fuel (and hydro) shares, and (2) the assumed heat rates (that is, Btu's of fuel input per net kwh), both for utility and for industrial generation.

With regard to fuel (and hydro) shares in utility generation, a composition has been stipulated that takes as its point of origin the past trend and is shaped by both the opinion of experts and the authors' own judgment. As shown in Appendix Table H-15, other projections provide also for nuclear energy; the projection in this study does not. Thus, the other estimates are not directly comparable to this study. In addition, it is considered unlikely that, on the assumption of 1955 price conditions, the share of gas would drop as forecast in other projections. These other projections probably take into account the possibility of a relative increase in the price of gas delivered to electric utilities, whereas for this study the 1955 price pattern has been frozen. From the point of view of geographical distribution alone, there is the additional point that gas lines are continuing to expand into new areas and will, for economic operation, probably require the off-peak markets that electric utilities can provide. The 1975 fuel composition will, of course, depend also on the location of new power plants, which, in turn, will be affected by advances in electricity transmission. No assumptions have been made on this score.

As to heat rates in utility-produced electric energy, investigation of the subject led to acceptance of the judgment of Philip Sporn, one of the foremost U.S. authorities in the field, with regard to 1975 rates for each of the three fuels. As shown in Appendix Table H-25, the projected heat rates continue the upward trend in thermal efficiency, though at a somewhat less rapid pace—1.35 per cent compounded annually—than has prevailed, at times, in the past (Appendix Table H-26). As in 1955, we have used the resulting average heat rate as the hypothetical ratio for converting hydro generation into Btu's (Appendix Table H-24).

A final set of assumptions relates to fuel consumption in the industrial generation of electricity (Appendix Table H-18). Here, it has been assumed that there will be no change in fuel composition between 1955 and 1975. As for heat rates, an annual improvement of 1.25 per cent in fuel efficiency over the 1955 rate for industry is assumed. This has the effect of widening the gap in efficiency between utility and non-utility generation of electricity.

Growing disparity in efficiency between these two sources of electricity does not seem unwarranted for a number of reasons. Non-utility generation is often tied in with other phases of the industrial plant's operation (for example, steam or exhaust utilization or sometimes pressure differentials, as in the case of natural gas). Or it is wanted as a stand-by facility or as a source of power that, for a variety of reasons, has minimum voltage variations, or on other grounds which are not specifically oriented to cost with respect to electricity generation. In addition, the industrial stations tend to be small compared to utility stations,[38] and a growing differentiation in this respect can be confidently expected, given the much faster rate of capacity expansion in utilities, with increasingly larger units. This again will tend to widen the gap in efficiency.

A major assumption pertains to the amount of hydro-generated power that has been assumed for 1975 (Appendix Table H-16). This is not based on demand, since there is no such thing as separate demand for hydropower (although in certain localities demand for electricity may, in effect, mean demand for hydropower as the main, or only, source of supply in the area). Rather, it is based on

[38] In 1955, industrial electricity was generated by 2,852 plants with an average installed capacity of approximately 5,600 kw each, compared with an average capacity of approximately 30,000 kw each among all public utility stations. See U.S. Department of Commerce, *Statistical Abstract of the United States, 1957* (Washington, D. C.: U.S. Government Printing Office), p. 527, Table No. 656. The 455 largest steam-electric utility plants reporting to the Federal Power Commission in 1955 were responsible for 92 per cent of all net thermal generation in the United States, and had an average installed capacity of approximately 166,000 kw.

the 1975 estimate for developed hydro capacity (see Chapter 11). In the light of a declining utilization factor for hydroelectric capacity in the past, as indicated in Appendix Table H-14, a 1975 factor of only 45 per cent as compared to 54 per cent in 1955 has been assumed. Although this may appear low, the conservatism in the hydro assumption is deliberate: as hydro generation makes no claim on fuel resources, fuel requirements should not be underestimated on the basis of too high a projected rate of hydro utilization. This is consistent, moreover, with the allowance made in Chapter 11 for the use of pumped storage on a large scale for peaking purposes.

CHAPTER 6

Summary of the energy consumption estimates

The estimates derived according to the procedures and assumptions described in the preceding chapter may be examined from many different points of view. The most important for this study as a whole is to compare these estimates of consumption with the estimated availability of energy supplies in order to determine what difficulties, if any, might be encountered in satisfying the country's future needs. Another important aspect within the context of the total study is to consider the estimated future level and composition of consumption against the background of the historical record of energy use in the United States. Examination of the consumption estimates from these two points of view requires, however, the joint consideration of findings from Parts I, II, and III of this volume. It, therefore, is not undertaken in this chapter, but is done instead in Chapter 1.

The focus of this chapter, instead, is fixed on consumption only and on the terminal years of the projection: 1955 which serves as the base year and 1975 which marks the end of the twenty-year projection span. First presented within this setting are the 1975 projections and their comparison to the 1955 base, in terms both of total energy and of the individual energy sources from which the aggregate arises. Thereafter, an additional dimension, in the shape of what here is called the energy-consuming sectors, is examined from two points of view. The first point of departure is the energy sources, and attention is devoted entirely to the 1955 and 1975 pattern in which each of the sources is used by the consuming sectors. Next, emphasis shifts to the consuming sectors as the primary classification, and the estimates are examined in terms of the relative importance in each sector of each of the energy sources, both for 1955 and 1975.

By and large, energy consumption in 1955 is a matter of record, although establishing the 1955 patterns of consumption often involved considerable esti-

233

mation. But the assumptions made in projecting twenty years forward from the 1955 base are a matter of judgment, not fact. Although a great volume of factual information was analyzed in making these judgments, their validity can be assessed only as the future unfolds.

The results are implied in the assumptions employed, which are described in full detail in the preceding chapter and the Appendix to Part II. This chapter does not evaluate the estimates; it is purely descriptive. The large number of bits and pieces which have been separately estimated are added together to yield totals for the various energy sources, the several energy-consuming sectors, and the economy as a whole, and these are described from the three points of view indicated above. Although 1975 will be referred to repeatedly in the following pages as the year to which the estimates of the future apply, it should be taken as a shorthand way of designating a year which follows the base period by about twenty years.

THE LEVEL AND COMPOSITION OF ENERGY CONSUMPTION

To provide perspective on the estimated changes in energy consumption between 1955 and 1975 it is helpful to begin with the aggregate level of energy consumption and compare this with two other aggregates—gross national product (GNP) and population. Although such aggregate relationships do not provide a dependable basis for making projections, they do offer a convenient means of summarizing results at the most general level.

The relevant figures are summarized in Table 64 and Figure 31. When the various energy commodities which have been separately estimated are added together in terms of British thermal units (Btu's) contained, the total is found

TABLE 64.   ENERGY CONSUMPTION, GROSS NATIONAL PRODUCT, AND POPULATION, 1955 AND ESTIMATED 1975

Item	1955 (1)	1975 estimates (2)	Percentage change 1955–75 (3)	Average annual rate of change 1955–75 (4)
Energy consumption (trillion Btu)[a].	39,723	74,541	+88%	+3.2%
Gross national product (billion 1955 dollars)[b]	$391	$857	+119	+4.0
Population (millions)[b]	165.3	233.0	+41	+1.7
GNP per capita (1955 dollars)	$2,365	$3,678	+56	+2.2
Energy consumption per capita (million Btu)	240.3	319.9	+33	+1.4
Energy consumption per unit of GNP (thousand Btu per 1955 dollar of GNP)	102	87	−15	−0.8

[a] From Table 66.
[b] From Appendix Table I-1.

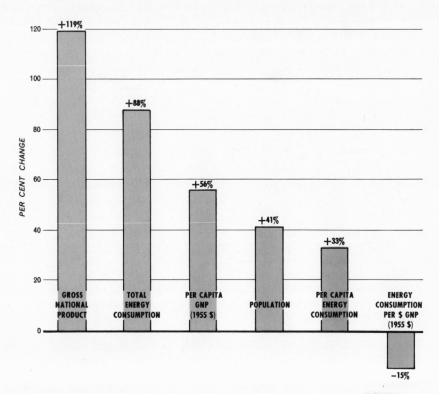

Figure 31. Energy consumption, gross national product, and population; percentage change, 1955–75.

to grow by 88 per cent between 1955 and 1975. Thus, the growth in energy consumption in the twenty-year period turns out to be more than twice as great as the assumed population increase of 41 per cent, but falls short of the increase of 119 per cent assumed for GNP. On a per capita basis, the assumed increase in GNP of more than 50 per cent is found to require an increase of 33 per cent in energy consumption. Over the twenty-year period, therefore, there is a resultant 15 per cent decline in the quantity of energy consumption necessary to support a fixed amount of total national product (that is, a constant dollar of GNP). Expressed in terms of average rates of change, the assumed increases of 4 per cent per year in GNP and 1.7 per cent per year in population call forth an annual increase in energy consumption of 3.2 per cent.

The figures for the individual energy sources which underlie the energy aggregate are shown in Tables 65 and 66 and Figures 32, 33, and 34. In Table 65 they are measured in the physical units customary for the particular energy commodity, and in Table 66 they are measured in Btu's which, when summed, yield the energy total shown in Table 64.

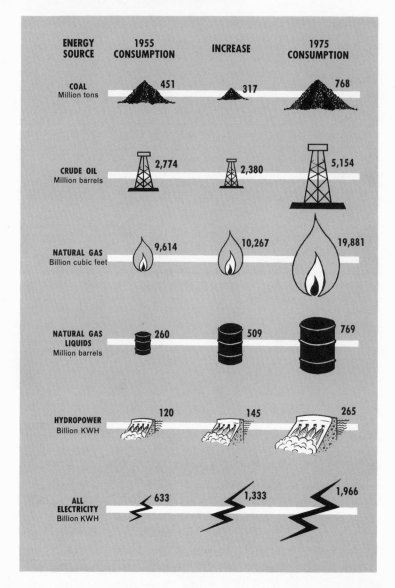

Figure 32.   Energy consumption in physical units, 1955 and estimated 1975.

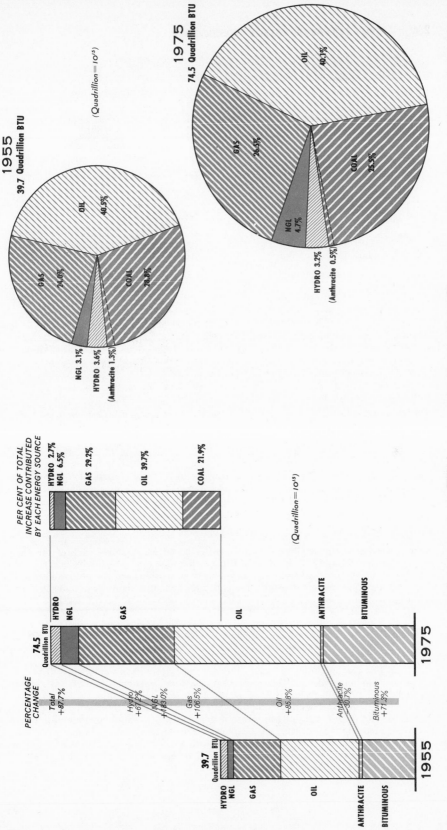

Figure 34. *The energy source mix—percentage of total by energy source—1955 and estimated 1975.*

Figure 33. *The energy source mix, 1955 and estimated 1975.*

TABLE 65. PHYSICAL UNITS OF ENERGY CONSUMPTION,
BY SOURCE, 1955 AND ESTIMATED 1975

Energy source	Consumption		Absolute change (3)	Percentage change (4)
	1955 (1)	1975 (2)		
Coal (million tons).....................	451	768	+ 317	+ 70.3
Bituminous[a]........................	431	754	+ 323	+ 74.9
Anthracite[a]........................	20	14	− 6	− 30.0
Crude oil (million bbl.)[b].................	2,774	5,154	+ 2,380	+ 85.8
Natural gas (billion cu. ft.)[c].............	9,614	19,881	+10,267	+106.8
Natural gas liquids (million bbl.)[d]........	260	769	+ 509	+195.8
Hydropower (billion kwh)[e]..............	120	265	+ 145	+120.8
Consumed as electricity (billion kwh)[f]....	633	1,966	+ 1,333	+210.6

[a] From Appendix Tables A–37, B–9, C–6, C–39, D–59, H–9, and H–17. The allocation between anthracite and bituminous is not exact: about 3 million tons of anthracite consumed at electric utilities in 1955 (see Appendix Table A–6) are included within the bituminous coal total, because in projecting coal consumption by electric utilities in 1975 no separate estimate was made for anthracite.

[b] Derived from total of petroleum product mix (see Table 71), assuming 5.8 million Btu per barrel of crude oil.

[c] From Appendix Tables A–37, B–9, C–6, C–39, D–59, E–13, G–1, H–9, and H–17. Includes that portion of natural gas which is stripped in extraction of NGL (see Appendix Tables A–3 and A–19).

[d] Data from Appendix Tables A–37, B–9, C–6, C–39, D–59, E–13, F–3, and G–1. Total thus derived adjusted by subtracting amounts of LPG originating in petroleum refining (see footnote b, Table 66). The resulting increase in the rate of extraction of NGL from natural gas consumption is in line with past experience. It is well within the practical limits of NGL extraction (see Chapter 10).

[e] From Appendix Tables H–9 and H–17.

[f] From Table 76.

NOTE: This table is generally comparable to Table 66 which shows each of the energy sources in 1955 and 1975 in terms of Btu's rather than in physical units as in this table. However, the physical unit-Btu conversion relationships are not always identical in 1955 and 1975 and consequently the percentage changes shown here differ in varying degrees from those shown in Table 66. The physical unit-Btu relationships differ in the two years for the following reasons:

1) Somewhat different Btu values are applicable to fuels used in electricity generation than in other uses (see Appendix Tables H–2 and H–6). Hence, the changing relative importance of electricity generation in a fuel's total consumption between 1955 and 1975 will affect the over-all physical unit-Btu relationship.

2) The various products constituting the NGL total have somewhat different Btu values per physical unit. Hence the changing product composition of NGL between 1955 and 1975 affects the over-all physical unit-Btu relationship.

3) Total electricity and hydropower are measured in this table in terms of kwh. In Table 66 they are measured in terms of the fuels which would be required to produce these amounts of electricity. Since an increase in efficiency in electric power generation is assumed between 1955 and 1975, the kwh increase (shown in this table) is substantially greater than the increase in fuel requirements or the fuel equivalent of hydro (shown in Table 66).

TABLE 66. BTU'S OF ENERGY CONSUMPTION, BY SOURCE,
1955 AND ESTIMATED 1975

Energy source	Consumption (trillion Btu)		Percentage share of each fuel in total change	Percentage change in Btu consumption	Percentage share of each energy source in total Btu consumption	
	1955 (1)	1975 (2)	(3)	(4)	1955 (5)	1975 (6)
Total..............	39,723	74,541	100.0%	+ 87.7%	100.0%	100.0%
Coal..............	11,422	19,043	+ 21.9	+ 66.7	28.8	25.5
Bituminous ª......	10,910	18,688	+ 22.3	+ 71.3	27.5	25.1
Anthracite ª.......	512	355	− 0.4	− 30.7	1.3	0.5
Oil ᵇ..............	16,090	29,896	+ 39.7	+ 85.8	40.5	40.1
Natural gas ᶜ........	9,552	19,726	+ 29.2	+106.5	24.0	26.5
Natural gas liquids ᵈ..	1,235	3,495	+ 6.5	+183.0	3.1	4.7
Hydropower ᵉ.......	1,424	2,381	+ 2.7	+ 67.2	3.6	3.2
Consumed as electricity ᵉ........	7,680	18,053	+ 29.8	+135.1	19.3	24.2

ª From Appendix Tables A–37, B–9, C–6, C–40, D–60, H–9, and H–17. The allocation between anthracite and bituminous is not exact: about 85 trillion Btu of anthracite consumed at electric utilities in 1955 (see Appendix Table A–6) are included within the bituminous coal total, because in projecting coal consumption by electric utilities in 1975 no separate estimate was made for anthracite.

ᵇ Total from Table 69 increased by 169 and 321 trillion Btu in 1955 and 1975 respectively. These are amounts of LPG which originate in petroleum refining and are generally included with NGL in statistics in this study. The 1955 figure—1,768,772,000 gallons—is taken from U. S. Bureau of Mines, *Minerals Yearbook, 1956*, Vol. II (Washington, D. C.: U. S. Government Printing Office), p. 302. The 1975 figure is derived by raising the 1955 figure by 90 per cent which represents the approximate estimated increase in petroleum demand between 1955 and 1975.

ᶜ From Table 72, but, to eliminate double counting, is adjusted to exclude the Btu equivalent of the hydrocarbons stripped from the gas in the production of NGL (see Appendix Tables A–3 and A–19).

ᵈ From Table 74, with deduction for LPG originating in oil industry rather than in natural gas industry, as explained in footnote ᵇ above.

ᵉ From Appendix Tables H–9 and H–17.

NOTE: Totals may not add because of rounding and may, for the same reason, differ slightly from comparable totals in other text tables.

The quantities in column 2 of Table 65 are, in a sense, the end products of the entire estimating procedure. Here are the estimated quantities of energy materials that, under the given assumptions, will be called upon to satisfy the needs of the economy in 1975. In all instances except anthracite, which shows a decline, estimated consumption in 1975 reaches into new high levels. Compared to 1955, bituminous coal increases about 75 per cent, crude oil about 85 per cent, natural gas more than doubles, and consumption of natural gas liquids (NGL) almost triples. The greatest increase of all is estimated not for a primary energy source, but for electricity, which rises to over three times the 1955 level; hydropower, a component of the electricity total, is estimated to more than **double**.

When the quantities are reduced to the Btu common denominator, as in Table 66, the changes in the relative importance of the various energy materials can be measured. By and large, as columns 5 and 6 reveal, the relative shares are not estimated to change much between 1955 and 1975. The most significant change among the primary energy sources involves a switch in the relative positions of coal and natural gas. Coal, which held second place in 1955 with 28.8 per cent of the total, is estimated to fall back to third place in 1975, with just over one-quarter of all energy; while gas, which was third in 1955 with 24 per cent, is estimated to move to second place in 1975 with 26.5 per cent of the total. Oil, with about two-fifths of the total, holds first place in both years. The largest increase in relative importance is experienced by natural gas liquids, which rise from 3.1 per cent to 4.7 per cent of the total, and by the aggregate Btu value of the energy sources consumed in electric power generation, which rises from about one-fifth of the total in 1955 to almost one-quarter in 1975.

In Btu terms, it is possible also to measure the percentage contribution of each fuel to the total estimated increase of energy consumption from 1955 to 1975 (Table 66, column 3). In the total increase of almost 35,000 trillion Btu (equivalent say to about one and a third billion tons of bituminous coal), oil contributes almost 40 per cent; gas close to 30 per cent; and coal about 22 per cent. The remaining 9 per cent consists of natural gas liquids and hydro-generated power (expressed in terms of the fuel equivalents which would have been required in its generation). These statistics indicate also that 30 per cent of the estimated increase in 1975 compared to 1955 is accounted for by fuels required for the generation of electric power.

These estimates of the future are in sharp contrast with past developments, as described in Part I, in one important respect: The drastic losses experienced historically by coal relative to oil and gas are replaced in this period by comparative stability in the percentage shares of these three energy sources in the total. The main reasons underlying this change are discussed in Chapter 1; however, it is relevant to point out here that the relative stability of coal's position depends in substantial degree on its estimated role in providing fuel for the projected expansion of electric power generation.

THE ENERGY SOURCES:
CONSUMPTION PATTERN ACCORDING TO SECTORS

The preceding section has dealt with the relationships between total energy consumption and other economic aggregates, and has described the composition of the energy total in 1955 and as estimated for 1975 in terms of the specific energy sources comprising the total. Here, each energy source is accounted for in 1955, and as estimated for 1975, in terms of the amounts used in the various consuming sectors. The breakdown by sectors is useful in uncovering the factors underlying the foregoing estimated changes in the level of consumption for the different energy sources.

The main burden of the description is in every instance borne by the tables and figures containing the statistics for 1955 and 1975; the text serves chiefly to identify some of the leading features revealed by them. Tables are presented for the primary energy sources—coal (including bituminous and anthracite), oil, natural gas, and natural gas liquids—and also for electric energy (which is not an additional primary source except as it is hydro-generated, but is instead transformed from primary energy sources). Electricity is covered also in the tables for those primary energy sources which are consumed in the generation of electric energy. Electricity appears twice in such tables, once as a direct consumer of fuel on an equal footing with each of the consuming sectors, and again in a separate column in which it is considered an indirect form of fuel consumption. In the latter case, the fuel required in the generation of electricity is distributed among the sectors in which the fuel has been indirectly consumed via electricity. "Direct consumption" in these tables refers to the consumption of fuels before they have gone through the transformation to electric energy, although they may have gone through other transformations such as the refining of crude oil to produce gasoline, diesel oil, the stripping of liquids from natural gas, etc. (Use of the term "direct" is shorthand for "not by way of electricity." It does not establish any presumption that there are not other flows of energy that might legitimately be called indirect.)

For purposes of uniformity in presentation and in order to maintain comparability among the statistics presented in this and the following section, measurement for the primary energy sources is in Btu terms (see Appendix "Note on Problems of Measurement"). Thus, these results differ somewhat from measurements based on the customary physical units—tons, barrels, etc.

. . .

Coal

Total coal consumption, including bituminous coal and anthracite, is estimated to rise about two-thirds between 1955 and 1975. The outstanding characteristic of this increase, as revealed by Tables 67 and 68 and Figures 35 and 36, is that it results almost entirely from the estimated increase in the use of coal for generating electricity. In all other uses, the net growth in coal consumption between 1955 and 1975 is only 5 per cent, while coal for electricity generation is estimated to grow by over 170 per cent. The importance of electricity to coal's future growth is illustrated also by other measures: electricity generation accounts for over 95 per cent of the total increase in estimated 1975 consumption above consumption in 1955, and electricity's share of total coal consumption rises from less than 40 per cent in 1955 to over 60 per cent in 1975.

A significant characteristic of coal consumption is revealed by comparing its direct consumption in each of the different sectors with that sector's coal consumption, including the amounts indirectly consumed via electricity. Thus, in terms of direct coal consumption the only consuming sector which shows an estimated increase between 1955 and 1975 is industry—by about 30 per cent. The other sectors for which separate statistics are available—commercial, house-

TABLE 67. BITUMINOUS COAL AND ANTHRACITE CONSUMPTION, BY SECTOR, 1955 AND ESTIMATED 1975

(Trillion Btu)

Sector	1955			1975		
	Direct consumption (1)	Via electricity (2)	Total (3)	Direct consumption (4)	Via electricity (5)	Total (6)
Total..............	} 11,422 [a] } 7,179 [b]	4,242	11,422	} 19,043 [a] } 7,525 [b]	11,518	19,043
Industry [c]..........	5,012	2,112	7,124	6,528	6,067	12,595
Commercial [d].......	896	570	1,466	597	1,773	2,370
Households [e].......	938	870	1,808	400	2,748	3,148
Transportation [f].....	333	54	387	0	30	30
Government [g].......	[h]	581	581	[h]	822	822
Agriculture [i].......	[h]	56	56	[h]	79	79
Miscellaneous uses and losses........	[h]			[h]		
Electricity generation [j].............	4,242			11,518		

[a] Including amounts consumed in electricity generation.
[b] Excluding amounts consumed in electricity generation.
[c] From Appendix Table A-37.
[d] From Appendix Table B-9.
[e] From Appendix Tables C-6 and C-40.
[f] From Appendix Table D-60.
[g] From Appendix Table E-13.
[h] Included in other categories; not separately reported or derived.
[i] From Appendix Table F-4.
[j] Including non-utility generation.

NOTE: Totals may not add because of rounding.

holds, and transportation—all show substantial declines: 33 per cent, 57 per cent, and 100 per cent, respectively. However, the picture changes considerably when coal consumption via electricity is added to direct consumption. On this basis, the estimated growth in industry's consumption is about 77 per cent, in commercial about 62 per cent, and in households close to 75 per cent. Only transportation shows a substantial decline in both instances, because of the assumed disappearance of coal-fired locomotives—almost an accomplished fact at this time—and the assumed decline in electrically powered rail transport (including railroads and urban and interurban transit systems).

The marked effect of allocating to the consuming sectors the coal consumed in electricity generation may be seen also in the measure of each sector's contribution to the total increase in coal consumption in 1975 compared to 1955, and in the measure of the percentage share of each sector in total coal consumption in 1955 and 1975. The latter statistics show that the decline in relative importance of various sectors as direct consumers between 1955 and 1975 is replaced by an over-all comparative stability when indirect consumption via electricity is included. Thus, including coal consumed via electricity, industry's relative share rises from 62 per cent to 66 per cent, and commercial and house-

TABLE 68. COAL: CHANGES IN THE PATTERN OF CONSUMPTION, 1955-75

Sector	Percentage share in total consumption				Percentage change 1955-75		Percentage share of each sector in total increase	
	Direct consumption		Direct consumption and consumption via electricity		Direct consumption (5)	Direct consumption and consumption via electricity (6)	Direct consumption (7)	Direct consumption and consumption via electricity (8)
	1955 (1)	1975 (2)	1955 (3)	1975 (4)				
Total..................	100.0%	100.0%	100.0%	100.0%	+66.7%[a] / +4.8[b]	+66.7%	100.0%	100.0%
Industry.................	43.9	34.3	62.4	66.1	+30.2	+76.8	19.9	71.8
Commercial.............	7.8	3.1	12.8	12.4	-33.4	+61.7	-3.9	11.9
Households.............	8.2	2.1	15.8	16.5	-57.4	+74.1	-7.1	17.6
Transportation..........	2.9	0	3.4	0.2	-100.0	-92.2	-4.4	-4.7
Government.............	[c]	[c]	5.1	4.3	[c]	+41.5	[c]	3.2
Agriculture.............	[c]	[c]	0.5	0.4	[c]	+41.1	[c]	0.3
Miscellaneous uses and losses......	[c]	[c]			[c]		[c]	
Electricity generation[d]............	37.1	60.5			+171.5		95.5	

[a] Including amounts consumed in electricity generation.
[b] Excluding amounts consumed in electricity generation.
[c] Included in other categories; not separately reported or derived.
[d] Including non-utility generation.

SOURCE: Based on Table 67.

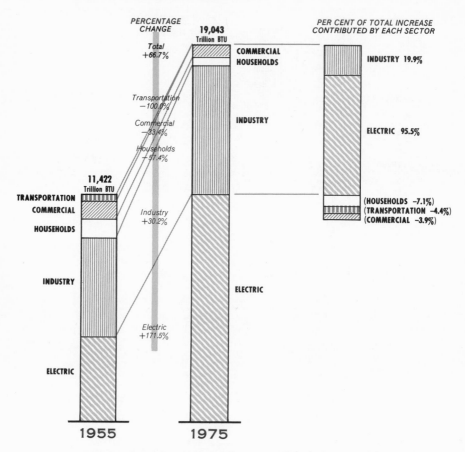

Figure 35.   Coal consumption, by sectors, 1955 and estimated 1975.

holds hold firm at about 12 per cent and 16 per cent, respectively, in contrast to the sizable declines in relative shares of all three as direct coal consumers.

The allocation to the sectors of coal consumed indirectly via the use of electricity is, of course, an analytic device which has no counterpart in the world of commerce. From a commercial point of view, the markets for coal consist of the customers who consume coal directly. Only the houseowner who burns coal in his furnace is a customer, not the purchaser of electric power who consumes kilowatt hours to cook his meals or watch television. Looking at coal consumption from the seller's point of view—that is, ignoring the diversity of coal's customers when coal has been transformed into kilowatts—estimated coal consumption in 1975 is composed almost wholly of two broad markets which together account for 95 per cent of the total. The first is industry, with more than one-third of the total; the second, electricity, with about three-fifths. These two markets were already dominant in 1955, when together they accounted for somewhat more than 80 per cent of the total consumption. Between 1955 and 1975,

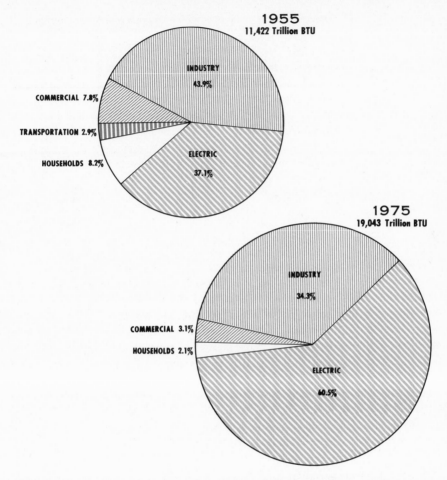

Figure 36. Coal consumption—percentage of total by sector—1955 and estimated 1975.

the estimates indicate not only a strengthening in the dominant position of the two markets, but also a reversal in the relative importance of industry and of electricity. While industry was first among coal consumers in 1955, with 44 per cent of the total, and electricity second with 37 per cent, the far greater growth in electricity than in industry during the twenty-year period makes electricity first by a wide margin in 1975.[1]

---

[1] The statistics on direct consumption in Tables 67 and 68 include that portion of electricity which is self-generated by industry within the electricity totals rather than the industry totals. In fact, therefore, industry's direct purchases of coal in 1955, and as estimated for 1975, are greater than the figures cited in this paragraph would indicate. About 16 per cent of all coal consumed for electricity generation in 1955, and about 10 per cent as estimated for 1975, is for electricity self-generated within industry. (See Appendix Tables H-9 and H-17.)

Industry is, of course, a broad category which includes a large number of specific manufacturing and mining industries, but within this total one manufacturing industry—iron and steel—is of dominant importance as a coal consumer. For all purposes (including self-generated electricity), coal consumption by the iron and steel industry was about 110 million tons in 1955 and is estimated to rise to 175 million tons in 1975 (Appendix Tables A-1 and A-18), equivalent to about 50 per cent and 58 per cent, respectively, of total industrial coal consumption (including amounts used for self-generated electricity) in these two years. Coal's future fortunes thus seem tied decisively to two specific consumers, electric utilities and iron and steel, with electric utilities by far the more important.

. . .

Oil

There are divergent movements within the increase of 86 per cent in annual oil consumption estimated to take place between 1955 and 1975, and presented in Tables 69 and 70 and Figures 37 and 38. But, by and large, oil consumption increases more uniformly in all the consuming sectors than does coal. The major exception is the continuing concentration of oil consumption in the field of transportation: first in 1955, with somewhat more than 40 per cent of the total, it affirms its rank in 1975, with an increase in its percentage share to more than 50 per cent of the total. Transportation's growth in relative importance in the total is, of course, a reflection of the much greater increase in the estimated consumption of oil products in transportation services than in any of the other consuming sectors (columns 5 and 6, Table 70). As a consequence, almost two-thirds of the estimated net increase in the annual consumption of oil products in 1975 as compared to 1955 is accounted for by transportation.

Within the transportation total, a large share is accounted for by private automobiles ("transportation self-performed by households" in the terminology of Tables 69 and 70). In 1955, about one-fifth of all oil products consumed was used by private automobiles, and in 1975 it is estimated that close to one-quarter of the total will be so used. Thus, in both years, the private automobile accounts for close to one-half of all oil products used in transportation; but owing to the even faster growth estimated for general transportation, its relative importance within the transportation total is estimated to decline somewhat between 1955 and 1975.

Although between 1955 and 1975 households are estimated to increase in relative importance as oil consumers via the private automobile, consumption of oil for direct use within the home (essentially space and water heating) is estimated to fall sharply in relative importance: from 14.5 per cent of the total in 1955, to 8 per cent in 1975. These percentages are changed only slightly if oil consumed indirectly via electricity is also taken into account. The decline in the relative importance of households as direct consumers of oil reflects the

TABLE 69. OIL CONSUMPTION,[a] BY SECTOR, 1955 AND ESTIMATED 1975

(Trillion Btu)

Sector	1955			1975		
	Direct consumption (1)	Via electricity (2)	Total (3)	Direct consumption (4)	Via electricity (5)	Total (6)
Total..............	15,921[b] 15,291[c]	630	15,921	29,575[b] 28,375[c]	1,200	29,575
Industry[d]..........	2,666	370	3,036	4,621	729	5,350
Commercial[d].......	737	91	828	1,321	168	1,489
Households[d].......	2,316	139	2,455	2,356	260	2,616
Transportation[d].....	6,698	5	6,703	15,435	3	15,438
of which:						
Self-performed by households......	3,276		3,276	7,033		7,033
Self-performed by government (excluding military)	90		90	177		177
General transportation...........	3,332	5	3,337	8,225	3	8,228
Government[d].......	760	16	776	1,048	33	1,081
Agriculture[d].......	515	9	524	766	7	773
Miscellaneous uses... and losses[e]........	1,598	[f]	1,598	2,827	[f]	2,827
Electricity generation[g].......	630			1,200		

[a] Measured in terms of petroleum products, converted to their Btu equivalents.

[b] Including amounts consumed in electricity generation.

[c] Excluding amounts consumed in electricity generation.

[d] From Appendix Table I-13.

[e] From Appendix Table G-1.

[f] Included in other categories; not separately reported or derived.

[g] Including non-utility generation.

NOTE: Totals may not add because of rounding.

comparatively small percentage increase estimated for direct household oil consumption between 1955–75 (columns 5 and 6, Table 70). In the main, oil's relatively poor showing in direct household consumption mirrors the assumptions which have been made about the further inroads of gas in home heating at the expense of oil (Appendix Tables C-9 and C-10).

Of the three major consuming sectors in 1955, the two just discussed—transportation and direct household use—show opposite movements in terms of relative shares; transportation sharply upward, direct household use sharply downward. The third sector, industry, shows almost no change in relative importance, accounting for about 16 per cent of direct consumption of oil products in both years, and about 19 per cent of direct consumption plus consumption via electricity. Industry as an oil consumer consequently takes a firm hold on second place among the sectors in 1975 (although far behind transportation), and is also second to transportation in its contribution to the estimated net increase in annual oil consumption in 1975 above the 1955 level.

TABLE 70. OIL: CHANGES IN THE PATTERN OF CONSUMPTION, 1955–75

Sector	Percentage share in total consumption				Percentage change 1955–75		Percentage share of each sector in total increase	
	Direct consumption		Direct consumption and consumption via electricity		Direct consumption (5)	Direct consumption and consumption via electricity (6)	Direct consumption (7)	Direct consumption and consumption via electricity (8)
	1955 (1)	1975 (2)	1955 (3)	1975 (4)				
Total..........	100.0%	100.0%	100.0%	100.0%	{+85.8%[a] / +85.6%[b]	+85.8%	100.0%	100.0%
Industry...........	16.7	15.6	19.1	18.1	+73.3	+76.2	14.3	16.9
Commercial.........	4.6	4.5	5.2	5.0	+79.2	+79.8	4.3	4.8
Households.........	14.5	8.0	15.4	8.8	+1.7	+6.6	0.3	1.2
Transportation.....	42.1	52.2	42.1	52.2	+130.4	+130.3	64.0	64.0
of which:								
Self-performed by households.....	20.6	23.8	20.6	23.8	+114.7	+114.7	27.5	27.5
Self-performed by government (excluding military)......	0.6	0.6	0.6	0.6	+96.7	+96.7	0.6	0.6
General transportation......	20.9	27.8	20.9	27.8	+146.8	+146.6	35.8	35.8
Government.........	4.8	3.5	4.9	3.7	+37.9	+39.3	2.1	2.2
Agriculture........	3.2	2.6	3.3	2.6	+48.7	+47.5	1.8	1.8
Miscellaneous uses and losses......	10.0	9.6	10.0	9.6	+76.9	+76.9	9.0	9.0
Electricity generation [c]......	4.0	4.1			+90.5		4.2	

[a] Including amounts consumed in electricity generation.
[b] Excluding amounts consumed in electricity generation.
[c] Including non-utility generation.

SOURCE: Based on Table 69.

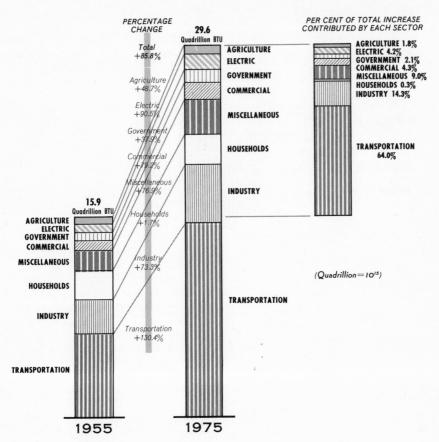

Figure 37. Consumption of petroleum products, by sector, 1955 and estimated 1975.

Oil shares with coal the characteristic of being highly dependent, and increasingly so, on two consuming sectors for supporting its future growth. The character and degree of dependence differ, however, in the two instances. First, the main consuming sector is different: coal's future is dominated by electric generation, while oil's future is tied—though less strongly—to transportation. Second, transportation as a sector is composed of a large number of different types of uses subject to different influences, whereas electric generation is a homogeneous category. Industry, a heterogeneous sector, is in second place for both coal and oil as a source of future growth, although coal is more dependent on industry as a market than is oil.

Oil's lesser degree of dependence than coal on one or two markets is further helped by the importance of the category "miscellaneous uses and losses" which is the fourth largest category in 1955 and third largest in 1975. Non-energy uses (comprising asphalt, road oil, lubricants, and miscellaneous oils) make

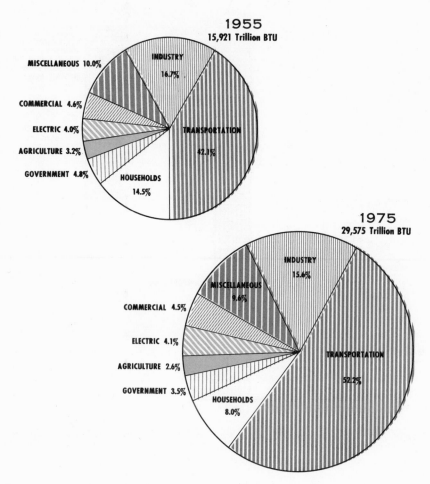

Figure 38.   Consumption of petroleum products—percentage of total by sector —1955 and estimated 1975.

up the bulk of the category and are a further source of strength in the growth of oil consumption. The equivalent non-energy (chemical) uses of coal are insignificant relative to total coal use. All in all, there is greater diversity in oil's sources of future growth than in coal's, despite the concentration of growth in two consuming sectors for both fuels.

More so than any of the other energy sources, crude oil appears on the market in the form of a large number of different fuel products. The pattern of consumption in 1955 and as estimated for 1975 in terms of the various products is presented in Table 71 and Figures 39 and 40. The petroleum product mix, as the term is used in Table 71, consists of the petroleum commodities that enter the domestic economy, and therefore includes imported products such

TABLE 71.   PETROLEUM PRODUCT MIX, 1955 AND ESTIMATED 1975

Product	Consumption (trillion Btu)		Per cent increase in consumption 1955–75 (3)	Percentage share in total consumption	
	1955 (1)	1975 (2)		1955 (4)	1975 (5)
Gasoline [a]	6,127	12,922	110.9%	38.1%	43.2%
Kerosine [a]	711	1,636	130.1	4.4	5.5
Distillates [a]	3,342	4,881	46.1	20.8	16.3
Residual [a]	3,542	5,825	64.5	22.0	19.5
Still gas [b]	887	1,828	106.1	5.5	6.1
Lubricants [c]	258	360	39.5	1.6	1.2
Coke (in all uses) [d]	146	444	204.1	0.9	1.5
Asphalt and road oil [c]	614	748	121.8	3.8	2.5
Naphtha [c]	126	239	89.7	0.8	0.8
All other and losses [e]	168	692	311.9	1.0	2.3
Liquefied refinery gases [f]	169	321	89.9	1.1	1.1
Total	16,090 [g]	29,896 [g]	85.8	100.0	100.0

[a] Appendix Table I-13.
[b] Appendix Table A-37.
[c] Appendix Table G-1.
[d] Appendix Tables A-37 and G-1.
[e] Appendix Table G-1 (miscellaneous oils, petroleum wax, gasoline losses) and Table A-37 (acid sludge).
[f] Table 66, footnote b.
[g] Differs from totals in Table 69 because of inclusion of liquefied refinery gases ordinarily carried in the statistics with NGL (see Table 66, footnote b).

NOTE: Totals may not add because of rounding.

as residual fuel oil. Thus, it differs from the refinery mix, for which statistics are ordinarily cited, which refers to the composition of products as they emerge from domestic refinery operations.

Three items dominate the petroleum product mix—gasoline, distillates, and residual fuel oil. Gasoline is the only one of the three which is estimated to increase in relative importance between 1955 and 1975—from 38 to 43 per cent of the total product mix. This increase is, of course, a reflection of the assumptions made regarding automotive transportation and is consistent with the increasing importance of transportation as a consuming sector. Distillates show a relatively small growth between 1955 and 1975, leading to a decline in their relative importance in the total product mix from roughly 21 per cent to 16 per cent. This is due chiefly to the modest increase in fuel oil for household use, which constitutes the major market for distillates. Residual fuel oil is also estimated to grow less than the average between 1955 and 1975, leading to a decline in its relative importance. This product is not dominated by a particular use to anything like the same extent as gasoline and distillates, so that there is no single development which is especially responsible for its relatively slow absolute increase and its consequent decline in relative importance. A fuller understanding of the factors lying behind the estimated developments in residual fuel oil and the other principal petroleum products will be gained through examining Appendix Table I-13.

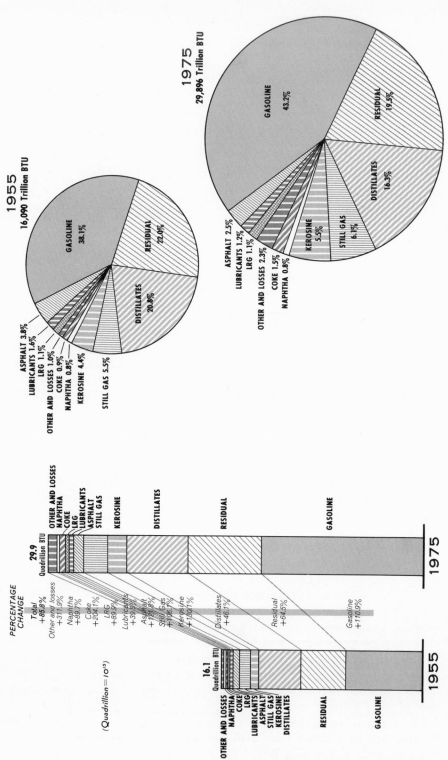

Figure 40. Petroleum product mix—percentage of total by
and estimated 1975

Figure 39. Petroleum product mix, 1955
and estimated 1975

Natural Gas

In the estimated increase in natural gas consumption of more than 100 per cent between 1955 and 1975 (as shown in Tables 72 and 73, and Figures 41 and 42), three uses predominate: industry, households, and electricity generation. These three consumption categories, in the order listed, were most important in 1955 and are estimated to rank in the same order in 1975. Stability in pattern among the major consumers is, of course, a reflection of the fact that the estimated percentage increases in the three categories between 1955 and 1975 do not differ widely (column 5, Table 73).

Of the three consumer classes, industry is by far the most important, accounting for 41 per cent of all direct gas consumption in 1955 and an estimated 43 per cent in 1975. Reference to Appendix Tables A-1, A-3, A-9, and A-23, which provide information on the subcategories underlying the industrial total, indicates that more than 35 per cent is consumed in what is termed "field use," which consists of the quantities used for pumping, drilling, NGL production,

TABLE 72. NATURAL GAS CONSUMPTION, BY SECTOR, 1955 AND ESTIMATED 1975

(Trillion Btu)

Sector	1955			1975		
	Direct consumption (1)	Via electricity (2)	Total (3)	Direct consumption (4)	Via electricity (5)	Total (6)
Total.............	} 9,908 [a] } 8,524 [b]	1,384	9,908	} 20,473 [a] } 17,519 [b]	2,955	20,473
Industry [c]..........	4,081	738	4,819	8,848	1,612	10,460
Commercial [d].......	603	220	823	1,271	470	1,741
Households [e]........	2,239	336	2,574	5,086	728	5,814
Transportation [f].....	254 [g]	12	266	533 [g]	8	541
Government [h].......	293	57	350	487	115	602
Agriculture [i]........	[j]	22	22	[j]	21	21
Miscellaneous uses and losses [k].......	1,054	[j]	1,054	1,294	[j]	1,294
Electricity generation [l].......	1,384			2,955		

[a] Including amounts consumed in electricity generation.
[b] Excluding amounts consumed in electricity generation.
[c] From Appendix Table A-37. Includes extraction of NGL.
[d] From Appendix Table B-9.
[e] From Appendix Tables C-6 and C-40.
[f] From Appendix Table D-60.
[g] Consumed by gas pipelines.
[h] From Appendix Table E-13.
[i] From Appendix Table F-4.
[j] Included in other categories; not separately reported or derived.
[k] From Appendix Table G-1, Includes gas vented and wasted.
[l] From Appendix Tables H-9 and H-17. Includes non-utility generation.

NOTE: Totals may not add because of rounding.

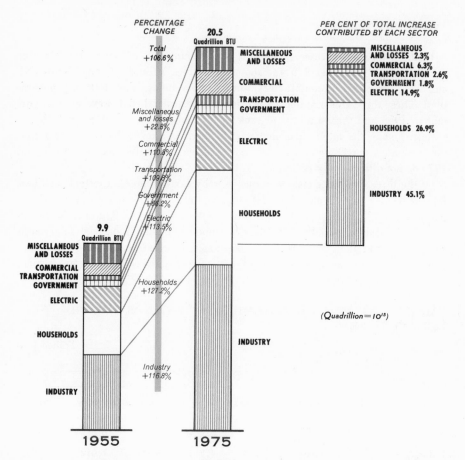

Figure 41. Natural gas consumption, by sector, 1955 and estimated 1975.

etc. in the oil and gas fields, and another 15 per cent in petroleum refining.[2]

The second most important consuming sector, households, shows the greatest estimated increase between 1955 and 1975. As a result, its percentage share in the direct consumption of gas is estimated to rise from 22.6 per cent in 1955 to almost 25 per cent in 1975. The increase in the relative importance of households in the total is in marked contrast to their relative decline in importance as direct consumers of coal and oil products.

The generation of electricity, the third ranking consumer class, accounts for about the same percentage of total gas consumption in 1955 and 1975—14 per cent and an estimated 14.4 per cent, respectively. Because natural gas con-

[2] Other data, not here shown, indicate that the use of the remaining 50 per cent was diversified among a large number of industrial users in 1955 and is likely to be more diversified in 1975.

TABLE 73. NATURAL GAS: CHANGES IN THE PATTERN OF CONSUMPTION, 1955-75

Sector	Percentage share in total consumption				Percentage change 1955-75		Percentage share of each sector in total increase	
	Direct consumption		Direct consumption and consumption via electricity		Direct consumption (5)	Direct consumption and consumption via electricity (6)	Direct consumption (7)	Direct consumption and consumption via electricity (8)
	1955 (1)	1975 (2)	1955 (3)	1975 (4)				
Total..............	100.0%	100.0%	100.0%	100.0%	}+106.6%[a] / +105.5[b]	+106.6%	100.0%	100.0%
Industry.............	41.2	43.2	48.6	51.1	+116.8	+117.1	45.1	53.4
Commercial.........	6.1	6.2	8.3	8.5	+110.8	+111.5	6.3	8.7
Households.........	22.6	24.8	26.0	28.4	+127.2	+125.9	26.9	30.7
Transportation......	2.6	2.6	2.7	2.6	+109.8	+103.4	2.6	2.6
Government.........	3.0	2.4	3.5	2.9	+66.2	+72.0	1.8	2.4
Agriculture.........	c	c	0.2	0.1	c	-4.5	c	negl.
Miscellaneous uses and losses......	10.6	6.3	10.6	6.3	+22.8	+22.8	2.3	2.3
Electricity generation[d]........	14.0	14.4			+113.5		14.9	

negl. Negligible.

[a] Including amounts consumed in electricity generation.

[b] Excluding amounts consumed in electricity generation.

[c] Included in other categories; not separately reported or derived.

[d] Including non-utility generation.

SOURCE: Based on Table 72.

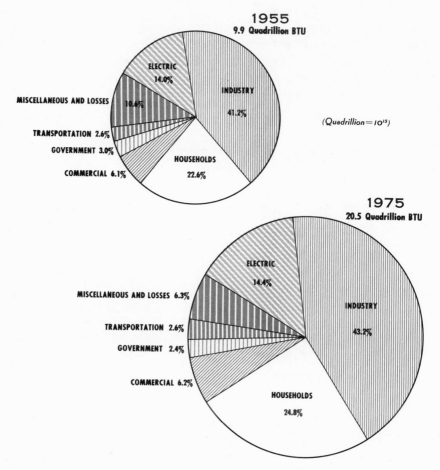

Figure 42. Natural gas consumption—percentage of total by sector—1955 and estimated 1975.

sumed in electricity is an important component of the total, the percentage share of some of the other consuming sectors in total gas consumption is noticeably increased when the gas required in generating electricity is assigned to them in proportion to their electricity consumption. On this basis, industry in 1975 is estimated to account for more than half of all natural gas consumption, and household use approaches 30 per cent of the total. In respect to the marked effect on different consuming sectors of the fuel consumed indirectly via electricity, natural gas resembles coal, although in relative terms the influence of indirect consumption on the comparative importance of the sectors is far greater for coal than for natural gas.

The category called miscellaneous uses and losses consists in large part of natural gas vented and wasted in the field (about 80 per cent of the entire category in 1955 and almost 90 per cent in 1975). The amounts so lost are regarded here as a concomitant of production and are, therefore, included as an element in total consumption in Tables 72 and 73 and Figures 41 and 42. When the amounts vented and wasted are added to field use, which is included in the industrial figure, the totals are a sizable portion of all natural gas consumption:

	1955	Percentage of total gas	1975	Percentage of total gas
	Trillion Btu		*Trillion Btu*	
Field use (including extraction for NGL production).............................	1,560	15.7%	3,277	16.0%
Vented and wasted......................	801	8.1	1,146	5.6
Total.............................	2,361	23.8%	4,423	21.6%

These amounts represent that part of total natural gas consumption which, although sensitive to price, is treated here as a function of the level of gas production. Thus, in the final analysis, it is determined by the demands originating in the other consuming sectors.

· · ·

Natural Gas Liquids

Natural gas liquids, although of comparatively small importance among the primary energy sources, are characterized by the largest estimated growth between 1955 and 1975. As shown in Tables 74 and 75 and Figures 43 and 44, three sectors—transportation, household, and miscellaneous uses—dominate the use pattern in 1955 and 1975, and account for more than 90 per cent of the total increase in 1975 consumption above the 1955 level.

Transportation is by far the largest consuming sector, accounting for about half of total consumption, and for more than 40 per cent of the amount by which estimated 1975 NGL consumption exceeds that of 1955. The dominance of transportation, which resembles the situation in oil discussed earlier, is to be expected because natural gasoline is a major component of natural gas liquids. In this study, a fixed percentage of gasoline in all its uses—12 per cent—has been assumed to be natural gasoline (Appendix Table I-10); consequently, the assumptions made about the growth of automotive transportation equally affect the gasoline component of oil consumption and the natural gasoline component of NGL. In addition, a portion of liquid petroleum gas (LPG) is used for automotive transportation. This item, which is very small compared to gasoline is nevertheless estimated to grow far more than gasoline between 1955 and 1975 (Appendix Tables D-20 and D-40).

TABLE 74.   NATURAL GAS LIQUIDS CONSUMPTION, BY SECTOR,
1955 AND ESTIMATED 1975

(Trillion Btu)

Sector	1955	1975
Total...	1,404	3,816
Industry ª..	56	169
Commercial ᵇ..	26	47
Households ᶜ..	233	477
Transportation ᵈ....................................	732	1,796
Self-performed by households..............................	466	1,150
Self-performed by government (excluding military)...........	12	23
General transportation......................................	254	623
Government ᵉ..	61	84
Agriculture ᶠ.......................................	101	151
Miscellaneous uses and losses ᵍ.....................	196	1,092

  ª From Appendix Table A-37.
  ᵇ From Appendix Table B-9.
  ᶜ From Appendix Tables C-6 and C-40.
  ᵈ From Appendix Table D-60.
  ᵉ From Appendix Table E-13.
  ᶠ From Appendix Table F-4.
  ᵍ From Appendix Table G-1.

NOTE: Totals may not add because of rounding.

TABLE 75.   NATURAL GAS LIQUIDS: CHANGES IN THE PATTERN OF
CONSUMPTION, 1955–75

Sector	Percentage share in total consumption		Percentage change 1955–75 (3)	Percentage share of each sector in total increase (4)
	1955 (1)	1975 (2)		
Total................................	100.0%	100.0%	+171.8%	100.0%
Industry.............................	4.0	4.4	+201.8	4.7
Commercial...........................	1.9	1.2	+ 80.8	0.9
Households...........................	16.6	12.5	+104.7	10.1
Transportation.......................	52.1	47.1	+145.4	44.1
Self-performed by households...........	33.2	30.1	+146.8	28.4
Self-performed by government (excluding military).......................	0.9	0.6	+91.7	0.5
General transportation.................	18.1	16.3	+145.3	15.3
Government...........................	4.3	2.2	+37.7	1.0
Agriculture..........................	7.2	4.0	+49.5	2.1
Miscellaneous uses and losses..............	14.0	28.6	+457.1	37.1

SOURCE: Based on Table 74.

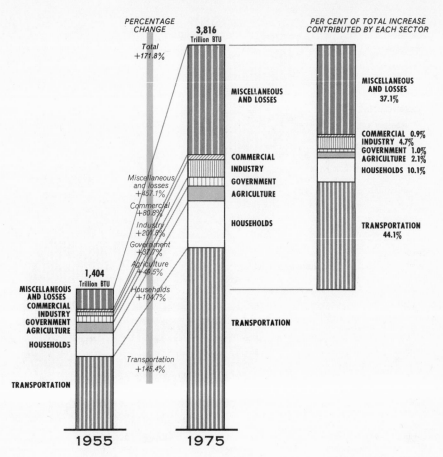

Figure 43. Natural gas liquids consumption, by sector, 1955 and estimated 1975.

The use pattern for NGL also resembles oil in the fact that private automobiles account for a large percentage of total consumption. This item—referred to as "transportation self-performed by households" in Tables 74 and 75—accounts for about one-third of all NGL consumption, and is of even greater relative importance here than in oil.

Although transportation is the dominant NGL consuming sector, and although its estimated growth between 1955 and 1975 is greater for NGL than for oil products, transportation declines somewhat in relative importance as a consumer of NGL in the twenty-year period, while in oil it shows a substantial rise. This decline results from the fact that transportation's growth as a consumer of NGL is far exceeded by the growth of the category "miscellaneous uses and losses" which consists essentially of the nonfuel uses of NGL. The percentage growth in this category is estimated at almost 460 per cent, which results in an approxi-

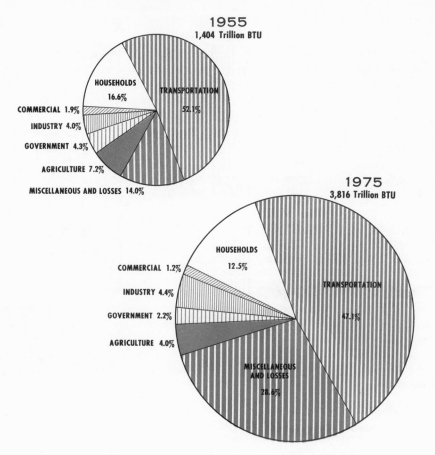

Figure 44. Natural gas liquids consumption—percentage of total by sector—1955 and estimated 1975.

mate doubling of its relative share among NGL consumers from 14 per cent to 29 per cent. This remarkable expansion is a consequence of the estimated growth in the petrochemical industry's take of NGL (Appendix Table G-1).

Between 1955 and 1975, the nonfuel uses are estimated to exchange ranks with households among the consuming sectors for NGL. Households, which were second in importance in 1955, move to third place in the 1975 estimates. Although household consumption of NGL is estimated to more than double, its share in total consumption drops from about 16.6 per cent to 12.5 per cent. Household consumption of LPG might have been estimated to grow more during this period but for the expected expansion of the natural gas network (and to a lesser extent, electricity transmission) into remote areas now most conveniently served by bottled gas.

Electricity

The reason for separately describing the pattern of total electricity consumption, even though the major parts—that is all but hydro-generated electric power—have already been accounted for under the fuels, is that electric energy is a unique product in the market place. It is, moreover, an important energy product, one which accounts for about one-fifth of all energy consumed in 1955 and one-quarter of the estimated 1975 total. Therefore, it is as important to examine the pattern of electricity use among the consuming sectors as it is to study those of the primary energy sources.

The homogeneity of electricity is equally the reason why hydro-generated power is the only item that has not been accounted for among the primary energy sources in the preceding discussion and is not examined separately now. In the first place, there is no demand for hydro-generated electricity as such, but only for electricity. Thus, the consumption pattern for all electricity also constitutes, by definition, the consumption pattern for hydro-generated electricity, as it does for electricity generated by coal, gas, and oil. The need for allocating—by essentially arbitrary calculations—to each consuming sector specific portions of the total electricity supply arising, respectively, from combustion of coal, gas, or oil, and converting these portions into fuel equivalents lies in the convenience of combining quantities of fuels so derived with the consumption of the same fuels used in other ways. In the case of hydro-generated electricity, this need noes not exist as hydro-generated electricity is the only significant mode left today in which water produces energy.

The electric power consumption patterns in 1955, and in 1975 as they result from the growth rates in individual consuming sectors, are presented in Tables 76 and 77 and Figures 45 and 46. These tables measure electricity in terms of

TABLE 76. ELECTRICITY CONSUMPTION, BY SECTOR, 1955 AND
ESTIMATED 1975

(Billion kwh)

Sector	1955	1975
Total	633.1	1,965.5
Industry	308.3	1,023.3
Commercial	94.6	315.2
Households	144.5	488.6
Transportation	6.8	5.3
Government	69.5	119.0
AEC	52.5	57.8
Agriculture	9.4	14.0
Miscellaneous uses and losses	a	a

ᵃ Allocated among the various consuming sectors. Consists of difference between net amounts generated and amounts identified as consumed in sectors shown.

NOTE: Totals may not add because of rounding.

SOURCES: Appendix Tables H-9 and H-17.

TABLE 77. ELECTRICITY: CHANGES IN THE PATTERN
OF CONSUMPTION, 1955–75

Sector	Percentage share in total consumption		Percentage change 1955–75 (3)	Percentage share of each sector in total increase (4)
	1955 (1)	1975 (2)		
Total................................	100.0%	100.0%	+210.5%	100.0%
Industry..............................	48.7	52.1	+231.9	53.7
Commercial...........................	14.9	16.0	+233.2	16.6
Households...........................	22.8	24.9	+238.1	25.8
Transportation........................	1.1	0.3	−22.1	−0.1
Government...........................	11.0	6.1	+71.2	3.7
AEC...............................	8.3	2.9	+10.1	0.4
Agriculture...........................	1.5	0.7	+48.9	0.3
Miscellaneous uses and losses.............	ᵃ	ᵃ		

ᵃ Allocated among the various consuming sectors. Consists of difference between net
amounts generated and amounts identified as consumed in sectors shown.

SOURCE: Based on Table 76.

kilowatt hours and thus differ from Table 66 and the tables dealing with coal,
oil, and natural gas, which measure the Btu's required in electric power generation. Owing to the higher fuel efficiency assumed in 1975, the growth rate is
much smaller for Btu's than for kilowatt hours produced by them (see the general note to Table 65).

Electricity's estimated increase of 210 per cent between 1955 and 1975 is,
as indicated earlier, greater than that of any of the primary energy sources.
Table 14 shows that, within the over-all growth, the three major consuming
sectors—industry, households, and commercial—are estimated to grow at rates
which are greater than the average and which are quite similar for all three.
Consequently, the concentration of consumption in these three sectors grows
from about 86 per cent in 1955 to an estimated 93 per cent in 1975.

More than half of the estimated net difference in consumption between 1955
and 1975 is accounted for by industry's use of electric power (Table 77, column
4). Industry was first among the sectors in electricity consumption in 1955 with
slightly less than one-half of the total and, as a result of the estimated increase
between 1955 and 1975 of about 230 per cent, stands first in 1975 with somewhat more than half of total consumption. Households remained in 1975 as
second-highest consuming sector and commercial as third. The percentage
importance of household consumption increases slightly from about 23 per cent
to 25 per cent of the total, and that of commercial from 15 per cent to 16 per
cent.

The increase in relative importance of the three major sectors is mainly at
the expense of a relative decline in the importance of government as a consuming sector, from 11 per cent of the total in 1955 to an estimated 6 per cent in
1975. This decline, however, is not to be found in the routine activities of government, but rather is because, as Tables 76 and 77 show, use of electricity by

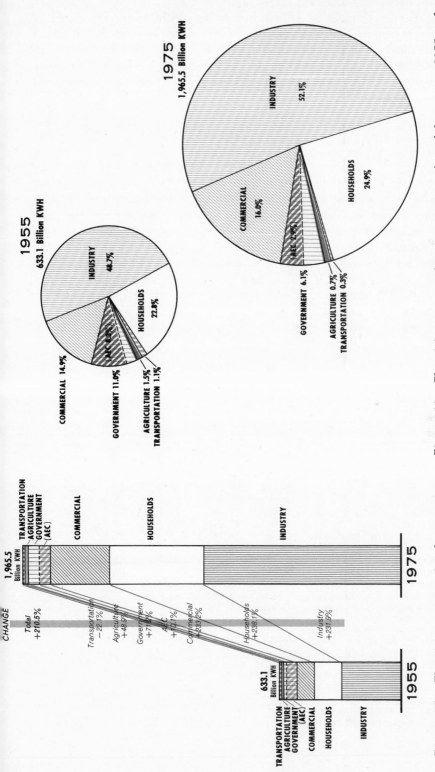

Figure 46. *Electricity consumption—percentage of total by sector—1955 and estimated 1975.*

Figure 45. *Electricity consumption, by sector, 1955 and estimated 1975.*

Atomic Energy Commission (AEC) installations is the major component of government consumption in 1955. The assumption made about the growth in AEC consumpton—that it will not rise much beyond the 1955 level—accounts for the sharp decline in the relative share of government in estimated electricity consumption. If AEC were omitted, the relative importance of the remainder of government would increase slightly.

THE CONSUMING SECTORS: CONSUMPTION PATTERN ACCORDING TO ENERGY SOURCES

Shifting from the examination of the 1955 and 1975 use of each energy source by its consuming sectors, this section takes a different view of the same structure. It considers one consuming sector at a time, and identifies the quantity as well as the proportion of total energy consumption supplied by each energy source.

Before undertaking the description of energy source patterns within each of the consuming sectors, it is well to have some measure of the relative importance of the different sectors as energy consumers in 1955 and as estimated for 1975. This is provided in Table 78 and Figures 47 and 48, which break down total energy consumption, measured in terms of Btu's, into the major consuming sectors used in this study. These figures indicate that industry, transporta-

TABLE 78. TOTAL ENERGY CONSUMPTION, BY SECTOR, 1955 AND ESTIMATED 1975

Sector	Consumption (trillion Btu)		Per cent increase in consumption 1955–75 (3)	Percentage share of each sector in total consumption	
	1955 (1)	1975 (2)		1955 (4)	1975 (5)
Total[a]	40,079	75,288	87.8%	100.0%	100.0%
Industry[b]	15,712	29,761	89.4	39.2	39.5
Commercial[c]	3,395	6,067	78.7	8.5	8.1
Households[d]	7,456	12,706	70.4	18.6	16.9
Transportation[e]	8,103	17,811	119.8	20.2	23.7
Self-performed by households	3,742	8,184	118.7	9.3	10.9
Self-performed by government (excluding military)	102	200	96.1	0.3	0.3
General transportation	4,259	9,428	121.4	10.6	12.5
Government[f]	1,837	2,688	46.3	4.6	3.6
Agriculture[g]	729	1,042	42.9	1.8	1.4
Miscellaneous uses and losses[h]	2,848	5,213	83.0	7.1	6.9

[a] Includes NGL as well as gas extraction loss in production of NGL. Totals, therefore, are larger by that amount than totals in Table 66.
[b] From Appendix Table A-37.
[c] From Appendix Table B-9.
[d] From Appendix Tables C-6 and C-40.
[e] From Appendix Table D-60.
[f] From Appendix Table E-13.
[g] From Appendix Table F-4.
[h] From Appendix Table G-1.

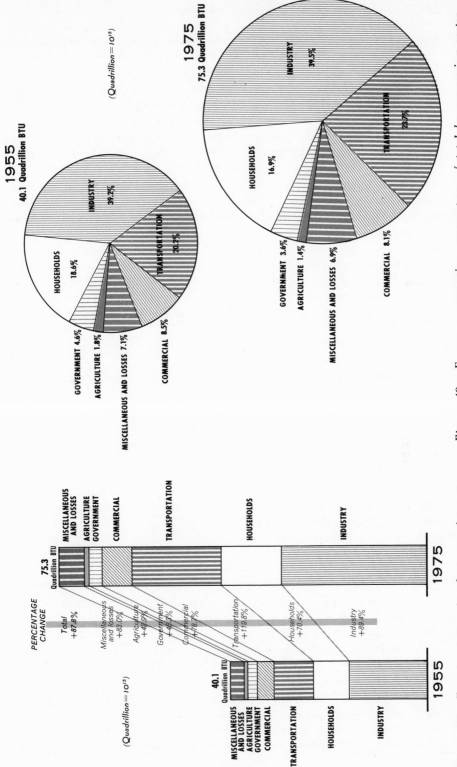

(Quadrillion = 10¹⁵)

1955
40.1 Quadrillion BTU

INDUSTRY
39.2%

HOUSEHOLDS
18.6%

GOVERNMENT 4.6%

AGRICULTURE 1.8%

MISCELLANEOUS AND LOSSES 7.1%

COMMERCIAL 8.5%

TRANSPORTATION
20.2%

1975
75.3 Quadrillion BTU

INDUSTRY
39.5%

HOUSEHOLDS
16.9%

GOVERNMENT 3.6%

AGRICULTURE 1.4%

MISCELLANEOUS AND LOSSES 6.9%

COMMERCIAL 8.1%

TRANSPORTATION
23.7%

Figure 48. Energy consumption—percentage of total by consuming sector— 1955 and estimated 1975.

PERCENTAGE CHANGE

75.3
Quadrillion BTU

MISCELLANEOUS AND LOSSES
AGRICULTURE
GOVERNMENT
COMMERCIAL

TRANSPORTATION

HOUSEHOLDS

INDUSTRY

Total +87.8%

Miscellaneous and losses +83.0%

Agriculture +42.9%

Government +46.3%

Commercial +78.7%

Transportation +119.8%

Households +70.4%

Industry +89.4%

40.1
Quadrillion BTU

MISCELLANEOUS AND LOSSES
AGRICULTURE
GOVERNMENT
COMMERCIAL

TRANSPORTATION

HOUSEHOLDS

INDUSTRY

(Quadrillion = 10¹⁵)

1975

1955

Figure 47. Energy consumption, by consuming sector, 1955 and estimated 1975.

tion, and households, in that order, were the three largest consuming sectors in 1955, and are estimated to hold the same relative positions in 1975. Industry, with almost two-fifths of total consumption, is first in both years, increasing only slightly in relative importance between 1955 and 1975. Transportation, which is second in 1955, with one-fifth of total consumption, continues to hold second place in 1975, with close to 24 per cent of the total. Although transportation's rank does not change, it is the only sector that shows a significant increase in the percentage share from 1955 to 1975. Households, the third-ranking sector in both years, drops in percentage share of the total from 18.6 per cent to about 17 per cent. If, however, the household sector is defined to include the energy consumed in private automobiles (shown as "transportation self-performed by households" in Table 78), it becomes the second most important consuming sector, with about 28 per cent of the total in both 1955 and 1975.

Taken together, industry, households, and transportation account for about 80 per cent of all energy consumption in the United States. The other three sectors—commercial, government, and agriculture—account for close to 15 per cent. Of these, commercial, with more than 8 per cent, is the largest sector; government, with about 4 per cent, is second; and agriculture, with less than 2 per cent, is the smallest. All three are estimated to decline somewhat in relative importance between 1955 and 1975.

The energy unaccounted for by the six identified sectors is shown in Table 78 as "miscellaneous uses and losses." The amounts involved are quite large— about as much as energy consumption in the commercial sector. Since this category is not truly a consuming sector, in the sense that the activities covered have some common frame of reference, but is instead a catch-all, it will not be covered in the discussion of sectors which follows. The items which make up the total for the class, and their derivation, may be found by examining Section G of the Appendix to Part II. The nature of miscellaneous uses and losses is indicated also in the preceding section discussing the sector composition of consumption of the individual energy sources.

As in the preceding sections, the description here is chiefly by way of the statistical tables and graphs, with the text serving only to identify the major elements in the sectors' fuel-consumption patterns in 1955 and as estimated for 1975. Since the statistics contained in the tables and graphs are summary statements of materials which have been developed in much greater detail in the Appendix to Part II, the text is, in fact, a generalized statement of results which is twice removed from the underlying statistical calculations.

The tables showing energy consumption by source are not identical in form for the different sectors because certain important aspects are unique to one or another of the sectors. However, with the exception of transportation, the tables divide each sector's total energy consumption into at least two broad classes— direct fuel consumption and consumption via electricity—and show the amounts of the various fuels consumed in each. The former category includes all fuels consumed as such; the latter includes the estimated quantities of particular fuels

(and hydro) represented in the sector's consumption of electricity, whether purchased or self-generated. With very few exceptions—such, for example, as the
production of primary aluminum—the identification of the exact energy sources
used in producing the electricity consumed by a particular industry or activity,
even after extensive research, would still depend on arbitrary allocations. Therefore, most figures presented under this heading are estimates based on the
simplifying assumption that the electricity consumed in a particular sector
draws on the different fuels (and hydro) in the same proportion as does electricity generation in the economy as a whole.[3]

.   .   .

Industry

Industry,[4] the largest of the energy-consuming sectors, shows an estimated
increase in total consumption of almost 90 per cent between 1955 and 1975,
and an increase in direct fuel consumption of about 71 per cent over the same
period (see Tables 79 and 80 and Figures 49 and 50). Among the fuels consumed directly within the industrial sector (Table 80, columns 1 and 2) coal

TABLE 79. INDUSTRY: ENERGY CONSUMPTION BY SOURCE, 1955
AND ESTIMATED 1975

(Trillion Btu)

Energy source	1955	1975
Direct fuel consumption.............................	11,816	20,167
Coal..	5,012	6,528
Oil...	2,666	4,621
Gas..	4,081	8,848
NGL...	56	169
Consumption via electricity, utility and self-generated....	3,896	9,594
Coal..	2,112	6,067
Oil...	370	729
Gas..	738	1,612
Hydro...	677	1,186
Total...	15,712	29,761
Coal..	7,123	12,595
Oil...	3,036	5,350
Gas..	4,819	10,461
NGL...	56	169
Hydro...	677	1,186

NOTE: Totals may not add because of rounding.

SOURCE: Appendix Table A-37.

[3] See Chapter 5, section titled "Electricity, by Source of Energy," for detailed description
of the techniques and assumptions used in estimating the fuel (and hydro) inputs into
electricity consumed by the various sectors.

[4] For a description of the coverage of the industrial sector and of the methods and assumptions used in deriving its energy consumption patterns, see the discussion of Industry in
Chapter 5; for the detailed statistical materials underlying Tables 79 and 80, see Section A
in the Appendix to Part II.

TABLE 80. INDUSTRY: CHANGES IN THE PATTERN OF
ENERGY CONSUMPTION, 1955-75

	Percentage share in sector's total energy consumption				Percentage change in quantity consumed 1955-75	
	Direct fuel consumption		Direct fuel consumption and consumption via electricity		Direct fuel consumption	Direct fuel consumption and consumption via electricity
Energy source	1955 (1)	1975 (2)	1955 (3)	1975 (4)	(5)	(6)
Total..........	100.0%	100.0%	100.0%	100.0%	+ 70.7%	+ 89.4%
Coal..........	42.4	32.4	45.3	42.3	+ 30.2	+ 76.8
Oil............	22.6	22.9	19.3	18.0	+ 73.3	+ 76.2
Gas...........	34.5	43.9	30.7	35.1	+116.8	+117.1
NGL..........	0.5	0.8	0.4	0.6	+201.8	+201.8
Hydro.........			4.3	4.0		+ 75.2
Consumed as electricity.....			24.8%	32.2%		+146.3%

SOURCE: Based on Table 79.

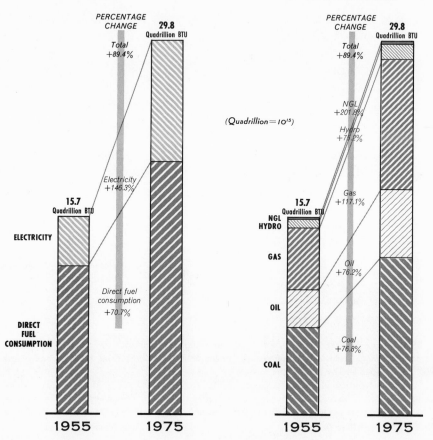

BY TYPE OF USE   **BY ENERGY SOURCE**

*Figure 49. Industrial sector: energy consumption by type of use and energy
source, 1955 and estimated 1975.*

was in first place in 1955, with more than two-fifths of the total, and natural gas was second, with almost 35 per cent. By 1975, gas and coal are estimated to change places in the ranks of the fuels consumed directly: gas is first, with more than two-fifths, and coal is second, with less than one-third. Oil is in third place in both years, with about 23 per cent of the total.

Electricity is of substantial importance in industry's total energy supply (Table 80, columns 3 and 4). Measured in terms of the Btu's contained in the fuels required in its generation, electricity accounted for about one-quarter of all energy consumption in 1955 and is estimated at almost one-third in 1975. The estimated percentage increase of almost 150 per cent in fuels consumed in generating electricity between 1955 and 1975 is more than twice as large as the estimated increase of about 70 per cent in direct fuel consumption between the two years (Table 80, columns 5 and 6).

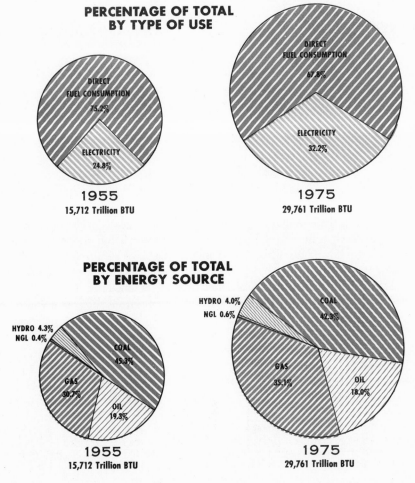

Figure 50. Industrial sector: percentage of total energy consumption by type of use and energy source, 1955 and estimated 1975.

Because of the large and increasing relative importance of electricity, the percentage importance of the several fuels as suppliers of industrial energy is quite different when measured including their use in generating industrially consumed electricity, than when measured in terms of industrial direct fuel consumption only. Thus, including its use in electricity, coal is in first place as an industrial energy source in both 1955 and in 1975, its relative importance declining only slightly from 45 per cent of the total in 1955 to an estimated 42 per cent in 1975. Gas ranks second in both years, with its relative importance increasing from 30 per cent to an estimated 35 per cent. Oil is third in both 1955 and 1975, with something less than one-fifth of the total.

In broad outline, therefore, the industrial energy picture is characterized by a marked shift in the relative importance of coal and gas in direct fuel use between 1955 and the projected levels for 1975: coal declines, gas rises. With fuel use via electricity consumption taken into account, the pattern of consumption for the two years is considerably more stable, although the percentage of natural gas still gains at the expense of coal.

.   .   .

Commercial

The commercial sector,[5] which is the fourth largest energy consumer, is estimated to increase its total consumption of energy by almost 80 per cent and its direct consumption of fuels by almost 45 per cent between 1955 and 1975 (Tables 81 and 82 and Figures 51 and 52). Among the fuels consumed directly, coal was the most important in 1955 with almost two-fifths of the total; oil second, with almost one-third; and natural gas third, with about one-quarter (Table 82, columns 1 and 2, and Figure 52). By 1975, a sharp change is estimated to take place in these proportions: coal drops to third place, with less than one-fifth of the total, while oil and gas are of almost equal importance, with each accounting for about two-fifths of the total. The most significant changes are estimated for coal and gas. Coal's sharp decline in relative importance is brought about by an estimated absolute decline of one-third in the quantity of coal used directly in commercial establishments—principally as a source of heat. The large relative increase in natural gas, replacing coal in identical tasks, reflects an estimated absolute growth in consumption of more than 100 per cent.

As is true of industry, the picture changes sharply when fuels burned in generating the electricity consumed in the commercial sector are added to the sector's direct fuel consumption. This is so because energy input consumed as elec-

[5] For a description of the coverage of the commercial sector and of the methods and assumptions used in deriving its energy consumption pattern, see the discussion in Chapter 5; for the detailed statistical materials underlying Tables 81 and 82, see Section B in the Appendix to Part II.

tricity is estimated to grow by about 150 per cent between 1955 and 1975, as compared to an estimated growth of less than 45 per cent in fuels consumed directly (Table 82, columns 5 and 6, and Figure 52). Including the amounts consumed in electricity, the fuel consumption pattern in the commercial sector is estimated to remain comparatively stable between 1955 and 1975; coal, with about 43 per cent of the total in 1955, is estimated to decline to just under 40 per cent in 1975; natural gas increases from about 25 per cent to almost 30 per cent; and oil holds firm at about 25 per cent (Table 82, columns 3 and 4).

TABLE 81. COMMERCIAL: ENERGY CONSUMPTION BY SOURCE, 1955 AND ESTIMATED 1975

(Trillion Btu)

Energy source	1955	1975
Direct fuel consumption	2,262	3,237
Coal	896	597
Oil	737	1,321
Gas	603	1,271
NGL	26	47
Consumption via electricity	1,133	2,830
Coal	570	1,773
Oil	91	168
Gas	220	470
Hydro	253	420
Total	3,395	6,067
Coal	1,466	2,370
Oil	828	1,489
Gas	823	1,741
NGL	26	47
Hydro	253	420

NOTE: Totals may not add because of rounding.

SOURCE: Appendix Table B-9.

TABLE 82. COMMERCIAL: CHANGES IN THE PATTERN OF ENERGY CONSUMPTION, 1955–75

Energy source	Percentage share in sector's total energy consumption				Percentage change in quantity consumed 1955–75	
	Direct fuel consumption		Direct fuel consumption and consumption via electricity		Direct fuel consumption (5)	Direct fuel consumption and consumption via electricity (6)
	1955 (1)	1975 (2)	1955 (3)	1975 (4)		
Total	100.0%	100.0%	100.0%	100.0%	+ 43.1%	+ 78.7%
Coal	39.6	18.4	43.2	39.1	− 33.4	+ 61.7
Oil	32.6	40.8	24.4	24.5	+ 79.2	+ 79.8
Gas	26.7	39.3	24.2	28.7	+110.8	+111.5
NGL	1.1	1.5	0.8	0.8	+ 80.8	+ 80.8
Hydro			7.5	6.9		+ 66.0
Consumed as electricity			33.4%	46.7%		+149.9%

SOURCE: Based on Table 81.

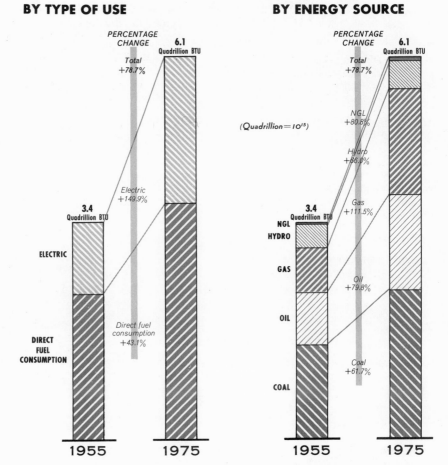

Figure 51. Commercial sector: energy consumption by type of use and energy source, 1955 and estimated 1975.

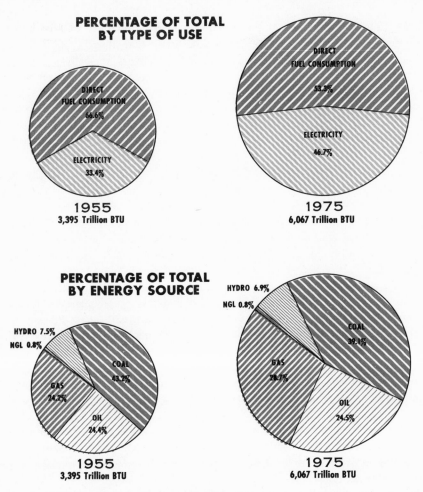

Figure 52. Commercial sector: percentage of total energy consumption by type of use and energy source, 1955 and estimated 1975.

Consumption via electricity in the commercial sector is thus even more important than in industry in affecting the relative position of the various energy sources. This reflects the fact that electricity is of far greater relative importance in energy consumed in the commercial sector than it is in industry. By 1975, energy consumed via electricity constitutes almost one-half of the estimated total energy consumption of the commercial sector as compared to not quite one-third in the industrial sector. By the same token, in the commercial sector, coal's maintenance of its relative position in the face of losses to oil and gas in direct fuel consumption depends on electricity consumption even more than in the industry sector.

·   ·   ·

Households

According to the statistics shown in Table 78, households[6] are the third most important energy-consuming sector when defined to include the fuels and electricity used within the physical confines of the home only. However, energy consumption in the household sector could be defined as well to include the fuel used in private automobiles. When the latter item (which is called "transportation, self-performed" in Tables 78, 83, and 84) is included, households appear as the second most important consuming sector, with about 28 per cent of the economy's total energy consumption in 1955, and as estimated for 1975.

Energy use in the household sector is shown in Tables 83 and 84 and Figures 53 and 54, both in terms of energy consumption within the home and in terms of fuel used in private automobiles. Energy consumed within the home is divided into two broad classes: direct fuel consumption and consumption via electricity. Direct consumption, in turn, is divided into two uses: space heating, which accounts for 70 to 80 per cent of the total for the class, and the other direct fuel uses in the home, consisting mainly of water heating and cooking. The tables thus provide a threefold breakdown of the use of each primary energy source within the home.

It is apparent from this breakdown that oil and gas dominate direct fuel use in the home in 1955 and in the 1975 estimates, with gas estimated to grow greatly at the expense of oil over the twenty-year period. Each accounted for about 40 per cent of direct fuel consumption in 1955, but by 1975 the share of gas in the total is estimated to rise to more than 60 per cent while that of oil falls to about 30 per cent (Table 84, columns 1 and 2). Coal, which was already of small relative importance in direct fuel consumption within the home in 1955, is estimated to decline in absolute terms by more than 57 per cent between 1955 and 1975, and to reduce its percentage share of total direct fuel consumption from about 15 per cent to 5 per cent.

---

[6] For a description of the coverage of the household sector and of the methods and assumptions used in deriving its energy consumption pattern, see Chapter 5; for the detailed statistical materials underlying Tables 83 and 84, see Section C of the Appendix to Part II.

TABLE 83.   HOUSEHOLDS: ENERGY CONSUMPTION BY SOURCE, 1955 AND ESTIMATED 1975

(Trillion Btu)

Item	Coal		Oil		Gas		NGL		Hydro		Total			
											Btu		Percentage of all household uses	
	1955 (1)	1975 (2)	1955 (3)	1975 (4)	1955 (5)	1975 (6)	1955 (7)	1975 (8)	1955 (9)	1975 (10)	1955 (11)	1975 (12)	1955 (13)	1975 (14)
Direct fuel consumption in the home	938	400	2,316	2,356	2,239	5,086	233	477			5,726	8,319	51.1%	39.8%
Space heating	891	400	1,873	2,104	1,423	3,650	128	262			4,316	6,416	38.5	30.7
Other uses	47	0	443	252	815	1,436	105	215			1,410	1,903	12.6	9.1
Consumption in the home via electricity	870	2,748	139	260	336	728			386	650	1,729	4,387	15.4	21.0
Transportation, self-performed			3,276	7,033			466	1,150			3,742	8,184	33.4	39.2
Total	1,808	3,148	5,731	9,650	2,574	5,814	699	1,628	386	650	11,198	20,890	100.0%	100.0%

NOTE: Totals may not add because of rounding.

SOURCES: Appendix Tables C-6 and C-40.

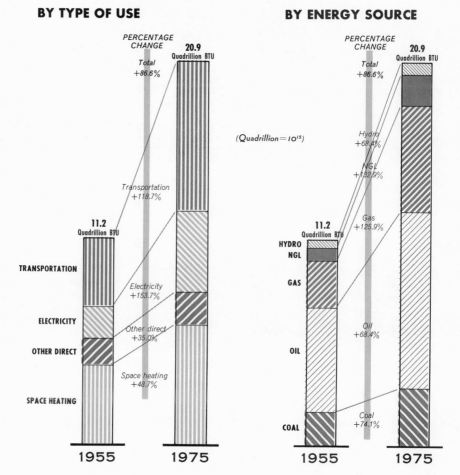

Figure 53.   Household sector: energy consumption by type of use and energy source, 1955 and estimated 1975.

TABLE 84. HOUSEHOLDS: CHANGES IN THE PATTERN OF ENERGY CONSUMPTION, 1955-75

| Energy source | Direct fuel consumption in the home | | Percentage share in sector's total energy consumption | | | | Percentage change in quantity consumed 1955-75 | | |
| | | | Direct fuel consumption in the home and consumption in the home via electricity | | Direct fuel consumption in the home and consumption in the home via electricity and self-performed transportation | | Direct fuel consumption in the home | Direct fuel consumption and consumption via electricity | Direct fuel consumption and consumption via electricity and self-performed transportation |
	1955 (1)	1975 (2)	1955 (3)	1975 (4)	1955 (5)	1975 (6)	(7)	(8)	(9)
Total	100.0%	100.0%	100.0%	100.0%	100.0%	100.0%	+ 45.3%	+ 70.4%	+ 86.6%
Coal	16.4	4.8	24.3	24.8	16.1	15.1	− 57.4	+ 74.1	+ 74.1
Oil	40.4	28.3	32.9	20.6	51.2	46.2	+ 1.7	+ 6.6	+ 68.4
Gas	39.1	61.1	34.5	45.8	23.0	27.8	+127.2	+125.9	+125.9
NGL	4.1	5.7	3.1	3.8	6.2	7.8	+104.7	+104.7	+132.9
Hydro			5.2	5.1	3.4	3.1		+ 68.4	+ 68.4
Consumed as electricity			23.2%	34.5%	15.4%	21.0%		+153.7%	+153.7%

SOURCE: Based on Table 83.

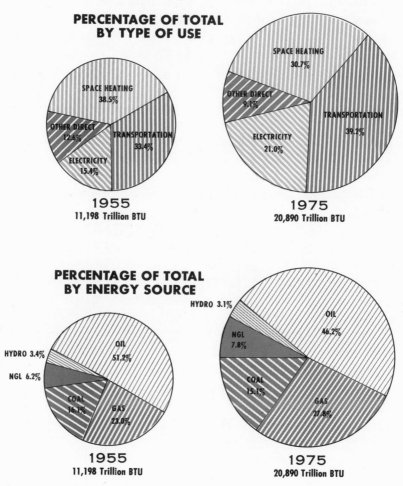

Figure 54. Household sector: percentage of total energy consumption by type of use and energy source, 1955 and estimated 1975.

The estimated twenty-year growth of household fuel consumption via electricity is about 150 per cent. This is more than three times as large as the estimated growth of 45 per cent in direct fuel consumption. Consequently, fuel consumption via electricity is estimated to increase from less than one-quarter to almost 35 per cent of the total of direct fuel plus fuel via electricity between 1955 and 1975 (Table 84, columns 3 and 4). Taking fuel consumption via electricity into account yields a substantially different picture of the relative importance of the different fuels, owing to the predominance of coal in power generation: oil and gas are of almost equal relative importance in 1955—as they are among the fuels consumed directly—but with about one-third of the total rather than 40 per cent. Coal is again third in importance, but with almost one-quarter of the total, as compared to 16 per cent among the fuels consumed directly. In 1975, the estimates again show gas first, with 45 per cent of the total—considerably less than its 60 per cent as a portion of direct fuel consumption. Coal, with less than 5 per cent of direct fuel consumption in 1975, accounts for almost 25 per cent when fuel use in electricity is added. Coal thus maintains the same percentage share as in 1955, and is in second place among the 1975 energy sources—rather than in last place when only direct consumption is considered. Oil, with an estimated 20 per cent of the total, drops to third position. Even more so than in the case of the industrial and commercial sectors, coal's future in the home is tied to the growth of electricity and to coal's estimated role in providing fuel for the power plants of 1975.

Broadening the definition of households to include, in addition, fuel used in private automobiles serves to enhance greatly the relative importance of oil (Table 84, columns 5 and 6, and Figure 54). On this basis, oil is far and away the primary household fuel in 1955, with more than one-half of total consumption. It holds first place also in the 1975 estimates, but with a decline in share to about 45 per cent of the total. Thus, even the very large comparative growth estimated for private automobile fuel consumption (see Table 78) is not enough to preserve oil's share of the household total in the face of the decline estimated in its direct fuel use within the home and the even steeper rise in the household application of electricity and natural gas. The latter, which is first by far in its share of estimated 1975 direct fuel consumption in the home, falls to second place in its share of the more comprehensive total, which includes electricity and private automobiles. But, even on this basis, natural gas shows up as the only major energy source estimated to increase its share of the household total between 1955 and 1975.

Transportation

Transportation as an energy-consuming sector is defined in Tables 78, 85, and 86 to include all transportation services performed in the economy whether

TABLE 85. TRANSPORTATION: ENERGY CONSUMPTION BY SOURCE, 1955 AND ESTIMATED 1975

(Trillion Btu)

Type	Coal 1955 (1)	Coal 1975 (2)	Oil 1955 (3)	Oil 1975 (4)	Gas 1955 (5)	Gas 1975 (6)	NGL 1955 (7)	NGL 1975 (8)	Hydro 1955 (9)	Hydro 1975 (10)	Total Btu 1955 (11)	Total Btu 1975 (12)	Percentage of all transportation uses 1955 (13)	Percentage of all transportation uses 1975 (14)
General transportation	388	30	3,337	8,228	266	541	254	623	14	7	4,259	9,428	52.6%	52.9%
Automotive			1,845	4,821			235	603			2,080	5,423	25.7	30.4
Marine	39	0	833	1,579			negl.	1			873	1,579	10.8	8.9
Railroads a	348	30	524	702	12	8			14	7	899	746	11.1	4.2
Aviation			135	1,126			18	19			153	1,146	1.9	6.4
Pipelines b					254	533					254	533	3.1	3.0
Transportation self-performed by households			3,276	7,033			466	1,150			3,742	8,184	46.2	45.9
Transportation self-performed by government (excluding military) c			90	177			12	23			102	200	1.3	1.1
Total	388	30	6,703	15,438	266	541	732	1,796	14	7	8,103	17,811	100.0%	100.0%

negl. Negligible.

a Category includes railroads and urban and interurban transit lines. Includes direct fuel consumption and relatively small amounts of fuel consumed in generating electricity for electrically powered railroads and nonmotive purposes. Excludes direct fuel consumption for nonmotive purposes (see Appendix Table A-3).

b Adequate information available only for natural gas consumed in operating natural gas pipelines.

c Energy materials consumed in military transport are included in the statistics shown for the government sector (Tables 89 and 90).

NOTE: Totals may not add because of rounding. Transportation self-performed in households and government also included in the energy consumption by sectors.

SOURCE: Appendix Table D-60.

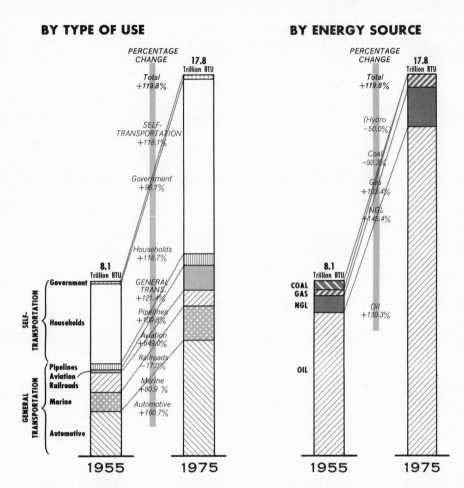

Figure 55. Total transportation: energy consumption by type of use and energy source, 1955 and estimated 1975.

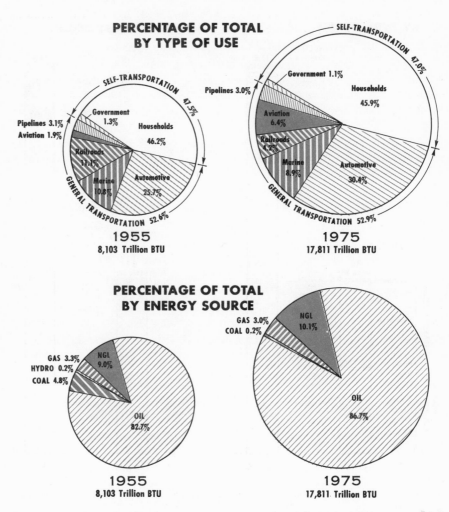

Figure 56. Total transportation: percentage of total energy consumption by type of use and energy source, 1955 and estimated 1975.

for purchase or whether self-performed by the user.[7] Thus defined, transportation is the economy's second largest energy-consuming sector. The classification system used in Tables 78 and 85 for presenting the statistics for the sector is designed to provide a measure of the energy consumed in three classes which constitute the total: general transportation, transportation self-performed by households (the private automobile), and transportation self-performed by government (excluding military transportation). General transportation, which breaks down into the five subclasses shown in Table 85, consists conceptually of which constitute the total: general transportation; transportation self-performed in other consuming sectors, such as industry and commercial, for which separate estimates of fuel use in transportation are only partially or not at all available.[8] Although fuel consumed in transportation self-performed by government is separately estimated, this category is unimportant in the total, and in the following discussion is thrown together with fuels consumed in transportation self-performed by households, which constitutes almost all of this combined total.

Between 1955 and 1975, energy consumption in transportation is estimated to grow by about 120 per cent, which is the greatest increase among all the sectors (see Table 78 and Figure 47). The amounts of the various fuels used in 1955 and estimated for 1975 are shown in Table 85 and Figure 55 in terms of a number of different types of transportation services. From this breakdown, some of the forces lying behind the growth in transportation's energy use can be discerned. However, in considering this table it must be borne in mind that the changes in energy consumption do not necessarily reflect proportionate changes in levels of transportation activity. In aviation, the anticipated expansion of jet aircraft increases Btu requirements more rapidly than the estimated increase in passenger-miles, ton-miles, or hours flown, while in railroads the continuing dieselization implies fewer Btu's per unit of activity. Thus, the estimated absolute drop in railroads' energy consumption is not the result of decreased activity, but (as may be seen from Appendix Tables D-3 and D-7) of anticipated changes in the type of propulsion used.

As shown in Table 85 and Figure 56, total energy consumption in transportation may be divided into two broad classes which are of almost equal importance: general transportation, which accounts for slightly more than 50 per cent of the total, and transportation self-performed in households and government, which accounts for slightly less than 50 per cent. The latter class consists wholly of automotive transportation, and since automotive accounts also for between

[7] Transportation self-performed by the military is an exception. The fuel so consumed is included in the government sector (Tables 87 and 88) and is not separately identified. For a description of the coverage of the transportation sector and the methods and assumptions used in deriving its energy consumption pattern, see Chapter 5; for the detailed statistical materials underlying Tables 85 and 86, see Section D in the Appendix to Part II.

[8] Deviations from this concept, dictated by considerations of statistical availability or techniques—such as aircraft or pleasure-boat operation self-performed by households but included in general transportation—are of but little substance in the face of the overwhelming magnitude of the categories properly assigned to their groups.

50 and 60 per cent of general transportation, approximately three-fourths of the energy consumed in transportation is for use in automotive vehicles.

All other forms of transportation are of small importance alongside the overwhelming share of the total accounted for by automotive uses. Marine transportation and railroads, with about 11 per cent of fuel consumption each, were next in importance in 1955. By 1975, the share of these two is estimated to decline to about 9 per cent and 4 per cent of the total respectively. Aviation, which used less than 2 per cent of transportation's energy total in 1955, is estimated to grow greatly and to account for more than 6 per cent of the total in 1975, thus outranking energy consumption by railroads in that year.

Liquid fuels are, of course, of dominant importance in the transportation sector. As shown in Table 86 and Figure 56, oil and NGL were the source of about 92 per cent of all energy consumed in transportation in 1955, and of almost 97 per cent of the estimated 1975 consumption. In 1955, the remainder was accounted for by coal and gas; the former fuel used primarily in railroads where it had already lost much of its historically important market to diesel fuel, and was continuing to lose the remainder at a fast rate; the latter used as a fuel in the operation of natural gas pipelines. By 1975, coal's disappearance from the transportation scene is estimated to be virtually complete;[9] what little it does provide will be for nonmotive purposes and also through its indirect use as a fuel source for the electricity consumed by railroads.

TABLE 86.   TRANSPORTATION: CHANGES IN THE PATTERN OF ENERGY CONSUMPTION, 1955–75

| | Percentage share in sector's total energy consumption | | | | Percentage change in quantity consumed 1955–75 | |
| | General transportation | | General transportation and transportation self-performed by households and government | | General transportation | General transportation and transportation self-performed by households and government |
Energy source	1955 (1)	1975 (2)	1955 (3)	1975 (4)	(5)	(6)
Total..........	100.0%	100.0%	100.0%	100.0%	+121.4%	+119.8%
Coal..........	9.1	0.3	4.8	0.2	− 92.3	− 92.3
Oil............	78.4	87.3	82.7	86.7	+146.6	+130.3
Gas..........	6.2	5.7	3.3	3.0	+103.4	+103.4
NGL..........	6.0	6.6	9.0	10.1	+145.3	+145.4
Hydro.........	0.3	0.1	0.2	negl.	− 50.0	− 50.0

negl. Negligible.

SOURCE: Based on Table 85.

[9] This does not imply that disappearance will be at an even rate between 1955 and 1975. In fact, indications are that this will be an accomplished fact long before 1975.

Government

Energy consumption by government constitutes less than 5 per cent of the total for the economy, which makes government (including federal, state, and local) the second smallest of the energy-consuming sectors. Its estimated growth of less than 50 per cent between 1955 and 1975 also ranks as second smallest among the sectors (Table 78). Problems of coverage heavily color the statistics and must be kept in mind when considering this sector.[10]

As shown in Table 87 and Figures 57 and 58, two classes of use dominate the government's energy consumption in 1955: the military establishment and the Atomic Energy Commission. Consequently, the assumptions made about changes in their energy consumption between 1955 and 1975 exert a heavy weight on the 1975 estimates for the sector. Together, these two components account for close to 70 per cent of the total for government in 1955 and about 55 per cent of the estimated total for 1975. By way of comparison, such a familiar governmental energy use as street and highway lighting accounts for less than 10 per cent of the total in 1955 and less than 19 per cent in 1975.

Among the energy sources, liquid fuels (oil and NGL) are the most important, accounting in 1955 and 1975 for around 75 per cent of direct fuel consumption (Table 88, columns 1 and 2). This high percentage is essentially a reflection of the importance of the military establishment in the government's direct fuel consumption. When fuel consumption via electricity is taken into account, oil's percentage share of the total drops sharply, while coal's importance rises to about 30 per cent of the total. The latter aspect reflects coal's indirect use via electricity consumption of the AEC and in street and highway lighting.

·   ·   ·

Agriculture

With less than 2 per cent of the economy's total energy consumption, agriculture[11] is the smallest of the consuming sectors. Its estimated increase in consumption of 43 per cent between 1955 and 1975 is also the smallest among the sectors. Problems of coverage heavily influence the statistics presented for this sector; usable information is available only for the consumption of liquid fuels and electricity, and even for these the information is quite inadequate.[12]

Within the coverage afforded by the data, liquid fuels are of dominant importance in argriculture; according to the statistics in Tables 89 and 90 and Figures 59 and 60, oil and NGL account for 100 per cent of the sector's direct

[10] For a description of the coverage of the government sector and of the methods and assumptions used in deriving its energy consumption pattern see Chapter 5; for the detailed statistical materials underlying Tables 87 and 88, see Section E in the Appendix to Part II.

[11] For a description of the coverage of the agriculture sector and of the methods and assumptions used in deriving its energy consumption pattern see Chapter 5; for the detailed statistical materials underlying Tables 89 and 90, see Section F in the Appendix to Part II.

[12] For example, electricity covers only the amounts used in pumping and irrigation, and the liquid fuels statistics do not include the amounts consumed by trucks used on the farm.

TABLE 87. GOVERNMENT: ENERGY CONSUMPTION BY SOURCE, 1955 AND ESTIMATED 1975

(Trillion Btu)

Item	Coal		Oil		Gas		NGL		Hydro		Total			
											Btu		Percentage of all government	
	1955 (1)	1975 (2)	1955 (3)	1975 (4)	1955 (5)	1975 (6)	1955 (7)	1975 (8)	1955 (9)	1975 (10)	1955 (11)	1975 (12)	1955 (13)	1975 (14)
Direct fuel consumption...	n.a.	n.a.	850	1,225	293	487	72	107			1,215	1,819	62.7%	63.0%
Military establishment [b]	n.a.	n.a.	735	975	n.a.	n.a.	57	74			792	1,048	40.8	36.3
Transportation, self-performed [a]			90	177	293	487	12	23			102	200	5.3	6.9
All other...........	n.a.	n.a.	25	74	57	115	3	10			322	570	16.6	19.7
Consumption via electricity	581	822	16	33					69	99	723	1,069	37.3	37.0
Atomic Energy Commission..........	478	477			18	24			24	18	520	519	26.8	18.0
All other, including street and highway lighting..	102	345	.16	33	40	91			45	82	204	550	10.5	19.0
Total...........	581	822	866	1,258	350	602	72	107	69	99	1,939	2,888	100.0%	100.0%

n.a. Not available.

[a] Self-performed military transportation included within "military establishment."

NOTE: Totals may not add because of rounding.

SOURCES: Appendix Tables E-8, E-13, H-9, and H-17.

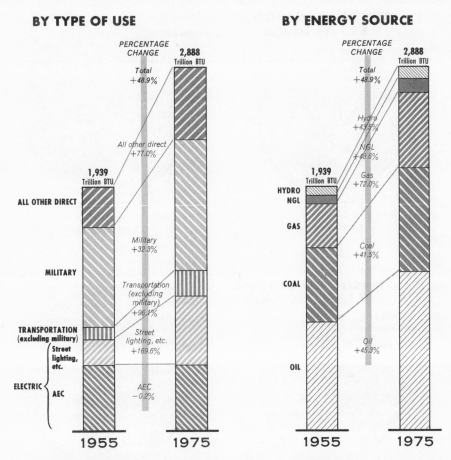

Figure 57. Government sector: energy consumption by type of use and energy source, 1955 and estimated 1975.

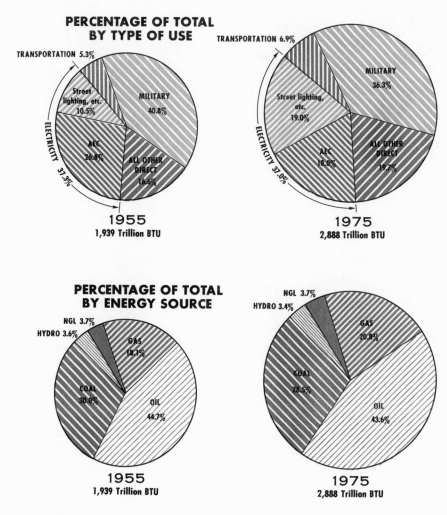

Figure 58. Government sector: percentage of total energy consumption by type of use and energy source, 1955 and estimated 1975.

TABLE 88. GOVERNMENT: CHANGES IN THE PATTERN OF
ENERGY CONSUMPTION, 1955–75

| Energy source | Percentage share in sector's total energy consumption | | | | Percentage change in quantity consumed 1955–75 | |
| | Direct fuel consumption | | Direct fuel consumption and consumption via electricity | | Direct fuel consumption (5) | Direct fuel consumption and consumption via electricity (6) |
	1955 (1)	1975 (2)	1955 (3)	1975 (4)		
Total..........	100.0%	100.0%	100.0%	100.0%	+49.7%	+48.9%
Coal..........	n.a.	n.a.	30.0	28.5	n.a.	+41.5
Oil............	70.0	67.3	44.7	43.6	+44.1	+45.3
Gas...........	24.1	26.8	18.1	20.8	+66.2	+72.0
NGL..........	5.9	5.9	3.7	3.7	+48.6	+48.6
Hydro.........			3.6	3.4		+43.5
Consumed as electricity.....			37.3%	37.0%		+47.9%

n.a. Not available.

SOURCE: Based on Table 87.

TABLE 89. AGRICULTURE: ENERGY CONSUMPTION BY SOURCE,
1955 AND ESTIMATED 1975

Trillion (Btu)

Energy source	1955	1975
Direct fuel consumption.....................................	617	916
Coal...	n.a.	n.a.
Oil..	515	766
Gas...	n.a.	n.a.
NGL...	101	151
Consumption via electricity.............................	112	126
Coal...	56	79
Oil..	9	7
Gas...	22	21
Hydro...	25	19
Total...	729	1,042
Coal...	56	79
Oil..	524	773
Gas...	22	21
NGL...	101	151
Hydro...	25	19

n.a. Not available.

NOTE: Totals may not add because of rounding.

SOURCE: Appendix Table F-4.

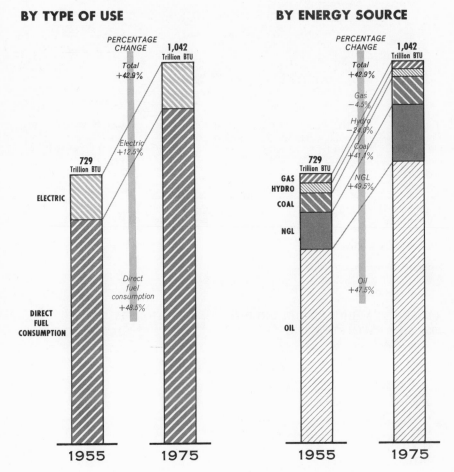

Figure 59.   Agriculture sector: energy consumption by type of use and energy source, 1955 and estimated 1975.

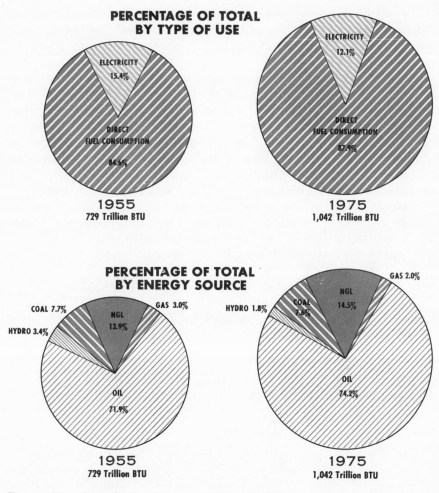

Figure 60. Agriculture sector: percentage of total energy consumption by type of use and energy source, 1955 and estimated 1975.

energy consumption. Although this percentage obviously is incorrect (since adequate statistics covering the use of other fuels are not available), it is likely that liquid fuels in fact account for close to 100 per cent of the mineral fuels used for productive—as opposed to household—purposes. The importance of liquid fuels results from the fact that work within this sector is dominated by tractor-type vehicles.

Electricity is the only other energy input into agriculture accounted for in the statistics in this study. In terms of the fuel needed in its generation, electricity consumed on the farm accounted for 15 per cent of agriculture's energy consumption in 1955, and an estimated 12 per cent in 1975 (Table 90, columns 3 and 4, and Figure 60). The decline in relative share reflects the fact that the estimated growth in electricity between 1955–75 of 12.5 per cent is only about one-quarter as much as the estimated growth in direct fuel consumption (Table 90, columns 5 and 6). This does not reflect a similar small rise in activity; on the contrary, the underlying use—power for irrigation and drainage—increases by some 50 per cent, but when translated into fuel requirements the assumed gain in the thermal efficiency of electric power generation serves to offset much of the growth in the amount of electricity used in agriculture.

When fuels consumed indirectly via electricity are taken into account, the share of liquid fuels in the total energy consumption in agriculture drops to about 85 per cent in 1955 and an estimated 89 per cent in 1975. The remainder is supplied by the energy sources in generating electricity, mainly coal, which, on this basis, accounts for almost 8 per cent of agriculture's total energy consumption in 1955 and 1975.

TABLE 90. AGRICULTURE: CHANGES IN THE PATTERN OF ENERGY CONSUMPTION, 1955-75

| Energy source | Percentage share in sector's total energy consumption | | | | Percentage change in quantity consumed 1955–75 | |
| | Direct fuel consumption | | Direct fuel consumption and consumption via electricity | | Direct fuel consumption (5) | Direct fuel consumption and consumption via electricity (6) |
	1955 (1)	1975 (2)	1955 (3)	1975 (4)		
Total..........	100.0%	100.0%	100.0%	100.0%	+48.5%	+42.9%
Coal..........	n.a.	n.a.	7.7	7.6	n.a.	+41.1
Oil............	83.5	83.6	71.9	74.2	+48.7	+47.5
Gas...........	n.a.	n.a.	3.0	2.0	n.a.	− 4.5
NGL..........	16.4	16.5	13.9	14.5	+49.5	+49.5
Hydro.........			3.4	1.8		−24.0
Consumed as electricity.....			15.4%	12.1%		+12.5%

n.a. Not available.

SOURCE: Based on Table 89.

PART III

The future of energy supply

CHAPTER 7

The conceptual basis
of energy supply estimation

TERMINOLOGY

In the preceding part of this study a basic assumption in estimating future energy consumption was the continuation of 1955 price interrelationships in the period through 1975. Thus the resultant estimate is not a forecast of "demand" in 1975 in the sense of the specific quantities that will actually be taken up by economic activity in that year. Similarly, the estimates on the supply side developed in Part III are based on special circumstances which mean that they do not constitute forecasts or predictions of what actually will be produced in 1975, hence the term "supply" should not be applied to them.

The special point of view from which supply is examined assumes that the only limitation on the capacity to produce the several fuel sources (and in a certain sense, hydropower) is the extent and nature of the stock afforded by the environment. Prospects for future supply, in other words, are determined for present purposes only by the physical availability of the energy sources and the technologic feasibility of "producing" them at a certain capacity level (that is, at a certain annual rate of output). The effect of this approach to supply is to exclude from consideration demand and other important factors, such as the level of imports, which determine the actual level of production. Finally, it is assumed that production costs, in constant dollar terms, remain constant or, more precisely, do not rise. This assumption is introduced to simplify the analysis and to limit the consideration of technology to what is expected to be feasible *and* economic in the period through 1975.

The term "availability" is used to describe the resultant estimates. It may be defined as: what *could* be produced, or made available in the year in ques-

295

tion, at no appreciable increase in constant-dollar costs. This carries with it the assumption that the growth in output between now and 1975 will be constant, by and large, whatever the possible productive capacity in the terminal year may be. And this assumption, in turn, requires that natural stocks be adequate to permit such growth—that production at no increase in costs will not be lower in 1975 than in some preceding year due to the depletion of natural stocks. The findings of this study are consistent with this requirement.

In examining the natural stock of the energy materials, it is necessary to introduce additional new terminology because of the lack of adequate concepts and precise definitions. The common terms "reserves" and "resources" are ordinarily applied to the natural occurrences of useful mineral substances in the earth's crust—including coal, crude oil, and natural gas—with which this study is concerned. This usage suffers, however, from the absence of a clearly understood conceptual basis and from the traditional habit of employing the terms without defining them. Indeed, the two terms are often used interchangeably.

Specifically, there are three conceptual shortcomings in current terminology: First, there is a failure to comprehend the economic aspect within the terminology. That is to say, there is no relating of costs to what exists in the environment. Do "reserves" and "resources" imply current costs or higher costs, and if the latter, at what level? Second, there is no systematic means of comprehending both the known and the unknown portions of the natural stock. There is no clear demarcation between what has been discovered and what is not yet discovered but which may be presumed to exist. And, finally, there is no systematic provision for technological progress. Existing terminology does not allow for material, either known or presumed to exist, exploitation of which, regardless of cost, is presently infeasible, but which conceivably some day could become feasible with greater knowledge and technological progress.

These shortcomings may be of small importance in looking at the present or the short-term future, but in any consideration of the medium-term or long-term future they cannot be ignored. A perspective for the long term that does not recognize them is utterly inadequate. One cannot talk meaningfully of the future in terms of the present alone. To be sure, the current terminology has often been used with qualifying adjectives or phrases to acknowledge one or the other of these aspects, but the result is an inadequate makeshift. The need is for a new terminology derived from concepts that remove all of the shortcomings and are at the same time unambiguous.

To this end this study employs three concepts—"reserves," "resource base," and "resources." Conceptually, "reserves" are the stocks of a mineral raw material *in situ* as viewed by the operator producing it. They are explicitly defined in terms of immediate or short-term economic feasibility of extraction. The cost limits are consistent with normal risk taking and commercial production, and exclude material known to exist but which cannot be profitably extracted with current techniques. This usage is consistent with the most common industry definition of the term "reserves."

The "resource base" is conceived to include the sum total of a mineral raw material present in the earth's crust within a given geographic area. If reserves are denoted by A, the resource base, C, equals A plus B, where B comprehends all the stock not included in A, whether its existence is known or unknown and regardless of cost considerations and of technologic feasibility of extraction. The resource-base concept is thus absolute in that it includes *all* the occurrences within the geographic area specified.[1]

The concepts of reserves and resource base establish the outer limits within which to consider the source of supply of a mineral raw material. The former is restricted to only what is known and economic; the latter passes over these two criteria and extends to the limits of the physical environment. Between these limits exists a wide middle ground where various technological and economic criteria may apply—where one may wish to consider various "middle" quantities of the natural stocks coupled with technology and costs different from those currently prevailing.

Here, the term "resources" is employed to cover this middle ground. The "resources" of a mineral raw material may be defined according to any technical and economic criteria that may be considered relevant and appropriate. The resources consist of that part of the resource base (including reserves) which seems likely to become available given certain technologic and economic conditions. The petroleum resources of the United States, for example, may be indicated as X billion barrels if one assumes that costs are triple those of the present and that there is full exploitation of the continental shelf, but only Y billion assuming a doubling of costs and a limitation of offshore operations to 200 feet of water. Or, to use coal as an example, the resources of the United States may be defined in terms of all coal producible with current technology at one and a half times current costs; or one may wish to consider the coal resources that exist down to a depth of 5,000 feet (the limiting criterion in this instance being physical and indirectly, rather than directly, technologic or economic). As still another illustration, one might wish to consider the uranium resources that could be exploited at current costs with the (hypothetical) technique of leaching *in situ.*

Whether any particular definition of resources is useful depends on the context in which it is to be used and the possibility and need for expressing it quantitatively. It is essential in any event that an explicit definition always be given in conjunction with the use of the term. This study is interested in the resources of coal, crude oil, natural gas, and hydropower that can be

---

[1] The application of the resource base concept to many mineral raw materials, particularly the metals, creates problems in defining the conceptual limits (although it is believed these can be successfully coped with). In the present instance, however, there are no such problems, and the conceptual limits are "clean." The resource-base concept applied to the energy minerals (as well as to hydropower) comprehends the total occurrence of these energy sources in the natural environment, and can be meaningfully related to technology. This is demonstrated for each of the energy sources in the following chapters.

exploited at approximately current costs with foreseeable technological advancement by 1975.

The relation of the three concepts to the three fundamental aspects of the natural stocks that must be considered is summarized in Table 91. Although the concepts are unambiguous and simply defined, it may well happen that the quantitative expression of the resource definition—or, for that matter, the terms "reserves" and "resource base"—is not wholly satisfactory, or cannot be done at all, but this does not necessarily detract from the usefulness of the concepts. The lack of quantitative data may be unfortunate, but it does not need to be stultifying. The great advantage of this terminology is that it enables the particular point of view adopted here, or anywhere else, to be presented in the appropriate perspective.

The perspective afforded by the resource-base concept, for example, emphasizes the truly large possibilities awaiting realization through technology. With thinking based on the traditional reserve concept, even those attempts to take a longer view with latitude for technological advance are apt to remain in the general vicinity of the reserve magnitude. The generalized relationships between the magnitudes of reserves, resources, and the resource base for most minerals are illustrated in Figure 61.

The resource base is represented in Figure 61 by the entire rectangle; resources defined on one set of criteria are represented by the shaded area in the lower right; and reserves are denoted by the solid area in the lower right corner. The resources portion, it should be remembered, may be any size, for one can define resources by any criteria one chooses. The lighter shading away from reserves is intended to represent the lesser degree of knowledge concerning actual quantities as a progressively larger portion of the resource base is encompassed by the resources definition.

Figure 61 is also designed to indicate the generalized relative magnitudes of the three conceptual levels. In most instances, reserves constitute only a very small percentage of the resource base, and even optimistically defined resources

TABLE 91. RELATION BETWEEN RESERVE-RESOURCE TERMINOLOGY
AND BASIC ASPECTS OF THE NATURAL STOCKS

ASPECTS →	Occurrence	Economic	Technologic
TERMS ↓			
Reserves	Known	Present cost level	Currently feasible
Resources	Known + unknown	Any cost level specified	Currently feasible and feasibility indicated in future
Resource base	Known + unknown	Irrelevant	Feasible + infeasible

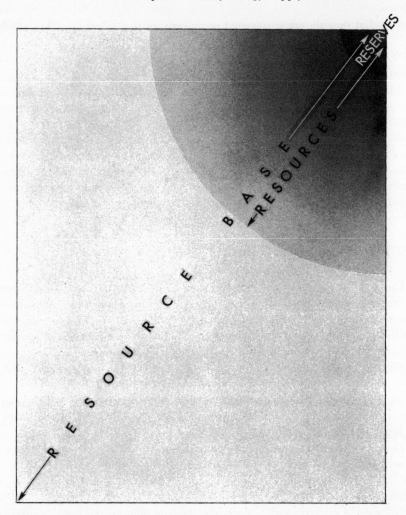

Figure 61. Relative magnitudes of reserves, resources, and resource base for any mineral raw material.

usually will include only a small proportion of the resource base. Figure 61 illustrates the fact that the introduction of the resource-base concept greatly enlarges the scope which may be given to a resources definition. The results of this widened scope are demonstrated in the conclusions reached in each of the following chapters.

Unfortunately, the specific definitions above are applied herein to a body of information that cannot be set forth with equivalent precision in meaning. The results, therefore, are less than perfect—ambiguities in the literature cannot be wholly cleared up, and the figures employed are not always satisfactory measures in that they do not correspond completely to the definitions. Nevertheless, the introduction of precise terminology is believed to be a desirable end in itself, and it is hoped that its use in the present study will contribute to a better understanding of the subject.

Although the term "resource base" and the flexible definition of the term "resources" are here introduced for the first time,[2] the basic distinction between reserves and resources is not original. Present usage makes these terms interchangeable, but the distinction was recently proposed in a report on reserve-resource terminology by an international committee of geologists.[3] This study acknowledges its debt to the committee report, and suggests that the terminological innovations presented herein add logical completeness to the concepts and definitions set forth in the committee report.

ESTIMATING TECHNIQUE

The problem of estimating future consumption is essentially statistical. Certain arithmetic relations are established, growth factors are selected and applied, and numerical results are obtained in considerable detail. The data necessary for this procedure are, generally speaking, readily obtainable, and the procedure can be undertaken by anyone who is interested in the subject.

The estimation of availability involves an entirely different process—one which is essentially nonstatistical in nature. Many past supply studies have been preoccupied with statistical trends without paying much attention to the possible future behavior of the variables that determine the trends. The present study is in large part an examination of the variables.

The problem to begin with is geological. It concerns the occurrence of energy minerals in the earth's crust—characteristics of distribution (geographically and vertically), concentration (the absolute and/or proportionate content of the material in a given volume of the earth's crust), and quantity (total and size distribution of occurrences).[4] Moreover, the data on occurrence are fragmentary

---

[2] More correctly, the terminology was set forth in the prior publication of the chapters on oil and gas availability. See B. C. Netschert, *The Future Supply of Oil and Gas* (Baltimore: Johns Hopkins Press, 1958). In his recent book, *Conservation in the Production of Petroleum* (New Haven: Yale University Press, 1957), p. 7, E. W. Zimmermann also stresses the dynamic aspect of resources as the product of technology in defining resources as "environmental aspects for use by man." Zimmermann relates resources solely to need, however, rather than to their availability as determined by technology. His concept thus has elements of both "resources" and the "resource base" as here defined. Moreover, he does not attempt to relate his resource concept to the conventional reserve concept, nor does he consider the possibility or usefulness of quantifying petroleum resources in estimates.

[3] F. Blondel and S. G. Lasky, "Mineral Reserves and Mineral Resources," *Economic Geology*, Vol. LI, No. 7 (November 1956), pp. 686–97.

[4] This is not, of course, literally applicable to hydropower, but equivalent statements can be made for hydropower by changing the appropriate terms, beginning with the substitution of hydrology for geology (see Chapter 11).

or at best incomplete, and the task of assembling and analyzing them is a full undertaking in itself.

Under these circumstances, in the procedure used here the first part of the analysis for each of the energy sources is addressed to the position of the United States with respect to reserves, resources, and the resource base for that energy source. Estimates are obtained for each level by listing, describing, and interpreting—in the light of their demonstrated shortcomings—existing estimates of "reserves" and "resources," however defined, in the perspective of this study's terminology. This is followed by a similar listing and description of existing estimates of future capacity and production in the period through 1975. As production estimates, they carry certain assumptions about the demand which would call forth such production and about an import level, where relevant, that would supplement that production in meeting the demand. They are thus not necessarily estimates of availability as considered in this study. At the same time, there is an availability implication in the estimates—if a forecaster believes production in a certain year will be at a certain level, it seems proper to conclude that in his opinion the potential capacity for that year should be *at least* that level. Thus the various estimates of production can be used to give an indication of expert opinion (since they are almost all made by members of the industry) as to the general level of availability from domestic production. The perspective of availability ex demand used in this study can then be applied.

The analysis next examines the indicated future course of technology in the respective industry and its relation to future productive capacity; and then the findings with respect to the resource position and technology are applied to the existing estimates of future production and capacity to obtain an estimate of domestic availability in 1975. The analysis concludes with a brief consideration of the possible role of alternative sources of supply, such as imports and synthetic equivalents, where appropriate.

In summary, for each energy source published estimates of future production are surveyed, a consensus is adjudged, and this is modified to obtain an availability estimate in the light of what appear to be relevant data and reasonable opinions on the various determinants of availability.

CHAPTER 8

Coal

The coal industry provides a good example of the terminological confusion mentioned in the preceding chapter.[1] In current industry usage (and, for that matter, in any discussion in the literature), "reserves" and "resources" are rarely defined with precision and are often employed interchangeably. Most discussions of the basis of future coal supply apply the term "reserves" to estimates based on criteria which would be defined as "resources" in the terminology adopted herein. In the following discussion, the two terms are put in quotation marks when used in the context of discussions or estimates being cited. When so marked, they may or may not correspond to the definitions given in the preceding chapter. The use of the two words without quotation marks signifies that they *are* being used according to those definitions. Although it would be preferable to use quotation marks only for those terms that do not correspond to the definitions adopted in this study, this cannot be done, since in many instances the terms are ambiguous in their original context and it is not possible to determine to which of the definitions in this study they correspond.

THE RESERVE-RESOURCE POSITION

Consideration of coal reserves and resources requires a different approach than is used in the following chapters on the other energy sources. An assessment of current resource estimates necessitates a survey of the background of the estimates if their full significance is to be understood in the light of the concepts of this study. Accordingly, this chapter begins with an historical survey of estimates of coal resources in the United States.

[1] The scope of this chapter covers all ranks (kinds) and grades (quality) of coal. Anthracite is not considered separately because of its minor significance in the total energy picture.

Historical Survey of Estimates of Coal Resources

The first over-all estimate of U.S. coal resources was published in a paper by Campbell and Parker of the Geological Survey in 1909.[2] An estimate of 3.157 trillion tons[3] was given for the "quantity of coal contained within the known area of the United States when mining first began." Of this amount, 1.9 trillion tons was considered "easily accessible or minable under present conditions," and 1.2 trillion tons was "nonminable under present conditions or accessible with extreme difficulty."[4] The authors added that some 500 billion tons of low-rank coal in western states were not really accessible or minable under current conditions, so that the figure of 1.9 trillion tons should be reduced to 1.4 trillion tons. The limiting criteria for bituminous coal (the most important part of the total) were a seam thickness of 14 inches, a maximum depth of 3,000 feet, and 30 per cent ash content.

In 1917, Campbell presented an expanded version of his original paper,[5] and in 1922 a further revision appeared.[6] The revised total was given as 3.5 trillion tons, constituting the "coal reserve" remaining in the ground as of January 1, 1919. Presumably this revised figure was based on new data.

In discussing his choice of limiting criteria, Campbell observed that his approach was not limited to "present mining practice," but constituted an "attempt to estimate the total quantity of coal that ever would be mined in the United States, looking ahead 40, 50, or perhaps even 100 years." Although "present mining practice" was considered, he placed the physical limits higher "because it is almost certain that the future will go far beyond all present operations."[7]

Campbell noted, in establishing the depth limit, that the deepest coal mines in the world at that time were 4,000 feet and other mining operations were going deeper than 5,000 feet, hence "it was thought that future mining might be carried to a depth of 6,000 feet." Campbell actually established two depth limits, "in order to meet various requirements" which he did not specify. The limit of 6,000 feet he considered as the ultimate; another, at 3,000 feet, he established as the limit "for easily minable coal." The 3,000-foot limit became the effective criterion, however, since almost no data existed beyond that depth. On the thickness criterion, Campbell noted that the minimum thickness of seams

[2] M. R. Campbell and E. W. Parker, "Coal Fields of the United States," U.S. Geological Survey Bulletin No. 394, Papers on the Conservation of Mineral Resources (Washington, D. C.: U.S. Government Printing Office, 1909).

[3] All tons in this study are short, or net, tons of 2,000 pounds.

[4] *Ibid.*, p. 8

[5] M. R. Campbell, *The Coal Fields of the United States*, General Introduction, U.S. Geological Survey Professional Paper No. 100 (Washington, D. C.: U.S. Government Printing Office, 1917).

[6] M. R. Campbell, *The Coal Fields of the United States*, U.S. Geological Survey Professional Paper 100-A (Washington, D. C.: U.S. Government Printing Office, April 27, 1922).

[7] *Ibid.*, p. 24.

then being worked in the United States was 15 inches, and arbitrarily established 14 inches, as a point beyond that minimum, for his limit for high-rank coal. A similar procedure (with greater thicknesses) was followed for the other ranks of coal. On the question of ash content, Campbell remarked that "30 per cent has been regarded as the limit, but it is questionable whether it would not better be placed at 25 per cent."[8]

From Campbell's explanations it is clear that his estimates pertain to the concept of resources used in this study. They were resource estimates defined according to specific physical criteria but with less explicitly stated economic and technological parameters.[9]

Campbell's 1922 estimate was also published by the Geological Survey in 1929.[10] Prior to the last republication, the Engineer's Advisory Valuation Committee of the U.S. Coal Commission issued a report in 1924 which estimated recoverable coal "reserves," with known and possible mining methods, to be 1.625 trillion tons.[11] In 1939, the National Resources Committee published a report which used a figure of 3.2 trillion tons for coal resources,[12] and in 1947 the Bureau of Mines and the Geological Survey gave to Congress a joint estimate of 3.1 trillion tons of coal resources as of 1944.[13]

The basis of the three additional estimates was in each instance one of the Campbell estimates, expressed either in gross or net (recoverable) terms. The Campbell estimates thus remained current, either as originally expressed or as the basis for modified estimates, for some forty years. This surprisingly long tenure, considering the crudity of Campbell's data (which he himself noted) was the result of a lack of any further work on national coal resources. The general lack of interest in a re-examination of coal resources is understandable because of the general belief that coal resources were of an astronomic magnitude relative to current consumption and even for requirements in the foreseeable future.

Interest in the magnitude of total coal resources was, however, revived in 1948, when A. B. Crichton, a member of the coal industry, declared that existing estimates were obsolete and called for a thorough reappraisal of the nation's

---

[8] *Idem.*

[9] It should be noted that Campbell's reference to original coal in place makes no difference in this instance. Total coal production cumulated through 1908 was some 31 billion tons, whereas the estimate by Campbell is here rounded to the nearest 100 billion tons.

[10] M. R. Campbell and J. A. Bownocker, *The Coal Fields of the United States*, U.S. Geological Survey Professional Paper No. 100 (Washington, D. C.: U.S. Government Printing Office, 1929).

[11] Engineer's Advisory Valuation Committee, "Report to the U.S. Coal Commission," *Transactions*, American Institute of Mining and Metallurgical Engineers, Vol. 70 (1924), pp. 794–804.

[12] T. A. Hendricks, "Coal Reserves," in National Resources Committee, *Energy Resources and National Policy* (Washington, D. C.: U.S. Government Printing Office, January 1939).

[13] U.S. Bureau of Mines and Geological Survey, *Mineral Resources of the United States* (reprint, Washington, D. C.: Public Affairs Press, 1948).

coal "reserves." [14] Crichton charged that Campbell's (latest) estimate had very little validity—too much of the total was inferred on geologic grounds that had since been demonstrated to be overoptimistic. (Coal, that is, had been assumed to be continuous between outcrops and to maintain the outcrop thickness, whereas subsequent investigation, Crichton claimed, had all too often disclosed thickness between outcrops to be highly irregular, with large areas of no coal at all.) Moreover, Crichton contended, the limiting criteria of seam thickness, depth, and ash content were so broad as to be unrealistic; it had never been economic to mine coal in the United States under circumstances approaching the 14-inch seam or 3,000-foot depth that Campbell had used as limits and subsequent authors had accepted.

In support of his contention that the original estimate was unrealistic, Crichton claimed that most subsequent survey work by the states in any detail had yielded state totals well below those carried by the U.S. Geological Survey. Crichton concluded that the total recoverable "reserves" of the United States were more probably on the order of 223 billion tons, or only 16 per cent of Campbell's original estimate of "easily accessible and minable" coal.

It can be demonstrated that Crichton's comparison of state and U.S. Geological Survey totals was in many instances improper; because of different bases and limiting criteria the estimates were not directly comparable. A detailed account of Crichton's comparisons is not necessary here, however, since in the present context it will be recognized that much of Crichton's criticism was based on terminological differences. Crichton was disputing the Campbell and Campbell-based estimates in large part because they were resource estimates and not reserve estimates. Crichton's own estimate, questionable even in its own context, was being offered in lieu of the others as if they were directly comparable.

Crichton's dramatic reduction of national coal "reserves" received little support, but it was tacitly agreed that a new look at the nation's coal endowment was in order. The U.S. Geological Survey began in the same year a ten-year program of reappraisal on a state-by-state basis involving detailed field investigations in co-operation with state geological surveys, and with somewhat different limiting criteria.

In early 1949, a few months after the Crichton paper, A. C. Fieldner of the U.S. Bureau of Mines published an estimate of 1.562 trillion tons as the recoverable "reserves" of the country. [15] His paper took note of the Crichton criticisms but maintained adherence to the Campbell basis.

The first governmental break from the Campbell basis occurred in 1950, with publication by the U.S. Geological Survey of its first progress report on its

[14] A. B. Crichton, "How Much Coal Do We Really Have? The Need for an Up-to-date Survey," Technical Paper 2428 of the American Institute of Mining and Metallurgical Engineers, *Coal Technology*, Vol. 3, No. 1 (February 1948).

[15] A. C. Fieldner, "Solid Fuels," *Oil and Gas Journal*, Vol. 47, No. 46 (March 17, 1949), pp. 138–40, 142, 145.

long-term reappraisal program.[16] With only some 15 per cent of the previous resource total re-examined (and with no revision of previous state estimates not yet re-examined), the revised estimate of the total as of 1950 was 2.5 trillion tons, and of recoverable "resources" was 1.2 trillion tons (of which about one-quarter was lignite). The revised total figure represented a decrease of 19 per cent from the 1944 estimate of resources; and that for recoverable "resources," a decrease of 32 per cent from the equivalent Campbell estimate.

The Geological Survey published its second progress report in 1953.[17] The new listing, based on a re-examination of two-thirds of the 1944 total, gave a total figure of 1.9 trillion tons, with currently recoverable resources of 950 billion tons. This represented a further reduction of about 20 per cent from the 1950 total figure, and a reduction of 46 per cent from the Campbell estimate.

In 1953, there also appeared a broad study of energy in the future by Palmer Putnam in which the author subjected the Campbell estimate and its successors to severe criticism, extending Crichton's criticisms and applying "correction factors" to the 1944 estimate.[18] Whereas Crichton had emphasized the disparity between federal estimates of state totals and the states' own estimates of their resources, Putnam listed specific criticisms of the Geological Survey's methodology and criteria. Putnam's criticisms and conclusions are not really pertinent to this analysis, but since they have received wide credence and have continued to be cited as a valid view of coal resources in preference to those of the Geological Survey[19] his argument is examined in a Note at the end of this chapter.

Current Estimates of the Makeup and Characteristics of Coal Resources

From the above survey of coal reserve-resource estimates it is apparent that there is only one estimate that can be considered current—the figures contained in the 1953 progress report of the U.S. Geological Survey.[20] These figures constitute the only official estimate as well as the only recent, detailed, and comprehensive breakdown of coal resources. The following paragraphs summarize the Survey's report.

It should be noted to begin with that the Survey uses "reserves" and "resources" as synonyms. The title speaks of "coal resources," but the word is not used at all in the text; following past usage, the term "reserves" is employed throughout. This does not, of course, affect the validity or usefulness of the figures themselves, but it is an example of the present lack of distinction in

[16] P. Averitt and L. R. Berryhill, *Coal Resources of the United States*, U.S. Geological Survey Circular No. 94, November 1, 1950.

[17] P. Averitt, L. R. Berryhill, and D. R. Taylor, *Coal Resources of the United States*, U.S. Geological Survey Circular No. 293, October 1, 1953.

[18] P. Putnam, *Energy in the Future* (New York: Van Nostrand, 1953), pp. 124–33.

[19] See E. Ayres, "The Fuel Situation," *Scientific American*, Vol. 195, No. 4 (October 1956), p. 47.

[20] Averitt *et al., op. cit.*

reserve-resource terminology in the literature. Under the definition followed herein all the figures in the Survey report pertain to resources.

The state figures comprising the total are heterogeneous as to source and criteria. Of the thirty-two state totals comprising the national total, sixteen are the result of recent detailed work, the other sixteen are earlier, more generalized estimates. The 1953 report notes that the earlier estimates are used in unmodified form, for modification could be done only on an arbitrary basis. The sixteen recent state figures represent, however, about two-thirds of the total national resource estimate.

Although there is some variation in the criteria used by the different states for their estimates, the Geological Survey believes that modification of the state figures would be arbitrary and essentially meaningless. Where new estimates for individual states are lower than preceding estimates, the major reason is the adoption of more conservative assumptions as to continuity and thickness of beds back of outcrops. Another contributing cause is the elimination of areas for which available data are so scanty as to be useless. Thus, large portions of the probable and coal-bearing areas of several states are entirely omitted from consideration. (In terms of the resources definition used herein this results in significant underestimation.)

In classifying coal resources on the relative degree of knowledge and reliability of the information on which the individual estimate is based, the Survey uses three categories. "Measured reserves" are those for which sufficient data are available to render the estimate error 20 per cent or less; in area terms, points of observation are about one-half mile apart. "Indicated reserves" are computed partly from measurements and partly from geological projections; points of observation average about one mile apart, but may be as much as one and one-half miles. "Inferred reserves" are derived almost entirely from general geologic information on a bed or region, with perhaps a few thickness measurements. "In general, inferred coal lies more than two miles from the outcrop."[21] In only ten states have estimates been made in sufficient detail to permit a percentage breakdown on this basis. Within these states—whose resources comprise 50 per cent of the total—about two-thirds of the "reserves" are inferred, a bit more than one-quarter are indicated, and the remaining 5 per cent or so are measured.

With respect to coal rank, the Geological Survey categorizes the resources in the sixteen states for which recent estimates have been made. Within this total— equivalent to two-thirds of the national resource figure—two-fifths are bituminous, somewhat over one-third lignite, one-quarter subbituminous, and the remainder anthracite. It is noted that in terms of heat value the lignite and subbituminous proportions would be slightly less, and bituminous slightly greater. Because of the large proportion of the national resource total represented in this rank categorization, the distribution, according to the Survey, "may be considered as being substantially correct for the United States as a

[21] *Ibid.*, p. 12.

whole."[22] It is interesting to compare these figures with those of Table 1 of the Survey report, in which all coal-bearing states are represented by estimates, some of which date from the Campbell report. According to these over-all data (see Table 92 of this study), bituminous is a considerably greater proportion of the total, lignite much less. This is one illustration of the effects of the Survey's recent work on coal-resource data.

Under the criteria of thickness and depth, a breakdown is again available for only ten states. More than 85 per cent of this portion of resources is at a depth of 1,000 feet or less, 10 per cent is between 1,000 and 2,000 feet, and the remaining few per cent is between 2,000 and 3,000 feet. The Survey notes in this connection that the high concentration of shallow resources is due in part "to the fact that less information is available for the more deeply buried beds," but again concludes that "the observed distribution percentages should

TABLE 92. SUMMARY OF THE MAKEUP AND COMPOSITION OF U.S. COAL RESOURCES AS CURRENTLY ESTIMATED

Basis of categorization	No. of states represented[a]	Per cent of total resource figure represented[b]	Subcategories	Per cent of the resources covered by the categorization that are within each subcategory
Type of "reserves"....	10	49.5%	Measured.........	6%
			Indicated..........	27
			Inferred...........	67
Rank................	16	65.3	Anthracite.........	1
			Bituminous........	39
			Subbituminous.....	24
			Lignite............	36
	48	100.0	Anthracite.........	1
			Bituminous........	55
			Subbituminous.....	20
			Lignite............	24
Thickness.............	10	49.5	Thick.............	31
			Intermediate.......	27
			Thin..............	42
Depth................	10	49.5	Less than 1,000 ft..	87
			1,000–2,000 ft......	10
			2,000–3,000 ft......	3

ᵃ Reserve type, thickness, and depth breakdown based on data available for only ten states. Rank breakdown given for the sixteen states for which recent estimates supersede the Campbell estimates, and also for forty-eight states, using the Campbell estimates for the thirty-two without subsequent estimates.

ᵇ Total resource figure used here is figure for "remaining reserves," or reserves not yet mined as of January 1, 1953, as given in P. Averitt, L. R. Berryhill, and D. R. Taylor, *Coal Resources of the United States*, U.S. Geological Survey Circular No. 293, October 1, 1953, Tables 1 and 2.

SOURCE: Averitt *et al.*, *op cit.*

[22] *Ibid.*, p. 14.

show the general order of magnitude of distribution for the United States as a whole." [23]

The Survey defines special categories with regard to seam thickness. "Thick" coals are bituminous and anthracite seams greater than 42 inches, and sub-bituminous and lignite more than 10 feet. "Intermediate" coals are 28- to 42-inch seams of anthracite and bituminous, 5- to 10-foot seams of subbituminous and lignite. "Thin" seams are defined as those of anthracite and bituminous 14 to 28 inches thick, of subbituminous and lignite 2.5 to 5 feet thick. On this basis, the 50 per cent of the total resources in the ten states with detailed data are listed as a bit more than two-fifths thin, almost one-third thick, and somewhat more than one-quarter intermediate. The Survey points out that "the smaller percentage of reserves in the 'intermediate' category is due probably for the most part to the conservativeness of the appraisers. This is particularly true in the estimation of inferred reserves, where little information is available to determine the thickness satisfactorily, and the tendency is to assume minimum thickness." [24]

The thirteen subcategories under the foregoing criteria provide a breakdown of current coal resource estimates (see Table 92) which can be summarized very generally as follows:

a) The bulk of national coal resources are of subbituminous or lower rank.
b) Most of the resources are in the inferred category; very little are measured.
c) Most of the resources are at a depth of less than 1,000 feet.
d) A large proportion are in "thin" seams.

.   .   .

Special Aspects of Coal Resources

In order to make the discussion of coal resources complete there must be considered three aspects of these resources in addition to those looked at thus far. These are recovery, the use of coal to make metallurgical coke, and regional distribution.

RECOVERY

The recovery factor is primarily significant as a determinant of the proportion of coal resources that can be counted on as available. It is also important as a determinant of the rate of exhaustion of individual seams and districts, hence the extent of location changes in coal production. Thus, examination of the current recovery level and the foreseeable future influence of technology on it, is appropriate. Actually, there is no such statistic as *the* recovery level. Not only does recovery differ among the various mining techniques, but there

[23] *Ibid.*, p. 16.
[24] *Ibid.*

is considerable dispute in many instances over what the recovery level is even for an individual mine. A brief survey of recovery levels in the several mining techniques will suffice here.

Auger mining is a technique in which mechanically powered augers up to several feet in diameter bore horizontally as much as 200 feet into coal seams exposed on a hillside or cut bank. Here the theoretical maximum recovery is 75 per cent of the coal in place, based on the geometry of putting round holes in the edge of a tabular mass.[25] In a recent Bureau of Mines study of eight auger-mining operations, recovery ranged from 20 to 50 per cent.[26] Even if these data are typical, the influence this technique is likely to have on the over-all recovery rate in coal production should be small, since the combination of special site requirements and low recovery should continue to limit coal mined by this technique to a negligible percentage of total production.

Strip mining, a second surface-mining technique, exposes the coal seam by progressively removing the overburden, or covering rock and soil, and scooping up the coal thus uncovered. Theoretical recovery in this instance is 100 per cent; actual recovery is less because of loss by spillage, loss in transit, loss by leaving a fender of coal next to the spoil bank (the pile of dumped overburden), and by dirt from the spoil banks covering part of the stripped coal.[27] The Geological Survey considers average strip-mining recovery to be about 80 per cent;[28] others believe it to be even higher. Maize, for example, gives a recovery range of 88 to 92 per cent, which allows for a loss in cleaning of 3 to 5 per cent (depending on the nature of the cleaning plant and the quality of the coal).[29] According to the staff of the National Coal Association, efficient stripping operations may recover 87 to 97 per cent of the coal,[30] and Lamb and Koenig both consider the figure to be 90 per cent.[31]

One point of view includes as loss that part of a coal seam being strip-mined that is under too much overburden to be economically uncovered. Such coal is considered irretrievably lost, in this view, because the exposed face is buried when the original land surface is restored, yet it is at too shallow a depth to be mined by underground methods. "It is idle to assume that the marginal coal (which in some cases represents ten or even a hundred times the coal recovered by surface mining) will ever be sought by underground-mining technique. So, in an over-all sense, . . . surface mining may prove to have been

[25] *Ibid.*, p. 18.

[26] W. A. Haley and J. J. Dowd, *The Use of Augers in Surface Mining of Bituminous Coal,* U.S. Bureau of Mines Report of Investigations 5325, March 1957, pp. 14–15.

[27] R. Maize, Discussion of Technical Paper 1885, *Transactions,* American Institute of Mining and Metallurgical Engineers, Vol. 168 (1946), p. 17.

[28] Averitt *et al., op. cit.*

[29] Maize, *op. cit.*

[30] Communication to the author.

[31] R. P. Koenig, "Economics and Technique of Strip Coal Mining," *Colorado School of Mines Quarterly,* Vol. 45, No. 2B (April 1950), p. 28; G. A. Lamb's communication to the author.

wasteful." [32] This view rests on the assumption that because the unmined coal is unrecoverable at current costs with present technology it is beyond recovery forever, or would at the very least require technological changes to recover it. But stripping operations do not necessarily affect the accessibility of that part of the seam that was not worked, and the assumption that the unworked coal is permanently lost—that it should not be counted as resources under any criteria —seems unduly severe. On the contrary, it can be argued that strip mining adds to total recoverable resources by allowing recovery of coal under shallow overburden, in faulted (broken) seams, and in isolated pockets. [33]

In view of the distinctive characteristics of strip mining and the fact that only coal under certain prescribed circumstances of occurrence is amenable to such operations, it is logical to speak of "strippable reserves" and "strippable resources." Although there is obviously a certain part of total coal resources that is so amenable, data for quantifying this category on a national scale are lacking. In only a few states has there been any attempt at estimating such reserves, and the definition of such resources can be made only in terms of a flexible and dynamic technology. [34]

Again, site conditions circumscribe the opportunities for using stripping technology, but its place in current coal production is vastly more significant than that of auger mining. Whereas auger production is only 1.0 per cent of total output, strip-mine production is one-quarter of the total. Thus, the high recovery factor in strip mining has an important bearing on total recoverable resources. To the extent that technological progress makes it possible to strip coal that would otherwise be left unmined or would be mined by underground methods (with their lower recovery), total recoverable resources are increased.

The best available data on recovery in underground mining are given in a series of Reports of Investigations by the Bureau of Mines on reserves of coking coals in certain counties of Pennsylvania, West Virginia, and Kentucky. Most of these have been published since 1950 and indicate an average recovery of 50 per cent in mines covered by the reports over the years they have been in operation. A figure of 50 per cent has also been used for the national average, [35] but this cannot be taken too literally. In the first place, there is a source of confusion in the practice of operators in citing recovery in terms of only that

---

[32] E. Ayres and C. Scarlott, *Energy Sources—The Wealth of the World* (New York: McGraw-Hill Book Company, 1952), p. 60.

[33] Averitt *et al., op. cit.*

[34] See, for example, W. H. Smith, *Strippable Coal Reserves of Illinois*, Illinois State Geological Survey Circular 228, Urbana, 1957, p. 4. Smith uses a commendably broad perspective: "Although 100 feet of overburden represents the upper limit for overburden in Illinois strip mining to date, it seemed appropriate to include resources at depths greater than those currently considered strippable so that the results of this inventory may have the broadest possible application." He uses the term "resources" as defined in this study and takes the limit of overburden to 150 feet.

[35] See A. C. Fieldner, *Coal for Coke Production*, U.S. Bureau of Mines Information Circular 7559, March 1950; W. E. Wrather *et al.*, "Energy Resources of the United States," *Transactions*, Vol. I, Fourth World Power Conference, London, 1950, p. 22.

part of the coal seam from which they are actually extracting coal. An operator may claim a recovery level as high as 95 per cent, yet may be leaving in place 15 to 25 per cent of the coal at the top and bottom of the seam because of poor quality or necessity for roof or floor control.[36] Second, in mining metallurgical coal, which is very valuable, the attempt is to get full recovery, and actual performance may average as high as 75 to 80 per cent.[37] Third, the recovery level depends on the mining method employed. About 90 per cent of underground mining in this country employs the "room-and-pillar" method, in which large blocks of coal are left in place as "pillars" to support the roof. The extent to which the pillars can be recovered in working out a mine depends, among other things, on the operator. It is often profitable to recover the pillars, but is is not certain how much of the coal abandoned in them is lost only because pillar recovery is beyond the resources and skill of the operator.[38] There is also the possibility of legal liability by the mine operator for surface subsidence (and consequent damage to structures and facilities) caused by general roof collapse following pillar removal. This may deter pillar recovery that is otherwise physically and economically feasible and which the operator might desire to undertake. In any event, the loss of coal in pillars is on the average very high in this country, and in extreme circumstances, as in some of the western mines in very thick seams, recovery is only 15 per cent.[39]

European experience has demonstrated that, where necessary, losses of only 2 or 3 per cent can be achieved in underground mining,[40] although this can be done only at greater cost. Nevertheless, there is clearly much room in physical terms for improvement in coal recovery in the United States.

Equally important along with the attitude and general practice of industry in determining the future trend of recovery levels is mining technology, especially the general adoption of continuous-mining machinery. Continuous mining, in which a machine removes coal from the working face in a single operation, is a technological revolution comparable to the earlier introduction of "mechanization." Until the continuous miner arrived about 1950, mechanization consisted chiefly in the substitution of mechanical loading and continuous transport underground in place of the previous hand loading into individual cars and their transport in trains. With mechanization there still remains the need for blasting the coal loose, during which time other operations in the vicinity are not possible. Continuous mining in one operation breaks up the coal and removes it from the face, eliminating an entire phase from the cycle. The rapid

[36] H. N. Eavenson, "Wasting a Valuable National Resource (Bituminous Coal)," *Transactions*, American Institute of Mining and Metallurgical Engineers, Vol. 168 (1946), p. 11.

[37] G. A. Lamb's communication to the author.

[38] The loss of coal in pillars is irrevocable once the workings have been abandoned. This is because the collapse of the roof makes it physically infeasible to rework the area.

[39] President's Materials Policy Commission (PMPC), *Resources for Freedom*, Vol. IV (Washington, D. C.: U.S. Government Printing Office, 1952), p. 5.

[40] C. A. Carlow, "World Coal Resources," *Seventy-Five Years of Progress in the Mineral Industry*, American Institute of Mining and Metallurgical Engineers, New York, 1947, p. 677.

rate of growth in the use of these machines is shown in the sharply increasing percentage of total underground production for which they are responsible:

Year	Percentage
1958	19.7
1957	14.9
1956	10.9
1955	8.0
1954	5.6
1953	3.4
1952	2.3

But there is as yet disagreement on the effect of continuous mining on recovery and its likely effect in the future. The only published survey of continuous mining, based on reports from twelve mines in which pillar extraction, either wholly or in part, is practiced, shows recovery ranging from 60 per cent to 96 per cent. The percentage of total operations within the mine in which continuous mining machines were employed ranged from 4.8 per cent to 100 per cent. The recovery figures in nine of the twelve mines refer to the mine operations as a whole, so that the results are, unfortunately, ambiguous.[41]

Expectations as to the effect of continuous mining on the recovery factor nevertheless appear to be optimistic. It has been pointed out, for example, that with continuous mining it is possible to work areas within a seam that are uneconomic with methods previously used.[42] Where the room-and-pillar method is used with continuous mining, smaller pillars are possible, for the coal remaining in place is not shattered and the roof is stronger. Even if no pillars are recovered, the absence of shattering permits pillar coal to be left in more orderly form, again permitting greater recovery. With pillar removal, the smaller working space needed for continuous mining permits the recovery of pillars that are otherwise unrecoverable.[43]

The most important single determinant of over-all recovery levels will be the relative proportion of stripping to underground operations. Unfortunately, the future position of strip mining in total coal production is by no means clear.[44] Since strippable sources are indeterminate, there is no way of telling when and to what degree resource limitations will begin to be apparent in strip-mine production. Although, in the opinion of some, strip mining east of the Mississippi

[41] J. J. Shields *et al.*, *Methods of Mining with Continuous Mining Machines*, U.S. Bureau of Mines Information Circular No. 7696, September 1954, p. 3.

[42] J. H. Truax, "Use of Continuous Miners in Pillaring," *Mechanization*, Vol. XIX, No. 6 (June 1955), pp. 57–58.

[43] See W. L. Wearly, "Trends in Continuous Mining Underground," *Colorado School of Mines Quarterly*, Vol. 45, No. 2B (April 1950), pp. 41–56; W. E. Hess, "Pillar Extraction in the Pittsburgh Seam With Continuous Miners," *Mining Engineering*, Vol. 7, No. 2 (February 1955), pp. 162–65; and S. Krickovic, "Pillaring With Continuous Miners," *Mining Engineering*, Vol. 7, No. 2 (February 1955), pp. 165–66.

[44] See discussion of productivity, and Table 95.

may reach a peak before 1975,[45] it is also suggested that surface operations are likely to be a much higher proportion of the total in the western fields,[46] which in turn will probably bulk much larger in total U.S. production. All that can be said is that resource estimates that use the currently estimated recovery factor for underground mining applied to all coal understate the recoverable coal resources to some degree. Advances in stripping technology may well extend strippable reserves beyond limiting physical criteria set by current equipment and techniques.

In underground operations, it can be assumed that—even if the advantage of continuous miners in pillar recovery may not prove to be as significant as currently claimed—the increasing adoption of such machines will at least permit more pillar recovery than at present because of better mine layouts, if for no other reason. And the greater possibility of full-seam mining should cause some upward trend in recovery levels. With full-seam mining, seam thickness is apparently no obstacle to the use of continuous-mining machines, which are already working seams as low as 28 inches. In the same vein is the expectation that "as we get into thinner coal, a combination of machinery development and a trend to longer working faces will tend to make longwall[47] or semi-longwall mining more customary,"[48] and recovery will be greater as a consequence.

Finally, there should be mentioned such other technological advances as roof bolting. The use of bolts to strengthen the roof has permitted full-seam mining as well as the mining of certain areas that could not be worked with timber supports, thus raising the recovery level.

All in all, there are grounds for optimism concerning future higher recovery levels in coal mining in the United States. To the extent that this occurs, recoverable resources will thereby be increased.

METALLURGICAL COAL

The use of coal to make metallurgical coke requires certain physical properties and qualities so as to produce coke with size uniformity, absence of dust, and with low sulfur and ash content. The importance of coke as a basic raw material in such a fundamental industrial activity as steelmaking raises the question of reserves and resources for this specific use.

The prime determinant of whether a coal is suitable for conversion to coke is the property of "caking." A caking coal becomes plastic when heated, and through further heating in the range of 1,650°F. to 2,000°F. in the absence of air, the contained volatile material is driven off, leaving a porous, carbonaceous

[45] Ayres and Scarlott, op. cit., p. 59.

[46] Koenig, op. cit., p. 36.

[47] Longwall mining is a system in which the whole seam is mined on a single face and pillars are left only around the shaft or main entry. The roof is allowed to collapse parallel to the face as the mining progresses.

[48] G. A. Lamb et al., "There's Coal in Your Future," Utilization, Vol. 5, No. 12 (December 1951), p. 35.

mass—coke. The coals having the best caking qualities are those of bituminous rank with a moderate percentage of contained volatile material, or "medium-volatile bituminous." Specific reserve data on caking coal are lacking, but the general magnitude of such reserves is known to be small.

Although there is a concept of "coking coal" roughly related to the percentage of contained volatiles, it is not feasible to apply the concept to estimate such reserves and resources. Modern blast furnaces require a strong, but not brittle, coke able to support the heavy weight of the furnace charge without crushing. The "structure" of the coke, which provides these properties, is in turn determined by the expansion characteristics of the coal charged to the coking oven. The dimensional behavior of coal in the coking process is complex, and is variable not only among coals of different volatile categories, but among coals of the same volatile category from different fields. At the same time, economic operation of the blast furnace requires uniformity of charge (that is, consistency over time), hence uniformity in the properties and characteristics of the coke used in the charge. For this reason, "blending" or mixing of the coal charge to the coke oven is the common practice, and each oven company has its own formula to produce a consistent product. The proportions of the different types of coal used in the charge vary widely. In 1958, for example, the percentage of low-volatile in the charge ranged from 4 per cent to 40 per cent. The average proportions for the country as a whole were approximately 67 per cent of the more abundant high-volatile, 20 per cent low-volatile, 13 per cent medium-volatile.[49] (In addition, there is the practice, begun during World War II and since continued on a minor scale, of blending anthracite fines in the charge, but this is less a matter of improving coke structure than of increasing carbon throughput.)

There is no trouble in defining what is meant by "low-volatile bituminous," but again there are no data for estimating total low-volatile reserves (although some attempts at estimates have been made). There is, however, good evidence that the drain on known areas of low-volatile bituminous reserves has been severe, chiefly because of their highly localized occurrence. In 1958, 67 per cent of the total coal delivered to coke ovens came from Pennsylvania and West Virginia, in roughly equal amounts from each state. But of the total low-volatile coal delivered, 91.3 per cent came from these two states—73 per cent from West Virginia and 18 per cent from Pennsylvania.[50] It is misleading, however, to equate "coking reserves" too closely with low-volatile bituminous. There is a limit, because of the expansion characteristics of this type of coal, to the gain in quality and yield that can be obtained through its use in the charge.

The second criterion of coking coal is its sulfur content. Sulfur is present in measurable amounts in almost all coals. It is an annoying source of corrosive

[49] U.S. Bureau of Mines, *Minerals Yearbook, 1958*, Vol. II (Washington, D. C.: U.S. Government Printing Office), pp. 222-23.

[50] *Idem.*

gas when coal is burned for any purpose, and it is a critical impurity in metal smelting. About three-quarters of the sulfur present in the coal remains in the coke, and in the blast furnace is carried over into the metal product, where it constitutes a deleterious impurity difficult and expensive to remove. Sulfur can, however, be removed from run-of-mine coal, the cost and degree of success depending on the mode of occurrence of the sulfur (whether organic or pyritic, finely disseminated or in nodules). At present, very finely disseminated pyrite cannot be removed during coal preparation because the coal must be reduced to too small a size for economic processing; nor can organic sulfur be removed, since it is combined with the coal substance. It has been observed, however, that if at some future time the sulfur present in the coke from this source reaches the limit of blast furnace tolerance, the technique of chemical desulfurization of the coal is available for commercial development.[51]

The third criterion is ash content, which lowers the productivity of the blast furnace. A reduction of 1.0 per cent in ash content increases the rate of pig iron production, for example, by 3 to 6 per cent.[52] The average ash content in coal charged to coke ovens is 10 per cent or less.

Just as blending makes possible the use of coals whose volatility differs from the ideal, so the use of coals with high ash and sulfur content is made possible through "preparation." Preparation utilizes various techniques to separate certain proportions of the impurities from the mined coal and thus provide a delivered product of higher quality. It is possible, with proper preparation techniques, to produce from many coals a product with most sulfur and ash removed. Often, indeed, a low-ash, low-sulfur product can be produced for coking, together with a middling product for fuel use.[53]

Coking and blast furnace operations are on such a large scale that changes in raw materials are made only when and if they cannot be avoided. Nevertheless, a decline in coke quality does not necessarily pose an insurmountable difficulty to the iron and steel industry. Indeed, the economic efficiency of coke from poor quality coals is not necessarily inferior. High ash is not always harmful, and it has been demonstrated that a higher sulfur content can be tolerated than was previously thought possible. Actually, the quality of any individual coal for use in the coking charge is less significant than consistency.[54]

[51] C. Robinson and L. R. Smith, "Modern Trends in Coal Preparation," *Mining Congress Journal*, Vol. 38, No. 2 (February 1952), p. 127.

[52] A. C. Fieldner and L. L. Newman, "Overcoming Shortages of Metallurgical Coke," *Proceedings*, United Nations Scientific Conference on the Conservation and Utilization of Resources, Vol. III (New York: United Nations, 1951), p. 165.

[53] A. C. Richardson, *The Role of Technology in Increasing Mineral Supplies by Suppression of Waste in Beneficiation*, unpublished report by Battelle Memorial Institute to the President's Materials Policy Commission, September 26, 1951, p. 13.

[54] See H. W. Nelson, *The Role of Technology in the Future of Coking Coals*, unpublished report by Battelle Memorial Institute to PMPC, September 21, 1951, pp. 2, 9; and H. H. Lowry, Discussion remarks in *Proceedings*, United Nations Scientific Conference on the Conservation and Utilization of Resources, *op. cit.*, p. 196.

The situation with respect to coking coal resources outlined in the foregoing paragraphs is aptly summarized in the following statement from the U.S. Geological Survey progress report:

> Because of the almost limitless possibilities of blending coals and other hydrocarbons in the manufacture of coke, and because of the certainty that the acceptable amounts of impurities in coke will be allowed to increase and coking properties to decrease as the higher rank and higher grade coals are depleted, it is impossible to define coking coal in precise terms. It may be possible, however, to establish certain categories of coal based on coking properties, and ash and sulfur contents, conforming to ranges now regarded as acceptable for use in making coke, and to report coal reserves in these categories, but this has not yet been done.[55]

Reliance on technology in this statement seems well founded. Technology in this field is dynamic, and the literature abounds in references to the technological possibilities in coke production and utilization. The role of preparation technology, for example, in increasing reserves of metallurgical coal has been described as spectacular. "Investigations have demonstrated that some deposits not now used for coking can be improved sufficiently for metallurgical use by skillful preparation."[56] For the period under consideration here, significant advances in the use of coal for metallurgical coke could come from research such as that suggested in a Bureau of Mines circular[57] along the following lines:

1) Determination of the behavior of the petrographic constituents of coals during cleaning and coking, and the application of this knowledge to improving the coking qualities of coals through selective preparation and blending.

2) Determination of the possible advantages of crushing separately the high- and low-volatile components of coke-oven blends to control the size distribution of each component.

3) Investigation of the effect of blending low-temperature chars on the carbonizing properties of coals.

4) Investigation of methods of pretreating weakly coking or noncoking coals to make them suitable for manufacturing metallurgical coke, either alone or in blends with strongly coking coals.

5) Investigation of the behavior of coals during carbonization with reference to the effect of the rank and type of coal and operating variables on the carbonizing process.

6) Development of full-size test ovens or pilot-scale test ovens and procedures that will give reliable results for predicting the behavior of coals or coal mixtures in commercial coke ovens.

---

[55] Averitt *et al., op. cit.*, p. 17. Some progress in establishing such categories, however, has been made by the Survey's work on Appalachian coking coal reserves by county (*ibid.*, p. 20).

[56] T. Fraser, "Preparation of Coal in America," *Proceedings,* United Nations Scientific Conference on the Conservation and Utilization of Resources, p. 129.

[57] *Outlook and Research Possibilities for Bituminous Coal,* U.S. Bureau of Mines Information Circular 7754, May 1956, p. 44.

7) Study of the effect of pretreating coal, below the plastic temperature, on carbonizing characteristics.

8) Investigation of the coking of special mixtures, such as mixtures of coal and iron ore, to produce "Ferrocoke" for blast furnaces.

9) Study of methods for eliminating sulfur during carbonization and of minimizing the effects of sulfur in the blast furnace.

Finally, it should be noted that the entire question of coking coal could become academic through realization of the possibility—at present beyond the horizon but being pursued in many quarters—of a continuous large-scale process to win iron from its ore without the use of coke (such as the reduction of iron ore with hydrogen or carbon monoxide). At the least, the increasing use of pelletizing and other techniques leading to a richer blast furnace charge will mean a decline in the amount of coke required to produce a ton of pig iron.

REGIONAL DISTRIBUTION

Although there is considerable substitutability as a heat source among coals of neighboring ranks, the greater the difference in rank the more difficult the substitution, and for such uses as coke there is considerable specificity. Coal, on the other hand, is not a homogeneous resource; its geographical distribution, both in toto and by rank and grade, varies widely. There is a high regional concentration of the various ranks of coal within the country. Although only 40 per cent of the total coal resources as estimated by the Geological Survey is east of the Mississippi, this region contains some 60 per cent of the higher rank bituminous and anthracite (the most desirable). Conversely, the 60 per cent of total resources west of the Mississippi consists chiefly of the lower rank coals, from low-rank bituminous down through lignite. The low-rank coals of the West can be utilized to generate steam power (although they have a lower heating value than the higher rank coals) and as a source of gas, synthetic liquid fuels, and chemicals. Nevertheless, they possess a serious handicap as coal resources because of their current remoteness from industrial and power-consuming centers. And, in addition, those of lower rank (subbituminous and lignite) are difficult to handle—they crumble during transportation and tend to ignite spontaneously in storage.[58]

The production pattern parallels the resource pattern. As shown in Table 93, production from the northern portion of the Eastern Coal Province (the Northern Appalachian Region) has accounted for 70 per cent of the total national output of bituminous coal and lignite in recent years. (Anthracite, as a special coal produced from limited districts for a limited market, can be disregarded here.) Thus, any major regional shift in coal mining could not occur without a drastic change in the type of coal produced, which would mean economic problems of great import and difficulty quite aside from those of the locational shift alone.

[58] Averitt et al., op. cit., p. 13.

TABLE 93. PRODUCTION OF BITUMINOUS COAL IN STATES OF THE NORTHERN PORTION OF THE EASTERN COAL PROVINCE, AS A PERCENTAGE OF U.S. COAL PRODUCTION OTHER THAN ANTHRACITE, 1945–59

State	1945	1946	1947	1948	1949	1950	1951	1952	1953	1954	1955	1956	1957	1958	1959
Pennsylvania	23.0%	23.5%	23.3%	22.4%	20.4%	20.5%	20.3%	19.1%	20.4%	18.2%	18.4%	17.9%	17.3%	16.8%	16.1%
West Virginia	26.3	27.0	27.9	28.2	28.0	27.9	30.6	30.4	29.1	29.6	30.0	30.5	31.8	29.2	28.8
Ohio	5.7	6.0	6.0	6.4	7.1	7.3	7.1	7.8	7.6	7.7	8.2	8.1	7.5	7.4	8.5
Virginia	3.0	2.9	3.2	3.0	3.3	3.4	4.0	4.6	4.2	4.5	5.1	5.5	6.0	6.7	7.0
Maryland	0.3	0.4	0.3	0.3	0.2	0.1	0.1	0.1	0.1	0.1	0.1	0.1	0.2	0.2	0.2
Eastern Kentucky	8.5	9.2	9.8	10.0	10.2	10.5	9.9	9.6	9.6	9.6	9.2	9.6	9.3	9.4	8.5
Total	66.8%	69.0%	70.5%	70.3%	69.2%	69.7%	72.0%	71.6%	71.0%	69.7%	71.0%	71.7%	72.1%	69.7%	69.1%

SOURCE: U.S. Bureau of Mines, *Minerals Yearbook*, various issues (Washington, D. C.: U.S. Government Printing Office).

Reserves and Resource Cost Schedules

Thus far, nothing has been said about the reserves of coal as defined here. Unfortunately, there is little that can be said, for unlike the practice in the oil and gas industry (see Chapters 9 and 10), there is no industry-wide collection of reserve data by either government or industry. There have been attempts, nevertheless, at estimating total reserves.

The most recent attempt is that of Given (the editor of an industry trade journal) in 1957. Given begins his estimating procedure with published data, by mine, of 1955 production and expected remaining mine life for mines producing over two-thirds of all U.S. coal production located east of the Mississippi. He multiplies the production and mine-life figures to obtain a "committed reserve" figure, or reserves assigned to operating properties. The result is 12.6 billion tons of bituminous. The next step is to include the reserves of present operations with the committed reserves of current mines. Using data in company and industry reports, Given finds that the average ratio of total reserves to committed reserves is 3 : 1. He is not very sanguine on the applicability of this ratio even to that part of the coal industry east of the Mississippi. "It is based on holdings of larger and stronger companies presumably better able to acquire and hold reserves. At the other end of the scale is a fair number of properties with no reserves beyond those already committed. Between are properties with varying holdings. . . . One assumption is that one-fifth of the present producing capacity has no reserves beyond those already committed. The second is that the remaining 30 per cent [of the smaller companies have] an average of 50 yr."[59] On these sweeping assumptions, Given obtains a figure of 28.3 billion tons of "total" bituminous reserves for present mining operations east of the Mississippi.

Given then refers to the Geological Survey resource estimates summarized above, and notes that ten states, considered typical of the country as a whole by the Survey, in which reserves have been classified in considerable detail, are noted by the Survey to contain 5 per cent of total "measured reserves" in beds at least 28 inches thick and at less than 1,000-foot depth, and 20 per cent in beds of the same thickness limit at less than 2,000-foot depth. Given considers this 25 per cent the equivalent of reserves. He applies this ratio to the Survey's resource estimate for states east of the Mississippi (adjusted for a later Ohio estimate by that state's Geological Survey) and obtains a figure of 152 billion tons of "overall reserves mineable at the prices of today or the near future."[60]

In addition to the Given estimate, two previous attempts were made by the Department of the Interior which included a reserve estimate as part of a "cost schedule" of coal resources; that is, the establishment of a schedule listing the quantity available at current prices and at successively higher prices (in con-

[59] I. A. Given, "How Much Bituminous . . . East of the Mississippi?" *Coal Age*, Vol. 62, No. 5 (May 1957), pp. 79–80.

[60] *Ibid.*, p. 80.

stant dollars). The first attempt was in a report furnished to the President's Materials Policy Commission by the Department. The estimate was given in terms of the mining costs that would be entailed in exploiting selected percentages of total recoverable coal resources, in terms of the man-hours and materials relative to labor and materials requirements in early 1951.[61] This was superseded by a similar attempt, in a report to the Panel on the Impact of the Peaceful Uses of Atomic Energy, published in 1956. This report estimated the "economically recoverable reserves"[62] at various price levels (in constant dollars) as follows:

Price level	*Billion short tons*
At or near 1954 prices	237
Additional at 1¼ to 1½ times 1954 prices	285
Cumulated total	522
Additional at 1½ to 4 times 1954 prices	426
Cumulated total	948

These estimates were based on the Geological Survey resource estimates published in 1950 and 1953, respectively.

.   .   .

Critique of Current Reserve-Resource Estimates

The various estimates of the U.S. reserves and resources of coal having been presented, they can now be examined in the light of the purposes of this study and of the reserve-resource concepts set forth in Chapter 7. Since the reserve and cost-schedule estimates are based on the U.S. Geological Survey's resource data, these data should appropriately be considered first.

It must be recognized to begin with that the Survey's latest report is the result of still unfinished work. Only nine of the sixteen new state estimates in the 1953 progress report represent a reappraisal of previous estimates in the true sense—a completely new look, with detailed field work on the basis of the Survey's standardized criteria. Figures for three of the states are "provisional" in that the new detailed field work does not cover the entire state and the totals are extrapolations. The new figures for the remaining four states are the result of state Survey work which used different categories and criteria from those of the U.S. Geological Survey.

To call attention to the incompleteness of its work is no criticism of the Survey, which itself stresses this aspect. The task is a large one, and the work can be accomplished by the Survey and the co-operating state Survey agencies only to the extent that funds are provided. It can be assumed that the current

---

[61] PMPC, *op. cit.*, Vol. II, pp. 164–65.

[62] Panel on the Impact of the Peaceful Uses of Atomic Energy, *Peaceful Uses of Atomic Energy*, Vol. 2, Report to the Joint Committee on Atomic Energy, 84th Congress, 2nd Session (Washington, D. C.: U.S. Government Printing Office, January 1956), p. 74.

reappraisal program will be carried through to completion, so that it is only a matter of time until there will exist national data based on reasonably uniform categories and criteria among the several states. Nevertheless, because the program is not finished at the present time, the national totals contain an indeterminate but unquestionably wide margin of error—a margin that, whatever it may be, is wider now than it will be when the work is done.

In the context of this study, the Survey's work can also be considered unfinished on another score, where there is no program for eventual completion. This criticism is made to suggest the advantages that would be provided by the Survey's coal resource work through adoption of the resource-base concept and the perspective it affords.

The Survey currently carries its data on coal resources to the same general limits as those used by Campbell in his original estimate. The depth limit is 3,000 feet, the minimum seam thickness for high-rank coal is 14 inches—both identical with Campbell's practice. The maximum ash content is 33 per cent, however, compared with Campbell's 30 per cent.

These limits are valid resource criteria in the terminology of this study. But this does not mean that 1.9 trillion tons, the quantification of resources at these limits, constitute *the* coal resources of the United States, or, as the Survey puts it, that 950 billion tons constitute "*the* recoverable reserves of the United States . . . based on the assumption that half of the coal reserves in the ground will be lost in mining, and half will be recovered."[63] (Italics added.) It is misleading to make any quantitative statement on resources without direct accompanying reference to the limiting criteria on which the quantification is based. There is no absolute figure for the estimated coal resources of the United States, but there are resources estimated up to an established limit for ash content, etc. To equate the Survey estimate with the absolute coal resources of the nation would be to assume that no coal will or conceivably can be mined beyond the limits on which the estimate is based. Yet without specific emphasis on the limits along with mention of the estimate, this is implied.

To be meaningful, moreover, the limiting criteria must be chosen keeping in mind the purpose of the estimate and the use that is likely to be made of it. In referring to its criteria, the Survey makes such statements as "less information is available for the more deeply buried beds,"[64] and "although the definitions and procedures used in calculating coal reserves generally permit the inclusion of beds containing as much as 33 per cent ash, very little coal of such high ash content is included in modern estimates, in part, because of the natural conservatism of the estimators, and in part, because all layers of parting and bone more than 3/8-inch thick are excluded in determining the thickness of the beds."[65] These, together with the fact that the current limits correspond in general to those of Campbell, suggest that the use of the limits is pragmatic—that, due

[63] Averitt *et al.*, *op. cit.*, p. 1.
[64] *Ibid.*, p. 16.
[65] *Ibid.*, p. 7.

partly to the long use of the Campbell limits and partly to the infeasibility of exceeding those limits (for example, depths below 3,000 feet), data beyond those limits are too scanty to bother with.

Consider now the purpose of the estimate, which can be fairly described as providing a figure for the total inventory of the natural stock of coal in the United States. Ideally, this would cover the resource base, but it is neither practicable nor necessary to suggest that this be the goal. However, it is both feasible and desirable to adopt the *concept* of the resource base[66] in the sense that data should be collected, so far as possible, without any limiting criteria. If the above-stated purpose of the Survey's coal resources estimate is correct, then the wider its perspective the better it fulfills that purpose. It could be said, for example, that coal resources down to 3,000 feet are an estimated 1.9 billion tons, and down to 6,000 feet are *at least* x tons, using whatever fragmentary data are available.

The use of the reserve-resource terminology adopted here is not incompatible with the currently accepted usage of "measured," "indicated," and "inferred reserves" that the Survey follows. On the contrary, these terms can and should be integrated with the new terminology and even with the resource-base concept.[67] Moreover, the foregoing criticisms of the Geological Survey's coal resource estimate are not intended to disparage the agency's work in that field. It is concluded here that the estimate presented in the 1953 progress report does not provide all the information one would like to have. At the same time, it is recognized that the estimate is considerably more meaningful than its predecessors and its physical basis is given in commendable detail and clarity. In fact, data on coal resources approach closer to the resource-base concept than those for any other mineral resource. Within a wide margin of error, the coal resources of the United States can be considered to be at least 2 trillion tons. Although the estimate may be reduced by further revision of individual state totals, it is reasonable to believe that this will be more than offset when and as known coal-bearing areas now excluded are brought within the total. And, as the Survey observes, "As exploration and development are carried to greater depths, it is certain that the total estimated reserves in the United States will be considerably increased by the addition of reserves in the deeper overburden categories."[68]

[66] Note that the conceptual limits of the resource base applied to coal are unambiguous. A substance in the earth's crust is either coal or it is not coal, according to detailed physical and chemical characteristics that are commonly accepted criteria. Concerning the depth limit in applying the concept, under certain temperature-pressure conditions coal is converted to graphite, hence there is a finite limit to the depth at which coal can occur as such. There is, in other words, a physical limitation to the environment in which the resource base occurs. Whether such depths could ever be reached in mining operations is irrelevant to the concept.

[67] See F. Blondel and S. G. Lasky, "Mineral Reserves and Mineral Resources," *Economic Geology*, Vol. LI, No. 7 (November 1956), pp. 686–97, *passim*.

[68] Averitt *et al., op. cit.*, p. 16.

Given's reserve and cost-schedule estimates, since they are based on the Survey's resource estimates, share the shortcomings of the latter, and in addition, possess some egregious flaws of their own. Given is, of course, the first to point out the crudeness of his approximations, although he believes his estimate of " 'total' mine reserves" is a "closer approach to the actual total of reserves held by bituminous mining companies east of the Mississippi" than any alternative method would yield.[69] In the absence of other attempts with which to compare it, this can be taken as probably true, but his derivation of an " 'overall' reserve" figure for the eastern half of the United States from the Geological Survey data is another matter.

In effect, Given equates the Survey resource data to the 28-inch thickness and 2,000-foot depth limits with reserves as defined here. That is to say, coal within these limits could be mined with current technology at current (constant dollar) costs. It is significant, however, that Averitt and his colleagues, to whom the importance of relating their resource data to current costs was certainly apparent, deliberately refrain from any remarks on the subject. The inference is clear—they saw no basis in the data on which to construct this relation. Given's assumption must therefore be regarded as totally arbitrary and his reserve estimate for the eastern United States as having little value since it is totally indeterminate.

The reserve estimates of the Department of the Interior and the cost schedules in which they appear are no better. Although the Survey estimates are given as the basis, no background or explanation is provided to show how the cost breakdown was obtained. The detailed data in the Survey report could not have been the basis of the costing, for the physical criteria used by the Survey must be translated into cost equivalents. Yet there is no systematic means of obtaining such equivalents; there is only the most general relationship—so general as to be useless—between seam thickness and cost, depth and cost, and so forth. The relationship can possibly be established, assuming other things equal (that is, given a coal seam of certain rank, thickness, and ash content, accessible only by shaft mining, one might state a rule of thumb that each additional 100 feet in depth would represent a certain increase in cost). But a costing of coal resources requires more than the physical factors considered by the Survey. In addition it involves such things as the nature of the roof rock, the thickness and distribution of partings in the seam, the dip of the seam in relation to topography and drainage, ground water conditions, local labor costs, and the degree of mechanization.

Even with the assumption that the Interior Department's costing somehow represents a valid translation of physical parameters into cost, the results are unsuitable for present purposes, for they fail to take into account foreseeable advances in the technology of coal production. As will be seen in the following section,[70] a consideration of future availability, or even supply as commonly

[69] Given, *op. cit.*, p. 80.
[70] And emphasized in all the following chapters.

defined, must include the indicated effects of foreseeable technological progress. Not to do so is unrealistic.

The purposes of this study would best be satisfied on the score of availability by an adequate costing of coal resources. Although detailed analyses of coal resources covering some of the necessary physical aspects have been made for a limited number of counties by the U.S. Bureau of Mines and individual state Surveys, there is no such information on a national level, nor is it possible to extrapolate it from existing data. To sum up: there exist no estimates that measure the resource base; nor is it known how much coal could be mined with existing technology at current costs—the magnitude of coal reserves is unknown. The official estimate of coal resources is subject to large error and the economic and technologic parameters are indeterminate. The lack of national reserve data suggests the desirability of a costing of coal resources, based on detailed data collected for this purpose. The magnitude of the resource base in coal, as indicated by existing resource estimates, does not lend urgency to the need for resource costing. Nevertheless, the fact remains that not only is there no reasonably certain knowledge of how much coal is available at present costs, also there is no knowledge of where the cost curve would begin to steepen. Despite this lack of knowledge, it is useful in estimating future coal availability to assess the probable course of coal costs as they are influenced by the course of technology.

COSTS AND TECHNOLOGY

Production Costs

An outstanding economic characteristic of coal production is that labor constitutes a relatively large proportion of the total inputs to coal production. This, in turn, should be reflected in the industry's costs. Current published data are lacking, but the evidence suggests that labor costs constitute at least half of total costs, on the average, for bituminous and lignite mines in the United States.[71]

[71] This can be demonstrated by using the industry-wide statistics available for 1956. Taking $2.81 as average hourly earnings during 1956 in the industry (Bureau of Labor Statistics data), the wages for an eight-hour day are $22.48. Dividing this by 10.79 tons, the average production per man-day in 1956 (Bureau of Mines data), gives "straight" labor costs of $2.08 per ton. This includes overtime and shift differentials but does not include vacation payments and the royalty to the union welfare fund. Vacation pay can be considered as amounting to 8¢ per ton ($180 annual vacation payment divided by total tons produced per man-year) which, when taken together with the 40¢ per ton royalty payment and added to the straight labor costs, gives total labor costs of $2.56 per ton. Dividing this by $4.93 per ton, the average f.o.b. mine value of coal produced in 1956 (Bureau of Mines data), yields a figure of 51.9 per cent for labor costs versus total costs.

Actual cost data of the Office of Price Administration for the period 1938–46 show an even higher proportion of labor costs in total costs. Mine labor costs as a percentage of total

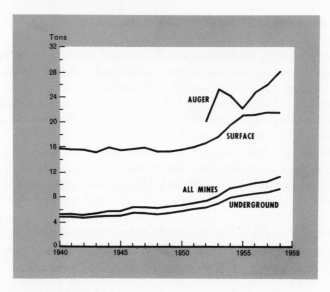

Figure 62.   U.S. bituminous coal and lignite mines, average output per man-day, 1940–1958.

With labor such a significant cost factor, it follows that wage increases will exert a strong leverage on coal prices, except insofar as they are offset by increases in productivity. What changes are likely to occur in coal wage levels versus productivity in the future? On the wage score, it appears reasonable to adopt as a working assumption the conclusions of the President's Materials Policy Commission: "Now that coal miners have reached the top of the wage scale, further wage increases are likely to be more nearly in proportion to the general rise of wage levels."[72] This leaves the matter of productivity to be examined in detail.

The level of productivity in bituminous and lignite mining increased by 30 per cent in the period 1920 through 1940. Thereafter, the over-all figure has undergone an accelerated growth, especially in the 1950's, as shown in Table 94 and Figure 62. The later growth is due in part to the closing of many inefficient producers caused by a decline in total demand (including exports) from the high war and immediate postwar level. Although there is wide variation

producing, administrative, and selling costs in U.S. bituminous coal mines in 1946, for example, were 62.6 per cent. For "hand-loading" mines (i.e., with more than 50 per cent of the output hand-loaded), labor costs were 69.3 per cent; for "mechanized mines" (i.e., more than 50 per cent of the output machine-loaded), they were 62 per cent; and for strip mines, 46.1 per cent. See U.S. Office of Price Administration, *Survey of Commercial Bituminous Coal Mines*, OPA Economic Data Series No. 15, Washington, D. C., 1947, p. 16.

[72]PMPC, *op. cit.*, Vol. III, p. 28.

from the national averages, both regionally and among mines within a given district, the general growth in productivity is unquestionable.

It will be observed that, except for an increase in the period 1950–55, the productivity of strip mining has remained on a plateau. The reasons for this are not immediately apparent. It may be that for a while reductions in man-hours of direct labor per ton were obscured by the lack of progress in reducing service labor requirements, but that the trend toward larger units of machinery and better co-ordination of shovels, bulldozers, and other equipment perhaps was responsible for the upturn in stripping productivity in the early 1950's. Possibilities have been mentioned of further advances in stripping technology, with resultant productivity increases, through the development of machines that spend more time digging while performing the auxiliary functions of conveying and depositing spoil more cheaply and efficiently.[73]

But, regardless of whether such advances occur, it is possible for strip mining to raise over-all productivity by enhancing its position among all coal mining.

TABLE 94. U.S. BITUMINOUS COAL AND LIGNITE MINES, AVERAGE OUTPUT PER MAN-DAY, 1940–59

(Tons)

Year	Underground mines	Auger mines	Surface mines	All mines
1959	n.a.	n.a.	n.a.	12.12
1958	9.38	28.15	21.54	11.33
1957	8.91	26.19	21.64	10.59
1956	8.62	24.85	21.18	10.28
1955	8.28	22.22	21.12	9.84
1954	7.99	24.12	19.64	9.47
1953	7.01	25.30	17.62	8.17
1952	6.37	20.07	16.77	7.47
1951	6.08		16.02	7.04
1950	5.75		15.66	6.77
1949	5.42		15.33	6.43
1948	5.31		15.28	6.26
1947	5.49		15.93	6.42
1946	5.43		15.73	6.30
1945	5.04		15.46	5.78
1944	5.04		15.89	5.67
1943	4.89		15.15	5.38
1942	4.74		15.52	5.12
1941	4.83		15.59	5.20
1940	4.86		15.63	5.19

n.a. Not available.

SOURCE: U.S. Bureau of Mines, *Minerals Yearbook*, various issues (Washington, D. C.: U.S. Government Printing Office).

[73] See R. P. Koenig, *op. cit.*, p. 36; and *Coal Age*, Vol. LX, No. 2 (February 1955), p. 77.

TABLE 95. PER CENT OF TOTAL U.S. BITUMINOUS COAL AND
LIGNITE PRODUCTION BY TYPE OF OPERATION, 1940–59

Year	Underground	Auger	Strip
1959	68.0	2.0	30.0
1958	69.9	1.8	28.3
1957	73.2	1.6	25.2
1956	73.0	1.6	25.4
1955	73.9	1.3	24.8
1954	73.8	1.1	25.1
1953	76.4	0.5	23.1
1952	76.4	0.3	23.3
1951	78.0		22.0
1950	76.1		23.9
1949	75.8		24.2
1948	76.7		23.3
1947	77.9		22.1
1946	78.9		21.1
1945	81.0		19.0
1944	83.7		16.3
1943	86.5		13.5
1942	88.5		11.5
1941	89.3		10.7
1940	90.6		9.4

SOURCE: U.S. Bureau of Mines.

Since stripping is some two and one-half times more productive than underground mining, an increase in the proportion of total output that comes from stripping would have a favorable effect on over-all productivity. As shown in Table 95 and Figure 63, the proportion of strip-mined production rose rapidly during and immediately after World War II and has since risen more slowly.

To some, the record of recent years is an indication of "reserve" limitations, but as demonstrated above, the strippable resource position is rather open-ended, at least until the present wave of technological progress has been exploited. Nevertheless, it is possible that there will be a geographic shift in the location of a considerable portion of strip-mining operations during the coming decades. This would reflect not so much resource limitations in the East as the fact that so much of the western coals that have not yet been worked are amenable to stripping. With an increasing use of western coals possible, the relative proportion of stripping to total mining would likely increase, and as a consequence so would over-all productivity. The disparity between underground and auger productivity is even greater than that relative to strip mining, but, in view of the resource position for this technique, it can be reasonably dismissed as a factor in over-all productivity.

The possibilities of technological progress in strip mining and the growth of strip production relative to the total are, however, overshadowed by the promis-

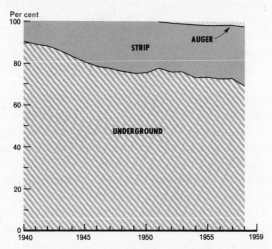

Figure 63. Per cent of total U.S. bituminous coal and lignite production, by type of operation, 1940–1958.

ing opportunities underground. Opinion in the industry is unanimous that underground productivity will continue to improve, although there is disagreement as to whether it will continue at the rate of the 1950's. This optimism is based chiefly on a looked-for expansion of the already proved benefits of the continuous miner as its adoption spreads in underground mining. In the industry's opinion, the true potential of this technological revolution will be realized with: (1) the adoption of underground haulage methods that can keep up with the continuous miner's productive capacity, (2) the design and layout of new mines specifically for the use of continuous mining equipment, and (3) further improvements in design and operation of the equipment as further experience is gained.[74]

These advantages have, indeed, already been demonstrated in certain instances.[75] Manpower requirements with continuous miners have been reduced as much as 70 to 85 per cent in certain mines.[76] A 1956 Bureau of Mines Survey of 24 mines employing only continuous mining revealed an average output per man-day of 14.08 tons.[77] According to a 1956 survey of 79 coal companies accounting for roughly one-third of total bituminous production in that year, the weighted average for underground mines represented was 8.7 tons per man-day and for strip mines, 21.6 tons. These same companies expected that their

---

[74] See *Coal Age, ibid.*; and PMPC, *op. cit.*, Vol. III, p. 27.

[75] "Continuous Mining Approaches Reality," *Mechanization*, Vol. XIX, No. 5 (May 1955), pp. 47–49.

[76] H. M. Forester, "A Review and Forecast of Continuous Mining," *Mining Congress Journal*, Vol. 39, No. 4 (April 1953), p. 88.

[77] Reported in the *American Metal Market*, May 7, 1958.

productivity by 1960 would rise to 11.9 tons per man-day for underground operations, and 25.3 tons for strip mining.[78] These levels are, respectively, double and
60 per cent higher than the 1950–51 averages. On this general basis, underground
productivity has been projected by some as tripling, and total productivity for
underground and surface operations as at least doubling over 1950–51 levels by
1975.[79]

It should be observed, however, that the large reductions in labor requirements
with the continuous miner are at the working face. The effect on requirements for
service labor (for maintenance, haulage, materials, etc.), on whose productivity
the technology has little or no direct effect, is much less significant. To the extent
that such labor constitutes a large proportion of total mine labor, the over-all
effect on productivity is considerably reduced. If, for example, for every man
working at the face there are two men employed elsewhere, the increase in total
productivity is only one-third the increase of productivity at the face. The record
shows that despite such dilution, the advances in face productivity with
the continuous miner to date have been so great that substantial improvement in
over-all productivity has been achieved. Although it would be expected in the
normal course of events that the rate of increase in over-all productivity would
begin to diminish as the new technology of continuous mining is fully exploited,
the rate of diminution of the increase will be accelerated by the dilution effect of
service labor. The expectations referred to in the preceding paragraph may thus
be overoptimistic. To what extent it is impossible to say.

The continuous miner has also yielded cost benefits in addition to increased
productivity. An analysis in 1953 showed that the use of continuous miner had
enabled total production costs to be cut by 22 per cent, including labor cost savings. Savings in specific areas included: production supply cost, 19 per cent;
maintenance, 80 per cent; power, 5 per cent; and other operating costs, 15 per
cent.[80] Still another area in which the new technology can yield savings is in the
great reduction made possible in the development time for a new mine. Whereas
traditionally it has taken two or more years to bring a mine to a level of some
5,000 tons per day, with continuous miners this should be possible in a matter of
weeks. In fact, it should be possible to bring a mine to full production "within
three months of the time that slope and tipple facilities have been completed."[81]

---

[78] "Building for 1960," *Coal Age*, Vol. LXI, No. 9 (September 1956), pp. 55–56. According
to the survey, this improvement was to be closely related to plans for the opening of 55 new
mines, with an annual capacity of 45,780,000 tons, in the period 1957–60 as part of meeting
an expected required total capacity of 675–700 million tons in 1960.

[79] See C. J. Lyons and H. W. Nelson, *The Role of Technology in the Future of Coal*, un-
published report by Battelle Memorial Institute to PMPC, September 21, 1952, p. 2;
PMPC, *op. cit.*, Vol. III, p. 27; "Billion tons—1975," *Mechanization*, Vol. XV, No. 11
(November 1951), p. 99; and G. C. Lindsay, "Coal's New Threshold," *Mechanization*, Vol.
XIX, No. 11 (November 1955), p. 64.

[80] Forester, *op. cit.*, p. 88.

[81] Wearly, *op. cit.*, p. 51. This does not mean three months from the time the first earth
is turned. The slope, shaft, and tipple will still take one to two years to construct. But
once actual mine production begins, full-scale output can be achieved quickly.

The extent to which all these saving may affect the over-all cost of coal depends, of course, on many things. Savings in labor costs, for example, may be partly offset by increases in material and supply costs and in depreciation. Thus, at the same time that the proportion of labor costs to total costs has declined, as noted above (see footnote 71, p. 325), supply and depreciation cost have increased, from 10 per cent of total costs in the mid-1930's to 25 per cent in 1956.[82] The effect on over-all coal cost also depends upon the degree to which continuous miners are adopted by the industry and the extent to which, once adopted, their full potentialities are realized. It has been observed that "continuous mining equipment cannot completely justify the use of the term until there are parallel developments in auxiliary equipment for transportation, rock dusting, dust control, ventilation, roof support and face lighting."[83] There is little question that the new technology is still at the pioneering stage, and that its full benefits will be obtained only when it is employed in mines laid out for its use, and with associated equipment and techniques that take full advantage of its high productivity.

Doubts have been expressed about the physical limitations under which the machines can be used—whether they will prove successful in seams less than 36 inches thick, with abrupt and severe changes in roof and bottom, or even moderate pitches.[84] Until 1956, the minimum seam thickness for which a continuous miner was designed was 40 inches. Recently, however, new machines have been introduced for use in seams as low as 28 inches. The vexing problem of maintaining haulage capacity from the face at the continuous miner's rate of output also appears to have been solved with the provision of extensible belts to convey the miner's output to main haulage ways.

As for the extent of the adoption of continuous mining, there is some opinion within the industry that in the near future, for mines adopting the new technique, the continuous miner would account for 70 to 100 per cent of the mine's output.[85] Even if this range is overoptimistic by a factor of two for the period through 1975, the contribution of continuous mining should become significant within a decade, and should exert a strong influence on costs during the remainder of the period. The same opinion holds that "the attainment of cost improvement" in the future can be projected on the basis of the new technique with, at the minimum, the same rate as that achieved with mechanized equipment in the past.[86]

The foregoing advantages pertain to the mining costs and, although continuous mining apears to offer great promise in lowering such costs through increased

[82] J. W. Kepler, "Bituminous Coal and the Fuel Market," paper presented at Fuels Forum, National Association of Purchasing Agents, Atlantic City, New Jersey, May 29, 1957.

[83] R. E. Kirk, "Mechanical Coal Mining," *Mining Congress Journal*, Vol. 42, No. 2 (February 1956), p. 704.

[84] *Ibid.*, p. 71.

[85] Lindsay, *op. cit.* But 100 per cent of mine output would be rare, indeed, since it would depend on the unlikely event that physical conditions (seam thickness, roof condition, etc.) were satisfactory for continuous mining throughout the mine.

[86] *Ibid.*, p. 60.

productivity, the underground gain of the new technology must be balanced against certain disadvantages in quality and physical characteristics of the product that appears at the mine mouth.

It has been pointed out that continuous mining leaves the roof undisturbed, so that fewer impurities are introduced into the coal from this source, and the machine can work on the exact proportion of a seam it is desired to mine (impurities often tend to be concentrated in the top and bottom margins of a seam). An example of such results is the reduction in ash content from 14 to 15 per cent with previous methods to 10 to 11 per cent with continuous miners.[87] But it has also been observed that the cost and operating advantages of continuous miners will lead to more full-seam mining in dirty coal beds, with resultant higher ash content.[88] Considering the ever-present economic pressure toward higher productivity, the latter argument appears stronger. The net effect of the growth of continuous mining is likely to be greater impurities in run-of-mine coal.

This in itself is not, however, a net disadvantage because of the practice of coal preparation. Although some coal was prepared in the late nineteenth century, the growth of coal preparation dates from the early 1920's. At that time, some 5 per cent of the total output was cleaned; since then its importance has grown uninterruptedly until now over 60 per cent of all bituminous coal mined is cleaned at the mine. Basically, the necessity for preparing, or cleaning, coal developed with the increasing ash content of the mined product, as higher quality resources were depleted, and as the quality of run-of-mine coal declined with increased mechanization (that is, mechanical loading, which cannot be as selective as hand mining). In part, also, it was a defensive measure, as higher transportation costs led utility companies to pay increasing attention to the Btu content of their fuel. Some large utility consumers, indeed, began to clean the delivered coal themselves, and many plants currently buy coal on an energy-content or cost-per-Btu basis, rather than on a weight basis, as a means of minimizing the effect of higher freight rates on their coal costs.

The significance of all this is that the tendency of continuous mining to lower the quality of the mine product finds a well developed technique already in existence to deal with this problem, a technique firmly established on pre-existing circumstances. But the balancing of advantage against disadvantage is not yet complete—there remains the matter of physical size of the mine product as it affects coal preparation. The crucial element in size is the proportion of "fines" in the mine product, that is, the proportion of smaller sized particles. This is really of greater significance than impurities, since the magnitude of the preparation job depends on the number of particles per unit quantity to be cleaned. Current mechanical loading yields coal of which 25 per cent is less than one-quarter inch in size, which is about the smallest size commonly amenable to

[87] Wearly, op. cit., p. 53.
[88] R. I. Billings, "Five Years of Continuous Mining," Mining Congress Journal, Vol. 42, No. 6 (June 1956), p. 54.

economic cleaning of raw-coal feed. If cleaned, fines tend to increase the losses in preparation.

Whether continuous mining will further the trend toward more fines is a matter of dispute, as illustrated by the following points of view. "In general, but depending on the structure of the coal, type of roof and floor, and presence and location of the partings, the coal mined by continuous mining machines will contain a substantially higher proportion of fines,"[89] and the proportion of mined coal under one-quarter inch in size may be almost 40 per cent.[90] In contrast, some types of continuous miners are reported to give a size distribution comparable to that of conventional mining.[91] And, in a study of continuous mining by the Bureau of Mines, the reject from the continuous mining operations in two cleaning plants was about one-half that of the mechanically loaded coal in the same plants.[92]

A previous problem with fines was lack of a market, but this is now much less true and it can be confidently assumed that the problem will not be of great significance in the future, especially as price adjustments between sized and slack (fine) coal take place. A large share of current coal uses does not require a sized coal product, and it has been observed that "the use of fines for the production of smokeless fuels, particularly low temperature cokes or semicokes . . . will be greatly extended, since it has been shown that a satisfactory product can be produced and that there is a steady market for such a fuel."[93] In fact, use of pulverized coal for some plants as boiler fuel is so advantageous that small-sized coal can be shipped for pulverizing by the consumers.[94]

All of this nevertheless seems to indicate that broader use of continuous mining should raise the cost of coal preparation. It has been suggested that this cost will increase in direct proportion to the percentage of material of three-eighths inch and under in the mine product, leading to an increase of 50 per cent in cleaning costs on this score until improvements in continuous mining machines reduce the proportion of fines produced.[95]

Yet there is still the possibility of a net gain through continuous mining. Preparation facilities and continuous mining are economically complementary. Preparation offers a means of offsetting the lower value of the continuous mining product, and the lower mining costs with the new technique permit more costs to

[89] Nelson, *op. cit.*, p. 3.

[90] Lyons and Nelson, *op. cit.*

[91] Forester, *op. cit.*

[92] Shields *et al.*, *op. cit.*

[93] D. P. Mitchell, ed., *Coal Preparation*, 2nd ed., American Institute of Mining and Metallurgical Engineers, New York, 1950, p. 28.

[94] For a thoughtful commentary on the economics of coal preparation as seen by the user of pulverized coal, see J. E. Tobey, "Effects of Preparation and Other Factors on the Economics of Coal Buying" (and discussion thereon), *Proceedings of the American Power Conference, Eighteenth Annual Meeting, Volume XVIII, 1956* (Chicago: Illinois Institute of Technology), pp. 179–91.

[95] Nelson, *op. cit.*, p. 5.

be incurred at the preparation stage. Thus, coal in place, of lower quality, can be mined to yield a full quality product at no net increase in cost.[96] All this can occur with no further progress in preparation technology, but "when there is an economic need for cleaning fine coal to low ash, the technical difficulties will be solved. The utilization of the 'fines' below 28-mesh will determine the extent to which beneficiation will be carried. Whenever these 'fines' will be processed into smokeless fuels or used as raw material for the chemical industry or for hydrogenation, a higher degree of cleaning will be economically justified."[97]

On balance, it appears reasonable to assume no increase, on the average, in the constant-dollar cost of coal at the mine through the period to 1975. The average quality of coal being mined may well decline slowly and preparation difficulties will be accentuated, perhaps only temporarily, by the growth of continuous mining. But advances in preparation technology should maintain the general quality of coal shipped from the mine without a significant increase in the constant-dollar cost of coal at the mine. This, together with the productivity gains that should accrue during the coming decades, provides the ground for the expectation that the price of coal at the mine should rise little, if any, in constant dollar terms.

.   .   .

Transportation

Fully as important as production costs in the determination of the delivered price of coal is the transportation cost. Of the total bituminous and lignite output, 98 per cent is transported to the point of use, some three-quarters of it by rail. The very great significance of transportation cost in the price of coal is indicated by Table 96 and Figure 64. Although the data in the table cover only Class I railroads, and are therefore incomplete, they provide a useful measure of the place of transportation costs in total costs of delivered coal. The very sharp decline and subsequent rise in the percentage series in Figure 64 may be noted in passing. The important aspect of these changes is that in the last twenty years transportation costs by this measurement have never been less than half of production costs, and if the current trend continues could possibly again equal production costs in the coming two decades. In any event, it is apparent that the opportunity is large for achieving savings in the delivered cost of coal through any means that yields savings in the transportation cost.

The economics of coal transportation are complex. According to a Congressional study of the subject, freight charges for coal haulage have little rational basis. The rate structure is unnecessarily complicated and bears less relation to distance than that for any other commodity in rail traffic; and there is often a wide range of rates for equivalent distances on different routes.[98] In

[96] See Lyons and Nelson, op. cit., pp. 16–17; and T. Fraser, op. cit., pp. 128–30.
[97] Mitchell, op. cit.
[98] Economics of Coal Traffic Flow, Senate Document No. 82, 79th Congress, 1st Session, September 20, 1944.

TABLE 96. AVERAGE RAIL REVENUE PER TON OF BITUMINOUS
COAL HAULED, AS PERCENTAGE OF AVERAGE MINE VALUE, 1936-59

Year	Average value per ton, f.o.b. mine (1)	Average revenue per ton hauled on Class I railroads (2)	(2) as percentage of (1) (3)
1959 ᵃ	$4.86	$3.57	73.4%
1958	4.86	3.58	73.7
1957	5.08	3.57	70.3
1956	4.82	3.45	71.6
1955	4.49	3.24	72.2
1954	4.51	3.23	71.6
1953	4.92	3.33	67.7
1952	4.90	3.35	68.4
1951	4.92	3.16	64.2
1950	4.84	3.09	63.8
1949	4.88	3.00	61.5
1948	4.99	2.74	54.9
1947	4.16	2.49	59.8
1946	3.44	2.27	66.0
1945	3.06	2.20	71.9
1944	2.92	2.21	75.7
1943	2.69	2.30	85.5
1942	2.36	2.31	97.9
1941	2.19	2.22	101.4
1940	1.91	2.22	116.2
1939	1.84	2.23	121.2
1938	1.95	2.27	116.4
1937	1.94	2.17	111.8
1936	1.83	2.25	123.0

ᵃ Preliminary.

SOURCE: U.S. Bureau of Mines, *Minerals Yearbook*, various issues :(Washington, D. C.
U.S. Government Printing Office).

such a context, it is less fruitful to speculate on or project future railroad freight
rates than to examine the economically significant aspects of coal transportation
as they are likely to affect those rates. One of these is competing forms of
haulage, either existing or possible. The other is the elimination of coal transportation in those instances where the use is as fuel, either through its conversion into energy or another fuel form and its transportation as such, or by location of the industrial consumer at the mine. These aspects set limits on possible
future increases in rail freight rates.

The recent place of rail versus water and truck transport, the competing forms
of transportation, is shown in Table 97 and Figure 65. The data show that water
and truck shipments have increased as a proportion of the total at the expense of
rail shipments. This can be interpreted generally as a trend away from expensive

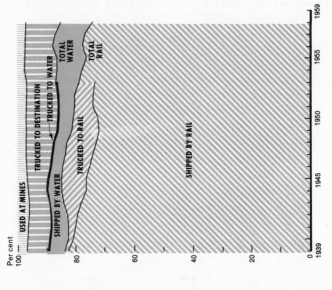

Figure 65. Percentage of total production of bituminous coal and lignite moved by various transport means, 1939–58.

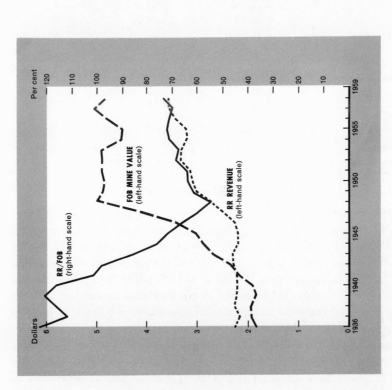

Figure 64. Average rail revenue per ton of bituminous coal hauled, as percentage of average mine value, 1936–58.

TABLE 97. PERCENTAGE OF TOTAL PRODUCTION OF BITUMINOUS
COAL AND LIGNITE MOVED BY THE VARIOUS TRANSPORT
MEANS IN THE UNITED STATES, 1939–58

Year	Shipped by rail	Trucked to rail	Total rail	Shipped by water	Trucked to water	Total water	Trucked to final destination	Used at mines[a]
1958	n.a.	n.a.	74.5	n.a.	n.a.	10.7	12.3	2.5
1957	n.a.	n.a.	77.2	n.a.	n.a.	10.4	10.2	2.2
1956	n.a.	n.a.	77.9	n.a.	n.a.	10.1	9.9	2.1
1955	n.a.	n.a.	76.6	n.a.	n.a.	10.2	11.1	2.1
1954	n.a.	n.a.	78.1	n.a.	n.a.	8.4	11.4	2.1
1953	73.5	5.7	79.2	7.2	.6	7.8	10.3	2.7
1952	74.2	6.3	80.5	5.6	.3	5.9	10.8	2.8
1951	74.3	6.4	80.7	5.4	.2	5.6	10.9	2.8
1950	72.7	8.1	80.8	5.1	.2	5.3	11.3	2.6
1949	72.2	9.2	81.4	4.7	.3	5.0	10.9	2.7
1948	73.2	9.9	83.1	4.2	.3	4.5	9.7	2.7
1947	74.3	9.3	83.6	4.4	.3	4.7	8.9	2.8
1946	75.5	8.9	84.4	4.4	.2	4.6	8.0	3.0
1945	76.7	8.2	84.9	4.5	.3	4.8	7.2	3.1
1944	76.9	8.2	85.1	4.9	.2	5.1	6.5	3.3
1943	78.7	5.3	84.0	5.0	.1	5.1	7.2	3.7
1942	79.8	3.1	82.9	5.7	.1	5.8	7.7	3.6
1941	80.5	2.2	82.7	5.6	.3	5.9	7.8	3.6
1940	81.5	1.1	82.6	6.2	.2	6.4	7.7	3.3
1939	82.9	1.0	83.9	5.3	.3	5.6	7.5	3.0

n.a. Not available.
[a] Includes delivery to nearby destination by conveyer or tram.

SOURCE: U.S. Bureau of Mines, *Minerals Yearbook*, various issues (Washington, D. C.:
U.S. Government Printing Office).

rail haulage toward the cheaper barge transport.[99] Truck transport, although
most expensive over-all, is most economical for the shortest hauls. Barge movement, although the cheapest inland transport medium, cannot compete with rail
or truck over short distances where transshipment is involved. That is, if coal has
already been loaded on a truck at the mine mouth, it is often cheaper to finish
the short haul by truck rather than transship from truck to barge and again from
barge to truck for final delivery. Although the relative differences in the cost of
the three means of transport may change in the future, it can be confidently assumed that any change in their competitive position could occur only through a
radical unforeseen technological innovation.[100]

[99] One of the reasons for the shift in proportions was the dieselization of the railroads.
They no longer haul the coal they formerly bought as fuel. Since the dieselization is almost
complete, any continued shift away from rail movement of coal will be a clear reflection
of relative coal transport costs.

[100] It should be noted, however, that a change in regulatory policy that allowed the railroads to set competitive rates would probably result in the recapture of a significant portion
of the coal traffic lost to truck haulage.

One of the possible new forms of coal transportation is by conveyer belt. A specific proposal for such a belt between a southeastern Ohio coalfield and a Lake Erie port, with iron ore to be carried in the opposite direction, was based on engineering studies which found that the over-all costs of moving coal for the 100-mile distance would be comparable with rail costs.[101] The proposal was frustrated, however, by the inability to secure the necessary right of eminent domain. Because of this, the future of the technique is obscure. Until the legal obstacles to the development of long-distance conveyer transport of coal are overcome, it cannot be considered as a significant factor in reducing coal transport costs in the period through 1975.

Of much greater potential is the equally radical innovation of coal transport by pipeline. In this technique pulverized coal is mixed with water to form a "slurry" in which the coal is carried by suspension, and which can be pumped like any fluid. Progress here has reached the stage of commercial installation. The pioneer coal pipeline, running 108 miles between southeastern Ohio and Cleveland, went into full operation in 1958. The line delivers coal from the preparation plant at a strip mine to a power plant, and is expected by its participants to yield cost savings of around 40 per cent compared with rail costs for the same route. The contract calls for delivery of over 18 million tons of coal over a fifteen-year period.[102]

A second pipeline has been proposed between East Liverpool and Ashtabula, Ohio (a distance of ninety miles) to carry coal to Great Lakes power plants after barging down the Monongahela, Allegheny, and Ohio Rivers. It is anticipated that this should save about $1 a ton on freight costs.[103] In another development, the Bureau of Mines began a study in July 1955 to determine the feasibility of pipeline transport of low-grade Colorado bituminous to industrial consumers. The project includes the eventual construction of an experimental line.[104]

Although the coal pipeline exists as a commercial reality, it would again be an unjustified extrapolation to assign the technique an established position in the transportation of coal during the next decade and a half. It has been pointed out by one of the engineers connected with the pipeline that certain conditions must be satisfied if a pipeline is to be competitive with conventional transport. Because of the high capital investment, for example, large quantities of coal must be involved, and the pipeline must have a high use factor.[105] Moreover, unless provision is made for returning the water (at large additional expense), pipelines

---

[101] "Moving Coal to Market," Coal Age, Vol. LVI, No. 11 (November 1951), p. 71.

[102] See D. Hale, "Coal Commutes from Cadiz to Cleveland," The Petroleum Engineer, Vol. XXVIII, No. 10 (September 1956), p. D-24; and C. A. Dauber, "Pipeline Transportation of Coal," Proceedings of the American Power Conference, op. cit., Vol. XIX, 1957, pp. 328–36.

[103] American Metal Market, January 1, 1960.

[104] Engineering News-Record, January 27, 1955, p. 27. The United States, incidentally, does not appear to be alone in exploring coal pipeline possibilities. A forty-mile line was scheduled to go into operation in 1958 in the Ukraine, U.S.S.R. (Petroleum Press Service, May 1958, p. 193).

[105] Dauber, op. cit.

are limited to situations in which there is an ample water supply at the head and ample disposal facilities at the terminal. Finally, the first commercial long-distance coal pipeline is competing against a freight rate between the same two points that is triple the national average.

Yet the pipeline unquestionably has greater significance than the conveyer. It is not an innovation in long-distance transport—pipelines for natural gas, petroleum, and refined products have afforded a wide technological basis for the adaptation of the pipeline to coal transport. (Although, to be sure, the coal pipeline has an economic handicap. Oil and gas lines carry commodities that are fully usable at the terminal. The water bearing the coal, on the other hand, is unlikely to have any value at the terminal and indeed, may mean disposal costs.) And, although technical problems for coal pipelines are formidable, there is the evidence of progress to date that they are not insoluble.[106] In the words of the engineer cited above, "pipeline transportation is here to stay if present freight rates are maintained."[107] Thus, just as rising rail freight costs encouraged an increase in water transport, so the possibility exists for a future growth in pipeline transport if a further rise in rail rates on coal provides sufficient stimulus.

Where coal is used directly as a fuel the elimination of transport cost by location at the mine is theoretically very attractive. But the net gain by this means must, for an industrial plant, meet the higher transport bill for raw materials and delivery of the product to market (assuming that present location practices constitute a reasonably profitable balance on this score). Considering the location of the large markets versus that of the coal resources of the United States, it is apparent that there are comparatively narrow limits within which an industrial plant can achieve net gains by choosing a coal field site. However, in those industries in which electricity is a large input factor, such as alumina reduction, there has been a noticeable tendency in the past few years to locate new plants in the coalfields.[108]

The electric power industry is a special case in this respect. Here the comparison is directly a matter of energy transport—coal versus electricity. Again, the current situation reflects past circumstances. There has been a tendency to locate coal-fired generating stations near electricity consuming centers rather than near the coal fields, because the cost of moving electricity has generally exceeded the cost of transporting the equivalent net energy product in the form of coal. Advances in recent years, however, have begun to affect this relationship. It may be cheaper to transmit electricity than haul coal if other circumstances are favorable—a result of improvements in transmission technology. Thus, a new

---

[106] See *Engineering News-Record*, August 4, 1955, pp. 38, 40; D. M. Taylor, "Coal Pipe Lines . . . A More Competitive Price with Oil and Gas Fuels?" *Pipe Line Industry*, Vol. 3, No. 1 (July 1955), p. 55; "Moving Coal to Market," *Coal Age, op. cit.*, p. 74; Dauber, *op. cit.*; and Resources for the Future, *The Nation Looks at its Resources*, Report of the Mid-Century Conference on Resources for the Future, Washington, D. C., 1954, p. 235.

[107] Dauber, *op. cit.*, p. 336.

[108] See H. G. Schmidt, "The Aluminum Industry Turns to Coal," *Public Utilities Fortnightly*, Vol. 59, No. 8 (April 11, 1957), pp. 515–19.

large coal-fired generating station is being built in Indiana 200 miles from the load center of the utility system it will serve. This has been made possible by the development of 345,000-volt transmission. But parallel progress in the technology of steam and power generation are at least partially offsetting this tendency by decreasing the amount of coal needed to generate a unit of electricity.

Nevertheless, current work in transmission at extra high voltage indicates the possibilities of significant further reduction in the cost of transporting electricity, from which it would appear logical to deduce that a large-scale trend toward the generation of electricity in the coal field is equally possible. A solution of the large water requirements for condensing is the location of the power plant on a navigable waterway near the coal fields, even if power transmission is thereby over a longer distance.[109] This is a compromise which shortens the distance of coal transport at the same time that it utilizes cheap water transport, provides the essential condenser water, and takes advantage of progress in power transmission.

Another development of great promise in connection with the location of power plants is the low-temperature carbonization of coal. This process drives off part of the volatiles, which can be used as raw materials for chemicals or liquid fuels, and leaves a solid residue termed "char," which can be used as boiler fuel. The potential significance of the process lies in the joint production of both fuel and chemicals from coal, offering the opportunity of low-cost char. There is a limitation on the scale of char use, however, in the markets for the co-product chemicals. At present prices for the chemical products the process is economic, but if charring were to become widespread the markets for these products would be flooded and the resulting prices would be too low to allow commercial operations.

The process does, however, exist commercially. The pioneer operation is a plant in Texas that for several years has been charring lignite, selling the chemicals and using the char for power supplied to an aluminum plant. A second application of this approach was more recently put into operation in the Appalachian coalfields in West Virginia, again to supply power for an aluminum plant. A large power station was built atop one billion tons of coal reserves. A mine next to the power plant delivers coal, at the rate of 2 million tons a year, directly from the mine entry to the plant stockpile. A char plant also on the site can intercept and process as much of the coal as is desired, delivering the char to the power plant and the tar to a chemical processing plant also built on the site.[110]

In the opinion of the coal company co-operating with a chemical company in this venture, "this type of large-scale development will be best suited, in this lifetime at least, to Eastern coal deposits on navigable waters and adjacent to

[109] See G. A. Lamb, "The Future of Coal in Power Generation," *Proceedings of the American Power Conference, op. cit.*, Volume XVI, 1954, p. 214; and C. S. Ball, "Coal Reserves of the United States for Future Use," paper presented at Joint Solid Fuels Conference, Columbus, Ohio, October 19, 1955.

[110] J. Pursglove, Jr., "New Markets From Coal Research," *Coal Age*, Vol. LXII, No. 1 (January 1957), pp. 70–73.

large-scale electrical power plants." But charring also offers attractive possibilities in connection with pipeline transportation, since the size of pipeline coal is the same as that used in the charring process. Thus charring at the pipeline terminal could yield sizable credits: "The future combination of pipelining coal and then processing it hundreds of miles from the mines could greatly alter the geographical distribution of our energy supplies and the geographic points of production of coal chemicals [currently obtained from coke ovens]."[111]

Still another possibility of eliminating coal transport is to gasify the coal at the mine and send the gas to the consuming center by conventional gas pipeline.[112] It is contended that the possibilities on this score are truly large, for "every [gas] transmission line of any size in this country crosses a substantial coalfield. Thus, coal can be processed at the mine and immediately delivered to the pipeline for movement to market."[113] But this glosses over the fact that plant and pipeline investment are of secondary importance in determining the economic feasibility of such a procedure. The greatest problem is low-cost coal production and low-cost gas generation.[114]

The competition with gas from coal comes not so much from coal itself as from natural gas. The troubles begin with the fact that natural gas has a high heat value (high Btu content), hence not only has a high unit value but can carry a high unit transport cost and can thus be transported over long distances. Unfortunately, the gas produced from coal by simple, inexpensive processes has a low Btu content. It cannot carry high transport costs and may, indeed, cost more per Btu at the point of use than gas produced from coal transported to the point of use. It is feasible—and under the appropriate conditions may be profitable —to raise the Btu content of the gas from coal by synthesizing the same constituent that makes up natural gas. But this is expensive.

The problem would be partially solved if the cost of coal at the mine could be significantly reduced. On this score, the introduction of continuous mining represents an important advance, but the cost savings are far from sufficient for this purpose. Another approach is to use strip-mined coal. Those engaged in recent work on such coal in Illinois and Indiana believe that with coal available at the mine for $3 per ton it can be gasified and delivered for space heating at a lower cost than the delivered coal.[115] The necessary price is, however, about 25 per cent lower than the national average for strip-mined coal in the period 1951–53.

The ideal solution to the mining cost problem is to eliminate such costs entirely by burning the coal in place—a process termed "underground gasification." Only limited experimental work has been done in this field in the United States

[111] *Ibid.*, p. 73.

[112] Coal gasification is referred to here solely with respect to possible effects on the costs of coal at the point where its energy is obtained. The probability, timing, and extent of the future development of coal gasification are examined in detail in Chapter 10.

[113] E. S. Pettyjohn, "Coal: Gas Source of the Future," *Coal Age*, Vol. LX, No. 3 (March 1955), p. 57.

[114] "Moving Coal to Market," *Coal Age, op. cit.*

[115] Pettyjohn, *op. cit.*

(although the Russians claim commercial operations), and results are thus far discouraging. The great handicap is the fact that the resultant gas consists largely of combustion products; the Btu content is even lower (100–200 Btu per cubic foot) than that obtained through conventional simple gasification. However, if means can be found to upgrade this gas to pipeline quality it is possible that the cost per Btu could be the lowest of any synthetically produced gas.[116]

Despite existing possibilities for radical developments in coal transport, published opinion generally does not foresee large-scale changes. One study concludes, for example, that the transportation pattern of coal in 1975 will be roughly the same as in 1950; conveyers and pipelines will have advantages under certain favorable conditions, though this will not necessarily hold true on the average.[117] In the opinion of another observer, the bulk of coal will continue to move by rail despite the fact that costs are high and will continue to rise. "The fact remains that the railroads do own enough coal-hauling equipment to move most of the coal produced. . . . It would take a long time and lots of money to build another transportation network that would equal the railroads."[118] It should be observed, however, that this view minimizes the possibility of a diversion, into facilities to substitute for rail transport or more or less to eliminate transport, of the capital that would otherwise be put into rail facilities to replace those being worn out.

According to a more balanced viewpoint, "Present indications are that lower grades of coal will be utilized at or near their sources for conversion into liquid or gaseous form, while the best coal will be shipped predominantly by rail or water for use in industry. But it will get cleaned before shipment, and transport agencies will not be called upon to carry tons of dirt around the country. This means the railways will necessarily find it to their best interests to reduce rates in order that they may transport over long distances at low rates rather than for short distances at high rates. Coal will not move by pipeline over long distances in the foreseeable future to steel mills, and steel mills will not be relocated near coal mines."[119]

For present purposes, however, the characteristics of future coal transportation patterns are unimportant. The most clearly indicated conclusion would seem to be that, regardless of the pace and extent of the development of new transportation techniques and patterns—including power generation at or near the mine—the cost, in constant dollars, of delivered coal or its derived energy is not likely to change significantly. To the extent that the railroads, in self defense, become more efficient in their movement of bituminous coal and attempt to slow down the pace of increase in freight rates, this conclusion will be fortified.

[116] M. Chandler, "Outlook for Gas Industry," *Gas Age*, August 25, 1955, p. 24.
[117] Lyons and Nelson, *op. cit.*, p. 8.
[118] "Moving Coal to Market," *Coal Age*, *op. cit.*, p. 76.
[119] L. K. Sillcox, "Will Railway Movement of Coal Decline?" *Railway Age*, Vol. 133, No. 25 (December 22, 1952), p. 38.

CONCLUSIONS

Although it is generally expected that the coal industry will be called upon during the next twenty years to furnish a much greater supply of its product to the economy, there appears to be little cause for concern as to the problems this may raise. The current estimate of coal resources justifies the conclusions that there should be no physical limitation on the over-all availability of coal to meet any foreseeable demand level in the period through 1975. Local resource limitations may effect some locational changes,[120] but these should not be of such magnitude as to generate economic dislocations other than those that can be taken care of through normal economic growth and development.

Although reserves of coking coal as currently defined are limited, and are probably insufficient as such, there is good reason to believe that technological progress in both coke manufacture and coke utilization will provide sufficient flexibility to create, out of total coal resources, ample coking reserves.

Advances in mining technology, and their general application, should provide substantial cost benefits in coal production. These are likely to be offset, at least partially, by a decline in the quality of run-of-mine product and by associated difficulties in preparation. There are good grounds for believing, nevertheless, that improvements in preparation techniques should not only meet these problems, but perhaps even yield a net cost benefit.

Transportation adjustments, together with coal conversion, should at the least largely offset any trend toward rising transportation costs (in constant dollars), and under favorable combinations of circumstances should yield a net reduction in transport costs.

In summary, there should be sufficient supplies for all uses, of coal of all types, either as such or in converted fuel or energy form, to meet any foreseeable demand through 1975.[121] This should be possible with a negligible increase, if any, in delivered cost, and in the most optimistic interpretation of current indications, at a slightly lower cost in constant dollars.

---

[120] In any mining district economic forces dictate the practice of mining the best coal first and moving progressively to coal of lower grade, hence it appears likely that there would be shifts of operations within districts. (This does not necessarily mean, however, that the best coal is always available first. There is the problem of assembling, under clear title, coal land that can be blocked out for mining. This may take many years, during which time less valuable coal may be mined in the same district.)

[121] The conclusion on coal availability differs in manner of presentation from those on the availability of the other energy sources in that there is no attempt to quantify the availability. Quantification is not considered necessary in this instance since there is clearly enormous unutilized potential productive capacity on the basis of known resource data. There is, in other words, no indication of resource limitation on present capacity or on any future capacity level that might be required in 1975. Whatever the demand may be in that year, there is no question that the resources exist to bring the desired capacity into being. This is an entirely different circumstance from those of the other energy sources, where there is a fairly clear relationship between resources and productive capacity, the need to discover the resources to sustain 1975 output, and even serious question as to whether the necessary resources exist.

ADDENDUM TO CHAPTER 8

A Note on Putnam's Approach to Coal Reserves and Resources *(The context for this discussion is found on page 306.)*

Putnam begins by cutting in half the 1944 gross estimate of the U.S. Geological Survey to allow for excessive geologic inference, recognizing that this is quite arbitrary, but noting that "until the completion of the resurvey . . . the true value of this correction factor can only be guesssed at by means of the collective judgment of those familiar with the problem."[122] To date, and on a national scale, this judgment appears to have been substantiated: a comparison of the total resources for the 16 states "reappraised" in the 1953 Survey report with the total for the same states in the 1947 report (1944 data) shows a decline of 49.2 per cent.[123]

Putnam applies a second reduction factor to compensate for what he considered the unrealistic limiting criteria of the Geological Survey for seam thickness and depth. He notes that current coal and lignite mining operations on seams less than 3 feet thick accounted for only a few per cent of the total output, and from seams less than 2 feet thick there was only a little over 1 per cent of total output.[124] Putnam cites a previous estimate that some 45 per cent of the bituminous resources of Pennsylvania are in beds less than 2 feet thick;[125] and the fact that as of 1950 "no bituminous coal is being mined with a thickness less than double Campbell's 14-inch limit nor at more than one-half his depth of 3,000 feet."[126] Putnam accordingly establishes his second reduction factor at 50 per cent.

In the light of the definitions adopted herein, it is obvious that Putnam is merely substituting a "reserve" concept for a "resource" concept—a procedure that can be meaningful only with a clear definition of terms. The second reduction factor is therefore not justified in the context in which it is presented.

Putnam is also unjustified in his footnoted remark that the first progress report of the Survey, issued after his study was written, confirmed "in a general way the conclusions already reached in this report by means of the analysis developed."[127] A 1951 Survey report had, in fact, already recognized the significance of limiting criteria. The report noted that there is really no agreement as to the practical limits for thickness of seam and overburden in defining "reserves." "A very conservative estimate may include only the original reserves in thick beds and under slight overburden—in other words, reserves that could be recovered profit-

---

[122] Palmer Putnam, *Energy in the Future* (New York: Van Nostrand, 1953), p. 127.

[123] There is, however, a wide range in the changes for individual state estimates. Three of the state figures show increases ranging from 66.7 per cent to 197.7 per cent. The greatest individual decrease is 91.7 per cent. The agreement between the average change and Putnam's judgment hinges on the fact that for the four states with the largest resources, which comprise 78.6 per cent of the 1944 resource total, the decrease is 58.7 per cent.

[124] Putnam, *op. cit.*

[125] G. H. Ashley, *The Underdeveloped Mineral Resources of Pennsylvania,* Pennsylvania Topographic and Geological Survey, Bulletin M 18-A, 1933.

[126] Putnam, *op. cit.*, p. 128.

[127] *Ibid.*, p. 125 n.

ably under current mining conditions. A more inclusive estimate, on the other hand, may consider thinner, more impure, and more deeply buried coal as recoverable by improved methods when more easily mined deposits have been exhausted."[128] Thus the Survey allows for possible changes in the limiting criteria as technological and economic conditions change (even if it did not choose to incorporate the conceptual distinction between "reserves" and "resources" into any definitions), whereas Putnam does not.

Putnam continues with a third reduction of 50 per cent to allow for recoverability. He assumes, in other words, that only one-half of the coal present in the ground can be recovered; and on this he is in full agreement with the Survey. In the present context, there is no criticism of the use of a recovery limitation, but recovery is basically a matter of technology, and with a given technological level the term "recoverable resources" is misleading unless that level is clearly indicated. To be useful, the term must be stated as "currently recoverable resources," providing a technological limit that can be considered together with economic limits. (See the discussion of the recovery level over the long term in the body of Chapter 8.)

Putnam's fourth reduction factor is based on his disagreement with the Survey's limiting criterion of 30 per cent ash content (raised to 33 per cent in the 1953 progress report) and the failure to set a limit on sulfur content. Having made a cumulative reduction of 87.5 per cent in the 1944 government estimate with his first three factors, Putnam adds another reduction factor of 0.5 per cent on this score. A correction factor of this magnitude is obviously insignificant relative to the inevitably wide range of error in both reserve and resource estimates.

Putnam also employs a fifth correction factor, which he applied to the energy content (in terms of Btu's) of Campbell's 1909 estimate, adjusted for subsequent production. Noting that about 75 per cent of the total reserves west of the Mississippi are of low rank and hence cannot be shipped far because of deterioration, Putnam assumed that 10 per cent of such reserves would be used locally, the other 90 per cent used only through conversion to synthetic gas or liquid fuel, with a loss of half of the contained energy. The product of these composite assumptions is a reduction factor of 17 per cent. Regardless of the validity of the underlying assumptions, the fifth factor is irrelevant to a discussion of physical quantity estimates, since it is applied to a thermal equivalent and is merely an allowance for efficiency in use.

The composite of Putnam's five correction factors is a reduction of 90 per cent. This composite factor he applies to the thermal equivalent of the estimate presented to Congress by the Survey in 1947. The resultant figure is in Btu's, rounded to one significant figure in nineteen places (that is, a seven, followed by 18 zeros). This rounded figure he subsequently converts to an equivalent 260

[128] U.S. Geological Survey, *Fuel Reserves of the United States*, statement submitted to Senate Committee on Interior and Insular Affairs, 82nd Congress, 1st Session, Committee Print, 1951, p. 5.

billion tons of bituminous coal. The statistical error this introduces into the coal tonnage figure is itself considerable.

It is to be regretted that Putnam's quantity figure has received uncritical acceptance in some quarters. The figure is based on limiting criteria that have no consistent basis; some of them are wholly arbitrary and some have no relation to coal actually in the ground. It is not a reserve estimate because it goes beyond current limitations, yet it is not a resource estimate because of the inclusion of criteria pertaining to efficiency of use. It cannot be regarded, therefore, as a valid alternative estimate to that of the U.S. Geological Survey.

CHAPTER 9

Crude oil

THE RESERVE-RESOURCE POSITION

Before surveying the opinion of technical authorities within the industry on the present U.S. reserve-resource position in petroleum, it is necessary to relate the industry terminology in which existing estimates are presented to the terminology used in this study. The term "reserves" as used in the petroleum industry is normally a contraction of the term "proved recoverable reserves." The American Petroleum Institute provides an authoritative and explicit definition as follows:

> Proved reserves are both drilled and undrilled. The proved drilled reserves, in any pool, include oil estimated to be recoverable by the production systems now in operation, whether with or without fluid injection, and from the area actually drilled up on the spacing pattern in effect in that pool. The proved undrilled reserves, in any pool, include reserves under undrilled spacing units which are so close, and so related, to the drilled units that there is every reasonable probability that they will produce when drilled.[1]

Although additions to proved reserves can accrue through improved recovery techniques, through more favorable economic conditions, or through better knowledge of the reservoirs in which the oil occurs, the magnitude of proved reserves at any point in time is in the last analysis a function of the drilling of wells. And, since the industry is interested in production, not in proving reserves for their own sake (which would involve tying up large capital sums), the ratio of proved reserves to production tends to be small. Proved reserves as of the end of 1959 were 31.7 billion barrels, 12.8 times production in that year. In the period since 1945 the proved reserves-production ratio has averaged 12.4, ranging from a high of 13.6 to a low of 11.6.

[1] Committee on Petroleum Reserves, *1960 Report* to the American Petroleum Institute, March 16, 1960.

In the numerous discussions of the probable course of future oil discoveries in this country the tendency of most has been to hold technology as well as costs constant, either explicitly or implicitly. These discussions have commonly employed the term "ultimate reserves," meaning all oil so far produced, plus current proved reserves, plus "reserves" (defined in terms of current technology and costs) that will be discovered in the future.

The literature, save for a few exceptions, has been surveyed only for 1950 and subsequent years in order to review only current opinion. For convenience, the estimates are first examined and compared on an ultimate-reserve basis. But it is evident that this basis, by limiting technology to its current status, ignores the element of technological progress in the determination of future productive capacity. When used as a basis for estimating future production and future resource positions, there is a strong downward bias. There is, of course, a legitimate and proper use for a reserve concept even as restrictive as proved reserves. But it is certainly illogical, in estimating the course of future production, to assume that technology remains frozen. Estimates on this basis may be admissible if presented as minimal figures because of the definitional restriction on technology (although most estimates are unaccompanied by this caveat); yet the fact remains that they represent only a partial, incomplete look at the future.

It is necessary, therefore, in line with the concepts used herein, to convert the ultimate-reserve estimates into resource-base figures. It is believed that this conversion is accomplished in this study without violating the essential meaning and intent of the authors of the ultimate-reserve estimates. The advantage gained is the very large one of subsequently being able to introduce into the all-inclusive resource-base concept the levels of technology that appear as plausible and probable future developments.[2] The procedure followed is somewhat circuitous, but it is hoped that as the exposition proceeds the benefits of its use will be apparent. The final result is that the conclusions arrived at in this study, although based on new and different concepts, also reflect the opinion of recognized authorities who have employed the conventional concept.

In order to compare and examine the various estimates, certain distinctions must be recognized. One of these is the conventional one between "primary" and "secondary" production. Broadly speaking, primary production is that obtained through the development, by drilling, of an oil reservoir. Such production may

[2] There is no question as to what should be included under the terms crude oil, natural gas, and natural gas liquids. There is no gradation in these hydrocarbon occurrences corresponding to the tenor of ore; a hydrocarbon occurrence is either one of these materials or it is not. The hydrocarbon content of such materials as bituminous shales or "tar sands," for example, is by universal custom excluded from the definition of petroleum. As for the environmental limits, these too are "clean" with respect to the hydrocarbons under consideration. Using the Mohorovičić discontinuity as the line of demarcation, the earth's crust underneath the continents is some 115,000 feet thick. But the theoretical limit to the possible depth of occurrence of the hydrocarbons is around 65,000 feet. (J. S. Cloninger, "How Deep Oil or Gas May Be Expected," *World Oil*, Vol. 130, No. 6 (May 1950), p. 60.) Although the maximum penetration to date is somewhat more than one-third that depth, it is conceivable, even if not plausible, that technological progress could utlimately make penetration to such depths feasible.

be accompanied by recycling the associated natural gas back into the reservoir to maintain pressure. And as a further means of increasing the total cumulative recovery of the oil in the reservoir, such production may be aided by "fluid injection," defined by the American Petroleum Institute as "a method of recovery of oil, gas and/or related hydrocarbons in which part of the energy effective in moving these hydrocarbons through a reservoir is applied from extraneous sources by injection of liquids or gases into the reservoir." Primary production with fluid injection is obtained when the technique is applied "early in the producing life of a reservoir when there has been little or no loss of natural reservoir energy." In contradistinction, "secondary recovery is an application of fluid injection when a reservoir is approaching or has reached economic production limits."[3]

A second distinction can be made between "continental," or "onshore," oil and "offshore" oil. The offshore oil occurs under submerged lands of the continental shelf and is obtainable only through specialized techniques of directional drilling and drilling in open water.

In order to aid the analysis of the estimates of future reserves, these production categories are translated into the following reserve categories: (a) "primary reserves"—obtainable through primary onshore production; (b) "secondary reserves"—obtainable through secondary onshore production; and (c) "offshore reserves"—as defined above (and including oil obtainable through secondary production offshore).

The published estimates fail to recognize or specify these distinctions in many instances and are thus frequently ambiguous or even wholly lack definition. Whether or not an estimate so states, for example, it is likely to include an indeterminate proportion of secondary reserves if it was derived from data on proved reserves, since the latter include a varying but indeterminate proportion of secondary reserves. Nevertheless, the several estimates have been brought together in Table 98 and listed under what seems to be the appropriate reserve category. Where possible, the estimate is shown for comparison purposes as an "ultimate-reserves" figure, which is further related to a quantity "yet to be produced" (as of January 1, 1960), and the ratio of this unproduced total to 1959 output.

Because of ambiguity and lack of definition, the placement of many of the estimates in the respective reserve category in Table 98 as well as the conversion to an ultimate-reserves figure may involve considerable error or distortion of the original intent or meaning behind the estimate. Nevertheless, it is believed that the presentation is in general sufficiently faithful to provide a useful basis for analyzing published opinion.[4] As a first step in the analysis, the estimates under the respective reserve categories are described in chronological order. (Unless otherwise specified in a footnote, a reference to the original estimate may be assumed to be that listed in Table 98.)

[3] P. D. Torrey, "Significance of Fluid Injection in United States Oil Fields," *The Oil Forum*, Vol. X, No. 12 (Mid-November 1956), p. 425.
[4] This study has had the benefit of comments from most of the authors whose estimates are listed in Table 98.

TABLE 98.　ESTIMATES OF FUTURE CRUDE OIL RESERVES OF THE UNITED STATES

(In billion barrels)

Source and date (1)	Ultimate Reserves				Yet to be produced (1/1/60) (6)	Col. 6 as multiple of 1959 production (7)
	Primary (2)	Secondary (resources) (3)	Offshore (4)	Total (5)		
a) Weeks, 1948	110 (165)[1]	—	—	—	—	—
b) Pratt, 1950	109	—	33[2]	142[2]	80	32
c) USGS, 1951	—	—	>15	—	—	—
d) Thompson, 1951	—	75	—	—	—	—
e) Egloff, 1951	500–1,000	—	500–1,000	1,000–2,000	938–1,938	375–775
f) Murphree, 1952	—	111	—	—	—	—
g) Petersen, 1952	—	69	—	—	—	—
h) Schultz, 1952	170	⋯⋯30⋯⋯		>200	138	55
i) Carmical, 1955	—	—	>15	—	—	—
j) Ayres, 1955	—	—	—	140	78	31
k) Interior Dept., 1956	—	—	—	300	238	95
l) Pogue and Hill, 1956	—	—	—	165	103	41
m) Murrell, 1956	—	—	—	200	138	55
n) Hubbert, 1956	130	—	20	150	88	35
o) Hill et al., 1957	—	—	20	>250	188	75
p) Weeks, 1957	—	—	—	240	178	71
q) Torrey, 1960	—	59 (105)[3]	—	—	—	—

[1] See text, p. 351.
[2] Imputed.
[3] See text, p. 353.

SOURCES:

a) L. G. Weeks, "Highlights on 1947 Developments in Foreign Petroleum Fields," *Bulletin of the American Association of Petroleum Geologists*, Vol. 32, No. 6, p. 1,094.

b) W. E. Pratt, "The Earth's Petroleum Resources," *Our Oil Resources*, L. M. Fanning, ed. (2nd ed., New York: McGraw-Hill Book Co., 1950), p. 151.

c) U.S. Geological Survey (USGS), *Fuel Reserves of the United States*, Senate Committee on Interior and Insular Affairs, 82nd Congress, 1st Session (Washington, D. C.: U.S. Government Printing Office, 1951).

d) E. O. Thompson, "Freedom's Oil," *Proceedings*, American Petroleum Institute, Vol. XXXII, No. 1 (1952), p. 32.

e) G. Egloff, "Oil and Gas as Industrial Raw Materials," *Resources for Freedom*, Vol. IV, Report of the President's Materials Policy Commission (Washington, D. C.: U.S. Government Printing Office, 1952), p. 193.

f) E. V. Murphree, "Where Will Tomorrow's Oil Come From?" *Oil and Gas Journal*, November 3, 1952, pp. 123–24.

g) T. S. Petersen, "Oil in the Next Quarter-Century," *Proceedings*, American Petroleum Institute, *op. cit.*

h) P. R. Schultz, "What Is the Future of Petroleum Discovery?" *Oil and Gas Journal*, July 28, 1952, p. 259.

i) J. H. Carmical, *New York Times*, August 7, 1955.

j) E. Ayres, "Energy Resources for the Future," *Oil and Gas Compact Bulletin*, Vol. XIV, No. 1 (June 1955), p. 20.

k) Panel on the Impact of the Peaceful Uses of Atomic Energy, *Peaceful Uses of Atomic Energy*, Vol. 2, Report to the Joint Committee on Atomic Energy, 84th Congress, 2nd Session (Washington, D. C.: U.S. Government Printing Office, January 1956), p. 82.

(*Footnotes continued on next page.*)

(Footnotes to Table 98, continued.)

l) J. E. Pogue and K. E. Hill, *Future Growth and Financial Requirements of the World Petroleum Industry* (New York: Chase Manhattan Bank, 1956). Presented at annual meeting of American Institute of Mining, Metallurgical and Petroleum Engineers, Petroleum Branch, February 21, 1956.

m) J. H. Murrell, as reported in *Petroleum Week*, March 16, 1956, pp. 9–10.

n) M. K. Hubbert, "Nuclear Energy and the Fossil Fuels," *Drilling and Production Practice—1956* (New York: American Petroleum Institute, 1957), pp. 14–15.

o) K. E. Hill, H. D. Hammar, and J. G. Winger, *Future Growth of the World Petroleum Industry* (New York: Chase Manhattan Bank, 1957). Presented at meeting of American Petroleum Institute Division of Production, Rocky Mountain District, Caspar, Wyoming, April 25, 1957.

p) L. G. Weeks, "Fuel Reserves of the Future," *Bulletin of the American Association of Petroleum Geologists*, Vol. 42, No. 2 (February 1958), p. 434.

q) P. D. Torrey, "Can We Salvage Another 44 Billion Barrels?" *The Oil and Gas Journal*, June 13, 1960, pp. 97-102.

Primary Reserves

The 1948 estimate by Weeks is included because it is a reference mark for subsequent estimates. Weeks' figure was based on a systematic analysis of the various sedimentary basins and oil provinces of the world. "Preliminary and basic studies include the origin and development of basins, and their classification based on origin, history, physical form or architecture and composition. They involve a study of sedimentation and deposition environment, the effects of the changes that occur progressively with different stages of the deposition cycle."[5] These studies were used to obtain an estimate of the "potential ultimate recoverable oil" from individual sedimentary areas and basins, using as guides or bases for comparison measurements of productivity from current or previously producing units of the earth's crust. Measurements were in the form of barrels of oil per square mile, per cubic mile, per unit of exploratory effort, and the like.

Weeks' estimate was originally presented as the amount of undiscovered recoverable reserves as of 1948, which he concluded were about equal to past discoveries. Secondary reserves were not meant to be included,[6] and offshore reserves were explicitly excluded. Weeks considered that, although he has gone beyond the proved-reserve concept in his figure, the conclusion was a very conservative one, and the final figure for primary production from the land area of the United States was more likely to be 50 per cent larger, or 165 billion barrels, than 10 per cent less.

Pratt's estimate, like that of Weeks, is based on geological inference. But, whereas Weeks uses a detailed analysis of individual petroliferous areas, Pratt relies on a general relationship between production and the area from which production comes. Excluding the offshore province, he estimates reserves of 100 billion barrels based on the extent and productivity of proved producing areas.

[5] L. G. Weeks, discussion in *Proceedings*, United Nations Scientific Conference on Conservation and Utilization of Resources, Vol. I (New York: United Nations, 1950), p. 108.

[6] Communication to the author.

Assuming on the basis of past experience that some 1.5 per cent of the "distinctly favorable" parts of the total U.S. area (amounting to about 577 million acres) were eventually productive, such productive area would total 8.6 million acres. Cumulative discoveries through 1948 totaled 57.2 billion barrels from a producing area of 4.5 million acres, hence reserves (excluding the continental shelf) would be about 109 billion barrels (rounded in Pratt's presentation to an even 100 billion).[7]

Egloff cites Weeks' estimate of 100 billion barrels (as originally presented, in round numbers) and points out that this quantity of oil would occupy somewhat less than 4 cubic miles. If the estimate were correct, it would mean that 4 cubic miles of oil would be produced from 1.5 million cubic miles of sediments. In Egloff's view this is disproportionately small; the ultimate reserves of the land area of the United States are more likely to range between 500 and 1,000 billion barrels, or 20 to 40 cubic miles of oil from 1.5 million cubic miles of sediments.

Schultz's estimate of 170 billion barrels is based on a projection of the "trend of cumulative discoveries." Although he does not specify what this means, it is probable that he applied a logistic growth curve to the cumulative discovery statistics. Such a curve yields an upper asymptote which represents the ultimate total. Schultz implies that with existing data the asymptote is still ambiguous by noting that his figure is a "minimum ultimate potential" and that it will probably continue to grow.

Hubbert's estimate is a modification of Weeks' original figure based on the good production record of the past two decades made possible through improved recovery practices.

·   ·   ·

Secondary "Reserves"

Consideration of the basis of future secondary production again calls attention to the reserve-resource distinction discussed in Chapter 7. The authors who have made specific estimates of future total secondary recovery allow for improved recovery methods or more favorable economic conditions—criteria used herein as part of the definition of "resources." For this reason the heading of this section has been put in quotation marks and the word "resources" is in parentheses above column 3 of Table 98.

[7] A later estimate by Pratt appears in the report of the Panel on the Impact of the Peaceful Uses of Atomic Energy to the Joint Committee on Atomic Energy, *Peaceful Uses of Atomic Energy,* Vol. 2 (Washington, D. C.: U.S. Government Printing Office, January 1956), p. 94. The estimate of 170 billion barrels as the ultimate reserves of the United States is in terms of "liquid hydrocarbons," which includes natural gas liquids (see Chapter 10 of this study). Although it is possible to assume a certain proportion of the latter in the total figure on the basis of statistical relationships, Pratt gives no indication as to what proportion is subsumed in his estimate. In the absence of such knowledge, it is considered here that the assumption of any given proportion would be an unwarranted interpretation of Pratt's figure. The estimate is therefore omitted from discussion in this study.

Thompson's estimate of secondary resources is not supported by any argument. He merely remarks that possible secondary recovery might be as high as 75 billion barrels.

Murphree's estimate is accompanied by more detail. He notes that in 1950 the estimated oil content of known fields was 175 billion barrels. Of this, 64 billion barrels could be expected through primary recovery and 4 billion more through conventional secondary methods such as water flooding. The remaining 107 billion barrels await improved secondary-recovery methods, and "there is indication that secondary methods will be developed in the future that will be able to recover the bulk of this remaining oil."[8] This yields a secondary-resource estimate composed of 4 billion barrels of reserves and 107 billion that will ultimately become reserves because of technological progress. Technically, however, it is not a complete secondary-resource estimate because it does not include the undiscovered oil that will be producible only through secondary operations. It could perhaps be termed "known secondary resources."

Petersen's estimate is apparently a passing reference to the Murphree figure. Petersen forecasts that secondary recovery will yield 65 billion barrels of the total known 107 billion barrels unrecoverable in 1950. The 4 billion of Murphree's secondary reserves has been added to Petersen's 65 billion barrels in Table 98. Again, this estimate provides only a figure for known secondary resources.

The Torrey estimate is the latest of several he has presented in recent years as part of comprehensive, continuing statistical work by the Committee on Secondary Recovery and Pressure Maintenance of the Interstate Oil Compact Commission. The work involves a field-by-field study of the oil fields of the United States. The Committee estimates the original oil content of known reservoirs to have been 328 billion barrels.[9] After primary production under present economic and technological conditions, some 234 billion barrels of this total would remain unrecovered. Of this amount, according to the Committee, about 15 billion barrels can be recovered with conventional secondary methods under economic conditions as of January 1, 1960 (that is, secondary reserves are 15 billion barrels). In addition, "oil that is physically recoverable by improved recovery methods" (see section on Drilling and Production Technology, below) totals 44 billion barrels,[10] so that known secondary oil resources with present technology are an estimated 59 billion barrels, as shown in Table 98. The figure of 44 billion is considered a minimum, however, and could well be in the range of 90 billion.[11] A figure of 105 billion (15 + 90) has therefore been placed in parentheses in Table 98.

[8] E. V. Murphree, "Where Will Tomorrow's Oil Come From?" *Oil and Gas Journal*, November 3, 1952, pp. 119–24.

[9] P. D. Torrey, "Can We Salvage Another 44 Billion Barrels?" *op. cit.*

[10] *Ibid.*, pp. 98, 100.

[11] *Ibid.*, p. 102.

Offshore "Reserves"

Again the term "reserves" must be put in quotation marks, since some of the estimates include offshore oil beyond the water depth limits of current technology.

The figure of 33 billion barrels attributed to Pratt in Table 98 is a double inference; it is not his actual estimate. Pratt's only figure for the continental shelf area is one trillion barrels for the earth as a whole, based on the recoverable oil content per unit volume of sediments in the United States applied to the volume of the continental shelves of the world. Taking the U.S. and Alaskan portion of the total shelf area of the world as 10 per cent, the U.S. Geological Survey (USGS) suggests that it is possible to infer from Pratt's estimate a figure of 100 billion barrels.[12] The figure for the United States (excl. Alaska) was obtained for this study by taking the same ratio between the continental shelf of Alaska and the rest of the United States as was used by the USGS, in its inference from the Weeks figure. The Survey does not offer its own estimate for the total continental shelf area of the United States but considers, on the basis of discoveries to date in coastal Texas and Louisiana, that their offshore resources approximate 13 billion barrels and, by similar reasoning, the California offshore resources are some 2 billion barrels. "It should be emphasized, however," the USGS report states, "that these two areas probably have greater oil and gas possibilities than any other parts of the Continental Shelf adjacent to the United States."

Egloff concludes that as much oil will probably be found under the continental shelves as will be produced under the land areas. He cites a figure of 14 million square miles, however, as the area of the continental shelves bordering the United States as the basis for this conclusion. This makes his estimate invalid, since the figure pertains to the total continental shelf area of the world, not that of the United States alone.

Carmical's estimate is derived from industry geologists' opinion plus his own judgment.[13] According to him, the total offshore reserves out to a depth of 250 feet of water are estimated to be over 15 billion barrels, based on 300 discoveries to date and known production and proved-reserve data for adjacent shore areas.

Hubbert cites the Geological Survey's offshore estimate together with an estimate for California, by Jenkins of the California Division of Natural Resources, which is larger by 2 billion barrels than the USGS figure. This total of 17 billion barrels is rounded to 20 billion by Hubbert.

The estimate of 20 billion barrels by Hill *et al.* is merely mentioned by them as included in their ultimate reserve estimate.

[12] Geological Survey, *Fuel Reserves of the United States*, Senate Committee on Interior and Insular Affairs, 82nd Congress, 1st Session (Washington, D. C.: U.S. Government Printing Office, 1951), p. 32. The Survey also suggests the inference of a figure of 12 billion barrels for the U.S. continental shelf from an estimate by Weeks for the total of the world's continental shelf area. Weeks, however, denies (in a communication to the author) the implication and strongly criticizes the procedure of assuming the same area-occurrence ratio for different areas of the world.

[13] Communication to the author.

Ultimate Reserves

The Pratt figure for total ultimate reserves in Table 98 is derived, as noted above, through the addition to his "basic" estimate of a figure for offshore resources inferred from his published statements. It is therefore an imputed figure, as noted in Table 98, not an estimate specifically made by Pratt.

The Egloff estimate, presented as a range, is merely the equivalent of his statement that offshore reserves equal onshore reserves.

Schultz bases his estimate on a projection of the trend of cumulative discoveries plus an estimate for secondary recovery and offshore potential. He considers this a minimum that will probably grow in the future.

Ayres' estimate is stated as follows: "Using Weeks' estimates including both on- and off-shore oil [*sic*], adjusted to January 1, 1955, and the A.P.I. evaluation of proved reserves, it seems that we may have about 90 billion barrels of oil yet to be produced. . . ."[14] Together with cumulative past production, this is the equivalent of a total of 140 billion barrels through time. Ayres had previously taken note of Schultz's 200-billion barrel estimate, contending that such higher estimates of the ultimate reserve are not based on firm physical data but "on a passionate desire to postpone the time when production will be inadequate."[15]

The Interior Department estimate prepared for the Panel on the Impact of Peaceful Uses of Atomic Energy is derived from the Schultz estimate, modified by the considerations that "trends in production and discovery are still headed upward, and that significant improvements in recoverability are now being accomplished or promised for the future. . . ."[16] In the terminology of this paper, this is clearly a resource estimate because of the allowance for improved technology.

The estimate by Pogue and Hill is included in Table 98 only because it is the basis of their projection of future production. Actually, it is not an estimate but merely the assumption that future discoveries will equal past discoveries. No justification is offered for the choice of this particular assumption.

Murrell's estimate of 200 billion barrels represents his judgment compared to other estimates in the range of 160-165 billion barrels. He considers these too small in the light of the production record, which has thus far surpassed all earlier estimates of reserves.

The supporting data and arguments for Hubbert's estimate of 150 billion barrels as the ultimate reserve have been referred to above, under the individual reserve components.

In making their estimate of 250 billion barrels, Hill *et al.* refer to the previous Pogue and Hill estimate as a minimum one, acknowledge that other recent esti-

[14] E. Ayres, "Energy Resources for the Future," *Oil and Gas Compact Bulletin*, Vol. XIV, No. 1 (June 1955), p. 20.

[15] E. Ayres, "U.S. Oil Outlook: How Coal Fits In," *Coal Age*, Vol. LVIII, No. 8 (August 1953), p. 72.

[16] Panel on the Impact of Peaceful Uses of Atomic Energy, *op. cit.*, pp. 81–82.

mates have ranged between 200 and 300 billion barrels, and "accept as plausible" a figure of 250 billion barrels.

Weeks' presentation of his second estimate does not refer to his earlier one. He observes that "in forecasting the extent of our ultimate potential oil resources" there are only two determinants "that have any general application and which can be classified as basic today . . . (1) geology, and (2) experience on the broadest possible scale in what the geology means in terms of oil occurrence." His estimate is thus built up, "Basin by basin, after careful study of each basin's geology over a long period, and [is] based on world-wide experience and analysis of the relation between oil occurrence and facies."[17] It can be inferred from these remarks that the procedure was the same in making both the 1948 and 1957 estimates. The coverage is, however, slightly different. Secondary reserves are again excluded (the estimate applies to oil "recoverable by conventional primary methods in terms of current economics"), but offshore reserves are included. In calling attention to the wide range of error inherent in any such estimate, Weeks adds that this "ultimate resource" figure is "very conservative."

RESERVE ESTIMATES AND THE RESOURCE BASE

As shown in Table 99, the ultimate-reserve estimates may be divided into three groups: those below 200 billion barrels, those in the range of 200–300 billion, and the single estimate in the range of trillions of barrels. (The individual estimates in columns 3 and 4 of Table 98 will not be discussed here, for reasons that will shortly become apparent.) This wide range in the estimates

TABLE 99. ESTIMATES OF ULTIMATE RESERVES OF CRUDE OIL IN THE UNITED STATES ARRANGED IN ORDER OF SIZE

(In billion barrels)

Source	Estimate
Egloff	1,000–2,000
Interior Department	300
Hill *et al.*	>250
Weeks	240
Schultz	>200
Murrell	200
Pogue and Hill	165
Hubbert	150
Pratt	142
Ayres	140

[17] L. G. Weeks, "Fuel Reserves of the Future," *Bulletin of the American Association of Petroleum Geologists,* Vol. 42, No. 2 (February 1958), p. 434.

is symptomatic of a fundamental gap in knowledge concerning oil occurrence—the lack of a theory of the incidence of oil in the earth's crust. Weeks points out that oil occurrence is related to (1) "the nature of the environments in the basin of deposition and their pattern of distribution relative to each other, relative rates of deposition, etc.;" and (2) "the existence of timely traps, strategically located to collect the hydrocarbons on their early migration."[18] But the recognition of these relationships is a weak analytical tool compared with a systematic statement of the relationships that would furnish a sound basis for prediction. In the absence of the latter, the available information is, as Weeks observes, "subject to wide interpretation."

Among the estimators, only Weeks and Pratt have made any attempt to derive an ultimate-reserve figure from the circumstances of natural occurrence. The others either derive such a figure from discovery statistics, proclaim a figure as their flat judgment, or use their judgment to modify Weeks' or Pratt's original conclusions. And, although Weeks' 1958 estimate is the product of the most comprehensive and systematic analysis, the extrapolation of the data is inevitably so open-ended that the predominant element in the estimate is, in the last analysis, the estimator's individual judgment. All of the estimates involving undiscovered oil are thus individual interpretations which are subject to large error. This is not meant to be an invidious judgment; it is a statement with which the authors listed would be the first to agree.

It remains now to consider the ultimate-reserve estimates in terms of the resource-base concept as set forth earlier in this study. For convenience and simplicity, the estimates were discussed in their own terms but these terms carry with them the concept of proved reserves and its limiting criterion of current technology. Even when Weeks, for example, speaks of the "potential ultimate recoverable oil" he is basing his estimate on area-productivity relationships *measured in terms of proved reserves*, hence under current technology. On the other hand, with the resource-base concept one can view the "oil environment" within which future technology will operate.

The translation from ultimate reserves to the resource base can be accomplished directly and simply by means of the "recovery factor," which is the percentage of the total oil content of the reservoir that can be recovered over the producing life of that reservoir. The relation is as follows:

a) Ultimate-reserve estimates are based on the proved-reserve concept.

b) Proved reserves are defined in terms of current recovery (that is, only that oil is included which is recoverable with current technology).

c) Therefore, to convert an ultimate-reserve estimate (A) into an inferred resource-base equivalent (C) (see Chapter 7) the formula is

$$C = \frac{A}{\text{recovery factor}}$$

[18] *Ibid.*, pp. 433–34.

A figure frequently used in the literature as the average recovery factor (including primary and secondary) in the United States today is 40 per cent. This has not been accompanied by any substantiation, however, and it is dismissed in favor of the estimate by the Committee on Secondary Recovery and Pressure Maintenance of the Interstate Oil Compact Commission. According to the Committee, under the technologic and economic conditions prevailing at the end of 1959 there would be an ultimate recovery of 33 per cent of the original oil in place from known reservoirs.[19] This figure is an average of data from the Committee's field-by-field studies and is derived from information from the files and records of the various state regulatory authorities not available to any other investigators. Thus it may be said that to the best of current knowledge recovery averages about one-third of the total oil present in a reservoir.

Under the procedure outlined above, the ultimate-reserve estimates are multiplied by a factor of three (the reciprocal of the recovery factor) to obtain an inferred resource-base equivalent. The results when applied to the estimates in Table 99 are listed in Table 100. Because of its magnitude and ambiguous basis, the Egloff estimate does not seem suitable for conversion. The Interior Department estimate contains an unspecified allowance for improvement in recovery, hence cannot be converted. The conversion of the remaining estimates is not considered to do violence to the originals since all of them are based, either explicitly or implicitly, on current recoverability.

A few words of caution and qualification are in order. First, multiplication by three on the basis of a recovery factor of approximately one-third does *not* carry any implications concerning the future recovery level. The conversion in Table 100 merely shows the equivalent resource base inferable from the respective ultimate-reserve estimates. Second, the adjective "equivalent" is used advisedly. The result is not, in fact, the total resource base. Only recovery technology is taken into account by conversion, whereas the total resource base

TABLE 100.   ESTIMATES OF ULTIMATE RESERVES CONVERTED TO INFERRED RESOURCE-BASE EQUIVALENT

(In billion barrels)

Source and date (1)	Ultimate reserve estimate (2)	Inferred equivalent resource base (3)	Yet to be discovered (1/1/60) (4)	Possibly available for future recovery (5)
Hill *et al.*	250	750	422	687
Weeks	240	720	392	657
Schultz, 1952	>200	>600	>272	>537
Murrell, 1956	200	600	272	537
Pogue and Hill, 1956	165	495	167	432
Hubbert, 1956	150	450	122	387
Pratt, 1950	142	426	98	363
Ayres, 1955	140	420	92	357

SOURCES: See Table 98.

[19] P. D. Torrey, "Can We Salvage Another 44 Billion Barrels?" *op. cit.*, p. 100.

could be obtained from the estimates only by taking account of the fact that current discovery and drilling technology is not able to probe the limits of the petroleum environment. The results of the conversion thus logically apply only to the crude oil that exists down to the current depth limit of drilling, since the ultimate-reserve estimates do not suggest the eventual probing of the total environment in which petroleum may possibly occur. Nevertheless, with due allowance for the shortcomings of the conversion procedure, its application to the ultimate-reserve estimates gives inferred resource-base equivalents that are sufficiently useful for present purposes by indicating general orders of magnitude.

In column 4 of Table 100 the resource-base figures are reduced by the original oil content of known reservoirs as of January 1, 1960 (all oil discovered in the United States to that date), estimated to be 328 billion barrels.[20] This yields the oil yet to be discovered according to the various estimates. Column 5 of Table 100 is obtained by subtracting from the figures in column 3 the total production through 1959, or 63 billion barrels. The figures of column 5, adapted to the conceptual basis of this study, thus present the total quantity of oil from which future production will come as inferred from expert opinion on ultimate reserves.

The conclusion from Table 100 is that the resource base for future oil production in this country is on the general order of magnitude of 500 billion barrels. It is worth repeating what this means so that the reader will avoid the error of interpreting it in the light of conventional concepts.

The total crude oil awaiting (potentially available for) future recovery in the United States can be inferred from expert opinion to be on the order of 500 billion barrels. This includes present proved reserves, the currently unrecoverable content of known reservoirs, and the total content of undiscovered reservoirs, without regard to present or future technologic feasibility of discovery and recovery.[21]

ESTIMATES OF FUTURE CAPACITY AND PRODUCTION

Just as authoritative opinion on future reserves was examined as an aid in estimating the resource base, so it is useful to examine opinion on future production and productive capacity in estimating the future availability of oil

[20] *Idem.*

[21] It must be noted that this approach and the resulting conclusion are anticipated in this succinct statement: "Scientific estimates of ultimate production appear to be based on recovering only about 40 per cent of the oil in place, reflecting past experience and current practices. Estimates that ultimate production will be 200–300 billion barrels of oil really indicate discovery of reservoirs with 500–700 billion barrels of oil in place." See R. J. Gonzalez, "U.S. Not Running Out of Oil," *World Oil*, Vol. 144, No. 4 (March 1957), p. 66. Nevertheless, the full implications of this conclusion, especially in terms of the results of increased recovery over the medium term, have not, in this writer's opinion, received the recognition they deserve.

from domestic sources. The various published estimates of future annual production and/or capacity during the period through 1975 are brought together for this purpose in Table 101.

There is less ambiguity here than in the reserve estimates, although there is one aspect in which the use of the estimates may be inconsistent with the authors' original intentions. Most of the estimates are forecasts or projections of actual U.S. crude oil production for a given year or years in the future. As production estimates, they carry certain assumptions about the demand which would call forth such production and about an import level that would supplement that production in meeting the demand. Thus, they are not necessarily estimates of *availability* as considered in this study. At the same time, there is an availability implication in the estimates—if a forecaster believes production in a certain year will be X billion barrels, it seems proper to conclude that in his opinion the potential capacity for that year should be *at least* that same X billion barrels. The various estimates of production, therefore, can be used to give an indication of expert opinion as to the general level of crude oil availability from domestic production. The perspective of availability ex demand used in this study can then be applied.

.   .   .

Description of Capacity and Production Estimates

The estimates of future capacity and production are listed chronologically, by the year in which they were made, in column 1 of Table 101. Again, the estimates are individually described before they are discussed. (Unless noted otherwise in the following paragraphs, references to the original estimates and the author's explanation of his estimate can be assumed to be that listed in Table 101.)

The estimates of the President's Materials Policy Commission (PMPC) are presented in the Commission's report only in graphic form as "three possible trends in U.S. crude production," with no supporting discussion or argument. They are not considered here to be comparable with other estimates listed in Table 101, for which there are supporting arguments. In their original form they were apparently meant to indicate the range of optimistic, pessimistic, and moderate expectations.

The Egloff estimates in the PMPC report likewise appear without supporting argument, although it is apparent from the accompanying optimistic reserve estimate (see Table 98) that Egloff did not envisage any peaking of output due to physical limitations during the period considered herein.

Ayres' 1952 estimate of a peak production of under 3 billion barrels in 1960 is derived directly from an assumption that ultimate reserves amount to 100 billion barrels. According to Ayres, given a total cumulative output for the United States as a whole and the production record of a considerable fraction of the total producing life, there is, at least in terms of order of magnitude, a

TABLE 101. ESTIMATES OF FUTURE CRUDE OIL CAPACITY AND/OR PRODUCTION IN THE UNITED STATES

Source and date (1)	Peak[1] (2)	Year[2] (3)	Daily rate[3] (million barrels) (4)	Annual rate[3] (billion barrels) (5)	Explicit ultimate reserves(*) or implied cumulative discoveries through terminal date (col. 3), as of 12/31/59[4] (billion barrels) (6)	Col. 5 as percentage of 1959 production[5] (7)
a) PMPC, 1951..	X	1963	(7.7)	2.8 ⎫	123 minimum	112
		1975	(5.0)	1.8 ⎭		72
	X	1967	(8.8)	3.2 ⎫	138 minimum	128
		1975	(7.9)	2.9 ⎭		116
		1975	(10.0)	3.6	147 minimum	144
b) Egloff, 1951...		1960	(8.2)	3.0 ⎫	1,000*–2,000*	120
		1975	(12.3)	4.5 ⎭		180
c) Ayres, 1952...	X	1960	(<8.2)	<3.0	100*	120
d) Swearingen, 1952........		1967	9.0	(3.3)	158 minimum	132
e) Ayres, 1955....	X	1965	(8.2)	3.0 ⎫	140*	120
		1975	(5.5)	2.0 ⎭		80
f) Lasky, 1955...	X	1960–65	(8.2)	3.0	150*	120
		1975–?	(7.5–8.0)	2.6–2.9	250*	104–116
g) Cadle, 1955....		1975	11.2	(4.1)	156 minimum	164
h) Hubbert, 1956.	X	1965	(7.4)	2.7 ⎫	150*	108
		1975	(5.8)	2.1 ⎭		84
	X	1970	(8.2)	3.0 ⎫	200*	120
		1975	(7.9)	2.9 ⎭		116
i) Pogue and Hill, 1956........	X	1973	(9.6)	3.5 ⎫	165*	140
		1975	(8.8)	3.2 ⎭		128
j) Ion, 1956......		1965	8.3–9.3	(3.0–3.7)	109–118 minimum	120–148
		1975	8.3–9.3	(3.0–3.7)	136–149 minimum	120–148
	X	1960–80–?	8.3	(3.0)	92–150 minimum	120
		1975	11.0	(4.0)	153 minimum	160
k) AIME, 1956...		1975	11.2	(4.1)	156 minimum	164
		1975	11.1	(4.1)	156 minimum	164
l) Hill *et al.*, 1957.	X	1966	9.5	(3.5) ⎫	250*	140
		1970–80	(11.0)	4.0 ⎭		160
m) Davis, 1958....	X	1965	9.0	(3.3) ⎫	150*	132
		1975	6.3	(2.3) ⎭		92

[1] The X's in column 2 indicate whether the author specifies that the figure will be the historical peak of domestic annual crude oil production.

[2] Column 3 indicates the year to which each estimate refers.

[3] In columns 4 and 5, the estimate as presented by its author is shown without parentheses.

[4] Column 6 is discussed on page 365.

[5] Column 7 shows the estimates, for purposes of comparison, on a common basis as a percentage of 1959 production.

SOURCES:

a) President's Materials Policy Commission (PMPC), *Resources for Freedom*, Vol. I (Washington, D. C.: U.S. Government Printing Office, 1952), p. 108.

b) G. Egloff, "Oil and Gas as Industrial Raw Materials," *Resources for Freedom, ibid.*, Vol. IV, p. 193.

c) E. Ayres, "Synthetic Liquid Fuels—When and How?" *Petroleum Processing*, January 1952, pp. 41–44.

d) J. E. Swearingen, "Meeting Future Petroleum Demands," *Oil and Gas Journal*, November 17, 1952, pp. 328–36.

(*Footnotes continued on next page.*)

narrow range of possibility for the future course of oil production. With a given ultimate total, the higher the production peak the sooner it must occur and the steeper it will be.[22] Ayres further notes that if the date of the peak proves to be much later than 1960 it must mean that ultimate reserves are much higher than his assumption. But, he continues, extrapolations seem to indicate that 100 billion barrels is not too high, and even if reserve estimates were increased by 50 per cent the production peak would be delayed by only a few years. Ayres concludes: "We seem to have a choice between prediction of expansion for the indefinite future, based upon hope, and prediction of the more probable shape of things to come, based upon reason."[23]

The method of treating aggregate national production over time in the same manner as the production of an individual field may be termed as a "decline-curve" technique. In the record of any field the production level rises to a peak as the field is developed, then falls as the effect of depletion exerts an ever greater limitation on output. Such a production curve for a single field is called a "decline curve" because it traces the long period of decline subsequent to peak production. By analogy, according to this method, national production should reach a peak and then go into a long period of decline as ultimate reserves are depleted. The area under the decline curve for the entire life of an individual field equals the cumulative production of that field during its lifetime. By the

---

[22] This latter point has also been stressed by M. K. Hubbert in *Proceedings*, United Nations Scientific Conference on Conservation and Utilization of Resources, *op. cit.*, pp. 1 and 104. Note, however, the opposite assumption in the PMPC figures.

[23] E. Ayres, "Synthetic Liquid Fuels—When and How?" *Petroleum Processing*, January 1952, pp. 41–44.

(Footnotes to Table 101, continued.)

e) E. Ayres, "Energy Resources for the Future," *Oil and Gas Compact Bulletin*, Vol. XIV, No. 1 (June 1955), pp. 20–21.

f) S. G. Lasky, unpublished manuscript.

g) A. Cadle, "An Appraisal of Future Energy Demand and Supply in the United States," paper presented before American Petroleum Institute Petroleum Industry Buyers, San Francisco, November 15, 1955.

h) M. K. Hubbert, "Nuclear Energy and the Fossil Fuels," *Drilling and Production Practice—1956* (New York: American Petroleum Institute, 1957), interpolated from Hubbert's Fig. 21, p. 17.

i) J. E. Pogue and K. E. Hill, *Future Growth and Financial Requirements of the World Petroleum Industry* (New York: Chase Manhattan Bank, 1956). Presented at annual meeting of the American Institute of Mining, Metallurgical and Petroleum Engineers, Petroleum Branch, February 21, 1956.

j) D. C. Ion, "Oil Resources in the Next Half Century," paper presented at Institute of Petroleum Summer Meeting, Torquay, England, June 6–10, 1956.

k) Production Review Committee, *Oil and Gas Development and Production* (Dallas: Petroleum Branch, American Institute of Mining and Metallurgical Engineers [AIME], February 1956).

l) K. E. Hill, H. D. Hammar, and J. G. Winger, *Future Growth of the World Petroleum Industry* (New York: Chase Manhattan Bank, 1957). Presented at meeting of American Petroleum Institute Division of Production, Rocky Mountain District, Casper, Wyoming, April 25, 1957.

m) W. Davis, "Future Productive Capacity and Probable Reserves of the U.S.," *Oil and Gas Journal*, February 24, 1958, pp. 114, 117.

same token, given ultimate reserves for the nation as a whole and the record of production, the decline-curve approach assumes that the curve can be extrapolated to take into account the current trend and at the same time imply a cumulative production equal to ultimate reserves.

In a later article, Ayres takes note of an ultimate-reserve estimate of 200 billion barrels and extrapolates U.S. production to 1993 based on both the 100-billion and 200-billion figures. According to his analysis, a doubling of the reserve total results merely in the postponement of the production peak from 1960 to 1970. If the 200-billion figure is valid, he says, the evidence should become clear by 1960.[24]

In his 1955 estimate, Ayres has raised the peak to a flat 3 billion barrels and postponed its occurrence to 1965, with a decline to 2 billion barrels a year by 1975. Ayres provides no further details as the basis for this change.

The Swearingen estimate is based on individual forecasts of the productive capacity in 1967 for the five districts into which the Petroleum Administration for Defense divided the United States. The estimate allows for a large secondary production but assumes no drastic technological changes or new secondary-recovery methods. His forecasts are, he contends, more than mathematical projections, for they reflect the representative opinion of geologists and geophysicists in the various districts.

Lasky obtains his first estimate (3 billion barrels) from the first derivative of a logistic growth curve fitted to the cumulative record of U.S. oil production, which is another mathematical way of handling the decline-curve concept. This logistic analysis indicates ultimate cumulative production of 150 billion barrels. The second estimate, ranging from 2.6 to 2.9 billion barrels as the annual rate of production, "is the result of fitting a logistic curve to the annual production series." It indicates a plateau within that range reachable by about 1975; this implies about 250 billion barrels of ultimate cumulative production. Lasky concludes that the point of inflection on the growth curve of cumulative production is as yet indeterminate. He adds that a compromise between the two estimates indicates a flat peak of about 2.8 billion barrels a year annual production persisting over the period 1965–75 before beginning to decline. The implied ultimate cumulative production for this compromise estimate is about 200 billion barrels. The basic assumption of this method, according to Lasky, is that "the past interplay of forces indicates the course of their future interplay."[25]

The Cadle estimate is what the author terms a "guess-estimate" applied to a consideration of the proportions of total energy requirements in the United States that will be supplied from domestic production of the various fuels. "The indications are," says Cadle, "that crude oil production in the U.S. will be over 11,000,000 b/d in 1975," or 4.1 billion barrels a year.

Hubbert is a pioneer in the use of the decline-curve approach to estimate future national production. He extrapolates a production curve through time

[24] E. Ayres, "U.S. Oil Outlook: How Coal Fits In," *op. cit.*, pp. 70–73.
[25] Communication to the author.

on the basis of the production record to date and an assumption as to the size of ultimate reserves. Taking alternative assumptions of 150 and 200 billion barrels as ultimate reserves, he derives mathematically in the first instance a peak output of 2.7 billion barrels in 1965, in the second a peak output of 3 billion barrels in 1970.

The estimates of Pogue and Hill are based on an analysis of past production trends, proved reserve-production ratios, and discovery rates which carries their projection through 1965, the course of subsequent years being a decline curve such as that used by Hubbert and Ayres. The decline curve in this instance is based on the assumption that approximately one-half of ultimate reserves had been discovered by 1956, implying a total figure of 165 billion barrels for ultimate reserves (see p. 355).

The several estimates by Ion are contained in a paper in which he forecasts world oil demand and supply through 1975. The highest figure among his estimates in Table 101 represents the U.S. production that would be forthcoming if Middle East oil were for any reason not available. It is therefore closest to the "availability" concept of the present discussion. Ion notes that all the output levels he lists would, however, be possible only because of offshore production in quantity. If Middle East oil is allowed "to play the part it could," U.S. production, according to Ion, might hit a peak of 8.3 million barrels a day (3 billion barrels a year) within a few years and then hold near that level for about twenty years.

The estimate of the American Institute of Mining and Metallurgical Engineers (AIME) is derived from two independent sources. The higher figure is based on an estimate by the PMPC for total free world output in 1975. The AIME committee resolved this total into U.S. and foreign production through unspecified calculations. The lower figure was obtained by projecting the trend of recent U.S. production as calculated by Pogue and Hill (although this was not the basis of the Pogue and Hill projections).

The first estimate by Hill et al. is a trend projection based on the assumption of a discovery rate of 3.6 billion barrels per year and a decline in the reserve-production ratio from 11.6 in 1956 to 10.3 by 1966. The second is the peak production indicated by a decline curve drawn on a 250-billion-barrel ultimate reserve.

The Davis estimates are derived with the aid of an elaborate statistical projection of trends in "drilling return" (barrels of proved reserves developed per foot drilled), drilling activity, and drilling costs. The data were projected and adjusted for consistency, on a year-by-year basis, with an electronic computer. Davis concludes: "With the average drilling return, a maximum crude oil price of $4 per barrel [in 1956 dollars] and a producing capacity based on good conservation practices, United States crude-oil production should reach a peak of about 9 million barrels per day in 1967 and decline thereafter. The time of peak producing rate may be extended beyond 1967, but to do so requires crude-oil prices that are unrealistic. If the price of crude only keeps up with inflation it is likely that the peak production will occur before 1967." (Davis distinguishes between production and capacity in his calculations. His capacity figures were used in Table 101 and therefore do not correspond with the production figures quoted here.)

In column 6 of Table 101, the estimates of future production are compared on the basis of implied or explicitly stated reserves. The latter, noted by an asterisk, are the figures for ultimate reserves (referred to by some of the authors as total cumulative production through time) from which the production estimates are derived or with which they are associated. With the remaining estimates, for which no explicit reserve figure is stated, a straight-line growth in production was assumed from 1959 to the terminal year or between intermediate years, if noted, and an allowance of a ratio of 10 between proved reserves and production was made for the terminal year.[26] This figure was added to cumulative production as of the end of 1959. The straight-line growth and reserve-production ratio are, of course, wholly arbitrary assumptions, and are used solely as a simple means of obtaining, on a uniform basis, some idea of the *minimum* total reserves through time required by the respective production estimates.

In addition to the foregoing primary production-capacity estimates, there is a single estimate of future secondary production by itself. Sweeney has taken Torrey's 1955 estimates of secondary reserves and resources and constructed a decline curve linked to the Pogue and Hill decline curve for primary production. "The peak water-flood production was estimated as an approximate 25 per cent of the total production at that time. This point was predicted to occur shortly after the total production had reached a peak when new discoveries would be insufficient to maintain the rate of production. If the present growth of water flood is extrapolated, this peak could be achieved as early as 1965. However, a less optimistic rate of increase was assumed so that this peak was reached in 1980. The total annual production at that time from the curve prepared by Pogue and Hill is 3,000,000 bbl. [*sic*]. The peak annual water-flood production is then 750,000,000 bbl."[27]

.   .   .

Comparison of Capacity-Production Estimates

Table 102 shows a comparison of 1975 capacity-output estimates and the corresponding ultimate reserves or minimum cumulative discoveries by listing the appropriate figures from columns 5 and 6 of Table 101. The first group of figures in Table 102 consists of estimates of 1975 production or capacity that

[26] Data provided by Swearingen allow the calculation of cumulative total discoveries based on the course of production he specified to the terminal year. The figure in Table 101, column 6, also employs the proved reserve-production ratio of 13 used by Swearingen for that year. Davis does not carry his projection through to ultimate cumulative production, but mentions 150 billion barrels as consistent with his production series.

[27] A. E. Sweeney, Jr., "The Future of Water Flooding in the U.S.," *The Petroleum Engineer*, Vol. 28, No. 5 (May 1956), p. B-82.

TABLE 102. COMPARISON OF 1975 CAPACITY-OUTPUT
ESTIMATES AND CORRESPONDING ULTIMATE RESERVES OR
MINIMUM CUMULATIVE DISCOVERIES

(In billion barrels)

Source	1975 figure	Ultimate reserves	Minimum cumulative discoveries
Group I			
Hill *et al.*	4.0	250	
Lasky	2.6–2.9	250	
Hubbert	2.9	200	
Pogue and Hill	3.2	165	
Hubbert	2.1	150	
PMPC	2.9		
Davis	2.3	150	131
Ayres	2.0	140	
PMPC	1.8		123
Group II			
Cadle	4.1		156
AIME	4.1		156
Ion	4.0		153
Ion	3.0–3.7		136–149
PMPC	3.6		147

Group I: Production peak 1975 or earlier.
Group II: No production peak expectation by 1975.

SOURCE: Table 101.

are accompanied by the expectation of a production peak in the period through
1975. The estimates in the second group do not carry that expectation.[28]

Except for the PMPC estimates, all those in Group I are associated with a
specific ultimate-reserve estimate, and the figures for 1975 were obtained by
means of the decline-curve approach or its equivalent. The essential difference
between the two groups, as expressed in the expectation or nonexpectation of a
production peak, is the assumption that resources either will or will not exercise
a limit to the growth in production (at more or less constant real costs) within
the period through 1975.

Not only is the decline-curve approach utilized by almost all the estimators
in the first group, but it is the preponderant basis for all estimates of future oil
production. Such popularity seems to result from the fact that the approach
has a seductive simplicity that masks its fundamental fallacies. The simplicity
in turn derives from the neatness of its *ex post* application. That is, the production record of an exhausted field, when charted, typically describes a rise
to a peak and a subsequent protracted decline to zero. Of course, the nearer a
field is to the end of production, the more accurate will be the estimate of total
cumulative production (that is, ultimate reserves on the aggregate level) and

[28] The unexplained estimate of Egloff in Table 101 is omitted from Table 102.

the level of production throughout the remainder of the producing life. But by the same token, the earlier the point of estimation is in the life history of the field, the less accurate will be the assumption as to total cumulative production and the wider the range of possible production for any given year in the future. To put it another way, unless the production cycle has proceeded well toward its end the estimator can never be certain where he stands on the cycle, especially if it is still in the growth phase. This point is well illustrated in Tables 101 and 102 by the wide range of estimates for a given year and by the change of given estimates in the light of a slightly longer production record.

A second major shortcoming of the decline-curve technique is its exclusion of technological change. This is embodied in the assumption of a given magnitude of ultimate reserves, based on the proved-reserve concept—hence, current technology. It is paradoxical that the devotees of the decline curve ignore in the basis of their analogy—the curve for the individual field—the abundant evidence that the premise of a unique curve is false. Many fields show two or even more peaks in their production record, the result of secondary recovery or the discovery and exploitation of deeper reservoirs. These events are essentially the application of improved technology. (Ayres even displays such curves and discusses their basis, but denies that this aspect of the analogy can be carried from the individual field to the national aggregate.)[29] An observer of the production record as it climbed to the first peak, however, would falsely conclude from the record that there would be only a single cycle. This is not to argue the likelihood or even possibility of multiple cycles in the aggregate production record, but as noted in the discussion of the reserve-resource estimates, the static treatment of technology is inconsistent with any consideration of the future.

Still another serious shortcoming of the decline-curve technique is the fallacious assumption that on the aggregate level (that is, in dealing with national production) the resource position is the only significant determinant of production. This ignores the fact that demand, the level of imports, and the relative prices of substitute fuels are actually more important than the resource position in determining the level of production in any year or period such as a decade. This means that even with a given resource position the course of production over time will be influenced by the level of preceding production. For example, a low level of demand (due, for instance, to a decline in economic activity), a high level of imports, or lower prices of substitute fuels in the near future would, even within the internal logic of the decline curve, affect the nature and the timing of the production peak and the period of decline. Thus, with a given resource position the peak could be postponed, it could be higher, and the period of decline longer.

In addition to the conceptual flaws in the decline-curve approach, there are also errors in the derivation and use of the curve itself. The curve is often

[29] E. Ayres and C. A. Scarlott, *Energy Sources—The Wealth of the World* (New York: McGraw-Hill Book Co., 1952), pp. 35–36.

drawn, for example, with perfect symmetry and rounded peak, in seeming confusión with the normal distribution curve; yet the examples of individual fields show that wide variation is possible. The decline curve is, in short, the kind of mechanical extrapolation of statistics which this study seeks to avoid. Indeed, the more rigid mathematical pursuit of the technique employed by some of its proponents implies that the results are more unqualified predictions than forecasts.

The Davis estimates, as the product of the most refined statistical approach to the projection of crude oil production and capacity yet attempted, warrant individual consideration. Although a point-by-point analysis and criticism of the Davis technique could be made, a discussion of a few of his major premises and procedures should suffice to demonstrate its shortcomings for present purposes.

Davis' fundamental datum is the "drilling return," or "the ratio of total reserve additions to total footage drilled in all wells."[30] He notes that the drilling return has been generally declining since 1930; this decline is a "critical fact" on which he bases all his calculations and conclusions. Now, the declining trend in the data cannot be denied, but there are several reasons for regarding them as an unsuitable measure of the actual results of the search for oil. In the first place, the figures on drilling return are tied to the proved-reserve concept. This means that potential secondary reserves (where secondary operations are economically feasible but facilities are not yet provided) are not covered. A considerable portion of yearly additions to reserves, moreover, are what are known as "revisions"—changes in reserves due to more knowledge of specific reservoir conditions—and these are not necessarily related to drilling activity. And on yet another score, the data on drilling return are considerably affected by unitization (unified development of an oil pool through co-operation by the several owners of surface rights) and state conservation practices requiring wider spacing. Both these factors tend to reduce "overdrilling" within the limits of a pool, with its depressing effect on the drilling-return data. In sum, too many determinants of the drilling return are ignored to allow it to be considered as an accurate measure in terms of available data, and there are indications that it significantly understates the actual drilling return.

A second weakness of the Davis approach is the assumed relation of the drilling return to ultimate reserves. "It is reasonable to expect," says Davis, "that as more reserves are developed, there are less left to develop and the effort required to find and develop a barrel of oil increases."[31] In a sense, this is the decline-curve concept, and just as in the application of that concept the logical jump is too great. It must be proved that the declining drilling return, as measured, is an indication of more than the fact that diminishing returns may be appearing *among the oil prospects that can currently be located*. It assumes that

[30] W. Davis, "Future Productive Capacity and Probable Reserves of the U.S.," *Oil and Gas Journal*, Vol. LVI, No. 8 (February 24, 1958), p. 106.

[31] *Ibid.*

there are no other oil habitats than those currently being probed, and equates current discovery ability with the actual limits of oil occurrence.

A third comment concerns the downward bias that seems to be built into the calculating procedure. The procedure works back for each year from annual production to annual reserve additions, assuming in each of seven stages of calculation the same quantitative or causal relationship that currently prevails in the statistics. Since the projection is built cumulatively, on a year-to-year basis, even a slight downward bias in the original assumptions (and it is suggested that one is present in the drilling return) becomes absolutely larger through time and its effect on the results, being cumulative, increases geometrically.

Finally, it should be observed that Davis is the only estimator who specifically takes price into account. It is done, however, by the extrapolation and simultaneous manipulation of no less than six separate relationships between costs, price, and drilling activity. This is, in essence, the same rigid employment of statistics in which the decline-curve approach goes astray.

The current popularity of the decline curve justifies the emphasis placed here on its shortcomings in principle and in interpretation, although such criticism casts doubts on the usefulness of nearly all the estimates in Group I of Table 102. At the same time, however, with respect to the figures in Group II, it must be recognized that it is all too easy to ignore the possibility of resource limitations and to assume, in effect, infinite reserves. The estimate then refers more to potential demand, given the corresponding availability on the supply side. Some of the estimates in the second group do, perhaps, have such an "infinite reserve" flavor.

The foregoing discussion may seem to suggest that the present study will provide a "better" estimate than any that has been made heretofore. But there is no such thing as a "true" or "correct" estimate of the future. Any of the figures in Tables 98 through 102 could turn out to be the same as those that will develop historically, yet the actual occurrence of such figures could be for reasons quite different from those in the mind of the estimator. As stated in the Introduction and Summary, the intention of the analysis is not to match a new estimate with existing ones but to build on the latter in the light of considerations that have not, in the opinion of the author, received sufficient acknowledgment or emphasis. The use of the multiplication factor on reserves, for example, is a recognition of technological improvements in recovery that can now be expected, as will be demonstrated. Likewise, in attempting to judge the reasonable expectations with respect to availability in 1975, it is appropriate to examine the indicated significance of technology as a determinant of future domestic crude oil availability.

TECHNOLOGY AS A DETERMINANT OF FUTURE AVAILABILITY

It was inferred from current opinion, in column 4 of Table 100, that some-where between 100 billion and 500 billion barrels of oil remain to be discovered. Unless and until this oil is discovered, however, it might as well not exist. What are the prospects that the bulk of undiscovered oil will in fact be found?

.   .   .

Discovery Technology

Discussions of future discovery prospects tend to produce a welter of statistics concerning the ratio of successful holes to dry holes, and oil discovered per exploratory well, per foot drilled, and the like. Such statistics cannot be wholly ignored, but it is all too easy to become preoccupied with trend projections, instead of focusing on the determinants of the future behavior of the variables. The proved-reserve concept, moreover, again confuses matters, since discovery, when defined in relation to it, includes additions to proved reserves in both known and newly found reservoirs. This, in turn, makes it difficult to define discovery in relation to time (that is, oil added to proved reserves in one year may be in a reservoir actually discovered in a previous year). In short, the use of statistical evidence in the manner cited involves an a priori assumption of the continuation of present trends and the exclusion of further technological progress.

An example of such use of statistics is found in a recent study which projects the following percentage declines between 1945 and 1965: oil discovered per exploratory well, 67 per cent; oil discovered per oil well drilled, 50 per cent; oil discovered per foot of hole drilled, 67 per cent.[32] The statistical evidence can be recognized, however, without becoming involved in trend projection and detailed data. It is sufficient to observe that according to the evidence, oil is currently becoming more difficult to find, in the sense that more preliminary work is needed to find favorable geologic circumstances, and the average depth of newly found reservoirs is increasing.

To some observers (Davis, for example), this is in itself an indication of scraping the bottom of the barrel, a warning that the finite limit of actual resources in the ground is being approached. Such argument implies that current technology is approaching the limit of human capability to probe all the possible physical locations of oil under the area of the United States and the adjacent continental shelf—that no oil exists beyond where we may be tempted to look with present technology. But the possible relation of discovery rates to resource limitations is at best tenuous. Discoveries of proved reserves thus far have tended to increase in proportion with annual production.[33]

[32] K. E. Hill, H. D. Hammar, and J. G. Winger, *Future Growth of the World Petroleum Industry* (New York: Chase Manhattan Bank, 1957). Presented at meeting of American Petroleum Institute Division of Production, Rocky Mountain District, Casper, Wyoming, April 25, 1957.

[33] Gonzales, *op. cit.*, pp. 64–69.

The argument is meaningful, however, if stated in relation to economic and technological circumstances. A declining success level in the search for oil may indicate that the limit of oil discoverable with current technology at current costs is being approached. But there are strong reasons for believing that even this is unlikely. In the first place, a large portion of the area of the United States is geologically favorable to potential oil production but has not been given the intensive exploration and development effort of present and past producing "provinces." In 1951, it was estimated that this area was some 100 times greater than the area proved productive to date.[34] Of course, this does not mean that the ultimate productive area in the United States will necessarily be increased by a hundred-fold, fifty-fold, or even ten-fold. It does mean, however, that there is plenty of room in which the continued search for oil is justified.

Among the relatively unexplored areas, the possibilities of the continental shelf are generally acknowledged to be extraordinarily good. "A factor which gives added assurance of the ultimate high productivity of the continental shelf regions is that throughout most of their extent they consist of and are a part of the Tertiary sequence of rocks. These . . . have accounted for over 60 per cent of all the past petroleum discoveries. They are generally soft rocks, easily folded and deformed into traps, and they are high in organic content. They have suffered less erosion than the older rocks which may account in part for their higher productivity. For reasons such as these, they are much favored geologically."[35]

At the same time, it is questionable whether the possibilities of known productive areas are being exhausted. According to one claim "there is no evidence that old areas respond to exploratory effort any less than new ones."[36] In any

[34] Committee on Oil and Gas Availability, *Petroleum Productive Capacity* (Washington, D. C.: National Petroleum Council, 1952), pp. 9, 10, 85–93; see also, D. D. Moore, *Role of Technology in the Future of Petroleum*, unpublished report by Battelle Memorial Institute to the President's Materials Policy Commission, September 15, 1951, p. 10. According to Moore, "the vast bulk of reserves are in a very few large fields comprising roughly 1,900 square miles, or only two-tenths of one per cent of the favorable area." There is some ambiguity, however, as to the proved reserves to which Moore refers. Slightly more than one-half of reserves are in "giant fields," that is, those with ultimate reserves of 100 million barrels or more.

[35] A. I. Levorsen, "Estimates of Undiscovered Petroleum Reserves," *Proceedings*, United Nations Scientific Conference on the Conservation and Utilization of Resources, *op. cit.*, p. 97. According to a recent study of the worldwide occurrence of petroleum, 50 per cent of the world's major oil fields (236 fields, excluding the Soviet bloc, with ultimate reserves of more than 100 million barrels each) are of Tertiary age, and account for 38 per cent of total proved reserves. If the influence of the great Middle East fields is excluded, Tertiary fields account for 50 per cent of the remainder, containing 54 per cent of the reserves. See G. M. Knebel and Guillermo Rodriguez-Eraso, "Habitat of Some Oil," *Bulletin of the American Association of Petroleum Geologists*, Vol. 40, No. 4 (April 1956), p. 557.

[36] F. J. Gardner, "Dear John, We're Not Running Out of Oil," *Oil and Gas Journal*, April 18, 1955, p. 251.

event, there has been failure in the past to explore known structures thoroughly, and there has tended to be a preoccupation with some types of geological traps at the expense of other types. Negative results in one portion of a structure, such as the crest of an anticline, have not always been followed up by tests of the flanks. And if it should develop that about three-quarters of all the oil ultimately found in the United States occurred in stratigraphic traps, as one authority believes may be true,[37] then the opportunities for future exploratory work are large indeed, for approximately three-quarters of all exploratory effort to date has been in the search for structural traps.[38] Even in known oil country large favorable areas are not adequately explored and drilled.

A third factor in the probability that resource limits are not being approached is that of depth, which presents possibilities in both known and unexplored areas. It was estimated in 1951 that 80 per cent of all producing fields in the United States had deeper possibilities.[39] It has been observed by Cloninger that, theoretically, oil could occur in sandstones down to 65,260 feet below the surface and in limestones down to 51,300 feet. This would make it possible, says Cloninger, given the necessary source rocks and traps, for oil to be found near the bottom of all favorable sedimentary sections in the United States except the San Joaquin-Sacramento Basin in California, which has an estimated depth of 65,000 to 75,000 feet.[40] This observation cannot be taken too literally, for the influence of depth on such factors as permeability, porosity, temperature, and pressure, as well as purely geological aspects of depth, will affect the incidence of oil in the deep environment. Thus Lees holds that:

> The increase in drilling depths now possible must also lead to many deep discoveries, but not in the ratio of increase of depth. For a number of reasons the depths between 10,000 and 20,000 feet will not be so prolific as were the levels from grass roots to 10,000 feet. In many oil-bearing areas basement rocks are met at lesser depths than 10,000 feet; in deeper levels the productivity per unit volume of pore-space will be less because of surface shrinkage of the crude, and porosity may be somewhat less. Drilling costs to such depths are so much greater that only an expectation of substantial results will justify the costs, and, superimposed on all this, the discovery of deep objectives, is im-

[37] P. L. Lyons, "Future of Geophysics," *Bulletin of the American Association of Petroleum Geologists*, Vol. 39, No. 7 (June 1955), p. 1210.

[38] A. I. Levorsen, "Geologists Are Talking About . . .," *The Petroleum Engineer*, Vol. 28, No. 2 (February 1956), pp. B-39 ff. The Knebel and Rodriguez-Eraso study, *op. cit.*, pp. 553–55, reported that 80 per cent of the oil covered by the study occurs in anticlinal traps, and excluding the Middle East this type of occurrence still accounts for 40 per cent of oil discoveries. By number of fields, 16 per cent are categorized as stratigraphic traps. It is curious in this regard that all the more important stratigraphic fields are in the Western Hemisphere, and most of them in North America. This may, of course, be no more than a reflection of the more intensive exploration in North America. Stratigraphic traps require more effort to locate.

[39] E. Holman, "Oil's Horizons at Mid-Century," *Proceedings*, American Petroleum Institute, Vol. XXXI, No. 1 (1951), p. 34.

[40] J. S. Cloninger, "How Deep Oil or Gas May Be Expected," *op. cit.*, p. 60.

measurably more difficult by both geological and geophysical methods, and the clue of seepage is mostly absent.[41]

But the physical possibilities are largely measured against the relatively limited penetration to date. The fact is, little is really known about the occurrence of oil at depth. Through 1959, only 1,021 wells had been drilled deeper than 15,000 feet (see Table 103) and, as seen in Figure 66, although the depth of the deepest well is growing fairly rapidly, the average of all wells deeper than 15,000 feet is more or less constant. The bulk of proved reserves, moreover, are shallow. Of the proved reserves in the free world, 44 per cent are at depths of 4,000 feet or less and 84 per cent at 7,000 feet or less, and—excluding the large influence of the Middle East reserves on the total—56 per cent of the remaining free world proved reserves are at 4,000 feet or less and 88 per cent at 7,000 feet or less (see Table 104 and Figure 67).

The compilers of Table 104 observe: "It is to be expected that the deeper picture will probably improve with time as more and deeper wildcats are drilled. However, this is the depth habitat of oil as it is known today. There must be some reason for the occurrence of the bulk of our oil, 85 per cent, at depths between 2,000 and 8,000 feet."[42] It would seem that the reason sought for the pattern of depth distribution may be largely supplied by the authors themselves.

TABLE 103. WELLS DEEPER THAN 15,000 FEET DRILLED THROUGH 1959

Year	Number of deep wells by date of completion		Average depth of deep wells drilled (feet)	Deepest well drilled to date (feet)
	Total	Wildcat		
1938	1	1	15,004	15,004
1944	1	1	15,279	15,279
1945	3	3	15,870	16,655
1946	1	1	15,452	16,655
1947	8	8	15,891	17,823
1948	7	6	16,047	17,823
1949	11	8	16,421	20,521
1950	5	2	15,713	20,521
1951	12	5	15,822	20,521
1952	25	17	15,874	20,521
1953	26	14	16,117	21,482
1954	58	30	15,929	21,482
1955	101	64	16,031	22,559
1956	154	77	15,988	22,559
1957	189	116	16,064	22,559
1958	191	134	16,019	25,340
1959	228	142	16,056	25,340

SOURCE: E. Adams, "Deep Drilling Finds Deep Production" (14th Annual Deep Well Survey), *The Petroleum Engineer*, Vol. 32, No. 3 (March 1960), p. B–20.

[41] G. M. Lees, "Review of Techniques for Oil and Gas Discovery," *Proceedings*, United Nations Scientific Conference on Conservation and Utilization of Resources, Vol. III (New York: United Nations, 1951), p. 5.

[42] Knebel and Rodriguez-Eraso, *op. cit.*, p. 559.

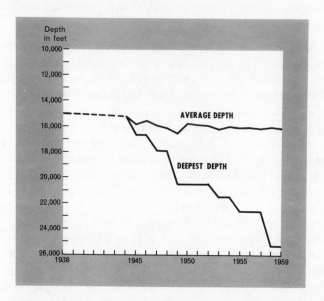

Figure 66.   Average depth and greatest depth of wells drilled below 15,000 feet, 1938–59.

TABLE 104.   SUBSURFACE DEPTH OF OCCURRENCE OF OIL IN THE MAJOR OIL FIELDS OF THE FREE WORLD

Depth range (feet)	Total free world		Free world except Middle East	
	Per cent of reserves in each depth range	Per cent of fields in each depth range	Per cent of reserves in each depth range	Per cent of fields in each depth range
1,000 and under .	1.5	4.7	3.9	4.8
1,000–2,000	6.2	9.4	13.3	9.6
2,000–3,000	10.2	12.9	18.0	13.1
3,000–4,000	26.2	13.7	20.9	14.2
4,000–5,000	16.8	13.5	10.6	13.6
5,000–6,000	9.5	12.1	13.6	11.5
6,000–7,000	14.0	9.9	8.0	9.6
7,000–8,000	8.5	7.9	5.4	7.3
8,000–9,000	3.5	6.3	2.5	6.2
9,000–10,000	1.6	3.5	1.7	3.7
10,000–11,000	1.5	3.8	1.3	3.8
11,000–12,000	0.4	1.8	0.4	1.9
12,000 and over . .	0.1	0.5	0.4	0.7

SOURCE: G. M. Knebel and Guillermo Rodriguez-Eraso, "Habitat of Some Oil," *Bulletin of the American Association of Petroleum Geologists*, Vol. 40, No. 4 (April 1956), p. 560.

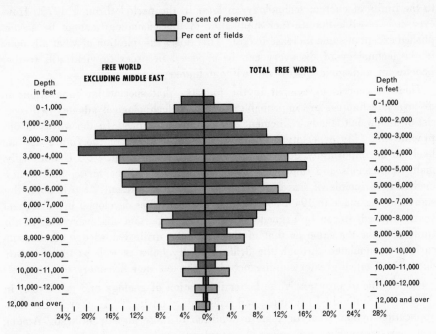

Figure 67. World oil reserves by depth of occurrence.

The pattern is only a reflection of present knowledge. Until the record of deep drilling has proved otherwise the potential of deeper oil occurrence cannot be arbitrarily minimized.

Still another factor is the oil potential in unorthodox sources. Thus, Levorsen argues that full-scale discovery efforts should be made on such currently novel sources as pre-Cambrian and basement rocks, crystalline rocks, volcanics, and continental (or fresh-water) deposits. All these sources have yielded reservoirs where conditions were favorable; all are present in large volumes and have been tested in relatively few places. Levorsen also points out that Cambrian rocks, in addition, seem to represent almost ideal potential reservoir conditions, nor has it yet been proved that no oil was formed in Cambrian rocks during the Cambrian period. Moreover, many traps do not reach up into younger rocks, hence many Cambrian traps are not yet tested. Levorsen concludes that whether or not the Cambrian are, or can be, source rocks, their large-scale occurrence, permeability, and many large untested traps offer the "extremely inviting possibility that the Cambrian will become the next great producing system in the U.S. and Canada."[43]

There seems to be no reason to believe, in view of the many unexploited or partially exploited opportunities, that discovery will be hampered by approach

[43] A. I. Levorsen, "Where Will Tomorrow's Oil Be Found?" *World Oil,* Vol. 140, No. 5 (April 1955), pp. 76–81.

to the limits of current technology, at least in the period through 1975. However, it is possible that further application of this technology cannot be accomplished except at some increase in cost. This raises the question of what advances in the technology of discovery can be expected in order to yield still further benefits in additional discoveries without higher costs.

There is general agreement in the industry that spectacular innovations in discovery techniques are improbable; or rather, technological advance will consist of a slow but steady refinement of existing techniques. In the words of one practitioner, "My expectation is that the discovery tools of the future are not likely to be importantly different from those of the present. . . . Undoubtedly, many refinements and improvements of all methods will be made, but no new method or principle of search is remotely in sight at present."[44] Although this statement was made in 1949, no evidence to refute it has developed in subsequent years. Indeed, it can be argued that the most important discovery tool of the future will be the same as that of the past—the drill. Knowledge of the subsurface accumulated through the drilling of dry holes as well as through producers is of much greater significance than possible new discovery techniques.[45]

One avenue of progress is the better integration of geology and geophysics in the study of individual provinces and sedimentary basins.[46] Another is the wider application of new analytic tools in addition to those already utilized. Among such new approaches are micro-photogeology, remapping of surface structure on small contour intervals, stratigraphic correlation by continuous velocity logging and pollen and spore analysis, the magnetic recording of seismic data, and the applied study of regional geologic history.[47] Not all such progress in discovery techniques will yield lower costs, to be sure, but the significant point is that discovery technology, although currently being strained to maintain the necessary pace, is still open-ended with currently foreseen improvements. The reasonable expectation is that future discovery technology will contribute to the finding of oil where present technology is unable to do so.

·   ·   ·

Drilling and Production Technology

With the mounting evidence that future production will mean an ever greater number of wells, including those for exploration, drilled deeper and under more difficult conditions (such as offshore location), there is increasing pressure on

[44] Lees, op. cit.; see also A. I. Levorsen, "Outlook for Petroleum Exploration," Paper 23, Section I, Fifth World Petroleum Congress, New York, May 30–June 5, 1959.

[45] E. B. Noble, World Oil, Vol. 140, No. 5 (April 1955), p. 83.

[46] P. R. Schultz, "Oil Discovery Trends," Bulletin of the American Association of Petroleum Geologists, Vol. 37, No. 7 (July 1953), p. 1574; and C. S. Shenkel, Jr., "Superposed Geologic Data as an Exploration Tool," paper given at meeting of American Association of Petroleum Geologists, Chicago, April 25, 1956. (Abstract in Bulletin of the American Association of Petroleum Geologists, Vol. 40, No. 2 (February 1956), p. 428.)

[47] A. I. Levorsen, "Geologists are Talking About . . .," op. cit., pp. B-39 ff.

the oil industry to develop better, more efficient, and hence less costly, drilling techniques. Recent important advances have been made with the development of jet drilling, which utilizes high-velocity jet streams of the drilling fluid at the bit head for efficient removal of cuttings; new bit designs for hard formations; improved drilling mud additives that lengthen bit life and reduce friction; and the use of water, gas, or air as the drilling "fluid." These new techniques and equipment have made possible spectacular increases in rate of penetration and have brought consequent drilling economies. With perfection of the new techniques and knowledge of their limitations, their general adoption should aid the drilling of more and deeper wells.

A new approach using conventional equipment that is being adopted on an increasing scale is "slim-hole" drilling. This technique uses equipment of smaller size to provide a hole of smaller diameter than is used in conventional practice. Dramatic cost savings have been reported. Although the limitations on slim-hole work are still being defined, it seems apparent that the major benefit of slim holes will be in exploratory rather than development wells. Nevertheless, it is reasonable to expect that the slim-hole technique will be adopted to the limit of its usefulness, with consequent benefits of increased footage and lower cost.

More radical departures from conventional practices, currently in the development stage, are such techniques as sonic drilling, percussion drilling, and the turbodrill. The conventional technique imparts a rotary motion to a drill bit on the end of a string of pipe by rotating the pipe at the surface. When the length of pipe reaches several miles the stresses to which it is subjected are very great, necessitating the use of the highest grade steel. At the same time, the efficiency of energy transmission through the length of pipe falls off seriously due to the high frictional losses down the hole.

All three of the new approaches employ a self-contained unit at the bottom of the hole, thus reducing or eliminating energy losses between the surface and the bottom. Sonic drilling utilizes a transducer just above the drill bit to translate sonic frequencies (about 300 cycles per second) into mechanical vibrations of the drill bit. Experimentation with this technique is currently in progress.

The percussion drill makes use of a reciprocating hammer unit (similar in principle to the pneumatic drill) operated by the circulating drilling mud at the bottom of the hole to drive a conventional bit into the rock. At the same time the bit is rotated at a comparatively slow speed, as in pneumatic drilling. Originally developed for use in excessively hard formations, the method shows promise for more general use. Penetration rates have been increased by 25 to 50 per cent and at the same time bit life has been prolonged by as much as three times.[48] This percussion technique has already reached the licensing stage.

[48] *The Petroleum Engineer*, Vol. 29, No. 7 (July, 1957), pp. B-32–34; also *Petroleum Week*, June 7, 1957, p. 12.

The turbodrill principle also employs a self-contained unit at the bottom of the hole, consisting of the bit and a turbine to rotate it. Fluid circulated through the pipe from the surface supplies the motive force to operate the turbine. The U.S. oil industry experimented sporadically with the turbodrill for more than thirty years without real success, which is perhaps explained by the lack of real need for its development. In 1956, however, the principle received wide attention because of the introduction of a Russian version of the turbodrill into this country. The glowing claims made for the Russian equipment served to remind the U.S. industry of the significant possibilities of the turbodrill in the light of future drilling requirements and circumstances. Subsequent developments involving both Russian-designed and French-designed equipment indicate the early introduction of the method into U.S. operations. Probable intensification of the pressure for improvement in drilling methods makes it likely that the potentialities of the turbodrill will be thoroughly exploited in this country during the coming two decades,[49] especially since the relative advantage of the turbodrill increases with depth.

There is now being voiced within the industry the sentiment that the efficiency and capability of existing equipment and methods are being strained to the limit. Radical new approaches are being discussed that would eliminate entirely the conventional derrick and would revolutionize almost every surface operation in drilling.[50] This is significant not as an indication of dramatic developments in the near future but as evidence that the industry will respond, with technological advances, to the greater drilling demands of the coming decades.[51]

A host of special drilling problems are raised by offshore operations, where the chief difficulty is the provision of a base or platform from which to do the drilling. As brought out in the discussion of resources earlier in this study, an important fraction of total resources is believed to lie under the continental shelf—but the shelf extends to a depth of 600 feet under water. Can the shelf areas be exploited to a sufficient degree to yield significant supply benefits?

The answer would appear to be an almost unqualified "yes." The pace of progress to date in surmounting the obstacles to offshore operations has been truly astounding. Only a few years ago, a depth of about 100 feet of water seemed to be the foreseeable limit to offshore drilling. Artificial islands, submersible barges, and platforms were thought to be limited to such relatively shallow depths. By 1956, however, mobile platforms were being designed for use in 300 feet of water; and the complete solution of the depth problem is

[49] J. A. LeVelle, "An Engineer's Look at Turbine Drilling," *The Petroleum Engineer*, Vol. 28, No. 11 (October 1956), pp. B-39-44.

[50] T. A. Huber, "The Challenge in Oil Field Mechanical Development," *The Petroleum Engineer*, Vol. 30, No. 8 (July 15, 1958), p. B-26. See also *Petroleum Week*, June 8, 1956, p. 18.

[51] See J. A. LeVelle, "New Concepts Spark Drilling Developments," *The Petroleum Engineer*, Vol. 29, No. 8 (July 15, 1957), pp. B-39-40; also Huber, *op. cit.*, and *Oil and Gas Journal*, Vol. 57, No. 46 (November 9, 1959), pp. 126-29.

now all but assured with the development of floating rigs that are already being used to obtain stratigraphic information through such drilling. Again, this is not to say that producing oil fields on the edge of the continental shelf will be a feature of the near future. One can conclude, however, that the full *potential* of the petroleum resources under the continental shelf is likely to be within reach for exploitation, if economic circumstances call for it.

There is good evidence that onshore, at least, technological advances in drilling have been holding the line against the increased costs of drilling at greater depth. Industry-sponsored studies of drilling costs in 1953, 1955, and 1956 reveal the following (the 1954 figures are from the *Census of Mineral Industries*, as used in the 1959 industry report) :[52]

Year	Average cost per well	Average cost per foot drilled
1956	$50,200	$12.35
1955	46,500	11.55
1954	46,300	11.03
1953	50,200	12.43

In constant dollar terms (that is, deflated by the Bureau of Labor Statistics Wholesale Price Index) the showing of technology is even better:

Year	Average cost per well (1953 $)	Average cost per foot drilled (1953 $)
1956	$48,400	$11.90
1955	46,300	11.49
1954	46,200	11.01
1953	50,200	12.43

The *Joint Association Survey* notes that in the light of better data for the years 1955 and 1956 "it now appears that the actual expenditures and costs per well were about 6 per cent less than were first estimated for that year [1953]." Taking this adjustment into account, the 1953 figure becomes $47,200, and the change from 1953 to 1956 is an increase of 2.5 per cent. Such a short period, it should be observed, offers small grounds on which to draw conclusions as to developments over the longer term, but even a substantial increase within a few years would not necessarily indicate inevitably rising costs over the coming years. Costs *could* get out of line in the short term and still not be inconsistent with the expectation that the long-term progress in technology would later be able to catch up.

Deep drilling has yet to exert a significant influence on the average depth of all new wells being drilled, but it is likely that the rate of increase in the

[52] American Petroleum Institute, Mid-Continent Oil and Gas Association, and Independent Petroleum Association of America, *Joint Association Survey of Industry Drilling Costs—1955 and 1956* (1959, mimeo.) ; *ibid., 1953* (1955, mimeo.) ; see also D. Ragland, "The Effect of Modern Drilling Technology on Well Cost," *Drilling and Production Practice—1956* (New York: American Petroleum Institute, 1957), pp. 146–47; and Huber, *op. cit.*

average depth of new wells will accelerate in the future. In Ragland's opinion, a further increase of 11 per cent in average depth of new wells, reflecting a larger proportion of deep wells, could raise well costs by almost 75 per cent in the absence of continued technological progress. But the greatest benefits of such progress to date, he observes, have accrued at depth. According to Ragland, in the period 1950–55, in constant dollar terms, "total well costs decreased from 10 per cent for 3,000-foot wells to about 40 per cent for wells in the 15,000-foot depth range."[53] It would be, perhaps, too much to expect that the average depth of new wells can continue to increase indefinitely at little or no increase in cost, but the achievement of technology to date is reasonable ground for assuming, at worst, only a modest cost increase in the period through 1975.

Although petroleum production includes several aspects in addition to drilling, the only other aspect of real significance in the present context is recovery. The currently mounting discovery difficulties and costs have caused the oil industry to give great attention in recent years to possibilities of increased recovery. The known secondary resources carry no discovery costs, and increased recovery from future oil discoveries would lower the discovery costs per unit of oil production. The accumulation of knowledge by the industry in its production activities has gradually given it an understanding of the physical nature of underground oil reservoirs and of the forces present in those reservoirs. "Reservoir engineering" has spurred the trend toward operation of a reservoir as a unit, making possible maximum utilization of the energy within the reservoir to produce oil at the surface. The maintenance of reservoir pressure is now a common practice, and in the postwar period there has been a very rapid growth of water injection projects to drive the oil out of the reservoir rock. Along with these developments has come the establishment of state conservation bodies to encourage and even enforce such practices.

The basic determinants of recovery with any technique are: (1) properties of the reservoir rock, (2) properties of the crude oil, and (3) reservoir structure (including depth, dimensions, and attitude). Thus, even without the addition of such variables as the degree of primary depletion and the type of secondary-recovery technique, the problems and potentials of increased recovery vary greatly between reservoirs. It is nevertheless possible to generalize. On the average, waterflooding increases total recovery to about 50 per cent of the original oil in place.[54]

Much higher recovery possibilities are indicated by current research and development with new techniques. Thus, what has been termed "improved gas drive" or "solvent flooding" (involving the injection of either natural gas under very high pressure, natural gas "enriched" with ethane, propane, and

[53] Ragland, op. cit., p. 147.

[54] G. Roberts, Jr., "Applications and Limitations of Fluid Injection for Oil Recovery," Proceedings, Eleventh Oil Recovery Conference, Bulletin 67 (Austin: Texas Petroleum Research Committee, 1958), p. 68.

butane in proper proportions, or the latter three components directly) may allow as much as 70 per cent recovery, on the average, of the original oil in place;[55] and under appropriate conditions can give total recovery.[56] The most recent avenue of research to be opened up is *in situ* combustion, or "fireflooding," in which the burning of part (some 10 per cent) of the oil in place vaporizes, cracks, and generally reduces the viscosity of the remaining oil and permits its recovery. This is especially applicable to highly viscous crude which, in the most extreme circumstances, may be totally unrecoverable by other means. Recovery levels through thermal techniques may equal or exceed those obtainable with "improved gas methods."[57]

Torrey has estimated that as of January 1, 1960, a total of 234 billion barrels of oil would remain unrecovered after primary production.[58] The new techniques now in sight would, of course, be applicable not only to these known resources but also to the indeterminate secondary portion of the 200–300 billion barrels of undiscovered oil included in the resource-base estimate made above. Indeed, the distinction between primary and secondary production is already tending to become blurred, as more secondary techniques are applied early in the life of producing reservoirs.[59] But the most significant portion of secondary resources is the 234 billion barrels now known to exist. Although future discoveries should contribute to secondary resources that could be exploited in the period through 1975, it is the known resources that can sustain a rapid exploitation of new secondary-recovery techniques and which could contribute an explosive boost to total yearly crude oil production.

Expert opinion can be found on both sides of the question of whether the possibilities of increased recovery favor a rapid expansion in output. One of the trade journals, for example, makes the following comments on the miscible phase displacement technique, in the same issue that carries an enthusiastic description of it:

> There will be limitations, to be sure. In most instances, . . . propane and ethane will be required to make up the critical composition of injected gas . . . and, this mixture will vary from reservoir to reservoir. Availability of propane and ethane in adequate quantities will be a controlling factor . . . which means that the oil field must be located in an area where ample supplies of these vital hydrocarbons are available at an economic advantage. . . .

[55] *Ibid.*, p. 67.

[56] N. J. Clark, W. P. Schultz, and H. M. Shearin, "New Injection Method Affords Total Oil Recovery," *The Petroleum Engineer*, Vol. 28, No. 11 (October 1956), pp. B-45–51.

[57] Eighty per cent recovery has been achieved with the thermal technique. See J. S. McNiel, Jr. and J. T. Moss, "Recent Progress in Oil Recovery by In-Situ Combustion," *Proceedings, Eleventh Oil Recovery Conference, op. cit.*, pp. 84–99. Another investigator observes that although 90 per cent recovery is theoretically possible, "the practical limit may turn out to be somewhere around 65 per cent." See J. S. Breston, "Oil Recovery by Heat from *In Situ* Combustion," *Journal of Petroleum Technology*, Vol. X, No. 8 (August 1958), p. 17.

[58] Torrey, *op. cit.* See p. 353, above.

[59] See *Petroleum Week*, July 18, 1958, pp. 54–62.

It is not likely that all this will transpire overnight, but will require costly experimentation in both the laboratory and field, as well as take considerable time for individual reservoir study to select the best prospects. Waterflooding took a mighty long time to find widespread application. No doubt, the condensing gas drive process, too, will be around for some time before it is as well known as waterflooding is today.[60]

Hubbert also foresees a rise in the recovery level but contends that this could not yield results of much importance. "Because of the slowness of the secondary recovery process . . . it appears unlikely that any improvement that can be made within the next 10 or 15 years can have any significant effect" upon the historical peak of production. The more likely result, he thinks, will be to reduce the rate of decline after culmination of production at the peaks he projects.[61] Similarly, Hill *et al.* note that such advancements in technique as pressure maintenance and secondary-recovery methods "tend chiefly to arrest production decline rather than increase output."[62]

On the other hand, the secondary-reserve estimates given in Table 98 show considerable optimism regarding secondary prospects, and articles by industry experts are beginning to carry allusions to the large possibilities of increased recovery that are now opening up. The experts (perhaps because they are experts) do not exhibit the temerity of the present study in essaying a quantitative estimate of these possibilities. But Pratt, for example, observes that "the industry is not content to continue to leave 60 per cent [assuming 40 per cent recovery] . . . of its oil in the ground. The reward for more efficient recovery is too great. . . . Much greater recoveries are certain to be achieved."[63] And Gonzalez comments that "unitization and pressure maintenance projects and other significant new developments may mean much higher rates of recovery in future than in the past."[64] Finally, Torrey, the outstanding authority on secondary recovery, observes: "A realistic appraisal of the effect of improved recovery technology might be that sufficient additional oil will be produced by this means during the next 20 years to *in large measure* supplement the anticipated increased demand."[65] (Italics added.)

In adopting the view of the optimists among the experts, certain specific points can be made in argument against the opposing views that have been cited. To answer the quotation from *The Petroleum Engineer*, there are certain differences between the circumstances surrounding the growth of waterflooding and those in which the new techniques can be expected to develop. The full

[60] *The Petroleum Engineer*, Vol. 28, No. 11 (October 1956), p. B-45.

[61] M. K. Hubbert, "Nuclear Energy and the Fossil Fuels," *Drilling and Production Practice—1956* (New York: American Petroleum Institute, 1957), p. 18.

[62] Hill *et al., op. cit.*

[63] W. E. Pratt, "A Geologist's Long-Term Forecast of Petroleum Supply," paper given before Pacific Section, American Association of Petroleum Geologists, Los Angeles, November 9, 1956.

[64] Gonzalez, *op. cit.*, p. 66.

[65] P. D. Torrey, "Oil Resources of the United States," *The Oil and Gas Compact Bulletin*, Vol. XIV, No. 1 (June 1955), p. 49.

benefits of waterflooding are coming through the advanced state of knowledge of reservoir engineering. The technological environment for the new methods is thus far more favorable at the initial stage; they can be developed more rapidly, given sufficient stimulus. Such stimulus will arise from the pressures on the oil industry to keep pace with a demand that is already large and gives evidence of growing in the future at an accelerating pace. Because of the constantly larger quantities involved, there is a much stronger incentive to develop and apply new techniques than was true when waterflooding began its recent growth. If a given effort expended on secondary recovery will yield greater, more certain, and quicker results than the same effort devoted to discovery, it can be expected that the oil industry will pursue this advantage on a large scale.[66] And, what may be most important, the 234 billion barrels of oil in the ground offer attractive cost advantages. Secondary oil is, of course, not free, but the cost of secondary operations must be measured against the costs of discovering new oil. Even with equivalent costs, the absence of the discovery risk in secondary oil should certainly tip the balance.

Hubbert's argument concerns the possible magnitude and pace of the secondary operations themselves rather than the development of techniques. But the secondary-recovery process is not slow, as he contends. On the contrary, it is much more rapid than that of primary recovery. Most secondary projects have a life of eight to twelve years, whereas the regulated primary production from many existing fields is over a period from five to ten times longer.[67] Indeed, the very decline curves cited by Hubbert show the high peak output attainable shortly after the application of secondary-recovery techniques to a given reservoir. Even if production restrictions were extended to secondary operations, the total effect of a widespread simultaneous adoption of a new high-recovery technique could be very large. The total additions to production from hundreds or thousands of individual secondary operations could have a significant effect, over a short period, on total output. Such would be the case if there were an industry rush to take advantage of a highly profitable new technique, and the indications do point to the imminent occurrence of a sudden, large jump in the recovery factor. A doubling, for example, is wholly plausible. A recovery factor of two-thirds as the average for the United States within the next fifteen years or so would be well within the possibilities currently being opened up.[68]

[66] There are already independent operators who specialize in buying up producing fields and applying secondary-production methods. See *Petroleum Week*, August 30, 1957, p. 21, and September 13, 1957, pp. 48–49.

[67] P. D. Torrey in a communication to the author.

[68] See M. B. Spangler, *New Technology and the Supply of Petroleum*, Research Paper No. 2 (Chicago: University of Chicago Program of Education and Research in Planning, 1956), Chap. VIII, for an unusual discussion of future progress in recovery. Spangler concludes that the most probable recovery level in 1975 will be 70 per cent. Although the conclusion is preceded by an elaborate probability analysis presented in obscure terminology, it is in essence a judgment based on an interesting and useful survey of technological possibilities.

CONCLUSIONS ON DOMESTIC CRUDE OIL AVAILABILITY

Before presenting the conclusions on domestic crude oil availability in 1975 it is worth repeating the statements made in Chapter 7: The purpose of the study is not to make projections or forecasts of actual production. The discussion, moreover, is not a technical analysis, offering new basic data from which original estimates can be derived. The conclusions are rather a distillation of expert technical opinion as interpreted in the light of the concepts and assumptions introduced herein.

The following paragraphs present the conclusions on primary and secondary availability separately. Again, it must be observed that supply is not being matched against a given demand. The indicated availability levels may therefore look startlingly high, but it is believed they represent reasonable expectations as to the quantity of crude oil that *could* be forthcoming in 1975 from both primary and secondary operations, at no appreciable increase in constant dollar costs.

.   .   .

Primary Availability

Two major conclusions concerning primary availability can be drawn from the preceding discussion. First, the magnitude of U.S. crude oil resources at current costs is such that there should be no resource limitation on continued growth in primary capacity in the period through 1975. Second, it can be expected that technology will continue to expand the possibilities of probing the environment of oil occurrence so that continued growth in primary capacity can be sustained.

On the basis of these conclusions, a quantitative estimate of primary crude oil availability in 1975 may be adopted from among existing expert opinion as being representative. The first conclusion eliminates from consideration the first group of estimates in Table 102, since their basic assumption of a peak in output before 1975 is incompatible with it. The second places the author among the optimists on future oil discovery prospects. The estimates in the second group of figures in Table 102, which are not based on a resource-limiting assumption, range between 3 and 4.1 billion barrels as the production or capacity in 1975. Of these, the Cadle estimate of 4.1 billion and the high estimate of Ion, of 4 billion barrels, appear to approximate the conclusions reached herein. (The AIME estimate is not a truly independent one but is based on PMPC and Pogue and Hill estimates.) It should be observed that the Ion and Cadle figures as projections of current output implicitly refer to both primary and secondary production. Secondary output in the base years for the projections was a minor percentage of the total, however, and since neither author specifies any disproportionate increase in secondary production their use here for primary alone is not considered to be inconsistent with the authors' intentions. Accordingly, it is concluded that primary domestic crude oil availability in 1975 could be as high as 4 billion barrels, in round numbers.

Again, it should be noted that the choice of a figure equivalent to Ion's estimate and approximating one by Cadle does not mean that these are considered the "best" estimates. Indeed, it will be recalled that Cadle himself describes his figure as a "guess-estimate," and he does not present any systematic justification of it. The Ion and Cadle figures, however, are most consonant with the conclusions stated above and best express the judgment of the present study.

.   .   .

Secondary Availability

The conclusion to be drawn from the discussion of secondary-recovery technology is that the industry is about to enter a period of explosive growth in such recovery. There exists a wide technological opportunity, there is the incentive to exploit that opportunity, and it is likely that there will be a general movement to do so. For these reasons, it is believed that the pace of development and use of the new high-recovery techniques will be rapid, and the level of secondary production in 1975 could be very large compared with the present.

An attempt to quantify these expectations in an estimate of secondary availability in 1975 is more difficult than was true for primary availability. There is, to begin with, no collection of expert estimates upon which to base a judgment in the light of the perspective developed herein. Sweeney's secondary-production estimate is clearly minimal. It is linked with the restrictive Pogue and Hill decline curve for primary output; it is based on secondary-reserve (resource) estimates by Torrey since superseded by larger ones by the same author; and the estimate is itself a product of the decline-curve technique, with its static treatment of technology, the most crucial element in the future of secondary production.

The derivation of an independent estimate of 1975 secondary availability is hampered by the lack of statistics on past and current secondary output. Such statistics are not compiled, but there are available figures for total production from fluid injection operations. In 1953, this output totaled 425 million barrels, and it is estimated that the purely secondary output in that year amounted to some 117 million barrels.[69]

In the absence of any systematic means of arriving at an estimate of 1975 availability, a figure of 2 billion barrels is chosen to indicate the general magnitude by which total annual crude output could be increased by 1975 at no increase in constant dollar costs. The range of error in this estimate is obviously very great, but if the preceding arguments are accepted, the estimate appears to be, if anything, on the conservative side. It should be noted again that this is not a prediction of 2 billion barrels of secondary production in 1975; it is

[69] A. E. Sweeney, Jr., "The Magnitude of Fluid Injection Operations in the U.S.," *The Petroleum Engineer*, Vol. 28, No. 2 (February 1956), pp. B-120, B-125–26.

a judgment as to what *could* be produced if present circumstances and forces continue to evolve throughout the intervening period as they currently appear to be doing.

The conclusion of this study, therefore, is that the indicated total domestic availability of crude oil in the United States in 1975, at no appreciable increase in constant dollar costs, is on the order of 6 billion barrels.

It should be clearly understood what this judgment concerns and implies. It has already been emphasized that it is not a prediction or forecast of actual primary and secondary production in 1975, but is a judgment of what production could be, under constant costs, in the light of the resource position and foreseeable technological progress (see chapter 7). These two determinants of capacity are not in themselves, however, sufficient to make an annual output of 6 billion barrels in 1975 actually feasible. Such an output level carries obvious implications, not only for that year but for the period from now until then. For example, unless exploration and discovery efforts were maintained at a fairly high level in the period through, say, 1970, it would be impossible to obtain 4 billion barrels of primary production in 1975 by making up an earlier deficiency in such activity by intensified efforts in the years 1971–74. The maintenance of such levels of activity depends in turn, on public policy decisions in such fields as imports and the regulation of production.

OTHER SOURCES OF SUPPLY

Imports

Although the preceding discussion has been concerned solely with domestic crude availability, it is not meant to carry the implication that domestic crude output would in that year be the sole source for satisfying whatever demands may exist. On the contrary, it can be assumed that imports would also contribute to total supply. Not only should Canada and Venezuela continue to have exportable surpluses available to this country throughout the period to 1975, but there also exist the resources of the Middle East. The known potential capacity of the latter region alone is so enormous[70] that, given normal world trade relations and a modicum of political stability in that area, no reasonably projected world demand on that capacity in the period through 1975 could reach the level at which resource limitations would come into play. All this oil constitutes a large reservoir that can be tapped, at lower costs than domestic oil, to an extent that will be determined by world supply-demand relationships, U.S. import policy, and other factors that are beyond the scope of this study.

Inextricably related to the role of imports in total supply is the matter of

[70] Pratt estimates the *proved reserves* of the Middle East at 230 billion barrels as of the end of 1954. See Panel on the Impact of Peaceful Uses of Atomic Energy, *op. cit.*, p. 93.

price. To a large extent, the two are interdeterminate, but there is a substitute source of domestic supply that appears likely to put a ceiling on the possible domestic price level of crude oil. The significance of this possibility is sufficient to warrant additional consideration.

.   .   .

Shale Oil

The substitute source for domestic supply is shale oil, a material obtained from a type of rock known as "oil shale."[71] This rock contains a variable proportion of hydrocarbon material that can be separated from the rock and produced in liquid form as shale oil. The shale oil, in turn, can be hydrogenated and processed by conventional oil refinery practices to yield the same products as crude oil. Rocks that can be termed oil shales occur in more than half of the 48 states. The total shale oil content of these rocks is not yet possible to estimate, but the U.S. Geological Survey estimates that the shale oil resources of Colorado alone total about a trillion barrels, including only rock that would yield at least 15 gallons of oil per ton.[72] The richest beds constitute a section up to 90 feet thick assaying 30 gallons to the ton, which alone contain an estimated 126 billion barrels of shale oil.[73] It has been recently estimated that 30–40 billion barrels are currently economically recoverable from these beds.[74]

It is thus evident that the shale oil resources of the United States constitute an abundant potential domestic source of liquid fuels that is considerably larger than the estimated crude oil resource base. The significance of these resources, which do not involve future discovery and which can be measured, as resources, with much greater accuracy than petroleum resources, has been apparent for some time to both industry and government. Between 1944 and 1956, the Bureau of Mines carried on extensive experimentation which included the operation of an oil shale mine and several shale oil pilot plants. The technical feasibility of shale oil recovery was proved beyond question by this work. In addition, investigations by private companies have been under way during the past decade, progressing through the operation of two pilot plants in 1957. One plant was shut down in 1958 to permit assessment of the data obtained;

[71] Other domestic sources of liquid fuels, present or potential, such as gilsonite and oil sands, are excluded from consideration because of the limited scale of output they could support. For example, the total content of all oil sands in the United States has been estimated to be only 2–3 billion barrels. See U.S. Senate Committee on Interior and Insular Affairs, *Stockpile and Accessibility of Strategic and Critical Materials to the U.S. in Time of War*, Hearings before the Special Subcommittee on Minerals and Materials and Fuels Economics, Part 6, 83rd Congress (1953–54), p. 118.

[72] F. L. Hartley and C. S. Brinegar, "Oil Shale and Bituminous Sand," *The Scientific Monthly*, Vol. LXXXIV, No. 6 (June 1957), p. 278.

[73] U.S. Bureau of Mines, *Synthetic Liquid Fuels, Annual Report of the Secretary of the Interior for 1955*, Part II, "Oil From Oil Shale," Report of Investigations 5237, July 1956, p. 3.

[74] Hartley and Brinegar, *op. cit.*, p. 279.

simultaneously, the operators of the other plant announced plans to construct, in the near future, a semicommercial plant with a capacity of 1,300 to 2,600 barrels a day.

Both geography and the indicated future supply-demand situation on the Pacific Coast, particularly in Southern California, point to that area as the most logical initial market for shale oil. For this reason, early cost estimates in the period 1951–56 referred to the cost of gasoline from shale oil produced for the Southern California market. These estimates ranged from 11.1 cents to 16.2 cents per gallon for gasoline produced at refineries in the Los Angeles area from partly processed shale oil pipelined 700 miles from Colorado.[75] One of these estimates, a figure of 14.7 cents published in a study by the National Petroleum Council based on 1951 circumstances,[76] was subsequently updated by other investigators to allow for changed economic conditions as of 1957. According to this source, whereas shale oil gasoline would cost an estimated 14.7 cents per gallon compared with petroleum gasoline at 12 cents in 1951, in 1957 shale oil gasoline based on the same National Petroleum Council data would cost 19 cents per gallon compared with gasoline from petroleum at 14 to 15 cents.[77] The explanation given by Miller and Cameron for the larger inflationary increase in the shale oil product is that the petroleum industry has been absorbing some of the cost increase in the intervening period.

Currently, however, there is a difference of opinion as to the actual basis on which shale oil will compete with crude oil—whether the former is more significant as a source of jet and diesel fuels, with gasoline only as a by-product.[78] Recent cost estimates have coincidentally been in terms of crude rather than refined products. Actual production costs appear to be well below the price of crude in California. Union Oil claims a cost of $2 per barrel in its pilot operations,[79] and the Oil Shale Corporation states that it could lay down shale oil on the Pacific Coast at a cost of $1.42 to $1.92 per barrel.[80] This compares with posted prices for California crude of $2.35 and delivered West Texas crude of about $3 a barrel.

But what would be the actual selling price of delivered shale oil, allowing for interest, profit, taxes, depletion, and royalties? Miller and Cameron offer estimates (shown in Table 105) for operations at a level of 250,000 barrels a day. Estimates are given for two methods of shale retorting, the Union Oil process and the Bureau of Mines process. Data for the Aspeco process, a third method, were not available to the authors at that time. The return of 6 per

[75] See B. C. Netschert, *The Future Supply of Oil and Gas* (Baltimore: Johns Hopkins Press, 1958), p. 62, Table 8.

[76] *Final Report of Committee on Synthetic Liquid Fuels Production Costs* (Washington, D. C.: National Petroleum Council, February 26, 1953), p. 8.

[77] E. P. Miller and R. J. Cameron, "Shale Oil Nears Competitive Level with Domestic Petroleum," *Journal of Petroleum Technology*, Vol. X, No. 8 (August 1958), p. 26.

[78] *Petroleum Week*, February 22, 1957, p. 75; *Journal of Commerce*, July 10, 1958.

[79] *Business Week*, February 15, 1958, p. 44.

[80] *Journal of Commerce*, July 10, 1958; *Petroleum Week*, July 18, 1958, p. 76.

cent represents the allowance made in the earlier studies of shale oil economics. The authors consider this unrealistic, however, in comparison with the return obtained in the petroleum industry, and present the return of 12 per cent as a better alternative.

TABLE 105. SELLING PRICE PER BARREL OF OIL DELIVERED IN CALIFORNIA, 1957

	Union Oil Process	Bureau of Mines process
6% return on capital:		
No depletion..............................	$2.85	$2.35
15% depletion.............................	2.65	2.10
12% return on capital:		
No depletion..............................	4.10	3.30
15% depletion.............................	3.75	2.95

SOURCE: E. P. Miller and R. J. Cameron, "Shale Oil Nears Competitive Level with Domestic Petroleum," *Journal of Petroleum Technology*, Vol. X, No. 8 (August 1958), p. 26.

It is evident that published data do not provide an unequivocal indication of the current place of shale oil relative to crude oil. Miller and Cameron observe that "significantly different shale oil prices can be presented depending only on the basis of evaluation selected."[81] The true competitive position of this supply source will not be known until the first commercial plants are in operation. If current indications are correct, however, and shale oil is already marginal, a significant price rise in crude oil would be a powerful stimulus in developing the new industry. Shale oil would be meeting crude at a higher price, but shale oil costs would be no greater, thus attracting capital from the petroleum industry into shale oil development. Nor should it be overlooked that the cost of shale oil should go down, not up, as the benefits of operating experience are applied. At some point, at least in theory, a sufficiently high price for crude would enable the shale oil industry to effectively supplant the petroleum industry. A final word of caution is in order, however. The oil shale district in Colorado is in a water-short area, and pessimists question the availability of water to support large-scale operations. The most that has been claimed on this score by proponents is sufficient water, with suitable storage facilities, to sustain shale oil operations on a level of 2 million barrels a day.[82] The conclusion of the present study is that shale oil, unless given government encouragement or support, is likely to constitute at best only a minor supplemental source of oil supply in 1975.

[81] Miller and Cameron, *op. cit.*, p. 27.
[82] C. H. Prien and J. W. Savage, "A Shale-Oil Industry is on its Way," *Chemical Engineering Progress*, Vol. LII, No. 1 (January 1956), p. 18-J.

CHAPTER 10

Natural gas and natural gas liquids

NATURAL GAS

The future of natural gas is a difficult subject because of peculiarities in natural gas occurrence and production. Data from which to infer the magnitude of unknown resources and the various components of future supply are even more scanty than is corresponding information for petroleum. The assumptions required are therefore less well founded, and it is not surprising to find relatively few public discussions and estimates concerning the subject.

Natural gas has two major modes of occurrence: It is often found by itself, in distinct gas reservoirs, and it can occur together with crude oil. Because the effect of these purely physical circumstances on production characteristics is important, the American Gas Association distinguishes two types of gas occurrence on the basis of production characteristics:

Non-associated gas is free gas not in contact with crude oil in the reservoir, and free gas in contact with oil where the production of such gas is not significantly affected by the production of crude oil.

Associated gas is free gas in contact with crude oil in the reservoir where the production of such gas is significantly affected by the production of crude oil.[1]

Associated gas constitutes either a "gas cap" overlying the crude oil in the underground reservoir, or gas dissolved in the crude oil, held in solution by the reservoir pressure. This dissolved gas is liberated when the pressure is reduced either at the surface or in the subsurface, when the reservoir pressure drops below the saturation pressure because of withdrawals. To date, non-associated

---

[1] Definitions adopted by the Natural Gas Reserves Committee of the American Gas Association, 1957.

gas has been the most important mode of occurrence; it currently constitutes about two-thirds of total proved reserves of natural gas, with the two kinds of associated gas accounting for roughly equal portions of the remainder.

The various published estimates and opinions concerning future reserves and production of natural gas are examined in the following sections in the same manner as were the oil estimates. Additional features of occurrence, discovery, and production peculiar to natural gas as compared with crude oil are brought into the discussion where relevant. Again, only the literature for the past few years has been surveyed, in order to restrict the discussion to current opinion.

.   .   .

Reserve Measurement and Definitions

The proved-reserve concept used for oil is also applied to natural gas in the estimation by industry of its reserves: "Proved recoverable reserves of natural gas are those reserves estimated to be producible under present operating practices, with no consideration being given to their ultimate use."[2] But, as is true of oil, there are the same uncertainties and ambiguities to be resolved in deciding whether a known gas occurrence is sufficiently well-defined to be so included, and the recovery factor must also be taken into account since there are both physical and economic limits to the proportion of the gas in place that currently can be recovered.

One of these limits concerns the pressure at which a gas field is likely to be abandoned. Gas can be forced or pulled to the surface, but ordinarily reaches the surface with the naturally existing pressure in the underground reservoir. This pressure is often very high—thousands of pounds per square inch—and the problem is then the reduction of pressure to a level that can be economically handled in the gathering system. As gas is removed from the reservoir, the pressure drops and there exists for each field a pressure differential (between the reservoir and the gathering pipeline system) at which further operation would be uneconomic. At this point the field must be abandoned. Usually this pressure is rather low and, as noted, can even be negative, but in certain instances abandonment pressures as high as 300 to 500 pounds per square inch are the cutoff point beyond which the gas is considered "unrecoverable."[3]

There is, in addition, the problem of the inclusion in the proved-reserve estimate of individual small gas fields. Many of these are excluded from the estimates on the grounds that it would be impracticable to consider them and that the quantities involved are insignificant relative to the total. The errors inherent in any estimation of natural resources are, of course, very large—so large, in fact, that they probably override errors peculiar to natural gas. This discussion does not use the gas industry's proved-reserve estimates as such, although they are

---

[2] Natural Gas Reserves Committee of the American Gas Association, *1960 Report.*

[3] J. R. Stockton, R. C. Henshaw, Jr., and R. W. Graves, *Economics of Natural Gas in Texas* (Austin: Bureau of Business Research, University of Texas, 1952), p. 120.

included in total future supply estimates and are employed in examining certain relationships between natural gas and crude oil.

Future reserves of natural gas cannot be considered in terms of total cumulative reserves through time, as was possible with oil. This results from the lack of knowledge as to the total past "production" of gas, defining production to include waste through "venting" (escape of gas without burning), and "flaring" (escape with burning). In the earlier decades of the oil industry, an unknown but undoubtedly very large amount of gas was wasted through ignorance, carelessness, and the lack of economic incentive to do otherwise. Until modern technology made pipeline construction economically feasible there was at best a limited market for the gas, which consequently had little or no value. Since the waste was probably a substantial proportion of total past "production," estimates of that production, or of total discoveries to date, are of little use in the present context. This has not prevented some writers on the subject from making an assumption as to the magnitude of total past losses and so constructing an estimate of cumulative discoveries, or reserves to date. Most estimates of ultimate reserves of natural gas, as that term is defined in the preceding discussion of oil, have been made, however, in terms of the "total future supply," which consists of current proved reserves plus anticipated future discoveries of such reserves.

. . .

The Reserve-Resource Position

ESTIMATES OF TOTAL FUTURE SUPPLY

Table 106 lists the current estimates of the total future supply of natural gas in the United States. The estimates are reduced to a common basis in column 4 of the table, where proved reserves as of January 1, 1960, have been subtracted from the total future-supply estimate in column 2. Column 5 gives an indication of the relative magnitude of each estimate through the ratio between it and 1959 production. (Unless otherwise stated, references for the following descriptions of the estimates are the same as those given in Table 106.)

Terry's 1950 estimate was based on Weeks' estimate of "onshore" oil reserves.[4] Terry estimated that the ratio of gas discoveries to oil discoveries in the future should run about 6,000 cubic feet (6 Mcf) of gas per barrel of oil, hence Weeks' figure should result in 280 trillion cubic feet of onshore gas discoveries.[5] (The gas-oil ratio is discussed in detail below.) To this figure, Terry added an arbitrary estimate of 50 trillion cubic feet for offshore gas discoveries, which together with the then proved-reserve level of 180 trillion cubic feet yielded a total future supply of 510 trillion cubic feet. Terry used his gas-oil ratio as a compromise between the then current ratios of 4.1 Mcf per barrel in gas and oil produc-

[4] See discussion in Chapter 9 of L. G. Weeks' estimates.
[5] Weeks estimated ultimate oil reserves at 110 billion barrels, leaving 46.5 billion barrels to be discovered as of January 1, 1950 (6,000 × 46.5 billion = 279 trillion).

TABLE 106. ESTIMATES OF TOTAL RECOVERABLE RESERVES OF
NATURAL GAS IN THE UNITED STATES

(In trillion cubic feet)

Source and date (1)	Estimated total future supply (2)	To be discovered		Ratio of total future supply to 1959 production (5)
		(as of time of estimate) (3)	(as of 1/1/60)[1] (4)	
a) Terry, 1950	>510	>330	>247	>41
b) Hinson, 1954	586	375	323	47
c) Interior Dept., 1956	875	663	612	71
d) Pratt, 1956	725	513	462	58
e) Pogue and Hill, 1956	570	358	307	46
f) Hubbert, 1956	730	506	467	59
g) Terry and Winger, 1957	>1,200	>984	>937	>97

[1] Column 2 minus proved reserves as of January 1, 1960.

SOURCES:
   a) L. F. Terry, "The Future Supply of Natural Gas," *Proceedings*, American Gas Association, 1950, pp. 155–59.
   b) H. H. Hinson, "What's the Present Picture for Natural Gas Reserves?" report presented before the American Gas Association Financial Forum, October 8, 1954.
   c) Panel on the Impact of Peaceful Uses of Atomic Energy, *Peaceful Uses of Atomic Energy*, Vol. 2, report to the Joint Committee on Atomic Energy (Washington, D. C.: U.S. Government Printing Office, January 1, 1956), p. 83.
   d) W. E. Pratt, *Peaceful Uses of Atomic Energy, ibid.*, p. 94.
   e) J. E. Pogue and K. E. Hill, *Future Growth and Financial Requirements of the World Petroleum Industry* (New York: Chase Manhattan Bank, 1956). Presented at annual meeting of American Institute of Mining, Metallurgical and Petroleum Engineers, Petroleum Branch, February 21, 1956.
   f) M. K. Hubbert, "Nuclear Energy and the Fossil Fuels," *Drilling and Production Practice—1956* (New York: American Petroleum Institute, 1957), p. 15.
   g) L. F. Terry and J. G. Winger, "Sees 1,200 Trillion of U.S. Recoverable Gas," *American Gas Association Monthly*, Vol. XXXIX, Nos. 7–8 (July–August 1957), pp. 10 ff.

tion and 7.3 Mcf per barrel in proved reserves. He considered that the 6-Mcf figure was actually conservative, and that his future-supply figure of 510 trillion cubic feet should be regarded as a minimum.

Hinson's estimate is based on a gas-oil ratio of 5 Mcf per barrel applied to a somewhat larger (but unspecified) oil-reserve estimate than the Weeks figure employed by Terry.

The Department of Interior estimate is contained in its report to the McKinney Panel on the impact of the peaceful uses of atomic energy on the natural gas industry.[6] The Interior Department report first cites Terry's estimate, noting that his gas-oil ratio "has turned out to be too low." "Considering that it has been necessary in the past to increase both the estimate of ultimate oil reserves and the ratio of gas to oil discoveries," the report continues, "and taking into

[6] Panel on the Peaceful Uses of Atomic Energy, *Peaceful Uses of Atomic Energy*, Vol. 2, report to the Joint Committee on Atomic Energy (Washington, D. C.: U.S. Government Printing Office, January 1956), p. 83.

account the trend toward deeper and deeper drilling, it is likely that larger and larger reserves of natural gas will continue to be found. Thus a considerable upward adjustment of the Terry estimate is now required." The Department thinks that this adjustment should be by at least a factor of two. But the Department mistakenly interprets Terry's original estimate to be "ultimate gas reserves," and so terms it. The doubling of Terry's figure to a level of 1,000 trillion cubic feet is the Interior Department's revised estimate of "ultimate gas reserves." In Table 106 this is adjusted to an equivalent total future supply figure.

The Pratt estimate was also presented in a report to the McKinney Panel, in which he voiced the industry consensus as to future developments but emphasized that the actual estimates were his own. Pratt uses a gas-oil ratio of 5 Mcf per barrel, applied to an estimate of total liquid hydrocarbon reserves (including natural gas liquids, which are discussed later). Pratt implies conservatism in his estimate by citing the fact that outside the United States the ratio is 4 Mcf per barrel of oil, against the current 6–7 Mcf in this country.[7]

The Pogue and Hill estimate is presented as their basis for deriving the trend of future production, with no supporting statements or analysis.

Hubbert's gas estimate is based on his estimate of 150 billion barrels as the ultimate oil reserves of the United States (see discussion of Table 98 in Chapter 9) which, as of January 1, 1958, left 91.5 billion barrels to be produced. "Then, if we use the gas-oil ratio of current production, we obtain 410 trillion cubic feet of gas as the future reserve. If we assume the ratio of 7,500 cubic feet per barrel, obtained from proved reserves, we obtain a future reserve of 730 trillion cubic feet. . . . Of these figures the latter appears the more reliable since the reserves represent a much larger sample than the annual production."[8] For his own use, Hubbert adopted the Pratt estimate, as a round number with which his own estimate is in substantial agreement.

The Terry and Winger estimate is based on their colleagues' estimate of ultimate oil reserves of 250 billion barrels. Deducting 86 billion barrels of cumulative discoveries, Terry and Winger apply a gas-oil ratio of 6 Mcf per barrel to the 164 billion barrels of oil remaining to be discovered. This yields indicated future gas discoveries of 984 trillion cubic feet, to which are added 238 trillion of current proved reserves for a total future gas supply of about 1,200 trillion cubic feet. Terry and Winger consider this a "reasonable minimum estimate based upon present evidence."[9]

[7] *Ibid.*, p. 94.

[8] M. K. Hubbert, "Nuclear Energy and the Fossil Fuels," *Drilling and Production Practice—1956* (New York: American Petroleum Institute, 1957), p. 15. Hubbert's future-supply figure differs from Pratt's even though derived from the latter's "ultimate reserve" figure of 850 trillion cubic feet because Hubbert takes past production as 130 rather than 125 trillion cubic feet.

[9] See Hill *et al.*, Table 98; and L. F. Terry and J. G. Winger, "Sees 1,200 Trillion of U.S. Recoverable Gas," *American Gas Association Monthly*, Vol. XXXIX, Nos. 7–8 (July-August 1957), p. 39.

Two other estimates, not included in Table 106, concern the offshore gas reserves only. Kastrop, in discussing the Gulf Coast offshore province, mentions that "some have estimated as much as . . . 70 trillion cubic feet of natural gas are to be found ultimately" in this area alone.[10] The U.S. Geological Survey (USGS) has estimated total continental shelf natural gas resources as 68.5 trillion cubic feet, slightly lower than Kastrop's reference.[11]

RESERVE ESTIMATES AND THE RESOURCE BASE

Each of the estimates of total future natural gas supply discussed in the previous section has as a common basis a double assumption—(a) an estimate of total future crude oil supply (derived from an estimate of ultimate reserves), and (b) a gas-oil ratio applied to the crude oil figure. This compounding of assumptions naturally leads to considerable variation in results. Different crude oil assumptions are used, and the gas-oil ratios employed vary from Hubbert's 7,500 cubic feet to the Interior Department's 3,333.[12] At this point, it is possible to say that in the present context some of the figures appear to be unduly conservative because of the low oil-reserve figure on which they are based. Terry's first estimate is now obsolete; the Pogue and Hill and the Hubbert estimates are associated with oil estimates in the low group (see Table 102). Nevertheless, it is instructive to consider the estimates in the larger perspective of the resource base, as was done earlier in the discussion of oil.

With the exception of the Interior Department estimates, the proved-reserve basis of the total future supply estimates means that they all contain the current technology limitation; the estimates refer only to gas that is, or would be, recoverable with techniques and under economic conditions prevailing here and now. There is a paucity of information on the recovery factor in gas production, but the Bureau of Statistics of the American Gas Association has furnished an estimate that the "ratio of proved economically recoverable natural gas to total original gas in place within a given reservoir averages approximately 75 to 80 per cent."[13] This estimate is taken here as representative of authoritative technical opinion.

It will be recalled that the conversion of the estimates of ultimate oil reserve to the resource-base equivalent was accomplished by multiplying the ultimate-reserve estimate by the reciprocal of the recovery factor. The procedure cannot be so neat or simple with the gas estimates. The total future-supply estimates contain current proved reserves, whereas the recovery factor as given relates to original reserves. The recovery factor cannot be applied to current proved re-

---

[10] J. E. Kastrop, "Louisiana's Offshore Picture," *The Petroleum Engineer*, Vol. 27, No. 13 (December 1955), p. B-40.

[11] American Petroleum Institute, *Petroleum Facts and Figures* (11th ed., 1954), p. 120.

[12] The Interior Department gas-oil ratio is deduced from its estimate of ultimate oil reserves at 300 billion barrels (see Chapter 9) and the use of the estimate of one quadrillion cubic feet as "ultimate gas reserves."

[13] Communication to the author.

serves because the production of gas from a reservoir changes the percentage recovery that will be obtained from the remaining gas. Without attempting to compute the original reserves of known reservoirs with current proved reserves, the best that can be done is to calculate a "minimum approximation" of the resource-base equivalent of the estimates of future supply. The figures in column 3 of Table 106 represent the proved reserves (in the sense of total cumulative production to be expected in the future) of the reservoirs as yet undiscovered, and hence can appropriately be multiplied by the reciprocal of the recovery factor. Current proved reserves cannot be so expanded but it is known they do not include the total gas in place in known reservoirs. Thus, the result of this multiplication, shown in Table 107, as the minimum resource-base equivalent of the total future-supply estimates, understates this equivalent by an unknown amount.

TABLE 107.   ESTIMATES OF TOTAL FUTURE NATURAL GAS SUPPLY CONVERTED TO MINIMUM RESOURCE-BASE EQUIVALENT

(In trillion cubic feet)

Estimate and date (1)	Total future supply (2)	Minimum resource-base equivalent (3)	Ratio of col. 3 to 1959 production (4)
a) Terry, 1950	510	592	48
b) Hinson, 1954	586	681	55
c) Interior Dept., 1956	875	1,041	84
d) Pratt, 1956	725	853	69
e) Pogue and Hill, 1956	570	660	53
f) Hubbert, 1956	730	856	69
g) Terry and Winger, 1957	1,200	1,468	118

SOURCES: See Table 106.

Column 2 of Table 107 lists the total future-supply estimates as given in column 2 of Table 106. The figures in column 3 result from division of the undiscovered portion of the estimates (listed in column 3 of Table 106) by 0.8—the upper range of estimated current recovery, chosen to give current technology the benefit of the doubt and to make the minimum resource-base equivalent somewhat more conservative—and from addition of proved reserves as of the time of the estimate. Column 4 provides a measure of the relative magnitude of the minimum resource-base equivalents in terms of current production levels.

The gas-oil ratio, the second basis of the several estimates, has yet to be examined, but before doing so it will be helpful to consider the estimates of future gas production. The determinants of future domestic natural gas supply can then be viewed as they relate to both the reserve-resource and production estimates.

Estimates of Future Production

The discussion in Chapter 9 concerning implied demand level in future oil production estimates and the relevance of those estimates to the availability approach used herein, also applies to estimates for natural gas. The various gas estimates are summarized in Table 108.

TABLE 108. ESTIMATES OF FUTURE U.S. NATURAL GAS PRODUCTION

Source and date (1)	Peak[1] (2)	Year[2] (3)	Estimated production (trillion cubic feet) (4)	Explicit total future supply(*) or implied minimum future supply through terminal date as of January 1, 1960[3] (trillion cubic feet) (5)	Per cent of 1959 production[4] (6)
a) PMPC, 1951		1975	15.3	528 minimum	123
b) Egloff, 1951		1960	11.4⎱	595 minimum	92
		1975	18.0⎰		145
c) Pettyjohn, 1955	X	1960	12.0	240 minimum	97
d) Ayres, 1955	X	1965	12.0⎱	*600	97
		1975	11.0⎰		89
e) Interior Dept., 1956		1975	19.0	*875	153
f) Pratt, 1956		1965	13.5⎱	*725	109
		1975	15.0⎰		121
g) Pogue and Hill, 1956		1965	14.2	364 minimum	115
		1965	15.2⎱		123
	X	1970	16.0⎬	*570	129
		1975	15.5⎰		125
h) A.G.A., 1956		1975	22.5	*850	181
i) Tippy, 1956	X	1970	13.0⎱	*475	105
		1975	12.5⎰		101
	X	1975	15.0	*725	121
	X	1980	17.0	*875	137
j) Hubbert, 1956	X	1970	14.0⎱	*725	113
		1975	13.5⎰		109
k) Ayres, 1956	X	1965–70	13.0	*600	105
l) Terry and Winger, 1957 . .		1966	16.3⎱	*1,200	131
	X	1980–90	20.0⎰		161

[1] An X in column 2 indicates that the production for the year shown in column 3 is projected as the historical peak of production by the author of the estimate.

[2] Year to which each estimate refers.

[3] Column 5 is explained on p. 400.

[4] Estimates as per cent of 1959 production of 12.4 trillion cubic feet.

SOURCES:

a) President's Materials Policy Commission (PMPC), *Resources for Freedom*, Vol. I (Washington, D. C.: U.S. Government Printing Office, 1952), pp. 127–28.

b) G. Egloff, "Oil and Gas as Industrial Raw Materials," *Resources for Freedom*, Vol. IV, *ibid.*, p. 193.

c) E. S. Pettyjohn, "Coal . . . Gas Source of the Future," *Coal Age*, Vol. LX, No. 3 (March 1955), p. 57.

d) E. Ayres, "Energy Resources for the Future," *Oil and Gas Compact Bulletin*, Vol. XIV, No. 1 (June 1955), p. 21.

e) Panel on the Impact of the Peaceful Uses of Atomic Energy, *Peaceful Uses of Atomic Energy*, Vol. 2, Report to the Joint Committee on Atomic Energy (Washington, D. C.: U.S. Government Printing Office, January 1956), p. 87.

(*Footnotes continued on next page.*)

DESCRIPTION OF ESTIMATES

The figure attributed to the President's Materials Policy Commission (PMPC) is taken from a table in Volume I of the Commission's report which portrays "A Hypothetical Picture of Energy Flow in 1975." Although there are discussions of future possibilities at several places in the five volumes of the report, the only specific comment on the subject is the acceptance of "relatively optimistic assumptions . . . as to future discovery."[14]

Egloff also does not present specific support of his estimate, but in a subsequent article on the subject he cites Terry's original reserve estimate, commenting that it is a very conservative figure. Essentially his position is the same as the one he takes regarding the future of oil—only a very small fraction of the possible occurrence has been probed. His outlook is summed up in the statement that "estimators," whom he does not name, "consider that supplies will be maintained well beyond the present century."[15]

Pettyjohn merely mentions in passing that "it has been estimated" that a peak production of 12 trillion cubic feet of gas will occur in 1960. Ayres derives his 1955 estimates through the same decline-curve technique he used for his oil estimates. He obtains his figures from a total future supply of 600 trillion cubic feet, which he assumes arbitrarily as a recognition of Terry's 1950 characterization of his own total supply estimate as too conservative (see Table 106 and accompanying discussion).

The Interior Department estimate is in the form of a statement that a 1975 demand of 19 trillion cubic feet can be met "if exploratory drilling for petroleum

[14] President's Materials Policy Commission (PMPC), *Resources for Freedom*, Vol. I (Washington, D. C.: U.S. Government Printing Office, 1952), p. 127. According to Cornelius J. Dwyer (in a letter to the author), the PMPC gas figure was related to the estimate of 1975 crude oil production through an assumption of a 6,000-cubic-foot gas-oil ratio, a twenty-year life for gas fields, and the greater use of repressuring (which tends to postpone a certain portion of gas output).

[15] G. Egloff, "The Place of Natural Gas, Present and Future," *Proceedings*, American Gas Association, 1952, p. 32.

(Footnotes to Table 108, continued.)

f) *Ibid.*, p. 92.

g) J. E. Pogue and K. E. Hill, *Future Growth and Financial Requirements of the World Petroleum Industry* (New York: Chase Manhattan Bank, 1956). Presented at annual meeting of American Institute of Mining, Metallurgical and Petroleum Engineers, Petroleum Branch, February 21, 1956.

h) Bureau of Statistics, American Gas Association, "Supply of, and Demand for, Natural Gas in 1975," August 3, 1956.

i) W. B. Tippy, "Where Does the Gas Industry Go from Here—" *American Gas Journal*, Vol. XVIII, No. 3 (October 1956), pp. 66–67.

j) M. K. Hubbert, "Nuclear Energy and the Fossil Fuels," *Drilling and Production Practice—1956* (New York: American Petroleum Institute, 1957), p. 18.

k) E. Ayres, "The Fuel Situation," *Scientific American*, Vol. 195, No. 4 (October 1956), p. 47.

l) L. F. Terry and J. G. Winger, "Sees 1,200 Trillion of U.S. Recoverable Gas," *American Gas Association Monthly*, Vol. XXXIX, Nos. 7–8 (July–August 1957), pp. 10 ff.

and gas continue to increase over the next 25 years, as seems inevitable." Pratt's figures are presented as the estimated consumption in 1965 and 1975, but since he makes no mention of imports it is assumed here that his figures are equivalent to production estimates.

The several Pogue and Hill figures appearing in Table 108 have a double basis. The estimate of 14.2 trillion cubic feet for 1965 production is based on "discovery momentum," that is, an assumption that future annual discoveries will average 25 per cent more than those of the postwar period to date, at the same time that the ratio of proved reserve to production falls from 22 to 20 during the period 1956–65. The other three estimates of Pogue and Hill are derived from a decline curve based on the assumption of 570 trillion cubic feet of total future supply. The figures for 1970 and 1975 are interpolated from Figure 11 of the Pogue and Hill paper.

The basis of the American Gas Association estimate is summarized in its statement as follows:

> The reasoning in this memorandum assumes that appropriate economic incentives will be present to foster an accelerated discovery rate so that new supplies will become available when needed for supplying the nation's increased demands. It also assumes that deliverability will be maintained adequately to provide the increased requirements of natural gas in spite of declining pressures in some of the older producing fields. Presumable technological improvements in recovery technique will assist in this area by permitting substantially higher proportions of gas in underground reservoirs to be made economically available.[16]

In addition, the estimate is based on a total future supply of 850 trillion cubic feet.

Tippy's several estimates are taken from decline curves based on varying assumptions of total future supply. (The estimate for the non-peak year 1975 is read from Chart 4 of Tippy's paper.) Hubbert notes that the peak of 14 trillion cubic feet is "about the maximum that appears likely while allowing for the necessary period of prolonged decline," and comments that Pratt's 1975 estimate requires a total future supply "considerably in excess" of Pratt's total reserve assumption.

Ayres' 1956 estimate is a revision of his 1955 figure, but he again uses the decline-curve method. He projects his curve on the "conservative assumption" that gas production will increase at about 4 per cent per year, about half the present rate, during the next few years. Ayres contends that the peak will be held down by the fact that as the peak is approached, pipeline builders "will hesitate to build new lines if they are not assured that the gas will last long enough to amortize their investment."[17]

The Terry and Winger estimate for 1966 assumes an annual growth rate in demand of 4.7 per cent in the coming decade. Their peak estimate of 20 trillion

[16] Bureau of Statistics, American Gas Association, "Supply of, and Demand for, Natural Gas in 1975," August 3, 1956, p. 6.

[17] E. Ayres, "The Fuel Situation," *Scientific American*, Vol. 195, No. 4 (October 1956), p. 46.

cubic feet in the 1980–90 decade is indicated by a rough decline curve which they fit to their estimate of total future supply. Although a figure for 1975 could be taken from this curve, it would place more emphasis on the curve than the authors themselves are willing to do, since they imply that it is only one of the many possible curves that can be based on their estimate of total future supply. Noting that the latter "is taken as a conservative minimum," they conclude, "we expect that future reviewers will probably find the curve too small and the indicated peak to occur later than here forecast."

Column 5 of Table 108 compares the production estimates on the basis of the implied or explicitly stated reserve magnitude to which they are related. The figures marked with asterisks are the total future-supply assumptions from which the production estimates were derived or to which they are related. Some of these assumptions are not listed in Table 106 and considered individually because they are only hypothetical total supply levels, viz., "If we assume a total future supply of 10, then production in year T should be Z." The unmarked figures in column 5 were computed in a similar manner to the equivalent figures in Table 101 in Chapter 9. Specifically, (a) a straight-line growth in production was assumed from 1959 to the terminal year or between intermediate years, if noted; (b) an allowance of a reserve-production ratio of 20 was made for the terminal year. This ratio was chosen because of its common use as the proved-reserve basis in the supply contracts for transmission pipelines. Again, the straight-line growth and reserve-production ratio are arbitrary assumptions adopted solely to provide a basis for comparing the *minimum* total future supply implied by the various production estimates.

COMPARISON OF ESTIMATES

Table 108 can be summarized as follows: (a) Estimates of the *year of peak production* (columns 2 and 3) range from 1960 past 1980. (b) Estimates of *peak output* (columns 2 and 4), where specified in the period through 1975, range from 12 trillion to 16 trillion cubic feet. And (c) estimates of *output in 1975* (column 4) range from 11 to 22.5 trillion cubic feet. As would be expected from the wide variation in the bases of the estimates, there is also a wide range among the estimates themselves. Also in accordance with expectation, the estimates of 1975 output show a rough correlation with the total future supply estimate with which they are associated:

Range of explicit total future supply estimates listed in Table 108 (trillion cubic feet)	Number of corresponding 1975 output estimates in Table 108	Average of corresponding 1975 output estimates in Table 108 (trillion cubic feet)
475	1	12.5
570–600	2	13.25
725	3	14.5
850–875	2	20.7

The favored basis of estimation is the decline curve. The conceptual limitation of this technique has been discussed with respect to the oil estimates. Here the estimates demonstrate, in addition, the dependence of the results on the judgments of the estimator, despite the fact that the estimate is mathematically derived. Five of the authors listed in Table 108 use the technique to obtain an estimate for 1975 production. Ayres, with an assumed total future supply of 600 trillion cubic feet, gets a 1975 output of 11.0 trillion. Yet Tippy, using 475 trillion cubic feet,[18] and Pogue and Hill, with 570 trillion cubic feet, get results of 12.5 trillion and 15.5 trillion respectively, as 1975 output. In each case, an estimate of total future supply smaller than Ayres' yields a higher projected output for the same year. Again, Tippy and Hubbert, using the same assumption of a total future supply of 725 trillion cubic feet, project 1975 output as 15 trillion and 13.5 trillion, respectively, a difference of 10 per cent when using the same basis.

Nevertheless, it is not intended to deny that there is any relationship between the reserve-resource position and the level of future production in a given year. Obviously there is at any time a level of output beyond which production would be uneconomic, if not physically impossible, because of the reserve-resource position. But one of the principal arguments of this study is that there should be room for the exercise of judgment with regard to *all* the determinants of future output levels, not the reserve-resource aspect alone, in estimating future output.

.   .   .

Technology as a Determinant of Future
Domestic Natural Gas Availability

DISCOVERY

The fundamental fact concerning natural gas discovery is that much of it is intimately and inextricably related to the search for oil. Until the postwar era and the creation of a nation-wide market for gas, the discovery of new reservoirs could be described as the result of a search for oil, not gas. The postwar rise in the value of gas has stimulated the search for gas in known gas areas, but as long as oil is the more valuable commodity, it is reasonable to assume that a large proportion of gas discoveries will continue to be a by-product of oil discovery efforts. This does not mean, however, that future gas discovery will be any more dependent on oil discovery than in the past.

Appropriately, then, the general conclusions with respect to prospects for oil discovery which were reached in the preceding chapter apply equally to natural gas. It will be recalled that these conclusions are optimistic because there are large unexplored areas, among which the continental shelf is prominent; there are further possibilities in known productive areas; there are unexplored possibil-

---

[18] Tippy uses an adjusted Terry figure of 600 trillion cubic feet for total future supply as if it were an ultimate-reserve estimate. It has been converted here to a total future-supply equivalent.

ities everywhere at greater depth; there are undertermined potentials in unorthodox sources; and there is room for further exploitation of current discovery
technology. For all of these reasons, the general outlook for gas discovery (considering associated and non-associated together) is also considered good.

At the same time, it is necessary to note a peculiarity of current proved gas
reserves—a large percentage of total proved reserves are in a few giant, non-
associated gas fields, which "accumulated" over the preceding forty years because
there was no market, or at best a limited market, for the gas. In Texas, containing
almost one-half the total proved reserves of natural gas in the United States, some
three-quarters of the total state reserves are non-associated reserves, and are
largely in twenty-two major fields.[19]

Moreover, the giant fields are a proportionately larger source of current supply
than the smaller fields, since they constitute the logical first source to tap with
long-distance transmission pipelines. Thus, the great expansion in natural gas
production in the past decade has been disproportionately from the giant fields.
Although associated and non-associated discoveries will continue in the future, it
appears questionable whether the number of giant non-associated fields discovered
will be sufficient to maintain the present ratio between associated reserves on the
one hand and non-associated reserves on the other. As shown in Table 109, a
small but evident decline in the proportion of non-associated reserves took place
between 1946 and 1956. The subsequent rise in 1957–1959 may signify a

TABLE 109. NON-ASSOCIATED RESERVES AS A PERCENTAGE OF
TOTAL PROVED RESERVES OF NATURAL GAS,[a] 1946–59

Year	Percentage
1959	70.1%
1958	70.0
1957	68.3
1956	67.3
1955	68.4
1954	69.4
1953	69.8
1952	69.1
1951	69.2
1950	70.5
1949	70.0
1948	71.0
1947	72.2
1946	72.5

[a] Excluding reserves in underground storage.

[19] C. A. Breitung, "Present Available Natural Gas Reserves in Texas as of January 1,
1956," *Proceedings*, Ninth Oil Recovery Conference, Bulletin No. 54, Texas Petroleum Research Committee, April 9–10, 1956, pp. 10–26. The total number of gas fields in Texas in
1956 was 1,755 (*ibid.*, p. 12).

reversal of this trend, but at present there is no preponderant evidence one way or the other.

The crucial element in estimating the total future natural gas supply remains the choice of the appropriate gas-oil ratio. There is a limitation in this choice arising from the fact that none of the ratios derivable from published statistics can be a measure of the *true* ratio between the natural occurrence of oil and natural gas, since none of the data refers to the actual reservoir content of total gas and oil in place. Both production and proved reserves depend on the recovery factor. The problem, then, is to determine whether—despite this limitation— there is a useful measure among the several choices of ratio available from published data.

One possible choice is the ratio of the proved reserves of associated and dissolved gas to the proved reserves of oil. This indicates the relative proportion of recoverable oil and gas where they occur together in the same reservoir. Table 110 lists this ratio for recent years; the data are charted in Figure 68. Table 110 and Figure 68 indicate an apparent rise in this gas-oil ratio over time. The average of the last seven years is 10 per cent greater than that of the first seven years, and the figures since 1955 are considerably higher than those of previous years. But the figures are ambiguous—they may mean that recently discovered reservoirs have a higher gas-oil ratio than older ones, or they may merely reflect the different courses of gas and oil production, which are among the determinants of the proved-reserve position. About all that can be concluded is that the ratio of gas and oil in proved reserves, where they occur in conjunction, has been between 2 and 3 Mcf per barrel and that it may be rising.

TABLE 110. RATIO OF ASSOCIATED GAS TO OIL IN PROVED RESERVES, 1946–59

Year	Cu. ft. per bbl.
1959	2,413
1958	2,441
1957	2,511
1956	2,505
1955	2,342
1954	2,177
1953	2,225
1952	2,196
1951	2,169
1950	2,162
1949	2,190
1948	2,116
1947	2,149
1946	2,114
Average	2,265

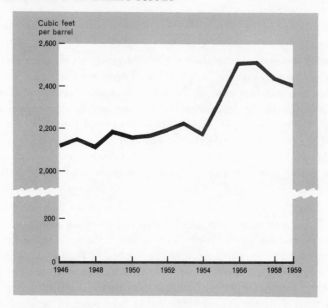

Figure 68.   Ratio of associated gas to oil in proved reserves, 1946–59.

Another possible measure of the oil-gas relationship is the ratio in the cumulative production of both gas and oil. Through 1959, this ratio was 4.2 Mcf per barrel of oil. (The ratio in 1959 production was 5,010 cubic feet per barrel.) But the record of "production" has included wastage only since 1935, so that the ratio on this basis cannot be said to bear much relationship to the ratio of recoverable oil to *recoverable* gas. In addition, the production of oil and of non-associated gas have no relationship whatever.

A third possibility is the ratio in cumulative discoveries (production plus wastage plus present proved reserves) of both gas and oil. In his original work on total future supply of natural gas, Terry attempted to estimate the wastage to obtain such a ratio. He estimated that about 30 trillion cubic feet had been lost and wasted in the natural gas industry through 1949, and "an enormous but unknown quantity of gas in solution with oil . . . wasted in the production of oil," so that total gas "produced" through 1949, including marketed production, was from 150 to 175 trillion cubic feet.[20] Terry thus estimated the additional wastage of gas in oil production at 36 to 61 trillion cubic feet. He rounded his cumulative "production" figure to 160 trillion cubic feet, implying 46 trillion cubic feet of such wastage, for a total loss of 76 trillion cubic feet including wastage from both oil and gas wells. When Terry's cumulative totals are carried through 1959, the resultant gas-oil ratio is 5.8 Mcf per barrel. (Terry obtained a ratio of 4.1. The reason for the increase is the much higher ratio in recent dis-

[20] L. F. Terry, "The Future Supply of Natural Gas," *Proceedings,* American Gas Association, 1950, p. 157.

coveries than in the past.) The usefulness of this ratio depends upon two things: the accuracy of the wastage estimate and the degree to which discoveries reflect the ratio of *occurrence* of recoverable oil to recoverable gas rather than mere discovery experience. In view of the large quantities of gas wastage involved, the large range of the wastage estimate, and the lack of any detailed basis for the estimate, Terry's figure is of little use here. The discovery aspect is considered separately.

A fourth possibility is the ratio in current proved reserves, which was 8.3 Mcf per barrel as of 1959. Here again, past wastage is an element of error. The gas that was wasted in the past, if it had not been wasted, would be in the ground today, and would be part of proved reserves. In the strict sense, this is not true; that is, the very same gas that was wasted might not be part of proved reserves today, since it might have been produced in place of other gas that entered into production, because of more favorable location or mere chance. But *net* production would have remained unchanged if there had never been any waste, for the only limitation on production was demand, not supply. Thus, proved reserves of gas, as a net or residual quantity, would have been larger throughout the history of the oil and gas industry. Since no suitable estimate of wastage exists, the proved-reserve ratio understates the true situation to an unknown degree. A more serious drawback, however, is the fact that proved reserves, as a net or residual quantity, are as much a function of production as of discovery, being the net result of both activities. Proved reserves of oil have tended to bear a rather constant relationship to production, but for several decades before the postwar period gas reserves tended to mount because of the lack of a market for what was found. Gas reserves therefore reflect the course of previous production as much as the fruits of discovery, and introduce an indeterminate error in the other direction.

This leads to consideration of the fifth possibility, the discovery ratio. To the extent that discovery activity is chiefly a search for oil, the results of that activity, through the unexpected findings of gas, would reflect the natural ratio of occurrence between recoverable oil and recoverable gas. Conversely, to the extent that discovery effort is deliberately for gas alone and is independent of the oil search, the ratio reflects the value of gas (that is, a higher value of gas stimulates the search for gas, hence leads to greater gas discoveries relative to oil discoveries). To complicate the matter, the definition of proved reserves leads to two kinds of discoveries as defined in the statistics: "Extensions and revisions" are the result of the development of known fields, and are "discoveries" only in the sense that they are additions to proved reserves through the proof of what was previously suspected or expected. "Discoveries of new fields and new pools in old fields" are the result of exploration in the true sense, known as "wildcatting." This exploration is undertaken with, at the most, indirect evidence of the possible occurrence of oil or gas, and sometimes in the absence of any evidence at all.

Which of these discovery ratios is most representative of the relative abundance, in the ground, of recoverable oil and recoverable gas? The ratio in old pools and fields, as revealed in the figures for extensions and revisions, is invalid to the extent that it depends on the specific characteristics of the pools and fields being developed. Those in which development is essentially completed (hence contribute little to the "discovery" statistics) are not adequately represented in the ratio. The ratio in new pools and fields alone is a truer representation of discovery, yet there is an advantage to a third ratio—in total discoveries or additions to proved reserves—in the sense that it constitutes a larger sample.

The significance of the choice between the three discovery ratios is demonstrated in Table 111 and Figure 69. During the period for which proved-reserve statistics are available, the gas-oil ratio in new fields and new pools has been consistently higher than that in extensions and revisions, averaging almost two and one-half times the latter during the thirteen-year period. (The ratio in total discoveries is closer to that in extensions and revisions because of the great preponderance of the latter in the total.) Thus, the use of a ratio based on one or the other can yield widely varying estimates of total future supply. The immediate question, however, is not what the choice should be, but why there is a dramatic difference between the results of wildcatting and of the development of known pools and fields.

One factor would appear to be depth and its relation to the gas-oil ratio. Terry describes this as follows: "Since gas is compressed somewhat in proportion to pressure, the quantity, by weight, of gas contained in a cubic foot of pore space is greater with increasing depth. . . . Deposits of oil found at great depths and under correspondingly high pressure contain larger proportions of gas in solution than oil in shallow reservoirs." Moreover, at greater depths the proportion of free gas

TABLE 111. GAS-OIL RATIO IN "DISCOVERIES" OF PROVED RESERVES, 1947–59

(Cubic feet per barrel)

Year	Extensions and revisions	New fields and pools	Total discoveries
1959	4,529	15,705	5,655
1958	5,838	17,828	7,285
1957	5,535	21,622	8,296
1956	7,664	12,064	8,355
1955	6,812	11,991	7,666
1954	2,025	8,479	3,462
1953	4,944	11,969	6,205
1952	3,966	10,900	5,218
1951	3,233	7,808	3,637
1950	4,591	5,093	4,702
1949	3,509	5,180	3,976
1948	2,874	10,414	3,662
1947	3,749	7,656	4,455
Average	4,559	11,285	5,583

SOURCE: Annual proved-reserve estimates of American Petroleum Institute and American Gas Association.

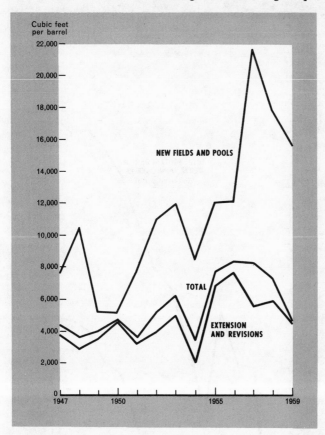

Cubic feet per barrel

NEW FIELDS AND POOLS

TOTAL

EXTENSION AND REVISIONS

Figure 69.   Gas-oil ratio in "discoveries" of proved reserves, 1947–59.

present is likely to be greater, "since the deeper the deposit the higher the reservoir temperature and the greater the possibility for more complete transformation of the original oil in place with resulting increased formation of gas."[21]

Statistics on the distribution of existing wells by depth are lacking, and for new wells the statistics are available for only a few years, but it is evident that a very high proportion of all development wells are in shallow pools less than 4,000 feet below the surface (see table 104). The average depth of all wells drilled in the United States in 1958 was 4,019 feet. However, the number of deep wildcats (those 15,000 feet and below) has been increasing as deep drilling activity has grown (see Figure 70, based on Table 103), and discoveries at these depths should come to constitute a correspondingly higher proportion of total wildcat

[21] *Ibid.*, p. 158. Weeks (in a communication to the author) suggests, in addition, the possibility that gas may flush oil from the deeper reservoirs, causing it to migrate up-dip into shallower traps.

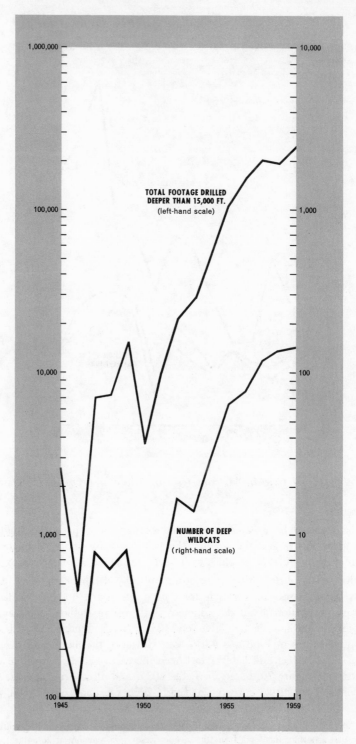

Figure 70. Total footage and number of wildcats drilled each year deeper than 15,000 feet, 1945–59.

discoveries. Further, the wildcatting in the offshore Gulf province is deep drilling, and both the success ratio and gas-oil ratio are high.[22]

Nevertheless, it is possible that the difference between the gas-oil ratio in wildcatting and in development has a nongeologic basis. The ratio may reflect the rapid increase in the field price of natural gas in the postwar era which, through anticipation of still higher prices, would lead to more wildcatting for gas and a consequent higher ratio. Thus, Table 112 shows that in this period the proportion of additions to reserves from wildcatting to total additions to reserves in gas has consistently been higher than the same proportion in oil, and the ratio between the two proportions has averaged 2.03 in the past thirteen years. (That is, the proportion of wildcat discoveries to total discoveries of gas in each year has averaged 2.03 times the same proportion in oil for that year.) To the extent that this influence holds, the gas-oil ratio in wildcat discoveries is a reflection of the relative value of gas.

For present purposes, it is not necessary to decide which of the two influences, depth or value, is primarily or wholly responsible for the higher gas-oil ratio in wildcat discoveries. It can be assumed that future discoveries will be deeper on the average and that the value of natural gas will certainly not fall, and may even continue its present rising trend. On balance, therefore, it seems reasonable to use a figure higher than Terry's but not on the order of recent wildcat experience.

TABLE 112. YEARLY ADDITIONS TO RESERVES IN NEW FIELDS
AND POOLS AS PERCENTAGE OF TOTAL YEARLY ADDITIONS
TO RESERVES, 1947–59

Year	In gas	In oil	Ratio, gas to oil
1959	28.0%	10.1%	2.77
1958	29.5	12.1	2.44
1957	44.7	17.2	2.60
1956	22.7	15.7	1.44
1955	26.0	16.6	1.56
1954	51.7	20.4	2.53
1953	34.6	18.0	1.92
1952	37.7	18.0	2.09
1951	18.9	8.8	2.14
1950	23.9	22.0	1.08
1949	36.4	27.9	1.30
1948	29.7	10.4	2.85
1947	31.0	18.1	1.71
Average			2.03

[22] *Petroleum Week*, February 22, 1957, pp. 41–70; also I. H. Cram, "The Outlook Offshore," paper given at meeting of American Petroleum Institute, Chicago, November 14, 1956. Gulf Coast offshore wells currently average 9,700 feet in depth; by 1970, such wells are expected to average over 12,000 feet. (See C. R. Graham, "The Big Offshore Picture—to 1970," *The Petroleum Engineer*, Vol. 29, No. 5 [May 1957], pp. B-21–27). Wildcats will lead the way down, and can be expected to be consistently deeper, on the average, than the average for all wells.

A ratio of 7,000 is chosen here as a figure higher than 6,000 that is not too drastic an increase. Admittedly, as an arbitrary choice this is no more refined than the ratio assumptions used in preceding estimates of total future natural gas supply, but at least it reflects the position developed here that the ratios previously used are too low.

PRODUCTION ASPECTS

Again, the general conclusions regarding drilling technology and the exploitation of the offshore provinces that were reached in the discussion of oil apply equally well to natural gas. There are, in addition, certain physical limitations on gas production that require mention.

Since dissolved gas (known as "casinghead" gas to producers) is produced by oil wells, it is difficult or even impossible to vary the rate of production independently of the oil production of the well. Its availability is thus determined by the rate of oil production. To some extent, this is modified by state conservation regulations, as in Texas, where the common permissible gas-oil ratio in oil-well output is 2,000 cubic feet per barrel. That is, the production of casinghead gas from a given oil well normally cannot exceed this ratio; any excess gas "produced" by the well must be recycled back to the reservoir.

The prime reason for such control is to conserve reservoir energy and thus increase the total primary production of oil from the reservoir. This same objective applied to a gas cap tends to postpone gas production until the reservoir's producing life for primary oil is about exhausted. The degree to which this may be necessary or desirable depends on many factors—for example, the gas-oil ratio in a reservoir. With a minor quantity of oil present, the reservoir may be treated as a non-associated gas occurrence. The significant distinction, however, is that the output of gas wells from a gas cap occurrence is not closely related to the rate of oil output from the reservoir.

The recovery factor for gas was mentioned at the start of this chapter. In addition to the "secondary resources" implied there, which are known to exist but which on economic criteria have been excluded from the estimate of proved reserves, there are other categories of such resources. One such category stems from the recovery limitations imposed by the presumed sealing off of small pockets of gas in the reservoir through the encroachment of water as gas is withdrawn and the pressure declines. The formation of such small pockets may not be detectable or, if known, their recovery may not be worth the necessary special measures. Another is the dissolved gas content of secondary oil resources; such gas probably cannot be recovered except through production of the oil, so if the oil is secondary, the gas is also.

It would be advantageous to have some idea of the extent of known secondary reserves of gas, such as were provided by Torrey for oil. Since they cannot be quantified, the most that can be said is that there exists an unknown quantity of gas which will become available given improved gas recovery techniques (such as "fracturing" to increase the effective permeability of the area around a gas well, thus making it economically feasible to carry a given reservoir to a lower abandonment pressure) and the use of secondary oil resources.

. . .

Conclusions on Domestic Natural Gas Availability

The first step in deriving conclusions on domestic natural gas availability in 1975 is to estimate total future supply. In the absence of data, there is no alternative to the method used by all previous estimators—the application of an assumed gas-oil ratio to an assumed future oil supply. The ratio adopted above is 7,000 cubic feet per barrel, and the resource base for future oil production has been estimated to be on the order of 500 billion barrels. The gas-oil ratio is, however, in terms of current recoverability, since it is derived from data based on the proved reserve concept. Thus, the figure of 500 billion barrels must be converted back to a current recoverability basis by dividing by three (the reverse of the resource-base conversion), which yields a figure of 167 billion barrels.[23] It will be seen that the total future supply estimate derived here is, in round numbers, the same as that of Terry and Winger, although the basis is different. Nevertheless, this study in effect agrees with those authors that the total future supply of natural gas in the light of present knowledge is on the order of 1.2 quadrillion cubic feet.

There remains to be considered the availability of natural gas in the year 1975. As a first step, existing estimates of natural gas output in that year are referred to. None of the estimates for that year given in Table 108 is related to a total future supply estimate as large as that adopted here (the Terry and Winger estimate of 1.2 quadrillion cubic feet is for 1980). The highest existing estimate for 1975 is related to an estimated total future supply of 850 trillion cubic feet. In adopting an estimate of 1975 availability for present purposes, it is instructive to test this highest estimate—the A.G.A. figure of 22.5 trillion cubic feet—for plausibility.

What does the A.G.A. figure imply in relation to the availability estimate developed for oil? It was concluded that domestic primary availability of oil in 1975 would be some 4 billion barrels, and secondary availability would be on the order of 2 billion barrels. But secondary output must be ignored on the presumption that, being secondary, the reservoir energy is essentially exhausted, hence the gas available from secondary output would be negligible. On this basis, a gas output of 22.5 trillion cubic feet would mean a gas-oil ratio of 5,625 cubic feet

---

[23] When the above gas-oil ratio is applied to this, the result is 1.169 quadrillion cubic feet of gas. If this, in turn, is converted to a resource-base equivalent by dividing by a factor of 0.8, there is an indicated quantity of almost 1.5 quadrillion cubic feet potentially available for future recovery. The latter figure can be passed over in this instance since, due to the relatively high level of recovery that already exists, the total supply available for future production should be on the order indicated whether no improvement in recovery levels occurs or whether full recovery is attained. The difference between the two figures, in other words, is within the error of estimation.

per barrel of primary oil output. Although this is 12 per cent greater than the 1959 production ratio of 5,010, it is consistent with the conclusions previously stated concerning a higher gas-oil ratio in the future than in the past.

A second ratio implied in the A.G.A. estimate relative to that for oil availability is associated gas output to oil output. Assuming a ratio of 2,500 cubic feet per barrel, the highest level yet recorded in proved reserves,[24] the output of associated gas in 1975 would be 48 per cent of total gas output. Dissolved gas alone currently accounts for 30 to 33 per cent of total current output (see Table 113, column 6, and Figure 71), so that total associated gas constitutes a greater but unknown proportion of the total.

It is apparent from the foregoing that a level of gas output such as estimated by the A.G.A. carries with it in the present study certain key assumptions: (1) a high gas-oil ratio in total output; and (2) either (a) a high gas-oil ratio where the hydrocarbons occur together, or (b) a very high gas-oil ratio in future discoveries, sufficient to allow future non-associated gas discoveries to replace the proved reserves in giant gas fields which currently constitute a large proportion of total proved reserves.

The first assumption and (a) under the second are consistent with the general conclusions reached previously in this study, but it is also clear that any higher figure for 1975 gas output would begin to stretch this consistency. It has been concluded that the proportion of non-associated gas in total proved reserves is likely to decline. To the extent that this occurs, more of the yearly output must come from associated reserves. But this, in turn, means that gas output is to a greater extent a function of oil output, and the higher the estimated gas output, the higher the required ratio for associated gas. Thus the A.G.A. figure of 22.5 trillion cubic feet must be taken, on the basis of present knowledge, as the limit of domestic natural gas availability in 1975 despite the fact that this study obtains a higher estimate of total future supply than that to which the A.G.A. figure for 1975 is related.

This does not weaken the plausibility of the estimated total future supply of 1.2 quadrillion cubic feet. The key assumption on which this is based is a higher gas-oil ratio in the future than in the past. It was not possible to determine whether the higher ratio would be due to geologic factors at depth or to the influence of economic factors (price) on gas discovery; the adoption of 22.5 trillion cubic feet as the availability in 1975 stems from this open question. If depth is the basic determinant, then the limitation of oil output on gas output is called more strongly into play (that is, the gas-oil ratio will be higher because *more gas with oil*, as well as more gas reservoirs, occurs at depth). But if price is fundamental, then the plausibility of an output level above 22.5 trillion is increased (the gas-oil ratio can be greater if exploration for gas *per se* is stimu-

---

[24] See Table 110. Unfortunately, there are no production statistics for associated gas alone. Figures are available for gas from oil wells and gas from gas wells (see Table 113). The former gives dissolved gas output, but the latter includes both gas from gas caps and gas from non-associated gas reservoirs.

lated by a higher price, and more unassociated gas discoveries are made relative
to total oil discoveries).

A word should be added concerning the meaning of the availability estimate
of 22.5 trillion cubic feet in the light of the A.G.A. and Bureau of Mines production statistics. The two sets of figures are arrived at independently and do not
correspond exactly, but tie in fairly well with each other. The A.G.A. figures are
for "net production," defined as gas permanently removed from the natural
reservoir, excluding gas that is cycled for natural gas liquids recovery or reinjected for repressuring purposes. The Bureau of Mines furnishes a set of statistics,
listed in Table 113, that begin with "total gross withdrawal" (column 1). This
refers to all gas taken out of the ground, for whatever purpose and regardless of
whether it is returned to the reservoir. "Marketed production" (column 4) refers
to the quantity of gas that is actually sold. The difference between gross withdrawal and marketed production consists of gas returned to the reservoir for
repressuring (column 5) and gas lost, wasted, and consumed in production (not
shown in Table 113). If one deducts the quantity of gas used in repressuring

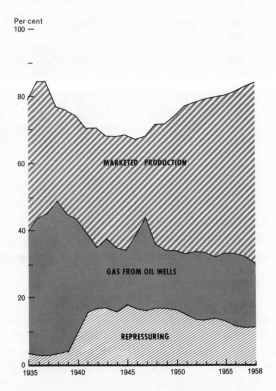

*Figure 71. Marketed production, gas from oil wells, and repressuring, as per-
centage of gross natural gas withdrawals, 1935–58.*

TABLE 113. GAS WITHDRAWAL AND DISPOSITION, 1935-58

(In billion cubic feet)

| | | | | | Per cent of total | | |
Year	Total gross withdrawal (1)	From gas wells (2)	From oil wells (3)	Marketed production (4)	Repressuring (5)	From oil wells (3) ÷ (1) (6)	Marketed production (4) ÷ (1) (7)	Repressuring (5) ÷ (1) (8)
1958..	13,147	9,154	3,993	11,030	1,483	30.4%	83.9%	11.3%
1957..	12,907	8,717	4,190	10,680	1,417	32.4	82.7	11.0
1956..	12,373	8,307	4,066	10,082	1,427	32.9	81.5	11.5
1955..	11,720	7,842	3,878	9,405	1,541	33.1	80.2	13.1
1954..	10,985	7,466	3,519	8,743	1,519	32.0	79.6	13.8
1953..	10,646	7,095	3,551	8,397	1,439	33.4	78.9	13.5
1952..	10,273	6,839	3,433	8,013	1,411	33.4	78.0	13.7
1951..	9,689	6,481	3,208	7,457	1,439	33.1	77.0	14.8
1950..	8,480	5,603	2,876	6,282	1,397	33.9	74.1	16.5
1949..	7,547	4,986	2,561	5,420	1,273	33.9	71.8	16.9
1948..	7,179	4,589	2,590	5,148	1,221	36.1	71.7	17.0
1947..	6,733	3,770	2,963	4,582	1,083	44.0	68.0	16.1
1946..	6,190	3,808	2,383	4,153	1,038	38.5	67.1	16.8
1945..	5,902	3,888	2,014	4,042	1,062	34.1	68.5	18.0
1944..	5,614	3,650	1,964	3,815	883	35.0	68.0	15.7
1943..	5,161	3,227	1,934	3,516	885	37.5	68.1	17.1
1942..	4,454	2,885	1,569	3,146	753	35.2	70.6	16.9
1941..	4,104	2,491	1,613	2,894	644	39.3	70.5	15.7
1940..	3,694	2,095	1,599	2,734	363	43.3	74.0	9.8
1939..	3,334	1,833	1,501	2,538	171	45.0	76.1	5.1
1938..	3,061	1,567	1,494	2,358	101	48.8	77.0	3.3
1937..	2,939	1,614	1,326	2,473	85	45.1	84.1	2.9
1936..	2,645	1,484	1,161	2,225	74	43.9	84.1	2.8
1935..	2,498	1,493	1,005	1,969	90	40.2	78.8	3.6

SOURCE: U.S. Bureau of Mines, *Minerals Yearbook*, various issues (Washington, D. C.: U.S. Government Printing Office).

from the total gross withdrawal figure one gets the Bureau of Mines equivalent to the A.G.A. net production figure—in 1958 this was 11.7 trillion cubic feet. In the language of this study, total gross withdrawal is equivalent to "gross availability." The above estimate of "net availability" in 1975 does not conform to the definition of either the A.G.A. or the Bureau of Mines terms, but it can be considered closer to a net production figure than to anything else.

It remains, then, to examine the relation between the estimate of 1975 net availability and the other items in Table 113. Columns 7 and 8 in Table 113 list marketed production and repressuring as a percentage of gross withdrawals, and the data are graphed in Figure 71. It will be seen that there was a marked decline in the proportion of gas withdrawals marketed (equivalent to net availability) from 1937 through 1946 and, beginning in 1947, a subsequent return to the earlier level. In the earlier years of the period, most of the nonmarketed gas was wasted. The recent rise in the marketed proportion, despite the rise in repressuring (column 8), reflects the adoption of gas conservation measures as well as the decline in the proportion of gas produced from oil wells. It can be expected that in the period through 1975 the proportion of total withdrawals wasted will further decline, so that virtually all of the withdrawals not marketed will represent repressuring use, the course of which has been the opposite of marketed production relative to total gross withdrawals. The earlier rise is also due to conservation measures; the more recent decline can be ascribed to the postwar growth of non-associated gas output. The course of this relation in the future again depends on the place of associated and dissolved gas output in the total. It seems reasonable to conclude that net availability, because of repressuring, should range between 10 and 15 per cent lower than gross withdrawals in 1975.

. . .

Other Sources of Supply

IMPORTS

As was true of crude oil, allowance must also be made for imports as an element of total natural gas supply, for there is no reason to assume that domestic supply will satisfy demand in 1975, regardless of the level of demand. On the contrary, regional factors in the supply and demand of natural gas generate strong pressures towards the international movement of natural gas in North America.

In contrast to oil imports, natural gas imports have been negligible to date in relation to total natural gas supply (see Table 114). Large-scale contracts for imports from both Canada and Mexico over a twenty-year period, however, have already been entered into, and these indicate that in the coming decades foreign supply could become a formidable competitor to domestic supply in several important regions of the country.

TABLE 114.   IMPORTS AS A PERCENTAGE OF TOTAL NATURAL GAS SUPPLY

Year	Per cent
1958	1.15
1957	0.29
1956	0.10
1955	0.11
1954	0.07
1953	0.10
1952	0.09

SOURCE: U.S. Bureau of Mines, *Minerals Yearbook*, various issues (Washington, D. C.: U.S. Government Printing Office).

The export potential of Canada has been assessed for that country's own purposes in a study sponsored by the Royal Commission on Canada's Economic Prospects. According to this study, Canada could sustain an annual export level to the United States of one trillion cubic feet in the 1975 period without affecting supply or price in the domestic (Canadian) market. This is also considered the upper limit that could be contracted for without endangering the Canadian supply position after 1980.[25] No equivalent figures are available concerning the import possibilities from Mexico in 1975. Although such imports might rise, there is no basis on which to make a quantitative estimate of their growth.

In addition to gas imports received via the traditional pipeline method of transportation, there is the revolutionary possibility involving the transport of natural gas by barge or tanker. This procedure involves liquefying the natural gas in the field at a temperature of approximately minus 260°F. and transporting it in the liquid state in insulated tanks, at atmospheric pressure, using the vapor from the liquid gas as fuel for the voyage. The gas is transferred to storage tanks at the market terminal still in the liquid state; it is delivered to consumers in the gaseous state, and in the process of vaporizing at the terminal it absorbs large quantities of heat. (Each 20 to 22 Mcf of gas evaporated and warmed provides one ton of refrigeration capacity.)[26] With suitable arrangements, this by-product refrigeration capacity can be utilized for such operations as cold-storage warehousing or the liquefaction of air (the latter could be marketed in turn or could be used on the spot in a petrochemical plant based on the natural gas).

The water-transport approach for liquefied gas has undergone pilot operations in this country and there is considerable interest in the development of the method in several parts of the world.[27] One rather detailed analysis of the economic and technical problems concludes that "the proposed system under the worst conditions equals the present system of pipeline transmission."[28] According to this same study, the major physical problems concern the choice and design of

[25] J. Davis, *Canadian Energy Prospects* (Ottawa: Royal Commission on Canada's Economic Prospects, 1957), p. 182.

[26] *Power Engineering*, Vol. 59, No. 6 (June 1954), pp. 92–93.

[27] Examples of this international interest are: The Japanese have reportedly been attempting to work out a project to import liquefied natural gas by tanker from Borneo, Sumatra, and other Southeast Asian sources, and even from Iran (*Petroleum Week*, July 5, 1957, p. 50, and September 27, 1957, p. 51). The use of tanker transport of liquefied natural gas across the Mediterranean, to market the recently discovered Algerian gas in Europe, is receiving serious consideration (*Oil and Gas Journal*, April 11, 1960, p. 98). A British experiment with the importation of liquefied natural gas from the U.S. Gulf Coast began in 1959. For a concise summary of the background of this experiment see C. I. Kelly, "Liquefied Natural Gas, Part I," *The Petroleum Times*, Vol. LXII, No. 1,578 (January 31, 1958), pp. 84–86. A thorough examination of all aspects of the subject of liquefied natural gas is provided in Parts II-VII of the paper, which appear in successive issues of the same journal (Nos. 1,579–1,586). For an early report on the British import project see J. A. Murphy and C. G. Filstead, "Ocean Transport of Liquid Methane," Paper 3, Section VIII, Fifth World Petroleum Congress, New York, May 30–June 5, 1959.

[28] J. D. Crecca, Jr., "Liquid Gas . . . an Investigation" (Part VI—Summary), *Gas Journal*, Vol. 287, No. 4,853 (July 18, 1956), p. 177.

container and insulating materials and the establishment of water transport safety standards.

In the present context, the significance of the concept of transporting liquefied gas by water is that it is applicable to the importation of natural gas from the oilfields of Venezuela. Although initial development of natural gas liquids recovery units and petrochemical plants is now beginning in Venezuela, such development will have to go a long way to absorb the available supply—56 per cent of the total yearly gas output of over a trillion cubic feet is currently flared.[29]

The more remote possibility of gas imports from the Middle East should also be mentioned. Gas wastage in the Middle East is also great: 500 million cubic feet per day in Saudi Arabia alone. Total flaring in the Middle East is about 1.5 billion cubic feet per day.[30] There is talk of getting the gas to energy-hungry Europe, and the possibility of liquefied natural gas imports from the Middle East to the United States by 1975 is not inconceivable.

In addition to his general analysis of the subject referred to above, Crecca has also published an economic analysis of a theoretical project to supply the Philadelphia area with its gas needs from Venezuela. According to this study, a fleet of seven converted T-2 tankers could supply 16 billion cubic feet a year at an over-all cost of 3.19 cents per therm (100,000 Btu), or about 32 cents per Mcf.[31] This compares with 1955 city gate prices for pipelined natural gas in Philadelphia of 34–39 cents per Mcf. The calculations were made for methane, which has a lower liquefaction temperature—hence higher liquefaction costs—than natural gas. Engineering assumptions at all stages were deliberately held conservative, and no credit for by-product refrigeration was allowed. Thus, on all counts, the economics appear favorable.

There is, of course, no means at present of foretelling whether importation of liquefied natural gas by water transport will ever come to pass, or if it does, when and on what scale. Evidence to date, however, indicates that this means of supply is technically and economically feasible on a significant scale. As such it is an important potential source.

In view of the above discussion, it can be concluded that a considerable expansion in natural gas imports could take place, both absolutely and relative to total domestic consumption. The growth of imports from contiguous countries will be determined by supply-demand relationships and government export policies in those countries. Overseas imports involve technology, in addition. If they become a reality their growth would be influenced both by world market circumstances and by U.S. import policy.

[29] See *Petroleum Press Service*, March 1960, p. 89.

[30] *Petroleum Press Service*, July 1960, p. 259.

[31] J. D. Crecca, Jr., "Venezuelan Natural Gas for U.S.?" *Oil and Gas Journal*, November 19, 1956, pp. 255, 257. See also Kelly, *op. cit.*, Part VI, for a complete summary of Crecca's original study. Economic feasibility is also indicated for the New York area by a more recent study by P. B. Lederman and B. Williams in "Economics of Gas Liquefaction," *Gas Age*, November 14, 1957, pp. 41–47.

PRICE ASPECTS

At this point, some observations concerning price are necessary. The assumption has been made throughout the discussion of both crude oil and natural gas that constant dollar costs will not increase significantly, but this does not mean that the price of gas will also be stable. In the past five years, there has been a very rapid rise in the price of natural gas. This is less related to costs, however, than to market forces. Gas is a premium fuel in that it supplies Btu's at the burner with high efficiency and with unequalled convenience and cleanliness. With large overcapacity in the field in earlier years due to lack of transmission facilities, the price of natural gas could not reflect this premium value; but with the development of markets based on its premium characteristics, price has come to reflect such value.

The recent rise in the price of natural gas has been by any standards both large and rapid. The average price at the wellhead for the years 1946–50 was 6.2 cents per Mcf. In 1959, it was 12.1 cents, and in 1956 new contracts were running as high as 22.5 cents and reserves were being valued as high as 40 cents.[32] (In 1958, new contracts for offshore gas were being written as high as 23.3 cents, and the wellhead price was 11.7 cents per Mcf.) The average value at the point of consumption (obtained by dividing sales volume into revenues received from consumers) was 24.5 cents per Mcf for the 1946–50 period. By 1958 this had risen to 46 cents.[33] (These national averages conceal wide regional ranges which result from the regional nature of gas markets and the variation that exists in field prices. A consideration of the regional aspects is, however, a study in itself, and it is believed that the figures above are meaningful as first-order approximations.)

Such an upward trend in both field and delivered prices cannot, of course, continue indefinitely, although some existing contracts contain escalation provisions for field prices reaching 36.4 cents in 1986. A continued rise in the average wellhead value will further stimulate discovery and will tend to increase the import potential. But a rise in the average delivered value will adversely affect the competitive position of natural gas versus other fuels despite the somewhat inelastic character of residential demand. This stems from the market pattern of natural gas. Large-volume industrial consumers account for somewhat more than half of the total natural gas consumption. They are able to obtain the gas at a much lower price than the residential and commercial retail price not only because the cost of distribution to them is lower but because their consumption is complementary to residential and commercial use. The latter uses fluctuate widely, especially between seasons, so that their annual load factor is on the order of 40 per cent. But transmission pipelines must operate as close to 100-per cent load factor as possible, and industrial sales are the means by which this is accom-

[32] A. K. Lee, "A Simple Solution for the Gas Producer Problem," *Public Utilities Fortnightly*, Vol. 58, No. 7 (September 27, 1956), p. 442; also T. P. Walker, "Some Comments on Gas Supply," *Public Utilities Fortnightly*, Vol. 58, No. 9 (October 25, 1956), p. 675.

[33] U.S. Bureau of Mines, *Minerals Yearbook*, various issues (Washington, D. C.: U.S. Government Printing Office).

plished. The development of underground storage to offset the seasonal peaking of residential and commercial consumption has been helpful in this respect, but it can replace only a portion of industrial consumption. The gas quantities involved—as much as 60 per cent of the total pipeline throughput—are simply too great for underground storage to be the entire solution to the peaking problem.

Yet industrial consumption of natural gas is elastic—it responds quickly and significantly to changes in the relative price of natural gas compared to that of competing fuels. Thus, wherever and whenever the gas price approaches that of its competitors in following an upward trend it can be expected that industrial consumption will fall off.[34] To the extent that such industrial sales no longer help carry the fixed charges on transmission and distribution systems, those charges must be taken on by the residential and commercial customers. Hence, at a certain level in a rising price trend, the effect on the prices to the residential and commercial consumers will become magnified and the inelasticity of their demand will tend to be offset. They, too, will begin to turn to competitive fuels.

In addition to these long-run market forces, there is the unresolved question of government regulation that remains at issue. Since the legislative outcome on this issue cannot be foreseen at this time, its possible effect on the price behavior of natural gas cannot be dealt with here.

SYNTHETIC GAS

Beyond this, in any event, there is the absolute ceiling set by synthetic gas. Oil and coal are, after all, not complete substitutes for gas and, to the extent that they are not, there remains a market for certain specific gas uses at almost any price. But synthetic gas can be a total substitute for natural gas and, given the proper price relationships, could completely replace it. The competitive relationship between synthetic and natural gas is rather complicated and necessitates some preliminary explanation.

Unlike synthetic liquid fuels, synthetic gas is not only a consideration for the future but has been important in the past. Indeed, synthetic gas preceded natural gas by a century as the major gaseous fuel in this country. The synthetic gas of the past and present, commonly termed "manufactured gas," is produced by several processes which depend in one way or another on coke or oil as the basis. However, due to a number of circumstances, these processes are no longer economically feasible as a means of supplying a full substitute for natural gas. Natural gas is generally cheaper; at the same time, the costs of coking coal and its shipment, and the operating costs of the gas-making process have all risen.

There is also an important physical distinction. The major constituent of natural gas is methane, a simple hydrocarbon compound. The major constituents

[34] See, for example, W. R. Connole, "Energy, Its Use and Abuse," address before Independent Natural Gas Association of America, Houston, Texas, September 10, 1957, for a recent analysis of this prospect.

of manufactured gas, on the other hand, are hydrogen and carbon monoxide. The monetary value of any fuel gas is determined by its energy content, which is measured in British thermal units (Btu's) per cubic foot and is termed the "heat value" of the gas. Manufactured gas has an average heat value of 500 to 600 Btu per cubic foot, whereas natural gas averages 1,035 Btu per cubic foot, as marketed.

The emergence of natural gas in generally available supply throughout the United States has meant that any competitive gaseous fuel should preferably be in the same range of heat value. That is, in order to utilize long-distance pipeline transportation and to avoid changeover problems in gas-burning equipment, the alternative gas should have a heat value between 750 and 1,000 Btu per cubic foot,[35] a specific gravity in the same range as natural gas, and burning characteristics comparable to those of natural gas. A high-Btu gas is necessary for pipeline operations because the gas must have a high value to sustain the cost of pipeline transmission; or, to put it another way, the pipeline must have a high throughput of energy, not just gas volume. It is possible to produce such a gas from any hydrocarbon material in the form of a product which is, like natural gas, predominantly or almost wholly methane. Such a gas may be considered the synthetic equivalent of the natural product.

Synthetic gas from crude oil or its products, known as "oil gas," is currently used as a gas source in certain areas, but only for meeting peak needs or to enrich manufactured gas. Its production is carried on near the market, since it is cheaper to transport Btu's as oil, either by tanker or pipeline, than to transport Btu's as gas. The use of oil gas on a national scale to supply firm demand can be considered unlikely, however, since natural gas should be in relatively abundant supply through 1975. Indeed, such use of oil gas would involve a major revolution in the prices of all petroleum products, for a large increase in the demand for refinery products suitable for gasification would seriously alter the refinery product mix. Oil gas is therefore ruled out of the discussion, leaving coal and oil shale as the sources to be considered.

The production of synthetic gas from coal on a large scale would not raise any problems of coal supply on the national level, but locational limitations are imposed by the requirements of individual plants. Roughly 100 pounds of coal are needed per thousand cubic feet of high-Btu gas produced. The present indicated economic minimum capacity for a coal gasification plant is about 100 million cubic feet daily, and the average would more likely be 200 million cubic feet. At the latter size, coal consumption would amount to 10,000 tons a day.[36] This necessitates that gasification be carried out close to the coal mine and that coal be used directly (that is, without an intermediate stage such as coke). The gas, in

---

[35] J. E. Tobey, "Gasification—Significance to the Bituminous Coal Industry," *Gasification and Liquefaction of Coal* (New York: American Institute of Mining and Metallurgical Engineers, 1953), pp. 207–09.

[36] W. Gumz and J. F. Foster, *A Critical Survey of Methods of Making a High BTU Gas from Coal*, Research Bulletin No. 6 (New York: American Gas Association, July 1953), p. 36.

turn, must be supplied to most markets via long-distance pipeline, since market areas and coalfields do not generally coincide.[37]

Pilot-plant operation has indicated promise in two approaches to coal gasification in this country. One is a two-stage process that produces first a low-Btu gas which is catalytically methanated to a high-Btu pipeline gas. The other is a direct hydrogenation process in which "two of three elements of bituminous coal are converted directly to pipeline gas under proper pressure and temperature conditions, perhaps in the presence of a catalyst, with the third element used as a source of heat."[38] Both of these processes are suitable for base-load operation; indeed, they require a high load factor.

Other processes have been investigated or conceived in attempts to reduce or eliminate the biggest economic obstacles to large-scale coal gasification—the cost of coal and the cost of gasification process itself. Coal is a major item in the total cost of synthetic gas, and each increase of $1 per ton in its cost means an increase in the gas cost of 6 cents per Mcf.[39] The mining cost could be eliminated entirely through gasification of the coal in place underground, but the general Btu content of the resultant gas would be very low, even if oxygen were employed. Considerable upgrading would thus be required to obtain a pipeline gas. Although continuing experiments are being carried out both in this country and abroad, commerical possibilities in the United States as yet are not in sight.[40]

A revolutionary attack on gasification cost is to use a nuclear reactor as the source of heat. The basic limitation on the heat obtainable from a nuclear reactor is not the fuel input but the limits put on the operating temperature by the materials used in the reactor. The bulk heat output of a reactor thus suggests that this might be a fruitful means of reducing gasification costs. (In a two-stage process, the cost of the low-Btu initial gas is about 80 per cent of the total cost of the high-Btu product.[41]) At present, this approach is still in the conceptual design stage, hence is not considered here as a commercial possibility in the period through 1975.

The supply of high-Btu gas from oil shale can be obtained in four ways: as

[37] W. C. Schroeder, "Chemicals, Pipeline Gas, and Liquid Fuels from Coal," *Transactions*, Tenth Annual Anthracite Conference of Lehigh University, May 8–9, 1952, p. 42.

[38] W. B. Tippy, "Some Aspects of Gas Supply," paper presented at Executive Conference, American Gas Association, Colorado Springs, June 21, 1956.

[39] C. F. De Mey, "Study of Synthetic Natural Gas," *American Gas Association Monthly*, Vol. XXXIV, No. 11 (November 1952), p. 28.

[40] Investigations have been carried on in the United Kingdom, France, Belgium, Italy, and Poland, but not beyond the pilot-plant stage. In the U.S.S.R., however, "commercial" underground gasification has been functioning on a large scale for several years, and plans have been announced for projects with capacities of 3–8 billion cubic meters a year (*Petroleum Press Service*, August 1958, p. 304). Nevertheless, the Soviet experience is more a demonstration of technical feasibility than an indication of possible economic feasibility in any other country. Research in this field in both Great Britain and the United States was abandoned in 1959. See Department of Interior comment, *Power Engineering*, Vol. 63, No. 9 (September 1959), p. 95.

[41] U.S. Bureau of Mines, *Synthetic Liquid Fuels, Annual Report of the Secretary of the Interior for 1953*, Part I, "Oil From Coal," Report of Investigations 5043, April 1954, p. iv.

a by-product of shale oil refining, as a by-product of shale oil production, through pyrolysis of the shale oil, or through hydrogasification of the hydrocarbon content of the oil shale.

To a significant degree, the supply as a refinery by-product suffers from the serious limitation of the scale of refinery operation. To be a significant source of by-product gas, oil shale operations would have to be on such a scale as to contribute a substantial portion of the nation's liquid fuel supply. At the feasibility limit of 2 million barrels a day for shale oil operations, mentioned in the chapter on crude oil, the by-product gas from refinery shale oil would amount to about 500 million cubic feet annually, only a minor percentage of the marketed production of natural gas in 1958. This by-product would be available, moreover, only from thermal cracking—an obsolescent process for gasoline production.[42]

The Aspeco shale oil process used by Union Oil Company has a larger on-site gas yield. According to the company's report, gas from the kiln can be purged of its liquefiable hydrocarbons, carbon dioxide and hydrogen sulfide content to yield a gas of 700 to 1,000 Btu content per cubic foot.[43] Scaling up from the level of 10,000 barrels a day, to which the published data pertain, to the "feasibility level" of 2 million barrels indicates a potential yield of a billion or 2 billion cubic feet per year. Although larger than the refinery by-product yield, it is still an insignificant percentage of total supply. Such production would, however, have the advantage of nominal cost, since liquid fuels with this process are claimed to be competitive even if the gas is flared.[44]

It has been claimed that pyrolysis of shale oil, either at the mine or in the market area at the end of a shale oil pipeline, would be economically feasible,[45] but there remains the market problem of the by-products of the oil gasification. The value of by-product tar and light oils in the face of a vastly expanded supply could be so low as to make insignificant the credit from their sale that could be applied to the cost of the gas.

The most recent proposal to utilize oil shale as a source of fuel gas calls for the conversion of the organic carbon and hydrogen content to methane in one step, through direct hydrogenation of crushed oil shale at high temperature and pressure. The important advantage of this approach is the absence of the by-product problem and, because the yield is all gas (representing 90 to 100 per cent, by weight, of the organic content of the shale, compared to about 80 per cent hydrocarbon recovery in the more conventional retorting processes), the total output is substantial. The proponents of this approach estimate the yield would be 8 billion cubic feet per day, or almost 3 trillion cubic feet annually, of 1,000-

---

[42] U.S. Bureau of Mines, *Synthetic Liquid Fuels, Annual Report of the Secretary of the Interior for 1951*, Part II, "Oil from Oil Shale," Report of Investigations 4866, July 1952, pp. 44–47.

[43] *Petroleum Week*, July 18, 1958, pp. 74, 76.

[44] *Idem.*

[45] H. M. Henry, "Where Will New England Get Its Future Gas Supplies?" *Gas*, Vol. XXXI, No. 4 (April 1955), pp. 71–76.

Btu gas, at an operating level equivalent to 2 million barrels a day.[46] (This level is the claimed feasibility limit set by water availability—see Chapter 9.)

Table 115 summarizes the recent estimates of the cost of synthetic gas from coal and from oil shale. The estimates lack equivalence in several respects: (a) Most pertain to the cost of synthetic gas at the fuel source, but some refer to the cost at the city gate (at the market but prior to distribution). (b) The estimates vary in the specified Btu content of the gas but, where possible, this has been offset through conversion to a common basis—cost per million Btu. (c) The assumed coal cost is variable—specified costs range from $2 to $6.07 per ton (reflecting locational differences, different ranks and grades, and price changes over time). (d) Costs are expressed in current dollars in different years. (e) Some estimates are specific as to process, others are general.

General equivalence has been provided through conversion of the estimates to a common basis of cost per million Btu (MM Btu). Nevertheless, the wide variation in the technical details from which the estimates are derived makes it impossible to compare them individually without becoming involved in an extensive technical discussion. But this is not necessary, since all that is needed is a rough approximation of the cost level of synthetic gas as a competitor with natural gas.

Estimates for underground gasification and gasification involving nuclear reactors can be eliminated at this point. Because of their very early stage of development, these processes can be considered only as possibilities rather than probabilities for the period with which this study is concerned. The use of oil shale with three of the four possible processes described above rules it out as a significant source because of the limitations of the by-product aspect, although it could, like crude oil, have local importance. Concerning the fourth process, hydrogasification, results available from research to date pertain to "raw materials costs" only. It is not possible to say what total costs would be with this process other than to note that "very substantial operating, capital and transportation costs" would be added to the raw material figure of 30–33 cents per Mcf listed in Table 115. It is reasonable to assume, however, that the representative cost figure for gas from coal that is adopted below can also serve for the total cost of the oil shale product, delivered at the major consuming centers.

It is evident from the remaining estimates of Table 115 that there is a wide range of disagreement among the experts, even allowing for changes in the price level between 1950 and 1958. At the one extreme are estimates up to $1 per million Btu, representing, in general, costs as they are now seen. At the other extreme are estimates ranging down to less than 50 cents, expressing the expectations of their authors as to the results of future technological progress. As a useful middle ground, a figure of 65 cents per million Btu can be used to express the general level of the cost at which it might be possible to produce synthetic gas in volume, in the coal field, in the period through 1975.

[46] E. B. Shultz, Jr., and H. R. Linden, "Production of Pipeline Gas by Batch Hydrogenolysis of Oil Shale," paper given at annual meeting of American Chemical Society, Chicago, September 10, 1958.

TABLE 115.   COST ESTIMATES FOR SYNTHETIC GAS

Source	Date	Cost estimate ¢ per Mcf	Cost estimate ¢ per MMBtu	Btu content	Place (source or market)	Remarks
Gas from coal						
a) Foster and Vorum..	1950	65.6¢	82¢	800	source	Oxygen use, upgraded from 454 Btu Lurgi gas.
		71.2–77.6	89–97	800	market	Same, delivered 250–500 miles.
		40	50	800	source	Hypothetical single-stage, high-pressure process with 80% thermal efficiency.
b) Alberts *et al.*......	10/52	55.35	<61.5	900+	source	Lurgi plus catalytic methanation. Fuel cost $4 per ton. 6% capital return. By-product credit.
c) De Mey...........	11/52	55–65	<61.1–<72.2	900+	source	Interpretation of Alberts *et al.* Each dollar increment of fuel cost means 6¢ increment in gas cost.
d) Gumz and Foster...	7/53	58.1	58.1–72.6	800–1,000	source	Lurgi plus catalytic methanation, 1 atmosphere pressure.
		48.8	48.8–61.0	800–1,000	source	Using oxygen, 20 atmospheres pressure.
		45.6	45.6–57.0	800–1,000	source	Using oxygen, 85 atmospheres pressure.
		58.1	58.1–72.6	800–1,000	source	Pulverized coal, 20 atmospheres pressure, catalytic methanation with credit for all surplus steam. Fuel $4 per ton.
e) Breck.............	1953	54.77* / 58.0**	59.21* / 62.70**	925 / 925	source / source	Lurgi plus catalytic methanation, 1,200 lbs. pressure, char as fuel. Coal $3.70 per ton, by-product credit. *100% load factor, **90% load factor.
f) Minet *et al.*.......	7/54	56	62.22	900	source	Process unspecified. Char as fuel. Coal $6.07 per ton (25.8¢ per MMBtu) by-product credits.
g) Tippy.............	1/55	65–75 / 59	65–75 / 59	(1,000 assumed)	source	Cost of "natural gas equivalent," known techniques. Cost of "natural gas equivalent," research advance over 5-year period.
h) Henry............	3/55	—	45–55	"high"	source	Ultimate possibilities with unconventional gasification process.
i) Chandler..........	8/55	55–75	55–75	1,000	source	Bureau of Mines estimate using heat from nuclear reactor for gasification. 250–300 Btu gas, subsequently upgraded. Upgrading costs possibly lower than allowed for.

TABLE 115 (continued)

Source	Date	Cost estimate		Btu content	Place (source or market)	Remarks
		¢ per Mcf	¢ per MMBtu			
j) Tippy...........	6/56	—	{90–100¢ / 70–75}	"high"	source	{ Current indications for two-stage process "possibility of improvement."
k) Bureau of Mines...	11/56	{37.6¢ / 32.0}	{268.6 / 228.6}	140	source	Natural lignite at $2 per ton. Plant 50 MM cu. ft. per day, output H_2 and CO at ratio of 2.5:1. Same with steam-dried lignite at $3.60 per ton, H_2CO ratio 2:1.
Underground gasification						
l) Gerdetz...........	11/53	3.297¢	11.648¢	283	source	Combined mining and underground gas operation, 20–25% of coal mined and shipped. $4.50 per ton coal to car and gas to collar.
Gas from oil shale						
m) Bureau of Mines...	7/52	{14.8¢ / 18.2}	{13.96¢ / 14.00}	1,060 / 1,300	market / market	{ By-products of thermal cracking of shale oil at California end of pipeline. / At refinery, St. Louis, gas as by-product.
n) Henry.........	4/55	{18.2 / 43.2}	{14.0 / 33.2}	1,300 / 1,300	market / market	At refinery, New England, allowing 20–25¢ per Mcf transportation costs, using new pipelines.
		60–65	60–65	1,000	market	Gas manufactured in New England from landed shale oil at $2.50 per bbl. Gasification bearing all charges, less by-product credits.
o) Oil Shale Corp....	7/58	.... nominal		700–1,000	source	Produced at kiln as by-product in Aspeco process.
p) Shultz and Linden..	9/58	—	—	1,000	source	"Raw material cost," 30–33¢ per Mcf, complete hydrogasification of oilshale hydrocarbon content at temperatures up to 1300°F. and pressures of 82–320 atmospheres. Hydrogen obtained from product gas. Source, shale with oil content of 22.9 gals. per ton.

(Sources on next page.)

An analysis of pipeline costs and rate structures indicates that the average cost for gas transport is about 1.5 cents per Mcf per 100 miles.[47] Assuming the distance from coal fields to major gas-consuming centers would range between 100 and 500 miles, the cost of synthetic gas transport would be from 1.5 cents to 7.5 cents per Mcf. It was concluded above that the average cost of synthetic gas at the point of production, with present technology, is likely to be 65 cents per million Btu. Assuming, for convenience, that the product is 1,000-Btu pipeline gas, the cost of such synthetic gas at the city gate would be in the range of 66.5 cents to 72.5 cents per Mcf—or 70 cents as a round number.

In contrast, recent typical city-gate prices in the several market regions were as follows:[48]

[47] F. K. Edwards, "The Relative Position of Coal and Natural Gas as Competitive Fuels," paper presented at 1956 Spring Conference, Southeastern Association of Railroad and Utilities Commissioners, Miami Beach, April 6, 1956.

[48] H. D. Ralph, "Price is the Key to Growth of Gas," *Oil and Gas Journal*, July 25, 1955, p. 165.

SOURCES TO TABLE 115:

a) J. F. Foster and D. A. Vorum, "Pipe-Line (high Btu) Gas," *Economics of Fuel Gas from Coal*, ed. R. J. Lund and J. F. Foster (New York: McGraw-Hill Book Co., 1950), p. 103.

b) L. W. Alberts *et al.*, "Production of Methane from Coal," *Chemical Engineering Progress*, Vol. XLVIII, No. 10 (October 1952), pp. 486-93.

c) C. F. De Mey, "Study of Synthetic Natural Gas," *American Gas Association Monthly*, Vol. XXXIV, No. 11 (November 1952), p. 28.

d) W. Gumz and J. F. Foster, *A Critical Survey of Methods of Making a High BTU Gas from Coal*, Research Bulletin No. 6 (New York: American Gas Association, July 1953).

e) C. R. Breck, "The Timing of an Initial Pipeline—Gas-From-Coal Enterprise," *Gasification and Liquefaction of Coal* (New York: American Institute of Mining and Metallurgical Engineers, 1953), pp. 189-94.

f) R. G. Minet *et al.*, "Economics of Coal Carbonization by the Low-Temperature Process," *Chemical Engineering Progress*, Vol. L, No. 7 (July 1954), pp. 342-47.

g) W. B. Tippy, "What Will Happen to the Price of Gas?" *Gas*, Vol. XXXI, No. 1, (January 1955), p. 49.

h) H. M. Henry, "What About Gas Supply and Price?" *Gas Age*, March 10, 1955, pp. 25-49.

i) M. Chandler, "Outlook for Gas Industry," *Gas Age*, August 25, 1955, pp. 24-25.

j) W. B. Tippy, "Some Aspects of Gas Supply," paper presented at Executive Conference of American Gas Association, Colorado Springs, June 21, 1956.

k) O. C. Ongstad, M. H. Chetrick, and W. H. Oppelt, *Cost Data for Gasification of Lignite in an Externally Heated Retort*, U. S. Department of Interior, Bureau of Mines, Report of Investigations 5272, pp. 8-10.

l) L. F. Gerdetz, "Controlled Underground Gasification," *Coal Age*, Vol. LVIII, No. 11 (November 1953), pp. 80 ff.

m) U. S. Bureau of Mines, *Synthetic Liquid Fuels, Annual Report of the Secretary of the Interior for 1951*, Part II, "Oil from Oil Shale," Report of Investigations 4866, July 1952, p. 53.

n) H. M. Henry, "Where Will New England Get Its Future Gas Supplies?" *Gas*, Vol. XXXI, No. 4 (April 1955), pp. 71-76.

o) *Petroleum Week*, July 18, 1958, pp. 72, 74, 76.

p) E. B. Shultz and H. R. Linden, "Production of Pipeline Gas by Batch Hydrogenolysis of Oil Shale," paper presented at annual meeting of American Chemical Society, Chicago, September 10, 1958.

Consuming region	City-gate price (¢ per Mcf)
New England	52¢
Middle Atlantic	34
South Atlantic	28
North Central	27
Pacific	26
Mountain	20

These figures suggest that on the average the city-gate price of natural gas would have to increase 2.5 times before synthetic gas would be competitive, while under the most favorable conditions (long-distance natural gas transport versus short-distance synthetic gas transport) the competitive level might be less than 50 per cent above the present city-gate price in certain areas. At the same time, if the price of natural gas continued to rise, efforts to reduce the cost of synthetic gas would be intensified, and if the more optimistic estimates in Table 115 are correct, there would begin to be competitive synthetic gas production on a large scale at something like a two-thirds increase in the average city-gate price of natural gas. Well before that, because of the wide regional range of city-gate prices, there would be local opportunities for synthetic gas, as well as further expansion in the current use of oil gas for peak shaving (that is, only during periods of peak gas consumption).

It can be concluded, therefore, that if the price of natural gas undergoes further rise during the period through 1975, the rate of increase should taper off markedly as local market competition from other fuels becomes more effective. And without a significant decline in the cost of synthetic gas—which cannot be foreseen at this time—synthetic is unlikely to provide more than minor local competition by 1975. Nevertheless, the price of synthetic gas, at whatever level it may be during the period, will constitute a potential ceiling on the price of natural gas

NATURAL GAS LIQUIDS

Definition, Occurrence, and Use

Natural gas was described in the previous section as consisting principally of methane, which is the simplest in the series of hydrocarbon compounds known as the "paraffin series." The remaining constituents of natural gas, other than non-hydrocarbon impurities, are heavier members of the paraffin series. These compounds have the property of either liquefying spontaneously at atmospheric temperature and pressure or else being amenable to liquefaction through simple pressure-temperature manipulation. Because this property is utilized to obtain them in liquid form these compounds are known as "natural gas liquids" (abbreviated to NGL). Their relative proportion, both singly and in sum, as constituents of natural gas varies widely among reservoirs, and is in some measure determined by production methods. If the NGL content is less than 0.1 gallon per thousand cubic feet, the natural gas is known as a "dry" gas. A "wet" gas has the following typical proportions (in per cent by volume): methane, 80–90 per cent; ethane, 5–10 per cent; propane, 3–5 per cent; isobutane and butane, 1–2 per cent; pentane and the heavier members of the paraffin series, 1–2 per cent.[49]

Natural gas liquids, as the source of many of the same hydrocarbon compounds obtainable from crude oil, are often lumped with the latter, especially in discussions of reserves and total production, under the term "liquid hydrocarbons," and the word "petroleum" has also been used synonymously with liquid hydrocarbons. Although, from this point of view, NGL might have been better discussed in the chapter on crude oil, the fact remains that they are a constituent of natural gas, hence their long-term supply is a function of natural gas supply. Moreover, as a hydrocarbon resource they are not synonymous with crude oil. They are, as will be seen, a source of a variety of hydrocarbon raw materials and products, but many of their uses are specific. In the broad sense they may be considered competitive with crude oil (some NGL are refinery feedstock), but they are really more supplementary to crude oil as a resource than as an alternative, as is shale oil.[50]

It should also be understood that NGL are anomalous in that they do not constitute a net addition to energy resources. They are by common practice included in natural gas reserve data in both physical (quantity) and energy terms. A gas reserve or resource estimate of x trillion cubic feet includes the cubic feet of NGL which are present in the reservoir in the gaseous phase; and the standard figure of 1,075 Btu per cubic foot used as the heat value of natural gas at the wellhead includes the energy content of the NGL.[51] But since NGL do constitute an

[49] B. R. Carney, "Natural Gas Liquids," *Progress in Petroleum Technology* (Washington, D. C.: American Chemical Society, 1951), p. 255.

[50] Since NGL correspond to the salable (as opposed to residual) products from crude oil, they are equivalent to a larger unit liquid volume of crude. It has been estimated that one barrel of NGL displaces one and a quarter barrels of crude in consumption (*Petroleum Week*, November 22, 1957, p. 11).

[51] The effect of the presence or absence of NGL in natural gas on the heat value of the gas raises a number of vexing questions. What happens to the total energy content of natural gas reserves if new discoveries increase the proportion of condensate reservoirs? What happens to the heat value of delivered gas if either or both the percentage of gas treated and the NGL recovery level increase? These and similar questions must be ignored in the present discussion because of the absence of the needed data. The figures 1,075 Btu and 1,035 Btu as the heat value of gas as produced and as delivered, respectively, are, as far as can be determined, conventional values with no statistical basis. The heat value of gas is highly variable among reservoirs, not only because of the varying NGL content but because of the presence of varying quantities of noncombustible constituents such as carbon dioxide and nitrogen. A true heat value of the natural gas produced in the United States would be a weighted average of the value of the gas from each reservoir, and for delivered gas, would be a weighted average of the gas going through each terminal. Such figures would, of course, fluctuate from year to year. The degree of arbitrariness in the standard figures is indicated by the impossibility of reconciling the wellhead and delivered Btu values with the energy content of the NGL removed. The entire subject of the heat value of natural gas badly needs statistical clarification.

alternative source of some petroleum products it is appropriate to consider them here in terms of their separate future supply.

The natural gas liquids are commonly divided into three categories in a classification scheme which is confusing not only because the categories overlap but because the classification is based on both mode of occurrence and type of use. The classification is nevertheless important in any analysis of future supply probabilities. One category consists of propane, isobutane, and butane—compounds which are gases at atmospheric pressure and temperature but are readily liquefied. Although they are extracted and handled in the liquid state they are consumed as fuel in the gaseous state, hence their designation "liquefied petroleum gases" (commonly abbreviated as LPG). A second category includes isobutane, butane, pentane, and heavier members which constitute a liquid mixture at ordinary temperatures and pressures. This mixture closely corresponds to manufactured gasoline and, although it has a low octane number, can be readily used as such, hence the term "natural gasoline." The third category consists of heavier paraffin series compounds which are also gaseous under high pressure and temperature in the reservoir, but which condense to a liquid under lower temperature-pressure conditions. These are known as "condensate."

Although the occurrence of NGL is highly variable, certain characteristics are significant in the present context. Associated gas is "wet" gas. Natural gasoline and LPG occur in all "wet" gas; condensate, on the other hand, occurs only in gas reservoirs with pressures above 2,000 pounds per square inch and temperatures above 200° F. Very few such reservoirs are found at depth of less than 6,000 feet.

Carney distinguishes four types of NGL production:[52] (1) Gas field plants extract NGL "to permit the satisfactory transportation and use of gas," and produce natural gasoline and condensate, with some LPG (propane and butane). (2) Oil field plants yield a similar product mix (except for condensate) in processing casinghead gas incident to oil production. (3) Cycling plants strip condensate and usually some LPG (propane and butane) from gas that is then returned to the reservoir. (4) Gas wells produce condensate, known as "lease condensate," at the wellhead due to the reduction in pressure and temperature at the wellhead in the course of gas production.

The uses of the three categories of NGL are also to some extent overlapping. The chief use of LPG is as a domestic and commercial fuel for heating and cooking. Other uses are chemical manufacturing, internal combustion engine fuel (directly, as well as a raw material), synthetic rubber manufacture, and general industrial uses, in that order. A peculiar feature of the LPG market is that there is direct competition from similar compounds produced by petroleum refineries (sometimes called liquefied refinery gases, or LRG). Currently about 30 per cent of the total supply of marketable LPG is from this source. Natural gasoline is used as a blend stock in motor fuel manufacture. The condensate liquids serve as petrochemical feedstock.

[52] Carney, *op. cit.*

Reserves and Future Supply Estimates

The anomalous nature of NGL as an energy source is further evident in the definition of proved reserves used by the American Gas Association. "Proved recoverable reserves of natural gas liquids are those contained in the recoverable gas reserves subject to being produced as natural gas liquids by separators or extraction plants, now in operation, under construction or planned for the immediate future."[53] In other words, not only is the current recoverability limitation included in the reserve definition, as in natural gas and crude oil, but the limitation of current productive capacity is further used.

This new limitation, which at first glance seems unnecessarily restrictive, has its rationale. As noted at the beginning of this study, the reserve concept is universally limited to what is currently economic. In one sense, natural gas liquids in reservoirs for which no extractive capacity exists are *not* economically recoverable at present. This cannot be taken too literally, but it would appear to be a pertinent generalization. Moreover, the situation is not as simple as that of most mineral raw materials—that anything not recoverable today is potentially recoverable in the future (either *in situ* or in a waste dump) at some cost. The fact is, NGL not currently recovered do not remain in the reservoir (except for what are not recovered in cycling) but are permanently removed from the reservoir along with the oil or gas that contains them. Indeed, one cannot say with certainty that even the total 6.5 billion barrels of currently proved NGL reserves will be produced as such. Depending on circumstances at the time of production (which will vary with each reservoir), they may be recorded as part of NGL, crude oil, or gas output.

Nevertheless, the concept of future NGL supply is not meaningless, although estimates are understandably few. The only published estimate of total future NGL supply is for an "indicated" 10 billion barrels, on the assumption that "the future supply of natural-gas liquids will maintain the same relationship to natural-gas discoveries in the future as it does now."[54] The validity of this estimate is considered below.

The few published estimates of future NGL production are listed in Table 116. All were originally expressed in terms of the daily production rate, here rounded to the nearest 100,000 barrels and converted into an annual total rounded to the nearest 25 million barrels. The Batchelder and Nelson estimate was read from Chart 4 of their paper and is consistent with their statement that production should almost double by 1975. None of the authors offers any basis for his estimate. Pogue and Hill indicate that their figure for the "computed recovery" of NGL is in some way related to their estimate of natural gas output, but the relation is not given. The Hill *et al.* estimate follows the statement that "should the market and price warrant, a substantially higher percentage of the liquid content of natural gas could be removed and utilized." With the exception of the earliest and

[53] Natural Gas Reserves Committee of the American Gas Association, *1960 Report.*
[54] J. R. Stockton, R. C. Henshaw, and R. W. Graves, *op. cit.*, p. 149.

TABLE 116.   ESTIMATES OF FUTURE U.S. PRODUCTION OF NATURAL
GAS LIQUIDS

Source and date	Year	Daily production (million barrels)	Equivalent annual production[1] (million barrels)	Per cent of 1959 production
a) Swearingen, 1952.............	1967	1.5	550	143%
b) Cadle, 1955..................	1975	1.4	500	130
c) Batchelder and Nelson, 1955...	1975	1.1	400	104
d) Pogue and Hill, 1956..........	1965	1.2	425	110
e) Hill *et al.*, 1957..............	1966	1.5	550	143

[1] Figures rounded.

SOURCES:

a) J. E. Swearingen, "Meeting Future Petroleum Demands," *Oil and Gas Journal*, November 17, 1952, pp. 328–36.

b) A. Cadle, "An Appraisal of Future Energy Demand and Supply in the United States," paper given before American Petroleum Institute Petroleum Industry Buyers, San Francisco, November 15, 1955.

c) H. R. Batchelder and H. W. Nelson, "Future of Synthetic Liquid and Gaseous Fuels," paper given before Joint Fuels Conference, Columbus, Ohio, October 19–20, 1955.

d) J. E. Pogue and K. E. Hill, *Future Growth and Financial Requirements of the World Petroleum Industry* (New York: Chase Manhattan Bank, 1956). Presented at annual meeting of American Institute of Mining, Metallurgical and Petroleum Engineers, Petroleum Branch, February 21, 1956.

e) K. E. Hill, H. D. Hammar, and J. G. Winger, *Future Growth of the World Petroleum Industry* (New York: Chase Manhattan Bank, 1957). Presented at meeting of American Petroleum Institute Division of Production, Rocky Mountain District, Casper, Wyoming, April 25, 1957.

most recent of the estimates, there is evident variation in opinion as to the likely level of future production.

·   ·   ·

Technology as a Determinant of Future NGL Availability

Statistics on recent NGL recovery, listed in Table 117 and shown graphically in Figure 72, show the ratios, first, of net production[55] of NGL to the quantity of natural gas treated for NGL recovery; and, second, the ratio of NGL recovery to natural gas treated.   Neither of these ratios is a true representation.

The American Gas Association net production figures used as a basis for column 1 of Table 117 cover production from all sources.   But the Bureau of Mines, in the figures on the quantity of natural gas treated for NGL recovery, excludes NGL burned in the field or that which never reached a processing plant because of loss or waste, and does not count the liquids recovered at pipeline compressor stations and gas-dehydration plants.   Thus, the ratio in column 1 involves NGL recovery from a total gas output greater than that reported by the Bureau of Mines as treated, and overstates the true recovery level to an unknown degree.

[55] "Net production" is undefined beyond "permanent removal from the ground." It presumably excludes the unrecovered NGL content of cycled gas.

TABLE 117.   RECOVERY OF NATURAL GAS LIQUIDS, 1945–58

(In barrels per million cubic feet)

Year	On A.G.A. basis [a] (1)		Bureau of Mines figures [b] (2)
1958	40.41		34.76
1957	41.07		34.29
1956	41.02		34.05
1955	39.14		34.29
1954	40.33		33.12
1953	45.27		35.00
1952	44.36		34.76
1951	43.05		33.10
1950	42.53		34.05
1949	42.76		33.81
1948	41.82		33.83
1947	39.50		32.38
1946	35.28		31.67
1945	n.a.		32.62
Average 1952–58	41.66	Average 1952–58	34.32
Average 1946–52	41.33	Average 1945–51	33.07

[a] Ratio of net production, as reported by American Gas Association (A.G.A.), to the quantity of gas treated for NGL recovery, as reported by the Bureau of Mines.

[b] Ratio of NGL recovery, as reported by the Bureau of Mines, to that agency's figures for natural gas treated.

SOURCES: American Gas Association, *Gas Facts;* U.S. Bureau of Mines, *Minerals Yearbook*, various issues (Washington, D. C.: U.S. Government Printing Office).

Although in column 2, where Bureau of Mines figures are used for comparison of NGL recovery and natural gas treated, the ratio represents the true recovery within the coverage of the data, the figures are biased downward on two counts. First, the data include such operations as the reprocessing of gas at the pipeline transmission stage. The NGL yield the second time around is, of course, bound to be very low, and would for this reason alone pull down any average in which it was included. But more than this, for a true measure of total recovery, the NGL recovery through the second processing should be added to that obtained in the first, while the quantity of gas processed should be counted only once, not twice as is done in the Bureau of Mines statistics. Second, the Bureau of Mines data include the results of operations in which the recovery level is deliberately set lower than capability in order to match NGL output to low seasonal demand. To this extent, the ratio is less a measure of current technological capability than of operating practice.

Both ratio series listed in Table 117 are useful, nevertheless, as the upper and lower limits to the actual recovery level in a given year, whatever that may have been. It cannot have been more than the ratio based on net production; it cannot have been less than the Bureau of Mines figure.

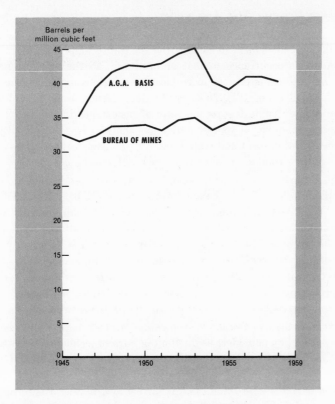

Barrels per
million cubic feet

A.G.A. BASIS

BUREAU OF MINES

Figure 72. Recovery of natural gas liquids, 1945–58.

Whatever the recovery factor actually is, there is evidence that it is held down less by technological capability than by economic factors that determine the provision of extraction facilities and the extent to which existing facilities are fully utilized. Carney estimated in 1951 that a recovery factor equivalent to 51 barrels per million cubic feet was "well within the limits of present methods." "Other students of this problem," he continued, "have reported that a very much greater potential is available whenever the demand may justify. It is recognized that this increased recovery will be attended by higher costs than present recoveries."[56] From this it can be inferred that a recovery factor of 51 barrels is feasible at present costs, with still higher recoveries technically obtainable at higher costs. It is probable that the current technological limit at present costs is already higher than Carney's estimate as a result of process improvements and innovations in subsequent years.

[56] Carney, *op. cit.*, p. 259. See also, *ibid.*, Table V, p. 256.

Conclusions on Domestic NGL Availability

Just as the crucial element in considering the future supply of natural gas itself is the ratio of its occurrence to that of crude oil, so the ratio of natural gas liquids to natural gas is crucial in reaching conclusions on the future supply of NGL. In an analysis of 1950 NGL production, Carney used something over 60 barrels per million cubic feet as the ratio of occurrence in nature, "based on a study of a large number of representative gas analyses from principal producing areas in the Mid-Continent and Gulf Coast." [57] This estimate is taken as authoritative and is here rounded to 60 barrels per million cubic feet.

With this occurrence ratio, it is possible to derive a resource-base estimate for NGL. Applied to the estimated total future gas supply of 1.2 quadrillion cubic feet, it yields an NGL minimum resource base of 72 billion barrels. Aside from the fact that the occurrence ratio was not applied to a natural gas resource-base estimate, the figure of 72 billion is conservative in that it is based on past experience. Condensate reservoirs are more frequent at depth, and if it is assumed that such reservoirs will constitute a higher proportion of future discoveries than in the past, the occurrence ratio could be greater than 60 barrels per million cubic feet. Ratios of 150 barrels have been reported for recent discoveries.

A reserve estimate can also be derived using Carney's data. Using the figure of 51 barrels per million cubic feet as the limit of current technology at current costs, NGL reserves ("discovered" and undiscovered) are on the order of 60 billion barrels as a probable minimum. In this light, the estimate of a total future supply of 10 billion barrels by Stockton *et al.* is far too low, tied as it is to the NGL-gas ratio in discoveries. The ratio of 20 barrels per million cubic feet implied in their estimate was apparently assumed from the most recent data for new field and new pool discoveries at the time the estimate was made. (The ratio in such discoveries in 1950 was 20.2.)

Since NGL do not constitute a net addition to energy resources because of their inclusion in quantity figures for natural gas, it is worth noting the significance of the above NGL resource-base estimate in terms of a net estimate of future natural gas supply. In adjusting natural gas reserve figures for the currently feasible increase in NGL recovery, Carney uses an equivalent of 1,343 cubic feet per barrel.[58] That is, the production of one barrel of NGL removes 1,343 cubic feet from the gas stream carrying it. Although this adjustment was for increased recovery, hence represented different proportions of compounds than is true for NGL in general, it is sufficient to indicate the order of magnitude of the effect on natural gas volume. Applying it, accordingly, to the resource base of 72 billion barrels, the result is 98.70 trillion cubic feet. It can be concluded from this that full exploitation of future NGL resources would reduce total future natural gas availability by less than 10 per cent.

[57] *Ibid.*, p. 259.
[58] *Ibid.*, p. 260.

The estimate of 1975 availability of NGL must also be derived from the estimate of 22.5 trillion cubic feet made for natural gas availability in that year. Since there is no basis for determining the degree of technological progress in NGL recovery that could be expected in the period through 1975, the figure of 51 barrels per million cubic feet taken from Carney as the limit of current technology under current costs is assumed for 1975. This yields a figure of 1,148 million barrels as the domestic availability of NGL in that year. In view of the compounding of assumptions, this can be rounded to a billion barrels as an order of magnitude.

For purposes of comparison, it may be noted that this is equivalent to some three times the 1959 output of NGL. But to reiterate—*the estimate is not for production.* The significance of the large magnitude is comparable to that of the oil-availability estimate; it emphasizes the large recovery potential. The evidence at hand indicates that domestic sources could supply a market for natural gas liquids on the order of a billion barrels. Whether such a market is likely to exist is a matter for separate investigation.

.   .   .

Other Sources of Supply

Natural gas liquids, especially LPG and natural gasoline, are well suited to pipeline and tank transport—the latter both for land (rail and truck) as well as marine transport. Given sufficient economic impetus, there is always the possibility that the potential NGL supplies of Canada and Venezuela could be developed for the U.S. market. The recent government-sponsored study of the energy prospects of Canada foresees an NGL export availability from that country of 7 million barrels in 1965 and 20 million barrels in 1980.[59] No estimates of Venezuelan capability exist.

As noted above, there is only one direct substitute for any of the NGL components—liquefied refinery gases for liquefied petroleum gases. Hence, only LPG can be considered to have an alternative "synthetic" source. Nevertheless, because NGL compete with crude oil as a source for both gasoline for the refinery gasoline pool and for petrochemical feed stock, NGL prices must be competitive with the prices of crude oil and refinery products.

This could exercise a ceiling effect on NGL prices, but aside from this, it does not seem likely that NGL costs would exert any upward pressure on NGL prices. The discovery and production costs of natural gas from any of its types of occurrence do not enter into NGL costs, since NGL are wholly by-products. Indeed, with the spread of conservation laws that require the repressuring of casinghead gas there has been a tendency to install NGL recovery facilities so that the return on the NGL output can help defray, even if it does not fully cover, the cost of handling the gas.

[59] J. Davis, *op. cit.*, p. 192.

The major element of production cost is actual recovery, and here the record to date has been one of cost reduction, as recovery processes have been improved and made more efficient. Prime cost deterrents in NGL marketing to date have been transportation and storage but, here too, costs have declined as facilities have been improved and economies of scale have been realized. The great handicap of seasonal demand for LPG can now be overcome with the development of large-scale storage, and the transportation handicap could be largely overcome by the installation of recovery plants at the terminals of long-distance transmission pipelines rather than in the field.

CHAPTER 11

Hydropower

What will the "availability" of hydropower in this country, in terms of installed capacity, be in the period through 1975? In attempting to answer this question, the chapter on hydropower, like the preceding ones, relies on a systematic review of the several published estimates of future capacity that have appeared in the past decade. These estimates are examined in the light of an independent analysis of two of the basic determinants of future hydro capacity.

The pace and extent of hydropower development depend in general on governmental policy decisions, the interest rate, regional growth in demand, the cost of competitive energy sources, the magnitude of unexploited hydro resources, and technological progress as it affects the exploitation of the hydropower potential. The emphasis of the present study is on the resource and technological determinants; the others are considered where relevant.

If unexploited hydro resources are conceived to be finite, then, as an increasing proportion of the total is developed, the rate and extent of further development is more and more influenced by the magnitude of the remainder. Equally significant is the technology of the various aspects of hydropower development—dam and facility design and construction, turbine and generator design and operation, and the transmission of the generated power—that determine, in the last analysis, the economic feasibility of exploiting the remaining potential. To be sure, the feasibility of developing a specific site may depend, perhaps even chiefly, on its place in an integrated power system or in the multipurpose development of a stream basin or region, but such considerations for the individual sites are not practicable in this discussion, which deals with the national aggregate.

Feasibility will also depend to a large extent on the "consumptive" uses of water and "head" (the difference in elevation), which in a sense compete with hydropower. The withdrawal of water from a stream for irrigation and for industrial, commercial, and household use reduces the streamflow and/or head by some degree

437

even if there is provision for return of the waste, since there is always some loss of water in use; thus the hydro potential represented by the streamflow is also reduced. The consumptive use of water can be expected to increase in the future, as it has in the past, through economic and population growth. The relation of this demand for water to future hydro availability is, however, a research project in itself, and cannot be attempted in this study. All that can be done here is to recognize that consumption is a limiting influence on hydropower availability that will manifest itself in an unmeasurable degree.

Accordingly, this chapter considers first the hydropower resources from which additions to capacity must come. The published estimates of future installed capacity in given years (that is, the total hydro generating capacity that will be in place in the given year) are then listed and the basis for each is described. There follows an examination of technology and its future prospects, as these may affect hydropower development. The various capacity estimates are evaluated as part of the conclusions of the chapter.

THE CONCEPT AND MEASUREMENT OF HYDROPOWER RESOURCES

The subject of hydropower resources has been the province of engineers; the literature is thus technical, with a specialized vocabulary. The present discussion attempts to review current authoritative opinion while avoiding oversimplification and generalization. Only a brief review of the characteristics of hydropower is necessary to show the peculiar problems of resource measurement they raise.

· · ·

Characteristics of Hydropower

Hydropower potential is created by the flow of water between different elevations, or the head. The energy of the water is used to turn a waterwheel and is converted into electricity by a generator driven by the waterwheel. The capacity of an actual or potential hydropower installation is measured in kilowatts (kw), and the energy produced, or producible, in kilowatt hours (kwh).

The outstanding characteristic of the demand for electricity in a typical electric power system is its periodic variation. Daily and seasonally the demand rises to peaks which may be considerably greater than the average level. The ratio of the average load, or demand for kilowatts, over a designated period to the peak load occurring in that period is termed the "load factor." The significance of this relationship is that generating capacity must be sufficient to take care of the peak load, hence in excess of the average load. Further, excess capacity must be provided over peak load to allow for equipment outages necessitated by maintenance or breakdown.[1] The ratio of the average load on the plant, for the

---

[1] Normally, excess capacity must be provided on a system basis. It would be taken into account for an individual plant only if the plant operates alone.

period of time considered, to the aggregate rating of all the generating equipment installed in the plant is known as the "plant factor." The higher the average use of the plant capacity during a given period, the higher is the plant factor for that period.

Against these universal characteristics related to the demand for electricity and the plants which supply it are production characteristics peculiar to hydropower. The flow of the stream being utilized for hydropower commonly varies over both long and short periods, reflecting rainfall and runoff patterns. In the ideal stream, these fluctuations would correspond precisely to the desired variations in the output of its hydro plants. Differences between short-period fluctuations in streamflow and desired variations in plant output can be overcome through the use of a small reservoir to provide pondage for the plant; long-term regulation of flow can be provided through storage reservoirs. Unless a plant has storage it is termed a "run-of-river" plant, either with or without pondage. Under any of these conditions, however, both flow and head can normally be expected to vary.[2]

Nevertheless, there is at any site a minimum flow below which the stream normally can be expected not to fall. The power capability that this flow and the available head represent is termed the "continuous power" or "prime power" that can or could be produced at that site. The principal function of a storage reservoir for power purposes is usually to increase the minimum flow, hence the continuous power level.

The use of waterpower for the generation of electricity is further complicated if such use is part of a multipurpose development. If the stored water is also used for irrigation or maintenance of a navigation channel not all of it may be available for power, and the continuous power level that can be assigned to the associated hydropower facilities is thereby lowered. Similarly, the use of a reservoir for flood control may be incompatible with maximum power development, for a reservoir must be kept low in periods when floods may occur if it is to fulfill its function of flood control, but this reduces the head available for power generation and may limit the amounts of water that can be stored for later use in power generation when natural streamflows are low. (Thus irrigation and navigation may also be in some degree incompatible with flood control.)

· · ·

Terminology of Hydropower Resources

Ideally, the reserve-resource terminology adopted in the preceding discussions of the mineral fuels should apply equally well to hydropower, but it it clear from this brief survey of hydropower characteristics that there is little in common with mineral resources. Nevertheless, there exists a hydro resource terminology

[2] Exceptional circumstances exist where natural storage is virtually unlimited, providing unusually constant streamflow, as at Niagara Falls and on the St. Lawrence River.

that is parallel in concept with the distinction between resource base, resources, and reserves as applied to minerals.

The rationale and methodology of estimating hydropower resources have received a good deal of attention in recent years, especially under the aegis of the World Power Conference. Interest has been stimulated in improving and standardizing concepts and measurement techniques. As a result, there is currently coming into acceptance outside the United States a standard terminology in defining and measuring hydropower resources.[3] The reason for the lack of enthusiasm for the subject in the United States does not appear in the literature but is obviously related to the difference of its energy position from that of most other countries. The United States possesses abundant energy resources of other kinds, and there has not been a strong sense of urgency toward maximum exploitation of hydro resources. In other countries, where energy resources in general are scarce, or at least of higher cost, the development of hydro resources acquires urgency and leads to a greater degree of interest in the identification and measurement of such hydro resources as remain undeveloped.

CONCEPTS

Conceptually, the starting point in the new hydro resource terminology is the natural environment within the geographic limits of the area or country considered. Since the physical basis of hydropower is a quantity of water descending a vertical distance, the maximum conceivable hydropower potential of a country is represented by the total quantity of water flowing in its streams, and the vertical distance it descends. This concept of total flow multiplied by head is the "theoretical hydroelectric potential."[4] It is defined in kilowatts for the period of a year as $\Sigma 9.81$ qh, where q is the arithmetic mean flow (cubic meters per second), over a period of years, of yearly average natural flows at the midpoint of each watercourse, and h is the gross head (in meters), or the difference in elevation between the terminal points of the streams. In terms of annual energy output (potential kwh), the definition is $\Sigma 85,848$ qh, or kw multiplied by 8,760, the number of hours in a year.[5] It will be seen that conceptually this is the exact equivalent of the *resource base* of a mineral.

This theoretical physical potential is forever unattainable for several reasons. It assumes a high degree of equalization of seasonal flow (theoretically attainable through perfect storage facilities perfectly utilized, but not necessary unless the load to be carried is absolutely uniform). It assumes complete utilization of the

---

[3] See, for example, the various reports of and to the Economic Commission for Europe and the Economic Commission for Asia and the Far East, several of which are cited below.

[4] Other concepts of the theoretical potential also exist, such as the "theoretical runoff potential" and the "theoretical rainfall potential," but these are irrelevant to the present discussion.

[5] Economic Commission for Europe, Committee on Electric Power, *Hydro-Electric Potential in Europe and its Gross, Technical and Economic Limits* (Geneva: United Nations, May 1953), p. 51.

flow (no competing uses or withdrawals of any kind); complete utilization of head; and 100 per cent efficiency (complete conversion of the hydro energy into electricity), and—in terms of annual energy—100 per cent utilization of the power capacity throughout the year. Within this theoretical limit there is distinguished a concept termed the "technical potential." This is considered to represent the total hydro resources that can be developed with a given state of technology. The technical potential can be derived from gross potential by deducting several types of losses of head. Among these are losses in headraces, penstocks, etc., and losses of flow due to alternative water uses, leakage past water-controlling apparatus, and incomplete flow regulation because of imperfect storage. Others, in terms of generated power, are the losses caused by turbine and generator inefficiency, and those resulting from the fact that continuous operation throughout the year is not feasible.[6]

A second method of deriving the technical potential is to add the potential at all developed and identifiable undeveloped sites. There is, however, an abrupt conceptual jump from *total* flow and head along a stream or all streams to the technological limits on usable flow and head *at specified generation sites*. The technical inability to capture and utilize all of the energy available at a given site means, of course, that the technical potential at that site is less than the theoretical potential of the site. But in considering the theoretical and technical potentials in the aggregate—for a country, a region, a drainage basin, or even an individual stream—the technical will also be less than the theoretical for an additional reason. The total potential of all hydropower sites does not equal the total energy represented by qh for the country, region, etc., even allowing for equipment inefficiency. There will be instances where it is technologically infeasible to specify a power site; the head may be too small to be usable, for example, or the geology or topography may be too unfavorable to cope with in considering the structures necessary for storage. Other reasons can be adduced.

The concept of technical potential has been criticized as being very unprecise on the grounds that it is too broad,[7] but it can also be criticized for failure to specify the place of the economic element in the concept. In one sense, the technological inability to make complete use of flow and head at a given site does not involve costs—the technological limits are not a matter of cost in that more expensive facilities or techniques would not increase significantly the technical potential as a percentage of the theoretical potential. In this sense, therefore, the technical potential at the level of the specific site disregards costs by taking them to the limit: regardless of cost, x kilowatts is all that is technically possible there. The same is true in general of the concept in the aggregate, although this cannot be stated categorically. The failure to identify sufficient

[6] See *ibid.*, pp. 61–62, and A. J. Dilloway, "Assessment of Hydro-Electric Potential in Regions Subject to Rapid Economic Development," Paper 47 B/3, Fifth World Power Conference, Vienna, June 1956, p. 5.

[7] See V. M. Yevdjevic, "Some Statistical Methods for Determining Water Power Resources," Paper 165 B/13, Fifth World Power Conference, *op. cit.*, p. 6.

sites to capture all the qh of a stream, etc., may be due in some part (how much is impossible to say) to implicit cost limitations. Geological and topographical and other disadvantages[8] could perhaps be overcome at some wholly extravagant cost. Hence, in this sense, the concept remains fuzzy, as Yevdjevic avers, unless the place of costs is noted. Costs are comprehended in the concept of technical potential, but are disregarded in the sense that they are not a limiting factor when the concept is correctly stated. In this discussion, the term "technical" is considered synonymous with "practicable," that is, it is a potential that could be realized some time in the future, but such realization is not necessarily fully justifiable under current costs. Again, in relation to the resource terminology of the preceding chapters it is the equivalent of the *resources* of a mineral, defined in this instance on the basis of practicability with existing technology.

Within the technical potential, there is a third conceptual limit for which costs are the limiting factor. The "economic potential" is thus the total hydro resources that can be developed with a given level of technology under given relative cost conditions—for purposes of this discussion, the capacity that would have a competitive margin over alternative energy sources. Again, the proportion of the technical potential that is economic does not necessarily remain constant, but can change with changing economic circumstances. It is determined by such things as the interest rate, construction and operating costs, competitive energy prices, and so forth. The economic potential thus corresponds to the *reserves* of a mineral.

The concepts behind the foregoing terminology provide the same kind of useful scale of perspectives in a consideration of the undeveloped hydropower resources of a country as does the reserve-resource terminology for minerals. The theoretical potential constitutes the environmental limit within which technology can be applied. The technical potential, in turn, is the limit of the resources that could be developed with a given level of technology under no cost limits. And the economic potential delimits the resources that can be developed according to prevailing costs and load conditions. There is thus a perspective suitable for whatever purpose is in mind. One may be interested in immediate additions to total generating capacity; or—going up the scale—in planning future additions that are, perhaps, not yet feasible; or one may even be speculating on new ways and means of harnessing potential hydropower. The appropriate perspective for each interest is available; the present study is interested in the entire scale.[9]

---

[8] Such as the cost of condemning a city that would be flooded by the reservoir.

[9] The following quotation exemplifies the prevailing attitude in this country toward the terminology and concepts just outlined. Speaking of the theoretical potential, F. L. Weaver in "Hydro Potentialities as Indicated by the Federal Power Commission," paper presented at Twenty First Annual Meeting, American Power Conference, Chicago, April 1, 1959, remarks: "This type of inventory obviously has limited usefulness. As an example, it is of little value to know that the lower Mississippi River has a power potential equivalent in capacity and generation to a very substantial proportion, possibly two-thirds, of that of all existing hydro plants in the country, if that potential cannot be developed physically or economically." But to criticize the usefulness of the concept of a theoretical limit because that limit is un-

MEASUREMENT

These concepts and the perspectives they afford are helpful despite the great difficulties of using the definitions as a basis for measurement. Although the definitions themselves are conceptually unambiguous, any attempt to quantify the technical and economic potentials involves the application of judgment in applying the limiting criteria. The definitions may remain objective but the measurement process unavoidably must be subjective to some degree. In addition, there is the difficulty of getting reasonable precision in the measurement of any of the potentials, since the most that can be expected is approximation. Nevertheless, even rough figures obtained with the foregoing concepts in mind are more meaningful and useful than estimates of hydro resources with no systematic basis or criteria.[10] The concepts provide a framework within which necessary judgments can be applied consistently rather than haphazardly and upon which approximations can be systematically constructed.

Among the three levels of potentials, it is least difficult to express the theoretical potential quantitatively, although even this requires the collection of large masses of data. One needs, in addition to fairly detailed topographic data for the entire country, hydro-meteorological data in considerable detail over a sufficient period of years to provide statistical reliability, but available data are inadequate. This inadequacy of data—as with inadequate terminology—has led to a lively discussion in other countries of statistical procedures and devices for estimating the theoretical hydro potential of a country, and it is believed possible by many students of the subject to approximate the theoretical potential with a minimum amount of data using various statistical shortcuts.[11] It should be noted, however, that regardless of how an estimate of the theoretical hydro potential may be obtained, it makes no allowance for the loss of potential represented by existing and potential demand for consumptive uses.

The measurement problem becomes more serious at the technical potential level. The losses due to equipment inefficiency can be averaged from current

---

attainable is to miss the point entirely. The theoretical limit of thermodynamic efficiency in the steam cycle is equally unattainable. Like that limit, the theoretical hydro potential is useful as a reference point against which achievement can be measured.

[10] As the Economic Commission for Europe observes, *op. cit.*, p. 4, periodic revisions of the technical potential "can be evaluated in terms of the theoretical upper limit as a datum. In areas where exploitable sites have not been surveyed, knowledge of gross upper limit also allows estimates of practical limits to be prepared."

[11] For example, certain simplified assumptions can be made regarding the relation between mean head of the drainage area and specific runoff on the one hand and the size of the drainage area on the other hand, using the relation kw/km along the watercourses. See T. L. Solotarjow, "Die Methodik der Berechnung von Wasserkraftvorräten," Paper 261 B/16, Fifth World Power Conference, *op. cit.*; see also Economic Commission for Europe, *op. cit.*; Dilloway, *op. cit.*; V. Felber, "Abflusskurven und Abflusskurvensysteme in der Gewässerkunde," Paper 45 B/2, Fifth World Power Conference, *op. cit.*; A. Lernhart, "Methodische Fragen der Wasserkraftstatistik, erläutert am Beispiel des österreichischen Wasserkraftkatasters," Paper 39 B/1, *ibid.*; and Yevdjevic, *op. cit.*

experience, summed, and subtracted from the theoretical potential. But a more meaningful and useful way to measure the technical level is to survey all potential hydropower sites to determine how much it is technically feasible to install at a given time—even though the question of just what is technically feasible can never be wholly settled. Such site-by-site surveys, however, are time-consuming and expensive, and if undertaken they are likely to understate the situation because they "tend always to stop at physical and cost limits which go little beyond expectations of use."[12]

Even more troublesome is the difficulty raised in obtaining an energy (kwh) estimate as distinguished from a capacity (kw) estimate. The technical potential in terms of energy is based on mean flow, but the installed or installable capacity bears no systematic relation to mean flow, being influenced rather by a variety of economic and physical considerations such as the range of flow conditions and the integration of the site into a power system. The best that can be done is to estimate the output in kilowatt hours for all installed and installable[13] capacity and to divide by 8,760 (the number of hours in a year) to get a continuous generation equivalent—termed "comparative capacity" by the Economic Commission for Europe—to compare with the constant (in the sense of unvarying) flow implied by the mean flow concept. This is probably the weakest element in the measurement of the hydro potentials.

The measurement problem becomes most acute at the level of the economic potential. Theoretically, it should be possible to construct a cost schedule of all undeveloped hydro sites, based on the cost per installed kilowatt or kilowatt hour output at each.

Of sites found to be technically exploitable, some will be structurally unsound, requiring costly excavation and strengthening. Others may be topographically complex and need extensive diversions, costly barrages or other special modifications before their full potentialities can be realized. Very large low-head installations on navigable rivers can fall within this category.

---

[12] Economic Commission for Europe, *op. cit.*, p. 1. This is stated more fully by J. Davis (*Canadian Energy Prospects* [Ottawa: Royal Commission on Canada's Economic Prospects, 1957], pp. 219–20): "With a caution customary among engineers, statistics pertaining to some of the lesser known (and yet possibly favorable) sites are frequently disregarded, until such time as the necessary runoff, topographic and dam foundation conditions have actually been subjected to exhaustive survey. . . . Where a high dam structure is envisaged, or considerable tunnelling is involved, the possibility of using new and improved techniques cannot always be anticipated. Often left out of account until the need arises, are the additional capacities possible through the greater use of storage and stream regulation. River diversions from one watershed to another may also result, sometimes quite unexpectedly, in new freedoms for increased hydro power generation. Thus potentials such as those recently established at Kitimat or envisaged for the Columbia or Fraser river systems had for years been disregarded either as unproven or visionary *if not entirely out of the question.*" (Italics added.)

[13] Again, it is difficult to delineate the cost element precisely. If costs were totally disregarded, it would generally be possible to install sufficient capacity at each site to utilize even maximum flows. "Practically installable" should be understood here.

Again, a project may be difficult of access, far removed from any consumption centre, or it may have to compete with others where a dual purpose would help to amortize power costs or where a cheap fuel supply holds greater attractions for baseload production.[14]

The traditional economic criterion for a hydropower installation was the cost of an equivalent block of power from thermal capacity, the cheapest alternative source. This was useful as long as a hydropower project could be assessed in terms of power only. But with the increasing emphasis in the United States on multipurpose development, a large part of the power aspect may be automatically incorporated in the over-all project, in which instance the even more complex and imprecise technique of benefit-cost ratios may be used to determine whether the over-all project is economic.[15]

Thus, in practice, the actual cost schedule[16] of potential hydropower projects is likely to be difficult to indicate even within wide limits, and there is the further difficulty of fitting specific increments under load curves. These difficulties led the President's Materials Policy Commission to conclude:

> There is no completely satisfactory measure of the remaining hydropower that could be developed. . . . There are extreme variations in the probable capital and operating costs of generating electricity at different sites. Even where costs are similar the economic possibilities of development will vary according to the differences in the prospects for power demand and the conditions of supply in the particular area. Moreover, the potential level of power that can be generated and the costs will vary widely for a single site according to how the whole river basin is developed. A river with a wide seasonal fluctuation in water flow will have a much greater year-round power potential if storage reservoirs are built upstream to even out seasonal fluctuations at power sites downstream.[17]

Judgment as to the efficacy of quantifying U.S. hydro potentials is deferred in this study until the concluding section. In the following section, the current estimates of the hydro resources of the United States are examined against the background of the concepts and definitions set forth above.

ESTIMATES OF HYDROPOWER POTENTIAL IN THE UNITED STATES

There are two government estimates of U.S. hydropower potential, one by the U.S. Geological Survey (USGS) and one by the Federal Power Commission

[14] Dilloway, *op. cit.*

[15] See J. J. Doland, *Hydro Power Engineering* (New York: Ronald Press, 1954), pp. 172–73. Indeed, the determination of whether the individual aspects of a multiple purpose project are economic is probably even more difficult.

[16] This term is used in the economist's sense (that is, a schedule of the cumulative capacity that would be available at each successive cost level) as in a "supply schedule."

[17] President's Materials Policy Commission (PMPC), *Resources for Freedom*, Vol. I (Washington, D. C.: U.S. Government Printing Office, 1952), p. 118.

(FPC). The estimates considered here are the latest in a series of periodic revisions published by the two agencies.

.   .   .

Description of the Estimates

The Geological Survey figures consist of estimates, over a range of assumptions, of "potential power," defined as that "estimated technically capable of being developed, economic infeasibility notwithstanding."[18] The definition is intended to include developed as well as undeveloped power. The estimates cover capacity available 50 per cent and 90 per cent of the time, with storage at known large reservoir sites, both developed and undeveloped; and capacity at mean flow (since time is not a parameter for mean flow, the estimate is the same with existing as with projected storage).[19] All of the estimates assume efficiency at 100 per cent and gross head. On this basis, the potential is:

> Available 90 per cent of the time..........48,479,000 kw
> Available 50 per cent of the time..........63,873,000 kw
> Based on mean flow.....................86,174,000 kw

The FPC describes the basis of its estimates as follows:

The Commission estimates and assembles data on the undeveloped hydroelectric power resources of the principal river basins of the country. This is done by making use of data obtained during the course of comprehensive river basin surveys, made either in connection with the Commission's hydroelectric power project licensing work or in cooperation with other federal agencies, and by using information obtained from investigations made by other federal agencies and by other interests, public and private. The Commission's estimates are based on the rated capacity of generators that normally would be installed at the power sites, assuming reasonable regulation of flow by storage. Allowance is made for depletions by irrigation and other consumptive use, and it is assumed that each site will be developed to achieve, in conjunction with the development of other sites, the best over-all development of the water resources of the river basin for power and other multiple uses.[20]

On this basis, with data as of January 1, 1959, the latest of FPC's periodic estimates of the "hydroelectric power resources" of the United States is:[21]

---

[18] L. L. Young, *Developed and Potential Waterpower of the United States and other Countries of the World*, December, 1954, U.S. Geological Survey Circular 367, 1955, p. 2.

[19] *Ibid.*, *passim*. Young also presents estimates of the potential "under existing conditions"; that is, existing storage facilities are taken into account but no allowance is made for reservoirs that could be established in the future. These estimates are not considered relevant to the present discussion.

[20] Federal Power Commission (FPC), *Hydroelectric Power Resources of the United States: Developed and Undeveloped, 1957* (Washington, D. C.: U.S. Government Printing Office, 1958), pp. 18–19.

[21] FPC, *Thirty Ninth Annual Report* (Washington, D. C.: U.S. Government Printing Office, 1960), p. 45.

Developed and installed capacity....30.2 million kw (153.1 billion kwh)
Estimated undeveloped capacity.....91.9 million kw (359.5 billion kwh)

Total......................122.1 million kw (512.6 billion kwh)

In addition to the estimates just described, many figures for the hydropower potential of the United States may be found, but most figures presented by individual writers cite one or the other of these government agencies as the source reference. The government estimates thus are the only estimates of hydropower potential derived from original statistics, and the figures given by individuals are, with a few exceptions, ignored in this study.[22]

The exceptions are a few misleading estimates, presented without source references. Because they appear in authoritative surroundings, it is desirable to indicate specifically in what respect they are in error. Harrison Brown, for example, uses a horsepower figure equivalent to 26.1 million kw as the generating capacity, based upon ordinary minimum flow, that would be made available by "full development of potential hydroelectric sites in the United States."[23] This can be taken as generally equivalent to the Geological Survey's estimate of the potential with existing flow available 95 per cent of the time, or 27.1 million kw. Under the conditions specified, Brown's figure describes the limit of continuous hydropower as seen at that time, but in no sense measures the "full development" of the hydropower potential. Indeed, installed capacity already exceeds that level.

Other authors use a different figure for the hydropower potential but similarly misstate the situation. Ayres and Scarlott state: ". . . the amount of electric power that can be ultimately produced from waterfalls is definitely limited to about 50 million kilowatts . . . ," and Pigott avers that "hydropower cannot exceed 50 million kilowatts capacity—that's all there is."[24] These unqualified statements correspond to the USGS estimate of 48.5 million kw as the potential hydropower available 90 per cent of the time with storage. This is also a measure of continuous power possibilities, but again, to suggest any figure of this kind as a flat upper limit to hydropower possibilities without any attempt to consider its relation to the theoretical potential is, at the least, misleading.

．　　　．　　　．

Critique of the Government Estimates

The purpose of the Geological Survey estimates by Young appears to be merely to make available for general use figures that were a by-product of other work. The Survey's specific function with respect to hydro potential is the classifica-

[22] One estimate not dealt with herein is quasi-official in that it is based on governmental data but appears in an unofficial paper by W. B. Langbein, "An American Survey," *Water Power*, November–December 1950. Langbein's estimates are based on Géological Survey data since superseded by the data that form the basis of the agency's official estimates in the 1955 publication described above.

[23] H. Brown, *The Challenge of Man's Future* (New York: Viking, 1954), p. 171.

[24] E. Ayres and C. A. Scarlott, *Energy Sources—The Wealth of the World* (New York: McGraw-Hill Book Co., 1952), p. 104; R. J. S. Pigott, "Fuel and Power Sources If and When Oil Fails," *Petroleum Refiner*, Vol. 28, No. 2 (February 1949), p. 88.

tion of public lands for hydropower purposes—it must identify potential power sites involving such lands as a basis for deciding whether the land should be withdrawn from other use because it may one day be flooded by a storage reservoir. The streamflow data developed by the Survey for this purpose (as well as for flood information) are detailed and comprehensive and were collected on a consistent basis, but where necessary they were supplemented from other sources to give the totals presented.

Young calls his results the "potential waterpower" of this country, but no thought seems to have been given to what their true meaning and significance might be, such as the implications of the assumptions on gross head and efficiency of 100 per cent. No indication is given, moreover, of what the Survey thinks of the relative usefulness and validity of the figures with different parametric values,[25] nor is there any indication of the coverage provided by the sites which undoubtedly will be developed at some future time but would not individually add materially to the potential of the stream or the country as a whole.[26] Even if the judgment of the Survey on the significance of the deliberate exclusion is accepted, it is reasonable to expect some statement of the adequacy of coverage, such as is provided in the Survey's estimates of coal resources, for example.

The Federal Power Commission comments on its estimates as follows:

> The estimates of undeveloped water power include projects on which economic feasibility has been demonstrated, as well as projects at sites where physical conditions indicate engineering feasibility and promise at some time of economic feasibility. The estimates with respect to the latter class of projects are subject to revision either by increase or decrease as additional information becomes available concerning stream flow, reservoir sites, costs, and other pertinent factors.

> The undeveloped hydroelectric power picture is constantly changing as new projects are constructed, and as continuing studies by federal, state and local public, and private interests uncover new potential projects, or their investigations demonstrate the desirability of modifications of older plans. Hence, estimates of undeveloped hydroelectric power must be revised from time to time as new studies are made and additional information is obtained. Although some of these potential projects may, upon detailed investigation, be found infeasible and impracticable of development from physical, or economic, or other standpoints, the estimates taken in the aggregate serve to indicate, from a long-range view, the over-all water-power potentialities of the United States and the water-power resources available for possible future development.[27]

Although this emphasizes the ephemeral nature of the total figure representing the "hydroelectric power resources" of the United States as estimated by the FPC, it fails to indicate that the estimate is the summation of a series of data from unrelated reports from various sources originally made for a variety of

[25] The use of 95 per cent availability with existing flow and 90 per cent with full storage is, for example, unexplained. It does not correspond with usage elsewhere. See J. J. Doland, op. cit., p. 48.

[26] Young, op. cit.

[27] FPC, Hydroelectric Power Resources of the United States: Developed and Undeveloped, 1957, op. cit., p. 19.

purposes. The data collected range from detailed specifications of the basis for an estimate of installed capacity to unsubstantiated guesses. The installed-capacity figures for undeveloped hydro have been taken by the Commission as given in the collected data, except for revision to accord with later information, and have no consistent basis. The figure also excludes small power sites with a potential of less than 2,500 kw. The total potential of such sites in the data available to the FPC amounts to less than 5 per cent of the total estimate, but it is not known what the total potential of all such sites would be. The Commission, moreover, does not accompany its estimates with a statement of the exclusion. The reader is left to infer that the coverage is complete. In any event, the FPC estimate is not, as Weaver describes it, "a summarization of resources available for possible development similar, for example, to summaries of the amount of coal or iron ore available in the country."[28] A "summarization of the resources *available* for development" (with no indication of feasibility) would be the theoretical potential or, with respect to iron ore and coal in the terminology of this study, an estimate of the resource base.

How can the estimates of U.S. hydro potential be described in the terminology adopted herein? It is impossible to assign the estimates to any of the three categories without qualification. On the one hand, there is no estimate that corresponds to the concept of theoretical potential, since there has been no all-inclusive survey of flow and head for the drainage basins of the United States (although comprehensive data probably exist in the files of the government agencies). The closest approach to the theoretical potential concept is Young's figure on mean flow, since it is accompanied by assumptions of gross head and 100 per cent efficiency. But it is the sum of identified sites, not a flow-head product, hence conceptually it falls short of the theoretical potential. On the other hand, the same estimate is taken to the technological limit (as stated by Young), which is the basis of the technical potential concept. But, even though the measurement is on a site-by-site basis, the coverage is incomplete, hence in this respect it falls short of being a measurement of technical potential. Conceptually, Young's estimate of mean flow is between the two potentials, making the flow-head and efficiency assumptions of the theoretical potential and the practicability assumption of the technical potential.

[28] Weaver, *op. cit.* In Canada, by contrast, there is greater awareness of the incompleteness of the equivalent official estimates: "With respect to hydraulic head, the figures . . . are based upon the actual drop, or feasible concentration of head, which has been measured or at least carefully estimated at existing falls, rapids and known power sites; no consideration has been given to possible economic concentrations of head on rivers and streams of gradual gradient, except at those locations where the feasible head has been definitely established by field investigations. Many unrecorded power sites exist on rivers and streams throughout the country, particularly in the less explored northerly districts, but these cannot be included in the tabulation until more detailed survey work has been made. Thus, regarding both the total number of sites and the possible head at each site, the listed figures of available power represent only the *minimum water power possibilities of Canada.*" (Italics in original.) See Department of Northern Affairs and National Resources, Water Resources Branch, *Water Power Resources of Canada*, Bulletin No. 2641, Ottawa, March 16, 1959, p. 3.

The Federal Power Commission's estimates pertain to installed capacity and kilowatt hour output, and can be related to the several potentials only through conversion to "comparative capacity," with all the shortcomings this brings with it. Aside from the measurement problem, however, it is conceptually equivalent to none of the potentials. It specifically goes beyond the current economic limit; at the same time, its coverage is also incomplete.

In addition to assessing the meaning and significance of the two resource estimates in the perspective of the "potentials" terminology, it is useful to consider their comparability, especially since Young raises the question. It is evident that they cannot be directly compared: The FPC estimates are in terms of the capacity that has been or could be installed at each site. Young's estimates refer to the power that would be available when the streamflow is utilized steadily at the streamflow rate which occurs with the frequency stated. Young also assumes gross head and efficiency of 100 per cent, although the result in each instance is something less than present plus probable installed capacity. How, then, can the two sets of estimates be equated?

Young attempts an explicit comparison of these two sets of estimates (using the figures in the FPC report for 1953) as follows:

> By adding the Federal Power Commission estimates of average annual output in kilowatt hours for developed and potential power and converting that total to a continuous [power] equivalent it will be seen that their estimate of the total waterpower resources of the United States is near the 56,060,000 kw . . . available 50 per cent of the time and that it is at the midpoint between the potential power estimated to be available 90 per cent of the time and 50 per cent of the time with development of known storage sites. . . .[29]

Young, in other words, converts the FPC estimates of the potential energy output of its estimated capacity into the equivalent power corresponding to that energy produced at a continuous rate. The arithmetic is as follows, using the figures in the FPC estimates of 1953:

FPC estimate, average annual generation by present hydro capacity. . . .112,479 million kwh
FPC estimate, average annual generation by undeveloped hydro capac-
    ity . . . . .378,508 million kwh
        Total . . . . .490,987 million kwh

$$\frac{490,987}{8,760 \text{ (hrs. in a yr.)}} = 56,048,000 \text{ kw (continuous capacity equivalent)}$$

He compares this figure with his own estimate of 56,060,000 kw available 50 per cent of the time with "existing flow," and the 56,311,000 kw he obtains by averaging his 90 per cent and 50 per cent availability potentials (with storage). The coincidence of the figures is satisfying, but the existing flow assumption in Young's figure is not the condition assumed by the FPC, as is evident from the description of its estimates quoted above. Nothing is adduced to show that the results are anything more than mere coincidence, or that the arithmetic procedure has any real meaning.

[29] Young, op. cit., pp. 13–14. The 56,060,000 kw cited by Young refers to his estimate of existing conditions (see footnote 19 above).

The two sets of estimates can also be compared on another basis. A Canadian study observes that estimates of installed capacity and streamflow capacity can be compared by following "the usual practice of industry of taking the commercially available capacity to be approximately one-third greater than consistent with the conditions of ordinary six months flow [flow available 50 per cent of the time]."[30] Applying this method to Young's estimates yields an implied installed capacity figure of 85.2 million kw with storage. The 1953 FPC figure of 109.5 million kw is 29 per cent greater than this result.

Young states that his estimates and those of the FPC "are in essential agreement"[31] but, although they are not necessarily inconsistent, or mutually contradictory, they simply cannot be compared as figures because of their very different bases. Any attempt to do so is a mere arithmetical exercise. Young's figures purport to be for technically feasible projects, even though they may be uneconomic, but the FPC figures are for sites which promise economic feasibility. And still again, the Young estimates assume gross head and efficiency of 100 per cent, whereas the FPC figures reflect net head and attainable efficiencies.

ESTIMATES OF FUTURE U.S. HYDROPOWER CAPACITY

A comparison of the published estimates of future hydropower capacity in the United States will help in making an independent judgment of the likely level of installed hydropower capacity in 1975. The estimates vary in completeness, in manner of expression, and in the year to which they refer. Ideally, they should be wholly comparable, but it was considered possible to reduce them to a common basis only in manner of expression—all estimates are listed as installed capacity of hydro facilities. Where estimates were incomplete and referred only to certain sectors of hydro capacity (such as federally owned, or interconnected systems only), it was not possible to impute to the estimates the unspecified remainder. However, the small place of industrial hydro in the total (less than 2.5 per cent at present) allows figures that exclude this sector to be taken as generally equivalent to the total hydro capacity.

Rather than do violence to implicit assumptions in those estimates for years other than 1975, it was considered preferable to list each estimate for the year stated rather than to attempt conversion by interpolation or extrapolation to the common year 1975. Finally, in several instances, the assumptions and definitions on which the estimates were based were not given in the respective sources. Where possible, these unstated bases were inferred. The estimates are presented in Table 118 in approximately the chronological order in which they were published. (Unless otherwise indicated in a footnote, discussion of the original estimate relates to the reference given in Table 118.)

[30] J. Davis, *op. cit.*, p. 219. It should be noted that this ratio looks low in the light of the situation described later in this chapter.

[31] Young, *op. cit.*, p. 13.

TABLE 118.   ESTIMATES OF FUTURE U.S. HYDROPOWER CAPACITY

Source and date (1)	Year for which estimate made (2)	Estimated capacity (thousand kw) (3)	Remarks (4)	Estimate ÷ base-year capacity, × 100 (5)	Implied average annual growth rate (per cent) (6)	Implied average annual growth rate, 1962 to projected year[1] (per cent) (7)	Estimate as per cent of hydro potential (FPC, Jan. 1959) (8)
a) Corps of Engineers–FPC (1948)	1968–73	59,540	Federal capacity only	(1947) 1,295	13.0%–10.4%	22.9%–12.7%	49%
b) Anonymous (1950)	1965	24,100	Federal capacity only	(1949) 417	9.3	14.6	20
c) PWRPC (1950)	1970	41,500	Total capacity	(1949) 235	4.1	0.6	34
d) Anonymous (1951)	1975	39,700	4 per cent of total energy supply	(1951) 200	2.9	negl.	33
e) PMPC (1952)	1975	33,000–57,750	See text	(1950) 200–350	2.8–5.1	*–2.9	27–47
	1975	49,500		300	4.5	1.7	41
	1975	60,000				3.2	49
f) Bur. Reclamation (1954)	1975	37,733	Total capacity	(1950) 321	4.8	3.2	49
g) Monteith (1954)	1963	31,500	Federal capacity only	(1954) 370	6.4	6.8	31
h) Cisler (1954)	1965	36,000	Total capacity	(1953) 137	3.2	*	26
			18 per cent of interconnected systems total	(1953) 163	4.2	*	29
i) Cisler (1954)	1975	42,800–54,200	Interconnected systems only	(1953) 194–246	3.1–4.2	0.7–2.6	35–44
j) Sporn (1954)	1978	41,000	10 per cent of total generating capacity	(1953) 178	2.3	0.3	34
k) Mayer (1954)	1975	56,000	Total capacity	(1954) 231	4.1	2.8	46
l) Mullendore (1955)	1975	50,000	Total capacity	(1954) 206	3.5	1.8	41
	1975	35,000	Total capacity?	(1955) 136	1.5	*	29
m) General Electric (1955)	1980	44,000	9 per cent of total generating capacity	(1955) 171	2.2	0.6	36

TABLE 118 (continued)

Source and date (1)	Year for which estimate made (2)	Estimated capacity (thousand kw) (3)	Remarks (4)	Estimate ÷ base-year capacity, x 100 (5)	Implied average annual growth rate (per cent) (6)	Implied average annual growth rate, 1962 to projected year[1] (per cent) (7)	Estimate as per cent of hydro potential (FPC Jan. 1959) (8)
n) *Coal Age* (1955).........	1965	50,000	Total capacity? (1955)	194	6.9	8.1	41
	1970	60,000		233	5.8	4.7	49
	1975	70,000		272	5.1	4.5	57
	1980	80,000		311	4.6	3.5	66
o) McKinney Report (1956).	1965	27,700–28,000	Lower figures excluding industrial (1954)	119–116	1.6–1.3	*–*	23–23
	1970	30,200–31,700		130–131	1.6–1.7	*–*	25–26
	1975	32,600–40,400		140–167	1.6–2.5	*–0.2	27–33
	1980	35,200–52,900		152–218	1.6–3.0	*–1.6	29–43
p) Sporn (1956).............	1975	48,000	Total capacity (1955)	186	3.1	1.5	39
q) Ebasco (1956)...........	1970	55,800	18 per cent of total utilities (excluding industrial) (1955)	223	5.5	4.6	46
r) FPC (1959).............	1965	40,700	Total capacity (1958)	135	4.4	0.9	33
	1970	45,700		152	3.5	1.8	37
	1975	51,700		172	3.2	2.0	42
	1980	57,700		192	3.0	2.1	47
s) *Electrical World* (1959).....	1975	50,740	Excluding industrial (1958)	186	3.3	2.1	42
t) FPC (1959)..............	1980	64,622	Total capacity (1958)	215	3.5	2.8	53

negl. Negligible.
[1] See text, footnote 38. Asterisk (*) means the projection is less than indicated 1962 capacity.

(*Sources on next page.*)

SOURCES TO TABLE 118:

a) *Public Utilities Fortnightly*, Vol. 42, No. 12 (Dec. 2, 1948), pp. 801–05.

b) *Electrical World*, May 22, 1950, p. 109.

c) President's Water Resources Policy Commission (PWRPC), *A Water Policy for the American People*, Vol. 1 (Washington, D. C.: U. S. Government Printing Office, 1950), p. 239.

d) *Mechanization*, Vol. XV, No. 11 (November 1951), pp. 89–100.

e) President's Materials Policy Commission (PMPC), *Resources for Freedom*, Vols. I–V (Washington, D. C.: U. S. Government Printing Office, 1952), *passim*.

f) Bureau of Reclamation, "Summary of Inventory of Future Development of Federally Identified Hydro-Electric Power Sites in the United States," unpublished staff study, January 8, 1954.

g) A. C. Monteith, "Future Energy Sources," *Proceedings of the American Power Conference, Sixteenth Annual Meeting*, Vol. XVI, 1954 (Chicago: Illinois Institute of Technology), p. 41.

h) W. L. Cisler, "Atomic Energy and its Industrial Applications," address to 1954 Coal Convention, American Mining Congress, Cincinnati, Ohio, May 3–5, 1954.

i) W. L. Cisler, "Looking Ahead to the Last Quarter of the First Century of Electric Power in the United States," *Bulletin*, Edison Electric Institute, Vol. 22, No. 6 (June 1954), p. 202.

j) P. Sporn, "Electric Power Demand and Supply in the United States and the Role of Research in the Quarter-Century Ahead," *Proceedings*, Institution of Electrical Engineers, Vol. 101, Part II, No. 82 (August 1954), p. 390.

k) K. M. Mayer, "A Study of the Economic Potential of Nuclear Energy in the United States Power Industry," unpublished doctoral dissertation, New York University, 1954.

l) W. C. Mullendore, "Hydroelectric Power," *Bulletin*, Edison Electric Institute, Vol. 23, No. 6 (June 1955), p. 171.

m) *Public Utilities Fortnightly*, Vol. 56, No. 5 (September 1, 1955), pp. 333 ff.

n) *Coal Age*, November 1955, p. 57.

o) Panel on the Impact of the Peaceful Uses of Atomic Energy, *Peaceful Uses of Atomic Energy*, Vol. 2, Report to the Joint Committee on Atomic Energy (Washington, D. C.: U.S. Government Printing Office, January 1956), pp. 24–30.

p) P. Sporn, "Sources of Energy for Electric Generation in the Two Decades Ahead," address to American Mining Congress, Cincinnati, May 7, 1956.

q) *Public Utilities Fortnightly*, Vol. 58, No. 11 (November 22, 1956), p. 850.

r) Federal Power Commission, Press Release No. 10,480, June 17, 1959.

s) *Electrical World*, September 14, 1959, p. 110.

t) Federal Power Commission, "Electric Power in Relation to the Nation's Water Resources," *Water Resources Activities in the United States*, Committee Print No. 10, Select Committee on National Water Resources, U. S. Senate (Washington, D. C.: U. S. Government Printing Office, 1960).

The Corps of Engineers-FPC estimate of 1948 represents the hydro capacity considered at that time feasible and economic for federal development during the following twenty to twenty-five years. It is thus not a true "estimate" of what *installed* capacity is likely to be in the future, but is the "planned" total of federal development at that time, based on authorized projects, reports to Congress, and plans in the course of preparation. Nevertheless, as an estimate of what *could* be installed it is considered here to be comparable with the other estimates of Table 118.

The anonymous estimate of 1950 is given without any stated basis. The estimate of the President's Water Resources Policy Commission (PWRPC) is related to an FPC estimate of total installed capacity of 160 million kw to meet energy requirements in 1970, which the Commission cites in concluding that "if present practices based on the most economical use of water power are followed, this will mean the development of about 25 million kw additional hydroelectric power."

The anonymous estimate of 1951 forecasts a doubling of 1951 capacity by 1975, based on the assumption that hydro would maintain its position in the total energy pattern at that time (that is, about 4 per cent of total supply) while the total energy output doubled.

The several estimates listed for the President's Materials Policy Commission (PMPC) have a varied basis. The figure of 60 million kw appears in a chart on page 119 of Volume I of the Commission's report. It is nowhere mentioned in the text of Volume I, where the discussion of future hydro capacity is in much broader terms:

> Opinions differ widely as to how much of the undeveloped potential it would be economical to establish before 1975, using either a single or multi-purpose approach as appropriate. It is quite possible, however, that our supply of hydroelectric energy could economically be doubled and conceivably be increased to 350 per cent of 1950 levels. Further study of each river basin and individual site would be necessary for a more exact appraisal.[32]

In the paragraph preceding the quotation, the report cites an FPC estimate of 16.5 million kw installed hydro capacity as of the beginning of 1950, although this excludes plants of 2,500 kw or less. Using the increases of two and three and one-half times mentioned by the PMPC, this would mean a range of 33 million to 57.75 million kw installed hydro capacity by 1975. A staff study in the PMPC report, however, makes the following statement:

> It is clearly feasible, within 10 to 15 years, to double the installed hydro capacity over the early 1950 level. In addition, there would remain other sites that probably could be economically developed before 1975. An output of hydroelectric energy on the order of three times the 1950 level might be achievable by 1975.[33]

[32] PMPC, *op. cit.*, p. 119.
[33] *Ibid.*, Vol. III, p. 38.

On the same basis, this would mean a capacity of 49.5 million kw by 1975. The chart thus uses a higher point than the range discussed by the Commission.

The Bureau of Reclamation figure is taken from a table prepared in answer to a request by the Atomic Energy Commission for a forecast of the schedule of federal hydro development through 1975. It is based on an inventory of "federally identified" power sites and an estimated schedule of their development.

The forecast by Monteith, an official in the electrical equipment industry, has no accompanying basis beyond the statement that hydro will "diminish in relative importance in the next ten to twenty years."

The first of the Cisler estimates is an unelaborated statement that hydro capacity will amount to 36 million kw in 1965, or 18 per cent of the total capacity of "interconnected power systems." The second Cisler estimate is derived from the following statement:

> It is almost certain that thermal generating units will constitute upwards of 90 per cent of the generating capacity to be installed in the next quarter century. This is because practically all the economic hydro sites have been developed in areas reasonably close to the heavy population centers, particularly in the eastern part of the country.[34]

Cisler listed actual and scheduled additions to hydro capacity from 1950 through 1955, and estimated maximum and minimum required additions to *total* generating capacity from 1955 to 1975. The figures imputed to Cisler in Table 118 were derived by taking the hydro additions together with 10 per cent of the subsequent total additions, and adding these to the FPC figure for installed utility hydro capacity at the end of 1949 (16.7 million kw). The use of 10 per cent means that the resulting figures are upper limits in the light of the quotation above.

The Sporn estimate is likewise an upper limit, with a very similar basis. Sporn believes that "water power may have difficulty in accounting for as much as 10 per cent" of the total capacity in 1978, which he projects as 410 million.

Mayer's estimate is based on the Bureau of Reclamation figures (see above) plus an assumption that future private hydro expansion will be at the rate of roughly 10 per cent of federal hydro expansion. This is on the basis of all current and announced hydro construction as of 1952.

The Mullendore estimate states that hydroelectric capacity "is expected to increase . . . to a maximum of 50 million kw in 1975." The use of the term "maximum" is somewhat ambiguous. It is probable that Mullendore believes that 50 million kw is as high as hydro capacity is likely to get by 1975.

The General Electric figures are taken from a published summary of an unpublished report by that company on the future of nuclear power. While focusing on the place of nuclear power in 1980, the report specifies a total of 44 million kw of hydro capacity among total generating capacity in that year. An

---

[34] W. L. Cisler, "Looking Ahead to the Last Quarter of the First Century of Electric Power in the United States," *Bulletin*, Edison Electric Institute, Vol. 22, No. 6 (June 1954), p. 202.

accompanying chart shows a projection of 35 million kw hydro capacity to 1975. No basis for these estimates is presented.

The *Coal Age* estimates are accompanied only by the information that they are based on those of General Electric, described in the preceding paragraph and of *Electrical World* (see below).

The figures labeled "McKinney Report" are derived from a section entitled "A Forecast of the Growth of Nuclear Fueled Electric Generating Capacity," in the report on Peaceful Uses of Atomic Energy. Here estimates are given for total, thermal, and nuclear generating capacity at five-year intervals through 1980. For Table 118, hydro capacity was obtained as a residual. Although the primary purpose of these estimates was to estimate the growth of nuclear capacity, the derived hydro figure is a valid imputation, since the report states that "the growth of hydroelectric generating capacity is assumed unaffected by nuclear plants."[35]

The Sporn estimate of 1956 is given as follows: "My own projections make me think that we shall have about 48 million kw of installed hydro by 1975. . . . This would mean that two decades from now slightly over one-eighth will be hydro. . . ."[36]

The Ebasco estimate represents the judgment of that firm based on an evaluation of other estimates and on such basic information as was available. The chart on which the estimate appears was not accompanied by any explanatory statements, nor is any such statement available elsewhere.

The Federal Power Commission serial estimates are derived, in the Commission's words, from "considerable information with respect to potential hydroelectric projects, hydroelectric construction work now in progress, and plans of both government agencies and private industry for developing power at the numerous river sites that have been studied . . . a careful analysis was made of such information in projecting hydroelectric generating capacity."[37]

The *Electrical World* estimate is based on the latest in that magazine's annual series of electrical industry forecasts. Yearly additions to hydro capacity are

[35] Panel on the Impact of the Peaceful Uses of Atomic Energy, *Peaceful Uses of Atomic Energy*, Vol. 2, Report to the Joint Committee on Atomic Energy (Washington, D. C.: U.S. Government Printing Office, January 1956), p. 9.

[36] Sporn in a letter assured the author that this estimate is, in fact, independently derived, and not the average of two government bureau estimates cited by Sporn, as suggested by M. S. Oldacre in "Energy Supplies for the Future," *Industrial Development*, Vol. 126, No. 3 (March 1957), p. 8. The two other estimates referred to by Sporn are (a) an unpublished Federal Power Commission estimate of 55 million kw made in 1956, and (b) a figure of 39 million kw for 1975 attributed to the Department of the Interior. This is derived from a figure by the Department given on page 74 of Volume 2 of the McKinney Report. The figure is given in British thermal units without any accompanying specific conversion factors for working back to kilowatt hours and installed hydro capacity. Sporn used his own conversion factors, which may or may not correspond to those used by the Department. Because of the absence of specified conversion factors, the Interior figure is not considered in this study.

[37] FPC, *Electric Power Requirements and Supply of the United States by Regions Present and Future to 1980*, FPC P-31, April 1958, p. 3.

given through 1962, and for the years 1963–75 are assumed to be at a constant rate. The sum of these additions was here added to the existing hydro capacity (excluding industrial) as of the end of 1958 to obtain the figure listed in Table 118. No attempt is made here to estimate retirement of obsolescent capacity.

The last estimate of the Federal Power Commission, a projection to the single year 1980, was made at the request of the Senate Select Committee on National Water Resources. No explanation of its derivation accompanies the estimate, but there is a reference to utilization of the data accompanying the estimates made earlier in 1959. It would be interesting to know the basis on which the FPC raised its estimate of 1980 installed capacity by 12 per cent in the space of a few months. Instead, the last estimate is accompanied by the statement that "All of the potential water power sites in the country have been studied by the Federal Power Commission and data have been developed on the available head, the capacity likely to be installed at these sites, and the amount of energy that would be generated in an average water year. Therefore, it can be assumed that the figures on future hydroelectric capacity . . . are fairly reliable." This is the most explicit statement yet by the FPC that its hydropower resource estimates represent a complete inventory. Those estimates nevertheless increase steadily from year to year.

The foregoing estimates have been reduced to common bases in columns 5, 6, and 7 of Table 118. In column 5 each estimate is given as a percentage of its respective base year. Column 6 lists the implied average annual growth rate during the period from the base year to the estimated year. Column 7 lists the implied average annual growth rate during the period from 1962 to the estimated year; the 1962 level of capacity was obtained by adding to the level as of the end of 1959 the additions planned during 1960, 1961, and 1962 as listed in the February 29, 1960 issue of *Electrical World*.[38]

Columns 6 and 7 reveal a wide range in implied rates of growth, with the estimates for federal capacity alone implying noticeably higher growth rates than all but one of those for total hydropower development. Both these features can be explained by the difference in past growth rates of federal and nonfederal hydro (see Figure 73), and the manner in which future federal development is viewed. The growth rates of the past and the immediate future are compared in Table 119, which demonstrates that an almost explosive development of federal hydro has in the past outweighed the modest pace of nonfederal development to yield the rate of 4–5 per cent that characterized total hydro development. Currently and for the next few years, however, this relationship is reversed, with a dramatic increase in the rate of nonfederal development outweighing an equally

[38] Total installed utility hydro capacity as of the end of 1959 was 30,977,000 kw, according to *Electrical World*, February 29, 1960, of which 14,154,000 was federal. To this must be added an estimated 700,000 kw of industrial capacity—allowing for a decline from the 725,000 kw as of 1957 reported in the U.S. Department of Commerce, *Statistical Abstract of the United States* (Washington, D. C.: U.S. Government Printing Office). The planned additions, 1960 through 1962, listed by *Electrical World* total 7,245,000 kw of which 1,862,000 are federal.

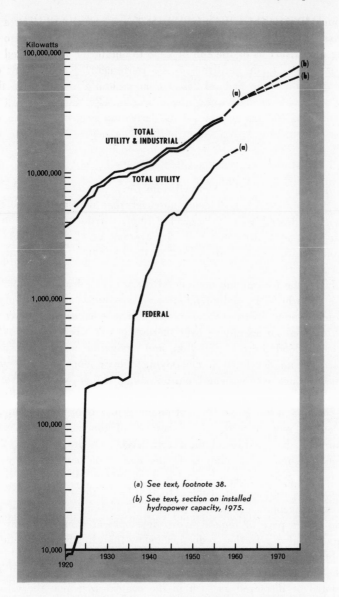

Figure 73. Installed hydropower capacity in the United States, 1920–59, and projection to 1975. (Industrial data for five-year intervals prior to 1936.) Source: Federal data, Statistical Bulletin *of* Edison Electric Institute; *other,* Federal Power Commission *Annual Report and* Industrial Power Summary, *all for years indicated.*

TABLE 119: AVERAGE ANNUAL GROWTH RATES OF HYDROPOWER
CAPACITY, SELECTED PERIODS, 1925–62

Period	Federal	Nonfederal	Total
1959–62.................	4.2%	10.4%	7.7%
1946–59.................	9.2	3.4	5.5
1935–45.................	34.9	1.1	4.3
1925–59.................	13.4	2.8	4.5

significant decline in the federal growth rate for a net increase in the pace of
total hydro development. It is evident, moreover, that almost all of the estimates
of future total hydro capacity in Table 118 imply a reduction from the current
growth rate of total hydro capacity. The average of all the implied growth
rates for total hydro capacity after 1962 in the estimates for the year 1975 is
2.1 per cent per year.

By and large, the federal and nonfederal sectors of hydro development reflect
the purpose for which the individual projects are undertaken. Simply stated,
otherwise uneconomic hydro—as viewed by private enterprise—may acquire
parity with or even an advantage over thermal power when it is a by-product
or coproduct of flood control, irrigation, and navigation works. The nature of
multipurpose stream development embodying one or more of these nonpower
purposes necessitates governmental participation, if not wholly governmental
action. With the possible exception of nuclear power, nowhere in the field of
energy resources and use is government policy (other than taxation and utility-
type regulation) more directly a determinant of the course of events. One
cannot approach the question of the future level of hydro capacity, therefore,
without making some assumption as to the nature of federal policy and the
extent of federal participation in hydro development. It may be reasonably
inferred from the estimates in Table 118 that, with the exception of those in
the government agencies concerned, the authors unanimously assume not only
a reduction in the pace of federal hydro development from that over the past
thirty years but also a further reduction below the already much-reduced rate
that will obtain in the next few years.

Since the implication of a lower rate of growth in future federal hydro is
nowhere stated or discussed as such in the context in which the estimates of
Table 118 originally appear, it is not possible to determine to what degree the
authors were consciously making such an assumption. Several of the estimates,
however, were associated with statements implying or explicitly noting either
economic or physical limitations, or both, on further development of hydro
capacity in the coming decade or two. Column 8 of Table 118 lists the estimates
as percentages of the FPC estimate of 122.1 million kw of total hydro potential
in terms of installed capacity. On this basis only the *Coal Age* and FPC estimates take development beyond roughly one-half the stated potential.

It is, of course, impossible to determine even roughly the level of hydro development at which economic and physical limitations would force the pace of further development below that of the present. But there would seem to be no *a priori* reason why such limitations should become effective at or below the level of one-half the potential. Nor should it be forgotten that, by limiting the coverage to what is now economic or is expected to be economic, the FPC understates the true potential (whatever it may be), so that all the estimates are overstated in column 8 of Table 118.

The foregoing applies to a consideration of the national hydro picture as a whole. But the regional variation in hydro resources cannot be wholly ignored. Like any natural resource, the occurrence of hydropower potential is, by human standards, fortuitous and haphazard, with high concentrations in certain relatively restricted regions and relative scarcity in others. This is illustrated in Table 120, which compares the regional occurrence of hydro potential according to the FPC and USGS estimates. Although specific percentages by region differ in the two reports, the wide regional variability is demonstrated in both, and they agree in the identification of the regions in order of concentration.

The pace of development in different regions is certain to vary, determined not only by the endowment of hydropower resources but also by the general complex of regional economic growth. Thus, different rates of hydro development in the past have resulted in different present levels of exploitation of the

TABLE 120.   REGIONAL DISTRIBUTION OF U.S. HYDROPOWER POTENTIAL

(Per cent of total potential in each region)

Region	FPC 1953	FPC 1958	USGS 90% availability [a]	USGS 50% availability
New England	4%	4%	2%	3%
Middle Atlantic	7	8	10	10
East North Central	4	3	2	3
West North Central	6	6	4	4
South Atlantic	11	10	6	7
East South Central	7	6	6	7
West South Central	4	4	2	2
Mountain	23	21	26	23
Pacific	34	37	41	42

[a] With storage.

SOURCES: L. L. Young, *Developed and Potential Waterpower of the United States and Other Countries of the World, December 1954.* U.S. Geological Survey Circular 367, 1955; Federal Power Commission, *Hydroelectric Power Resources of the United States, Developed and Undeveloped, 1953* (Washington, D. C.: U.S. Government Printing Office, 1954); and F. L. Weaver, "Hydro Potentialities as Indicated by the Federal Power Commission," paper presented at Twenty-First Annual Meeting, American Power Conference, Chicago, April 1, 1959. The earlier FPC data are included so as to make the dates of the agencies' estimates more comparable.

hydro potential in the several regions of the country. The FPC shows the current regional status, in terms of its own resource estimates, as follows:[39]

Region	Percentage development of hydro resources
New England	36%
Middle Atlantic	16
East North Central	25
West North Central	18
South Atlantic	33
East South Central	50
West South Central	20
Mountain	15
Pacific	23
United States as a whole	24%

Taken by river basins, the percentage of exploitation in 1957 ranged from a high of 92 per cent for the Tennessee to a low of 2 per cent for the Potomac.[40] The future pace of development will also depend, therefore, on the level of exploitation that has already been reached. Other things being equal, a high exploitation level would imply a relatively slow future development rate. For the country as a whole, it is significant that the regions with the greatest concentration of resources are relatively little developed.

TECHNOLOGY AS A DETERMINANT
OF FUTURE HYDROPOWER DEVELOPMENT

Technology, as manifest in technological progress, is both an "external" and "internal" determinant of the pace of hydropower development. It is external in the sense that the technology of other water use or management—such as for irrigation, navigation, flood control, and the various consumptive uses of industry and municipalities—affects the pace of hydro development. Improved irrigation techniques will, for example, through multipurpose projects, stimulate associated hydropower development. The feasibility of the St. Lawrence Seaway made possible the current construction of the associated power facilities. But these aspects are outside the scope of the present study, which can do no more than acknowledge them.

Technology as an internal determinant concerns the various aspects of hydropower proper already noted—the design, construction, and operation of dams; equipment and facilities; and the transmission of the generated power. It is an internal determinant in two ways: through the extension of the margin of technical feasibility, or practicability (that is, the "creation" of a larger tech-

[39] Weaver, op. cit.

[40] FPC, *Hydroelectric Power Reserves of the United States: Developed and Undeveloped, 1957, op. cit.*, p. 195.

nical potential); and through lowering the costs of new hydropower, in constant dollar terms (that is, an enlargement of the economic potential at any given time by intensive marginal development). The former is a straightforward matter of technology, but the latter, involving costs, requires consideration of the competitive position of hydropower as an energy source.

Superficially, the position of hydro versus thermal power in the continuing expansion of electric generating capacity can be viewed as an equilibrium arrived at and maintained by competition at the margin. Such competition in the past has resulted, according to this view, in the more or less complete development of the economic potential. Growth in the future will then be the result of a comparison of the power cost at each undeveloped hydro site with the alternative thermal plant that could be built. It has been stated, for example, that the undeveloped portion of what is here termed the technical potential can be developed "any time that the price of fuel makes the hydro competitive with the steam station for lower load factor. The reason no more hydro plants have been built [than already exist] is that . . . the initial investment is much higher than that for a steam plant, enough so that unless the load factor exceeds 65 per cent or so, the hydro total costs (operating and fixed charges) exceed those of a steam plant."[41]

This view is also expressed in the following argument that hydro has been saved from limbo in this country during the past period of large increase in thermal plant efficiency only by rising fuel costs.

> Of course, this does not mean that water power is immune to cost increases; for it, too, is afflicted with higher cost. But the point here is that the particular technological advancement whereby fuel electricity was to give hydroelectricity the coup de grace is not proving quite so powerful because its force has been blunted by the rising cost of fuel which overcompensates the savings.

> In this connection, one must keep in mind that, temporarily at least, the rapidly increasing use of natural gas . . . is injecting a new factor into the competitive struggle between diverse sources of energy and may offset here and there the benefits that otherwise might accrue to hydroelectricity as a result of the rising prices of coal and oil.[42]

But this view is an oversimplification that ignores the multipurpose basis of a large portion of recent and current additions to hydro capacity. It has been established that, as part of a multipurpose project, hydro capacity cannot be compared directly with alternative thermal capacity in simple cost terms. Direct comparison, moreover, carries the implication that the hydro capacity in question is, like the alternative thermal capacity, capable of supplying continuous power at a rate approximating the installed capacity. But this is not necessarily true:

> . . . in general, hydroelectric projects are best suited for operation at low capacity factors in the peak portions of area and regional loads. The relatively simple and rugged construction, with operations at low speeds and

[41] Pigott, *op. cit.*

[42] E. W. Zimmermann, *World Resources and Industries* (rev. ed., New York: Harper & Bros., 1951), p. 571.

temperatures, and the quick-starting ability make hydro projects adaptable for such peaking and reserve uses. Projects with ample pondage or with reservoir storage capacity are particularly valuable for such purposes. It is for such uses, therefore, that hydroelectric power derives its greatest value and provides its most valuable contribution toward meeting power demands. It may be noted that hydroelectric operation at low capacity factors results in the minimum possible conflicts with increasing consumptive uses of water.[43]

Nor is this merely a hypothetical consideration:

With rapidly increasing power loads in the United States, hydroelectric plants are being used to a greater extent in providing system reserves and in carrying short-time peak loads supplementing the baseload generation provided by fuel-electric plants. The hydroelectric plants, with limited amounts of energy available, *are designed to include large installed capacities to carry substantial portions of the peaks in the loads.* . . .

Even in the Pacific Northwest where today hydroelectric plants supply the bulk of the entire power loads and where until recently feasible hydroelectric power appeared to be available in such large potential quantities as to obviate the need for appreciable amounts of fuel-electric capacity, the long-range thinking and planning are in the direction of ultimately considering hydroelectric power for peaking as well as for baseload purposes in conjunction with fuel-electric sources of power supply.[44] (Italics added.)

Thus, it is particularly important, in attempting to estimate future *installed capacity*, not to identify hydro capacity in general with continuous power:

The evaluation of this resource must be on some basis other than the firm power that can be developed under minimum flows of the rivers. The factors of secondary usage and of coordination with other sources of electric energy represent the greatest means of applying technological knowledge to extend the resources of hydroelectric development.

Many existing projects can be redeveloped or enlarged to over capacity for the stream; but such plants can be counted on only when coordinated programs of interconnection and operation are utilized.[45]

Although the direct cost comparison of hydro and thermal is not the only, or necessarily the major determinant of whether a given hydro possibility is economically justified, this is not to say that hydro costs *per se* can be ignored. If they must be considered, then in the present context the crucial question is whether, in fact, hydro costs are subject to a secular increase, as the foregoing

[43] F. L. Weaver, "Prospects for Future Hydroelectric Development in the United States and What it is Likely to Cost," *Prospects for Nuclear Power* (New York: National Industrial Conference Board, 1957). See also F. A. Allner, "Economic Aspects of Water Power," *Transactions*, American Institute of Electrical Engineers, Vol. 52, No. 1 (March 1933), pp. 156–66.

[44] F. L. Weaver and G. G. Adkins, "Hydroelectric Power Development in the United States," Paper 64 A/15, Fifth World Power Conference, *op. cit.*

[45] S. L. Kerr, *Role of Technology in the Future of Hydroelectric Power*, Battelle Memorial Institute, unpublished report to the President's Materials Policy Commission, October 1, 1951, p. 1.

quotation from Zimmermann states. It should be noted that at least one authoritative source, the President's Materials Policy Commission, shares this belief:

> A few large water power sites remain to be developed which will produce low-cost power, but the remaining sites will require a higher capital outlay per unit of output and other expenses to be able to deliver electricity at the same low cost. As a consequence, the costs of hydropower also are subject, on an average, to upward pressures.[46]

To the extent that the lower cost hydro sites tend to be developed first, the tenor of the Commission's argument cannot be disputed. Whether it is too broad a generalization is less significant, however, than the fact that the argument ignores or denies the possibilities of future technological progress. The Commission seems to acknowledge this possibility a page or so later in noting the "opportunities for reducing capital outlay" through better construction technology and the avoidance of "the kind of 'overdesign' and 'overbuilding' which has characterized some hydropower structures in past years."[47] Conceivably, technologic advance in the design, construction, and operation of hydroelectric stations could considerably offset the general rise of marginal development costs with time and could even yield cost advantages for a significant portion of the undeveloped hydro potential. A study of European experience demonstrates that this has, in fact, occurred in that region in the past and may continue to hold in the future.[48] The purpose of this section is to ascertain whether, in this country, it is reasonable to expect that technology in the coming decade or two will be able to hold the line against the secular upward pressure on hydro costs owing to the exploitation of progressively more expensive sites.

·   ·   ·

Design and Construction

Since the major element in the cost of most hydropower installations is the dam, it is especially significant in the present context that the United States has been lagging behind other countries of the world in at least one aspect of dam technology. For a period, this country placed major reliance on the concrete gravity dam, which utilizes the sheer weight of the concrete mass to hold back the impounded water. Because of the large volume of processed materials that goes into such a dam it is not necessarily the most economical type of structure in all circumstances. (Note also the reference above to "overdesign" by the President's Materials Policy Commission.) Recently there has been a tendency in this country to make more use of earth and rock-fill dams, which realize the benefits of modern earth-moving technology. But there is some evidence that the arch dam has been unduly neglected in the recent past in this country, at least in the bold exploitation of its possibilities, while its use has been pushed aggres-

---

[46] PMPC, *op. cit.*, Vol. I, p. 117.
[47] *Ibid.*, pp. 119–20.
[48] Economic Commission for Europe, *op. cit.*, pp. 15–29.

sively abroad.[49] To the extent that this is true, there is the possibility that consideration of arch dams for specific hydro sites could make otherwise uneconomic projects economic,[50] and could result in a larger total developed capacity at any given time.

In addition to major cost savings that can be expected through the full exploitation of modern design possibilities in dams, it is reasonable to anticipate further modest savings from wider application (and continued further development) of present techniques of underground rock excavation. More and longer tunnels will mean more efficient use of hydro sites that would otherwise require more expensive structures and facilities. Similar benefits should accrue from the wider use of underground structures for turbines, transformers, and switching gear. (The provision of an underground powerhouse, for example, often increases the effective head and eliminates the costs of steel penstocks and surge tanks.) Again, it appears that European development on this score has been preceding development in this country.[51]

Similar opportunities appear to be present in turbine-generator design. Turbine efficiencies, to be sure, are already so high that there is little room for major improvement.[52] Nevertheless, there is still ample scope for increasing the heads with which each of the types can be used. The use of Kaplan and Francis types in the upper range of the heads for which they are adapted permits the use of turbine designs allowing the highest speed of water flow, higher turbine speed, a smaller sized turbine and generator, and smaller station size, thus yielding improved over-all efficiency and lower costs.[53]

Another aspect of technological advance in this field is the recent European development of the "bulb," or immersed Kaplan turbine, which operates horizontally under a very low head.[54] This should serve to extend the lower limit of economical hydro developments (in terms of low heads and smaller power potential), in what has been termed "micropower plants," to complement progress at the intensive margin of development made possible by the previously mentioned advances.

In the opinion of at least one observer, there is also a technological lag in turbine design in this country similar to that cited above with respect to the application of arch dams:

[49] See editorial, *Engineering News-Record*, April 12, 1956, and reader comment thereon, May 17, 1956 and June 28, 1956; also the issues of February 21, 1957 and September 11, 1958. This may be true of the buttress dam also. See G. S. Sarkaria, "Why Don't U.S. Dambuilders Build Buttress Type Dams?" *Engineering News-Record*, March 31, 1960, pp. 30–33.

[50] See, for example, *Engineering News-Record*, June 14, 1956.

[51] See Doland, *op. cit.*, p. 36.

[52] Current top turbine efficiencies are 93 per cent for the Kaplan type, 92 per cent for the Francis type, and 92 per cent for the Pelton wheel.

[53] E. R. DeLuccia and F. L. Weaver, "The State of Hydro-Electric Power Development in the United States," *Transactions*, Vol. IV, Fourth World Power Conference, London, 1950, p. 2090.

[54] See H. Chamayou, "Le groupe prototype de Castet et les perspectives d'avenir qu'il ouvre dans l'equipment hydroelectrique," Paper 97 H/17, Fifth World Power Conference, *op. cit.*

The nature of the hydraulic turbine industry is such that the design of the full-size units is based on model tests in research laboratories, and the performance guarantees of the manufacturers are predicated on the results of such work. The coordination of research and full-scale performance is essential to the progress of the industry. In the last 10 to 15 years, the performance testing of completed installations has been meager, and as a result, there is the same lag in technological progress that existed prior to 1918, at which time precise methods of water measurement became available to check the performance guarantees of hydraulic turbines.

The technical·developments in the United States as related to hydraulic turbine design thus have a major effect on the future scope of hydroelectric power as a national resource.[55]

Kerr cites two instances of this alleged lag: "In general, the range of specific speeds available for various heads from manufacturers in the United States is lower than offered in the world market, and this in turn makes the equipment more costly;" and "elsewhere in the world the vertical-shaft types [of turbine] with multiple jets have been in successful operation for many years with efficiencies and satisfactory performance far beyond anything found in the United States."[56]

One does not need to infer from these statements that great opportunities exist here for enlarging the economic potential or for significantly accelerating the pace of hydro development. But to the extent that such a situation may prevail, the opportunities are present for higher efficiencies, hence lower costs, in future hydro installations.

· · ·

Operation

It has been observed that the proper consideration of hydropower must include its place in electric power systems, where it may be integrated with other power sources. Under such circumstances, hydropower may be used for either base-load or peak-load purposes. A special technique of using hydro for the latter purpose is the method known as "pumped storage." This consists in the use of off-peak power available from a given system to pump water uphill into a reservoir, from which it can be drawn to generate hydropower to augment the system capacity under peak-load conditions.

The principle of pumped storage has been known and used for over half a century in Europe, where there are currently about 100 installations. In this country, however, there was only one pumped-storage plant prior to 1950. In that year, the reversible pump-turbine was brought out, constituting a basically new idea in hydropower, and the pumped-storage approach received a world-wide stimulus. This development significantly reduced capital costs for pumped storage and at the same time raised operating efficiency. The technique thus became

[55] Kerr, *op. cit.*, p. 2.
[56] *Ibid.*, pp. 3 and 5.

an immediately competitive alternative in planning additions to system capacity. By 1956, there were four pumped-storage installations in the United States and others existed in planning stages in all regions of the country.

The importance of this development warrants a brief survey of the advantages and opportunities it offers. In terms of cost advantage, it is the conclusion of one study that, allowing for "reasonable load-factor operation," pumped storage can sustain initial investment costs of up to $25 per kw more than the average cost of steam capacity.[57] (And, to the extent that investment costs for pumped storage are not greater than alternative steam capacity, the result can be net savings.) This, Loane says, is possible because of such advantages as:

1) Large reactive capacity available for system voltage regulation.

2) Almost zero cost of spinning reserve.

3) Relatively rapid load pickup or load drop.

4) Location of power plant where steam plant would be impractical, and in plant sizes that would be uneconomical for steam.

5) Use of smaller generating units, providing better opportunity for fitting capacity to load.

6) Relatively short lead time for additions to capacity of a developed site.[58]

These general advantages are supplemented by others that are determined by the type of system to which pumped storage is being added. The technique can be used on a limited scale at some hydro sites to add flexibility to the operation of the reservoir.

> To be most economically attractive such pumping has to be applied to a scheme designed for low load factor with restricted upper storage but preferably a large tail reservoir. . . . Besides offering opportunities for maintaining reservoir levels in times of drought and hence maintaining the kilowatt capacity at a higher "firm" figure, pumping may enable a higher average reservoir level to be achieved with consequent increased output. Alternatively, the pumping can be applied to enable the same results to be obtained with a lower dam.[59]

The need for only a small upper reservoir, moreover, "permits use of pumped-storage in places entirely unsuitable for the usual hydro plant. This flexibility of location should allow other economies through use of shorter penstocks or tunnels and proximity to transmission."[60]

With respect to the integration of pumped storage with steam capacity, the basic usefulness of the former stems from the desirability of providing as high

---

[57] E. S. Loane, "Pumped-Storage Hydro Attractive," *Electrical World*, September 23, 1957, p. 73.

[58] *Ibid.*, p. 77. The pumped-storage installation at the Sir Adam Beck station on the Canadian side of Niagara Falls had a slightly lower capital cost than equivalent thermal capacity. See O. Holden, "3 Pump-Turbines in Operation," *Electrical World*, Jan. 20, 1958, p. 57.

[59] A. A. Fulton, T. G. N. Haldane, and R. W. Mountain, "The Practical Application and Economics of Pumped Storage in Great Britain," Paper 227 H/38, Fifth World Power Conference, *op. cit.*

[60] Loane, *op. cit.*, p. 75.

a plant factor as possible for new steam plants. As the trend continues toward the construction of larger steam units employing more advanced technology, the high efficiency of these units yields incremental energy at low cost. Hence, it is desirable to get as much of the system supply as possible out of such units. The pumped-storage technique helps to accomplish this by offering a means of storing surplus off-peak, low-cost energy in a reservoir for release on peak. Since there are losses in pumping and regeneration, there must be other advantages, such as low capital costs, as compared with alternative new steam capacity, to offset these losses. Moreover, the effect of adding pumped storage to a steam system for peaking purposes is to increase fuel consumption in the system,[61] since the fuel requirements of existing steam capacity to power the pumps would be greater than the fuel requirements of new steam capacity equivalent to the pumped-storage capacity. This leads to the paradoxical conclusion that pumped storage may be more advantageous in low-cost fuel areas.

The situation concerning the future possibilities of integrating pumped storage with nuclear power plants is analogous to that of the advanced steam technology (assuming economic nuclear power to begin with). Again, units are large, capital costs are high, incremental generation cost is low, and the desirability of a high plant factor is accordingly enhanced. Not only are the possibilities on this score recognized, but at least one pumped-storage and nuclear combination is already projected in Great Britain.[62]

The evidence, in short, indicates strongly that pumped storage with reversible pump-turbines is a technological development of the greatest importance, for *pumped storage can create hydro capacity at sites where no natural flow exists.* Conventional thermal plants are often located at or near a stream or lake for transportation advantages and cooling purposes. "It is conceivable that utilities with conventional lakeshore or riverside thermal generation plants in hilly regions might construct artificial reservoirs for pumped storage systems to gain extra peak load generating capacity in the not too distant future." [63]

This raises the question of whether pumped storage really constitutes hydropower. The latter term usually implies "free" energy—energy realized from natural precipitation. Pumped storage, on the other hand, is a means of storing

[61] *Ibid.*, p. 77.

[62] *Nuclear Power*, Vol. 2, No. 15 (July 1957), p. 264; *Atom*, No. 11 (September 1957), p. 14; J. M. Kay and A. A. Fulton, "Combined Use of Nuclear Power and Pumped-Storage Hydro Stations," Paper 15/P/1448, Second United Nations International Conference on the Peaceful Uses of Atomic Energy, Geneva, September 1958.

[63] W. J. Rheingans, F. Jaski, and H. H. Roth, "Pumped Storage," *Proceedings*, Midwest Power Conference, Vol. XIII, 1951, p. 154. (Indeed, in 1956, a project was proposed that would put a pumped-storage plant on the shore of Lake Erie and form a reservoir by damming both ends of a nearby valley in the Allegheny Mountains. See *Power Engineering*, Vol. 60, No. 3 (March 1956), p. 105. And, in early 1960, a Missouri utility requested an FPC permit for a 350,000 kw pumped-storage project alongside a small stream in the southeast part of the state. A dam on the stream would merely provide the lower pool. Offpeak power from the St. Louis area would pump the water from this pool to a small reservoir 1,000 feet higher atop a nearby hill.

energy that may be derived from other sources than hydro for use at a more convenient time. If pumped storage is not hydro, it bears no relation to the hydro potential at any level, and must be considered separately. It is easy to get involved in a semantic snarl here, but it would appear that there is far more to be gained in simplicity of concepts and terminology by bringing pumped storage within the concept of hydro than by consigning it to its own category. Pumped storage, after all, does produce electricity from falling water, with the same equipment and technique used in hydro, regardless of the fact that it was human ingenuity rather than natural processes that raised the water to a position from which it could fall.

Accordingly, for the purposes of this discussion, pumped storage is considered to come under hydropower, but in so doing the effect of this definition on the concepts of hydro potentials must be acknowledged. Since pumped storage can "create" hydro potential where none exists in nature, this must be allowed for in the theoretical potential, the scope of which should be enlarged to this extent. Similarly, the technical and economic potentials should be raised by the inclusion of pumped storage, and any estimate of future installed hydro capacity should reflect this consideration. One writer has concluded that "in general, a system without other hydro capacity might utilize pumped-storage to the extent of 10 to 15 per cent of total system capacity,"[64] and there is already a widespread appreciation of the probable rapid growth of pumped storage in integrated systems.[65]

· · ·

Transmission

The relation between line voltage and transmission costs is inverse, and between line voltage and maximum distance is direct; that is, higher voltage is economically justified with larger blocks of power and longer distances. The significance of this with respect to hydropower concerns large remote hydro sites, and to a lesser extent all hydro sites. Since higher voltages make possible transmission of electric power over longer distances, the economic potential of hydro resources is affected. And to the extent that higher voltage contributes to more interconnection of power systems, the development of hydro in general is affected (it was brought out above that otherwise uneconomic hydro sites may be economic if considered as part of an integrated system). Current transmission technology in this country utilizes a maximum of 345 kilovolts (kv), with an economic limit of 200 to 300 miles in distance. (Voltage up to this level is known as "high voltage"; higher levels are often referred to as "extra high voltage" (ehv).

[64] Loane, *op. cit.*, p. 73.

[65] See, for example, F. L. Weaver, "Prospects for Future Hydroelectric Development in the United States and What it is Likely to Cost," *op. cit.*; and "Symposium on Pumped Storage," *Proceedings of the American Power Conference, Twentieth Annual Meeting, Volume XX, 1958* (Chicago: Illinois Institute of Technology), pp. 385–417.

The importance of future progress in transmission technology in the present context is indicated by this fact: If a distance of 600 miles for power transmission were to become both technically and economically feasible in this country, there would be sufficient radius for interconnections over the entire nation, and every hydro site would be within range of existing markets. (Not every site, to be sure, would thereby automatically become economic.) This distance is possible with the utilization of 500 kv. An example of the specific effects of this achievement on the hydro potential is given by a study of the Bureau of Reclamation which analyzes the possibilities of employing 500 kv on a grand scale in the United States west of the Mississippi River. According to the Bureau's analysis a supergrid for the twenty-two western states, tying in the source regions of hydro and coal-based steam power, would make feasible and economic by 1975 the development of almost two-thirds of the hydro potential of the area as a whole (as given by the FPC). This constitutes some three-quarters of the national potential as estimated by the FPC at the time.[66]

It is not necessary here to judge the practicality of the Bureau's scheme,[67] since it does not matter whether the scheme as proposed is realistic. For the purposes of this study the Bureau's analysis suggests the possible magnitude of the effects of extra high voltage on hydro development. The question then is, what degree of progress can be reasonably expected in the period under consideration?

Published opinion is divided on this question. According to the most pessimistic view:

> A great increase in the economic distance of electric-power transmission does not seem to be in the cards. To get it by pushing the voltage up much above the present maximum of 287 kilovolts, where it has been for nearly twenty years, does not seem likely. There is no foreseeable prospect for transmission lines operating in this country above about 315 kilovolts and certainly not above 380 kilovolts. . . .
> The fact is, the energy of our rivers will likely continue to be used within 200 or 300 miles—and mostly less—of its generation. History has shown that where low-cost power is, there energy-consuming industries go.[68]

A less extreme, but on the whole pessimistic, view is expressed by others. One discussion concludes that the advantages of extra high voltage in long-distance bulk transmission may be less than in superimposing it within existing systems because of the possibilities offered by greater development at existing voltages, particularly if this is 230,000 volts or above.[69] Another study compares the cost of fuel transport with the transmission of blocks of power up to 3.6 million kw and voltages up to 460 kv, for distances up to 700 miles. It notes that large power blocks combined with high load-factor loads tend to make fuel and electric

[66] Bureau of Reclamation, *A Study of Future Power Transmission for the West*, 1952.

[67] For an opinion on this score see *Business Week*, January 3, 1953, p. 34.

[68] Ayres and Scarlott, *op. cit.*, pp. 251–52.

[69] V. M. Marquis and H. P. St. Clair, "Transmission Looks to the Future," *Electrical World*, May 22, 1950, pp. 115–17.

power movement competitive, the balancing economies being determined by freight costs and the financing costs of transmission lines.

> Primarily because of the cost of getting the coal off and on wheels . . . electric transmission is far cheaper for short distances but more expensive as distance increases. The breakeven point depends primarily on the capital charges on the investment and on the block of power being transmitted. Even when handling 1,800,000 kw the breakeven point under American conditions is only . . . [160 miles] when total capital charges are 14 per cent and . . . [425] miles when they are 10 per cent. For really long distances, transmission of electric power is uncompetitive.[70]

Recent events, however, suggest that these opinions are in error, or at least that they seriously underestimate the possibilities of extra high voltage and the imminence of its use. An experimental 500-kv line is currently under test in the Colorado Rockies, and in June 1958 plans were announced for a five-year research program (titled "Project EHV") to advance knowledge of ehv transmission and to gain actual operating experience in the ranges of 460 to 750 kv. Operation at 460 to 500 kv is scheduled to take place in 1960. In the following year, the voltage will be raised to 600 to 750 kv; and in 1963 results of the tests will be evaluated to determine whether they should be continued at 1,000 kv. Of special significance to the present discussion is the prediction of the project director that eventually there will be in the United States a transcontinental power grid that will interconnect all major power generating areas of the country.[71]

Project EHV is described by its sponsor as helping to reestablish the United States as a world leader in ehv technology. Considering the relative abundance of low-cost fuels in most parts of this country, it is not surprising that the United States is not the most advanced in ehv technology. A 400-kv network involving a distance of 300 to 400 miles has been in service in Sweden since 1952, and the Soviet Union placed a similar transmission system in service in 1956 over a distance of 505 miles. This reflects a strong incentive in both countries to explore such an avenue of development because of their power resource position. Both have large hydro resources located long distances from consuming centers where fuel costs are high. Swedish engineers anticipate the need to transmit power over 500-mile distances by 1980, are prepared to use 500 kv, and believe that 650 kv can be controlled with current technical means.[72] Their Soviet

---

[70] C. N. Phillips, "Economics and Developments to Expect in Transporting Energy," *Bulletin*, Edison Electric Institute, Vol. 21, No. 7 (July 1953), pp. 271–76. See also the more recent paper by J. K. Dillard and M. Maxwell, "Economics of Extra-High-Voltage Transmission," Paper 40/D/10, World Power Conference Sectional Meeting, Montreal, September 7–11, 1958.

[71] *Electrical World*, June 9, 1958, pp. 54–55, 58. In the same vein, two General Electric engineers have predicted 650 kv will be in use in the United States in 1977. (See *American Metal Market*, Feburary 5, 1959.)

[72] Gunnar Jancke, "High Tension Transmission Problems with Special Reference to the Swedish Network," *Proceedings of the American Power Conference, op. cit., Volume XIX, 1957*, pp. 422–34.

counterparts intend also to raise their 400-kv system to 500 kv, and believe it is technically possible to extend transmission at such voltages to distances up to 2,000 miles.[73]

At such voltages and distances, however, the economic transmission of large blocks of power using direct current becomes competitive with the traditional alternating current. Again, the lack of incentive in this country has caused transmission of direct current (dc) to be largely ignored, but in Sweden and the USSR research has been going on for some time. At the research level, the two countries appear to be about even, but the Soviets have begun construction work on a truly grandiose scheme for an 800-kv, 340-mile dc line between Stalingrad and the Donbas, planned for 1960. This line would provide the experience for designing and operating a dc line at 1,000 kv, tying the hydro resources of far Siberia into various consuming centers. And even this is dwarfed by the Soviet intention, reported in early 1960, to have at least three 1,400-kv dc transmission lines in operation within twenty years.[74]

The specific Soviet intentions may be discounted for overconfidence, but the fact remains that in the period through 1975 ehv technology and operating experience with both alternating and direct current are likely to exist in Sweden and the USSR. The fundamental fuel-cost advantage of the United States can be assumed to continue throughout the period, hence there is no reason to suppose a wholesale swing in the United States to the most advanced ehv technology in Europe.[75] At the same time, it can also be reasonably assumed that experience and continued research with extra high voltage in Europe will reduce its costs in general, so that it would seem unwise to rule out its possible effects on the pace of future hydro development in this country. *The technology will be available if economic opportunities appear for its use.* The first paragraph of the quotation from Ayres and Scarlott (see above, p. 471) was obsolete almost as it was being written; the Bureau of Reclamation's visionary scheme is at present fully as plausible as the second paragraph of that quotation.

·   ·   ·

Small Power Sites

There remains one aspect of the impact of technology on the pace of hydro development that partakes of the benefits of advance in most, if not all, of the fields of technology surveyed above. It will be recalled that the estimates of potential hydropower by both the FPC and the Geological Survey exclude small sites of less than 2,500-kw capacity. The President's Materials Policy Com-

[73] J. H. M. Sykes, "Soviet Transmission Features," *Electrical World*, September 30, 1957, pp. 64–65.

[74] *Electrical World*, February 29, 1960, p. 67.

[75] Although the potentialities in high-capacity, low-cost transmission from coal fields to load centers could lead to the mutual stimulation of ehv and mine-mouth power generation. (See Chapter 8.)

mission noted that at the time of its investigations more than 1,000 potential hydro sites, mostly relatively small ones, "were apparently not receiving serious attention by anyone." But the PMPC shared the consensus that they were of little import in that "many of these may upon closer examination not prove economically feasible to develop by 1975."[76]

Clearly the significance of small sites is not very great in the total hydropower picture even if most of them are economically feasible. Assuming that the average potential capacity of the sites is 1,250 kw, or one-half of the upper limit with which they have been defined, the total capacity of the 1,000 sites would be on the order of 1.2 million kw. Although this is equivalent to only one very large hydro development the contribution should not necessarily be ignored. It is likely that the regional distribution of these small sites is as variable as is that of hydro capacity in general; hence, in certain regions the "small potential" may not be wholly insignificant.

There is, moreover, some evidence that a good portion of the potential is economic at present. Between 1948 and 1953, for example, a power company in North Carolina constructed five small plants ranging in size from 1,800 to 12,000 kilovolt amperes. The company considered the sites economically attractive in the light of three developments: (1) recent advances in supervisory control and tele-metering equipment, allowing fully automatic operation by remote control; (2) advances in turbine construction reducing required maintenance; and (3) the use of rock-fill dams, which cost less than one-twelfth the cost of concrete per unit volume and which have many other engineering advantages at small sites. On the basis of its experience, the company believes that "there still remains eco-nomically hydroelectric potential in many of the smaller streams which are more commonly available."[77]

This suggests that expected future progress in all areas of technology considered above, save ehv transmission, should tend to increase the economic potential of small sites. To this extent, existing resource estimates and estimates of future installed capacity all tend to understate the true possibilities.

CONCLUSIONS

The Hydropower Potential of the United States

The discussion of the government estimates of U.S. hydro resources earlier in this study ended on a critical note because of their misleading and ambiguous definitions, and incomplete coverage. But they do constitute the best available information on the subject, and the problem is to interpret them within the concepts employed in this study.

[76] PMPC, *op. cit.*, Vol. III, p. 37.
[77] H. H. Gnuse, Jr., "Small Hydro Sites Can Be Developed Economically," *Electrical World*, September 7, 1953, p. 80.

Young's estimate of 86 million kw as the hydro resources at mean flow was judged to be somewhere between the theoretical and technical potential in concept and something less than the technical potential in coverage. Conceptually, the estimate can be brought closer to the technical potential by replacing its assumptions of 100-per cent efficiency and gross head with a factor that corresponds to current technological capability. A figure of 70 per cent would appear to be reasonable and conservative for this purpose.[78] On this basis, the Survey figure becomes approximately 60 million kw.

The significance of this figure should be carefully understood. It does not refer to installed and installable capacity. It can best be described as the closest currently possible approximation to the technical potential of this country. When used as such, moreover, it means that the technical potential is *at least* 60 million kw. Its error is all on the low side due to the understatement that results from the incomplete coverage in the measurement procedure (and perhaps also on the score of a conservative efficiency factor). As a minimum figure, it therefore has considerable value.

The Federal Power Commission estimated 122 million kw of installed and installable capacity as the hydro resources of the United States. This estimate was put somewhere between the technical and economic potentials in concept and below the latter in coverage. The only way to make the figure consistent with the "potentials" terminology is to convert its associated generation estimate to the "comparative capacity" equivalent employed by the Economic Commission for Europe. Dividing the annual generation estimate of 512.6 billion kwh (that accompanies the capacity estimate) by 8,760 yields a figure of 58.5 million kw. Again, as an approximation of the economic potential it is a *minimum* figure because of the conservatism inherent in the individual site estimates, and the exclusion of pumped-storage possibilities. The latter may well be a serious deficiency.

It will be seen that the approximations of economic and technical potential obtained here are surprisingly close together. One would not expect, *a priori*, that costs would make little difference between what is technically feasible and what is economically feasible. Perhaps this is indeed the situation but, in any event, it is clear that the closeness is to some unmeasurable degree a reflection of the human factor. As pointed out previously, because of his innate caution, the engineer-estimator tends to infuse economic criteria into his view of the technical possibilities of a given site. Indeed, this closeness is exhibited to the same degree in European estimates of economic and technical potential.[79]

[78] Current over-all plant efficiency of the United States is given by an authoritative source as 80 to 83 per cent based on net head; with gross head, the over-all figure is 10 to 15 per cent less. See W. P. Creager and J. D. Justin, *Hydroelectric Handbook* (2nd ed., New York: Wiley, 1950), p. 160. The Economic Commission for Europe, *op. cit.*, p. 62, uses 75 per cent for over-all efficiency based on European practice. The Bureau of Reclamation assumes in its preliminary site studies an efficiency of 80 per cent for storage plants and 75 per cent for run-of-river plants. See *Bureau of Reclamation Manual*, Vol. IV, Chapter 4.2. Davis, *op. cit.*, uses 80 per cent for his Canadian estimate.

[79] Economic Commission for Europe, *op. cit.*, pp. 84, 93–95.

It would be highly desirable to have the third approximation, of theoretical potential, to round out this very rough assessment of U.S. hydro potentials at all levels. Unfortunately, there is no published figure extant that could be manipulated in a meaningful fashion to yield even a crude idea of what the theoretical potential of this country might be. The Economic Commission for Europe has made an exhaustive statistical analysis of the estimates for the river basins and countries of Europe at the various levels, and has obtained general relationships between the potentials. It concludes, for example, that existing national estimates of economic potential in Europe "in large areas comprising a wide range of natural conditions" are between 15 and 25 per cent of the gross potential.[80] Less sweeping, hence more meaningful, generalizations can be made based on these relations as a function of the "density" of the theoretical potential (that is, kw per square kilometer). It would be interesting to have such density data for this country to test the results by region. In their absence, the most that can be done is to speculate on the indicated theoretical gross potential if the relationships were the same in this country as in Europe. Using the above percentages, the results are a range of 230 to 390 million kw. Is the theoretical potential of the United States on this general level? In the absence of an adequate basis on which to reach any conclusion, the question is left unanswered for this study.

The figures do, however, suggest that the hydro resources of the United States, when viewed in the appropriate perspective, are appreciably larger than has heretofore been realized. The significance of this conclusion is emphasized by comparing current capacity with the approximate economic and technical potentials. The 1959 (year-end) installed capacity of some 32 million kw generated 138 kwh; converting the latter into a "comparative capacity" figure yields 15.7 million kw. On this basis, current capacity constitutes at the most only one-quarter of the actual economic and technical potentials. Or, to put it in terms of possibilities, available data suggest that the hydro resources of this country that can be economically developed at present are perhaps on the order of four times the current level of development. With due allowance for the crudeness of these results, it is reasonable to conclude that hydro capacity can be greatly expanded without running into serious cost limitations, and that the over-all resource limitations on hydro development are not yet within sight.[81] Indeed, the limitations that will effectively brake hydro development in the eventual future will be the competing consumptive water uses.

.   .   .

Installed Hydropower Capacity in the United States in 1975

The estimates of future installed capacity listed in Table 118 can now be viewed in the light of the survey of technology and the resource conclusions just

[80] *Ibid.*, p. 93.

[81] This is consistent with European findings where, despite the pressures of high-cost fuel resources and the consequent higher level of exploitation of hydro resources, "In no European country where significant hydro production is possible has more than one-half of the possible output yet been developed." See *ibid.*, p. 96.

presented. The implications of the technology survey are that general progress in the technology of hydroelectric design, construction and operation, and of power transmission should continue to favor the development of hydro resources by counteracting the less favorable physical circumstances of the remaining resources. In particular, the pumped-storage technique enhances the already growing value of hydro as peak capacity and gives promise, with the reversible pump-turbine, of leading to the widespread installation of hydro capacity employing this technique.

None of the estimates in Table 118, however, is accompanied by any similar statement or implication concerning the influence of technological progress on future hydro development. In the light of the foregoing, the most conspicuous lack is the failure to take account of an indicated rapid growth potential for pumped storage. This suggests that even the higher estimates in the table are not excessively optimistic. (The total, incidentally, of all currently planned additions —including those after 1962—reported in the 1960 *Electrical World* summary yields a figure of 52.3 million kw when added to existing capacity as of the end of 1959. This would indicate that, for 1975, all estimates of future installed capacity below this level are unrealistic. Indeed, according to the latest FPC figures for capacity under construction and in various planning stages,[82] the total installed and intended to be installed is 66.2 million kw.)

The assumed growth rates of even the latest of the estimates in Table 118 have disturbing implications when compared with those in Table 119. Part of the trouble has been a consistent underallowance for additions to capacity in the immediate future, as can be seen from the generally sharp contrast between the figures in columns 6 and 7 for each estimate in Table 118. Even the implied growth rate for the period of each estimate, however, has tended to be inconsistent with experience. Thus, the 3.5 per cent implied in the most recent estimate in Table 118 is less than two-thirds the rate that has prevailed to date in the postwar period, less than four-fifths of the rate over the past thirty-five years, and less than half the rate indicated in installations and planned installations in the period 1959–62. The imponderables of politics enter into the matter of federal power development policy, so that it would be unwarranted to assume that the growth of federal power would return to the rate of the 1946–59 period. Similarly, it would be unwise to infer any long-run significance from the current high rate of nonfederal power development. But at the same time, there appears to be no justification for assuming that the over-all pace would decline to well below past growth rates. This would mean a remarkably abrupt reversal, of which there is no current evidence, in the prevailing attitude toward the development of hydro resources. Rather, it is reasonable to expect a continuation of the current high level of interest in hydro development, under some aegis, whether private,

[82] *Energy Resources and Technology*, Hearings Before the Subcommittee on Automation and Energy Resources of the Joint Economic Committee, Congress of the United States, 86th Congress, 1st Session (Washington, D. C.: U.S. Government Printing Office, 1959), p. 111.

partnership, or public. On balance, then, even the latest FPC estimate would seem to be overly conservative.

Accordingly, a figure of 60 million kw is chosen to represent the lower limit to the range of likely installed hydropower capacity in 1975. For comparison purposes, the implied growth rates of this figure are 4.1 per cent per annum from 1959 to 1975, and 3.2 per cent from 1962 to 1975, based on currently planned capacity in 1962 (see Table 119 and Figure 73).

The upper limit should represent the extent to which the adoption of pumped storage expected in this study actually occurs. Systematic quantification of this expectation is impossible, since the effect of the technique is open-ended (that is, it can create new hydro potential). The best that can be done is to suggest that the probability of extensive adoption of the technique appears strong, and to represent this probability with a figure of 10 million kw. The upper limit to the range of likely installed hydropower capacity adopted as the estimate of this study is therefore 70 million kw. This implies a growth rate of 5.1 per cent in the period 1958–75 and 4.5 per cent for 1961–75. The choice of 10 million kw as representing an indicated level of pumped-storage installation is, of course, merely a reflection of the opinion of this study that the new technique will be widely adopted—widely enough in fact, to account for almost one-quarter of total hydro installations between 1963 and 1975. Note, however, that even these figures are conservative in the light of recent and current growth rates.

There remains the comparison of the 1975 installed capacity estimates with the conclusions on hydro resources. The FPC estimate was converted to a "comparative capacity" basis in order to compare it with the Geological Survey estimate, and both were labeled no more than crude approximations of economic and technical potentials, respectively. Assuming the FPC estimate is a useful approximation of the economic potential, it can be compared directly with the 1975 capacity estimates made above. The range of 60 to 70 million kw thus constitutes 49 to 57 per cent of the FPC resource estimate, which is definitely a minimal estimate of the economic potential. Hence, it is probably correct to suppose that such capacity in 1975 would constitute no more than one-half the present economic potential.

It can be concluded that not only should there be no decline in the pace of hydro development due to resource deficiency in the period through 1975, but that such development should not encounter a secular cost increase. The magnitude of undeveloped hydro resources is relatively large, and will remain so throughout the period. The combination of the wider adoption of known technology and anticipated further advances in technology should largely offset any tendency to cost increase, in constant dollars, that might otherwise appear.

APPENDICES

APPENDICES

A note on problems of measurement

The Btu as the Common Unit of Measurement

The British thermal unit, or Btu, recurs throughout this study as the common denominator through which the several energy sources and their products are added together and compared with each other. It is a calorific unit, representing the amount of heat necessary to raise the temperature of one pound of water one degree Fahrenheit. For each of the energy sources and their products there is a representative Btu content per unit of weight or volume which has been used in this study in converting to a common basis the physical units in which the various fuels are ordinarily measured.[1]

There is a special conversion problem for hydropower. Its output, which is measured in kilowatthours (kwh), may be converted to Btu's either in terms of the direct calorific equivalent of the kwh or the calorific equivalent of the fuels which would have been required if the same amount of electricity were generated in a thermal power station. In this study, the latter conversion factor was used. Since historical changes in the efficiency of converting fuels to electricity have been very great, this conversion factor has changed considerably over time. The direct calorific equivalent of the kwh, on the other hand, is a constant, but its use was considered inappropriate because this would have understated the relative importance of hydropower as compared with all other energy sources which are included in terms of their inherent Btu equivalents, even when used to generate electricity.[2]

[1] The totals thus derived measure the inherent Btu values of the primary energy materials consumed. The efficiency of use of the various energy sources in different applications are not taken into account. For a discussion of the efficiency question see the section in Chapter 4 dealing with the thermal and economic efficiency of energy utilization.

[2] Alternative methods are sometimes employed in which the kwh is used as the common denominator for all energy. One such method, used in United Nations statistics, is described in Chapter 4, in the section comparing per capita energy consumption in the United States and the rest of the world.

481

Another source of difficulty in using the Btu *numéraire*—or any other common denominator—is that although a given conversion factor may be broadly representative for a particular energy source it will not be valid in each and every case. Variations in quality are often reflected in differences in Btu content. In addition, a raw material such as crude oil which is converted into numerous secondary products is characterized by different representative Btu values per unit of its various products; and the products, in turn, are sufficiently lacking in homogeneity that there is a range in their Btu values. Hence, although the representative conversion factors which were used in the main in this study are enumerated in Table I-11 (Appendix to Part II) and in the footnotes to Tables II and VII (Appendix to Part I), the reader will note departures from them in some instances.

The Btu is a small unit of measure, especially in comparison with the units more commonly used in describing and analyzing the economy; gross national product (GNP) is expressed in hundreds of billions of dollars, population in hundreds of millions of people, and yearly per capita income in thousands of dollars; but yearly Btu consumption by the economy runs on the order of quadrillions, or, expressed exponentially, 10^{15}. Various devices have been used elsewhere to replace the Btu by a larger unit and thus reduce the magnitude of the numbers involved,[3] but for the purposes of this study the Btu was considered the most suitable unit.

In the Appendix to Part II figures are presented at the level of one billion (10^9) Btu. However, one billion Btu are equivalent to only some forty tons of coal and it is obvious that such a high degree of accuracy is not to be expected of the underlying statistics. We have chosen, nevertheless, to present the statistics at this level, despite the impression of spurious accuracy this conveys, in order to give the reader the working materials. Many of the calculations were carried out at this level, and we considered it desirable to retain the results as they came out rather than to round off. The billion level is also helpful in permitting the reconciliation between many of the tables in the Appendix to Part II.

·   ·   ·

Consistency Between Parts I and II

The reader working with both Parts I and II, and their respective Appendices, will find numerous differences between figures apparently referring to the same items for the year 1955, and in a few instances for earlier years. These discrepancies, which reflect the fact that the basic analyses in Part I and II were performed by different members of our group, have been allowed to remain. Since they are not quantitatively significant we considered it preferable to retain the figures used in the independent analyses than to strive for rigid consistency.

[3] The gas industry, for example, uses the "therm," defined as 100,000 Btu. A much larger unit is the "Q," to stand for 10^{18} Btu, introduced by Palmer Putnam in *Energy in the Future* (New York: Van Nostrand, 1953).

The differences occur both in details and in the totals for the different energy sources. The discrepancies between the totals in Parts I and II are summarized in Table A and discussed in the remainder of this note. As for the differences in details, the statistical annotations presented throughout this book should provide a sufficient explanation.

TABLE A. COMPARISON OF 1955 TOTAL CONSUMPTION FIGURES IN PARTS I AND II

Energy source	Part I	Part II
Coal (million tons)	447	451
Bituminous	423	431
Anthracite	24	20
Crude oil (million barrels)	2,803	2,774
Natural gas (billion cubic feet)	8,700	9,614
Natural gas liquids (million barrels)	278	260
Hydropower (billion kilowatt hours)	120	120

The broad explanation underlying the differences shown in Table A is that, in Part I, 1955 was but a single year in a long historical record, while in Part II it was the base year for projecting energy consumption to the year 1975. Hence, the 1955 energy consumption totals in Part I are measured in accord with definitions which maintain comparability with the statistics for earlier years. In Part II, on the other hand, the analysis was focused on the detailed structure of energy consumption in 1955, since the methodology involved the projection of consumption by categories of use. Thus, the total consumption of each energy source was built up from reported or derived statistics which purport to measure the quantities which went into specified sectors and activities. Although no rigid attempt was made to adjust the consumption aggregates reached in Part II to the historical totals used in Part I, the latter set of figures, as published by the Bureau of Mines, provided the broad framework within which the detailed analysis in Part II was performed. It is not surprising, therefore, that the totals in Parts I and II are not far apart, and that the main sources of difference are easy to identify.

In the coal total, the discrepancy stems from revisions made by the Bureau of Mines in its bituminous coal consumption statistics while this study was in progress. The Part I total incorporates these revisions in their entirety. In Part II, the mechanics of the detailed calculations permitted the incorporation of the revisions in some consumer classes but not in others, with the result that the Part II coal total exceeds the historical 1955 total by a small amount. Within the coal total a further difference results from the fact that for the sake of simplicity in making the projections, Part II treated all coal consumed by utilities as though it were bituminous, whereas in fact some 3 million tons consisted of anthracite (see Chapter 6, Table 65).

Although the numerical discrepancy in crude oil is slight, the two totals were derived in entirely different ways. Since actual consumption consists chiefly of products rather than crude oil itself, Part II studied the detailed structure of petroleum use in terms of refined products. These were then aggregated using the Btu values of the products as the common basis. The total oil consumption figure was then obtained by dividing the total Btu value of crude and its products by a conversion factor representing the Btu content of a barrel of crude. Part I, on the other hand, uses an apparent consumption figure derived from data on crude production, net stock changes, and net foreign trade in crude oil and its products.

The natural gas total in Part II substantially exceeds that in Part I principally because the former includes (a) the amounts of gas wasted and vented in the field, and (b) small amounts of gas other than natural gas distributed by utilities to their customers. The inclusion of these two items was judged important for the projection of natural gas use in 1975. However, it would have been inappropriate to include them in the historical 1955 total.

In natural gas liquids, Part I, in accord with the historical statistics on this subject, presents a measure of apparent consumption as derived from statistics of production, foreign trade, and stock changes. Part II, on the other hand, presents a measure of demand at the consumer level, partly on the basis of gasoline consumption in its various uses and partly on the basis of sales of liquefied petroleum gas to specified classes of customers.

A note on the measurement of direct waterpower and windpower in 1850, 1860, and 1870

The rough calculations on waterpower and windpower given in Chapter 4 are based on the following estimates of horsepower hours (hph) of mechanical work performed by direct-drive waterwheels and windpower on the one hand, and steam power derived from bituminous coal and the quantities of coal required to obtain this amount of mechanical work from steam engines on the other hand.[1] Work performance is defined as "final energy delivered as work done at the point of use." It has been estimated that, in 1850, on the average 11.4 pounds of bituminous coal were required per horsepower hour delivered at the shaft of the steam engine and that the losses in transmitting this power to the point of use amounted to 35 per cent. Thus, 17.6 pounds of coal were

ESTIMATED HORSEPOWER HOURS OF WORK PERFORMED

(Amounts in billions)

Derived from:	1850	1860	1870
Waterwheels..................................	0.9	1.3	1.7
Windpower....................................	1.4	2.1	1.1
Steam power (from bituminous coal)..............	0.4	1.0	3.0
Tons of bituminous coal required to generate steam power (thous.)............................	3,380	7,320	16,230
Efficiency of converting coal into mechanical work (per cent)......................	1.1%	1.3%	1.8%

[1] See J. F. Dewhurst and Associates, *America's Needs and Resources, A New Survey* (New York: The Twentieth Century Fund, 1955), Appendix 25-3, pp. 1103-04, 1106, and Tables B, C, E, K, and L.

485

consumed to obtain 1 hph of effectively utilized mechanical work. Since 1 pound of bituminous coal contains 13,100 Btu and 1 hph hour is the equivalent of 2,544.5 Btu, these estimates indicate an efficiency of converting coal into mechanical work of 1.1 per cent. For 1860 and 1870, the conversion factors are estimated to have been 1.3 per cent and 1.8 per cent, respectively.

If, in 1850, some 3,380,000 tons of bituminous coal were burned to obtain 0.4 billion hph of work at the point of use, while 0.9 billion hph were obtained by harnessing waterpower and 1.4 billion from windpower, some 7,605,000 tons of coal would have been required to replace the utilized waterpower and 11,830,000 tons to replace the windpower by horsepower hours derived from steam engines—a total of 19,435,000 tons of coal. For 1860 and 1870, the corresponding coal equivalents are shown below.

An alternative method of expressing waterpower and windpower in coal equivalents was used by Dewhurst. This method converts the energy "input" supplied by falling water and wind (that is, horsepower hours of work performed plus conversion and transmission losses) directly into coal equivalents. At 100 per cent efficiency of conversion 0.19 pounds of coal would equal 1 hph (2,544.5 Btu). Using this purely theoretical equivalent, 1 hph derived from falling water, which in 1850 according to Dewhurst's estimates was converted into mechanical work at an efficiency rate of 39 per cent, represents an energy input of 0.50 pounds of coal equivalent. One windmill horsepower hour, converted at 18 per cent efficiency, would be equal to 1.08 pounds of coal. The windpower utilized by sailing vessels was converted at the rate of 1 hph of work performed equals 2,544.5 Btu or a coal equivalent input of 0.19 pounds, which amounts to assuming an efficiency of conversion of 100 per cent. If this method is applied, the quantities of coal required to supply the horsepower hours furnished by wind and water would appear to be very small: not more than half a million tons of coal equivalent in the period 1850 to 1870. A somewhat different conversion method, applied to waterpower only, was used by Putnam.[2]

The results of these three methods of expressing waterpower alone (excluding windpower) in coal equivalents are (in thousands of tons of bituminous coal):

Year	Method I (This study)	Method II (Dewhurst)	Method III (Putnam)
1850	7,605	224	132
1860	9,516	292	187
1870	9,202	350	237

The corresponding coal input equivalents for energy obtained from windpower and waterpower combined are:

[2] Palmer Putnam, *Energy in the Future* (New York: Van Nostrand, 1953), pp. 377, 378, 383.

Year	Method I (This study)		Method II (Dewhurst)	
	1,000 *tons* bituminous coal	*Trillion* Btu	1,000 *tons* bituminous coal	*Trillion* Btu
1850........................	19,435	509	363	9.5
1860........................	24,888	652	500	13
1870........................	15,158	397	464	12

Depending on which concept one chooses in order to integrate waterpower and windpower into the nineteenth century energy economy, their Btu values will range from 500 trillion in 1850 to 400 trillion in 1870 (Method I) or from 9 to 12 trillion for the same period (Method II)—the decline in the first series being due to an increase in the efficiency of converting coal into mechanical power. In the first instance, the contribution of harnessed wind and water would add about one-fifth to the gross Btu value supplied by fuel materials in 1850 and 1860, and approximately one-tenth in 1870. In the second instance the role of these two energy sources would appear to be negligible.

The concept used in Method I for measuring windpower and waterpower is consistent with the treatment in this study of hydropower in later years, which is included in the energy total in terms of the Btu equivalents of the fuel which would have been required to generate the same amount of electricity (see "A Note on Problems of Measurement"). This approach has been adopted because fuels dominate the energy total in the United States throughout the period covered, and they are measured in this study in terms of inherent Btu values.

A note on sources of appendix tables

Several short-cuts have been taken for the sake of brevity in listing sources of the tables in the Appendices to Parts I and II. Abbreviations used for some of the most frequently cited sources are given below. Government publications are available either from the U.S. Government Printing Office in Washington or directly from the issuing government agency. Those of the private organizations listed below are from the cities noted.

AAR	Association of American Railroads, Washington, D. C.
AEC	Atomic Energy Commission, Washington, D. C.
A.G.A.	American Gas Association, New York, N. Y.
AISI	American Iron and Steel Institute, New York, N. Y.
AMA	Automobile Manufacturers Association, Detroit, Mich.
A.P.I.	American Petroleum Institute, New York, N. Y.
ATA	American Transit Association, New York, N. Y.
BLS	Bureau of Labor Statistics, U.S. Department of Labor, Washington, D. C.
CAA	Civil Aeronautics Administration (now Federal Aviation Agency), U.S. Department of Commerce, Washington, D. C.
Census	Bureau of the Census, U.S. Department of Commerce, Washington, D. C.
Commerce	U.S. Department of Commerce, Washington, D. C.
Ebasco	Ebasco Services, Inc., New York, N. Y.
E.E.I.	Edison Electric Institute, New York, N. Y.
FPC	Federal Power Commission, Washington, D. C.
FRB	Board of Governors, Federal Reserve System, Washington, D. C.
GAMA	Gas Appliance Manufacturers Association, New York, N. Y.
ICC	Interstate Commerce Commission, Washington, D. C.
Interior	U.S. Department of the Interior, Washington, D. C.
Labor	U.S. Department of Labor, Washington, D. C.
Mines	Bureau of Mines, U.S. Department of the Interior, Washington, D. C.
PMPC	President's Materials Policy Commission, reports from U.S. Government Printing Office, Washington, D. C.
Roads	Bureau of Public Roads, U.S. Department of Commerce, Washington, D. C.
USDA	U.S. Department of Agriculture, Washington, D. C.
USGS	Geological Survey, U.S. Department of the Interior, Washington, D. C.

Statistical appendix to part I,
a century of energy use, 1850-1955

Introductory Note

The first thirteen tables in this Appendix present measurements according to physical quantities and British thermal units (Btu's) in absolutes, percentage shares, and index numbers. Tables I through IX show production and consumption; Tables X through XIII, energy consumption per capita and per unit of gross national product (GNP).

Aggregate data on energy production and consumption are expressed in Btu's because a common denominator is necessary to add up such unlike quantities as tons of coal, barrels of oil, or cubic feet of gas. Since natural gas liquids (NGL) are not a primary energy source, but are obtained by the processing of natural gas, NGL are not included in the production tables, which show physical quantities or Btu values of natural gas prior to the extraction of NGL. They are, however, included in the consumption tables which—for the period since 1920—show physical quantities or Btu values of natural gas after allowance has been made for shrinkage in volume and reduction in Btu value through extraction of NGL.

Measurements according to dollar values appear in Tables XIV through XXII. Tables XIV through XVII present the value of production and consumption in current and 1947 dollars; Tables XVIII, XIX, and XX, percentage shares and the relation to GNP and total minerals production; and Tables XXI and XXII, indexes of production and consumption.

The unit dollar values represent averages at the point of production, in the case of coal at the mine and in the case of crude oil and natural gas at the well. The exception is NGL, the value of which cannot be measured at the original point of production (the natural gas well), but only at the plant in which they are extracted from natural gas. The value of NGL production is substantial, close to and in several years even exceeding that of natural gas production.

489

Hence, specific dollar values for NGL are included in the production statistics (Tables XIV and XV) because the unit value of natural gas at the well does not reflect the additional value represented by NGL. For comparison with production measured in Btu's, in which NGL are not shown separately, Tables XIV and XV also give a series excluding the value of NGL.

Price indexes are given in Tables XXIII and XXIV. Tables XXV through XXVIII have specific purposes in support of text tables and discussion.

Tables

TABLE I. PRODUCTION OF MINERAL FUELS, HYDROPOWER, AND FUEL WOOD, IN PHYSICAL QUANTITIES, 1850–1955

Year	Coal (thous. net tons)			Crude oil (thous. bbl.) (4)	Natural gas (mill. cu. ft.) (5)	Hydropower (mill. kwh) (6)	Fuel wood (thous. cords) (7)
	Bituminous (1)	Anthracite (2)	Total (3)				
1850...	4,029	4,327	8,356				102,000
1851...	4,590	5,814	10,404				
1852...	4,909	6,412	11,321				
1853...	6,100	6,653	12,753				
1854...	7,359	7,668	15,027				
1855...	7,543	8,607	16,150				114,000
1856...	7,992	8,960	16,952				
1857...	8,775	8,618	17,393				
1858...	8,846	8,808	17,654				
1859...	9,127	10,092	19,219	2			
1860...	9,057	10,984	20,041	500	n.a.		126,000
1861...	8,756	10,245	19,001	2,114	n.a.		
1862...	9,384	10,186	19,570	3,057	n.a.		
1863...	10,480	12,267	22,747	2,611	n.a.		
1864...	11,415	13,027	24,442	2,116	n.a.		
1865...	12,349	12,077	24,426	2,498	n.a.		132,000
1866...	13,015	15,784	28,799	3,598	n.a.		
1867...	13,837	16,067	29,904	3,347	n.a.		
1868...	16,244	17,708	33,952	3,646	n.a.		
1869...	19,903	18,341	38,244	4,215	n.a.		
1870...	20,471	19,958	40,429	5,261	n.a.		138,000
1871...	22,857	19,465	42,322	5,205	n.a.		
1872...	27,311	24,734	52,045	6,293	n.a.		
1873...	31,601	25,627	57,228	9,894	n.a.		
1874...	30,733	24,267	55,000	10,927	n.a.		
1875...	32,657	23,121	55,778	8,788	n.a.		137,000
1876...	31,822	22,793	54,615	9,133	n.a.		
1877...	34,385	25,660	60,045	13,350	n.a.		
1878...	36,418	21,690	58,108	15,397	n.a.		
1879...	40,425	30,208	70,633	19,914	n.a.		
1880...	50,757	28,650	79,407	26,286	n.a.		136,000

(*Table continued on next page.*)

TABLE I (continued)

Year	Coal (thous. net tons)			Crude oil (thous. bbl.) (4)	Natural gas (mill. cu. ft.) (5)	Hydropower (mill. kwh) (6)	Fuel wood (thous. cords) (7)
	Bituminous (1)	Anthracite (2)	Total (3)				
1881...	51,945	31,920	83,865	27,661	n.a.		
1882...	58,917	35,121	94,038	30,350	3,400		
1883...	64,860	38,457	103,317	23,450	7,770		
1884...	71,737	37,157	108,894	24,218	24,000		
1885...	71,773	38,336	110,109	21,859	76,000		128,000
1886...	74,645	39,035	113,680	28,065	157,000		
1887...	88,562	42,088	130,650	28,283	241,000		
1888...	102,040	46,620	148,660	27,612	343,000		
1889...	95,685	45,547	141,232	35,164	250,000		
1890...	111,302	46,469	157,771	45,824	239,000	250	120,000
1891...	117,901	50,665	168,566	54,293	183,000	n.a.	
1892...	126,857	52,473	179,330	50,515	159,000	n.a.	
1893...	128,385	53,968	182,353	48,431	149,000	n.a.	
1894...	118,820	51,921	170,741	49,344	144,000	n.a.	
1895...	135,118	57,999	193,117	52,892	137,000	1,000	110,000
1896...	137,640	54,346	191,986	60,960	140,000	n.a.	
1897...	147,618	52,612	200,230	60,467	149,000	n.a.	
1898...	166,594	53,383	219,977	55,364	173,000	n.a.	
1899...	193,323	60,418	253,741	57,071	223,000	n.a.	
1900...	212,316	57,368	269,684	63,621	236,000	2,786	100,000
1901...	225,828	67,472	293,300	69,389	263,000	3,030	
1902...	260,217	41,374	301,591	88,767	280,000	3,420	
1903...	282,749	74,607	357,356	100,461	297,000	3,927	
1904...	278,660	73,157	351,817	117,081	310,000	4,481	
1905...	315,063	77,660	392,723	134,717	351,000	5,054	95,000
1906...	342,875	71,282	414,157	126,494	388,843	5,613	
1907...	394,759	85,604	480,363	166,095	406,622	6,200	
1908...	332,574	83,269	415,843	178,527	402,141	6,974	
1909...	379,744	81,070	460,814	183,171	480,706	7,848	
1910...	417,111	84,465	501,596	209,557	509,155	8,626	91,000
1911...	405,907	90,464	496,371	220,449	512,993	9,458	
1912...	450,105	84,362	534,467	222,935	562,203	10,266	
1913...	478,435	91,525	569,960	248,446	581,898	11,229	
1914...	422,704	90,822	513,526	265,763	591,867	12,229	
1915...	442,624	88,995	531,619	281,104	628,579	13,238	87,000
1916...	502,520	87,578	590,098	300,767	753,170	14,321	
1917...	551,791	99,612	651,403	335,316	795,110	15,399	
1918...	579,386	98,826	678,212	355,928	721,001	15,974	
1919...	465,860	88,092	553,952	378,367	745,916	17,021	
1920...	568,667	89,598	658,265	442,929	812,338	18,779	83,000
1921...	415,922	90,473	506,395	472,183	673,770	17,529	
1922...	422,268	54,683	476,951	557,531	776,043	19,634	
1923...	564,565	93,339	657,904	732,407	1,024,800	21,788	
1924...	483,687	87,927	571,614	713,940	1,161,726	22,484	
1925...	520,053	61,817	581,870	763,743	1,209,609	25,496	79,000
1926...	573,367	84,437	657,804	770,874	1,336,259	29,249	
1927...	517,763	80,096	597,859	901,129	1,471,012	32,548	
1928...	500,745	75,348	576,093	901,474	1,595,895	37,683	
1929...	534,989	73,828	608,817	1,007,323	1,952,166	37,524	
1930...	467,526	69,385	536,911	898,011	1,978,911	35,878	75,000

TABLE I (continued)

Year	Coal (thous. net tons)			Crude oil (thous. bbl.) (4)	Natural gas (mill. cu. ft.) (5)	Hydropower (mill. kwh) (6)	Fuel wood (thous. cords) (7)
	Bituminous (1)	Anthracite (2)	Total (3)				
1931...	382,089	59,646	441,735	851,081	1,721,902	33,548	
1932...	309,710	49,855	359,565	785,159	1,593,798	36,529	
1933...	333,631	49,541	383,172	905,656	1,596,673	37,175	
1934...	359,368	57,168	416,536	908,065	1,815,796	36,747	
1935...	372,373	52,159	424,532	996,596	1,968,963	42,727	72,000
1936...	394,088	54,580	493,668	1,099,687	2,225,477	43,045	
1937...	445,531	51,856	497,387	1,279,160	2,473,483	46,173	
1938...	348,545	46,099	394,644	1,214,355	2,358,201	47,219	
1939...	394,855	51,487	446,342	1,264,962	2,538,383	46,355	
1940...	460,772	51,485	512,257	1,353,214	2,733,819	50,131	70,000
1941...	514,149	56,368	570,517	1,402,228	2,893,525	53,207	
1942...	582,693	60,328	643,021	1,386,645	3,145,694	66,706	
1943...	590,177	60,644	650,812	1,505,613	3,515,531	79,078	
1944...	619,576	63,701	683,277	1,677,904	3,815,024	78,905	
1945...	577,617	54,934	632,551	1,713,655	4,042,002	84,747	65,000
1946...	533,922	60,507	594,429	1,733,939	4,152,762	83,150	
1947...	630,624	57,190	687,814	1,856,987	4,582,173	83,066	
1948...	599,518	57,140	656,658	2,020,185	5,148,020	86,992	
1949...	437,868	42,702	480,570	1,841,940	5,419,736	94,773	
1950...	516,311	44,077	560,388	1,973,574	6,282,060	100,885	60,000
1951...	533,665	42,670	576,335	2,247,711	7,457,359	104,376	
1952...	466,841	40,583	507,424	2,289,836	8,013,457	109,708	
1953...	457,290	30,949	488,239	2,357,082	8,396,916	109,617	
1954...	391,706	29,100	420,789	2,314,988	8,742,546	111,640	
1955...	464,634	26,200	490,834	2,484,428	9,405,351	116,236	55,000

n.a. Not available.

SOURCES: The following general sources were used, except as noted under the individual commodity headings: Interior, USGS, *Mineral Resources of the United States* (Yearbooks, 1882–1923); Commerce, Mines, *Mineral Resources of the United States* (Yearbooks, 1924–31); Commerce, Mines, *Minerals Yearbook* (1932–33); and Interior, Mines, *Minerals Yearbook* (1934–56).

COAL: Bituminous coal, anthracite, and total coal figures, 1850–85 from Howard N. Eavenson, *The First Century and a Quarter of American Coal Industry* (Pittsburgh: privately printed, 1942), Appendix Tables 20 and 53.

NATURAL GAS: Data represent marketed production of wet and dry gas. The 1882–99 estimates by F. G. Tryon, USGS and Mines, based upon contemporary estimates of the quantity of coal displaced by gas or of the value of gas sold. Quoted in A. F. Burns, *Production Trends in the United States* (New York: National Bureau of Economic Research, 1934), p. 202. See also *Minerals Yearbook*, 1945, pp. 1155–59. Figures for 1900–05, physical volume calculated from Btu values of marketed production as published in recent issues of *Minerals Yearbook*. Note: Prior to 1920 the term "marketed production" refers to that portion of gross production that was commercially utilized. For 1920 and subsequent years, marketed production represents the amount of gas utilized plus the net volume stored and lost in transmission. Thus, for 1920–55, marketed production equals gross production minus repressuring, vent, and waste.

HYDROPOWER: 1890 figures supplied by L. D. Jennings of the FPC, quoted in J. Frederic Dewhurst and Associates, *America's Needs and Resources, A New Survey* (New York: The Twentieth Century Fund, 1955), Appendix 25-3, p. 1105. Estimate for 1895 based on

(*Sources continued on next page.*)

TABLE I (continued)

interpolation between 1890, 1900, and 1905 data. Those for 1900–55 from Mines tabulation "Production of mineral fuels and energy from waterpower in the continental United States," published in various issues of *Mineral Industry Surveys*, MMS No. 2830, 1958.

FUEL WOOD: Data represent estimated consumption, production data are not available. Estimates for 1850–1930 for every fifth year obtained by averaging decade consumption data in R. V. Reynolds and A. H. Pierson, *Fuel Wood Used in the United States*, 1630–1930, USDA Forest Service, Circular No. 641, February 1942, Table 2. Estimates for 1935–55 based on data in *A Reappraisal of the Forest Situation*, "Potential Requirements for Timber Products in the United States," Forest Service Report No. 2, 1946; and USDA, *Timber Resources for America's Future*, Forest Service Report No. 14, January 1958. Note: Quantities consumed in 1935 and 1940 may be somewhat underestimated, according to recent Forest Service estimates included in a letter to Resources for the Future.

TABLE II. PRODUCTION OF MINERAL FUELS, HYDROPOWER, AND FUEL WOOD; IN BTU'S, 1850–1955

(Trillion Btu)

Year	Coal			Crude oil (4)	Natural gas (5)	Total liquid and gaseous fuels (6)	Total mineral fuels (7)	Hydropower (8)	Mineral fuels and hydropower (9)	Fuel wood (10)	Total (11)
	Bituminous (1)	Anthracite (2)	Total (3)								
1850	106	110	216				216			2,138	2,354
1851	120	148	268				268				
1852	129	163	292				292				
1853	160	169	329				329				
1854	193	195	388				388				
1855	198	219	417				417			2,389	2,806
1856	209	228	437				437				
1857	230	219	449				449				
1858	232	224	456				456				
1859	239	256	495				495				
1860	237	279	516	3	n.a.		519			2,641	3,160
1861	229	260	489	12	n.a.		501				
1862	246	259	505	17	n.a.		522				
1863	275	312	587	14	n.a.		601				
1864	299	331	630	12	n.a.		642				
1865	324	307	631	14	n.a.		645			2,767	3,412
1866	341	401	742	20	n.a.		762				
1867	363	408	771	19	n.a.		790				
1868	426	450	876	20	n.a.		896				
1869	521	466	987	23	n.a.		1,010				
1870	536	507	1,043	29	n.a.		1,072			2,893	3,965
1871	599	494	1,093	29	n.a.		1,122				
1872	716	628	1,344	35	n.a.		1,379				
1873	828	651	1,479	55	n.a.		1,534				
1874	805	616	1,421	61	n.a.		1,482				
1875	856	587	1,443	49	n.a.		1,492			2,872	4,364

(Table continued on next page.)

TABLE II (continued)

Year	Coal Bituminous (1)	Coal Anthracite (2)	Coal Total (3)	Crude oil (4)	Natural gas (5)	Total liquid and gaseous fuels (6)	Total mineral fuels (7)	Hydropower (8)	Mineral fuels and hydropower (9)	Fuel wood (10)	Total (11)
1876	834	579	1,413	51	n.a.		1,464				
1877	901	652	1,553	74	n.a.		1,627				
1878	954	551	1,505	85	n.a.		1,590				
1879	1,059	767	1,826	111	n.a.		1,937				
1880	1,330	728	2,058	146	n.a.		2,204			2,851	5,055
1881	1,361	811	2,172	154	n.a.		2,326				
1882	1,544	892	2,436	168	4	172	2,608				
1883	1,699	977	2,676	130	8	138	2,814				
1884	1,880	944	2,824	134	26	160	2,984				
1885	1,880	974	2,854	121	82	203	3,057			2,683	5,740
1886	1,956	991	2,947	156	169	325	3,272				
1887	2,320	1,069	3,389	158	259	417	3,806				
1888	2,673	1,184	3,857	156	369	525	4,382				
1889	2,507	1,157	3,664	198	269	467	4,131				
1890	2,916	1,180	4,096	258	257	515	4,611	22	4,633	2,515	7,148
1891	3,089	1,287	4,376	306	197	503	4,879				
1892	3,324	1,333	4,657	285	171	456	5,113				
1893	3,364	1,371	4,735	273	160	433	5,168				
1894	3,113	1,319	4,432	279	155	434	4,866				
1895	3,540	1,473	5,013	299	147	446	5,459	90	5,549	2,306	7,855
1896	3,606	1,380	4,986	345	151	496	5,482				
1897	3,868	1,336	5,204	342	160	502	5,706				
1898	4,365	1,356	5,721	313	186	499	6,220				
1899	5,065	1,535	6,600	323	240	563	7,163	238	7,401		
1900	5,563	1,457	7,020	369	254	623	7,643	250	7,893	2,015	9,908

Year											
1901	5,917	1,714	7,631	402	283	685	8,316	264	8,580		
1902	6,818	1,051	7,869	515	301	816	8,685	289	8,974		
1903	7,408	1,895	9,303	583	319	902	10,205	321	10,526		
1904	7,301	1,858	9,159	679	333	1,012	10,171	354	10,525		
1905	8,255	1,973	10,228	781	377	1,158	11,386	386	11,772	1,843	13,615
1906	8,983	1,811	10,794	734	418	1,152	11,946	414	12,360		
1907	10,343	2,174	12,517	963	437	1,400	13,917	441	14,358		
1908	8,713	2,115	10,828	1,035	432	1,467	12,295	476	12,771		
1909	9,949	2,059	12,008	1,062	517	1,579	13,587	513	14,100		
1910	10,928	2,146	13,074	1,215	547	1,762	14,836	539	15,375	1,765	17,140
1911	10,635	2,298	12,933	1,279	551	1,830	14,763	565	15,328		
1912	11,793	2,143	13,936	1,293	604	1,897	15,833	585	16,418		
1913	12,535	2,325	14,860	1,441	626	2,067	16,927	609	17,536		
1914	11,075	2,307	13,382	1,541	636	2,177	15,559	636	16,195		
1915	11,597	2,260	13,857	1,630	676	2,306	16,163	659	16,822	1,688	18,510
1916	13,166	2,224	15,390	1,744	810	2,554	17,944	681	18,625		
1917	14,457	2,530	16,987	1,945	855	2,800	19,787	700	20,487		
1918	15,180	2,510	17,690	2,064	775	2,839	20,529	701	21,230		
1919	12,206	2,238	14,444	2,195	802	2,997	17,441	718	18,159		
1920	14,899	2,276	17,175	2,569	883	3,452	20,627	738	21,365	1,610	22,975
1921	10,897	2,298	13,195	2,739	732	3,471	16,666	620	17,286		
1922	11,063	1,389	12,452	3,234	843	4,077	16,529	643	17,172		
1923	14,792	2,371	17,163	4,248	1,113	5,361	22,524	685	23,209		
1924	12,673	2,233	14,906	4,141	1,263	5,404	20,310	648	20,958		
1925	13,625	1,570	15,195	4,430	1,314	5,744	20,939	668	21,607	1,533	23,140
1926	15,022	2,145	17,167	4,471	1,452	5,923	23,090	728	23,818		
1927	13,565	2,034	15,599	5,227	1,598	6,825	22,424	776	23,200		
1928	13,120	1,914	15,034	5,229	1,734	6,963	21,997	854	22,851		
1929	14,017	1,875	15,892	5,842	2,118	7,960	23,852	816	24,668		
1930	12,249	1,762	14,011	5,208	2,148	7,356	21,367	752	22,119	1,455	23,574

(Table continued on next page.)

Table II (continued)

Year	Coal			Crude oil (4)	Natural gas (5)	Total liquid and gaseous fuels (6)	Total mineral fuels (7)	Hydropower (8)	Mineral fuels and hydropower (9)	Fuel wood (10)	Total (11)
	Bituminous (1)	Anthracite (2)	Total (3)								
1931	10,011	1,515	11,526	4,936	1,869	6,805	18,331	668	18,999		
1932	8,114	1,266	9,380	4,554	1,729	6,283	15,663	713	16,376		
1933	8,741	1,258	9,999	5,253	1,733	6,986	16,985	711	17,696		
1934	9,415	1,452	10,867	5,267	1,970	7,237	18,104	698	18,802		
1935	9,756	1,325	11,081	5,780	2,136	7,916	18,997	806	19,803	1,397	21,200
1936	11,504	1,386	12,890	6,378	2,411	8,789	21,679	812	22,491		
1937	11,673	1,317	12,990	7,419	2,684	10,103	23,093	871	23,964		
1938	9,132	1,171	10,303	7,043	2,565	9,608	19,911	866	20,777		
1939	10,345	1,308	11,653	7,337	2,763	10,100	21,753	838	22,591		
1940	12,072	1,308	13,380	7,849	2,979	10,828	24,208	880	25,088	1,358	26,446
1941	13,471	1,432	14,903	8,133	3,162	11,295	26,198	934	27,132		
1942	15,267	1,532	16,799	8,043	3,436	11,479	28,278	1,136	29,414		
1943	15,463	1,540	17,003	8,733	3,839	12,572	29,575	1,304	30,879		
1944	16,233	1,618	17,851	9,732	4,176	13,908	31,759	1,344	33,103		
1945	15,134	1,395	16,529	9,939	4,423	14,362	30,891	1,442	32,333	1,261	33,594
1946	13,989	1,537	15,526	10,057	4,550	14,607	30,133	1,406	31,539		
1947	16,522	1,453	17,975	10,771	5,012	15,783	33,758	1,426	35,184		
1948	15,707	1,451	17,158	11,717	5,615	17,332	34,490	1,481	35,971		
1949	11,472	1,085	12,557	10,683	5,911	16,594	29,151	1,539	30,690		
1950	13,527	1,120	14,647	11,447	6,841	18,288	32,935	1,573	34,508	1,164	35,672
1951	13,982	1,084	15,066	13,037	8,106	21,143	36,209	1,559	37,768		
1952	12,231	1,031	13,262	13,281	8,705	21,986	35,248	1,581	36,829		
1953	11,981	786	12,767	13,671	9,116	22,787	35,554	1,522	37,076		
1954	10,263	739	11,002	13,427	9,488	22,915	33,917	1,449	35,366		
1955	12,174	665	12,839	14,410	10,204	24,614	37,453	1,447	38,900	1,067	39,967

NOTE: In converting physical quantities into Btu equivalents the following conversion factors were used:

Bituminous coal............26,200,000 Btu per net ton
Anthracite................25,400,000 Btu per net ton

Crude oil:
Pennsylvania Grade...... 5,550,000 Btu per bbl. of 42 gal.
Other................... 5,800,000 Btu per bbl. of 42 gal.
1859–99—weighted average of Pennsylvania Grade and Other.
1900–55—total production at 5,800,000 Btu per bbl.

NATURAL GAS: Conversion factor of 1,075 Btu per cu. ft. 1882–1919: marketed production at 1,075 Btu per cu. ft. 1920–55: gross production at 1,075 Btu per cu. ft. minus repressuring, vent, and waste gas at 1,035 Btu per cu. ft.

HYDROPOWER: In converting hydropower to its equivalent of fuel required to generate the same amount of electric power, the prevailing or average performance of all fuel-burning central electric stations has been used for each year. The fuel equivalent declined from 6.85 lbs. of coal per kwh in 1900 to 0.95 lb. in 1955. For 1890 and 1895, it has been estimated at 7 lbs. of coal.

FUEL WOOD:
1850–95................20,960,000 Btu per cord
1900...................20,154,000 Btu per cord
1905–55................19,407,000 Btu per cord
These conversion factors were derived from the following fuel equivalents (see J. F. Dewhurst and Associates, *America's Needs and Resources,
A New Survey* [New York: The Twentieth Century Fund, 1955], p. 1108):
1850–95................1.25 cords of fuel wood = 1 ton bituminous coal
1900...................1.30 cords of fuel wood = 1 ton bituminous coal
1905–55................1.35 cords of fuel wood = 1 ton bituminous coal

SOURCE: Appendix Table I.

TABLE III. SPECIFIC ENERGY SOURCES AS PERCENTAGES OF TOTAL PRODUCTION OF MINERAL FUELS, HYDROPOWER, AND FUEL WOOD, FIVE-YEAR INTERVALS, 1850–1955

(Based on Btu values)

Year	Coal			Liquid and gaseous fuels			Total mineral fuels (7)	Hydro-power (8)	Mineral fuels and hydropower (9)	Fuel wood (10)	Total (11)
	Bituminous (1)	Anthracite (2)	Total (3)	Crude oil (4)	Natural gas (5)	Total (6)					
1850	4.5%	4.7%	9.2%				9.2%			90.8%	100.0%
1855	7.1	7.8	14.9				14.9			85.1	100.0
1860	7.5	8.8	16.3	.1%			16.4			83.6	100.0
1865	9.5	9.0	18.5	.4			18.9			81.1	100.0
1870	13.5	12.8	26.3	.7			27.0			73.0	100.0
1875	19.6	13.5	33.1	1.1			34.2			65.8	100.0
1880	26.3	14.4	40.7	2.9			43.6			56.4	100.0
1885	32.8	17.0	49.8	2.1	1.4%	3.5%	53.3			46.7	100.0
1890	40.8	16.5	57.3	3.6	3.6	7.2	64.5	.3%	64.8%	35.2	100.0
1895	45.1	18.8	63.8	3.8	1.9	5.7	69.5	1.2	70.6	29.4	100.0
1900	56.2	14.7	70.9	3.7	2.6	6.3	77.1	2.5	79.7	20.3	100.0
1905	60.6	14.5	75.1	5.7	2.8	8.5	83.6	2.8	86.5	13.5	100.0
1910	63.8	12.5	76.3	7.1	3.2	10.3	86.6	3.1	89.7	10.3	100.0
1915	62.7	12.2	74.9	8.8	3.7	12.5	87.3	3.6	90.9	9.1	100.0
1920	64.9	9.9	74.8	11.2	3.8	15.0	89.8	3.2	93.0	7.0	100.0
1925	58.9	6.8	65.7	19.2	5.7	24.8	90.5	2.9	93.4	6.6	100.0
1930	52.0	7.5	59.4	22.1	9.1	31.2	90.6	3.2	93.8	6.2	100.0
1935	46.0	6.3	52.3	27.3	10.1	37.3	89.6	3.8	93.4	6.6	100.0
1940	45.7	5.0	50.6	29.7	11.3	40.9	91.5	3.3	94.9	5.1	100.0
1945	45.1	4.2	49.2	29.6	13.2	42.8	92.0	4.3	96.3	3.8	100.0
1950	37.9	3.1	41.1	32.1	19.2	51.3	92.3	4.4	96.7	3.3	100.0
1955	30.5	1.7	32.1	36.1	25.5	61.6	93.7	3.6	97.3	2.7	100.0

SOURCE: Appendix Table II.

TABLE IV. SPECIFIC MINERAL FUELS AS PERCENTAGES OF TOTAL
PRODUCTION OF MINERAL FUELS, 1900–55

(Based on Btu values)

Year	Coal			Liquid and gaseous fuels			Total mineral fuels (7)
	Bituminous (1)	Anthracite (2)	Total (3)	Crude oil (4)	Natural gas (5)	Total (6)	
1900....	72.8%	19.1%	91.8%	4.8%	3.3%	8.2%	100.0%
1901....	71.2	20.6	91.8	4.8	3.4	8.2	100.0
1902....	78.5	12.1	90.6	5.9	3.5	9.4	100.0
1903....	72.6	18.6	91.2	5.7	3.1	8.8	100.0
1904....	71.8	18.3	90.1	6.7	3.3	9.9	100.0
1905....	72.5	17.3	89.8	6.9	3.3	10.2	100.0
1906....	75.2	15.2	90.4	6.1	3.5	9.6	100.0
1907....	74.3	15.6	89.9	6.9	3.1	10.1	100.0
1908....	70.9	17.2	88.1	8.4	3.5	11.9	100.0
1909....	73.2	15.2	88.4	7.8	3.8	11.6	100.0
1910....	73.7	14.5	88.1	8.2	3.7	11.9	100.0
1911....	72.0	15.6	87.6	8.7	3.7	12.4	100.0
1912....	74.5	13.5	88.0	8.2	3.8	12.0	100.0
1913....	74.1	13.7	87.8	8.5	3.7	12.2	100.0
1914....	71.2	14.8	86.0	9.9	4.1	14.0	100.0
1915....	71.8	14.0	85.7	10.1	4.2	14.3	100.0
1916....	73.4	12.4	85.8	9.7	4.5	14.2	100.0
1917....	73.1	12.8	85.8	9.8	4.3	14.2	100.0
1918....	73.9	12.2	86.2	10.1	3.8	13.8	100.0
1919....	70.0	12.8	82.8	12.6	4.6	17.2	100.0
1920....	72.2	11.0	83.3	12.5	4.3	16.7	100.0
1921....	65.4	13.8	79.2	16.4	4.4	20.8	100.0
1922....	66.9	8.4	75.3	19.6	5.1	24.7	100.0
1923....	65.7	10.5	76.2	18.9	4.9	23.8	100.0
1924....	62.4	11.0	73.4	20.4	6.2	26.6	100.0
1925....	65.1	7.5	72.6	21.2	6.3	27.4	100.0
1926....	65.1	9.3	74.3	19.4	6.3	25.7	100.0
1927....	60.5	9.1	69.6	23.3	7.1	30.4	100.0
1928....	59.6	8.7	68.3	23.8	7.9	31.7	100.0
1929....	58.8	7.9	66.6	24.5	8.9	33.4	100.0
1930....	57.3	8.2	65.6	24.4	10.1	34.4	100.0
1931....	54.6	8.3	62.9	26.9	10.2	37.1	100.0
1932....	51.8	8.1	59.9	29.1	11.0	40.1	100.0
1933....	51.5	7.4	58.9	30.9	10.2	41.1	100.0
1934....	52.0	8.0	60.0	29.1	10.9	40.0	100.0
1935....	51.4	7.0	58.3	30.4	11.2	41.7	100.0
1936....	53.1	6.4	59.5	29.4	11.1	40.5	100.0
1937....	50.5	5.7	56.3	32.1	11.6	43.7	100.0
1938....	45.9	5.9	51.7	35.4	12.9	48.3	100.0
1939....	47.6	6.0	53.6	33.7	12.7	46.4	100.0
1940....	49.9	5.4	55.3	32.4	12.3	44.7	100.0
1941....	51.4	5.5	56.9	31.0	12.1	43.1	100.0
1942....	54.0	5.4	59.4	28.4	12.2	40.6	100.0
1943....	52.3	5.2	57.5	29.5	13.0	42.5	100.0
1944....	51.1	5.1	56.2	30.6	13.1	43.8	100.0
1945....	49.0	4.5	53.5	32.2	14.3	46.5	100.0

(*Table continued on next page.*)

TABLE IV (continued)

Year	Coal			Liquid and gaseous fuels			Total mineral fuels (7)
	Bituminous (1)	Anthracite (2)	Total (3)	Crude oil (4)	Natural gas (5)	Total (6)	
1946....	46.4%	5.1%	51.5%	33.4%	15.1%	48.5%	100.0%
1947....	48.9	4.3	53.2	31.9	14.8	46.8	100.0
1948....	45.5	4.2	49.7	34.0	16.3	50.3	100.0
1949....	39.4	3.7	43.1	36.6	20.3	56.9	100.0
1950....	41.1	3.4	44.5	34.8	20.8	55.5	100.0
1951....	38.6	3.0	41.6	36.0	22.4	58.4	100.0
1952....	34.7	2.9	37.6	37.7	24.7	62.4	100.0
1953....	33.7	2.2	35.9	38.5	25.6	64.1	100.0
1954....	30.3	2.2	32.4	39.6	28.0	67.6	100.0
1955....	32.5	1.8	34.3	38.5	27.2	65.7	100.0

SOURCE: Appendix Table II.

TABLE V. INDEXES OF PRODUCTION OF MINERAL FUELS, HYDROPOWER, AND FUEL WOOD BASED ON BTU VALUES: TOTALS AND BY SPECIFIC ENERGY SOURCES, 1850–1955

(1900 = 100)

| Year | Coal | | | Liquid and gaseous fuels | | | Total mineral fuels (7) | Hydropower (8) | Mineral fuels and hydropower (9) | Fuel wood (10) | Total (11) |
	Bituminous (1)	Anthracite (2)	Total (3)	Crude oil (4)	Natural gas (5)	Total (6)					
1850	1.9	7.5	3.1				2.8			106.1	23.8
1851	2.2	10.2	3.8				3.5				
1852	2.3	11.2	4.2				3.8				
1853	2.9	11.6	4.7				4.3				
1854	3.5	13.4	5.5				5.1			118.6	28.3
1855	3.6	15.0	5.9				5.5				
1856	3.8	15.6	6.2				5.7				
1857	4.1	15.0	6.4				5.9				
1858	4.2	15.4	6.5				6.0				
1859	4.3	17.6	7.1				6.5				
1860	4.3	19.1	7.4	0.8			6.8			131.1	31.9
1861	4.1	17.8	7.0	3.3			6.6				
1862	4.4	17.8	7.2	4.6			6.8				
1863	4.9	21.4	8.4	3.8			7.9				
1864	5.4	22.7	9.0	3.3			8.4				
1865	5.8	21.1	9.0	3.8			8.4			137.3	34.4
1866	6.1	27.5	10.6	5.4			10.0				
1867	6.5	28.0	11.0	5.1			10.3				
1868	7.7	30.9	12.5	5.4			11.7				
1869	9.4	32.0	14.1	6.2			13.2			143.6	40.0
1870	9.6	34.8	14.9	7.9			14.0				

(*Table continued on next page.*)

TABLE V (continued)

Year	Coal Bituminous (1)	Coal Anthracite (2)	Coal Total (3)	Liquid and gaseous fuels Crude oil (4)	Liquid and gaseous fuels Natural gas (5)	Liquid and gaseous fuels Total (6)	Total mineral fuels (7)	Hydropower (8)	Mineral fuels and hydropower (9)	Fuel wood (10)	Total (11)
1871	10.8	33.9	15.6	7.9	n.a.	n.a.	14.7				
1872	12.9	43.1	19.1	9.5	n.a.	n.a.	18.0				
1873	14.9	44.7	21.1	14.9	n.a.	n.a.	20.1				
1874	14.5	42.3	20.2	16.5	n.a.	n.a.	19.4				
1875	15.4	40.3	20.6	13.3	n.a.	n.a.	19.5			142.5	44.0
1876	15.0	39.7	20.1	13.8	n.a.	n.a.	19.2				
1877	16.2	44.7	22.1	20.1	n.a.	n.a.	21.3				
1878	17.1	37.8	21.4	23.0	n.a.	n.a.	20.8				
1879	19.0	52.6	26.0	30.1	n.a.	n.a.	25.3				
1880	23.9	50.0	29.3	39.6	n.a.	n.a.	28.8			141.5	51.0
1881	24.5	55.7	30.9	41.7	n.a.	n.a.	30.4				
1882	27.8	61.2	34.7	45.5	1.6	27.6	34.1				
1883	30.5	67.1	38.1	35.2	3.1	22.2	36.8				
1884	33.8	64.8	40.2	36.3	10.2	25.7	39.0				
1885	33.8	66.8	40.7	32.8	32.2	32.6	40.0			133.2	57.9
1886	35.2	68.0	42.0	42.3	66.5	52.2	42.8				
1887	41.7	73.4	48.3	42.8	102.0	66.9	49.8				
1888	48.0	81.3	54.9	42.3	145.3	84.3	57.3				
1889	45.1	79.4	52.2	53.7	105.9	75.0	54.1				
1890	52.4	81.0	58.3	69.9	101.2	82.7	60.3	8.8	58.7	124.8	72.1
1891	55.5	88.3	62.3	82.9	77.6	80.7	63.8	n.a.			
1892	59.8	91.5	66.3	77.2	67.3	73.2	66.9	n.a.			
1893	60.5	94.1	67.5	74.0	63.0	69.5	67.6	n.a.			
1894	56.0	90.5	63.1	75.6	61.0	69.7	63.7	n.a.		114.4	
1895	63.6	101.1	71.4	81.0	57.9	71.6	71.4	36.0	70.3	114.4	79.3

Year											
1896				n.a.	71.7	79.6	59.4	93.5	71.0	94.7	64.8
1897				n.a.	74.7	80.6	63.0	92.7	74.1	91.7	69.5
1898				n.a.	81.4	80.1	73.2	84.8	81.5	93.1	78.5
1899			93.8	95.2	93.7	90.4	94.5	87.5	94.0	105.4	91.0
1900	100.0	100.0	100.0	100.0	100.0	100.0	100.0	100.0	100.0	100.0	100.0
1901			108.7	105.6	108.8	109.9	111.4	108.9	108.7	117.6	106.4
1902			113.7	115.6	113.6	131.0	118.5	139.6	112.1	72.1	122.6
1903			113.4	128.4	133.5	144.8	125.6	158.0	132.5	130.1	133.2
1904			113.3	141.6	133.1	162.4	131.1	184.0	130.5	127.5	131.2
1905	137.4	91.5	149.1	154.4	149.0	185.9	148.4	211.7	145.7	135.4	148.4
1906			156.6	165.6	156.3	184.9	164.6	198.9	153.8	124.3	161.5
1907			181.9	176.4	182.1	224.7	172.0	261.0	178.3	149.2	185.9
1908			161.8	190.4	160.9	235.5-	170.1	280.5	154.2	145.2	156.6
1909			178.6	205.2	177.8	253.4	203.5	287.8	171.1	141.3	178.8
1910	173.0	87.6	194.8	215.6	194.1	282.8	215.4	329.3	186.2	147.3	196.4
1911			194.2	226.0	193.2	293.7	213.0	346.6	184.2	157.7	191.2
1912			208.0	234.0	207.2	304.5	237.8	350.4	198.5	147.1	212.0
1913			222.2	243.6	221.5	331.8	246.5	390.5	211.7	159.6	225.3
1914			205.2	254.4	203.6	349.4	250.4	417.6	190.6	158.3	199.1
1915	186.8	83.8	213.1	263.6	211.5	370.1	266.1	441.7	197.4	155.1	208.5
1916			236.0	272.4	234.8	409.9	318.9	472.6	219.2	152.6	236.7
1917			259.5	280.0	258.9	449.4	336.6	527.1	242.0	173.6	259.9
1918			269.0	280.4	268.6	455.7	305.1	559.0	252.0	172.3	272.9
1919			230.1	287.2	228.2	481.0	315.7	594.8	205.8	153.6	219.4
1920	231.9	79.9	270.7	295.2	269.9	554.1	347.6	696.2	244.7	156.2	267.8
1921			219.0	248.0	218.1	557.1	288.2	742.3	188.0	157.7	195.9
1922			217.6	257.2	216.3	654.4	331.9	876.4	177.4	95.3	198.9
1923			294.0	274.0	294.7	860.5	438.2	1,151.2	244.5	162.7	265.9
1924			265.5	259.2	265.7	867.4	497.2	1,122.2	212.3	153.3	227.8
1925	233.6	76.1	273.7	267.2	274.0	922.0	517.3	1,200.5	216.5	107.8	244.9

(*Table continued on next page.*)

TABLE V (continued)

Year	Coal			Liquid and gaseous fuels			Total mineral fuels (7)	Hydropower (8)	Mineral fuels and hydropower (9)	Fuel wood (10)	Total (11)
	Bituminous (1)	Anthracite (2)	Total (3)	Crude oil (4)	Natural gas (5)	Total (6)					
1926	270.0	147.2	244.5	1,211.6	571.7	950.7	302.1	291.2	301.8		
1927	243.8	139.6	222.2	1,416.5	629.1	1,095.5	293.4	310.4	293.9		
1928	235.8	131.4	214.2	1,417.1	682.7	1,117.6	287.8	341.6	289.5		
1929	252.0	128.7	226.4	1,583.2	833.9	1,277.7	312.1	326.4	312.5		
1930	220.2	120.9	199.6	1,411.4	845.7	1,180.7	279.6	300.8	280.2	72.2	237.9
1931	180.0	104.0	164.2	1,337.7	735.8	1,092.3	239.8	267.2	240.7		
1932	145.9	86.9	133.6	1,234.1	680.7	1,008.5	204.9	285.2	207.5		
1933	157.1	86.3	142.4	1,423.6	682.3	1,121.3	222.2	284.4	224.2		
1934	169.2	99.7	154.8	1,427.4	775.6	1,161.6	236.9	279.2	238.2		
1935	175.4	90.9	157.8	1,566.4	840.9	1,270.6	248.6	322.4	250.9		
1936	206.8	95.1	183.6	1,728.4	949.2	1,410.7	283.6	324.8	284.9		
1937	209.8	90.4	185.0	2,010.5	1,056.7	1,621.6	302.1	348.4	303.6		
1938	164.2	80.4	146.8	1,908.7	1,009.8	1,542.2	260.5	346.4	263.2		
1939	186.0	89.8	166.0	1,988.3	1,087.8	1,621.2	284.6	335.2	286.2		
1940	217.0	89.8	190.6	2,127.1	1,172.8	1,738.0	316.7	352.0	317.8	67.4	266.9
1941	242.2	98.3	212.3	2,204.0	1,244.9	1,813.0	342.8	373.6	343.7		
1942	274.4	105.1	239.3	2,179.7	1,352.8	1,842.5	370.0	454.4	372.6		
1943	278.0	105.7	242.2	2,366.6	1,511.4	2,017.9	387.0	521.6	391.2		
1944	291.8	111.0	254.3	2,637.4	1,644.1	2,232.4	415.5	537.6	419.4		
1945	272.0	95.7	235.5	2,693.5	1,741.3	2,305.2	404.2	576.8	409.6	62.6	339.1

1946	251.5	105.5	221.2	2,725.4	1,791.3	2,344.6	394.3	562.4	399.6	
1947	297.0	99.7	256.1	2,918.9	1,973.2	2,533.3	441.7	570.4	445.7	
1948	282.3	99.6	244.4	3,175.3	2,210.6	2,782.0	451.3	592.4	455.7	
1949	206.2	74.5	178.9	2,895.1	2,327.2	2,663.5	381.4	615.6	388.8	
1950	243.2	76.9	208.6	3,102.1	2,693.3	2,935.4	430.9	629.2	437.2	57.8 / 360.0
1951	251.3	74.4	214.6	3,533.0	3,191.3	3,393.7	473.8	623.6	478.5	
1952	219.9	70.8	188.9	3,599.2	3,427.2	3,529.0	461.2	632.4	466.6	
1953	215.4	53.9	181.9	3,704.8	3,589.0	3,657.5	465.2	608.8	469.7	
1954	184.5	50.7	156.7	3,638.7	3,735.4	3,678.1	443.8	579.6	448.1	
1955	218.8	45.6	182.9	3,905.1	4,017.3	3,950.8	490.0	578.8	492.8	53.0 / 403.4

n.a. Not available.

SOURCE: Appendix Table II.

TABLE VI. APPARENT CONSUMPTION[a] OF MINERAL FUELS, HYDROPOWER, AND FUEL WOOD, IN PHYSICAL QUANTITIES, 1850–1955

Year	Coal (thous. net tons)			Crude oil[b] (thous. bbl.)	Natural gas, dry[c] (mill. cu. ft.)	Natural gas liquids[d] (thous. bbl.)	Hydro-power (mill. kwh.)	Fuel wood (thous. cords)
	Bituminous (1)	Anthracite (2)	Total (3)	(4)	(5)	(6)	(7)	(8)
1850..	4,215	4,292	8,507					102,000
1855..	7,823	8,523	16,346					114,000
1860..	9,258	10,842	20,100	500	n.a.			126,000
1865..	12,534	11,988	24,522	1,700	n.a.			132,000
1870..	20,817	19,822	40,639	2,011	n.a.			138,000
1875..	32,919	22,770	55,689	2,002	n.a.			137,000
1880..	51,036	28,210	79,246	17,203	n.a.			136,000
1885..	71,868	37,689	109,557	7,172	76,000			128,000
1890..	110,785	45,614	156,399	27,652	239,000		250	120,000
1895..	133,998	56,667	190,665	29,726	137,000		1,000	110,000
1900..	207,275	55,515	262,790	39,564	235,000		2,786	100,000
1901..	221,687	65,239	286,926	43,158	261,000		3,030	
1902..	256,990	40,547	297,537	62,809	278,000		3,420	
1903..	279,217	72,554	351,771	77,442	295,000		3,927	
1904..	273,081	70,742	343,823	92,140	307,000		4,481	
1905..	308,823	75,201	384,024	105,119	346,000		5,054	95,000
1906..	335,605	68,836	404,441	95,699	382,000		5,613	
1907..	384,708	82,594	467,302	134,687	402,000		6,200	
1908..	323,600	80,205	403,805	141,369	397,000		6,974	
1909..	369,673	77,890	447,563	145,447	475,000		7,848	
1910..	406,633	81,110	487,743	173,559	502,000		8,626	91,000
1911..	391,017	86,486	477,503	179,330	506,000	177	9,990	
1912..	435,198	80,232	515,430	182,452	553,000	288	10,797	
1913..	459,330	86,873	546,203	208,681	577,000	573	11,884	
1914..	408,493	86,553	495,046	227,646	587,000	1,016	12,994	
1915..	424,978	85,033	510,011	243,230	626,000	1,556	13,886	87,000
1916..	482,114	82,919	565,033	258,031	750,000	2,464	15,335	
1917..	528,072	93,617	621,689	302,645	790,000	5,188	16,615	
1918..	556,798	93,896	650,694	329,473	717,000	6,726	17,095	
1919..	446,113	83,198	529,311	372,274	738,000	8,369	18,155	
1920..	508,595	85,786	594,381	454,242	785,120	9,167	19,719	83,000
1921..	391,849	81,950	473,799	461,447	646,752	10,715	18,538	
1922..	426,915	56,799	483,714	529,673	745,342	12,048	20,599	
1923..	518,993	86,914	605,907	648,619	979,232	19,429	23,119	
1924..	484,004	80,717	564,721	646,809	1,109,765	22,239	23,774	
1925..	499,193	64,061	563,254	716,096	1,150,253	26,833	26,753	79,000
1926..	532,581	77,221	609,802	745,092	1,266,676	32,358	30,742	
1927..	499,801	74,672	574,473	754,332	1,389,634	38,786	34,167	
1928..	498,828	73,650	572,478	819,598	1,506,463	43,429	39,256	
1929..	519,555	71,457	591,012	909,246	1,841,495	53,477	38,947	
1930..	454,990	67,628	522,618	970,762	1,866,504	53,095	37,470	75,000

TABLE VI (continued)

Year	Coal (thous. net tons) Bituminous (1)	Anthracite (2)	Total (3)	Crude oil[b] (thous. bbl.) (4)	Natural gas, dry[c] (mill. cu. ft.) (5)	Natural gas liquids[d] (thous. bbl.) (6)	Hydro-power (mill. kwh.) (7)	Fuel wood (thous. cords) (8)
1931..	371,869	58,408	430,277	854,462	1,621,961	44,025	34,757	
1932..	306,917	50,500	357,417	788,316	1,502,499	35,096	37,173	
1933..	317,685	49,600	367,285	832,546	1,505,119	32,048	38,142	
1934..	343,814	55,500	399,314	828,726	1,712,798	36,167	37,981	
1935..	356,326	51,100	407,426	945,857	1,854,413	38,476	44,064	72,000
1936..	408,293	53,200	461,493	1,053,621	2,099,454	42,406	44,601	
1937..	430,777	50,400	481,177	1,135,247	2,334,831	48,287	48,000	
1938..	336,281	45,200	381,481	1,110,760	2,220,759	49,096	49,027	
1939..	376,098	49,700	425,798	1,176,529	2,390,019	53,239	48,249	
1940..	430,910	49,000	479,910	1,284,954	2,575,133	60,095	52,245	70,000
1941..	492,115	52,700	544,815	1,410,834	2,689,728	80,929	55,538	
1942..	540,050	56,500	596,550	1,318,866	2,925,773	81,905	69,124	
1943..	593,797	57,100	650,897	1,413,836	3,281,691	84,571	81,575	
1944..	589,599	59,400	648,999	1,586,058	3,553,595	99,310	81,420	
1945..	559,567	51,600	611,167	1,661,487	3,740,543	110,762	87,309	65,000
1946..	500,386	53,900	554,286	1,715,647	3,847,656	111,000	85,541	
1947..	545,891	48,200	594,091	1,856,399	4,237,810	127,881	84,981	
1948..	519,909	50,200	570,109	2,052,627	4,735,641	140,690	88,535	
1949..	445,538	37,700	483,238	1,967,532	4,971,152	150,214	96,361	
1950..	454,202	39,900	494,102	2,180,291	5,766,992	178,833	102,671	60,000
1951..	468,904	37,000	505,904	2,398,620	6,810,162	200,214	106,554	
1952..	418,757	35,300	454,057	2,468,205	7,294,320	219,881	111,977	
1953..	426,798	28,000	454,798	2,590,054	7,639,270	232,024	111,625	
1954..	363,060	26,900	389,960	2,590,211	8,048,610	240,738	113,980	
1955..	423,412	23,600	447,012	2,802,856	8,700,259	277,500	120,304	55,000

n.a. Not available.

[a] Calculated from production plus imports minus exports. Figures for 1920 and subsequent years adjusted for net stock changes in mineral fuels.

[b] Figures reflect net exports and imports of crude oil and refined products. Prior to 1920, exports of products raised to approximate crude oil equivalent, allowing for losses ranging from 25 per cent in 1865 to 10 per cent in 1895 and less than 3 per cent after 1900; figures for apparent consumption reduced correspondingly. For 1920 and subsequent years, refinery losses considered sufficiently small to require no adjustment of data. For refinery losses in early period see S. F. Peckham, *Production, Technology and Uses of Petroleum and Its Products*, in *Tenth Census of the United States, Vol. X*, p. 270; and USGS, *Mineral Resources of the United States*, 1889–1890, p. 301.

[c] Prior to 1920, marketed production of dry and wet gas minus net exports. For 1920 and subsequent years, figures refer to dry gas (34 cubic feet of gas subtracted from marketed production for every gallon of natural gas liquids produced); transmission losses are excluded. See Mines, *Mineral Industry Surveys*, Monthly Petroleum Statement 402. In 1957, the Bureau of Mines revised its series "calculated consumption of natural gas, dry" to include transmission losses. The revised figures are shown in Table 39.

[d] See introductory note to Appendix to Part I. Figures above include natural gasoline and natural gasoline mixtures, finished gasoline and naphtha, condensate, kerosine, and distillate fuel produced from natural gas, and liquefied petroleum gases (such as propane, butane, isobutane, and other mixtures).

(Sources on next page.)

TABLE VI (continued)

SOURCES: 1850–95 for individual commodities as follows:

COAL: Imports and exports of total coal, 1850–65, H. N. Eavenson, *The First Century and A Quarter of American Coal Industry* (Pittsburgh: privately printed, 1942), Appendix Table 21. Imports and exports of bituminous coal and anthracite, 1950 and 1860, J. F. Dewhurst and Associates, *America's Needs and Resources, A New Survey* (New York: The Twentieth Century Fund, 1955), Appendix 25–3, p. 1106; 1855 and 1865 estimates, based on above data for 1850 and 1860 and annual import and export data, beginning 1867, published in *Mineral Resources of the United States, op. cit.* Imports and exports of bituminous coal and anthracite, 1870–95, *ibid.*

CRUDE OIL: Imports and exports, 1860–95, *ibid.*, and see explanation in footnote b above.

NATURAL GAS: 1885–95 data represent estimated marketed production (see footnote for natural gas in Appendix Table I, and above footnote c).

HYDROPOWER: 1890–95 identical with estimated production (see footnote for hydropower in Appendix Table I).

FUEL WOOD: See note for fuel wood in Appendix Table I.

Sources for years 1900–19 for individual commodities as follows:

ALL MINERAL FUELS AND HYDROPOWER: From worksheets underlying Census, *Raw Materials in the United States Economy: 1900–1952*, Working Paper No. 1, 1954.

FUEL WOOD: Same as 1850–95.

Sources for years 1920–55 as follows:

ALL MINERAL FUELS AND HYDROPOWER: Except as noted below, from Mines, *Monthly Petroleum Statement*, No. 402, and Mines, *Minerals Yearbook, 1956*, Vol. II.

NATURAL GAS LIQUIDS: Figures for 1925–40 adjusted to include marketed production of liquefied petroleum gases. See Mines, *Mineral Resources of the United States, 1929*, Vol. II, p. 310; Mines, *Minerals Yearbook, Review of 1940*, p. 1077; see also reprint from *Butane-Propane News*, January 1956 in Bulletin 350, Phillips Petroleum Company, Sales Department, Bartlesville, Oklahoma.

FUEL WOOD: Same as 1850–95.

TABLE VII. APPARENT CONSUMPTION OF MINERAL FUELS, HYDROPOWER, AND FUEL WOOD, IN BTU'S, 1850-1955

(Trillion Btu)

Year	Coal			Liquid and gaseous fuels				Total mineral fuels (8)	Hydropower (9)	Mineral fuels and hydropower (10)	Fuel wood (11)	Total (12)
	Bituminous (1)	Anthracite (2)	Total (3)	Crude oil [a] (4)	Natural gas (5)	Natural gas liquids (6)	Total (7)					
1850...	110	109	219					219		219	2,138	2,357
1855...	205	216	421					421		421	2,389	2,810
1860...	243	275	518	3	n.a.		n.a.	521		521	2,641	3,162
1865...	328	304	632	10	n.a.		n.a.	642		642	2,767	3,409
1870...	545	503	1,048	11	n.a.		n.a.	1,059		1,059	2,893	3,952
1875...	862	578	1,440	11	n.a.		n.a.	1,451		1,451	2,872	4,323
1880...	1,337	717	2,054	96	n.a.		n.a.	2,150		2,150	2,851	5,001
1885...	1,883	957	2,840	40	82		122	2,962		2,962	2,683	5,645
1890...	2,903	1,159	4,062	156	257		413	4,475	22	4,497	2,515	7,012
1895...	3,511	1,439	4,950	168	147		315	5,265	90	5,355	2,306	7,661
1900...	5,431	1,410	6,841	229	252		481	7,322	250	7,572	2,015	9,587
1901...	5,808	1,657	7,465	250	281		531	7,996	264	8,260		
1902...	6,733	1,030	7,763	364	299		663	8,426	289	8,715		
1903...	7,315	1,843	9,158	449	317		766	9,924	321	10,245		
1904...	7,155	1,797	8,952	534	330		864	9,816	354	10,170		
1905...	8,091	1,910	10,001	610	372		982	10,983	386	11,369	1,843	13,212
1906...	8,793	1,748	10,541	555	411		966	11,507	414	11,921		
1907...	10,079	2,098	12,177	781	432		1,213	13,390	441	13,831		
1908...	8,478	2,037	10,515	820	427		1,247	11,762	476	12,238		
1909...	9,685	1,978	11,663	844	511		1,355	13,018	513	13,531		
1910...	10,654	2,060	12,714	1,007	540		1,547	14,261	539	14,800	1,765	16,565

(*Table continued on next page.*)

TABLE VII (continued)

Year	Coal			Liquid and gaseous fuels				Total mineral fuels (8)	Hydropower (9)	Mineral fuels and hydropower (10)	Fuel wood (11)	Total (12)
	Bituminous (1)	Anthracite (2)	Total (3)	Crude oil a (4)	Natural gas (5)	Natural gas liquids (6)	Total (7)					
1911	10,245	2,197	12,442	1,040	544	1	1,585	14,027	597	14,624		
1912	11,402	2,038	13,440	1,058	594	1	1,653	15,093	615	15,708		
1913	12,034	2,207	14,241	1,210	620	3	1,833	16,074	645	16,719		
1914	10,703	2,198	12,901	1,320	632	5	1,957	14,858	676	15,534		
1915	11,134	2,160	13,294	1,411	673	7	2,091	15,385	691	16,076	1,688	17,764
1916	12,631	2,106	14,737	1,497	807	11	2,315	17,052	729	17,781		
1917	13,835	2,378	16,213	1,755	850	24	2,629	18,842	755	19,597		
1918	14,588	2,385	16,973	1,911	771	31	2,713	19,686	750	20,436		
1919	11,688	2,113	13,801	2,159	793	39	2,991	16,792	766	17,558		
1920	13,325	2,179	15,504	2,634	813	42	3,489	18,993	775	19,768	1,610	21,378
1921	10,266	2,082	12,348	2,674	669	50	3,393	15,741	656	16,397		
1922	11,185	1,443	12,628	3,071	771	56	3,898	16,526	675	17,201		
1923	13,598	2,208	15,806	4,030	1,014	90	5,134	20,940	727	21,667		
1924	12,681	2,050	14,731	3,764	1,149	103	5,016	19,747	685	20,432		
1925	13,079	1,627	14,706	4,156	1,191	124	5,471	20,177	701	20,878	1,533	22,411
1926	13,954	1,961	15,915	4,331	1,311	149	5,791	21,706	765	22,471		
1927	13,095	1,897	14,992	4,377	1,438	179	5,994	20,986	815	21,801		
1928	12,069	1,871	14,940	4,763	1,559	200	6,522	21,462	890	22,352		
1929	13,612	1,815	15,427	5,294	1,906	246	7,446	22,873	847	23,720		
1930	11,921	1,718	13,639	5,652	1,932	245	7,829	21,468	785	22,253	1,455	23,708
1931	9,743	1,484	11,227	4,965	1,679	203	6,847	18,074	692	18,766		
1932	8,041	1,283	9,324	4,590	1,555	161	6,306	15,630	726	16,356		
1933	8,323	1,260	9,583	4,844	1,558	148	6,550	16,133	729	16,862		
1934	9,008	1,410	10,418	4,818	1,773	166	6,757	17,175	721	17,896		
1935	9,336	1,298	10,634	5,499	1,919	176	7,594	18,228	831	19,059	1,397	20,456

Year												
1936...	10,697	1,351	12,048	6,124	2,173	194	8,491	20,539	841	21,380		
1937...	11,286	1,280	12,566	6,604	2,417	221	9,242	21,808	905	22,713		
1938...	8,811	1,148	9,959	6,465	2,298	225	8,988	18,947	899	19,886		
1939...	9,854	1,262	11,116	6,841	2,474	242	9,557	20,673	872	21,545		
1940...	11,290	1,245	12,535	7,487	2,665	273	10,425	22,960	917	23,877	1,358	25,235
1941...	12,893	1,338	14,231	8,204	2,784	364	11,352	25,583	975	26,558		
1942...	14,149	1,435	15,584	7,667	3,028	367	11,062	26,646	1,177	27,823		
1943...	15,557	1,450	17,007	8,228	3,397	379	12,004	29,011	1,347	30,358		
1944...	15,447	1,509	16,956	9,261	3,678	442	13,381	30,337	1,387	31,724		
1945...	14,661	1,311	15,972	9,619	3,871	491	13,981	29,953	1,486	31,439	1,261	32,700
1946...	13,110	1,369	14,479	9,987	3,982	493	14,462	28,941	1,446	30,387		
1947...	14,302	1,224	15,526	10,803	4,386	564	15,753	31,279	1,459	32,738		
1948...	13,622	1,275	14,897	11,938	4,901	619	17,458	32,355	1,507	33,862		
1949...	11,673	958	12,631	11,459	5,145	660	17,264	29,895	1,565	31,460		
1950...	11,900	1,013	12,913	12,706	5,969	783	19,458	32,371	1,601	33,972	1,164	35,136
1951...	12,285	940	13,225	13,974	7,049	874	21,897	35,122	1,592	36,714		
1952...	10,971	897	11,868	14,380	7,550	954	22,884	34,752	1,614	36,366		
1953...	11,182	711	11,893	15,092	7,907	1,006	24,005	35,898	1,550	37,448		
1954...	9,512	683	10,195	15,090	8,330	1,042	24,462	34,657	1,479	36,136		
1955...	11,104	599	11,703	16,328	9,005	1,196	26,529	38,232	1,497	39,729	1,067	40,796

n.a. Not available.

a Including net trade in oil products.

SOURCE: Appendix Table VI. In converting physical quantities into Btu's the conversion factors used were those listed in the Note to Appendix Table II, with the following exceptions:
Natural gas (dry and wet), prior to 1920, 1,075 Btu per cubic foot;
natural gas (dry), 1920 and subsequent years, 1,035 Btu per cubic foot; and
natural gas liquids, weighted average of 4,620,000 Btu per barrel for natural gasoline and
4,011,000 Btu per barrel for LPG (see Mines, *Monthly Petroleum Statement*, No. 402, May 1956)

TABLE VIII. SPECIFIC MINERAL FUELS AS PERCENTAGES OF TOTAL
CONSUMPTION OF MINERAL FUELS, 1900–55

(Based on Btu values)

Year	Coal			Liquid and gaseous fuels				Total mineral fuels (8)
	Bituminous (1)	Anthracite (2)	Total (3)	Crude petroleum[a] (4)	Natural gas (5)	Natural gas liquids (6)	Total (7)	
1900	74.2%	19.3%	93.4%	3.1%	3.4%		6.6%	100.0%
1901	72.6	20.7	93.4	3.1	3.5		6.6	100.0
1902	79.9	12.2	92.1	4.3	3.5		7.9	100.0
1903	73.7	18.6	92.3	4.5	3.2		7.7	100.0
1904	72.9	18.3	91.2	5.4	3.4		8.8	100.0
1905	73.7	17.4	91.1	5.6	3.4		8.9	100.0
1906	76.4	15.2	91.6	4.8	3.6		8.4	100.0
1907	75.3	15.7	90.9	5.8	3.2		9.1	100.0
1908	72.1	17.3	89.4	7.0	3.6		10.6	100.0
1909	74.4	15.2	89.6	6.5	3.9		10.4	100.0
1910	74.7	14.4	89.2	7.1	3.8		10.8	100.0
1911	73.0	15.7	88.7	7.4	3.9	b	11.3	100.0
1912	75.5	13.5	89.0	7.0	3.9	b	11.0	100.0
1913	74.9	13.7	88.6	7.5	3.9	b	11.4	100.0
1914	72.0	14.8	86.8	8.9	4.3	b	13.2	100.0
1915	72.4	14.0	86.4	9.2	4.4	b	13.6	100.0
1916	74.1	12.4	86.4	8.8	4.7	0.1%	13.6	100.0
1917	73.4	12.6	86.0	9.3	4.5	0.1	14.0	100.0
1918	74.1	12.1	86.2	9.7	3.9	0.2	13.8	100.0
1919	69.6	12.6	82.2	12.9	4.7	0.2	17.8	100.0
1920	70.2	11.5	81.6	13.9	4.3	0.2	18.4	100.0
1921	65.2	13.2	78.4	17.0	4.3	0.3	21.6	100.0
1922	67.7	8.7	76.4	18.6	4.7	0.3	23.6	100.0
1923	64.9	10.5	75.5	19.2	4.8	0.4	24.5	100.0
1924	64.2	10.4	74.6	19.1	5.8	0.5	25.4	100.0
1925	64.8	8.1	72.9	20.6	5.9	0.6	27.1	100.0
1926	64.3	9.0	73.3	20.0	6.0	0.7	26.7	100.0
1927	62.4	9.0	71.4	20.9	6.9	0.9	28.6	100.0
1928	60.9	8.7	69.6	22.2	7.3	0.9	30.4	100.0
1929	59.5	7.9	67.4	23.1	8.3	1.1	32.6	100.0
1930	55.5	8.0	63.5	26.3	9.0	1.1	36.5	100.0
1931	53.9	8.2	62.1	27.5	9.3	1.1	37.9	100.0
1932	51.4	8.2	59.7	29.4	9.9	1.0	40.3	100.0
1933	51.6	7.8	59.4	30.0	9.7	0.9	40.6	100.0
1934	52.4	8.2	60.7	28.1	10.3	1.0	39.3	100.0
1935	51.2	7.1	58.3	30.2	10.5	1.0	41.7	100.0
1936	52.1	6.6	58.7	29.8	10.6	0.9	41.3	100.0
1937	51.8	5.9	57.6	30.3	11.1	1.0	42.4	100.0
1938	46.5	6.1	52.6	34.1	12.1	1.2	47.4	100.0
1939	47.7	6.1	53.8	33.1	12.0	1.2	46.2	100.0
1940	49.2	5.4	54.6	32.6	11.6	1.2	45.4	100.0

TABLE VIII (continued)

Year	Coal			Liquid and gaseous fuels				Total mineral fuels (8)
	Bitumi- nous (1)	Anthra- cite (2)	Total (3)	Crude petro- leum ᵃ (4)	Natural gas (5)	Natural gas liquids (6)	Total (7)	
1941..........	50.4%	5.2%	55.6%	32.1%	10.9%	1.4%	44.4%	100.0%
1942..........	53.1	5.4	58.5	28.8	11.4	1.4	41.5	100.0
1943..........	53.6	5.0	58.6	28.4	11.7	1.3	41.4	100.0
1944..........	50.9	5.0	55.9	30.5	12.1	1.5	44.1	100.0
1945..........	48.9	4.4	53.3	32.1	12.9	1.6	46.7	100.0
1946..........	45.3	4.7	50.0	34.5	13.8	1.7	50.0	100.0
1947..........	45.7	3.9	49.6	34.5	14.0	1.8	50.4	100.0
1948..........	42.1	3.9	46.0	36.9	15.1	1.9	54.0	100.0
1949..........	39.0	3.2	42.3	38.3	17.2	2.2	57.7	100.0
1950..........	36.8	3.1	39.9	39.3	18.4	2.4	60.1	100.0
1951..........	35.0	2.7	37.7	39.8	20.1	2.5	62.3	100.0
1952..........	31.6	2.6	34.2	41.4	21.7	2.7	65.8	100.0
1953..........	31.1	2.0	33.1	42.0	22.0	2.8	66.9	100.0
1954..........	27.4	2.0	29.4	43.5	24.0	3.0	70.6	100.0
1955..........	29.0	1.6	30.6	42.7	23.6	3.1	69.4	100.0

ᵃ Including net trade in oil products.
ᵇ Less than 0.1%.

SOURCE: Appendix Table VII.

TABLE IX. INDEXES OF ENERGY CONSUMPTION BASED ON BTU VALUES: TOTALS AND BY SPECIFIC ENERGY SOURCES, 1850–1955

(1900 = 100)

Year	Coal			Liquid and gaseous fuels				Total mineral fuels (8)	Hydropower (9)	Mineral fuels and hydropower (10)	Fuel wood (11)	Total (12)
	Bituminous (1)	Anthracite (2)	Total (3)	Crude oil [a] (4)	Liquid hydrocarbons [b] (5)	Natural gas (6)	Total [c] (7)					
1850...	2.0	7.7	3.2					3.0		2.9	106.1	24.6
1855...	3.8	15.3	6.2					5.8		5.6	118.6	29.3
1860...	4.5	19.5	7.6	1.3		n.a.	0.6	7.1		6.9	131.1	33.0
1865...	6.0	21.6	9.2	4.4		n.a.	2.1	8.8		8.5	137.3	35.6
1870...	10.0	35.7	15.3	4.8		n.a.	2.3	14.5		14.0	143.6	41.2
1875...	15.9	41.0	21.1	4.8		n.a.	2.3	19.8		19.2	142.5	45.1
1880...	24.6	50.8	30.0	41.9		n.a.	20.0	29.4		28.4	141.5	52.2
1885...	34.7	67.9	41.5	17.5		32.5	25.4	40.5		39.1	133.2	58.9
1890...	53.4	82.2	59.4	68.1		102.0	85.9	61.1	8.8	59.4	124.8	73.1
1895...	64.6	102.2	72.4	73.4		58.3	65.5	71.9	36.0	70.7	114.4	79.9
1900...	100.0	100.0	100.0	100.0		100.0	100.0	100.0	100.0	100.0	100.0	100.0
1901...	106.9	117.5	109.1	109.2		111.5	110.4	109.2	105.6	109.1		
1902...	124.0	73.0	113.5	159.0		118.7	137.8	115.1	115.6	115.1		
1903...	134.7	130.7	113.9	196.1		125.8	159.3	135.5	128.4	135.3		
1904...	131.7	127.4	130.9	233.2		131.0	179.6	134.1	141.6	134.3		
1905...	149.0	135.5	146.2	266.4		147.6	204.2	150.0	154.4	150.1	91.5	137.8
1906...	161.9	124.0	154.1	242.4		163.1	200.8	157.2	165.6	157.4		
1907...	185.6	148.8	178.0	341.0		171.4	252.2	182.9	176.4	182.7		
1908...	156.1	144.5	153.7	358.1		169.4	259.3	160.6	190.4	161.6		
1909...	178.3	140.3	170.5	368.6		202.8	281.7	177.8	205.2	178.7		
1910...	196.2	146.1	185.9	439.7		214.3	321.6	194.8	215.6	195.5	87.6	172.8

Year	1	2	3	4	5	6	7	8	9	10	11	12
1911....	188.6	155.8	181.9	454.1	454.6	215.9	329.5	191.6	238.8	193.1		
1912....	209.9	144.5	196.5	462.0	462.4	235.7	343.7	206.1	246.0	207.5		
1913....	221.6	156.5	208.2	528.4	529.7	246.0	381.1	219.5	258.0	220.8		
1914....	197.1	155.9	188.6	576.4	578.6	250.8	406.9	202.9	270.4	205.2		
1915....	205.0	153.2	194.3	616.2	619.2	267.1	434.7	210.1	276.4	212.3	83.8	185.3
1916....	232.6	149.4	215.4	653.7	658.5	320.2	481.3	232.9	291.6	234.8		
1917....	254.7	168.7	237.0	766.4	776.9	337.3	546.6	257.3	302.0	258.8		
1918....	268.6	169.1	248.1	834.5	848.0	306.0	564.0	268.9	300.0	269.9		
1919....	215.2	149.9	201.7	942.8	959.8	314.7	621.8	229.3	306.4	231.9		
1920....	245.4	154.5	226.6	1,150.2	1,168.6	322.6	725.4	259.4	310.0	261.1	79.9	223.0
1921....	189.0	147.7	180.5	1,167.7	1,189.5	265.5	705.4	215.0	262.4	216.6		
1922....	205.9	102.3	184.6	1,341.0	1,365.5	306.0	810.4	225.7	270.0	227.2		
1923....	250.4	156.6	231.1	1,759.8	1,799.1	402.4	1,067.4	286.0	290.8	286.2		
1924....	233.5	145.4	215.3	1,643.7	1,688.6	456.0	1,042.8	269.7	274.0	269.9		
1925....	240.8	115.4	215.0	1,814.8	1,869.0	472.6	1,137.4	275.6	280.4	275.7	76.1	233.8
1926....	256.9	139.1	232.7	1,891.3	1,956.3	520.2	1,204.0	296.4	306.0	296.8		
1927....	241.1	134.5	219.2	1,911.3	1,989.5	570.6	1,246.2	286.6	326.0	287.9		
1928....	240.6	132.7	218.4	2,079.9	2,167.2	618.7	1,355.9	293.1	356.0	295.2		
1929....	250.6	128.7	225.5	2,311.8	2,419.2	756.3	1,548.0	312.4	338.8	313.3		
1930....	219.5	121.8	199.4	2,468.1	2,575.1	766.7	1,627.7	293.2	314.0	293.9	72.2	247.3
1931....	179.4	105.2	164.1	2,168.1	2,256.8	666.3	1,423.5	246.8	276.8	247.8		
1932....	148.1	91.0	136.3	2,004.4	2,074.7	617.1	1,311.0	213.5	290.4	216.0		
1933....	153.3	89.4	140.1	2,115.3	2,179.9	618.3	1,361.8	220.3	291.6	222.7		
1934....	165.9	100.0	152.3	2,103.9	2,176.4	703.6	1,404.8	234.6	288.4	236.4		
1935....	171.9	92.0	155.5	2,401.3	2,478.2	761.5	1,578.8	248.9	332.4	251.7	69.3	213.4
1936....	197.0	95.8	176.1	2,674.2	2,758.9	862.3	1,765.3	280.5	336.4	282.4		
1937....	207.8	90.8	183.7	2,883.8	2,980.3	959.1	1,921.4	297.8	362.0	300.0		
1938....	162.2	81.4	145.6	2,823.1	2,921.4	911.9	1,868.6	258.8	359.6	262.6		
1939....	181.4	89.5	162.5	2,987.3	3,093.0	981.7	1,986.9	282.3	348.8	284.5		
1940....	207.9	88.3	183.2	3,269.4	3,388.6	1,057.5	2,167.4	313.6	366.8	315.3	67.4	263.2

(Table continued on next page.)

TABLE IX (continued)

Year	Coal			Liquid and gaseous fuels				Total mineral fuels (8)	Hydropower (9)	Mineral fuels and hydropower (10)	Fuel wood (11)	Total (12)
	Bituminous (1)	Anthracite (2)	Total (3)	Crude oil [a] (4)	Liquid hydro-carbons [b] (5)	Natural gas (6)	Total [c] (7)					
1941...	237.4	94.9	208.0	3,582.5	3,741.5	1,104.8	2,360.1	349.4	390.0	350.8		
1942...	260.5	101.8	227.8	3,348.0	3,508.3	1,201.6	2,299.8	363.9	470.8	367.5		
1943...	286.5	102.8	248.6	3,593.0	3,758.5	1,348.0	2,495.6	396.2	538.8	400.9		
1944...	284.4	107.0	247.9	4,044.1	4,237.1	1,459.5	2,781.9	414.3	554.8	419.0		
1945...	270.0	93.0	233.5	4,200.4	4,414.8	1,536.1	2,906.7	409.1	594.4	415.2	62.6	341.1
1946...	241.4	97.1	211.7	4,361.1	4,576.4	1,580.2	3,006.7	395.3	578.4	401.3		
1947...	263.3	86.8	227.0	4,717.5	4,963.7	1,740.5	3,275.1	427.2	583.6	432.4		
1948...	250.8	90.4	217.8	5,213.1	5,483.4	1,944.8	3,629.5	441.9	602.8	447.2		
1949...	214.9	67.9	184.6	5,003.9	5,292.1	2,041.7	3,589.2	408.3	626.0	415.5		
1950...	219.1	71.8	188.8	5,548.5	5,890.4	2,368.6	4,045.3	442.1	640.4	448.7	57.8	366.5
1951...	226.2	66.7	193.3	6,102.2	6,483.8	2,797.2	4,552.4	479.7	636.8	484.9		
1952...	202.0	63.6	173.5	6,279.5	6,696.1	2,996.0	4,757.6	474.6	645.6	480.3		
1953...	205.9	50.4	173.9	6,590.4	7,029.7	3,137.7	4,990.6	490.3	620.0	494.5		
1954...	175.1	48.4	149.0	6,589.5	7,044.5	3,305.6	5,085.6	473.3	591.6	477.3		
1955...	204.5	42.5	171.1	7,130.1	7,652.4	3,573.4	5,515.4	522.2	598.8	524.7	53.0	425.5

n.a. Not available.

[a] Including net trade in oil products.
[b] Crude oil and natural gas liquids. Column 5 based on the sum of column 4 and column 6 in Appendix Table VII.
[c] Figures for 1860–80 refer to crude oil only; data for natural gas not available.

SOURCE: Appendix Table VII.

TABLE X.   PER CAPITA CONSUMPTION OF MINERAL FUELS,
HYDROPOWER, AND FUEL WOOD, IN PHYSICAL QUANTITIES, 1850–1955

| Year | Population (thousands) (1) | Coal (net tons) | | | Crude oil [a] (barrels) (5) | Natural gas, dry (thousand cu. ft.) (6) | Natural gas liquids (barrels) (7) | Hydro-power (kwh) (8) | Fuel wood (cords) (9) |
		Bitumi-nous (2)	Anthra-cite (3)	Total (4)					
1850..	23,261	0.18	0.18	0.36					4.39
1855..	27,386	0.29	0.31	0.60					4.16
1860..	31,513	0.29	0.34	0.63	0.02	n.a.			4.00
1865..	35,701	0.35	0.34	0.69	0.05	n.a.			3.70
1870..	39,905	0.52	0.50	1.02	0.05	n.a.			3.46
1875..	45,073	0.73	0.51	1.24	0.04	n.a.			3.04
1880..	50,262	1.02	0.56	1.58	0.34	n.a.			2.71
1885..	56,658	1.27	0.67	1.94	0.13	1.35			2.26
1890..	63,056	1.76	0.72	2.48	0.44	3.79		4	1.90
1895..	69,580	1.93	0.81	2.74	0.43	1.97		14	1.58
1900..	76,094	2.72	0.73	3.45	0.52	3.09		37	1.31
1901..	77,585	2.86	0.84	3.70	0.56	3.36		39	
1902..	79,160	3.25	0.51	3.76	0.79	3.51		43	
1903..	80,632	3.46	0.90	4.36	0.96	3.66		49	
1904..	82,165	3.32	0.86	4.18	1.12	3.74		55	
1905..	83,820	3.68	0.90	4.58	1.25	4.13		60	1.13
1906..	85,437	3.93	0.81	4.74	1.12	4.47		66	
1907..	87,000	4.42	0.95	5.37	1.55	4.62		71	
1908..	88,709	3.65	0.90	4.55	1.59	4.48		79	
1909..	90,492	4.09	0.86	4.95	1.61	5.25		87	
1910..	92,407	4.40	0.88	5.28	1.88	5.43		93	0.98
1911..	93,868	4.17	0.92	5.09	1.91	5.39		106	
1912..	95,331	4.57	0.84	5.41	1.91	5.80		113	
1913..	97,227	4.72	0.89	5.61	2.15	5.93		122	
1914..	99,118	4.12	0.87	4.99	2.30	5.92		131	
1915..	100,549	4.23	0.85	5.08	2.42	6.22	0.02	138	0.87
1916..	101,966	4.73	0.81	5.54	2.53	7.36	0.02	150	
1917..	103,414	5.11	0.91	6.02	2.93	7.64	0.05	161	
1918..	104,550	5.33	0.90	6.23	3.15	6.86	0.06	164	
1919..	105,063	4.25	0.79	5.04	3.54	7.02	0.08	173	
1920..	106,466	4.78	0.81	5.59	4.27	7.37	0.09	185	0.78
1921..	108,541	3.61	0.76	4.37	4.25	5.96	0.10	171	
1922..	110,055	3.88	0.52	4.40	4.81	6.77	0.11	187	
1923..	111,950	4.64	0.78	5.42	5.79	8.75	0.17	207	
1924..	114,113	4.24	0.71	4.95	5.67	9.73	0.19	208	
1925..	115,832	4.31	0.55	4.86	6.18	9.93	0.23	231	0.68
1926..	117,399	4.54	0.66	5.20	6.35	10.79	0.28	262	
1927..	119,038	4.20	0.63	4.83	6.34	11.67	0.33	287	
1928..	120,501	4.14	0.61	4.75	6.80	12.50	0.36	326	
1929..	121,881	4.26	0.59	4.85	7.46	15.11	0.44	320	
1930..	123,188	3.69	0.55	4.24	7.88	15.15	0.43	304	0.61

(*Table continued on next page.*)

TABLE X (continued)

Year	Population (thousands) (1)	Coal (net tons)			Crude oil [a] (barrels) (5)	Natural gas, dry (thousand cu. ft.) (6)	Natural gas liquids (barrels) (7)	Hydro-power (kwh) (8)	Fuel wood (cords) (9)
		Bitumi-nous (2)	Anthra-cite (3)	Total (4)					
1931..	124,149	3.00	0.47	3.47	6.88	13.06	0.35	280	
1932..	124,949	2.46	0.40	2.86	6.31	12.02	0.28	298	
1933..	125,690	2.53	0.39	2.92	6.62	11.97	0.25	303	
1934..	126,485	2.72	0.44	3.16	6.55	13.54	0.29	300	
1935..	127,362	2.80	0.40	3.20	7.43	14.56	0.30	346	0.57
1936..	128,181	3.19	0.42	3.61	8.22	16.38	0.33	348	
1937..	128,961	3.34	0.39	3.73	8.80	18.10	0.37	372	
1938..	129,969	2.59	0.35	2.94	8.55	17.09	0.38	377	
1939..	131,028	2.87	0.38	3.25	8.98	18.24	0.41	368	
1940..	132,122	3.26	0.37	3.63	9.73	19.49	0.45	395	0.53
1941..	133,402	3.69	0.40	4.09	10.58	20.16	0.61	416	
1942..	134,860	4.00	0.42	4.42	9.78	21.69	0.61	513	
1943..	136,739	4.34	0.42	4.76	10.34	24.00	0.62	597	
1944..	138,397	4.26	0.43	4.69	11.46	25.68	0.72	588	
1945..	139,928	4.00	0.37	4.37	11.87	26.73	0.79	624	0.46
1946..	141,389	3.54	0.38	3.92	12.13	27.21	0.79	605	
1947..	144,126	3.79	0.33	4.12	12.88	29.40	0.89	590	
1948..	146,631	3.55	0.34	3.89	14.00	32.30	0.96	604	
1949..	149,188	2.99	0.25	3.24	13.19	33.32	1.01	646	
1950..	151,683	2.99	0.26	3.25	14.37	38.02	1.18	677	0.40
1951..	154,360	3.04	0.24	3.28	15.54	44.12	1.30	690	
1952..	157,022	2.67	0.22	2.89	15.72	46.45	1.40	713	
1953..	159,643	2.67	0.18	2.85	16.22	47.85	1.45	699	
1954..	162,409	2.24	0.17	2.41	15.95	49.56	1.48	702	
1955..	165,248	2.56	0.14	2.70	16.96	52.65	1.68	728	0.33

n.a. Not available.

[a] Including net trade in oil products.

SOURCES: Column 1, estimated population on July 1 of each year. Figures for 1917–19 and 1929–55 include Armed Forces overseas. 1850–95, Census, *Historical Statistics of the United States, 1789–1945*, Series B 31. 1900–55, Census, *Statistical Abstract of the United States, 1955*, p. 13; and *ibid., 1956*, p. 5. Columns 2 through 9 from columns 1 through 8 of Appendix Table VI.

TABLE XI.   PER CAPITA CONSUMPTION OF MINERAL FUELS, AND HY-
DROPOWER; AND FUEL WOOD, IN BTU'S AND COAL EQUIVALENT, 1850–1955

Year	Mineral fuels and hydropower (million Btu) (1)	Fuel wood (million Btu) (2)	Total (million Btu) (3)	Total in bituminous coal equivalent (net tons) (4)
1850..............	9.4	91.9	101.3	3.9
1855..............	15.4	87.2	102.6	3.9
1860..............	16.5	83.8	100.3	3.8
1865..............	18.0	77.5	95.5	3.6
1870..............	26.5	72.5	99.0	3.8
1875..............	32.2	63.7	95.9	3.7
1880..............	42.8	56.7	99.5	3.8
1885..............	52.3	47.4	99.6	3.8
1890..............	71.3	39.9	111.2	4.2
1895..............	77.0	33.1	110.1	4.2
1900..............	99.5	26.5	126.0	4.8
1901..............	106.5			
1902..............	110.1			
1903..............	127.1			
1904..............	123.8			
1905..............	135.6	22.0	157.6	6.0
1906..............	139.5			
1907..............	159.0			
1908..............	138.0			
1909..............	149.5			
1910..............	160.2	19.1	179.3	6.8
1911..............	155.8			
1912..............	164.8			
1913..............	172.0			
1914..............	156.7			
1915..............	159.9	16.8	176.7	6.7
1916..............	174.4			
1917..............	189.5			
1918..............	195.5			
1919..............	167.1			
1920..............	185.7	15.1	200.8	7.7
1921..............	151.1			
1922..............	156.3			
1923..............	193.5			
1924..............	179.1			
1925..............	180.2	13.2	193.5	7.4
1926..............	191.4			
1927..............	183.1			
1928..............	185.5			
1929..............	194.6			
1930..............	180.6	11.8	192.5	7.3
1931..............	151.2			
1932..............	130.9			
1933..............	134.2			
1934..............	141.5			
1935..............	149.6	11.0	160.6	6.1

(*Table continued on next page.*)

TABLE XI (continued)

Year	Mineral fuels and hydropower (million Btu) (1)	Fuel wood (million Btu) (2)	Total (million Btu) (3)	Total in bituminous coal equivalent (net tons) 4)
1936.............	166.8			
1937.............	176.1			
1938.............	153.0			
1939.............	164.4			
1940.............	180.7	10.3	191.0	7.3
1941.............	199.1			
1942.............	206.3			
1943.............	222.0			
1944.............	229.2			
1945.............	224.7	9.0	233.7	8.9
1946.............	214.9			
1947.............	227.1			
1948.............	230.9			
1949.............	210.9			
1950.............	224.0	7.7	231.6	8.8
1951.............	237.8			
1952.............	231.6			
1953.............	234.6			
1954.............	222.5			
1955.............	240.4	6.5	246.9	9.4

SOURCES: Columns 1 through 3 from Appendix Table X, column 1; Appendix Table VII, columns 10, 11, and 12. Column 4: Conversion factor of 26.2 million Btu per net ton applied to column 3.

TABLE XII. INDEXES OF POPULATION, PER CAPITA REAL GROSS NATIONAL PRODUCT, AND PER CAPITA ENERGY CONSUMPTION, 1850–1955

(1900 = 100)

Year	Population (1)	Per capita GNP (2)	Per capita energy consumption	
			Excluding wood (3)	Including wood (4)
1850..............	30.6	n.a.	9.4	80.4
1855..............	36.0	n.a.	15.5	81.4
1860..............	41.4	n.a.	16.6	79.6
1865..............	46.9	n.a.	18.1	75.8
1870..............	52.4	n.a.	26.6	78.6
1875..............	59.2	n.a.	32.4	76.1
1880..............	66.1	75.7	43.0	79.0
1885..............	74.5	77.0	52.6	79.1
1890..............	82.9	82.8	71.7	88.3
1895..............	91.4	89.0	77.4	87.4

TABLE XII (continued)

Year	Population (1)	Per capita GNP (2)	Per capita energy consumption	
			Excluding wood (3)	Including wood (4)
1900...............	100.0	100.0	100.0	100.0
1901...............	102.0	109.4	107.0	
1902...............	104.0	108.2	110.6	
1903...............	106.0	111.5	127.7	
1904...............	108.0	108.0	124.4	
1905...............	110.2	113.8	136.3	125.1
1906...............	112.3	124.6	140.2	
1907...............	114.3	124.3	159.8	
1908...............	116.6	111.8	138.6	
1909...............	118.9	123.1	150.3	
1910...............	121.4	121.8	161.0	142.3
1911...............	123.4	123.8	156.6	
1912...............	125.3	127.6	165.4	
1913...............	127.8	130.1	172.8	
1914...............	130.3	117.9	157.5	
1915...............	132.1	119.7	160.7	140.2
1916...............	134.0	134.6	175.3	
1917...............	135.9	129.6	190.4	
1918...............	137.4	139.8	196.4	
1919...............	138.1	140.6	168.0	
1920...............	139.9	137.2	186.6	159.4
1921...............	142.6	131.4	151.8	
1922...............	144.6	137.2	157.1	
1923...............	147.1	152.7	194.5	
1924...............	150.0	154.3	179.9	
1925...............	152.2	155.7	181.1	153.6
1926...............	154.3	163.6	192.4	
1927...............	156.4	162.9	184.1	
1928...............	158.4	162.8	186.4	
1929...............	160.2	170.7	195.6	
1930...............	161.9	153.8	181.5	152.8
1931...............	163.2	143.5	151.9	
1932...............	164.2	121.8	131.5	
1933...............	165.2	117.6	134.8	
1934...............	166.2	127.2	142.2	
1935...............	167.4	143.0	150.4	127.5
1936...............	168.5	156.8	167.6	
1937...............	169.5	168.6	177.0	
1938...............	170.8	158.2	153.8	
1939...............	172.2	168.8	165.2	
1940...............	173.6	182.5	181.6	151.6
1941...............	175.3	207.1	200.1	
1942...............	177.2	228.5	207.3	
1943...............	179.7	248.0	223.1	
1944...............	181.9	264.3	230.4	
1945...............	183.9	257.6	225.8	185.5

(*Table continued on next page.*)

TABLE XII (continued)

Year	Population (1)	Per capita GNP (2)	Per capita energy consumption	
			Excluding wood (3)	Including wood (4)
1946..............	185.8	233.3	216.0	
1947..............	189.4	226.9	228.3	
1948..............	192.7	235.1	232.1	
1949..............	196.1	227.9	211.9	
1950..............	199.3	246.1	225.1	183.9
1951..............	202.9	257.4	239.0	
1952..............	206.4	262.0	232.7	
1953..............	209.8	268.5	235.7	
1954..............	213.4	261.2	223.6	
1955..............	217.2	275.2	241.6	196.0

n.a. Not available.

SOURCES: Appendix Tables X, XI, and XIII. Population, Table X, column 1; per capita
GNP: Table X, column 1, and Table XIII, column 1; per capita energy consumption:
Table XI, columns 1 and 3.

TABLE XIII. INDEXES OF ENERGY CONSUMPTION PER UNIT
OF GROSS NATIONAL PRODUCT, 1880–1955

(1900 = 100)

Year	Gross national product (1)	Total energy consumption including wood (2)	Mineral fuels and hydropower (3)	Coal (4)	Crude oil and natural gas (5)	Hydropower (6)
1880........	50.0	104.4	56.8	60.1	39.9	
1885........	57.3	102.7	68.2	72.4	44.2	
1890..:.....	68.6	106.6	86.6	86.6	125.2	12.8
1895........	81.4	98.2	86.9	88.9	80.5	44.2
1900........	100.0	100.0	100.0	100.0	100.0	100.0
1901........	111.5		97.9	97.9	99.0	94.7
1902........	112.6		102.2	100.8	122.4	102.7
1903........	118.1		114.5	113.3	134.8	108.7
1904........	116.7		115.1	112.2	154.0	121.4
1905........	125.3	110.0	119.8	116.7	162.9	123.2
1906........	139.9		112.6	110.2	143.6	118.4
1907........	142.1		128.6	125.3	177.5	124.1
1908........	130.4		124.0	117.9	202.1	146.1
1909........	146.3		122.1	116.5	192.5	140.2
1910........	147.9	116.8	132.2	125.7	217.4	145.8
1911........	152.7		126.5	119.1	215.8	156.4
1912........	159.8		129.8	122.9	215.0	153.9
1913........	166.2		132.9	125.3	229.3	155.2
1914........	153.5		133.7	122.9	265.0	176.1
1915........	158.2	117.1	134.2	122.8	274.8	174.7

TABLE XIII (continued)

Year	Gross national product (1)	Total energy consumption including wood (2)	Mineral fuels and hydropower (3)	Coal (4)	Crude oil and natural gas (5)	Hydropower (6)
1916........	180.3		130.2	119.5	266.9	161.7
1917........	176.1		147.0	134.6	310.4	171.5
1918........	192.1		140.5	129.2	293.7	156.2
1919........	194.1		119.4	103.9	320.3	157.8
1920........	191.9	116.2	136.0	118.1	377.9	161.5
1921........	187.4		115.6	96.3	376.4	140.0
1922........	198.4		114.5	93.0	408.5	136.1
1923........	224.7		127.4	102.8	475.1	129.4
1924........	231.3		116.7	93.1	450.8	118.5
1925........	237.0	98.6	116.3	90.7	479.9	118.3
1926........	252.4		117.6	92.2	477.0	121.2
1927........	254.8		113.0	86.0	489.0	127.9
1928........	257.9		114.5	84.7	525.8	138.0
1929........	273.4		114.6	82.5	566.2	123.9
1930........	249.1	99.3	118.0	80.1	653.5	126.1
1931........	234.2		105.8	70.1	607.8	118.2
1932........	200.0		108.0	68.1	655.4	145.2
1933........	194.2		114.7	72.1	701.2	150.2
1934........	211.5		111.8	72.0	664.3	136.4
1935........	239.4	89.1	105.1	64.9	659.5	138.9
1936........	264.2		106.9	66.7	668.2	127.3
1937........	285.7		105.0	64.3	672.6	126.7
1938........	270.3		97.2	53.9	691.4	133.1
1939........	290.6		97.9	55.9	683.8	120.0
1940........	316.8	83.1	99.5	57.8	684.1	115.8
1941........	363.1		96.6	57.3	650.0	107.4
1942........	404.9		90.8	56.3	568.0	116.3
1943........	445.6		90.0	55.8	560.1	120.9
1944........	480.6		87.2	51.6	578.8	115.4
1945........	473.7	72.0	87.7	49.3	613.6	125.5
1946........	433.6		92.6	48.8	693.5	133.4
1947........	429.7		100.6	52.8	762.2	135.8
1948........	453.0		98.7	48.1	801.3	133.1
1949........	446.7		93.0	41.3	803.4	140.1
1950........	490.6	74.7	91.5	38.5	824.5	130.5
1951........	522.1		92.9	37.0	872.0	122.0
1952........	540.7		88.8	32.1	879.9	119.4
1953........	563.2		87.8·	30.9	886.1	110.1
1954........	557.6		85.6	26.7	912.9	106.1
1955........	597.6	71.2	87.8	28.6	922.9	100.2

SOURCES: Energy consumption from Appendix Table VII. Gross national product from John W. Kendrick, *Productivity Trends in the United States* (New York: National Bureau of Economic Research, forthcoming). Kendrick measures GNP in 1929 dollars and expresses the index numbers with a 1929 base. In this study, Kendrick's indexes have been shifted to a 1900 comparison base.

TABLE XIV. VALUE OF MINERAL FUELS PRODUCTION, MEASURED IN CURRENT DOLLARS, 1880–1955

(Millions)

Year	Coal			Liquid and gaseous fuels					Total mineral fuels	
	Bituminous (1)	Anthracite (2)	Total (3)	Crude oil (4)	Natural gas ᵃ (5)	Total, crude oil and natural gas (6)	Natural gas liquids ᵇ (7)	Total (8)	Excluding natural gas liquids (9)	Including natural gas liquids (10)
1880	$ 63	$ 42	$ 105	$ 25	n.a.	n.a.			$ 130	
1885	81	77	158	19	$ 5	$ 24			182	
1890	110	66	176	35	17	52			228	
1895	116	82	198	58	10	68			266	
1900	221	85	306	76	17	93			399	
1901	237	113	350	67	15	82			432	
1902	291	76	367	71	16	87			454	
1903	351	152	503	94	17	111			614	
1904	307	139	446	101	18	119			565	
1905	334	142	476	84	18	102			578	
1906	381	132	513	92	18	110			623	
1907	450	164	614	120	21	141			755	
1908	372	158	530	129	21	150			680	
1909	406	149	555	128	24	152			707	
1910	467	161	628	128	27	155	n.a.	n.a.	783	n.a.
1911	451	176	627	134	29	163	ᶜ	$ 164	790	$ 790
1912	518	178	696	165	32	197	$ 1	198	893	894
1913	565	195	760	236	34	270	2	272	1,030	1,032
1914	495	188	683	215	36	251	3	254	934	937
1915	500	184	684	180	38	218	5	223	902	907

Year										
1916	663	202	865	331	46	377	14	391	1,242	1,256
1917	1,247	284	1,531	523	54	577	40	617	2,108	2,148
1918	1,495	336	1,831	705	58	763	50	813	2,594	2,644
1919	1,160	365	1,525	761	61	822	64	886	2,347	2,411
1920	2,133	435	2,568	1,360	76	1,436	72	1,508	4,004	4,076
1921	1,202	452	1,654	817	68	885	62	947	2,539	2,601
1922	1,275	274	1,549	898	86	984	73	1,057	2,533	2,606
1923	1,513	507	2,020	981	102	1,083	78	1,161	3,103	3,181
1924	1,064	477	1,541	1,021	108	1,129	82	1,211	2,670	2,752
1925	1,061	328	1,389	1,283	114	1,397	121	1,518	2,786	2,907
1926	1,181	475	1,656	1,449	127	1,576	136	1,712	3,232	3,368
1927	1,030	421	1,451	1,171	129	1,300	118	1,418	2,751	2,869
1928	931	393	1,324	1,055	142	1,197	140	1,337	2,521	2,661
1929	952	385	1,337	1,279	160	1,439	159	1,598	2,776	2,935
1930	795	355	1,150	1,069	150	1,219	129	1,348	2,369	2,498
1931	588	296	884	553	121	674	65	739	1,558	1,623
1932	406	222	628	683	102	785	50	835	1,413	1,463
1933	447	207	654	607	99	706	55	761	1,360	1,415
1934	629	244	873	908	109	1,017	62	1,079	1,890	1,952
1935	659	210	869	967	114	1,081	74	1,155	1,950	2,024
1936	773	227	1,000	1,199	122	1,321	89	1,410	2,321	2,410
1937	864	198	1,062	1,509	126	1,635	104	1,739	2,697	2,810
1938	680	181	861	1,372	116	1,488	93	1,581	2,349	2,442
1939	727	187	914	1,290	124	1,414	101	1,515	2,328	2,429
1940	880	205	1,085	1,380	123	1,503	77	1,580	2,588	2,665
1941	1,126	240	1,366	1,599	142	1,741	119	1,860	3,107	3,226
1942	1,375	271	1,646	1,650	160	1,810	123	1,933	3,456	3,579
1943	1,588	307	1,895	1,807	182	1,989	143	2,132	3,884	4,027
1944	1,809	355	2,164	2,030	195	2,225	181	2,406	4,389	4,570
1945	1,768	324	2,092	2,091	198	2,289	188	2,477	4,381	4,569

(Table continued on next page.)

TABLE XIV (continued)

Year	Coal			Liquid and gaseous fuels					Total mineral fuels	
	Bituminous (1)	Anthracite (2)	Total (3)	Crude oil (4)	Natural gas[a] (5)	Total, crude oil and natural gas (6)	Natural gas liquids[b] (7)	Total (8)	Excluding natural gas liquids (9)	Including natural gas liquids (10)
1946......	$1,837	$413	$2,250	$2,445	$220	$2,665	$180	$2,845	$4,915	$5,095
1947......	2,623	413	3,036	3,584	275	3,859	294	4,153	6,895	7,189
1948......	2,992	467	3,459	5,252	335	5,587	456	6,043	9,046	9,502
1949......	2,137	358	2,495	4,679	341	5,020	402	5,422	7,515	7,917
1950......	2,499	392	2,891	4,954	408	5,362	420	5,782	8,253	8,673
1951......	2,626	406	3,032	5,687	544	6,231	507	6,738	9,263	9,770
1952......	2,288	380	2,668	5,793	625	6,418	535	6,953	9,086	9,621
1953......	2,250	299	2,549	6,317	773	7,090	601	7,691	9,639	10,240
1954......	1,171	248	2,019	6,436	883	7,319	573	7,892	9,338	9,911
1955......	2,091	206	2,297	6,882	978	7,860	615	8,475	10,157	10,772

n.a. Not available.

[a] See Appendix Table XXIV, footnote b.
[b] See Appendix Table XXIV, footnote c.
[c] Less than $1 million.

SOURCES: Appendix Table I, columns 1 through 5, showing physical quantities of coal, crude oil, and natural gas produced (for natural gas liquids see introductory note to Appendix to Part I); Appendix Table XXIII, columns 1 and 4, showing average unit dollar values for coal f.o.b. mine; and Appendix Table XXIV, columns 1, 4, and 7, showing average unit dollar values for crude oil and natural gas at well and for natural gas liquids at plant.

TABLE XV. VALUE OF MINERAL FUELS PRODUCTION, MEASURED IN 1947 DOLLARS, 1870–1955

(Millions)

Year	Coal			Liquid and gaseous fuels					Total mineral fuels	
	Bituminous (1)	Anthracite (2)	Total (3)	Crude oil (4)	Natural gas[a] (5)	Total, crude oil and natural gas (6)	Natural gas liquids[b] (7)	Total (8)	Excluding natural gas liquids (9)	Including natural gas liquids (10)
1870	$ 85	$144	$ 229	$ 10	n.a.	n.a.			$ 239	
1875	136	167	303	17	n.a.	n.a.			320	
1880	211	207	418	51	n.a.	n.a.			469	
1885	299	277	576	42	$ 5	$ 47			623	
1890	463	336	799	88	14	102			901	
1895	562	419	981	102	8	110			1,091	
1900	883	414	1,297	123	14	137			1,434	
1901	939	487	1,426	134	16	150			1,576	
1902	1,083	299	1,382	171	17	188			1,570	
1903	1,176	539	1,715	194	18	212			1,927	
1904	1,159	528	1,687	226	19	245			1,932	
1905	1,311	561	1,872	260	21	281			2,153	
1906	1,426	515	1,941	244	23	267			2,208	
1907	1,642	618	2,260	321	24	345			2,605	
1908	1,384	601	1,985	345	24	369			2,354	
1909	1,580	585	2,165	354	29	383			2,548	
1910	1,735	610	2,345	404	31	435	n.a.	n.a.	2,780	n.a.
1911	1,689	653	2,342	425	31	456	[c]	$ 456	2,798	$2,798
1912	1,872	609	2,481	430	34	464	$ 1	465	2,945	2,946
1913	1,990	661	2,651	480	35	515	11	516	3,166	3,167
1914	1,758	656	2,414	513	36	549	2	551	2,963	2,965
1915	1,841	643	2,484	543	38	581	3	584	3,065	3,068

(Table continued on next page.)

TABLE XV (continued)

Year	Coal			Liquid and gaseous fuels					Total mineral fuels	
	Bituminous (1)	Anthracite (2)	Total (3)	Crude oil (4)	Natural gas (5)	Total, crude oil and natural gas (6)	Natural gas liquids [b] (7)	Total (8)	Excluding natural gas liquids (9)	Including natural gas liquids (10)
1916	$2,090	$632	$2,722	$ 580	$ 45	$ 625	$ 5	$ 630	$3,347	$3,352
1917	2,295	719	3,014	647	48	695	12	707	3,709	3,721
1918	2,410	714	3,124	687	43	730	15	745	3,854	3,869
1919	1,938	636	2,574	730	45	775	19	794	3,349	3,368
1920	2,366	647	3,013	855	49	904	20	924	3,917	3,937
1921	1,730	653	2,383	911	40	951	24	975	3,334	3,358
1922	1,757	395	2,152	1,076	47	1,123	27	1,150	3,275	3,302
1923	2,349	674	3,023	1,414	61	1,475	43	1,518	4,498	4,541
1924	2,012	635	2,647	1,378	70	1,448	50	1,498	4,095	4,145
1925	2,163	446	2,609	1,474	73	1,547	60	1,607	4,156	4,216
1926	2,385	610	2,995	1,488	80	1,568	72	1,640	4,563	4,635
1927	2,154	578	2,732	1,739	88	1,827	87	1,914	4,559	4,646
1928	2,083	544	2,627	1,740	96	1,836	96	1,932	4,463	4,559
1929	2,226	533	2,759	1,944	117	2,061	119	2,180	4,820	4,939
1930	1,945	501	2,446	1,733	119	1,852	118	1,970	4,298	4,416
1931	1,589	431	2,020	1,643	103	1,746	99	1,845	3,766	3,865
1932	1,288	360	1,648	1,515	96	1,611	83	1,694	3,259	3,342
1933	1,388	358	1,746	1,748	98	1,846	77	1,923	3,592	3,669
1934	1,495	413	1,908	1,753	109	1,862	84	1,946	3,770	3,854
1935	1,549	377	1,926	1,923	118	2,041	92	2,133	3,967	4,059
1936	1,827	394	2,221	2,122	134	2,256	101	2,357	4,477	4,578
1937	1,853	374	2,227	2,469	148	2,617	117	2,734	4,844	4,961
1938	1,450	333	1,783	2,344	141	2,485	123	2,608	4,268	4,391
1939	1,643	372	2,015	2,441	152	2,593	127	2,720	4,608	4,735
1940	1,917	372	2,289	2,612	164	2,776	141	2,917	5,065	5,206

1941	2,139	407	2,546	2,706	174	2,880	180	3,060	5,426	5,606
1942	2,424	436	2,860	2,676	189	2,865	186	3,051	5,725	5,911
1943	2,455	438	2,893	2,906	211	3,117	190	3,307	6,010	6,200
1944	2,577	560	3,037	3,238	229	3,467	223	3,690	6,504	6,727
1945	2,403	397	2,800	3,307	243	3,550	249	3,799	6,350	6,599
1946	2,221	437	2,658	3,347	249	3,596	258	3,854	6,254	6,512
1947	2,623	413	3,036	3,584	275	3,859	294	4,153	6,895	7,189
1948	2,494	413	2,907	3,899	309	4,208	327	4,535	7,115	7,442
1949	1,822	308	2,130	3,555	325	3,880	350	4,230	6,010	6,360
1950	2,148	318	2,466	3,809	377	4,186	405	4,591	6,652	7,057
1951	2,220	308	2,428	4,338	447	4,785	456	5,241	7,213	7,669
1952	1,942	293	2,235	4,419	481	4,900	498	5,398	7,135	7,663
1953	1,902	223	2,125	4,549	504	5,053	531	5,584	7,178	7,709
1954	1,629	210	1,839	4,468	525	4,993	552	5,545	6,832	7,384
1955	1,933	189	2,122	4,795	564	5,359	626	5,985	7,481	8,107

n.a. Not available.

[a] See Appendix Table XXIV, footnote b.
[b] See Appendix Table XXIV, footnote c.
[c] Less than $1 million.

SOURCES: Same as Appendix Table XIV.

TABLE XVI. VALUE OF MINERAL FUELS CONSUMPTION, MEASURED IN CURRENT DOLLARS, 1880–1955

(Millions)

Year	Coal Bitumi- nous (1)	Anthra- cite (2)	Total (3)	Liquid and gaseous fuels Crude oil[a] (4)	Natural gas[b] (5)	Natural gas liquids[c] (6)	Total (7)	Total mineral fuels (8)
1880.......	$ 64	$41	$105	$ 16	n.a.		n.a.	$ 121
1885.......	81	75	156	6	$ 5		$ 11	167
1890.......	110	65	175	21	17		38	213
1895.......	115	80	195	32	10		42	237
1900.......	215	83	298	47	17		64	362
1901.......	233	109	342	41	15		56	398
1902.......	288	75	363	50	16		66	429
1903.......	346	148	494	73	17		90	584
1904.......	300	134	434	79	17		96	530
1905.......	327	138	465	65	17		82	547
1906.......	373	127	500	70	18		88	588
1907.......	439	158	597	97	21		118	715
1908.......	362	152	514	102	21		123	637
1909.......	396	143	539	102	24		126	665
1910.......	455	154	609	106	27		133	742
1911.......	434	168	602	109	28	d	138	740
1912.......	500	169	669	135	32	$1	168	837
1913.......	542	185	727	198	33	2	233	960
1914.......	478	179	657	184	36	3	223	880
1915.......	480	176	656	156	38	5	199	855
1916.......	636	192	828	284	46	14	344	1,172
1917.......	1,193	267	1,460	472	54	40	566	2,026
1918.......	1,437	319	1,756	652	58	50	760	2,516
1919.......	1,111	344	1,455	748	61	64	873	2,328
1920.......	1,907	416	2,323	1,395	74	72	1,541	3,864
1921.......	1,132	410	1,542	798	65	62	925	2,467
1922.......	1,289	285	1,574	853	83	73	1,009	2,583
1923.......	1,391	472	1,863	869	98	78	1,045	2,908
1924.......	1,065	438	1,503	925	103	82	1,110	2,613
1925.......	1,018	340	1,358	1,203	108	121	1,432	2,790
1926.......	1,097	434	1,531	1,401	120	136	1,657	3,188
1927.......	995	393	1,388	981	122	117	1,220	2,608
1928.......	928	384	1,312	959	134	140	1,233	2,545
1929.......	925	373	1,298	1,155	142	159	1,456	2,754
1930.......	773	346	1,119	1,155	142	129	1,426	2,545
1931.......	573	290	863	555	114	65	734	1,597
1932.......	402	225	627	686	96	47	829	1,456
1933.......	426	207	633	558	96	51	705	1,338
1934.......	602	237	839	829	103	59	991	1,830
1935.......	631	206	837	917	108	69	1,094	1,931

TABLE XVI (continued)

Year	Coal			Liquid and gaseous fuels				Total mineral fuels (8)
	Bitumi- nous (1)	Anthra- cite (2)	Total (3)	Crude oil [a] (4)	Natural gas [b] (5)	Natural gas liquids [c] (6)	Total (7)	
1936........	$ 719	$221	$ 940	$1,148	$115	$84	$1,347	$2,287
1937........	836	192	1,028	1,340	119	95	1,554	2,582
1938........	656	177	833	1,255	109	82	1,446	2,279
1939........	692	181	873	1,200	117	94	1,411	2,284
1940........	823	196	1,019	1,311	116	73	1,500	2,519
1941........	1,078	225	1,303	1,608	132	119	1,859	3,162
1942........	1,275	254	1,529	1,569	149	120	1,838	3,367
1943........	1,597	289	1,886	1,697	171	142	2,010	3,896
1944........	1,722	331	2,053	1,919	181	179	2,279	4,332
1945........	1,712	304	2,016	2,027	183	186	2,396	4,412
1946........	1,721	368	2,089	2,419	204	172	2,795	4,884
1947........	2,271	348	2,619	3,583	254	285	4,122	6,741
1948........	2,594	410	3,004	5,337	308	437	6,082	9,086
1949........	2,174	316	2,490	4,998	313	385	5,696	8,186
1950........	2,198	355	2,553	5,473	375	413	6,261	8,814
1951........	2,307	352	2,659	6,069	497	496	7,062	9,721
1952........	2,052	330	2,382	6,245	569	526	7,340	9,722
1953........	2,100	271	2,371	6,941	703	585	8,229	10,600
1954........	1,641	229	1,870	7,201	813	556	8,570	10,440
1955........	1,905	185	2,090	7,764	905	606	9,275	11,365

n.a. Not available.

[a] Including net imports of oil products, see Appendix Table XXIV, footnote a.

[b] See Table XXIV, footnote b.

[c] See Table XXIV, footnote c.

[d] Less than $1 million.

SOURCES: Appendix Table VI, columns 1 through 6, showing physical quantities consumed; Appendix Table XXIII, columns 1 and 4, showing average unit dollar values for coal f.o.b. mines; and Appendix Table XXIV, columns 1, 4 and 7, showing average unit dollar values for crude oil and natural gas at well and for natural gas liquids at plant.

TABLE XVII. VALUE OF MINERAL FUELS CONSUMPTION, MEASURED
IN 1947 DOLLARS, 1870–1955

(Millions)

Year	Coal			Liquid and gaseous fuels				Total mineral fuels (8)
	Bitumi-nous (1)	Anthra-cite (2)	Total (3)	Crude oil [a] (4)	Natural gas [b] (5)	Natural gas liquids [c] (6)	Total (7)	
1870.........	$ 87	$143	$ 230	$ 4	n.a.		n.a.	$ 234
1875.........	137	164	301	4	n.a.		n.a.	305
1880.........	212	204	416	33	n.a.		n.a.	449
1885.........	299	272	571	14	$ 5		$ 19	590
1890.........	461	329	790	53	14		67	857
1895.........	557	409	966	57	8		65	1,031
1900.........	862	401	1,263	76	14		90	1,353
1901.........	922	471	1,393	83	16		99	1,492
1902.........	1,069	293	1,362	121	17		138	1,500
1903.........	1,162	524	1,686	149	18		167	1,853
1904.........	1,136	511	1,647	178	18		196	1,843
1905.........	1,285	543	1,828	203	21		224	2,052
1906.........	1,396	497	1,893	185	23		208	2,101
1907.........	1,600	596	2,196	260	24		284	2,480
1908.........	1,346	579	1,925	273	24		297	2,222
1909.........	1,538	562	2,100	281	29		310	2,410
1910.........	1,692	586	2,278	335	30	n.a.	365	2,643
1911.........	1,627	624	2,251	346	30	d	376	2,628
1912.........	1,810	579	2,389	352	33	$ 1	386	2,775
1913.........	1,911	627	2,538	403	35	1	439	2,977
1914.........	1,699	625	2,324	439	35	2	476	2,800
1915.........	1,768	614	2,382	469	38	3	510	2,892
1916.........	2,006	599	2,605	498	45	5	548	3,153
1917.........	2,197	676	2,873	584	47	12	643	3,516
1918.........	2,316	678	2,994	636	43	15	694	3,688
1919.........	1,856	601	2,457	718	44	19	781	3,238
1920.........	2,116	619	2,735	877	47	20	944	3,679
1921.........	1,630	592	2,222	891	39	24	954	3,176
1922.........	1,776	410	2,186	1,022	45	27	1,094	3,280
1923.........	2,159	628	2,787	1,252	59	43	1,354	4,141
1924.........	2,013	583	2,596	1,248	67	50	1,365	3,961
1925.........	2,077	463	2,540	1,382	69	60	1,511	4,051
1926.........	2,216	558	2,774	1,438	76	72	1,586	4,360
1927.........	2,079	539	2,618	1,456	83	86	1,625	4,243
1928.........	2,075	532	2,607	1,582	90	97	1,769	4,376
1929.........	2,161	516	2,677	1,755	110	119	1,984	4,661
1930.........	1,893	488	2,381	1,874	112	118	2,104	4,485
1931.........	1,547	422	1,969	1,649	97	98	1,844	3,813
1932.........	1,277	365	1,642	1,521	90	78	1,689	3,331
1933.........	1,322	358	1,680	1,607	90	71	1,768	3,448
1934.........	1,430	401	1,831	1,599	103	81	1,783	3,614
1935.........	1,482	369	1,851	1,826	111	86	2,023	3,874

TABLE XVII (continued)

Year	Coal			Liquid and gaseous fuels				Total mineral fuels (8)
	Bitumi-nous (1)	Anthra-cite (2)	Total (3)	Crude oil[a] (4)	Natural gas[b] (5)	Natural gas liquids[c] (6)	Total (7)	
1936.........	$1,698	$384	$2,082	$2,033	$126	$ 94	$2,253	$4,335
1937.........	1,792	364	2,156	2,191	140	107	2,438	4,594
1938.........	1,399	326	1,725	2,144	133	109	2,386	4,111
1939.........	1,565	359	1,924	2,271	143	119	2,533	4,457
1940.........	1,793	354	2,147	2,480	155	134	2,769	4,916
1941.........	2,047	380	2,427	2,723	161	180	3,064	5,491
1942.........	2,247	408	2,655	2,545	176	182	2,903	5,558
1943.........	2,470	412	2,882	2,729	197	188	3,114	5,996
1944.........	2,453	429	2,882	3,061	213	221	3,495	6,377
1945.........	2,328	373	2,701	3,207	224	247	3,678	6,379
1946.........	2,082	389	2,471	3,311	231	247	3,789	6,260
1947.........	2,271	348	2,619	3,583	254	285	4,122	6,741
1948.........	2,163	362	2,525	3,962	284	313	4,559	7,084
1949.........	1,853	272	2,125	3,797	298	334	4,429	6,554
1950.........	1,889	288	2,177	4,208	346	398	4,952	7,129
1951.........	1,951	267	2,218	4,629	409	446	5,484	7,702
1952.........	1,742	255	1,997	4,764	438	489	5,691	7,688
1953.........	1,775	202	1,977	4,999	458	516	5,973	7,950
1954.........	1,552	194	1,746	4,999	483	536	6,018	7,764
1955.........	1,761	170	1,931	5,410	522	618	6,550	8,481

n.a. Not available.

[a] Including net imports of oil products, see Appendix Table XXIV, footnote a.
[b] See Table XXIV, footnote b.
[c] See Table XXIV, footnote c.
[d] Less than $1 million.

SOURCES: Same as Appendix Table XVI.

TABLE XVIII. VALUE OF SPECIFIC MINERAL FUELS AS PERCENTAGES
OF THE VALUE OF TOTAL MINERAL FUELS CONSUMPTION, 1880–1955

(Based on average unit prices in current dollars)

| Year | Coal | | | Liquid and gaseous fuels | | | | Total mineral fuels (8) |
	Bitumi-nous (1)	Anthra-cite (2)	Total (3)	Crude oil (4)	Natural gas (5)	Natural gas liquids (6)	Total (7)	
1880...........	52.9%	33.9%	86.8%	13.2%	n.a.		13.2%	100.0%
1885...........	48.5	44.9	93.4	3.6	3.0%		6.6	100.0
1890...........	51.6	30.5	82.2	9.9	8.0		17.8	100.0
1895...........	48.5	33.8	82.3	13.5	4.2		17.7	100.0
1900...........	59.4	22.9	82.3	13.0	4.7		17.7	100.0
1901...........	58.5	27.4	85.9	10.3	3.8		14.1	100.0
1902...........	67.1	17.5	84.6	11.7	3.7		15.4	100.0
1903...........	59.2	25.3	84.6	12.5	2.9		15.4	100.0
1904...........	56.6	25.3	81.9	14.9	3.2		18.1	100.0
1905...........	59.8	25.2	85.0	11.9	3.1		15.0	100.0
1906...........	63.4	21.6	85.0	11.9	3.1		15.0	100.0
1907...........	61.4	22.1	83.5	13.6	2.9		16.5	100.0
1908...........	56.8	23.9	80.7	16.0	3.3		19.3	100.0
1909...........	59.6	21.5	81.1	15.3	3.6		18.9	100.0
1910...........	61.3	20.8	82.1	14.3	3.6		17.9	100.0
1911...........	58.7	22.7	81.4	14.7	3.8	.1%	18.6	100.0
1912...........	59.7	20.2	79.9	16.1	3.8	.1	20.1	100.0
1913...........	56.5	19.3	75.7	20.6	3.4	.2	24.3	100.0
1914...........	54.3	20.3	74.7	20.9	4.1	.3	25.3	100.0
1915...........	56.1	20.6	76.7	18.2	4.4	.6	23.3	100.0
1916...........	54.3	16.4	70.6	24.2	3.9	1.2	29.4	100.0
1917...........	58.9	13.2	72.1	23.3	2.7	2.0	27.9	100.0
1918...........	57.1	12.7	69.8	25.9	2.3	2.0	30.2	100.0
1919...........	47.7	14.8	62.5	32.1	2.6	2.7	37.5	100.0
1920...........	49.4	10.8	60.1	36.1	1.9	1.9	39.9	100.0
1921...........	45.9	16.6	62.5	32.3	2.6	2.5	37.5	100.0
1922...........	49.9	11.0	60.9	33.0	3.2	2.8	39.1	100.0
1923...........	47.8	16.2	64.1	29.9	3.4	2.7	35.9	100.0
1924...........	40.8	16.8	57.5	35.4	3.9	3.1	42.5	100.0
1925...........	36.5	12.2	48.7	43.1	3.9	4.3	51.3	100.0
1926...........	34.4	13.6	48.0	43.9	3.8	4.3	52.0	100.0
1927...........	38.2	15.1	53.2	37.6	4.7	4.5	46.8	100.0
1928...........	36.5	15.1	51.6	37.7	5.3	5.5	48.4	100.0
1929...........	33.6	13.5	47.1	41.9	5.2	5.8	52.9	100.0
1930...........	30.4	13.6	44.0	45.4	5.6	5.1	56.0	100.0
1931...........	35.9	18.2	54.0	34.8	7.1	4.1	46.0	100.0
1932...........	27.6	15.5	43.1	47.1	6.6	3.2	56.9	100.0
1933...........	31.8	15.5	47.3	41.7	7.2	3.8	52.7	100.0
1934...........	32.9	13.0	45.8	45.3	5.6	3.2	54.2	100.0
1935...........	32.7	10.7	43.3	47.5	5.6	3.6	56.7	100.0

TABLE XVIII (continued)

Year	Coal			Liquid and gaseous fuels				Total mineral fuels (8)
	Bitumi-nous (1)	Anthra-cite (2)	Total (3)	Crude oil (4)	Natural gas (5)	Natural gas liquids (6)	Total (7)	
1936	31.4%	9.7%	41.1%	50.2%	5.0%	3.7%	58.9%	100.0%
1937	32.4	7.4	39.8	51.9	4.6	3.7	60.2	100.0
1938	28.8	7.8	36.6	55.1	4.8	3.6	63.4	100.0
1939	30.3	7.9	38.2	52.5	5.1	4.1	61.8	100.0
1940	32.7	7.8	40.5	52.0	4.6	2.9	59.5	100.0
1941	34.1	7.1	41.2	50.9	4.2	3.8	58.8	100.0
1942	37.9	7.5	45.4	46.6	4.4	3.6	54.6	100.0
1943	41.0	7.4	48.4	43.6	4.4	3.6	51.6	100.0
1944	39.8	7.6	47.4	44.3	4.2	4.1	52.6	100.0
1945	38.8	6.9	45.7	45.9	4.1	4.2	54.3	100.0
1946	35.2	7.5	42.8	49.5	4.2	3.5	57.2	100.0
1947	33.7	5.2	38.9	53.2	3.8	4.2	61.1	100.0
1948	28.5	4.5	33.1	58.7	3.4	4.8	66.9	100.0
1949	26.6	3.9	30.4	61.1	3.8	4.7	69.6	100.0
1950	24.9	4.0	29.0	62.1	4.3	4.7	71.0	100.0
1951	23.7	3.6	27.4	62.4	5.1	5.1	72.6	100.0
1952	21.1	3.4	24.5	64.2	5.9	5.4	75.5	100.0
1953	19.8	2.6	22.4	65.5	6.6	5.5	77.6	100.0
1954	15.7	2.2	17.9	69.0	7.8	5.3	82.1	100.0
1955	16.8	1.6	18.4	68.3	8.0	5.3	81.6	100.0

n.a. Not available.

SOURCE: Appendix Table XVI.

TABLE XIX. VALUE OF MINERAL FUELS PRODUCTION AND CONSUMPTION AS A PERCENTAGE OF GROSS NATIONAL PRODUCT, 1880–1955

(Measured in current dollars)

Year	Production, excluding natural gas liquids (1)	Production, including natural gas liquids (2)	Consumption, including natural gas liquids (3)
1880	1.19%	1.19%	1.11%
1885	1.65	1.65	1.52
1890	1.74	1.74	1.63
1895	1.91	1.91	1.71
1900	2.13	2.13	1.94
1901	2.09	2.09	1.92
1902	2.10	2.10	1.99
1903	2.68	2.68	2.55
1904	2.47	2.47	2.31
1905	2.30	2.30	2.18
1906	2.17	2.17	2.05
1907	2.48	2.48	2.35
1908	2.45	2.45	2.30
1909	2.20	2.20	2.07
1910	2.34	2.34	2.22

(*Table continued on next page.*)

TABLE XIX (continued)

Year	Production, excluding natural gas liquids (1)	Production, including natural gas liquids (2)	Consumption, including natural gas liquids (3)
1911	2.30%	2.30%	2.16%
1912	2.39	2.40	2.24
1913	2.63	2.64	2.46
1914	2.57	2.57	2.42
1915	2.33	2.34	2.21
1916	2.49	2.52	2.35
1917	3.52	3.59	3.38
1918	3.40	3.47	3.30
1919	2.97	3.06	2.95
1920	4.50	4.58	4.35
1921	3.44	3.52	3.34
1922	3.42	3.52	3.49
1923	3.60	3.69	3.38
1924	3.05	3.14	2.98
1925	3.05	3.18	3.06
1926	3.31	3.45	3.26
1927	2.86	2.98	2.71
1928	2.57	2.71	2.59
1929	2.66	2.81	2.64
1930	2.60	2.74	2.79
1931	2.04	2.13	2.09
1932	2.42	2.50	2.49
1933	2.43	2.53	2.39
1934	2.91	3.00	2.82
1935	2.69	2.79	2.66
1936	2.81	2.91	2.77
1937	2.97	3.08	2.84
1938	2.76	2.87	2.67
1939	2.56	2.67	2.51
1940	2.57	2.65	2.50
1941	2.47	2.56	2.51
1942	2.17	2.25	2.12
1943	2.02	2.09	2.02
1944	2.08	2.16	2.05
1945	2.05	2.14	2.07
1946	2.35	2.44	2.33
1947	2.97	3.10	2.90
1948	3.52	3.69	3.53
1949	2.92	3.08	3.18
1950	2.89	3.04	3.09
1951	2.82	2.98	2.96
1952	2.63	2.79	2.81
1953	2.65	2.82	2.92
1954	2.59	2.75	2.89
1955	2.60	2.76	2.91

SOURCES: Value of mineral fuels production and consumption in current dollars: Appendix Tables XIV and XVI. Estimates of GNP in current dollars, 1880–1928 series developed by John Kendrick in *Productivity Trends in the United States* (New York: National Bureau of Economic Research, forthcoming); 1929–55: Commerce, various issues of *Survey of Current Business* and *National Income Supplement to the Survey of Current Business*.

TABLE XX.   VALUE OF MINERAL FUELS AS A PERCENTAGE OF THE
VALUE OF TOTAL MINERALS PRODUCTION, 1880–1955

(Measured in current dollars)

Year	Mineral fuels[a]	Year	Mineral fuels[a]
1880....................	41.80%	1926....................	63.42%
1885....................	48.79	1927....................	61.07
1890....................	45.97	1928....................	59.34
1895....................	48.10	1929....................	59.80
1900....................	43.99	1930....................	62.76
1901....................	45.47	1931....................	62.96
1902....................	45.26	1932....................	73.15
1903....................	51.38	1933....................	69.02
1904....................	49.22	1934....................	71.14
1905....................	44.84	1935....................	68.80
1906....................	42.58	1936....................	66.83
1907....................	46.23	1937....................	65.67
1908....................	49.24	1938....................	69.41
1909....................	46.15	1939....................	63.79
1910....................	47.11	1940....................	63.48
1911....................	48.51	1941....................	63.17
1912....................	48.06	1942....................	63.65
1913....................	50.69	1943....................	67.90
1914....................	51.65	1944....................	72.42
1915....................	45.08	1945....................	73.33
1916....................	43.07	1946....................	72.15
1917....................	53.16	1947....................	74.81
1918....................	59.14	1948....................	77.42
1919....................	61.71	1949....................	74.83
1920....................	68.31	1950....................	73.12
1921....................	69.81	1951....................	71.88
1922....................	64.33	1952....................	71.84
1923....................	62.18	1953....................	71.17
1924....................	59.74	1954....................	70.50
1925....................	60.41	1955....................	68.18

[a] Includes bituminous coal, anthracite, crude oil, natural gas, and natural gas liquids.

SOURCE: Appendix Table XIV, column 10. Value of mineral fuels production underlying
this table differs from the series in the Bureau of Census *Historical Statistics of the
United States, Colonial Times to 1957* (1960), because: (1) Natural gas was valued
at the well throughout (see Appendix Table XXIV, footnote b); in the *Historical
Statistics (ibid.)* series it was valued at point of consumption prior to 1925. In 1924,
this resulted in a discrepancy of $246 million, or 5.3 per cent of the total mineral fuels
production. In computing the percentage share of mineral fuels the value of total
minerals production was reduced correspondingly. (2) Total value shown in Appendix
Table XIV is the sum of the components listed whereas the *Historical Statistics (ibid.)*
mineral fuels series includes additional products (such as peat) not shown separately.
These discrepancies are minor. (3) Additional minor discrepancies are due to slightly
different data for physical quantities produced, as for instance for coal in 1880 and
natural gas liquids prior to 1941, and to rounding.

TABLE XXI. INDEXES OF TOTAL MINERAL FUELS PRODUCTION AND
CONSUMPTION, BASED ON 1947 PRICE WEIGHTS, 1870–1955

(1900 = 100)

Year	Production, excluding natural gas liquids (1)	Production, including natural gas liquids (2)	Consumption, including natural gas liquids (3)
1870..............	16.7	16.7	17.3
1875..............	22.3	22.3	22.5
1880..............	32.7	32.7	33.2
1885..............	43.4	43.4	43.6
1890..............	62.8	62.8	63.3
1895..............	76.1	76.1	76.2
1900..............	100.0	100.0	100.0
1901..............	109.9	109.9	110.3
1902..............	109.5	109.5	110.9
1903..............	134.4	134.4	137.0
1904..............	134.7	134.7	136.2
1905..............	150.1	150.1	151.7
1906..............	154.0	154.0	155.3
1907..............	181.7	181.7	183.3
1908..............	164.2	164.2	164.2
1909..............	177.7	177.7	178.1
1910..............	193.9	193.9	195.3
1911..............	195.1	195.2	194.2
1912..............	205.4	205.4	205.1
1913..............	220.8	220.9	220.0
1914..............	206.6	206.8	206.9
1915..............	213.7	213.9	213.7
1916..............	233.4	233.8	233.0
1917..............	258.6	259.5	259.9
1918..............	268.8	269.8	272.6
1919..............	233.5	234.9	239.3
1920..............	273.2	274.5	271.9
1921..............	232.5	234.2	234.7
1922..............	228.4	230.3	242.4
1923..............	313.7	316.7	306.1
1924..............	285.6	289.1	292.8
1925..............	289.8	294.0	299.4
1926..............	318.2	323.2	322.2
1927..............	317.9	324.0	313.6
1928..............	311.2	317.9	323.4
1929..............	336.1	344.4	344.5
1930..............	299.7	307.9	331.5
1931..............	262.6	269.5	281.8
1932..............	227.3	233.1	246.2
1933..............	250.5	255.9	254.8
1934..............	262.9	268.8	267.1
1935..............	276.6	283.1	286.3

TABLE XXI (continued)

Year	Production, excluding natural gas liquids (1)	Production, including natural gas liquids (2)	Consumption, including natural gas liquids (3)
1936...............	312.2	319.2	320.4
1937...............	337.8	346.0	339.5
1938...............	297.6	306.2	303.8
1939...............	321.3	330.2	329.4
1940...............	353.2	363.0	363.3
1941...............	378.4	390.9	405.8
1942...............	399.2	412.2	410.8
1943...............	419.1	432.4	443.2
1944...............	453.6	469.1	471.3
1945...............	442.8	460.2	471.5
1946...............	436.1	454.1	462.7
1947...............	480.8	501.3	498.2
1948...............	496.2	519.0	523.6
1949...............	419.1	443.5	484.4
1950...............	463.9	492.1	526.9
1951...............	503.0	534.8	569.3
1952...............	497.6	532.3	568.2
1953...............	500.6	537.6	587.6
1954...............	476.4	514.9	573.8
1955...............	521.7	565.3	626.8

SOURCES: Appendix Tables XV and XVII.

TABLE XXII. ILLUSTRATIVE CALCULATIONS OF PRODUCTION INDEXES OF MINERAL FUELS BASED ON ALTERNATIVE PRICE WEIGHTS (EXCLUDING NATURAL GAS LIQUIDS)

| Fuel | 1900 (1) | 1929 (2) | 1947 (3) | 1955 (4) | Columns 1 through 4 expressed as index numbers | | | |
					1900 (5)	1929 (6)	1947 (7)	1955 (8)
	Value of production in 1900 prices (production in given year, multiplied by unit prices in 1900; thousand 1900 dollars)				(Index—1900 price weights)			
Bituminous coal	$ 220,809	$ 556,389	$ 655,849	$ 483,219				
Anthracite	85,478	110,004	85,213	39,038				
Crude oil	75,709	1,198,714	2,209,815	2,956,469				
Natural gas	16,827	138,604	325,334	667,780				
Total	$ 398,823	$2,003,711	$3,276,211	$4,146,506	100.0	502.4	821.5	1,039.7
	Value of production in 1929 prices (production in given year, multiplied by unit prices in 1929; thousand 1929 dollars)				(Index—1929 price weights)			
Bituminous coal	$ 377,922	$ 952,280	$1,122,511	$ 827,049				
Anthracite	299,461	385,382	298,532	136,764				
Crude oil	80,799	1,279,300	2,358,373	3,155,224				
Natural gas	19,434	160,078	375,738	771,239				
Total	$ 777,616	$2,777,040	$4,155,154	$4,890,276	100.0	357.1	534.3	628.9
	Value of production in 1947 prices (production in given year, multiplied by unit prices in 1947; thousand 1947 dollars)				(Index—1947 price weights)			
Bituminous coal	$ 883,235	$2,225,554	$2,623,396	$1,932,877				
Anthracite	414,197	533,038	412,912	189,164				
Crude oil	122,789	1,944,133	3,583,985	4,794,946				
Natural gas	14,220	117,130	274,930	564,321				
Total	$1,434,441	$4,819,855	$6,895,223	$7,481,308	100.0	336.0	480.7	521.5

Value of production in 1955 prices (production in given year, multiplied by unit prices in 1955; thousand 1955 dollars)

	1900	1929	1947	1955	(Index—1955 price weights)			
					1900	1929	1947	1955
Bituminous coal	$ 955,422	$2,407,451	$2,837,808	$2,090,853				
Anthracite	450,912	580,288	449,513	205,932				
Crude oil	176,230	2,790,285	5,143,854	6,881,866				
Natural gas	24,648	203,025	476,546	978,157				
Total	$1,607,212	$5,981,049	$8,907,721	$10,156,808	100.0	372.1	554.2	632.0

UNDERLYING QUANTITIES AND PRICES USED IN ABOVE CALCULATIONS

Fuel	Unit	Quantities produced				Unit	Unit prices (dollars)			
		1900	1929	1947	1955		1900	1929	1947	1955
Bituminous coal	Thous. tons	212,316	534,989	630,624	464,634	Per net ton	$1.04	$1.78	$4.16	$4.50
Anthracite	Thous. tons	57,368	73,828	57,190	26,200	Per net ton	1.49	5.22	7.22	7.86
Crude oil	Thous. bbl.	63,621	1,007,323	1,856,987	2,484,428	Per barrel	1.19	1.27	1.93	2.77
Natural gas	Mill. cu. ft.	237,000	1,952,166	4,582,173	9,405,351	Per thous. cu. ft.	0.071	0.082	0.060	0.104

SOURCES: Appendix Table I, showing physical quantities produced; and Appendix Tables XXIII and XXIV, showing average unit values in current dollars.

NOTE: The purpose of the above calculations is to illustrate how the index of the physical volume of aggregate mineral fuels production varies according to the year to which the price weights refer. Changes in the composition of the mineral fuels basket combined with changes in the average unit prices of specific fuel materials result in the following indexes:

Index of the physical volume of aggregate mineral fuels production

	1900	1955
1900 price weights	100.0	1,039.7
1929 price weights	100.0	628.9
1947 price weights*	100.0	521.5
1955 price weights	100.0	632.0
An index constructed by linking overlapping segments, computed with different sets of price weights, results in:**	100.0	739.0
An index based on constant Btu weights for specific fuels results in:***	100.0	490.0

(Note continued on next page.)

TABLE XXII (continued)

Since between 1900 and 1955 the unit prices of crude oil and natural gas rose much less than those of coal (see Tables XXIII and XXIV), while the relative share of oil and gas in total mineral fuels production expanded greatly (see Table IV), the index based on 1900 price weights shows a much steeper rise than those based on price weights of later years.

Of the various price weights tested, those of 1947 result in an index of the physical volume of aggregate mineral fuels production which is closest to the index based on Btu weights (521.5 compared to 490.0 for 1955). This is fortuitous and reflects the fact that at that time the divergent movements of the relative quantities of specific fuels produced and of average unit prices of specific fuels happened nearly to offset each other, so that in 1947 prices, the value of an average unit of the mineral fuels basket in the composition prevailing in the 1950's was very close to the value of an average unit produced at the beginning of the century, which had a very different composition.

* These calculations (based on value figures rounded to thousand dollars) are more exact than those underlying Table XXI (which is based on value figures rounded to million dollars). Therefore, they result in slightly different index numbers:

	This table	Table XXI
1929	336.0	336.1
1947	480.7	480.8
1955	521.5	521.7

** This index was originally presented by Y. S. Leong in the *Journal of the American Statistical Association*, March 1950, Vol. 45, pp. 15–29. It was brought up to date by Robert E. Herman, of the Office of Chief Economist, Bureau of Mines; cf. *Minerals Yearbook, 1956*, Vol. I, pp. 2–5.

*** See Appendix Table V, column 7.

TABLE XXIII.   COAL: PRICES AND PRICE INDEXES, 1880–1955

(Index: 1947 = 100)

Year	Bituminous coal			Anthracite		
	Average price, $ per net ton^a (1)	Index (2)	Index relative to wholesale price index (3)	Average price, $ per net ton^a (4)	Index (5)	Index relative to wholesale price index (6)
1880..........	$1.25	30.0		$1.47	20.4	
1885..........	1.13	27.2		2.00	27.7	
1890..........	0.99	23.8		1.43	19.8	
1895..........	0.86	20.7		1.41	19.5	
1900..........	1.04	25.0	66.0	1.49	20.6	54.4
1901..........	1.05	25.2	67.7	1.67	23.1	62.1
1902..........	1.12	26.9	67.8	1.84	25.5	64.2
1903..........	1.24	29.8	74.3	2.04	28.3	70.6
1904..........	1.10	26.4	65.7	1.90	26.3	65.4
1905..........	1.06	25.5	62.8	1.83	25.3	62.3
1906..........	1.11	26.7	64.0	1.85	25.6	61.4
1907..........	1.14	27.4	62.3	1.91	26.5	60.2
1908..........	1.12	26.9	63.4	1.90	26.3	62.0
1909..........	1.07	25.7	56.5	1.84	25.5	56.0
1910..........	1.12	26.9	56.6	1.90	26.3	55.4
1911..........	1.11	26.7	61.0	1.94	26.9	61.4
1912..........	1.15	27.6	59.2	2.11	29.2	62.7
1913..........	1.18	28.4	60.3	2.13	29.5	62.6
1914..........	1.17	28.1	61.1	2.07	28.7	62.4
1915..........	1.13	27.2	58.0	2.07	28.7	61.2
1916..........	1.32	31.7	54.9	2.31	32.0	55.5
1917..........	2.26	54.3	68.5	2.85	39.5	49.8
1918..........	2.58	62.0	70.1	3.40	47.1	53.2
1919..........	2.49	59.9	64.1	4.14	57.3	61.3
1920..........	3.75	90.1	86.6	4.85	67.2	64.6
1921..........	2.89	69.5	105.6	5.00	69.3	105.3
1922..........	3.02	72.6	111.3	5.01	69.4	106.4
1923..........	2.68	64.4	95.0	5.43	75.2	110.9
1924..........	2.20	52.9	79.9	5.43	75.2	113.6
1925..........	2.04	49.0	70.2	5.30	73.4	105.2
1926..........	2.06	49.5	73.4	5.62	77.8	115.4
1927..........	1.99	47.8	74.3	5.26	72.9	113.4
1928..........	1.86	44.7	68.6	5.22	72.3	110.9
1929..........	1.78	42.8	66.7	5.22	72.3	112.6
1930..........	1.70	40.9	70.3	5.11	70.8	121.6
1931..........	1.54	37.0	75.2	4.97	68.8	139.8
1932..........	1.31	31.5	72.1	4.46	61.8	141.4
1933..........	1.34	32.2	72.5	4.17	57.8	130.2
1934..........	1.75	42.1	83.4	4.27	59.1	117.0
1935..........	1.77	42.5	78.8	4.03	55.8	103.5
1936..........	1.76	42.3	77.6	4.16	57.6	105.7
1937..........	1.94	46.6	80.1	3.81	52.8	90.7
1938..........	1.95	46.9	88.5	3.92	54.3	102.5
1939..........	1.84	44.2	85.0	3.64	50.4	96.9
1940..........	1.91	45.9	86.6	3.99	55.3	104.3

(Table continued on next page.)

TABLE XXIII (continued)

Year	Bituminous coal			Anthracite		
	Average price, $ per net ton [a] (1)	Index (2)	Index relative to wholesale price index (3)	Average price, $ per net ton [a] (4)	Index (5)	Index relative to wholesale price index (6)
1941...........	$2.19	52.6	89.3	$4.26	59.0	100.2
1942...........	2.36	57.5	86.3	4.50	62.3	93.5
1943...........	2.69	64.7	93.1	5.06	70.1	100.9
1944...........	2.92	70.2	100.1	5.57	77.1	110.0
1945...........	3.06	73.6	103.1	5.90	81.7	114.4
1946...........	3.44	82.7	101.3	6.83	94.6	115.9
1947...........	4.16	100.0	100.0	7.22	100.0	100.0
1948...........	4.99	120.0	110.8	8.17	113.2	104.5
1949...........	4.88	117.3	114.0	8.38	116.1	112.8
1950...........	4.84	116.3	108.7	8.90	123.3	115.2
1951...........	4.92	118.3	99.3	9.51	131.7	110.6
1952...........	4.90	117.8	101.7	9.36	129.6	111.9
1953...........	4.92	118.3	103.6	9.67	133.9	117.3
1954...........	4.52	108.7	95.0	8.52	118.0	103.1
1955...........	4.50	108.2	94.3	7.86	108.9	94.9

[a] Average values, f.o.b. mines.

SOURCES: Columns 1 and 4, USGS and Mines, *Mineral Resources of the United States* and *Minerals Yearbook*, various issues. Columns 3 and 6, based on BLS Wholesale Price Index for All Commodities (shifted to 1947 = 100).

TABLE XXIV. LIQUID AND GASEOUS FUELS: PRICES AND PRICE INDEXES, 1880–1955

(Index: 1947 = 100)

Year	Crude oil			Natural gas			Natural gas liquids		
	Average price, $ per barrel [a] (1)	Index (2)	Index relative to wholesale price index (3)	Average price, ¢ per cu. ft. [b] (4)	Index (5)	Index relative to wholesale price index (6)	Average price, ¢ per gallon [c] (7)	Index (8)	Index relative to wholesale price index (9)
1880...	$0.94	48.7		n.a.	n.a.				
1885...	0.88	45.6		7.0¢	116.7				
1890...	0.77	39.9		7.0	116.7				
1895...	1.09	56.5		7.0	116.7				
1900...	1.19	61.7	162.8	7.1	118.3	312.1			
1901...	0.96	49.7	133.6	5.7	95.0	255.4			
1902...	0.80	41.5	104.5	5.7	95.0	239.3			
1903...	0.94	48.7	121.4	5.7	95.0	236.9			
1904...	0.86	44.6	110.9	5.7	95.0	236.3			
1905...	0.62	32.1	79.1	5.0	83.3	205.2			
1906...	0.73	37.8	90.6	4.6	76.7	183.9			
1907...	0.72	37.3	84.8	5.1	85.0	193.2			
1908...	0.72	37.3	88.0	5.2	86.7	204.5			
1909...	0.70	36.3	79.8	5.0	83.3	183.1			
1910...	0.61	31.6	66.5	5.3	88.3	185.9			

TABLE XXIV (continued)

Year	Crude oil			Natural gas			Natural gas liquids		
	Average price, $ per barrel [a] (1)	Index (2)	Index relative to wholesale price index (3)	Average price, ¢ per cu. ft. [b] (4)	Index (5)	Index relative to wholesale price index (6)	Average price, ¢ per gallon [c] (7)	Index (8)	Index relative to wholesale price index (9)
1911...	0.61	31.6	72.1	5.6	93.3	213.0	7.2¢	135.8	310.0
1912...	0.74	38.3	82.2	5.7	95.0	203.9	9.6	181.1	388.6
1913...	0.95	49.2	104.5	5.8	96.7	205.3	10.2	192.5	408.7
1914...	0.81	42.0	91.3	6.1	101.7	221.1	7.3	137.7	299.3
1915...	0.64	33.2	70.8	6.1	101.7	216.8	7.9	149.1	317.9
1916...	1.10	57.0	98.8	6.1	101.7	176.3	13.8	260.4	451.3
1917...	1.56	80.8	101.9	6.8	113.3	142.9	18.4	347.2	437.8
1918...	1.98	102.6	115.9	8.1	135.0	152.5	17.8	335.9	379.5
1919...	2.01	104.1	111.3	8.2	136.7	146.2	18.3	345.3	369.3
1920...	3.07	159.1	152.8	9.4	156.7	150.5	18.7	352.8	338.9
1921...	1.73	89.6	136.2	10.1	168.3	255.8	13.7	258.5	392.9
1922...	1.61	83.4	127.9	11.1	185.0	283.7	14.4	271.7	416.7
1923...	1.34	69.4	102.4	10.0	166.7	245.9	9.5	179.2	264.3
1924...	1.43	74.1	111.9	9.3	155.0	234.1	8.8	166.0	250.8
1925...	1.68	87.0	124.6	9.4	156.7	224.5	10.7	201.9	289.3
1926...	1.88	97.4	144.5	9.5	158.3	234.9	10.0	188.7	280.0
1927...	1.30	67.4	104.8	8.8	146.7	228.1	7.2	135.8	211.2
1928...	1.17	60.6	92.9	8.9	148.3	227.2	7.7	145.3	222.9
1929...	1.27	65.8	102.5	8.2	136.7	212.9	7.1	134.0	208.7
1930...	1.19	61.7	106.0	7.6	126.7	217.7	5.8	109.4	188.0
1931...	0.65	33.7	68.5	7.0	116.7	237.2	3.5	66.0	134.1
1932...	0.87	45.1	103.2	6.4	106.7	244.2	3.2	60.4	138.2
1933...	0.67	34.7	78.2	6.2	103.3	232.7	3.8	71.7	161.5
1934...	1.00	51.8	102.6	6.0	100.0	198.0	3.9	73.6	145.7
1935...	0.97	50.3	93.3	5.8	96.7	179.4	4.3	81.1	150.5
1936...	1.09	56.5	103.7	5.5	91.7	168.3	4.7	88.7	162.8
1937...	1.18	61.1	105.0	5.1	85.0	146.0	4.7	88.7	152.4
1938...	1.13	58.5	110.4	4.9	81.7	154.2	4.0	75.5	142.5
1939...	1.02	52.8	101.5	4.9	81.7	157.1	4.2	79.2	152.3
1940...	1.02	52.8	99.6	4.5	75.0	141.5	2.9	54.7	103.2
1941...	1.14	59.1	100.3	4.9	81.7	138.7	3.5	66.0	112.1
1942...	1.19	61.7	92.6	5.1	85.0	127.6	3.5	66.0	99.1
1943...	1.20	62.2	89.5	5.2	86.7	124.7	4.0	75.5	108.6
1944...	1.21	62.7	89.4	5.1	85.0	121.3	4.3	81.1	115.7
1945...	1.22	63.2	88.5	4.9	81.7	114.4	4.0	75.5	105.7
1946...	1.41	73.1	89.6	5.3	88.3	108.2	3.7	69.8	85.5
1947...	1.93	100.0	100.0	6.0	100.0	100.0	5.3	100.0	100.0
1948...	2.60	134.7	124.4	6.5	108.3	100.0	7.4	139.6	128.9
1949...	2.54	131.6	127.9	6.3	105.0	102.0	6.1	115.1	111.9
1950...	2.51	130.1	121.6	6.5	108.3	101.2	5.5	103.8	97.0
1951...	2.53	131.1	110.1	7.3	121.7	102.2	5.9	111.3	93.5
1952...	2.53	131.1	113.2	7.8	130.0	112.3	5.7	107.5	92.8
1953...	2.68	138.9	121.6	9.2	153.3	134.2	6.0	113.2	99.1
1954...	2.78	144.0	125.9	10.1	168.3	147.1	5.5	103.8	90.7
1955...	2.77	143.5	125.0	10.4	173.3	151.0	5.2	98.1	85.5

(Footnotes on next page.)

TABLE XXIV (continued)

n.a. Not available.

ᵃ Average value at well. These crude oil values were applied to net imports of crude and oil products included in value of consumption figures, Appendix Table XVI, column 4.

ᵇ Average value at well. For years prior to 1922, for which only value at point of consumption is available, estimated assuming the same ratio between the two values as in 1922.

ᶜ Average value at plant. Figures for 1911–40 represent value of natural gas liquids excluding liquefied petroleum gases, figures for 1941 and subsequent years weighted average value of all natural gas liquids including LPG.

SOURCES (except as noted below):

Columns 1, 4, and 7, USGS and Mines, *Mineral Resources of the United States* and *Minerals Yearbook*, various issues.
Columns 3, 6, and 9, based on BLS Wholesale Price Index for All Commodities (shifted to 1947 = 100).
Natural gas, 1900–21, from worksheets underlying Census, *Raw Materials in the United States Economy: 1900–1952*, Working Paper No. 1, 1954; 1885–95, for which no information was available, estimated to have been similar to 1900 value.

TABLE XXV. FUEL CONSUMED COMPARED WITH MILES TRAVELED BY MOTOR VEHICLES, EXCLUDING MILITARY, 1936 AND 1955

Item	1936	1955	1955 ratio (1936 = 1)
Fuel consumed (gasoline, diesel and LPG, million gallons):			
Passenger cars	13,648	33,548	2.46
Trucks and combinations	4,003	13,308	3.32
Commercial buses	320	651	2.03
School and nonrevenue buses	58	120	2.07
All motor vehicles	18,029	47,627	2.64
Number of registered vehicles (thousands):			
Passenger cars	24,201	52,092	2.15
Trucks and combinations	4,071	10,413	2.56
Commercial buses	49	96	1.96
School and nonrevenue buses	75	159	2.12
All motor vehicles	28,396	62,760	2.21
Vehicle-miles traveled (millions):			
Passenger cars	208,654	487,540	2.34
Trucks and combinations	41,107	111,387	2.71
Commercial buses	1,764	3,256	1.85
School and nonrevenue buses	603	1,251	2.07
All motor vehicles	252,128	603,434	2.39
Miles per gallon:			
Passenger cars	15.29	14.53	0.950
Trucks and combinations	10.27	8.37	0.815
Commercial buses	5.51	5.00	0.907
School and nonrevenue buses	10.40	10.42	1.002
All motor vehicles	13.98	12.67	0.906

TABLE XXV (continued)

Item	1936	1955	1955 ratio (1936 = 1)
Operations of trucks and combinations on main rural roads:			
Vehicle-miles, loaded and empty (millions)..........	15,407	47,481	3.08
Ton-miles, loaded and empty (millions)............	28,004	154,050	5.50
Average load carried (tons)......................	2.90	5.92	2.04
Frequency of heavy loads (number per thousand loaded and empty trucks):			
Over 30,000 pounds...........................	43	206	4.79
Over 40,000 pounds...........................	11	128	11.64
Over 50,000 pounds...........................	3	80	26.67

SOURCE: Roads, *Highway Statistics, Summary to 1955*, pp. 33, 35-37, and 40.

TABLE XXVI. PETROLEUM PRODUCTS CONSUMED COMPARED TO WORK PERFORMED BY AIRCRAFT, SELECTED YEARS, 1935-55

Item	1935 (1)	1940 (2)	1945 (3)	1950 (4)	1955 (5)	1955 ratio (1935=1) (6)
Gasoline consumed (thous. gal.):						
Scheduled domestic flights	27,313	65,675	134,824	418,442	902,936	33
Scheduled international flights	5,948	8,860	25,087	153,804	237,511	40
General aircraft	11,104	22,400	98,576 a	131,200 b	190,000	17
Civil aircraft, total	44,365	96,935	258,487	703,446	1,330,447	30
All U.S. aircraft (including military)	73,684	n.a.	4,913,580	1,659,714	2,946,972	40
Jet fuel consumed (thous. gal.)				146,160	2,364,012 c	n.a.
Lubricating oil consumed (thous. gal.):						
Scheduled air carriers	880	1,288	2,025	6,675	13,832	16
General aircraft	334	660	2,191 a	2,916 b	4,222	13
Civil aircraft, total	1,214	1,948	4,216	9,591	18,054	15
Miles flown (mill.):						
Scheduled domestic revenue miles	55.9	110.1	209.0	364.3	620.7	11
Scheduled international revenue miles	7.9	9.7	32.6	93.8	131.5	18
General aircraft	84.8	264.0	n.a.	1,061.5 b	1,216.0	14
Civil aircraft, total	148.6	383.8	n.a.	1,519.6	1,968.3	13
Revenue passenger-miles flown (mill.):						
Scheduled, domestic	316	1,052	3,362	8,003	19,819	63
Scheduled, international	46	104	462	2,336	4,600	100
Ton-miles flown (thous.):						
Scheduled domestic express and freight	1,098	3,476	22,197	151,351	228,071	207
Scheduled international express and freight	n.a.	n.a.	8,718	60,563	90,969	n.a.
Scheduled, mail, domestic	4,133	10,118	65,093	47,009	87,445	21

n.a. Not available.

a Figure given refers to 1946; 1945 not available.

b Data computed from trend since no formal survey was conducted.

c Thereof, 1,827 thousand gallons consumed by scheduled air carriers.

SOURCES: A.P.I., *Petroleum Facts and Figures* (9th ed., 1950), pp. 96, 229; *ibid.* (12th ed., 1956), pp. 85-86, 203; Census, *Historical Statistics of the United States, 1789-1945*, series K 246-273; Census, *Statistical Abstract of the United States, 1957*, pp. 577-78; and CAA, *CAA Statistical Handbook of Civil Aviation* (1957 ed.).

TABLE XXVII. INDUSTRIAL CONSUMPTION OF NATURAL GAS BY USE, 1939 AND 1947

Use	Billion cubic feet		Per cent of total	
	1939 (1)	1947 (2)	1939 (3)	1947 (4)
Manufacturing industries, total................	969	1,754	49.3%	52.5%
a. Fuel use, total.........................	622	1,254	31.7	37.6
Food and kindred products.............	81	110		
Paper and allied products..............	30	69		
Chemical and allied products...........	58	156		
Petroleum refining....................	98	364		
Stone, clay and glass products..........	148	224		
Primary ferrous metals................	117	148		
Primary nonferrous metals.............	34	70		
Fabricated metal products.............	12	21		
Other................................	44	92		
b. Nonfuel use, total......................	347	500	17.7	15.0
Carbon black........................	347	485		
Methanol and ammonia................		15		
Electric utility plants.......................	191	373	9.7	11.2
Mines and quarries.........................	29	34	1.5	1.0
Field use, total............................	681	934	34.7	28.0
Gas plant use and shrinkage............	171	396		
Net field use.........................	510	538		
Other industrial uses.......................	94	244	4.8	7.3
Total industrial consumption.................	1,964	3,339	100.0%	100.0%

NOTE: Detailed statistics on natural gas consumption by the industrial sector are available only for a few census years. For 1939 and 1947, these data are shown in this table and Appendix Table XXVIII (the 1954 *Census of Manufactures* does not distinguish between natural and manufactured and mixed gas consumed by this sector). In those years, the manufacturing industries absorbed about one-half of the total industrial use. This information is included here because it contributes to a better interpretation of natural gas consumption by broad industrial use categories, shown in Table 42 of the text. In this breakdown, the category "other uses" accounted in recent years for more than one-third of the total industrial consumption. An analysis of the detailed statistics and their comparison with the corresponding broad use categories reveal that in 1937, 80 per cent and, in 1947, 75 per cent of all natural gas included in the omnibus category "other uses" was consumed by the manufacturing sector.

SOURCE: Mines, William H. Lyon and D. S. Colby, *Production, Consumption, and Use of Fuels and Electric Energy in the United States in 1929, 1939, and 1947*, Report of Investigations 4805, October 1951.

TABLE XXVIII. RECONCILIATION OF DETAILIED DATA ON
INDUSTRIAL CONSUMPTION OF NATURAL GAS WITH THE BROAD
INDUSTRIAL USE CATEGORIES USED IN TEXT TABLE 42

Use	Billion cubic feet		Per cent of total	
	1939 (1)	1947 (2)	1939 (3)	1947 (4)
Field use..................................	681	934	34.7%	28.0%
Carbon black.............................	347	485	17.7	14.5
Petroleum refineries.........................	98	364	5.0	10.9
Portland cement...........................	40	60	2.0	1.8
Central power stations.....................	191	373	9.7	11.2
Other uses................................	607	1,123	30.9	33.6
Total.....................................	1,964	3,339	100.0%	100.0%
Total consumption by manufacturing industries (from Appendix Table XXVII)..............	969	1,754		
Minus consumption by broad use categories (listed above), which are included in total consumption by manufacturing:				
Carbon black.........................	347	485		
Petroleum refineries.....................	98	364		
Portland cement.......................	40	60		
Leaving for consumption by manufacturing industries (included in "other uses" above).....	484	845		
Plus consumption by mines and quarries.......	29	34		
Plus other industrial uses (from Appendix Table XXVII)...............................	94	244		
Total "other uses" (as listed above)............	607	1,123		
Thereof consumed by manufacturing industries..	484	845		
Consumption by manufacturing industries as a percentage of total "other uses".............	79.7	75.2		

SOURCES: Mines, *Minerals Yearbook, Review of 1940*, pp. 1056–57; *Minerals Yearbook, 1948*, pp. 855–56; and Appendix Table XXVII.

Statistical appendix to part II, the future of energy consumption

Introductory Note

The material in this Appendix is organized into sections principally according to consuming sectors. The sequence of the sections is as follows:

The first seven sections (A through G) refer to separate consuming sectors. Section H deals with the allocation to specific consuming sectors of fuels used in electricity generation. Section I contains the major economic assumptions, as well as technical and summary material that refers to more than one sector; however, it is not the only section that does so. As the reader will quickly gather, interrelationships between the various parts necessarily make certain statistical tables germane to more than one consuming sector. Such tables are not marked in any special way, but since the origin of every figure in the Appendix is noted, by reference either to a published source, another table, or a calculation, the usefulness of one table for more than one sector becomes self-evident.

In accordance with the general approach employed in making these projections, all calculations are shown to a degree of detail that is in striking contrast to the broad estimating procedures. This may give an unwarranted appearance of precision to the estimates, but it was done in order to enable the reader to follow the calculations step by step and to prevent him from losing the thread among too many rounded figures, as well as to provide means of cross-checking the estimates. This is especially important where one assumption is pyramided upon another. Even so, it will be observed that occasionally additions do not check with totals shown, because of rounding.

As for reference to published sources, different editions of the same publication may be cited in different parts of the study, particularly in the case of monthly or annual government and trade association publications. This is caused mainly by the time elapsed during the study: where a later and more convenient source became available at a later stage of the study, the switch to that source was made and consistency of reference dates was sacrificed.

Section A. Industry

General Note

Tables A–1 through A–23 deal with the fuel input in industry for all purposes other than the industrial (i.e., non-utility) generation of electricity. The first nine tables develop the 1955 pattern; the remaining, that projected for 1975.

Attention is called to Tables A–5 through A–8, which underly the results shown in Table A–4. These tables show, in substantial detail, certain uses of fuels which are referred to also in sectors other than industry. They are in this sector because they are, quantitatively, most important in industry.

The following tables make up the three groups into which the sector has been divided:

(1) Iron and Steel, Cement, and Petroleum Refining:
    Table A–1, supported by Table A–2 for 1955, for the whole group
    Tables A–10 and A–11, for iron and steel projection
    Tables A–12 and A–13, for cement projection
    Table A–16, supported by Tables A–14, A–15, and A–17, for petroleum
        refining projection.

(2) Special Industrial Group:
    Tables A–3 and A–19.

(3) General Industrial Group:
    Table A–4, supported by Tables A–5 through A–8, for 1955.
    Table A–22, supported by Tables A–20 and A–21, for 1975.

The results are summarized in Tables A–9 and A–23 for 1955 and 1975 respectively.

Tables A–24 through A–36 deal with consumption of electricity in industry. Of these, the first two establish consumption in 1955, and the rest are devoted to the projection. Tables A–27 through A–29 contain the data for separating consumption by the Atomic Energy Commission (AEC) and by the separately treated aluminum and magnesium production. Tables A–30 through A–32 deal with the projection to 1975 of the narrower group, and Tables A–33 through A–36 with that of aluminum and magnesium. Table A–37 summarizes the results for both 1955 and 1975.

555

Industry Tables

TABLE A-1. FUEL INPUT TO IRON AND STEEL, PETROLEUM REFINING, AND CEMENT INDUSTRIES, 1955

Fuel	Fuel input for all purposes (physical units)				Fuels for electricity generation (physical unit)^d (5)	Fuels for purposes other than electricity generation	
	Iron and steel^a (1)	Petroleum refining^b (2)	Cement^c (3)	Total (4)		Physical unit (6)	Billion Btu (7)
Coal (thous. tons):							
Bituminous................	108,329	884	8,528	117,741	8,937	108,804	2,850,665
Anthracite................	791		199	990		990	25,146
Total................							2,875,811
Oil:							
Residual (thous. bbl.).....	54,233	53,387	8,506	116,126	7,060	109,066	696,277
Distillates (thous. bbl.)...		8,597		8,597		8,597	49,106
Acid sludge (thous. bbl.)...		2,228		2,228		2,228	10,013
Coke (thous. tons)........		2,450		2,450		2,450	73,500
Still gas (mill. cu. ft.).....		591,234		591,234		591,234	886,651
Total................							1,715,547
Natural gas liquids (thous. bbl.).....	293			293	293		1,175
Natural gas (mill. cu. ft.)......	266,602	625,243	133,402	1,025,247	58,560	966,687	1,000,521
Grand total............							5,593,054

^a AISI, *Annual Statistical Report, 1956*, p. 22, except for coal. Latter from Table A–2, item 1b, cols. 2 and 3 for coke, plus coal for all purposes other than coking, *ibid.*, p. 38.

^b Residual and distillate oil from Mines, *Mineral Market Report*, No. MMS 2517, p. 9, Table 12. All other from Mines, *Monthly Petroleum Statement*, No. 420, p. 18, Table 19. Comparison between the two sources suggests that 11,416,000 bbl. of the 53,387,000 bbl. of residual, and all of the 8,597,000 bbl. of distillates are for nonrefining oil company uses. Residual includes 1,992,000 bbl. of crude; the distillate includes 1,112,000 bbl. of diesel oil. Refinery gas includes small quantities of butane, propane, and other liquefied gases used as fuel.

^c Mines, *Minerals Yearbook, 1956*, Vol. I, p. 308.

^d Fuels consumed in own generation of electricity, from Appendix Table H-6.

TABLE A-2. COAL EQUIVALENT OF COKE CONSUMPTION, IN IRON
AND STEEL INDUSTRY, 1955

(Tons)

| Item | Coke (1) | Coal equivalent of coke[a] | | |
		Bituminous (2)	Anthracite (3)	Total (4)
1. Consumption:[b]				
a. Residential heating.....	1,126,065	1,606,444	5,478	1,611,922
b. Blast furnaces and foundries............	71,425,893	101,850,015	347,321	102,197,336
c. Other industries........	3,848,674	5,488,031	18,715	5,506,746
d. Net exports...........	404,163	576,318	1,965	578,283
e. Total.................	76,804,795	109,520,808	373,479	109,894,287
2. Production[c].............	75,301,826			
3. Coal carbonized:[a]				
a. Bituminous............	107,376,917			
b. Anthracite............	366,168			
c. Total.................	107,743,085			
4. Tons of coal carbonized per ton of coke produced....	1.43[d]			

[a] Figures derived on basis of coal-to-coke ratio given in item 4 and distribution between bituminous coal and anthracite as in item 3. Therefore, col. 4, items 1a through 1d obtained by multiplying col. 1 by ratio given in item 4. Col. 4, item 1e derived by totaling items 1a through 1d. Cols. 2 and 3 obtained by dividing col. 4 in same ratio as shown in items 3a through 3c.

[b] Mines, *Minerals Yearbook, 1955*, Vol. II, p. 170.

[c] *Ibid.*, p. 195. Difference between production and consumption principally due to decrease in stocks by 1,785,757 tons.

[d] Item 3c divided by item 2. Ratio carried to additional places in actual computation.

TABLE A-3. FUEL INPUT TO SPECIAL INDUSTRIAL GROUP, 1955

Item	Physical unit	Billion Btu
1. Mine consumption:		
a. Bituminous coal (thous. tons)[a].................	9,626	252,201
b. Anthracite (thous. tons)[b].......................	419	10,643
c. Total..		262,844
2. Railroad nonmotive:[c]		
a. Bituminous coal (thous. tons)...................	4,510	118,162
b. Anthracite (thous. tons).......................	457	11,608
c. Residual oil (thous. bbl.)......................	6,816	43,513
d. Diesel oil (thous. bbl.)	2,374	13,560
e. Total..		186,843
3. Field use of natural gas (mill. cu. ft.)[d]................	1,507,671	1,560,439
(excl. NGL extraction loss).......................	(1,158,421)	(1,204,320)

TABLE A–3 (continued)

Item	Physical unit	Billion Btu
4. Coke to "other industries": [e]		
a. Bituminous coal (thous. tons)...................	5,488	143,786
b. Anthracite (thous. tons).......................	19	483
c. Total......................................		144,269
5. All activities:		
Bituminous coal (thous. tons).....................	19,624	514,149
Anthracite (thous. tons).........................	895	22,734
Total coal.....................................		536,883
Residual oil (thous. bbl.)........................	6,816	43,513
Diesel oil (thous. bbl.)..........................	2,374	13,560
Total oil......................................		57,073
Natural gas (mill. cu. ft.).......................	1,507,671	1,560,439
Grand total..		2,154,395

[a] Mines, *Minerals Yearbook, 1956*, Vol. II, p. 99, includes coal used by mine employees, taken by locomotive tenders at tipples, used at mine for power and heat, transported from mines to point of consumption by conveyors or trains, made into beehive coke at mines, and all other uses at mines.

[b] Mines, *Minerals Yearbook, 1955*, Vol. II, p. 122.

[c] From Appendix Table D–4.

[d] Mines, *Minerals Yearbook, 1956*, Vol. II, p. 295: natural gas for field use, pumping, drilling, including NGL extraction, etc. On the basis of NGL production, it may be estimated that some 360 billion cu. ft. represents the so-called extraction loss or shrinkage, i.e., the reduction in volume caused by removal of the heavier hydrocarbon portions comprising the natural gas liquids. Elsewhere in this study, NGL demand is separately established and thus double-counting results when natural gas and NGL are aggregated in the Btu summary tables. As shown in the bracketed figures, the Btu figure, corresponding to the volume exclusive of the extraction loss, would be in the neighborhood of 1,200 000 billion Btu. A corresponding adjustment in the Btu figure has been made in text Table 66, which is thus free of any double-counting, but not in any of the appendix tables since none of them aggregates *all* natural gas and *all* NGL.

[e] From Table A–2, item 1c.

TABLE A–4. FUEL INPUT TO GENERAL INDUSTRIAL GROUP, 1955

Item	Physical unit			Btu's for purposes other than electricity generation (billion) (4)
	For all uses including electricity generation (1)	For electricity generation (2)	For purposes other than electricity generation (3)	
1. Coal (thous. tons):				
a. Bituminous............	79,892 [a]	21,935 [b]	57,957	1,518,473
b. Anthracite............	3,168 [c]		3,168	80,467
c. Total................				1,598,940
2. Oil (thous. bbl.):				
a. Residual..............	110,291 [d]	17,330 [e]	92,961	593,463
b. Distillates.............	43,606 [f]		43,606	253,656
c. Gasoline..............	8,958 [g]		8,958	46,651
d. Total................				893,770
3. NGL (thous. bbl.):				
a. Natural gasoline........	1,221 [h]		1,221	6,361
b. LPG.................	12,194 [i]		12,194	48,910
c. Total................				55,271
4. Natural gas (mill. cu. ft.)....	1,612,678 [j]	143,740 [k]	1,468,938	1,520,351
5. Grand total................				4,068,332

[a] Table A–5.

[b] Appendix Table H–6, col. 4.

[c] Table A–6, line 7.

[d] Table A–7, line 3.

[e] Appendix Table H–6, col. 6.

[f] Industrial sales of distillates other than oil company fuel. Consists of 16,753,000 bbl. of diesel and 26,853,000 bbl. of all other distillates. Mines, *Mineral Market Report*, No. MMS 2681, Tables 2 and 3.

[g] Roads, *Highway Statistics, 1955*, p. 7, Table G–24. Allocation between oil and natural gasoline as per Appendix Table I–10.

[h] *Ibid.*

[i] LPG sales to industry of 12,487,000 bbl., minus use in iron and steel industry (under NGL) as in Table A–1, col. 1. Mines, *Mineral Market Report*, No. MMS 2531.

[j] Table A–8, item 5.

[k] Appendix Table H–6, col. 5.

TABLE A-5.   CONSUMPTION OF BITUMINOUS COAL IN GENERAL
INDUSTRIAL GROUP, 1955 AND 1951

(Thousand tons)

Use	1955	1951
Other industrial[a]	91,856	105,634
Specified uses to be subtracted:		
Used at mine[b]	9,626	15,162
Purchased by gas utilities[c]	1,454	5,629
Petroleum refining[d]	884	1,170
Remainder for general industrial use	79,892	83,673

  [a] Mines, *Minerals Yearbook, 1956*, Vol. II, p. 104.
  [b] *Ibid.*, p. 99.
  [c] A.G.A., *1956 Gas Facts*, p. 49.
  [d] Mines, *Monthly Petroleum Statement*, No. 420, p. 18.

TABLE A-6.   CONSUMPTION OF ANTHRACITE IN GENERAL
INDUSTRIAL GROUP, 1955 AND 1951

(Tons)

Item	1955[a]	1951[b]
1. Anthracite, for all industrial uses:[c]		
a. Broken	73,066	115,355
b. Buckwheat No. 1	331,005	552,147
c. Buckwheat No. 2	1,052,183	1,459,548
d. Buckwheat No. 3	2,791,984	4,258,934
e. Buckwheat No. 4	} 4,163,203	2,050,286
f. All other		2,425,691
g. Total	8,411,441	10,861,961
2. Specified industrial uses to be subtracted:		
a. Used at collieries[d]	419,264	1,037,164
b. Coking[e]	366,168	237,136
c. Electric utilities[f]	3,209,218	3,869,512
d. Railroads[f]	457,349	678,229
e. Cement mills[g]	199,429	18,081
f. Iron and steel (excl. coke)[h]	443,483	492,087
g. Gas utilities[i]	180,000	322,000
h. Total	5,274,911	6,654,209
3. Remainder for general industrial use (item 1g − item 2h)	3,136,530	4,207,752
4. Total distribution for coal year[j]	23,363,653	37,807,743
5. Total domestic demand, calendar year[k]	23,600,000	37,000,000
6. Factor for adjusting coal year to calendar year		
(item 5 ÷ item 4)	(1.01)	(.98)
7. General industrial use, calendar year (item 3 × item 6)	3,167,895	4,123,597
8. Household and commercial use, coal year		
(item 4 − item 1g)	14,952,212	
9. Household and commercial use, calendar year		
(item 8 × item 6)	15,101,731	

(Footnotes on next page.)

TABLE A–6 (continued)

ᵃ Data through item 4 are on coal-year basis, April 1, 1955–March 31, 1956, from Mines, *Minerals Yearbook, 1955*, Vol. II, p. 156.

ᵇ Data through item 4 are on coal-year basis, April 1, 1951–March 31, 1952, from *ibid.*, *1951*, p. 434.

ᶜ Factors for allocating anthracite coal, by grades, to industrial use suggested by James A. Vaughan, of the U.S. Bureau of Mines.

ᵈ Mines, *Minerals Yearbook, 1956*, Vol. II, p. 120, and *1951*, p. 407.

ᵉ *Ibid.*, *1955*, p. 188 and *1951*, p. 482, Table 22.

ᶠ *Ibid.*, *1956*, Vol. II, p. 122 and *1951*, p. 408.

ᵍ *Ibid.*, *1956*, Vol. I, p. 307, Table 11, and *1951*, p. 257.

ʰ AISI, *Annual Statistical Report, 1956*, p. 38, and *1952*, p. 23.

ⁱ A.G.A., *1956 Gas Facts*, page 49, Table 33.

ʲ Mines, *Minerals Yearbook, 1956*, Vol. II, p. 156, and *1951*, p. 434.

ᵏ *Ibid.*, *1956*, Vol. II, p. 122, and *1951*, p. 407. In both cases, "apparent consumption."

TABLE A–7.   CONSUMPTION OF RESIDUAL OIL IN GENERAL
INDUSTRIAL GROUP, 1955 AND 1951

(Thousand barrels)

Item	1955	1951
1. Sales to smelters, mines, and manufacturing industries (excl. oil companies) ᵃ	173,030	157,279
2. Specified uses to be subtracted:		
a. Iron and steel ᵇ	54,233	60,088
b. Cement ᶜ	8,506	6,352
3. Remainder for general industrial use	110,291	90,839

ᵃ Mines, *Minerals Yearbook, 1956*, Vol. II, p. 412 and *1951*, p. 1032.

ᵇ AISI, *Annual Statistical Report, 1956*, p. 22, and *1952*, p. 16.

ᶜ Mines, *Minerals Yearbook, 1966*, Vol. I, p. 307, table 11, and *1951*, p. 257, table 15.

TABLE A–8.   CONSUMPTION OF NATURAL GAS IN GENERAL
INDUSTRIAL GROUP, 1955 AND 1951

(Million cubic feet)

Item	1955	1951
1. Other industrial sales of natural gas ᵃ	3,694,218	2,462,457
2. Specified uses to be subtracted:		
a. Electric utilities ᵃ	1,153,280	736,898
b. Cement mills ᵇ	128,386	
c. Iron and steel industry ᶜ	266,602	206,797
d. A.G.A. natural gas sales to "other" customers ᵈ	301,150	182,145
e. Natural gas used with manufactured gas ᵉ	304,605	201,382
3. Remainder to general industrial use (item 1 − item 2)	1,540,195	1,135,235
4. "Other" gas to industry ᶠ	72,483	66,029
5. Total gas to general industrial group	1,612,678	1,201,264

ᵃ Mines, *Minerals Yearbook, 1956*, Vol. II, p. 295, and *1951*, p. 888.

ᵇ 1955: *ibid.*, *1956*, Vol. II, p. 307, excluding 3,016 million cu. ft. of by-product and coke-oven gas; 1951: cement mills already excluded.

ᶜ AISI, *Annual Statistical Report, 1956*, p. 22, and *1952*, p. 16.

ᵈ A.G.A., *1956 Gas Facts*, p. 97, Table 82, last column. Converted from therms to cubic feet on basis of 100,000 Btu per therm and 1,035 Btu per cubic foot. "Other" than residential, commercial, and, industrial.

ᵉ Mines, *Minerals Yearbook, 1955*, Vol. II, p. 294, Table 13, and *1951*, p. 890, Table 13.

ᶠ A.G.A., *1956 Gas Facts*, p. 97. Computed as difference between total and natural gas sales to "industrial" classification, Tables 81 and 82. Converted to cubic feet as per footnote above.

TABLE A-9. SUMMARY: FUEL INPUT TO INDUSTRY FOR PURPOSES OTHER THAN ELECTRICITY GENERATION, 1955

Item	Physical unit				Billion Btu			
	Iron and steel, petroleum refining, and cement[a] (1)	Special industrial group[b] (2)	General industrial group[c] (3)	Total (4)	Iron and steel, petroleum refining, and cement[d] (5)	Special industrial group[b] (6)	General industrial group[e] (7)	Total (8)
1. Coal (thous. tons):								
Bituminous................	108,804	19,624	57,957	186,385	2,850,665	514,149	1,518,473	4,883,287
Anthracite................	990	895	3,168	5,053	25,146	22,734	80,467	128,347
Total................					2,875,811	536,883	1,598,940	5,011,634
2. Oil:								
Residual (thous. bbl.).........	109,066	6,816	92,961	208,843	696,277	43,513	593,463	1,333,253
Distillates (thous. bbl.)........	8,597	2,374	43,606	54,577	49,106	13,560	253,656	316,322
Gasoline (thous. bbl.).........			8,958	8,958			46,651	46,651
Acid sludge (thous. bbl.)........	2,228			2,228	10,013			10,013
Coke (thous. tons)...........	2,450			2,450	73,500			73,500
Still gas (mill. cu. ft.).........	591,243			591,243	886,651			886,651
Total................					1,715,547	57,073	893,770	2,666,390
3. Natural Gas Liquids (thous. bbl.):								
Natural gasoline............			1,221	1,221			6,361	6,361
LPG...................	293		12,194	12,487	1,175		48,910	50,085
Total................					1,175		55,271	56,446
4. Natural gas (mill. cu. ft.).........	966,687	1,507,671	1,468,938	3,943,296	1,000,521	1,560,439	1,520,351	4,081,311
5. Grand total................					5,593,054	2,154,395	4,068,332	11,815,781

[a] Table A-1, col. 6.
[b] Table A-3, item 5.
[c] Table A-4, col. 3.
[d] Table A-1, col. 7.
[e] Table A-4, col. 4.

564   APPENDICES

TABLE A-10.   IRON AND STEEL PRODUCTION AND THE FEDERAL
RESERVE BOARD INDEX OF INDUSTRIAL PRODUCTION, 1952–56
AND PROJECTION TO 1975

Year	FRB index of industrial production (1947–49 =100) (1)	Ingots and steel for castings (net tons) (2)	Tons per point of index (2) ÷ (1) (3)
1956...............	143	115,216,149	805,707
1955...............	139	117,036,085	841,986
1954...............	125	88,311,652	706,493
1953...............	134	111,609,719	832,908
1952...............	124	93,168,039	751,355
1952–56 a..........	665	525,341,644	789,987
1975...............	305 b	240,603,181 c	789,987 d

a Aggregate level for the five years 1952–56.
b Computed on basis of growth of 4 per cent per year, 1955 to 1975.
c Obtained as product of estimated tons per index point (col. 3) and index level reached in 1975 (col. 1; the precise factor used was 304.566, rather than 305). Based upon 1955 tonnage, the growth in iron and steel production is equivalent to 3.66 per cent per year, as 1955 production was substantially above 1952–56 average.
d Assumed to remain at 1952–56 level.

SOURCES: FRB index, see Table A–30; iron and steel production, 1952–56: AISI, *Annual Statistical Report, 1956*, p. 51.

TABLE A-11.   FUEL INPUT TO IRON AND STEEL INDUSTRY,
1955 AND PROJECTION TO 1975

Item	1955	1975
1. Ingots and steel for casting (tons) a............	117,036,085	240,603,181
2. Ingots and steel for casting, 1955 = 100.......	100	205.58
3. Assumed fuel used per unit of output, 1955 = 100 b	100	78
4. Projected fuel consumption, based upon 1955 = 100.....'...........................	100	160.35 c
5. Projected fuel consumption, by type of fuel: d		
a. Bituminous coal (thous. tons)............	108,329	173,708
b. Anthracite (thous. tons)................	791	1,268
c. Residual oil (thous. bbl.)...............	54,233	86,964
d. Natural gas liquids (thous. bbl.).........	293	470
e. Natural gas (mill. cu. ft.)................	266,602	427,503

a From Table A–10, col. 2.
b Based on assumed increase in fuel efficiency of 1.25 per cent per year.
c Item 2 × item 3. Ratio carried to additional places in actual computations.
d 1955–75 increase in consumption as per item 4 applied to 1955 consumption of each fuel as shown in Table A–1, col. 1.

TABLE A–12.   CEMENT PRODUCTION AND THE FEDERAL RESERVE BOARD
INDEX OF INDUSTRIAL PRODUCTION, 1952–56 AND PROJECTION TO 1975

Year	FRB index of industrial production (1947–49=100) (1)	Barrels of Portland cement produced (2)	Barrels of cement per point of index (2)÷(1) (3)
1956...............	143	316,438,253	2,212,855
1955...............	139	297,453,321	2,139,952
1954...............	125	272,352,557	2,178,820
1953...............	134	264,180,522	1,971,496
1952...............	124	249,256,154	2,010,130
1952–56 [a]...........	665	1,399,680,807	2,104,783
1975...............	305 [b]	641,045,339 [c]	2,104,783 [d]

[a] Aggregate level for the five years 1952–56.

[b] Computed on basis of growth of 4 per cent per year, 1955 to 1975.

[c] Obtained as product of estimated tons per point of index (col. 3) and index level reached in 1975 (col. 1; the precise factor used was 304.566, rather than 305). Based upon 1955 tonnage, the growth in cement production is just below 4 per cent per year, as 1955 production was slightly above 1952–56 average.

[d] Assumed to remain at 1952–56 level.

SOURCES: FRB index, see Table A–30; cement production: Mines, *Mineral Market Report*, No. MMS 2622, p. 2, except for 1956 which was obtained directly from the Mines ledger.

TABLE A–13.   FUEL INPUT TO CEMENT INDUSTRY,
1955 AND PROJECTION TO 1975

Item	1955	1975
1. Portland cement produced (bbl.) [a].................	297,453,321	641,045,339
2. Portland cement produced, 1955 = 100.............	100	215.51
3. Assumed fuel used per unit of output, 1955 = 100 [b]..	100	78
4. Projected fuel consumption, based upon 1955 = 100 (item 2 × item 3).............................	100	168.10 [d]
5. Projected fuel consumption, by type of fuel: [c]		
a. Bituminous coal (thous. tons)...............	8,528	14,335
b. Anthracite (thous. tons).....................	199	335
c. Residual oil (thous. bbl.)....................	8,506	14,298
d. Natural gas (mill. cu. ft.)....................	133,402	224,247

[a] From Table A–12, col. 2.

[b] Based on assumed increase in fuel efficiency of 1.25 per cent per year.

[c] 1955–75 increase in consumption as per item 4 applied to 1955 consumption of each fuel as shown in Table A–1, col. 3.

[d] Ratio carried to additional places in actual computations.

TABLE A-14.   FUEL CONSUMED AT PETROLEUM REFINERIES, 1925-55

Year	Oil [a] (thousand barrels) (1)	Acid sludge [a] (thousand barrels) (2)	Coal (thousand tons) (3)	Natural gas (million cu. ft.) (4)	Still gas (million cu. ft.) (5)	Petroleum coke (thousand tons) (6)
1955	41,971	2,228	884	625,243	591,234	2,450
1954	47,410	2,474	876	563,315	501,574	1,895
1953	41,342	2,910	735	558,695	477,931	1,806
1952	40,018	3,599	766	536,402	425,835	1,466
1951	39,883	4,178	1,170	537,774	422,810	1,458
1950	42,588	4,102	1,075	455,096	370,091	1,455
1949	44,510	4,326	1,011	422,357	361,671	1,254
1948	38,653	5,780	2,449	441,470	331,156	925
1947	38,717	5,824	2,273	363,892	324,737	721
1946	38,318	5,230	1,718	331,520	318,172	522
1945	38,557	5,222	1,532	338,458	348,736	596
1944	36,574	5,550	1,771	315,311	351,123	382
1943	29,011	4,614	1,831	243,584	296,518	114
1942	27,763	4,594	1,706	201,670	265,743	53
1941	33,105	4,517	1,091	148,127	283,021	73
1940	32,085	4,428	979	128,007	252,914	113
1939	31,756	4,009	742	97,685	246,188	123
1938	28,855	3,467	722	109,741	233,791	75
1937	27,849	4,750	1,209	113,005	224,698	84
1936	30,454	4,937	1,310	93,183	210,689	123
1935	31,497	5,178	1,221	80,175	183,383	117
1934	33,163	4,702	1,189	79,965	164,741	194
1933	33,292	4,990	1,069	66,333	172,085	263
1932	34,801	5,924	958	67,467	161,634	333
1931	38,913	5,743	1,412	75,548	149,924	529
1930	46,956		1,949	98,842	121,321	580
1929	51,544		2,300	103,729	98,727	488
1928	46,400		3,362	114,950	77,313	470
1927	41,462		5,031	123,395	53,465	450
1926	46,416		6,052	121,449	52,077	408
1925	50,455		6,153	87,842	35,041	314

[a] Oil includes acid sludge for 1925-30.

SOURCES: 1925-45: Mines, *Mineral Market Report*, No. MMS 1667, p. 4; 1946-55: Mines, *Monthly Petroleum Statement*, No. 429, p. 18, Table 19.

TABLE A–15. RELATIVE SHARE OF FUELS IN TOTAL BTU INPUT[a]
OF PETROLEUM REFINERIES, 1925–55

(In per cent)

Year	Oil[b] (1)	Acid sludge[b] (2)	Coal (3)	Natural gas (4)	Still gas (5)	Petroleum coke[c] (6)	Steam[e] (7)
1955.........	12.8%	.5%	1.2%	34.7%	46.8%	3.9%	.1%
1954.........	16.0	.7	1.3	34.4	43.8	3.3	.5
1953.........	14.6	.8	1.2	35.8	43.7	3.3	.6
1952.........	15.2	1.1	1.3	36.9	41.8	2.9	.8
1951.........	15.1	1.2	2.0	36.9	41.4	2.9	.5
1950.........	17.9	1.3	2.0	34.7	40.3	3.2	.6
1949.........	19.3	1.5	2.0	33.2	40.6	2.8	.6
1948.........	17.9	2.0	4.9	34.1	38.4	2.1	.6
1947.........	19.4	2.2	4.9	30.4	40.6	1.8	.7
1946.........	20.3	2.1	4.0	29.3	42.2	1.4	.7
1945.........	19.6	2.0	3.4	28.6	44.2	1.5	.7
1944.........	19.0	2.2	4.0	27.4	45.7	1.0	.7
1943.........	18.5	2.2	5.1	25.8	47.2	.4	.8
1942.........	19.9	2.4	5.3	24.0	47.5	.2	.7
1941.........	24.1	2.5	3.4	18.0	51.6	.4	
1940.........	25.7	2.6	3.4	17.1	50.7	.5	
1939.........	27.7	2.6	2.8	14.9	50.2	1.8	
1938.........	26.2	2.4	2.8	17.4	49.5	1.7	
1937.........	25.2	3.2	4.7	17.9	47.4	1.6	
1936.........	28.6	3.5	5.4	15.3	46.2	1.0	
1935.........	31.8	3.9	5.3	14.2	43.2	1.6	
1934.........	34.8	3.7	5.4	14.7	40.4	1.0	
1933.........	35.1	3.9	4.9	12.3	42.4	1.4	
1932.........	36.8	4.7	4.4	12.5	39.9	1.7	
1931.........	44.0		6.0	13.0	34.4	2.6	
1930.........	45.2		8.1	16.7	27.2	2.8	
1929.........	49.0		9.5	17.3	21.9	2.3	
1928[d].........	45.7		14.4	19.8	17.8	2.3	
1927.........	41.6		21.9	21.7	12.5	2.3	
1926.........	42.9		24.3	19.7	11.2	1.9	
1925[e].........	49.3		26.1	15.0	8.0	1.6	

[a] Btu values used, as stated in various issues of U.S. Bureau of Mines publication reporting refinery fuel consumption are:

Oil............. 6,000,000 Btu per bbl.
Acid sludge..... 4,500,000 Btu per bbl.
Coal...........26,000,000 Btu per ton
Natural gas:
  1925–39..... 1,050 Btu per cu. ft.
  1940–55..... 1,000 Btu per cu. ft.
Still gas:
  1925–39..... 1,400 Btu per cu. ft.
  1940–55..... 1,500 Btu per cu. ft.

Petroleum coke..30,000,000 Btu per ton
Steam:
  1936......... 1,013 Btu per lb.
  1937–38...... 1,113 Btu per lb.
  1939......... 1,193 Btu per lb.
  1940–55...... 1,200 Btu per lb.

[b] For 1925–31, acid sludge was combined with oil at 6,000,000 Btu per bbl.
[c] For 1935–42, petroleum coke included steam.
[d] Also 12,133 tons of refuse.
[e] Also 3,269 cords of wood.

SOURCES: 1925–38: from Mines, G. R. Hopkins, *Survey of Fuel Consumption at Refineries in 1938*, Report of Investigations 3485, December 1939, figure 2; 1939–45: Mines, *Mineral Market Report*, MMS 1667, p. 4; 1946–55: *Monthly Petroleum Statement*, No. 420, p. 19.

TABLE A–16. FUEL INPUT TO PETROLEUM REFINERIES, 1955 AND PROJECTION TO 1975

Fuel	1955		1975[a]	
	Physical units[b] (1)	Percentage of total Btu's consumed[c] (2)	Projected percentage of total Btu's consumed (3)	Projected physical units (4)
1. Coal (thous. tons).............	884	1.20%	1.20%[d]	1,680
2. Residual oil (thous. bbl.).......	41,971	12.80	6.74[e]	41,971[e]
3. Acid sludge (thous. bbl.).......	2,228	0.50	0.25[f]	2,117
4. Petroleum coke (thous. tons)...	2,450	3.90	6.00[g]	7,162
5. Still gas (mill. cu. ft.)..........	591,234	46.80	50.76[h]	1,218,397
6. Natural gas (mill. cu. ft.)......	625,243	34.70	35.00[i]	1,198,232
7. Steam purchased..............		0.10	0.05[j]	
Total........................		100.00%	100.00%	

[a] Projected percentages or quantities are based on two fundamental assumptions: First is that runs to stills in 1975 will be 90 per cent higher than in 1955. This constitutes a convenient approximation of the projected increase in domestic consumption which was made before the completion of the oil projection. Second is that fuel efficiency will remain unchanged between 1955 and 1975. Table A–17 demonstrates the wide extent of variation in fuel used per barrel of runs to stills on a geographic basis. A definitive projection of future fuel utilization in petroleum refineries is a highly complex matter, including locational questions and quality of product variations. In the absence of such an analysis, the simplifying "no change" assumption is preferred.

The combination of these two elements permits the projection to 1975 of the quantities shown in col. 1 by applying the percentages shown in col. 3 to the assumed growth in runs to stills, unless otherwise specified (item 2), i.e.,

$$\text{col. 4} = \text{col. 1} \times \frac{\text{col. 3} \times 190}{\text{col. 2} \times 100}$$

[b] Mines, *Monthly Petroleum Statement*, No. 420, p. 19, Table 20 (same as Table A–1, col. 2, with oil company fuel not used for refinery operations excluded, as per footnote b of Table A–1).

[c] *Ibid.*, page 19, Table 21. Percentages shown are of Btu equivalents of quantities in col. 1, derived by the U. S. Bureau of Mines on the basis of Btu conversion factors.

[d] It is assumed that coal will retain its 1955 relative share after a long history of decline (Table A–15, col. 3).

[e] Based on the assumption that the physical quantity consumed will remain unchanged between 1955 and 1975. This appears to be in accord with both the long-run and recent trends (Table A–14, col. 1). The corresponding percentage share in 1975 is then derived arithmetically on the further assumption that 1975 runs to stills will equal 190 per cent of 1955 runs, i.e.,

$$\frac{12.8}{190} \times 100 = 6.74 \text{ per cent.}$$

[f] Assumed to continue its long-run reduction (Table A–15, col. 2).

[g] Assumed to continue to increase in accordance with its recent trend (Table A–15, col. 6).

[h] Derived after all other shares have been determined as balancing item to total 100 per cent. The resultant level of over 50 per cent is in accord with the trend of the recent past.

[i] Natural gas is assumed to retain the relative position it has held in recent years.

[j] Steam is assumed to decline further, to one-half of its 1955 relative share. Carried only for sake of completeness, but not used in computations.

TABLE A-17. UNIT FUEL REQUIREMENTS IN U.S.
PETROLEUM REFINERIES, 1925-55

(Btu's per barrel of runs to stills)

Historical changes [a]

Year	U.S. Average	East Coast	Year	U.S. Average	East Coast
1955.......	694	580	1940.......	579	545
1954.......	677	573	1939.......	555	563
1953.......	641	540	1938.......	567	588
1952.......	626	538	1937.......	554	587
1951.......	646	543	1936.......	597	622
1950.......	658	564	1935.......	615	671
1949.......	687	565	1934.......	638	677
1948.......	638	509	1933.......	660	707
1947.......	651	504	1932.......	692	745
1946.......	653	494	1931.......	682	770
1945.......	688	504	1930.......	672	723
1944.......	692	518	1929.......	639	742
1943.......	659	570	1928.......	667	762
1942.......	629	616	1927.......	721	870
1941.......	584	541	1926.......	832	1,091
			1925.......	829	1,045

Geographic differences, 1955 [b]

East Coast.................... 580	Texas Gulf Coast.............. 823
Appalachian No. 1............. 717	Louisiana Gulf Coast........... 787
Appalachian No. 2............. 476	Arkansas, Louisiana Inland, etc... 706
Indiana, Illinois, Kentucky, etc... 606	New Mexico................... 356
Minnesota, Wisconsin, North	Other Rocky Mountain........ 700
Dakota, South Dakota........ 441	California.................... 682
Oklahoma, Kansas, Missouri, etc.. 628	
Texas Inland.................. 824	Total United States............ 694

[a] Figures from Mines. Years 1925-30 and 1931 through 1940 from following numbers of *Report of Investigations:* 3222, p. 8; 3198, p. 8; 3270, p. 6; 3281, p. 5; 3332, p. 4; 3367, p. 6; 3430, p. 7; 3554, p. 5; 3607, p. 6; and 3707, p. 2. Years 1941 through 1950 from following numbers of *Mineral Market Report:* 1667, pp. 9-10; 1922, p. 6; 2029, p. 6; and 2107, p. 4. Years from 1951 through 1955 from following numbers of *Monthly Petroleum Statement:* 367, p. 19; 391, p. 18; 403, p. 18; and 420, p. 18.

[b] Mines, *Monthly Petroleum Statement*, No. 420, Table 19.

TABLE A-18. SUMMARY: FUEL INPUT TO IRON AND STEEL, CEMENT, AND PETROLEUM REFINING, FOR PURPOSES OTHER THAN ELECTRICITY GENERATION, 1975 PROJECTION

| Item | Physical units | | | | | Net of electricity generation (4)−(5) (6) | Btu's for purposes other than electricity generation (billion) (7) |
| | For all purposes | | | | Used in generation of electricity[d] (5) | | |
	Iron and steel[a] (1)	Petroleum refining[b] (2)	Cement mills[c] (3)	Total (1)+(2)+(3) (4)			
1. Coal (thous. tons)							
Bituminous	173,708	1,680	14,335	189,723	13,842	175,881	4,608,082
Anthracite	1,268		335	1,603		1,603	40,716
Total							4,648,798
2. Oil:							
Residual (thous. bbl.)	86,964	63,661	14,298	164,923	11,807	153,116	977,493
Distillates (thous. bbl.)		16,334		16,334		16,334	95,015
Acid sludge (thous. bbl.)		2,117		2,117		2,117	9,514
Coke (thous. tons)		7,162		7,162		7,162	214,860
Still gas (mill. cu. ft.)		1,218,397		1,218,397		1,218,397	1,827,596
Total							3,124,478
3. Natural gas (mill. cu. ft.)	427,503	1,198,232	224,247	1,849,982	89,255	1,760,727	1,822,352
4. NGL (thous. bbl.)							
Natural gasoline	470			470		470	
LPG							1,885
5. Grand total							9,597,513

[a] Table A-11, item 5.
[b] Table A-16, col. 4; residual oil consists of 41,971,000 bbl. of refinery fuel plus oil company fuel for other than refinery uses. The nonrefinery use of residual is taken to increase at the same rate as the approximate increase in runs to stills, i.e, by 90 per cent, from 11,416,000 bbl. in 1955 to 21,690,000 bbl. in 1975. Distillates are also for nonrefinery uses by oil companies and are equally projected at increasing by 90 per cent, from 8,597,000 bbl. in 1955 to 16,334,000 bbl. in 1975.
[c] Table A-13, item 5.
[d] Appendix Table H-18, item 4c.

TABLE A-19.   FUEL INPUT TO SPECIAL INDUSTRIAL GROUP,
1975 PROJECTION

Item	Physical units	Billion Btu
1. Mine consumption:[a]		
a. Bituminous coal (thous. tons)..................	11,025	288,855
b. Anthracite (thous. tons).......................	240	6,096
c. Total..		294,951
2. Railroad nonmotive:[b]		
a. Bituminous coal (thous. tons)..................	4,510	118,162
b. Anthracite (thous. tons).......................	457	11,608
c. Residual oil (thous. bbl.)......................	6,816	43,513
d. Diesel oil (thous. bbl.)........................	2,374	13,560
e. Total..		186,843
3. Field use of natural gas (mill. cu. ft.)[c]...............	3,166,109	3,276,923
(excl. NGL extraction loss).....................	(2,432,000)	(2,529,000)
4. Coke to "other" industries:[b]		
a. Bituminous coal (thous. tons)..................	5,488	143,786
b. Anthracite (thous. tons).......................	19	483
c. Total..		144,269
5. All activities:		
Bituminous coal (thous. tons)....................	21,023	550,803
Anthracite (thous. tons)........................	716	18,187
Total coal.....................................		568,990
Residual oil (thous. bbl.).......................	6,816	43,513
Distillates and diesel oil (thous. bbl.).............	2,374	13,560
Total oil......................................		57,073
Natural gas (mill. cu. ft.)......................	3,166,109	3,276,923
Grand total..		3,902,986

[a] Estimated as a percentage of 1975 production. As projected production is determined only at the close of total 1975 energy demand, "working" figures of production were used at this stage to determine mine consumption. These are 735 million tons for bituminous coal, and 16 million tons for anthracite. Mine consumption was assumed at 1.5 per cent of production in continuation of a falling trend in the case of bituminous coal that brought it to 2.1 per cent in 1955 (Mines, *Minerals Yearbook, 1956*, Vol. II, p. 99), and roughly in line with current experience in anthracite (1.6 per cent in 1955, *ibid.*, p. 122).

[b] In absence of information left at 1955 levels.

[c] Assumed to increase in proportion to increase in gas consumption. As a working approximation, the latter, at this stage, was assumed to rise 110 per cent above the 1955 level (see Table A-3, item 3). This assumption contains a further simplification. As set out in Table A-3, the field-use category as published by the Bureau of Mines unfortunately includes, without separate identification, the volume of gas produced as such and stripped as NGL production. Since an increase has been assumed in NGL demand substantially in excess of gas demand, the projection of field use—of which NGL demand is an indirect, but indeterminate, component—could be expected to exceed that of gas demand.   On the basis of conversion factors between gas and liquid measures of NGL, it is possible to approxi-

(*Footnotes continued on next page.*)

TABLE A–19 (continued)

mate the portion of field use representing NGL production and to project it at a rate different from that used for all natural gas. Because of the statistical uncertainties involved this was not done. It can be estimated, however, that the understatement of field use on this account would be at most on the order of 10 per cent.

As in the case of the 1955 data, double-counting would result if the total demand for gas (including field use for NGL production) and that for NGL, in Btu terms, were aggregated. Consequently, an adjustment has been made in text Tables 64 and 66 but not in any other table, using the figure here bracketed.

TABLE A–20. FUEL INPUT TO GENERAL INDUSTRIAL GROUP, 1951

Item	Physical units			
	For all uses including electricity generation (1)	For electricity generation [a] (2)	For purposes other than electricity generation (3)	Btu's for purposes other than electricity generation (billion) (4)
1. Coal (thous. tons):				
Bituminous..............	83,673 [b]	18,034	65,639	1,719,742
Anthracite..............	4,124 [c]		4,124	104,750
Total...................				1,824,492
2. Oil (thous. bbl.):				
Residual................	90,839 [d]	9,070	81,769	522,013
Distillates..............	42,567 [e]		42,567	247,612
Gasoline................	13,361 [f]		13,361	69,584
Total...................				839,209
3. NGL (thous. bbl.):				
Natural gasoline..........	1,037 [f]		1,037	5,401
LPG...................	5,948 [g]		5,948	23,856
Total...................				29,257
4. Natural gas (mill. cu. ft.).....	1,201,264 [h]	76,660	1,124,604	1,163,965
5. Grand total................				3,856,923

[a] Derived in fashion analogous to method used in 1955 (see Table A–4).

[b] Table A–5.

[c] Table A–6, item 7.

[d] Table A–7.

[e] Mines, *Minerals Yearbook, 1955*, Vol. II, p. 399.

[f] Based on Roads, *Highway Statistics, 1951*, p. 6, Table G–24; natural gasoline portion based on same factor used for 1955 as shown in Appendix Table I–10.

[g] Mines, *Minerals Yearbook, 1955*, Vol. II, p. 306, Table 9; total industrial sale minus iron and steel consumption as shown in AISI, *Annual Statistical Report, 1956*, p. 22.

[h] From Table A–8.

TABLE A-21. CHANGES IN FUEL INPUT FOR PURPOSES OTHER THAN ELECTRICITY GENERATION, BY GENERAL INDUSTRIAL GROUP PER POINT OF THE FEDERAL RESERVE BOARD INDEX OF INDUSTRIAL PRODUCTION, 1951-55

Item	Fuel input in billion Btu		Btu's per point of FRB index [c]		Change in Btu per point of index, per year (5)	Specified fuel as per cent of noncoal Btu	
	1951 [a] (1)	1955 [b] (2)	1951 (3)	1955 (4)		1951 (6)	1955 (7)
1. Coal..................................	1,824,492	1,598,940	15,204.1	11,503.2	−7.22		
2. Noncoal:							
a. Oil (incl. natural gasoline)........	844,610	900,131	7,038.4	6,475.8	−2.10	41.6%	36.4%
b. NGL...........................	23,856	48,910	198.8	351.9	+15.36	1.1	2.0
c. Natural gas....................	1,163,965	1,520,351	9,699.7	10,937.8		57.3	61.6
d. Total.........................	2,032,431	2,469,392				100.0%	100.0%
3. Grand total........................	3,856,923	4,068,332	32,141.0	29,268.6	−2.34		

[a] Table A-20, col. 4.
[b] Table A-4, col. 4.
[c] Index for 1951 is 120; for 1955 is 139 (1947-49 = 100).

TABLE A-22.   FUEL INPUT TO GENERAL INDUSTRIAL GROUP,
1955 AND PROJECTION TO 1975

Item	Billion Btu		Physical units[b]	
	1955[a] (1)	1975 (2)	1955 (3)	1975 (4)
1. All fuels................	4,068,332	6,666,436 [c]		
2. Coal, total..............	1,598,940	1,310,402 [d]		
3. Bituminous coal (thous. tons).................	1,518,473	1,244,457 [d]	57,957	47,498
4. Anthracite (thous. tons) ..	80,467	65,945 [d]	3,168	2,596
5. Noncoal (item 1 − item 2)	2,469,392	5,356,034		
6. Oil (total incl. natural gasoline)..............	900,131	1,446,129 [e]		
7. Gasoline (incl. natural gasoline) (thous. bbl.) ..	53,012	53,012 [f]	10,179	10,179
8. Gasoline (excl. natural gasoline) (thous. bbl.) ..	(46,651)	(46,651)	(8,958)	(8,958)
9. Oil, other than gasoline (item 6 − item 7)......	(847,119)	(1,393,117)		
10. Residual (thous. bbl.).....	593,463	975,182 [g]	92,961	152,754
11. Distillates (thous. bbl.)....	253,656	417,935 [h]	43,606	71,847
12. Natural gas (mill. cu. ft.).	1,520,351	3,749,224 [i]	1,468,938	3,622,439
13. NGL (total).............	(55,271)			
14. Natural gasoline (thous. bbl.).................	(6,361)	(6,361)	(1,221)	(1,221)
15. LPG (thous. bbl.)........	48,910	160,681 [j]	12,194	40,060

[a] Table A-4, col. 4.

[b] 1955: Table A-4, col. 3; 1975: conversion from col. 2.

[c] It is assumed that nonelectric fuels used by the general industrial group will increase at 2.5 per cent per year. Output for the group is assumed to increase at 4 per cent and thermal efficiency is assumed to increase at 1.5 per cent per year. This is a substantially lower rate of improvement than for the 1951–55 period which showed an improvement in excess of 2.3 per cent per year (Table A-21, col. 5). This lower rate of improvement is used in recognition of the consideration that this industrial classification is in the nature of a residual in both its extent and (in particular) in the method by which fuel going to this sector is estimated. In addition, output in this group will have to increase at slightly more than 4 per cent per year in order to make the over-all Federal Reserve Board index of industrial production move at the rate of 4 per cent which has been assumed. The smaller allowance of improvement in fuel efficiency works arithmetically in that direction.

[d] It is assumed that coal Btu's decrease at 1 per cent per year, and that this rate of decrease is the same for both bituminous coal and anthracite. In terms of coal Btu's per point of the Federal Reserve Board index of industrial production, this means a rate of decrease of 5 per cent per point per year (since the index increases at 4 per cent and coal decreases at 1 per cent). This is less than the decrease of more than 7 per cent per year per point of the index during 1951–55 (Table A-21, col. 5), which is considered unlikely to continue at this rate.

[e] It is assumed that the oil proportion of the noncoal portion of Btu's decreases from 36.4 per cent to 27 per cent. This represents a modified continuation of the trend in noncoal

TABLE A-22 (continued)

Btu's which was seen for 1951–55 when the oil component decreased from 41.6 to 36.4 per cent (Table A-21, cols. 6 and 7).

[f] It is assumed that gasoline does not share in the growth of oil Btu's, the absolute level remaining unchanged.

[g] Of the oil Btu's excluding gasoline projected to 1975, it is assumed that residual oil retains the same share as in 1955.

[h] Of the oil Btu's excluding gasoline projected to 1975, it is assumed that distillates retain the same share as in 1955.

[i] The gas percentage of noncoal Btu's to this sector is assumed to increase to 70 per cent in a modified continuation of the tendency shown between 1951–55, when gas increased its percentage of noncoal Btu's from 57.3 to 61.6 per cent (Table A-21, cols. 6 and 7).

[j] Assumed as 3 per cent of noncoal Btu's in continuation of trend shown in Table A-21, cols. 6 and 7.

TABLE A-23. SUMMARY: FUEL INPUT TO INDUSTRY FOR PURPOSES OTHER THAN ELECTRICITY GENERATION, 1975

Fuel	Physical units				Billion Btu			
	Iron and steel, petroleum refining, and cement [a] (1)	Special industrial group [b] (2)	General industrial group [c] (3)	Total industry (1) + (2) + (3) (4)	Iron and steel, petroleum refining, and cement [d] (5)	Special industrial group [b] (6)	General industrial group [e] (7)	Total industry (5) + (6) + (7) (8)
Coal (thous. tons):								
Bituminous	175,881	21,023	47,498	244,402	4,608,082	550,803	1,244,457	6,403,342
Anthracite	1,603	716	2,596	4,915	40,716	18,187	65,945	124,848
Total					4,648,798	568,990	1,310,402	6,528,190
Oil:								
Residual (thous. bbl.)	153,116	6,816	152,754	312,686	977,493	43,513	975,182	1,996,188
Distillates (thous. bbl.)	16,334	2,374	71,847	90,555	95,015	13,560	417,935	526,510
Gasoline (incl. natural gasoline) (thous. bbl.)			(10,179)	(10,179)			(53,012)	(53,012)
Gasoline (excl. natural gasoline) (thous. bbl.)			8,958	8,958			46,651	46,651
Acid sludge (thous. bbl.)	2,117			2,117	9,514			9,514
Coke (thous. tons)	7,162			7,162	214,860			214,860
Still gas (mill. cu. ft.)	1,218,397			1,218,397	1,827,596			1,827,596
Total					3,124,478	57,073	1,439,768	4,621,319
Natural gas (mill. cu. ft.)	1,760,727	3,166,109	3,622,439	8,549,275	1,822,352	3,276,923	3,749,224	8,848,499
NGL (thous. bbl.):								
Natural gasoline			1,221	1,221			6,361	6,361
LPG	470		40,060	40,530	1,885		160,681	162,566
Total					1,885		167,042	168,927
Grand total					9,597,513	3,902,986	6,666,436	20,166,935

[a] Table A-18, col. 6.
[b] Table A-19, item 5.
[c] Table A-22, col. 4.
[d] Table A-18, col. 7.
[e] Table A-22, col. 2.

TABLE A-24. DERIVATION OF ELECTRICITY CONSUMED BY
INDUSTRY IN 1955[a]

Item	Million kwh
1. Large light and power sales of utilities[b]	249,206
2. Non-utility generation[c]	81,972
3. Transit generation[d]	1,480
4. Industrial generation net of transit generation (item 2 − item 3)	80,492
5. Non-utility sales to utilities[e]	6,037
6. Industrial generation used within industry (item 4 − item 5)	74,455
7. Total industrial consumption (item 1 + item 6)	323,661
8. AEC component of industrial consumption[f]	50,105
9. Industrial consumption net of AEC (item 7 − item 8)	273,556
10. Consumption for aluminum and magnesium[g]	29,828
11. Industrial consumption, excluding AEC and aluminum and magnesium (item 9 − item 10)	243,728

[a] Additional details concerning these computations are to be found in Section H dealing with electricity supply and distribution for 1955 and in Section B dealing with 1975 electricity for commercial consumption. The consumption figures given here do not include transmission losses, which are dealt with in Section H.

[b] It is assumed that this class of sales (E.E.I., *Statistical Bulletin for the Year 1957*, p. 27) is equivalent to sales to industry. The basis for this assumption is discussed in Appendix Table B-8.

[c] The FPC figure as listed on page 13 of E.E.I., *op. cit.*

[d] ATA, *Transit Fact Book, 1957 Edition*, p. 11.

[e] Assumed to be 7.5 per cent of non-utility generation excluding transit generation. For basis of assumption, see Appendix Table B-8, especially footnote d.

[f] From Table A-27.

[g] From Table A-28, col. 5.

TABLE A-25. METHOD OF DERIVING 1955 ELECTRICITY
CONSUMPTION BY INDUSTRY, CHECKED AGAINST 1954 CENSUS DATA

(Million kwh)

Item	1954 electricity consumption	
	1954 Census data (1)	Derivation by method used in Table A-24 (2)
1. Purchased	200,177[a]	200,155[b]
2. Generated	73,285[c]	71,449[d]
3. Sold	9,935[e]	5,359[f]
4. Net used (item 1 + item 2 − item 3)	263,527	266,245
5. Difference between col. 1 and col. 2		2,718[g]

[a] Includes all purchases from utility as well as from non-utility generation. Purchases consist of 187,027 million kwh for manufacturing, (*Census of Manufactures, 1954*, Bulletin MC-208, p. 5) and 13,150 million kwh for minerals (*Census of Minerals Industries, 1954*, Bulletin MI-F, p. F-5).

[b] Large light and power sales of electric utilities (E.E.I., *Statistical Bulletin for the Year 1957*, p. 27).

(*Footnotes continued on next page.*)

TABLE A-25 (continued)

ᶜ Consists of 69,683 million kwh in manufacturing and 3,602 in mining. (For sources, see footnote ᵃ.)

ᵈ Derived by subtracting transit generation (1,510 million kwh) from FPC non-utility generation of 72,959 million kwh (E.E.I., *op. cit.*, p. 13, and ATA, *Transit Fact Book, 1957 Edition*, p. 11). The difference between the two figures listed for generation is probably due to two sources: coverage and concept. There are some establishments for which the FPC may not obtain information. In addition, the Census respondents may have reported some quantities of electricity generation which are not regarded as "electricity generation" by the FPC. Such instances might materialize in the operations of mobile machinery.

ᵉ Of this, 9,044 million kwh were from manufacturing and 891 million kwh were from mining. (Same source as footnote a.) These are all sales, to utilities as well as within industry. The latter are presumably included in purchased power.

ᶠ At 7.5 per cent of non-utility generation excluding transit generation. These are sales to electric utilities only.

ᵍ Presumably industrial consumption other than mining and manufacturing. This difference is regarded as going to other activities such as construction, operation of natural gas pipelines, etc.

TABLE A-26. DERIVATION OF INDUSTRIAL CONSUMPTION OF ELECTRICITY, 1953-56, EXCLUDING TRANSMISSION LOSSES

(Million kwh)

Item	1953	1954	1955	1956
1. Large light and power sales ᵃ........	190,010	200,155	249,206	276,647
2. Non-utility generation ᵇ............	71,504	72,959	81,972	84,136
3. Transit generation ᶜ..............	1,590	1,510	1,480	1,450
4. Non-utility generation net of transit	69,914	71,449	80,492	82,686
5. Non-utility sales to utilities ᵈ........	5,244	5,359	6,037	6,201
6. Non-utility generation used in industry (item 4 − item 5)........	64,670	66,090	74,455	76,485
7. Total industrial consumption (item 1 + item 6)......................	254,680	266,245	323,661	353,132

ᵃ E.E.I., *Statistical Bulletin for the Year 1957*, p. 27.
ᵇ *Ibid.*, p. 13, under "other sources."
ᶜ ATA, *Transit Fact Book, 1957 Edition*, p. 11.
ᵈ At 7.5 per cent of non-utility generation excluding transit generation.

TABLE A-27. ATOMIC ENERGY COMMISSION ELECTRICITY CONSUMPTION, 1943–56

(Thousand kwh)

Source of electricity [a]	1950	1951	1952	1953	1954	1955	1956
Purchased							
Oak Ridge–TVA	1,681,230	3,113,873	5,818,336	5,986,815	9,121,949	15,714,183	18,147,482
Hanford–BPA	586,169	672,080	751,705	936,129	1,034,896	1,328,056	1,551,501
Paducah–TVA		6,684	83,814	2,894,665	6,790,282	11,505,022	12,471,627
Paducah–EEI		5,810	83,225	2,727,703	6,213,252	7,371,449	7,099,375
Savannah River–SCGC		28,819	38,800	40,806	239,425	371,018	502,536
Portsmouth–OVEC			2,400	20,600	422,413	10,812,667	17,123,296
Fernald–CG & E.						96,475	105,768
Portsmouth–OPC							778,365
Total	2,267,399	3,827,266	6,778,280	12,606,718	23,822,217	47,198,870	57,779,950
Generated and used in AEC installations							
Oak Ridge:							
Generated	1,688,581	2,158,138	2,065,195	2,543,248	2,493,742	2,138,438	1,773,323
Sold	161,769	452,887	370,663	423,128	481,212	414,867	45,719
Used	1,526,812	1,705,251	1,694,532	2,120,120	2,012,530	1,723,571	1,727,604
Savannah River, generated and used					724,027	1,183,028	1,147,781
Total	1,526,812	1,705,251	1,694,532	2,120,120	2,736,557	2,906,599	2,875,385
All sources	3,794,211	5,532,517	8,472,812	14,726,838	26,558,774	50,105,469	60,655,335

Source of electricity [a]	1943	1944	1945	1946	1947	1948	1949
Purchased							
Oak Ridge–TVA	21,382	609,923	1,610,480	1,866,029	1,616,717	1,718,783	1,855,150
Hanford–BPA	9,481	145,317	416,639	363,028	313,702	389,411	473,524
Total	30,863	755,240	2,027,119	2,229,057	1,930,419	2,108,194	2,328,674
Generated and used in AEC installations							
Oak Ridge:							
Generated		408,445	1,071,533	1,319,134	1,478,499	1,541,109	1,326,151
Sold					176,405	172,066	41,110
Used					1,302,094	1,369,043	1,285,041
All sources		1,163,685	3,098,652	3,548,191	3,232,513	3,477,237	3,613,715

[a] Abbreviations stand for following: TVA, Tennessee Valley Authority; BPA, Bonneville Power Administration; EEI, Electric Energy, Inc.; SCGC, South Carolina Generating Company; OVEC, Ohio Valley Electric Corporation; CG&E, Cincinnati Gas and Electric Company; and OPC, Ohio Power Company.

SOURCE: FPC, multilithed, undated release.

TABLE A-28. CONSUMPTION OF ELECTRICITY IN ALUMINUM AND
MAGNESIUM PRODUCTION, 1935–56

| Year | Primary aluminum | | | Electricity consumed in magnesium production (million kwh)[d] (4) | Electricity consumed in aluminum and magnesium production (million kwh) (2) + (4) (5) |
	Production (tons)[a] (1)	Electricity consumed (million kwh)[b] (2)	Kwh per ton[c] (3)		
1956....	1,678,954	30,641	18,250	1,366	32,007
1955....	1,565,721	28,600	18,266	1,228	29,828
1954....	1,460,565	26,700	18,281	1,395	28,095
1953....	1,252,013	22,900	18,290	1,862	24,762
1952....	937,330	17,100	18,243	2,116	19,216
1951....	836,881	15,300	18,282	818	16,118
1950....	718,622	13,207	18,378	315	13,522
1949....	603,462	11,032	18,282	232	11,264
1948....	623,456	11,339	18,187	200	11,539
1947....	571,750	10,344	18,092	247	10,591
1946....	409,630	7,659	18,697	106	7,765
1945....	495,060	9,555	19,300	656	10,211
1944....	776,446	15,454	19,903	3,142	18,596
1943....	920,179	18,869	20,506	3,672	22,541
1942....	521,106	11,000	21,109	979	11,979
1941....	309,067	6,765	21,888	326	7,091
1940....	206,280	4,532	21,970	125	4,657
1939....	163,545	3,597	21,994	67	3,664
1938....	143,441	3,154	21,988	64	3,218
1937....	146,340	3,218	21,990	58	3,276
1936....	112,464	2,597	23,092	49	2,646
1935....	59,647	1,402	23,505	29	1,431

[a] *Metal Statistics, 1958* (New York: *American Metal Market*), p. 605.

[b] Consumption in 1947, 1950–55 from *Load*, Vol. 14, No. 1 (Schenectady, N. Y.: General Electric Co., March 1958), Table III, p. 16. Consumption in 1935–42 from Nathanael Engle, Homer E. Gregory, and Robert Mossé, *Aluminum* (Chicago: Richard D. Irwin, Inc., 1945), p. 76, Table 12. Intermediate years estimated by assuming straight-line decreases between 1942 and 1947 and straight-line increases between 1947 and 1950 in kwh per ton, and multiplying resulting figures by annual production shown in col. 1. 1956 is based on the assumption of a further decrease, to 18,250 kwh per ton, from 1955.

The 1954 figure for total consumption reported by *Load, op. cit.*, is almost identical with the figure of 26,283 million kwh reported for primary aluminum production in *Census of Manufactures, 1954*, Bulletin MC–208, p. 15.

[c] Derived from col. 1 and col. 2 in 1947, 1950–55; estimated as explained in footnote b above for remaining years.

[d] Derived, on the assumption of 10 kwh per pound of magnesium throughout the period, from production data in *Metal Statistics, 1958, op. cit.*, p. 637.

TABLE A-29. ELECTRICITY CONSUMPTION IN INDUSTRY, EXCLUDING
AEC AND ALUMINUM AND MAGNESIUM PRODUCTION, 1920-56

(Million kwh)

Year	All industry [a] (1)	AEC installations [b] (2)	Aluminum and magnesium production [c] (3)	Industry, excluding AEC (4)	Industry, excluding AEC and aluminum and magnesium (5)
1956......	353,132	60,655	32,007	292,477	260,470
1955......	323,661	50,105	29,828	273,556	243,728
1954......	266,245	26,559	28,095	239,686	211,591
1953......	254,680	14,727	24,762	239,953	215,191
1952......	224,327	8,473	19,216	215,854	196,638
1951......	215,272	5,533	16,118	209,739	193,621
1950......	190,998	3,794	13,522	187,204	173,682
1949......	165,660	3,614	11,264	162,046	150,782
1948......	169,181	3,477	11,539	165,704	154,165
1947......	153,897	3,233	10,591	150,664	140,073
1946......	133,760	3,548	7,765	130,212	122,447
1945......	143,162	3,099	10,211	140,063	129,852
1944......	158,751	1,164	18,596	157,587	138,991
1943......	158,525	31	22,541	158,494	135,953
1942......	133,899		11,979		121,920
1941......	113,932		7,091		106,841
1940......	92,390		4,656		87,734
1939......	79,044		3,664		75,380
1938......	65,850		3,218		62,632
1937......	73,300		3,276		70,024
1936......	70,500		2,646		67,854
1935......	63,265		1,431		61,834
1934......	56,695		926		55,769
1933......	52,358		1,045		51,313
1932......	48,614		1,235		47,379
1931......	56,512		2,035		54,477
1930......	61,023		2,713		58,310
1929......	63,889		2,804		61,085
1928......	59,750		2,610		57,140
1927......	57,383		2,120		55,263
1926......	52,750		2,053		50,697
1925......	45,500		1,998		43,502
1924......	40,300		2,148		38,152
1923......	38,250		1,866		36,384
1922......	32,200		552		31,648
1921......	28,000		409		27,591
1920......	31,500		1,035		30,465

[a] 1953-56 from Table A-26.

1951-52 from *Electrical World*, January 23, 1956, p. 169, for manufacturing component. To this was added consumption in mining on assumption—derived from past trends— of 130 million kwh per point of Federal Reserve Board index of minerals production, which was 115 in 1951 and 114 in 1952. Total industrial electricity in 1951, therefore, consists of

(*Footnotes continued on next page.*)

TABLE A-29 (continued)

200,322 million kwh for manufacturing and 14,950 million for minerals. For 1952, the amounts are 209,507 million and 14,820 million kwh.

1946–50 from Commerce, *Continuation to 1952 of Historical Statistics of the United States, 1789–1945*, Series G–191–193, p. 23.

1920–45 from Commerce, *Historical Statistics of the United States, 1789–1945*, Series G–191–193, p. 157.

[b] From Table A-27.

[c] Electricity for aluminum for 1935–56, from Table A–28. For 1926–34, from Nathanael Engle, Homer E. Gregory, and Robert Mossé, *Aluminum* (Chicago: Richard D. Irwin, Inc., 1945), p. 76, Table 12.

The 1920–25 data are the product of primary production (*Metal Statistics, 1958, op. cit.*, p. 605) and estimated consumption of electricity per ton of production. Consumption was based on 30,000 kwh per ton in 1920–22; 29,000 kwh per ton in 1923; and 28,500 kwh per ton in 1924 and 1925. These assumptions are based on a personal communication from Stanley V. Malcuit of Aluminum Company of America in which he states in a letter dated November 8, 1957: "As near as our records show, the kilowatt hour consumption of aluminum produced in 1920 was at about 15 per pound; in 1930, 12; in 1940, 11 . . . these figures include the entire electrical consumption used at the smelting plants for services and other operations." The comparable FPC figures listed in *Aluminum, op. cit.*, are 12.37 kwh for 1930 and 10.985 kwh for 1940.

For magnesium, 20,000 kwh per ton of production, as shown in *Metal Statistics, 1958, op. cit.*, p. 637, was used throughout.

TABLE A-30. RELATIONSHIP OF ELECTRICITY CONSUMPTION IN INDUSTRY TO FEDERAL RESERVE BOARD INDEX OF INDUSTRIAL PRODUCTION, 1920-56

Year	Industrial electricity consumption, excluding AEC and aluminum and magnesium (million kwh) [a] (1)	FRB index (1947-49 = 100) [b] (2)	Industrial consumption per point of index (mill. kwh) (1) ÷ (2) (3)
1956	260,470	143	1,821.5
1955	243,728	139	1,753.4
1954	211,591	125	1,692.7
1953	215,191	134	1,605.9
1952	196,638	124	1,585.8
1951	193,621	120	1,613.5
1950	173,682	112	1,550.7
1949	150,782	97	1,554.5
1948	154,165	104	1,482.4
1947	140,073	100	1,400.7
1946	122,447	90	1,360.5
1945	129,852	107	1,213.6
1944	138,991	125	1,111.9
1943	135,953	127	1,070.5
1942	121,920	106	1,150.2
1941	106,841	87	1,228.1
1940	87,734	67	1,309.5
1939	75,380	58	1,299.7
1938	62,632	48	1,304.8
1937	70,024	61	1,147.9
1936	67,854	56	1,211.7
1935	61,834	47	1,315.7
1934	55,769	40	1,394.2
1933	51,313	37	1,386.8
1932	47,379	31	1,528.4
1931	54,477	40	1,361.9
1930	58,310	49	1,190.0
1929	61,085	59	1,035.3
1928	57,140	53	1,078.1
1927	55,263	51	1,083.6
1926	50,697	51	994.1
1925	43,502	49	888.2
1924	38,152	44	867.6
1923	36,384	47	774.1
1922	31,648	39	811.5
1921	27,591	31	890.0
1920	30,465	41	743.0

[a] Table A-29, col. 5.
[b] *Federal Reserve Bulletin*, August 1958, p. 972.

TABLE A-31.   RATES OF INCREASE IN INDUSTRIAL ELECTRICITY
CONSUMPTION PER POINT OF THE FEDERAL RESERVE BOARD INDEX
OF INDUSTRIAL PRODUCTION, SELECTED PERIODS, 1920-55

Period	Approximate annual rate of increase (Per cent)
1920-55	2.50%
1920-29	3.75
1922-55	2.33
1929-55	2.00
1929-39	2.30
1939-55	1.90
1939-47	0.94
1947-55	2.80
1951-55	2.00

SOURCE: Table A-30, col. 3. Excludes AEC and aluminum and magnesium production.

TABLE A-32.   ELECTRICITY CONSUMPTION IN INDUSTRY, 1975
PROJECTION (EXCLUDING AEC AND ALUMINUM AND MAGNESIUM)

Item	Million kwh	Per cent
1. Consumption in 1955, excluding AEC and aluminum and magnesium	243,728[a]	
2. Annual percentage increase of electricity used per point of the FRB index of industrial production		2%[b]
3. Annual rate of increase of FRB index of industrial production		4[c]
4. Annual rate of increase of electricity consumption in industry		6[c]
5. Projected 1975 level of electricity consumption expressed as multiple of 1955 (item 1 × 3.2[d])	781,669	

[a] From Table A-29, col. 5.

[b] Based on Table A-31 as most representative of both the long-run (1929-55) and the recent period (1951-55).

[c] Taken as a convenient approximation of growth rather than as an arithmetically accurate compound of the two preceding rates which are multiplicative, not additive.

[d] Amount at compound interest rate in twenty years (ratio carried to additional places in actual computation).

TABLE A–33.   CIVILIAN PURCHASES OF ALUMINUM, AND GROSS
NATIONAL PRODUCT, SELECTED PERIODS, 1910–55

Period	Annual percentage growth rate for civilian aluminum purchases[a] (1)	GNP growth rate[b] (2)	Excess of civilian aluminum purchases over GNP growth rate (1) − (2) (3)
1910–55............	10.41%	3.15%	7.26%
1910–39............	8.10	2.36	5.74
1910–28............	12.30	3.14	9.16
1928–55............	9.14	3.16	5.98
1928–39............	1.56	1.09	0.47
1939–55............	14.73	4.61	10.12
1939–47............	20.53	5.01	15.52
1947–55............	9.20	4.21	4.99

[a] Civilian aluminum demand for years prior to 1955 from James E. Rosenzweig, *The Demand for Aluminum, A Case-Study in Long-Range Forecasting,* University of Illinois Bulletin, Business Study No. 10 (Urbana, Ill.), p. 64; 1955 and 1957, from Commerce, Business and Defense Services Administration, Aluminum and Magnesium Division, *Aluminum Supply 1950–1960, and Shipments to Consumers,* mimeo. release, dated March 4, 1958.

[b] Statistical Appendix to Part I, Table XIII.

TABLE A–34.   SHARE OF PRIMARY ALUMINUM PRODUCTION IN
DOMESTIC DEMAND, 1950–57

(Million pounds)

Year	Domestic primary production (1)	Total supply (2)	Total shipments to consumers (3)	Difference between supply and shipments to consumers (2) − (3) (4)	Primary production[a] net of difference between supply and shipments (1) − (4) (5)	Net primary production as per cent of shipments to consumers (5) ÷ (3) (6)
1957........	3,295	4,677	3,848	829	2,466	64.1%
1956........	3,358	4,697	4,109	588	2,770	67.4
1955........	3,131	4,393	3,997	396	2,735	68.4
1954........	2,921	4,008	3,007	1,001	1,920	63.9
1953........	2,504	3,891	3,211	680	1,824	56.8
1952........	1,875	2,753	2,662	91	1,784	67.0
1951........	1,674	2,540	2,421	119	1,555	64.2
1950........	1,437	2,400	2,391	9	1,428	59.7

[a] This is equivalent to the simplifying assumption that the entire difference between total supply and total shipments is attributable to primary domestic aluminum. The main source of this difference is primary aluminum for the stockpile which is not included in the shipment data. In fact some of the aluminum entering the stockpile is imported.

SOURCE: Commerce, Business and Defense Services Administration, Aluminum and Magnesium Division, *Aluminum Supply 1950–1960, and Shipments to Consumers,* mimeo. release, dated March 4, 1958.

TABLE A-35. ELECTRICITY CONSUMPTION IN PRIMARY ALUMINUM
PRODUCTION, 1955 AND PROJECTION TO 1975

Item	Physical units 1955 (1)	Annual rate of change, 1955–75 (per cent) (2)	Physical units 1975 (3)
1. Aluminum shipments (tons)..........	2,000,000 [a]	8.4%	10,000,000 [b]
2. Primary aluminum production (tons)..	1,565,721 [c]	7.4	6,500,000 [d]
3. Kilowatt hours per ton of primary production......................	18,266 [e]	−0.46	16,666 [f]
4. Electricity consumed in primary aluminum production (million kwh) (item 2 × item 3).	28,600	6.9	108,329

[a] Table A-34, col. 3.

[b] Projection of Richard S. Reynolds, Jr., before meeting of the Investment Bankers
Association of America, December 4, 1957. This projection appears consistent with the
relationship between the civilian shipments of aluminum and gross national product shown
in Table A-33. If it is assumed that direct military purchases of aluminum reported as
such will total 300,000 tons in 1975—compared with shipments of 168,500 tons in 1955
and 133,500 tons in 1957 (Commerce, Business and Defense Services Administration,
Aluminum and Magnesium Division, *Aluminum Supply 1950–1960, and Shipments to
Consumers*, mimeo. release, dated March 4, 1958)—there would remain 9,700,000 tons of
aluminum for civilian shipments.

Civilian shipments of 9,700,000 tons in 1975 is equivalent to an increase of 8.7 per cent
per year over the 1,830,000 tons of 1955. With GNP growth assumed at 4 per cent per year,
civilian purchases would exceed the GNP growth rate by 4.7 per cent. While the growth
rates for civilian shipments (Table A-33) fail to show sufficient regularity to serve in themselves as the basis for the projection, the last decade or so appears to lend support to the
projection advanced by Mr. Reynolds.

Whereas total (civilian plus military) shipments are assumed to increase from 2 million
tons to 10 million tons, or at an annual rate of 8.4 per cent, primary aluminum production
is estimated to increase from 1,566,000 tons to 6,500,000 tons, or at a rate of 7.4 per cent.
This difference in rates is due solely to the implicit assumption that in 1975 there will be no
production for stockpiling, i.e., that production will be related to shipments as developed
in Table A-34, col. 6, and that there will be no discrepancy corresponding to the difference
between cols. 2 and 3 of that table.

[c] *Metal Statistics, 1958* (New York: *American Metal Market*), p. 605.

[d] It is assumed that 65 per cent of total aluminum shipments in 1975 will be met from
primary domestic production. This is regarded as being in accord with the general levels
shown in Table A-34, col. 6.

[e] Table A-28, col. 3.

[f] Represents a reduction of 1,600 kwh per ton from 1955, less than 0.5 per cent per year.
While there have been much more rapid rates of reduction in electricity consumption per
ton of primary aluminum in the past, the last decade or so has shown but slight reduction
in this relationship (Table A-28, col. 3). The following improvements in electricity consumption per ton of output have prevailed: 1920–55, 1.43 per cent; 1929–55, 1.13 per cent;
1935–55, 1.25 per cent; 1945–55, .5 per cent. The improvement in the last decade, moreover, has been concentrated in the earlier years. The record thus suggests a future trend
that is more in accord with recent experience.

TABLE A-36. ELECTRICITY CONSUMPTION IN PRIMARY MAGNESIUM PRODUCTION, 1955 AND PROJECTION TO 1975

Item	Physical units 1955 (1)	Annual rate of change, 1955–75 (per cent) (2)	Physical units 1975 (3)
1. Primary magnesium production (tons).	61,135[a]	8.8%	330,000[b]
2. Kilowatt hours per ton of primary production......................	20,000[c]	−1.12	16,000[d]
3. Electricity consumption (million kwh).	1,223	7.6	5,280

[a] *Metal Statistics, 1958* (New York: *American Metal Market*, p. 637).

[b] Letter of February 28, 1958, from A. W. Winston, Sr., Assistant Manager, Magnesium Department, Dow Chemical Company, Midland, Mich. This is his extrapolation of the projection to 1970 in the publication *Selected Magnesium Statistics 1928–1956*, Dow Chemical Company Bulletin No. 141–142, Midland, Mich.

[c] Throughout this section, the rate of 20,000 kwh per ton of primary magnesium has been used. The magazine *Load*, Vol. 14, No. 1 (Schenectady, N. Y.: General Electric Co., March 1958), p. 16, uses a factor of 24,000 kwh per ton. On the other hand, A. W. Winston, Sr. states, *op. cit.*, that the current use (February 1 58) is between 17 and 18 thousand kwh per ton.

[d] Based on interpretation of Mr. Winston's letter (see footnote a).

TABLE A-37. SUMMARY: INDUSTRIAL ENERGY CONSUMPTION, 1955 AND PROJECTION TO 1975

| Fuel | 1955 | | | | | | 1975 | | | | | |
| | Physical units | | | Billion Btu | | | Physical units | | | Billion Btu | | |
	For purposes other than electricity generation[a] (1)	For electricity generation[b] (2)	Total (3)	For purposes other than electricity generation[a] (4)	For electricity generation[b] (5)	Total (6)	For purposes other than electricity generation[c] (7)	For electricity generation[d] (8)	Total (9)	For purposes other than electricity generation[c] (10)	For electricity generation[d] (11)	Total (12)
Coal (thous. tons):												
Bituminous	186,385	87,724	274,109	4,883,287	2,111,803	6,995,090	244,402	252,781	497,183	6,403,342	6,066,729	12,470,071
Anthracite	5,053		5,053	128,347		128,347	4,915		4,915	124,848		124,848
Total				5,011,634	2,111,803	7,123,437				6,528,190	6,066,729	12,594,919
Oil:												
Residual (thous. bbl.)	208,843	58,556	267,399	1,333,253	369,681	1,702,934	312,686	115,655	428,341	1,996,188	728,627	2,724,815
Distillates (thous. bbl.)	54,577		54,577	316,322		316,322	90,555		90,555	526,510		526,510
Gasoline (thous. bbl.)	8,958		8,958	46,651		46,651	8,958		8,958	46,651		46,651
Acid sludge (thous. bbl.)	2,228		2,228	10,013		10,013	2,117		2,117	9,514		9,514
Coke (thous. tons)	2,450		2,450	73,500		73,500	7,162		7,162	214,860		214,860
Still gas (mill. cu. ft.)	591,243		591,243	886,651		886,651	1,218,397		1,218,397	1,827,596		1,827,596
Total				2,666,390	369,681	3,036,071				4,621,319	728,627	5,349,946
Natural Gas Liquids (thous. bbl.):												
Natural gasoline	1,221		1,221	6,361		6,361	1,221		1,221	6,361		6,361
LPG	12,487		12,487	50,085		50,085	40,530		40,530	162,566		162,566
Total				56,446		56,446				168,927		168,927
Natural Gas (mill. cu. ft.)	3,943,296	734,315	4,677,611	4,081,311	737,542	4,818,853	8,549,275	1,612,439	10,161,714	8,848,499	1,612,439	10,460,938
Hydro (mill. kwh)		56,777	56,777		676,803	676,803		131,586	131,586		1,185,790	1,185,790
Grand total				11,815,781	3,895,829	15,711,610				20,166,935	9,593,585	29,760,520

[a] Table A-9.
[b] Appendix Table H-9.
[c] Table A-23.
[d] Appendix Table H-17.

Section B. Commercial

General Note

This section consists of only nine statistical tables, since a good deal of the information is based upon data developed for households in Section C. All consumption except that via electricity for 1955 is given in a single table: B–1; the remaining eight tables relate to the 1975 projection. Tables B–2 and B–3 establish 1975 gas consumption, B–4 coal and oil consumption, and B–5 through B–8 electricity consumption. A summary of the 1975 data is given in Table B–9.

Commercial Tables

B–1. Commercial Consumption of Fuels, Except via Electricity, 1955
B–2. Relationship of Commercial to Residential Gas Consumption, 1932–57
B–3. Commercial Gas Consumption, Projection to 1975
B–4. Commercial Coal and Oil Consumption, Projection to 1975
B–5. Electricity Consumption per Customer, Residential and Commercial, 1926–57
B–6. Relationship of Households to Number of Commercial Electric Customers, Selected Years, 1930–56
B–7 Commercial Electricity Consumption, Projection to 1975
B–8. Determination of Representative Character of Small Light and Power Sales Classification for Commercial Consumption, 1926–55
B–9. Summary: Commercial Consumption of Energy, 1955 and Projection to 1975

TABLE B–1. COMMERCIAL CONSUMPTION OF FUELS, EXCEPT VIA ELECTRICITY, 1955

Item	Physical units	Billion Btu
1. Coal (thous. tons): [a]		
a. Bituminous	26,881	704,282
b. Anthracite	7,551	191,795
c. Total	34,432	896,077
2. Oil (thous. bbl.): [b]		
a. Heating oil No. 3	24,898	146,400
b. Heating oil No. 4	7,247	44,134
c. Heating oil No. 5	30,211	188,426
d. Heating oil No. 6	56,071	357,957
e. Total	118,427	736,917
3. NGL (thous. bbl.) [c]	6,453	25,882
4. Gas (mill. cu. ft.) [d]	582,541	602,930
5. Grand total		2,261,806

[a] Appendix Table C–5, col. 1 − col. 2.
[b] Mines, *Mineral Market Report*, No. MMS 2681, pp. 11, 12, Tables 13 and 14.
[c] Appendix Table C–4, item 4.
[d] Btu's from A.G.A., *1956 Gas Facts*, p. 97, Table 81; physical units based upon 1,035 Btu per cu. ft.

589

TABLE B-2. RELATIONSHIP OF COMMERCIAL TO RESIDENTIAL GAS CONSUMPTION, 1932–57

Year	Residential			Commercial			Relationship of commercial to residential		
	Number of customers (thous.) (1)	Consumption (bill. Btu) (2)	Consumption per customer (mill. Btu) (3)	Number of customers (thous.) (4)	Consumption (bill. Btu) (5)	Consumption per customer (mill. Btu) (6)	Average commercial consumption as multiple of residential consumption (6)÷(3) (7)	Number of commercial customers as per cent of residential customers (4)÷(1) (8)	Commercial consumption as per cent of residential consumption (5)÷(2) (9)
1957	28,101	2,598,500	92.47	2,211	698,890	316.10	3.42	7.87%	26.89%
1956	27,241	2,464,200	90.46	2,141	655,770	306.29	3.39	7.86	26.61
1955	26,283	2,238,670	85.18	2,048	602,930	294.40	3.46	7.79	26.93
1954	25,398	2,003,100	78.87	1,990	540,490	271.60	3.44	7.84	26.98
1953	24,647	1,803,280	73.16	1,926	498,020	258.58	3.54	7.81	27.62
1952	23,852	1,734,790	72.73	1,869	492,910	263.73	3.63	7.84	28.41
1951	23,042	1,620,450	70.33	1,787	455,940	255.14	3.63	7.76	28.14
1950	22,146	1,383,910	62.49	1,739	410,380	235.99	3.78	7.85	29.65
1949	21,264	1,182,740	55.62	1,657	372,420	224.76	4.04	7.79	31.49
1948	20,562	1,115,290	54.24	1,571	353,530	225.04	4.15	7.64	31.70
1947	19,835	1,008,650	50.85	1,474	310,670	210.77	4.14	7.43	30.80
1946	19,157	848,230	44.28	1,377	262,990	190.99	4.31	7.19	31.00
1945	18,607	774,930	41.65	1,278	249,730	195.41	4.69	6.87	32.23
1944	18,320	731,250	39.92	1,177	220,830	187.62	4.70	6.42	30.20
1943	17,838	700,140	39.25	1,141	208,310	182.57	4.65	6.40	29.75
1942	17,511	667,880	38.14	1,137	198,970	175.00	4.59	6.49	29.79
1941	16,904	586,200	34.68	1,137	164,950	145.07	4.18	6.73	28.14
1940	16,381	582,310	35.55	1,138	159,770	140.40	3.95	6.95	27.44
1939	15,926	528,940	33.21	1,121	146,850	131.00	3.94	7.04	27.76
1938	15,697	495,620	31.57	1,094	137,960	126.11	4.00	6.97	27.84
1937	15,466	498,730	32.25	1,056	138,150	130.82	4.06	6.83	27.70
1936	15,026	478,420	31.84	1,058	136,880	129.38	4.06	7.04	28.61
1935	14,725	444,450	30.18	1,014	121,110	119.44	3.96	6.89	27.25
1934	14,440	420,150	29.10	990	110,160	111.27	3.82	6.86	26.22
1933	14,141	423,720	29.96	978	115,030	117.62	3.93	6.92	27.15
1932	14,452	467,230	32.33	999	119,330	119.45	3.70	6.91	25.54

SOURCE: 1932–54: A.G.A., *Historical Statistics of the Gas Industry* (1956), for customers, p. 121, Table 69; for consumption, p. 121, Table 87. 1955–57: A.G.A., *1957 Gas Facts*, for customers, p. 80, Table 64: for consumption, p. 96, Table 82.

TABLE B-3.   COMMERCIAL GAS CONSUMPTION, PROJECTION TO 1975

Item	Cubic feet (million)	Btu (billion)
1. Residential consumption, space heating[a]	3,526,403	3,649,827
2. Residential consumption, other[b]	1,387,532	1,436,096
3. Total	4,913,935	5,085,923
4. Estimated commercial consumption (25% of residential consumption[c])	1,228,484	1,271,481

[a] Appendix Table C-13.
[b] Appendix Table C-17.
[c] Assumed on the basis of the slightly declining trend shown in this relationship in Table B-2, col. 9.

TABLE B-4.   COMMERCIAL COAL AND OIL CONSUMPTION, PROJECTION TO 1975

Item	Btu (billion)	Equivalent physical units
1. Aggregate fuel consumption, 1955[a]	2,261,806	
2. Projected fuel consumption, 1975[b]	3,236,644	
3. Projected commercial gas consumption[c]	1,271,481	1,228,484 mill. cu. ft.
4. Balance (item 2 − item 3) supplied by coal and oil	1,965,163	
5. Coal, at two-thirds of 1955 Btu consumption	597,385[d]	22,981 thous. tons
a. Bituminous	448,039	17,101 thous. tons
b. Anthracite	149,346	5,880 thous. tons
6. Oil, including NGL (item 4 − item 5)	1,367,778	
7. NGL[e]	46,504	11,594 thous. bbl.
8. Oil, excluding NGL (item 6 − item 7)[f]	1,321,274	212,337 thous. bbl.[g]
a. Heating oil No. 3	262,492	44,641 thous. bbl.
b. Heating oil No. 4	79,131	12,994 thous. bbl.
c. Heating oil No. 5	337,843	54,168 thous. bbl.
d. Heating oil No. 6	641,808	100,534 thous. bbl.

[a] From Table B-1, item 5.
[b] Increased over 1955 by percentage increase between 1955 and 1975 (43.1 per cent) in number of customers for commercial electricity use (Table B-7, item 3 and Table B-6, col. 2, average 1955–56—6,016,947).
[c] From Table B-3, item 4.
[d] 1955 consumption: Table B-1, item 1c; one-fourth assumed to be anthracite.
[e] Estimated as 3.4 per cent, which is proportion of NGL to total oil plus NGL in 1955 (Table B-1).
[f] Subtotals estimated as having increased from 1955 by same percentage as total (79.2975). The total in 1955 (Table B-1, item 2e) was 736,917 billion Btu.
[g] Derived as sum of types of oil shown below.

TABLE B-5. ELECTRICITY CONSUMPTION PER CUSTOMER, RESIDENTIAL AND COMMERCIAL, 1926-57

| Year | Consumption per customer | | Average commercial as multiple of average residential consumption (2) ÷ (1) (3) |
	Residential (kwh) (1)	Commercial a (kwh) (2)	
1957.............	3,174	15,432	4.86
1956.............	2,969	14,395	4.85
1955.............	2,751	13,422	4.88
1954.............	2,549	12,353	4.85
1953.............	2,346	12,007	5.12
1952.............	2,169	11,106	5.12
1951.............	2,004	10,432	5.21
1950.............	1,830	9,320	5.09
1949.............	1,684	8,871	5.27
1948.............	1,563	8,535	5.46
1947.............	1,438	7,915	5.50
1946.............	1,329	7,224	5.44
1945.............	1,229	7,062	5.75
1944.............	1,151	7,080	6.15
1943.............	1,070	6,722	6.28
1942.............	1,022	6,354	6.22
1941.............	986	5,754	5.84
1940.............	952	5,280	5.55
1939.............	897	4,968	5.54
1938.............	853	4,668	5.47
1937.............	805	4,578	5.69
1936.............	735	4,143	5.64
1935.............	677	3,682	5.44
1934.............	629	3,368	5.35
1933.............	600	3,208	5.35
1932.............	601	3,304	5.50
1931.............	583	3,686	6.32
1930.............	547	3,863	7.06
1929.............	502	3,681	7.33
1928.............	463	3,397	7.34
1927.............	446	3,307	7.42
1926.............	430	3,119	7.25

a These figures are for customers for "small light and power sales." Table B-8 contains the reason for considering this series representative of commercial consumption. The degree of representativeness, as also shown in Table B-8, deteriorates in the more remote years. No attempt has been made in this table to allow for any discrepancy in this regard.

SOURCE: 1945-57: E.E.I., *Statistical Bulletin for the Year 1957*, p. 50; 1937-44, *ibid., 1951*, p. 31; and 1926-36, *ibid., 1941*, p. 22.

TABLE B-6. RELATIONSHIP OF HOUSEHOLDS TO NUMBER OF COMMERCIAL ELECTRIC CUSTOMERS, SELECTED YEARS, 1930-56

Period	Number of households [a] (thous.) (1)	Number of commercial customers (December 31 of year shown in stub) [b] (2)	Number of commercial customers as per cent of number of households (3)
March 1956........	48,785	6,042,309	12.39%
April 1955.........	47,788	5,991,586	12.54
April 1954.........	46,893	5,863,210	12.50
April 1953.........	46,334	5,634,130	12.16
April 1952.........	45,504	5,528,117	12.15
April 1951.........	44,656	5,466,181	12.24
March 1950........	43,554	5,290,768	12.15
April 1949.........	42,182	5,131,730	12.17
April 1948.........	40,532	4,960,895	12.24
April 1947.........	39,107	4,692,850	12.00
April 1940.........	34,949	4,215,254	12.06
April 1930.........	29,905	3,594,115	12.02

[a] 1940-54: Census, *Current Population Reports*, Series P-20, No. 55, pp. 1-2; 1930, 1955, and 1956: Commerce, *Statistical Abstract of the United States, 1957*, Table 47, p. 45.

[b] Customers classified as "small light and power sales" (see Table B-8). Figures, from E.E.I., for 1947-56, *Statistical Bulletin for the Year 1957*, p. 33, Table 26; for 1940 and 1930, *ibid.*, for 1941, p. 20.

TABLE B-7. COMMERCIAL ELECTRICITY CONSUMPTION, PROJECTION TO 1975

Item	1975
1. Projected percentage number of commercial customers to households [a].	12.5
2. Projected number of households [b]..............................	68,878,000
3. Estimated number of commercial customers (item 2 × item 1).......	8,609,750
4. Projected consumption per commercial customer as multiple of consumption per residential customer [c]..........................	5
5. Projected consumption per residential customer (kwh) [d]............	6,250
6. Estimated consumption per commercial customer (item 4 × item 5) (kwh)..	31,250
7. Projected commercial consumption, 1975 (mill. kwh) (item 3 × item 6).	269,055
8. Commercial consumption, 1955 (mill. kwh) [e].......................	80,759

[a] Based upon material in Table B-6, col. 3.

[b] From Appendix Table I-1.

[c] Based upon material in Table B-5, col. 3.

[d] From Appendix Table C-38; average of family-type and over-all consumption per household. This average, which gives double weight to family-type households, recognizes that on a per-customer basis (which is the parameter here wanted) the family-type consumption is probably considerably higher than stated because of doubling up which is less frequent in individual primary households.

[e] "Small light and power sales," as per Table B-8, col. 11.

TABLE B–8. DETERMINATION OF REPRESENTATIVE CHARACTER OF SMALL LIGHT AND POWER SALES CLASSIFICATION FOR COMMERCIAL CONSUMPTION, 1926–55

(Million kwh)

Year	"Large light and power sales" a (1)	Industrial generation of electricity b (2)	Estimated industrial consumption (1) + (2) (3)	Transit generation c (4)	Nontransit industrial generation of electricity (2) − (4) (5)	Sales of industrial generation to utilities d (6)	Adjusted estimated industrial consumption (3) − (4) − (6) (7)	Actual industrial consumption e (8)	Utility sales to industry presumably included in "small light and power sales" f (8) − (7) (9)	"Small light and power sales" a (10)	Commercial sales = adjusted "small light and power sales" (10) − (9) (11)	Commercial sales as per cent of "small light and power sales" (11) ÷ (10) (12)
1955	249,206	81,972	331,178	1,480	80,492	6,037	323,661	323,661	0	80,759	80,759	100.00%
1954	200,155	72,959	273,114	1,510	71,449	5,359	266,245	266,245	0	73,373	73,373	100.00
1953	190,010	71,504	261,514	1,590	69,914	5,244	254,680	254,680	0	69,208	69,208	100.00
1952	167,358	63,831	231,189	1,770	62,061	4,655	224,764	224,327	− 433	62,080	62,515	100.70
1951	157,827	62,685	220,512	1,870	60,815	4,561	214,083	215,272	+1,189	57,278	56,089	97.92
1950	139,065	59,533	198,598	2,070	57,463	4,310	192,218	190,998	−1,220	50,446	51,666	102.41
1949	120,766	53,966	174,732	2,123	51,843	3,888	168,721	165,660	−3,061	46,262	49,332	106.63
1948	124,088	54,110	178,198	2,113	51,997	3,900	172,185	169,181	−3,004	43,193	46,197	106.95
1947	113,523	51,661	165,184	2,093	49,568	3,718	159,373	153,897	−5,476	38,379	43,855	114.26
1946	98,885	46,431	145,316	2,077	44,354	3,327	139,912	133,760	−6,152	33,016	39,168	118.63
1945	107,490	48,769	156,259	2,130	46,639	3,498	150,631	143,162	−7,469	30,438	37,907	124.53
1944	115,187	51,336	166,523	2,238	49,098	3,682	160,603	158,751	−1,852	29,837	31,689	106.20
1943	106,657	49,781	156,438	2,237	47,544	3,566	150,635	158,525	+7,890	28,192	20,302	72.01
1942	88,378	47,167	135,545	2,227	44,940	3,371	129,947	133,899	+3,952	27,233	23,281	85.49
1941	76,061	43,518	119,579	2,167	41,351	3,101	114,312	113,932	− 380	24,628	25,008	101.54
1940	59,557	38,070	97,627	2,255	35,815	2,686	92,685	92,390	− 295	22,373	22,668	101.31
1939	51,108	33,666	84,774	2,164	31,502	2,363	80,248	79,044	−1,204	20,722	21,926	105.81
1938	43,140	28,143	71,283	2,114	26,029	1,952	67,217	65,850	−1,367	19,137	20,504	107.14
1937	51,360	27,563	78,923	2,197	25,366	1,902	74,824	73,300	−1,524	18,075	19,598	108.43
1936	48,655	26,690	75,345	2,271	24,419	1,831	71,243	70,500	− 743	15,612	16,355	104.75

1935..	40,865	23,648	64,513	2,309	21,339	1,600	60,604	63,265	+2,661	13,588	10,927	80.41
1934..	36,944	23,146	60,090	2,352	20,794	1,560	56,177	56,695	+ 518	12,278	11,760	95.78
1933..	33,857	20,915	54,772	2,377	18,538	1,390	51,005	52,358	+1,353	11,589	10,236	88.32
1932..	30,964	19,966	50,930	2,433	17,533	1,315	47,183	48,614	+1,431	12,106	10,675	88.17
1931..	36,937	22,023	58,960	2,621	19,402	1,455	54,884	56,512	+1,628	13,544	11,916	87.98
1930..	40,148	23,525	63,673	2,770	20,755	1,557	59,346	61,023	+1,677	13,944	12,267	87.97
1929..	42,971	24,567	67,538	2,863	21,704	1,628	63,047	63,889	+ 842	13,106	12,264	93.58
1928..	37,715	25,275	62,990	2,935	22,340	1,676	58,379	59,750	+1,371	11,692	10,321	88.27
1927..	34,540	25,972	60,512	2,976	22,996	1,725	55,812	57,383	+1,571	10,766	9,195	85.40
1926..	31,993	24,869	56,862	3,108	21,761	1,632	52,122	52,750	+ 628	9,485	8,857	93.41

a E.E.I.: Figures for 1926–54 from *Statistical Bulletin for the Year 1954*, p. 25; 1955, *ibid.*, for *1957*, p. 27.

b E.E.I.: 1926–52, *ibid.*, *1954*, p. 13; 1953–55, *ibid.*, *1957*, p. 13.

c ATA, "Source and Distribution of Electrical Energy Consumed by the Transit Industry of the United States and Cost of Purchased Power—1920–1957, Inclusive," mimeo release by the Statistical Department, August 22, 1958.

d Assumed at 7.5 per cent of industrial generation excluding transit. There exists, from 1926–39, a series of electricity sales to utilities from "other sources." However, this series includes, besides industry, also "Federal, State and District Projects," sales to utilities (NELA, *Statistical Bulletin*, No. 5, June 1930, p. 5, Table VII). While the data are very close to those shown here from 1926–29, thereafter they begin to exceed the series here shown, as follows: 1930: 2,281; 1931: 2,031; 1932: 2,532; 1933: 2,865; 1934: 2,474; 1935: 2,351; 1936: 2,065; 1937: 3,429; 1938: 3,802; 1939: 4,045. No data are available after 1939. Rather than use this series, or estimates derived from the years that include public power project sales, 7.5 per cent, based on the years 1926–29, has been consistently assumed. A measure of the difference involved may be obtained by considering that even in the year in which there was the maximum gap between the two series—1938—sales, including those from public projects, would amount to some 14 per cent of generation.

e 1920–45: Commerce, *Historical Statistics of the United States, 1789–1945*, Series G 191–193, p. 157; 1946–50: Commerce, *Continuation to 1952 of Historical Statistics of the United States, 1789–1945*, Series G 191–193, p. 23; 1951–52: *Electrical World*, January 23, 1956, p. 169, adjusted to include mining by assuming that mining consumed 130,000,000 kwh per point of the FRB index of mining in 1951 and 1952; and 1953–55: assumed to equal figure shown in col. 7.

f The plus sign (+) designates amounts of energy sold by utilities to industry, but recorded as "small light and power sales," i.e., actual industrial consumption is larger by the amount indicated than that derived by adding "large light and power sales" and non-utility generation. The minus sign (−) designates amounts of energy sold by utilities to commercial consumers, but recorded as "large light and power sales," i.e., actual industrial consumption is smaller by the amount indicated than that derived by adding "large light and power sales" and non-utility generation.

TABLE B-9. SUMMARY: COMMERCIAL CONSUMPTION OF ENERGY, 1955 AND PROJECTION TO 1975

Fuel	Nonelectric		Fuels via electricity		Total	
	1975 [a] (1)	1955 [b] (2)	1975 [c] (3)	1955 [d] (4)	1975 (5)	1955 (6)
Physical units						
Coal (thous. tons)	22,981	34,432	73,868	23,628	96,849	58,060
Oil (thous. bbl.):						
Heating oil No. 3	44,641	24,898			44,641	24,898
Heating oil No. 4	12,994	7,247			12,994	7,247
Heating oil No. 5	54,168	30,211			54,168	30,211
Heating oil No. 6	100,534	56,071	26,659	14,367	127,193	70,438
Total oil	212,337	118,427	26,659	14,367	238,996	132,794
Gas (mill. cu. ft.)	1,228,484	582,541	469,944	218,577	1,698,428	801,118
NGL (thous. bbl.)	11,594	6,453			11,594	6,453
Hydro (mill. kwh)			46,840	21,490	46,840	21,490
Btu's (billion)						
Coal	597,385	896,077	1,772,821	569,636	2,370,206	1,465,713
Oil:						
Heating oil No. 3	262,492	146,400			262,492	146,400
Heating oil No. 4	79,131	44,134			79,131	44,134
Heating oil No. 5	337,843	188,426			337,843	188,426
Heating oil No. 6	641,808	357,957	167,955	90,820	807,763	448,777
Total oil	1,321,274	736,917	167,955	90,820	1,489,229	827,737
Gas	1,271,481	602,930	469,944	219,867	1,741,425	822,797
NGL	46,504	25,882			46,504	25,882
Hydro			419,516	252,638	419,516	252,638
Grand total	3,236,644	2,261,806	2,830,236	1,132,961	6,066,880	3,394,767

[a] Gas from Table B-3; all other from Table B-4.
[b] Table B-1.
[c] Appendix Table H-17.
[d] Appendix Table H-9.

Section C. Households

General Note

Tables C–1 through C–18 deal with consumption of fuels other than those used in the generation of electricity consumed in households.

Tables C–1 through C–5 develop the distribution pattern for 1955, which is summarized in C–6. With Table C–7, there begins a series of tables estimating the number of 1975 dwelling units heated with gas and oil, culminating in Table C–13 which contains the 1975 projection of oil and gas consumed for heating.

Table C–14 projects the use of the remaining fuels for space heating in 1975; Tables C–15 through C–17 develop the projection of gas used for purposes other than space heating, and Table C–18 shows uses of fuels, excluding gas, used for purposes other than space heating.

Tables C–19 through C–38 deal with electricity consumption, the first containing the 1955 pattern, and all the remaining tables developing the 1975 projection. Tables C–20 through C–22 present basic facts regarding past consumption and saturation rates. Tables C–23 through C–31 present data on appliance sales and distribution on the basis of which saturation rates for the various appliances are projected, both for electricity and for gas. Tables C–32 through C–36 supply average annual consumption data per appliance or use, for electricity and in some instances also for gas. Tables C–37 and C–38 combine the saturation and consumption rates with the number of customers to yield 1975 consumption of electricity. Table C–39 is a summary of all household energy consumption in 1975 in physical terms, and Table C–40 presents the summary in Btu terms.

Household Tables

C– 1. Household Consumption of Gas, Total and Per Customer, 1955
C– 2. Household Consumption of Heating Oils, 1955
C– 3. Determination of Use of No. 1 Heating Oil, 1955
C– 4. Household Consumption of LPG, 1955
C– 5. Household Consumption of Coal, 1955
C– 6. Summary: Household Energy Consumption, 1955
C– 7. Number of Households by Type of Heating, Mid-1956
C– 8. Heating Characteristics of New Nonfarm Family Houses Started in First Quarter of 1956
C– 9. Derivation of Distribution of Gas and Oil Heating Systems in New Housing Estimated to be Constructed in 1955–75
C–10. Estimated Distribution in 1975, by Heating System and Fuel, of Oil- and Gas-Heated Households Carried Over From 1956
C–11. Assumptions Concerning Number of Households Heated by Different Means in 1975
C–12. Distribution of New Oil- and Gas-Heated Dwelling Units, Estimated 1975
C–13. Consumption of Oil and Gas in Household Heating, Estimated 1975
C–14. Consumption of LPG and Coal in Household Heating, Estimated 1975
C–15. Household Consumption of Gas Per Customer in Uses Other Than Space Heating, 1975 Projection

TABLE C-1. HOUSEHOLD CONSUMPTION OF GAS, TOTAL AND PER CUSTOMER, 1955

Item	Residential sales of gas [a]					Number of residential customers [d] (thousand) (5)	Sales per residential customer (million Btu) (3) ÷ (5) (6)
	LPG, distributed through mains [b] (billion Btu) (1)	Other than LPG [c] (billion Btu) (2)	Total				
			Billion Btu (3)	Million cu. ft. (4)			
1. All uses....	5,480	2,233,190	2,238,670	2,162,966		26,283	85
2. Non-space heating..	2,610	812,640	815,250	787,681		26,283	31
3. Space heating..	2,870	1,420,550	1,423,420	1,375,285		14,711	97

[a] Btu's converted from therms in source material on basis of 100,000 Btu's per therm.

[b] A.G.A., *1956 Gas Facts*, p. 103, Table 90; non-space heating determined by consideration of geographic sales distribution.

[c] *Ibid.*, p. 131, Table 122; non-space heating assumed to be four times volume in third quarter; space heating derived as difference between item 1 and item 2.

[d] Total and non-space heating, *ibid.*, p. 82, Table 62; space heating, *ibid.*, p. 139, Table 133. It is assumed that space heating customers also use gas in one or more appliances other than space heating, and that, therefore, all customers use gas for other purposes than space heating.

TABLE C-2. HOUSEHOLD CONSUMPTION OF HEATING OILS, 1955

Fuel	Sales[a] (thous. bbl.) (1)	Non-household use in agriculture[b] (thous. bbl.) (2)	Household use					
			Physical units (thous. bbl.)			Billion Btu		
			Total (1)−(2) (3)	Space heating (4)	Other (5)	Space heating (6)	Other (7)	Total (8)
Kerosine..........	84,331	4,381	79,950	43,972 [c]	35,978	249,321	203,995	453,316
Distillate range........	17,374	3,035	14,339	7,170 [d]	7,169	40,955	40,949	81,904
No. 1 heating oil.......	48,977		48,977	36,620 [e]	12,357	209,170	70,587	279,757
No. 2 heating oil.......	258,093		258,093	236,155 [f]	21,938	1,373,714	127,613	1,501,327
Total..............	408,775	7,416	401,359	323,917	77,442	1,873,160	443,144	2,316,304

[a] Mines, *Mineral Market Report*, No. MMS 2681.
[b] From Appendix Table F-1.
[c] Based upon trade experience, 55 per cent to space heating.
[d] Divided equally between space heating and non-space heating, based upon trade experience.
[e] Distribution between space heating and non-space heating derived in Table C-3.
[f] Based upon trade experience, 91.5 per cent to space heating.

TABLE C-3.   DETERMINATION OF USE OF NO. 1 HEATING OIL, 1955

Item	Billion Btu	Thousand barrels
1. Estimated oil consumption in noncentral heating [a]............	432,000	
2. Supplied by kerosine [b].................................	249,321	
3. Supplied by distillate range oil [b]..........................	40,955	
4. Balance supplied by No. 1 heating oil (item 1 − item 2 − item 3)..	141,724	24,812
5. No. 1 heating oil for central heating use [c]..................	67,446	11,808
6. Total No. 1 for space heating (item 4 + item 5).............	209,170	36,620

[a] Based upon 4,800,000 households at 90 million Btu per unit. Number of households adjusted upward from 4.5 million in Table C-7 because of downward trend in number of families using noncentral heating. Unit consumption assumed to exceed that of gas-heated households by roughly 10 per cent. For consumption of latter see Table C-13.

[b] From Table C-2, col. 6.

[c] Assumed on basis of trade experience to equal 5 per cent of physical quantity of No. 2 heating oil used for space heating (for latter see Table C-2, col. 4). Btu's derived by conversion of physical quantity, not as 5 per cent of No. 2 heating oil Btu's.

TABLE C-4.   HOUSEHOLD CONSUMPTION OF LPG, 1955

Item	Thousand barrels	Billion Btu
1. Total domestic and commercial sales [a]..................	66,699.5	267,532
2. Agricultural use, other [b]..............................	2,172	8,712
3. Commercial and household use (item 1 − item 2)..........	64,527.5	258,820
4. Commercial use (10% of item 3)........................	6,452.8	25,882
5. Household use (90% of item 3)..........................	58,074.8	232,938
a. 55% of household for space heating..................	31,941	128,115
b. 45% of household for other uses....................	26,134	104,823

[a] Mines, *Minerals Yearbook, 1956*, Vol. II, p. 311.

[b] From Appendix Table F-3, cols. 3 and 4 of "other uses."

NOTE: The distribution between household and commercial, and space heating and other uses is largely arbitrary, based upon very fragmentary information.

TABLE C-5. HOUSEHOLD CONSUMPTION OF COAL, 1955

Coal	Physical units (thousand tons)						Billion Btu		
	Coal		Household use of coke, in coal equivalent [b] (3)	Total coal and coke			Space heating (7)	Other uses (8)	Total (9)
	Household and commercial use (1)	Household use only [a] (2)		All uses (2)+(3) (4)	Space heating [c] (5)	Other (4)−(5) (6)			
Bituminous	53,762 [d]	26,881	1,606	28,487	27,063	1,424	709,050	37,309	746,359
Anthracite	15,102 [e]	7,551	5	7,556	7,178	378	182,321	9,601	191,922
Total	68,864	34,432	1,611	36,043	34,241	1,802	891,371	46,910	938,281

[a] Examination of grades and industry experience suggest that 50 per cent of total goes to household consumption for space heating.
[b] From Appendix Table A-2, cols 2. and 3.
[c] Assumed to represent 95 per cent of all uses.
[d] Retail deliveries from Mines, *Minerals Yearbook, 1956*, Vol. II, p. 104.
[e] From Appendix Table A-6, item 9.

TABLE C-6. SUMMARY: HOUSEHOLD ENERGY CONSUMPTION, 1955

Fuel	Other than electricity and transportation [a]			Transportation [b] (4)	Fuels via electricity [c] (5)	Total (6)
	Space heating (1)	Other (2)	Total (3)			
Physical units						
Coal (thous. tons):						
Bituminous..............	27,063	1,424	28,487		36,066	64,553
Anthracite..............	7,178	378	7,556			7,556
Oil (thous. bbl.):						
Gasoline................				629,120		629,120
Kerosine................	43,972	35,978	79,950			79,950
Range oil...............	7,170	7,169	14,339			14,339
Heating oil No. 1.......	36,620	12,357	48,977			48,977
Heating oil No. 2.......	236,155	21,938	258,093			258,093
Residual................					21,930	21,930
Gas (mill. cu. ft.).....	1,375,285	787,681	2,162,966		333,648	2,496,614
Natural gas liquids (thous. bbl.):						
LPG....................	31,941	26,134	58,075	4,770		62,845
Natural gasoline........				85,789		85,789
Hydro (mill. kwh)......					32,804	32,804
Billion Btu						
Coal:						
Bituminous..............	709,050	37,309	746,359		869,523	1,615,882
Anthracite..............	182,321	9,601	191,922			191,922
Total.................	891,371	46,910	938,281			1,807,804

Oil:						
Gasoline				3,276,457		3,276,457
Kerosine	249,321	203,995	453,316			453,316
Range oil	40,995	40,949	81,904			81,904
Heating oil No. 1	209,170	70,587	279,757			279,757
Heating oil No. 2	1,373,714	127,613	1,501,327			1,501,327
Residual					138,632	138,632
Total	1,873,160	443,144	2,316,304	3,276,457	138,632	5,731,393
Gas	1,423,420	815,250	2,238,670		335,617	2,574,287
Natural gas liquids:						
LPG	128,115	104,823	232,938	19,132		252,070
Natural gasoline				446,789		446,789
Total	128,115	104,823	232,938	465,921		698,859
Hydro					385,640	385,640
Grand total	4,316,066	1,410,127	5,726,193	3,742,378	1,729,412	11,197,983

a Coal—from Table C-5; oil—from Table C-2; gas—from Table C-1; and LPG—from Table C-4.
b From Appendix Table D-22.
c From Appendix Table H-9.

TABLE C-7. NUMBER OF HOUSEHOLDS BY TYPE OF HEATING, MID-1956

(In millions)

Fuel	Central heating (1)	Noncentral heating (2)	Total (3)
Oil.....................................	10.1	4.5	14.6
Gas....................................	10.2	12.3	22.5
Utility gas..........................	9.8	7.9	17.7
LPG.................................	0.4	4.4	4.8
All other fuels or unheated..............			12.0
Total households......................			49.1

SOURCE: Estimate contained in a communication from Daniel Parson, former director, Bureau of Statistics, A.G.A. Mr. Parson generally characterizes the figures as approximations.

TABLE C-8. HEATING CHARACTERISTICS OF NEW NONFARM FAMILY HOUSES STARTED IN FIRST QUARTER OF 1956

Type of heating	Total (1)	Gas (2)	Oil (3)	Electricity (4)	Solid (5)	Unknown (6)
Percentage distribution:						
Boiler (steam or hot water)...........	100%	26%	73%	a	a	1%
Furnace (warm air with ducts)......	100	79	19	a	a	2
Space heaters......	100	82	10	8%	a	a
Absolute numbers:[b]						
Boiler (steam or hot water)...........	18,100	4,706	13,213			181
Furnace (warm air with ducts)......	159,000	125,610	30,210			3,180
Space heaters......	29,300	24,026	2,930	2,344		
Total.............	206,400	154,342	46,353	2,344		3,361

[a] Less than 0.5 per cent.

[b] Derived by applying percentages to totals as shown in *Characteristics of New Housing*, *op. cit.*, Tables 19–A and 19–B.

SOURCE: BLS, *Characteristics of New Housing, First Quarter—1956*, Part II, Tables 19–A and 19–B, and 19–C; based on number of units with heating systems.

TABLE C-9. DERIVATION OF DISTRIBUTION OF GAS AND OIL HEATING SYSTEMS IN NEW HOUSING ESTIMATED TO BE CONSTRUCTED IN 1955-75

I. 1st Quarter 1956 distribution by system [a]

System	Number of houses heated by—			Number of houses in each system as per cent of total (4)	Share of fuel in each system (per cent)		
	Gas (1)	Oil (2)	Gas or oil (3)		Gas (5)	Oil (6)	Gas or oil (7)
Central (boiler plus furnace).	130,316	43,423	173,739	86.57%	75.01%	24.99%	100.00%
Noncentral (space).........	24,026	2,930	26,956	13.43	89.13	10.87	100.00
Total....................	154,342	46,353	200,695	100.00%			

II. Assumed 1955-75 percentage distribution [b]

System	Distribution of systems (col. 4 above rounded) [c] (1)	Share of fuel in each system (from cols. 5 and 6 above)		Percentage distribution by fuels and systems	
		Gas (2)	Oil (3)	Gas[d] (1) × (2) (4)	Oil[d] (1) × (3) (5)
Central..........	87.5%	75.0%	25.0%	65.62%	21.88%
Noncentral.......	12.5	90.0	10.0	11.25	1.25
Total...........	100.0%			76.88%	23.12%

[a] From Table C-8.
[b] Based upon 1st quarter 1956 distribution.
[c] Rounded by emphasizing tendency towards central heating.
[d] When used in calculations, figures carried an additional place.

TABLE C-10. ESTIMATED DISTRIBUTION IN 1975, BY HEATING SYSTEM AND FUEL, OF OIL- AND GAS-HEATED HOUSEHOLDS CARRIED OVER FROM 1956

System and fuel	Oil- or gas-heated existing in 1956 [a]		Percentage distribution in new dwellings [b] (3)	Percentage distribution in carried-over households [c] (4)	Number of households carried over (thousands) [d] (5)
	Number (thousand) (1)	Per cent of total (2)			
Central:					
Gas.............	9,800	30.34%	65.62%	39.16%	11,474
Oil.............	10,100	31.27	21.88	28.92	8,474
Total..........	19,900	61.61	87.50	68.08	19,948
Noncentral:					
Gas.............	7,900	24.46	11.25	21.16	6,199
Oil.............	4,500	13.93	1.25	10.76	3,153
Total..........	12,400	38.39	12.50	31.92	9,352
Grand total........	32,300	100.00%	100.00%	100.00%	29,300

(*Footnotes on next page.*)

TABLE C-10 (continued)

ª From Table C-7.

ᵇ From Table C-9, part II, cols. 4 and 5.

ᶜ It is assumed that between 1956 and 1975 the distribution of households with oil and gas heating will move one-quarter of the difference between the 1956 pattern—col. 2—and the assumed 1975 pattern in new dwellings—col. 3.

ᵈ Col. 4 percentages applied to the total item in col. 5. The latter is the number existing in 1956 (col. 1) reduced by assumed demolition of 3 million units using oil or gas heat. The demolition rate of 150,000 oil- and gas-heated dwellings per year corresponds to the 300,000 per year rate for all types of dwellings advanced as reasonable by Leo Grebler, David M. Blank, and Louis Winnick, *Capital Formation in Residential Real Estate* (New York: National Bureau of Economic Research, 1956), p. 322. Allocating only half the demolitions to oil- or gas-heated dwellings, which constituted some 75 per cent of all households in 1956 (Table C-7), recognizes the fact that these are likely to be the more recent dwellings and, therefore, will undergo relatively less demolition.

TABLE C-11.   ASSUMPTIONS CONCERNING NUMBER OF HOUSEHOLDS HEATED BY DIFFERENT MEANS IN 1975

Item	Number
1. Total households ª	68,878,000
2. Households not heated with oil or gas:	
a. LPG ᵇ	5,000,000
b. Coal ᶜ	4,000,000
c. Electric ᵈ	3,788,000
d. Wood or not heated ᵉ	1,300,000
e. Total	14,088,000
3. Households to be heated with oil or gas (item 1 − item 2)	54,790,000
4. Household dwellings space-heated with oil or gas, carried over from 1956 ᶠ	29,300,000
5. Other or new oil- or gas-heated occupied dwelling units (item 3 − item 4)	25,490,000

ª Appendix Table I-1.

ᵇ Represents an increase of 200,000 units over 1956 (Table C-7). Extension of natural gas lines is expected to hold down the growth of LPG-heated households.

ᶜ There are no statistics as to number of coal-heated households, now or in the past. However, Table C-7 gives an estimated number of 12 million households heated by either coal, wood, electricity, or not at all. One may guess that on the basis of coal consumed by households (Table C-5) and annual consumption of 100 million Btu per household, there were some 9 million coal-heated households in 1955. It is assumed that these will decrease by more than 50 per cent to 4 million in 1975.

ᵈ Represents 5.5 per cent of total households; conceived as follows: 200,000 in 1955 and carried over; 200,000 converted to electric heating in 1955–75; and 3,388,000 of all new housing built in 1955–75 to be electrically heated. The latter figure is derived as 12.5 per cent of the 27,098,000 newly constructed households, this being the difference between 68,878,000 in 1975, and 47,780,000 in 1955, plus 6,000,000 to replace 1955–75 demolitions. (See discussion of electricity consumption, Chapter 5.)

ᵉ In 1956, of the 12 million non-oil and non-gas households (Table C-7), it is estimated that 9 million were coal-heated (*cf.* footnote c above). Of the remaining 3 million, on the order of 200,000 had electric heating, leaving 2.8 million wood-heated or without heat. Between 600,000 and 700,000 of these are estimated by Daniel Parson, former director, Bureau of Statistics, A.G.A., to have no heat at all, leaving 2,100,000 to 2,200,000 as wood-heated. It is assumed that the wood-heated units will decrease by two-thirds and the unheated units remain at 600,000, yielding the total of 1,300,000 here shown.

ᶠ Table C-10.

TABLE C-12. DISTRIBUTION OF NEW OIL- AND GAS-HEATED
DWELLING UNITS, ESTIMATED 1975

Fuel and system	Percentage[a]	Number of dwelling units
Total...	100.0%	25,490,000[b]
Gas, central....................................	65.62	16,727,813
Gas, noncentral................................	11.25	2,867,625
Oil, central....................................	21.88	5,575,937
Oil, noncentral................................	1.25	318,625

[a] From Table C-9, part II, cols. 4 and 5 (additional places used in actual computations).
[b] Total from Table C-11, item 5; breakdown secured by applying percentages to total.

TABLE C-13. CONSUMPTION OF OIL AND GAS IN
HOUSEHOLD HEATING, ESTIMATED 1975

	Number of households[a] (thousands) (1)	Assumed consumption per household[b] (million Btu) (2)	Total requirements Billion Btu (1) × (2) (3)	Total requirements Physical units (4)
Oil:				
Central.......	14,050	127.5	1,791,375	307,955 thous. bbl. No. 2 heating oil
Noncentral...	3,472	90.0	312,480[c]	{ 36,741 thous. bbl. kerosine 18,235 thous. bbl. No. 1 heating oil
Total........	17,522		2,103,855	
Gas:				
Central.......	28,202	103.7	2,924,547	2,825,650 mill. cu. ft.
Noncentral...	9,066	80.0	725,280	700,753 mill. cu. ft.
Total........	37,268		3,649,827	3,526,403 mill. cu. ft.
Grand total.....	54,790		5,753,682	

[a] Sum of numbers in Tables C-10, col. 5, and C-12 rounded.
[b] The rates shown are best estimates based upon current information of various degrees of exactness. The relatively fixed points are: Btu's per gas-heating customer (Table C-1); number of central oil burners in use; and number of central gas burners in use. The derivation of the oil estimate may be best shown in a supplementary tabulation as follows:

Number of central oil burners in use on:
1. January 1, 1955 [1]............................ 7,641,974
2. January 1, 1956 [2]............................ 8,255,228
3. January 1, 1957 [2]............................ 8,732,445

Estimated average number of central burners in use in:
4. 1956 [3]..................................... 8,398,393
5. 1955.. 7,825,950

(Footnotes continued on next page.)

TABLE C-13 (continued)

Number of households centrally heated by oil in:
6. Mid-1956 [4] 10,100,000

7. 1955 (est.) (item 10 × item 9)................ 9,391,140
Number of households per central burner:
8. Item 7 ÷ item 5............................   1.2
Consumption of oil in central heating in 1955:
9. Total (billion Btu's) [5] 1,441,160
10. Per household (million Btu's).................   153

[1] *Fueloil and Oil Heat*, Vol. 15, No. 4 (April 1956), p. 83.
[2] *Ibid.*, Vol. 17, No. 4 (April 1957), p. 84.
[3] Converted to average for year by adding to January 1 figure only 30 per cent of oil installations made during year, as most installations are made during second half of year. The figure of 30 per cent, which may appear high in this light, reflects the fact that full tanks are generally provided at time of installation, thus offsetting to some extent the seasonality.
[4] Table C-7.
[5] Sum of: No. 1 heating oil from Table C-3, item 5; and No. 2 heating oil from Table C-2, col. 6.

On the basis of past experience, it is assumed that efficiency will improve by one-sixth by 1975, and thus the figure of 127.5 million Btu from the 153 million Btu obtained in the above calculation is derived. The lower consumption in noncentral oil heating is largely arbitrary, though it appears to be of the right order of magnitude, as it should be above gas noncentral heating, but below oil central heating.

The finally adopted gas estimates are also arbitrary; the assumed rates of consumption are only one of the possible patterns that, when combined with the number of centrally and noncentrally heated households, will yield a total consumption similar to that found in Table C-1.

	Number of households (million)	Consumption per household (million Btu)	Total consumption (billion Btu)
Centrally gas-heated........	8.6 [1]	103.7	890,000
Noncentrally gas-heated.....	8.0 [1]	70.0 [2]	560,000
Total, gas-heated..........	—	—	1,450,000
Total, gas-heated (Table C-1)	—	—	1,423,420

[1] Adjusted from Table C-7, which reflects position as of mid-1956. Total differs from that given in Table C-1, col. 5, item 3, as the latter refers to customers, not households.
[2] Raised to 80 for 1975 to reflect higher heating standards at higher GNP level.

No lowering of consumption per central gas-heated household from the 1955 level was assumed, largely because efficiency is already high and any further improvement is likely to be offset by expansion and higher saturation rates of gas heating in colder locations in a generally northward direction.

[c] Btu's allocated between kerosine and No. 1 oil on 2:1 basis, and converted to physical units at their respective conversion rates.

TABLE C-14. CONSUMPTION OF LPG AND COAL IN
HOUSEHOLD HEATING, ESTIMATED 1975

Fuel	Number of households[a] (thousands) (1)	Assumed consumption per household[b] (million Btu) (2)	Total requirements	
			Billion Btu (1) × (2) (3)	Physical units (4)
LPG:				
Central.............	1,875	65	121,875	30,385 thous. bbl.
Noncentral.........	3,125	45	140,625	35,060 thous. bbl.
Total..............	5,000		262,500	65,445 thous. bbl.
Coal:				
Bituminous.........			318,400[c]	12,153 thous. tons
Anthracite.........			81,600[c]	3,211 thous. tons
Total..............	4,000	100	400,000	15,364 thous. tons

[a] Table C-11; division between central and noncentral is arbitrary, except that central is certainly much the smaller of the two.
[b] Rate based on comparison with oil and gas rates, taking into account differing efficiencies.
[c] Allocated on the basis of the relationship prevailing in 1955; see Table C-5, col. 7.

TABLE C-15. HOUSEHOLD CONSUMPTION OF GAS PER CUSTOMER
IN USES OTHER THAN SPACE HEATING, 1975 PROJECTION

Appliance	Average annual consumption per unit[a] (thousand Btu) (1)	Rate of saturation[b] (per cent) (2)	Annual consumption per unit per customer (thousand Btu) (3)
Range.........................	9,600	70%[c]	6,720
Water heater...................	25,740	95[d]	24,453
Clothes dryer..................	4,500	25[e]	1,125
Refrigerator...................	12,587	1[f]	126
Central air conditioner..........	47,290	2[g]	946
Incinerator....................	10,000	3[g]	300
Total.........................	109,717		33,670

[a] Table C-32, col. 2, except for incinerator which represents a rough guess.
[b] Homes with the given gas appliance as percentage of total homes serviced by gas.
[c] Table C-29, col. 2.
[d] Table C-26, col. 2.
[e] Table C-30, footnote b.
[f] It is estimated that, as of early 1958, there were some 3 million gas refrigerators in use, and that 1.9 million units were sold in the twelve years between 1945 and 1957 (release dated May 12, 1958, from Whirlpool Corporation, principal producer of gas refrigerators). It is also unofficially estimated that some 800,000 units were sold in the three years 1948–50 alone, suggesting that in recent years sales have lagged behind the volume required merely for replacement demand. A gradual decline to one-half million units by 1975 has therefore been assumed, equal to a saturation rate of 1 per cent in that year.
[g] Approximations based upon study of current trade literature and present spread of appliance.

TABLE C-16. RESIDENTIAL GAS CUSTOMERS USING GAS FOR SPACE
HEATING AS PERCENTAGE OF TOTAL RESIDENTIAL GAS CUSTOMERS,
1949-57, AND PROJECTIONS TO 1960, 1965, AND 1975

Year	Per cent	Year	Per cent
1975	82.0% [a]	1954	52.8%
1965	77.9 [a]	1953	49.9
1960	69.7 [a]	1952	46.9
1957	61.2	1951	44.1
1956	57.9	1950	40.7
1955	56.0	1949	35.5

[a] Rate shown assumed on basis of consistent upward trend.

SOURCE: A.G.A.: 1949-50—*Historical Statistics of the Gas Industry* (1956), p. 239, Table
142; 1951-57—*1957 Gas Facts*, p. 140; and 1960-65—Bureau of Statistics, release of
October 10, 1956.

TABLE C-17. HOUSEHOLD CONSUMPTION OF GAS IN USES OTHER
THAN SPACE HEATING, 1975 PROJECTION

Item	Total (1)	Family (2)	Primary individual (3)
1. Number of households	45,449,000 [a]	37,058,000	8,391,000
2. Average consumption per household (thous. Btu) [b]		33,670	22,447
3. Total consumption (bill. Btu)	1,436,096	1,247,743	188,353
4. Total consumption (mill. cu. ft.)	1,387,532		

[a]This total is derived from the figure previously estimated for the number of space-
heating customers for gas in 1975 (Table C-13). That total is assumed to represent 82 per
cent of all gas customers in 1975 as estimated in Table C-16. The total here shown is thus
the number of space-heating customers divided by 0.82. Division into family and primary
individual households based on proportion of those categories in 1975 household projection
(Appendix Table I-1).

[b]Family-type household consumption from Table C-15; primary individual household
consumption assumed to be one-third less.

TABLE C-18. HOUSEHOLD CONSUMPTION OF FUELS OTHER THAN GAS FOR NON-SPACE HEATING, 1955 AND PROJECTION TO 1975

Item	1955 Space heating (billion Btu) (1)	1955 Other[a] (billion Btu) (2)	1955 Other as per cent of space heating (2)÷(1) (3)	1955 Each as per cent of total (4)	1975 Space heating[b] (billion Btu) (5)	1975 As per cent of space heating[c] (6)	1975 Other Billion Btu[d] (7)	1975 Other Thousand barrels (8)
1. Kerosine	249,321	203,995		45.65%	208,321		115,249	20,326
2. No. 2 heating oil	1,373,714	127,613		28.56	1,791,375		72,103	12,395
3. Range oil	40,955	40,949		} 25.79	} 104,158		} 65,110	} 11,399
4. No. 1 heating oil	209,170	70,587						
5. Total, excl. LPG and coal	1,873,160	443,144	23.7%	100.0%	2,103,854	12.0%	252,462	44,120
6. LPG	128,115	104,823	81.8		262,500	81.8	214,725	53,532
7. Coal	891,371	46,910	5.3		400,000	[e]	53,532	

[a] LPG from Table C-4; coal from Table C-5; and all other from Table C-2.

[b] LPG and coal from Table C-14; all other from Table C-13.

[c] LPG assumed to retain 1955 relationship with space-heating use, as it is likely that LPG use in one instance will be combined with other. For all other fuels, it is assumed that non-space heating will decline sharply in relation to heating use; the decline here arbitrarily assumed is a halving of the relationship.

[d] Item 5 and item 6 obtained by multiplying col. 5 by col. 6. Items 1 through 4 derived by allocating total, excluding LPG and coal, among types of oil in the proportions that prevailed in 1955 (col. 4).

[e] Assumed to have disappeared in other than space-heating use.

TABLE C-19. HOUSEHOLD CONSUMPTION OF ELECTRICITY, 1955

(Million kwh)

Residential sales [a]	120,524
Rural sales [a]	10,751
Pumping and irrigation to be subtracted [b]	8,000
Net household consumption [c]	123,275

[a]E.E.I., *Statistical Bulletin for the Year 1957*, p. 27.
[b]FPC, *Estimated Future Power Requirements of the United States, 1955-1980*, December 1956, p. 17.
[c]The addition of all rural sales, except for pumping and irrigation, is a possible over-statement, since they not only include sales for residential consumption, but also for productive purposes on farms.

TABLE C-20. AVERAGE RESIDENTIAL PURCHASES OF ELECTRICITY, 1912-57

Year	Kwh per residential customer	Percentage increase over previous year	Year	Kwh per residential customer	Percentage increase over previous year
1957	3,174	6.9%	1934	629	4.8%
1956	2,969	7.9	1933	600	−0.2
1955	2,751	7.9	1932	601	3.1
			1931	583	6.6
1954	2,549	8.7	1930	547	9.0
1953	2,346	8.2			
1952	2,169	8.2	1929	502	8.4
1951	2,004	9.5	1928	463	3.8
1950	1,830	8.7	1927	446	3.7
			1926	430	8.0
1949	1,684	7.7	1925	398	5.3
1948	1,563	8.7			
1947	1,438	8.2	1924	378	2.7
1946	1,329	8.1	1923	368	2.5
1945	1,229	6.8	1922	359	3.5
			1921	347	2.4
1944	1,151	7.6	1920	339	15.7
1943	1,070	4.7			
1942	1,022	3.7	1919	293	7.7
1941	986	3.6	1918	272	1.5
1940	952	6.1	1917	268	1.1
			1916	265	1.9
1939	897	5.2	1915	260	−3.0
1938	853	6.0			
1937	805	9.5	1914	268	1.5
1936	735	8.6	1913	264	1.5
1935	677	7.6	1912	260	

SOURCES: E.E.I.: 1952-57—*Statistical Bulletin for the Year 1957*, p. 50; 1937-51—*ibid., 1951*, p. 31, Table 16; 1926-36—*Statistical Bulletin*, No. 9, March 1942, p. 22, Table 15; and 1913-25—*Supplement to Statistical Bulletin*, No. 4, January 1937, p. 2, Table II. Figures for 1912 derived from Commerce, *Historical Statistics of the United States, 1789-1945*, Series G 191-193, p. 159.

TABLE C-21. GROWTH RATES AND ACTUAL INCREASES IN AVERAGE
RESIDENTIAL ELECTRICITY CONSUMPTION, SELECTED PERIODS,
1912-56

Period	Annual growth rate (per cent)	Period	Average annual increase (kwh)
1912-56..........	5.99%	1925-30..........	30
1929-56..........	6.80	1930-35..........	26
1929-42..........	5.62	1935-40..........	55
1937-42..........	4.85	1937-55..........	108
1942-56..........	7.91	1940-45..........	55
1950-56..........	8.40	1945-50..........	120
		1950-55..........	184
		1955-57..........	212

SOURCE: Table C-20.

TABLE C-22. SATURATION RATES OF VARIOUS ELECTRIC
APPLIANCES, 1923-58[a], AND PROJECTION TO 1975

(Based on number of wired homes)

Date	Refrig- erators (1)	Ranges (2)	Water heaters (3)	Room air condi- tioners (4)	Tele- vision (5)	Bed cover- ings (6)	Food waste dis- posers (7)	Home freezers (8)	Dish- washers (9)	Clothes dryers[b] (10)
	%	%	%	%	%	%	%	%	%	%
1975.....	100.0[c]	50.0[d]	25.0[e]	60.0[f]	100.0[c]	n.s.e.	n.s.e.	40.0[g]	25.0[h]	45.0
Jan. 1:										
1958.....	97.3	31.5	17.4	9.6	86.0	15.2	7.5	19.2	5.2	13.7
1957.....	96.0	30.5	16.9	7.6	81.0	13.2	6.6	18.0	4.6	11.9
1956.....	94.1	28.2	16.3	5.6	76.1	11.6	5.5	16.8	4.0	9.2
1955.....	92.5	27.0	15.2	4.0	71.7	10.6	4.6	15.1	3.5	6.6
1954.....	90.4	25.7	14.6	2.6	63.4	9.8	3.9	13.4	3.2	5.1
1953.....	89.0	24.1	13.8	1.4	50.1	8.6	3.3	11.5	2.9	3.7
1952.....	86.8	22.9	12.8	.8	38.6	7.5	2.7	9.3	2.6	2.4
1951.....	86.3	20.9	11.6	.6	27.0	6.3	2.1	7.2	2.0	1.4
1950.....	79.3	18.0	10.1	.4	10.6	4.8	1.4	5.2	1.5	.7
1949.....	76.5	16.6	9.0	.3	2.8	3.8	1.0	4.3	1.2	.4
1948.....	71.0	14.4	6.8	.2						
1947.....	68.8	12.9	4.7	.2						
1946.....	67.2	12.1	3.7							
1945.....	69.4	12.5								
1944.....	71.0	12.8								
1943.....	71.8	12.9								
1942.....	71.8	12.6								
1941.....	62.8	11.2								
1940.....	55.7	10.2								
1939.....	51.5	9.6								
1938.....	49.1	9.0								
1937.....	40.9	7.9								
1936.....	34.1	6.8								
1935.....	29.1	5.9								

(*Table continued on next page.*)

TABLE C–22 (continued)

Date	Refrig- erators (1)	Ranges (2)	Water heaters (3)	Room air condi- tioners (4)	Tele- vision (5)	Bed cover- ings (6)	Food waste dis- posers (7)	Home freezers (8)	Dish- washers (9)	Clothes dryers[b] (10)
	%	%								
1934.....	24.5	5.7								
1933.....	21.7	5.6								
1932.....	17.4	5.4								
1931.....	12.9	4.9								
1930.....	9.3	4.4								
1929.....	6.4	3.8								
1928.....	4.2	3.3								
1927.....	2.4	2.9								
1926.....	.9	2.5								
1925.....	.5	2.0								
1924.....	.4									
1923.....	.3									

n.s.e. Not separately estimated.

[a] From data compiled and made available by the Market and Research Department, *Electrical Merchandising*, New York. The nature of the data is best illustrated by the following remarks contained in a personal communication from Marguerite Cook of the Market Analysis Department of *Electrical Merchandising:* "May we explain that *Electrical Merchandising's* yearly estimates of appliance ownership are not based on a house-to-house count of any kind. Rather they are arrived at through the use of industry sales totals, with allowances made for the amount of replacement and trade-in involved, together with such factors as the dealers' disposition of trade-ins accepted—in other words, the percentage that the dealer junks, rebuilds and resells, resells 'as is,' etc. Thus in the absence of a reliable census, we are obliged to work from as many factors as are available in the hope that our estimates will present a reasonably accurate picture of appliance ownership in the United States."

[b] The percentage rates in this column apply to electric and gas dryers together. The 1975 estimate is derived in footnote b to Table C–30. It is presented here as a rounded number.

[c] The 1975 saturation rate is one of convenience. On the one hand, some wired houses probably will not have this appliance. On the other, some are likely to have more than one.

[d] From Table C–29.

[e] From Table C–26.

[f] It is assumed that between 40 per cent and 50 per cent of all wired homes will, on the average, have 1 to 1.5 room units. The 60 per cent is in representation of such a development. While this appliance is too recent to be estimated with much confidence on the basis of a trend, it may be seen that even a mere continuation of the current annual growth of 2 per cent of wired households, would bring the 1975 saturation rate to 50 per cent. It may be expected that the growth will be steeper as more efficient and less cumbersome units are introduced. Pointing in the same direction is the very low percentage of replacement sales in total retail volume (Table C–31).

[g] The projected saturation rate is predicated upon a slowdown in the fast spread of home freezers in the immediate postwar years. This appears when the period 1955–58 is compared with the period 1952–55. On the other hand, the relatively small significance of replacement sales indicates that the appliance is still principally concerned with new installations, i.e., growth.

[h] Based upon a very slight speed-up in the growth of this appliance, as dishwashers tend to become standard equipment for higher priced new construction. A saturation rate of 25 per cent would mean some 17 million units. Compared with total new construction of approximately 27 million dwelling units, this appears a high figure, even when allowing for modernization of existing dwellings and purchases of dishwashers that are not built in. (Table C–11, footnote d.)

TABLE C–23.   WATER HEATERS IN USE AT YEAR'S END, 1948–56

Dec. 31:	Total (1)	Gas (2)	Electric (3)	Electric as per cent of total (4)
1956	27,302,000	19,287,000	8,015,000	29.36%
1955	25,866,000	18,366,000	7,500,000	29.00
1954	24,255,000	17,450,000	6,805,000	28.06
1953	23,113,000	16,700,000	6,413,000	27.75
1952	21,821,000	16,000,000	5,821,000	26.68
1951	20,630,000	15,400,000	5,230,000	25.35
1950	19,275,000	14,750,000	4,525,000	23.48
1949	17,760,000	14,000,000	3,760,000	21.17
1948	16,461,000	13,300,000	3,161,000	19.20

SOURCE: GAMA, "Nine Year Summary, 1948–1956," *GAMA Statistical Highlights*, June 23, 1957. Data exclude non-automatic gas heaters.

TABLE C–24.   WATER HEATER SALES, 1948–56

Year	Total (1)	Gas[a] (2)	Electric (3)	Electric as per cent of total (4)
1956	3,292,400	2,422,400	870,000	26.42%
1955	3,299,200	2,399,200	900,000	27.28
1954	2,880,900	2,074,900	806,000	27.98
1953	2,683,300	1,903,300	780,000	29.07
1952	2,361,600	1,641,600	720,000	30.49
1951	2,519,800	1,674,800	845,000	33.53
1950	3,044,400	2,054,400	990,000	32.52
1949	1,978,400	1,283,400	695,000	35.13
1948	2,325,900	1,285,900	1,040,000	44.71

[a] Automatic only; also excludes LPG.

SOURCE: GAMA, "Nine Year Summary, 1948–1956," *GAMA Statistical Highlights*, June 23, 1957.

TABLE C-25. TYPE OF WATER HEATERS IN NEW NONFARM ONE-FAMILY HOMES, 1940, 1950, AND STARTED FIRST QUARTER 1956, BY TYPE OF FUEL USED

(Per cent of total)

Year and characteristic	Gas (1)	Electric (2)	Others (3)	Unknown (4)	Total (5)
1940	90%	3%	7%	n.a.	100%
1950	72	16	12	n.a.	100
1956: All regions	76	16	2	6%	100
North East	58	17	17	8	100
North Central	88	9	a	3	100
South	67	27	a	6	100
West	91	7	a	2	100
1956, by price:					
Under $7,000	77	14	a	9	100
$7,000–$9,999	81	16	1	2	100
$10,000–$11,999	81	16	1	2	100
$12,000–$14,999	77	17	3	3	100
$15,000–$19,999	79	15	2	4	100
$20,000 and over	72	15	4	9	100

n.a. No comparable data available.
a Less than 0.5 per cent.

SOURCE: BLS, 1956: *Characteristics of New Housing, First Quarter—1956*, Part II, Table 24; 1940 and 1950: *New Housing and its Materials, 1940–1956*, Bulletin No. 1231, pp. 35–36, Table 6.

TABLE C-26. PROJECTION OF WATER HEATER USE, 1975

Heat source	Number of customers (1)	Saturation rate (2)	Number in use (3)
Electric	68,878,000 a	25% b	17,219,500
Gas	45,449,000 c	95 d	43,176,550
Total		87.7%	60,396,050

a Equals total number of households, on assumption that in 1975 all households will be wired for electricity.

b Electric water heaters in use in 1955 represent a saturation rate of 15.2 per cent. While electric water heaters in use have been gaining relative to gas heaters (Table C-23), the declining sales ratio (Table C-24) and the slowing pace of increase in the saturation rate (Table C-22) jointly suggest that by 1975 the saturation rate is unlikely to exceed 25 per cent, especially as an increasing percentage of sales has been in replacement of worn-out electric heaters rather than as new installation or in replacement of nonelectric heaters (Table C-31).

A higher saturation rate, in the face of the reasonable assumption made in footnote d below regarding gas heaters, would raise the total number of water heaters in use in 1975 to 90 per cent and above. Even the roughly 8.5 million households here implied to use other fuels for water heating, or to have no central water-heating appliance at all in 1975, might be on the low side, but in any event leaves little room for increasing the electric saturation rate.

At the assumed rates, electric heaters in use in 1975 will represent 28.5 per cent of all heaters, a level roughly the same as that of the mid-fifties (Table C-23, col. 4) but substantially above that emerging from new construction statistics as, for example, the BLS survey (Table C-25, col. 2).

c Table C-17.

d The saturation rate of gas heaters has been steadily rising and represents some 70 per cent in 1955. It is assumed that practically all gas-connected households will use gas water heaters by 1975.

TABLE C-27. RANGES IN USE AT YEAR'S END, 1948-56

(Thousands)

Dec. 31:	Total (1)	Gas (excluding LPG) (2)	Electric (3)	Electric as per cent of total (4)
1956.................	42,254	27,789	14,465	34.23%
1955.................	39,868	26,903	12,965	32.52
1954.................	38,033	25,947	12,086	31.78
1953.................	36,406	25,120	11,286	31.00
1952.................	34,505	24,305	10,200	29.56
1951.................	32,864	23,514	9,350	28.45
1950.................	30,792	22,597	8,195	26.61
1949.................	28,446	21,740	6,706	23.57
1948.................	26,721	20,881	5,840	21.86

SOURCE: GAMA, "Nine Year Summary, 1948-1956," *GAMA Statistical Highlights*, June 23, 1957.

TABLE C-28. RANGE SALES, 1948-56

(Thousands)

Year	Total (1)	Gas (excluding LPG) (2)	Electric (3)	Electric as per cent of total (4)
1956..............	3,327	1,742	1,585	47.6%
1955..............	3,468	1,868	1,600	46.1
1954..............	2,967	1,617	1,350	45.5
1953..............	2,991	1,741	1,250	41.8
1952..............	2,811	1,751	1,060	37.7
1951..............	3,287	1,887	1,400	42.6
1950..............	4,225	2,395	1,830	43.3
1949..............	2,664	1,608	1,056	39.6
1948..............	3,676	2,076	1,600	43.5

SOURCE: GAMA, "Nine Year Summary, 1948-1956," *GAMA Statistical Highlights*, June 23, 1957.

TABLE C-29. PROJECTION OF RANGE USE, 1975

Heat source	Number of customers (1)	Saturation rate (2)	Number in use (3)
Electric............	68,878,000 [a]	50% [b]	34,439,000
Gas...............	45,449,000 [c]	70 [d]	31,814,300
Total.............		96.2%	66,253,300

[a] Equals total number of households, on assumption that in 1975 all households will be wired for electricity.

[b] The 1955 saturation rate for electric ranges is 27 per cent (Table C-22). The steadily rising saturation rate in the past, the relative increase of electric versus gas ranges in use (Table C-27), and the relative increase in sales when compared to gas ranges (Table C-28), all argue for a further substantial increase in the saturation rate. The rate here stipulated represents a slight slowdown in the past trend, partially because the appliance is no longer in its infancy and thus is more vulnerable to gas competition, and partially because an increasing portion of sales has been for replacement rather than for new installations or substitution of other types of range (Table C-31).

(Footnotes continued on next page.)

TABLE C–29 (continued)

The rate of 50 per cent strikes a compromise between these tendencies and is, of course, statistically convenient. When measured against the assumed rate of growth in gas ranges, the 1975 percentage of electric to total ranges in use is 52 per cent, a relationship that is quite compatible with the past trend shown by this percentage in Table C–27.

  c Table C–17.

  d Gas ranges in use in 1955 would represent roughly a saturation rate of 100 per cent, if all were household ranges. Nonetheless, the rate must be close to 100 per cent. The projected decrease to 70 per cent is based largely upon the fact that the total number in use must, more or less, agree with the projected number of households, and that a certain number of households must be assumed to use other means of cooking. As it is, the fact that only 2.5 million households are left as using neither electricity nor gas suggests that either or both of the saturation rates are too liberal.

TABLE C–30. SALES AND USE OF CLOTHES DRYERS, 1948–56[a], AND 1975 PROJECTED USE[b]

| Year | Sales | | | Electric sales as per cent of total sales (4) | Total in use (5) |
	Gas (1)	Electric (2)	Total (3)		
1956............	470,000	1,190,000	1,660,000	71.69%	5,625,000
1955............	369,000	1,027,600	1,396,600	73.58	4,213,000
1954............	243,200	697,700	940,900	74.15	2,967,000
1953............	168,200	568,500	736,700	77.17	2,180,400
1952............	161,000	473,900	634,900	74.64	1,524,300
1951............	138,000	354,000	492,000	71.95	982,500
1950............	67,500	251,000	318,500	78.81	535,000
1949............	21,100	84,600	105,700	80.04	255,700
1948............	15,300	76,700	92,000	83.37	175,000
Total..........	1,653,300	4,724,000	6,377,300	74.08%	

  a GAMA, "Nine Year Summary, 1948–1956," *GAMA Statistical Highlights*, June 23, 1957.

  b On the basis of available data, dryers in use in 1955 probably consist of over 3 million electric and 1 million gas units. Both electric and gas units have been selling at rapidly rising rates, but all projections at this stage must be taken with a large grain of salt.

The A.G.A. Bureau of Statistics has estimated ("How Many Appliances in 1960–1974?", September 1956) that by 1975 half the households will have dryers and that 40 per cent of them will be gas-heated. The estimate here is that 30 per cent of all households will have electric dryers and 25 per cent of all gas-connected households will have gas dryers. Because of the smaller number of gas-connected households, this will give the electric dryers about two-thirds of the total then in use, and will lead to a saturation rate of all households of 46.5 per cent, as follows:

	Number of households	Saturation rate	Number in use
Electric[1].......	68,878,000	30%	20,663,000
Gas...........	45,449,000	25	11,362,000
Total[1]........	68,878,000	46.5%	32,025,000

  1 On the assumption that all households will be wired for electricity.

TABLE C–31.   REPLACEMENT SALES[a] OF SELECTED APPLIANCES, 1947–56, AND ESTIMATES FOR 1958 AND 1960–64

(Per cent of total retail volume)

Energy source	Ranges (1)	Water heaters (2)	Clothes dryers (3)	Freezers (4)	Room air conditioners (5)
Electric:[b]					
1956..............	59.7%	43.6%	12.5%	14.1%	3.9%
1955..............	63.6	51.1	8.3	12.6	2.4
1954..............	53.3	49.3	12.9	9.0	2.0
1953..............	44.1	37.2		15.7	
1952..............	44.2	18.9		7.0	
1951..............	35.0	20.5		10.2	
1950..............	37.8	29.4			
1949..............	38.2	18.4			
1948..............	30.7	25.4			
1947..............	18.3				
Gas:					
1958[c]...........	54.2	58.0	8.7[d]		
1960–64[e].........	60.6	63.3	25.1[d]		

[a] Replacement of same energy-source appliance only.
[b] Release by Market and Research Department, *Electrical Merchandising*, New York, N. Y.
[c] *American Gas Association Monthly*, Vol. XL, No. 4 (April 1958), pp. 15–16.
[d] Includes replacements of electric dryers.
[e] A.G.A., Bureau of Statistics, "How Many Appliances in 1960–1974?" September 1956, p. 11.

TABLE C–32.   ESTIMATES OF ANNUAL ELECTRICITY AND GAS CONSUMPTION RATES OF MAJOR APPLIANCES, VARIOUS YEARS

Appliance and source of estimate	Annual consumption			Ratio of gas Btu to direct Btu content of kwh (2) ÷ (3) (4)	Btu's required to generate electricity shown in col. (1) [2] (thous. Btu) (5)	Ratio of gas consumption to Btu's required to support electricity consumption [3] (2) ÷ (5) (6)
	Electricity (kwh) (1)	Gas (thous. Btu) (2)	Direct Btu equivalent of electricity [1] (thous. Btu) (3)			
Water heater:						
a) Tech. Bull. 1073.......	5,144	31,715	17,551	1.81	46,296	0.68
b) A.G.A...............				1.61		
c) Univ. of Illinois.......	4,716	25,740	16,095	1.60	42,444	0.61
d) Zinder...............	4,224	24,000	14,415	1.66	38,016	0.63
e) S.E.................	3,972	27,108	13,555	2.00	35,748	0.76
f) TVA................	3,247					
g) Sporn...............	4,700					
h) E.E.I., 1933..........	3,000					
i) Info. Bull. 161........	3,000					

(*Table continued on next page.*)

TABLE C-32 (continued)

Appliance and source of estimate	Annual consumption			Ratio of gas Btu to direct Btu content of kwh (2) ÷ (3) (4)	Btu's required to generate electricity shown in col. (1) [2] (thous. Btu) (5)	Ratio of gas consumption to Btu's required to support electricity consumption [3] (2) ÷ (5) (6)
	Electricity (kwh) (1)	Gas (thous. Btu) (2)	Direct Btu equivalent of electricity [1] (thous. Btu) (3)			
Range:						
j) Tech. Bull. 1073.......	1,606	10,942	5,481	2.00	14,454	0.76
b) A.G.A...............				2.00		
d) Zinder...............	1,620	11,520	5,529	2.08	14,580	0.79
k) C.U. low............	1,200	9,180	4,095	2.24	10,800	0.85
k) C.U. high...........	1,356	14,688	4,627	3.17	12,204	1.20
e) S.E..................	1,596	11,328	5,446	2.08	14,364	0.79
i) Info. Bull. 161.......	1,200					
l) Middle West..........	1,200					
f) TVA.................	1,160					
g) Sporn...............	1,400					
h) E.E.I., 1933..........	1,750					
Refrigerator:						
m) Tech. Bull. 1073.......	425	15,320	1,451	10.56	3,825	4.01
n) A.G.A...............		12,000				
d) Zinder...............	480	17,160	1,638	10.48	4,320	3.97
e) S.E..................	636				5,724	
i) Info. Bull. 161.......	360				3,240	
h) E.E.I., 1933..........	575				5,175	
o) E.E.I., 1955..........	353				3,177	
Clothes dryer:						
d) Zinder...............	1,164	4,440	3,974	1.12	10,476	0.42
n) A.G.A...............		4,800				
e) S.E..................	1,140	4,949	3,890	1.27	10,260	0.48
g) Sporn...............	1,100				9,900	
Central air conditioning:						
p) Zinder, conventional...	3,920	57,000	13,378	4.26	35,280	1.62
heat pump.....	4,300	57,000	14,675	3.88	38,700	1.47
q) S.E..................				4-5		
g) Sporn, heat pump......	3,300					
Estimates used in this study:						
Water heater..........	4,716	25,740	16,095	1.60	42,444	0.61
Range...............	1,200	9,600	4,095	2.34	10,800	0.89
Refrigerator...........	360	12,587	1,228	10.25	3,240	3.88
Clothes dryer........	1,150	4,500	3,925	1.15	10,350	0.43
Central air conditioning	3,300	47,290	11,262	4.20	29,700	1.59

[1] At 3412.76 Btu's per kilowatt hour.

[2] Computed at the rounded 1975 over-all heat rate of 9,000 Btu's per net kilowatt hour for utility generation (Appendix Table H-24).

[3] This column cannot be used to measure the advantage of one form of heating over the other, as the cost element is entirely eliminated. It does indicate, however, that the greatest *relative* advantage in fuel consumption of gas over electricity would tend to be found in clothes dryers and water heaters. The calculation is presented, however, mainly for the benefit of the reader who wishes to change the assumptions given here as to the future

TABLE C–32 (continued)

distribution of the households between gas and electricity appliances. The ratios shown provide a convenient short-cut in the pertinent recalculations.

SOURCES:

a) USDA, Technical Bulletin No. 1073, *Comparative Utilization of Energy by Household Electric and Liquefied Petroleum Gas Ranges, Refrigerators and Water Heaters*, October 1953, p. 51, Table 25. Computed for 50-gallon per day drawoff by taking 86.2 per cent of average 38-gallon and 78-gallon drawoff per day.

b) A.G.A., *Comparative Total Costs of Gas and Electricity for Cooking and Water Heating in Residences* (1955), derived from comparisons on page 1 (for water heater: 50-gallon drawoff).

c) University of Illinois, Engineering Experiment Station Bulletin No. 436, Eugene F. Hebrank, *Investigation of the Performance of Automatic Storage-Type Gas and Electric Domestic Heaters* (Urbana: October 1956), p. iv.

d) H. Zinder and Associates, Inc., *Gas and Electric Service in Multiple Housing* (Washington, D. C.: December 1957), p. 5. Figures relate to typical two-bedroom military housing.

e) Southeastern Electric Exchange, *Economic Study of Electric, Gas and Oil Usage for Capehart and Other Public Housing Projects*, Atlanta, Georgia, June 1958, p. 17.

f) *Electrical World*, March 19, 1956, Table 1, p. 126, "Serving the All-Electric Home," by William A. Bell, Jr., Special Studies Section, Tennessee Valley Authority. This is an average for two years (July 1953–June 1955).

g) Philip Sporn, address before the New York Society of Security Analysts, New York City, June 18, 1956.

h) E.E.I., *Statistical Bulletin*, No. 1, October 1934, p. 13.

i) USDA, Agricultural Research Service, Agriculture Information Bulletin No. 161, Joe F. Davis, *Use of Electricity on Farms*, November 1956, p. 27.

j) USDA, Technical Bulletin 1073, *op. cit.*, averages from p. 31, Table 12, and p. 29, Table 9, respectively, adjusted to cover 365 days.

k) Consumers Union, *Consumer Reports*, September 1958, p. 463. This represents a range of monthly consumption of 750 to 1,200 cu. ft. of natural gas at 1,020 Btu per cu. ft.

l) Middle West Service Company, communication to author from Malcolm R. Rodger, vice president.

m) USDA, Technical Bulletin No. 1073, *op. cit.*, p. 41, Tables 19 and 20.

n) Based on a direct communication to the author from A.G.A.

o) Communication to the author from Westinghouse Electric Corporation citing E.E.I., November 20, 1957.

p) H. Zinder and Associates, Inc., *op. cit.*, p. 37, Table 1A, shows 572 therms of gas or 4,300 kwh of electricity for central air cooling with the reversible heat pump. In "conventional" cooling unit the Zinder report places the kwh usage at 3,920 kwh (p. 38). This difference is explained as being due to size of the heat pump—being somewhat larger to meet heating needs (p. 28).

q) Southeastern Electric Exchange, *op. cit.*, based on following observations: "From what information is available, it appears that in its cooling operation, efficiencies of fuel utilization of the order of 50 per cent may be obtained at elevations near sea level where cooling water at 75° F. is used. When the elevation increases to about 2,000 ft. above sea level and the cooling water used is at 85° F., the resultant efficiency of fuel utilization may drop to about 40 per cent." (P. 42.) "On its cooling cycle, the heat pump will generally develop a coefficient of performance at, or above, 2.0 (200 per cent) under usual conditions of design and temperature difference." (p. 37.)

TABLE C–33. AVERAGE WATTAGE OF SELECTED HOUSEHOLD APPLIANCES

Appliance	Wattage	Appliance	Wattage
Room air conditioners:		Humidifier	185
½ ton	880	Ironer	1,455
¾ ton	1,255	Knife sharpener	50
1 ton	1,540	Pressure cooker	1,400
Blanket	175	Radio	30
Blender	275	Range	Up to 23,000
Broiler	1,400	Record player	50
Casserole	510	Refrigerator	230
Clock	2	Sandwich grill	960
Clothes dryer	4,760	Sewing machine	75
Coffee maker	Up to 1,000	Shaver	11
Dishwasher	1,325	Steam iron	1,040
Dry iron	1,025	Toaster	1,130
Fans:		Television receiver	205
Floor circulator	120	Vacuum cleaners:	
Attic	345	Bag type	340
Kitchen exhaust	75	Canister type	725
Portable	50	Tank type	555
Floor polisher	475	Hand type	310
Food freezer	Up to 460	Waffle baker	960
Hair dryer	415	Washer:	
Heating pad	60	Automatic	400
Heater	Up to 1,650	Non-automatic	380
Heating equipment:			
Warm air furnace fan	320		
Oil burner motor	230		

SOURCE: Release issued by Consolidated Edison Company, New York City.

TABLE C-34. ESTIMATES OF ELECTRICITY CONSUMPTION FOR LIGHTING, SELECTED YEARS, 1915–56

| | Average residential consumption (kwh per year) | | | | | Lighting as per cent of total residential consumption | | | |
| | Lighting only | | | | | | | | |
Year	All uses[a] (1)	Ebasco-Westinghouse[b] (2)	Ebasco-Gen. Elec.[c] (3)	Edison Electric Institute[d] (4)	Middle West Service Co.[e] (5)	Ebasco-Westinghouse (6)	Ebasco-Gen. Elec. (7)	Edison Electric Institute (8)	Middle West Service Co. (9)
1956	2,969		867	771			29.2%		26.0%
1955	2,751		842				30.6		
1954	2,549		818				32.1		
1953	2,346	744	793			31.7%	33.8		
1952	2,169	698	768			32.2	35.4		
1951	2,004	655	742			32.7	37.0		
1950	1,830	602	718			32.9	39.2		
1949	1,684	561	695			33.3	41.3		
1948	1,563	528	670			33.8	42.9		
1947	1,438	489	645			34.0	44.9		
1946	1,329	460	622			34.6	46.8		

TABLE C–34 (continued)

Year	Average residential consumption (kwh per year)					Lighting as per cent of total residential consumption			
		Lighting only							
	All uses [a] (1)	Ebasco-West-ing-house [b] (2)	Ebasco-Gen. Elec. [c] (3)	Edison Electric Insti-tute [d] (4)	Middle West Service Co. [e] (5)	Ebasco-West-ing-house (6)	Ebasco-Gen. Elec. (7)	Edison Electric Insti-tute (8)	Middle West Service Co. (9)
1945	1,229	428	597			34.8%	48.6%		
1944	1,151	407				35.4			
1943	1,070	383				35.8			
1942	1,022	369				36.1			
1941	986	360		337		36.5		34.2%	
1940	952	352		341		37.0		35.8	
1939	897	336		317		37.4		35.3	
1938	853	323		295		37.9		34.6	
1937	805	312		290		38.8		36.0	
1935	677			247				36.5	
1934	629			261				41.5	
1933	600			238				39.7	
1932	601			259				43.1	
1927–31	521			282				54.1	
1926	430			278				64.7	
1915	260				245				94.2%

[a] For sources, see Table C–20, except for 1927–31 average which is taken from E.E.I. *Statistical Bulletin*, No. 6, May 1939, p. 16. The latter is only approximate because of some inconsistencies in the source; for the same reason, no 1936 data are given.

[b] From *The Lighting Market* (New York: April 1954), p. 4, Table 1. This publication was prepared by Ebasco with lighting data supplied by the Westinghouse Electric Corporation. Per-customer estimates derived by applying percentage used for lighting to total per-customer consumption.

[c] From *Light for Living* (New York: December 1955), p. 36. This publication was prepared by Ebasco with lighting data prepared by the Lamp Division of the General Electric Company.

[d] E. E. I., *Statistical Bulletin*, various numbers—1937–41: No. 9, March 1942, pp. 22, 23; 1926–35: number of customers from No. 8, May 1941, p. 23; consumption for 1935, No. 3, June 1936, p. 15; 1934, No. 2, April 1935, p. 14; 1933, No. 1, October 1934, p. 13; and 5-year averages for 1926, 1932, No. 6, May 1939, p. 16.

[e] Middle West Service Company, "Residential Lighting," a paper presented by M. R. Rodger, vice president, before the Electrical Industry Coordinating Group, New York City, May 9, 1957, p. 4.

TABLE C-35. ELECTRICITY CONSUMPTION PER RESIDENTIAL CUSTOMER FOR SEVEN MIDWESTERN UTILITY COMPANIES, 1956

Company	Consumption per customer (kwh)			Consumption for lighting only as per cent of consumption for—	
	Lighting only (1)	Lighting and misc. appliances[a] (2)	All uses (3)	All uses (4)	Lighting and misc. appliances (5)
Central Power and Light Co.....	400	548	2,297	17.4%	73.0%
Consumer Power Co............	660	974	3,530	18.7	67.8
Detroit Edison Co.............	700	1,070	2,986	23.4	65.4
Empire District Electric Co.....	365	516	2,078	17.6	70.7
Iowa Southern Utilities Co......	400	580	2,460	16.3	69.0
Kansas Power and Light Co....	332	502	2,638	12.6	66.1
Lake Superior District Power Co.	460	771	3,599	12.8	59.7

[a] Minor appliances such as radios, vacuum cleaners, irons, clocks, grills, hair dryers, etc.

SOURCE: From undated table entitled "A Comparison of Residential and Rural Percent Saturation and Electric Consumption per Customer for Seven Utility Companies by Appliances—1956," Middle West Service Company, Chicago, Illinois.

TABLE C-36. SOME ESTIMATES OF FUTURE ELECTRICITY CONSUMPTION FOR LIGHTING

Source of estimate	Year (1)	Average consumption per customer (kwh)		Lighting as per cent of all uses (4)
		All uses (2)	Lighting only (3)	
a) Federal Power Commission.................	1980	7,000	725	10.4%
b) Middle West Service Co. (target)...........	1965	7,500	1,725	23.0
(base)............	1965	5,650	940	16.6
c) General Electric Co. (with special program)..	1965	6,608	2,093	31.7
(without special program)...............	1965	5,608	1,093	19.5
(with special program)..................	1963	5,595	1,722	30.8
(without special program)...............	1963	4,915	1,042	21.2
d) Westinghouse Corp........................	1963	4,600	1,250	27.2

SOURCES:

a) FPC, *Estimated Future Power Requirements of the United States, 1955–1980*, December 1956, p. 9.

b) Middle West Service Company, "Residential Lighting," a paper presented by M. R. Rodger, vice president, before the Electrical Industry Coordinating Group, New York City, May 9, 1957, pp. 17–18.

c) *Light for Living* (New York: December 1955), a publication prepared by Ebasco with lighting data prepared by the Lamp Division of the General Electric Company. The higher lighting use is G.E. Lamp Division's projection of the impact which a program of "light conditioning" can have. The lower amount, in each of the two years, is the G.E. Lamp Division's forecast of what will happen without a special program. For total consumption, G.E. uses the *Electrical World* 1955 projection. The difference in the total consumption figures in each of the two years is, of course, due to the lighting program which would "light condition" half of the houses in ten years.

d) *The Lighting Market* (New York: April 1954), p. 4, a publication prepared by Ebasco with data supplied by the Westinghouse Electric Corporation. Electricity utilization is given in aggregates rather than on a per-customer basis. The results shown are based roughly on 55 million customers.

TABLE C-37. DERIVATION OF ESTIMATED KILOWATT HOUR
CONSUMPTION PER RESIDENTIAL CUSTOMER, 1975

Item	Estimated annual consumption per unit[a] (kwh) (1)	Assumed percentage of saturation[b] (2)	Average consumption per customer (kwh) (3)
Total...................			6,448
1. Lighting...................	1,200	100%	1,200
2. Dishwasher.................	300	25	75
3. Steam iron.................	120	50	60
4. Television.................	250	100	250
5. Vacuum cleaner.............	30	80	24
6. Refrigerator..............	360	100	360
7. Freezer...................	900	40	360
8. Range....................	1,200	50	600
9. Water heater..............	4,716	25	1,179
10. Dryer...................	1,150	30	345
11. Heating.................	11,000	5.5	605
12. Central cooling..........	3,300	20	660
13. Room coolers.............	800	60	480
14. Miscellaneous appliances......	250	100	250

[a] Item 1 from Chapter 5, pp. 215–16. Items 2, 3, 4, and 5 assumed at reasonable
weekly rates of operation, at wattages given in Table C–33—dishwasher, 4 hours; steam
iron, 2¼ hours; television, 20 hours; vacuum cleaner, 1 hour. Items 6, 8, 9, 10, and 12 from
Table C–32. Item 7 from USDA, Agricultural Research Service, Joe F. Davis, *Use of Electricity on Farms*, Information Bulletin No. 161, November 1956, p. 27. Item 11 based on
informal survey of expert opinion—see Table C–11, footnote d, and discussion in Chapter 5,
pp. 214–15. Item 13 based on the assumption that about four room units are equivalent
to one central unit. Item 14 is arbitrary assumption.

[b] Saturation is defined as the percentage of wired homes (which in 1975 is assumed to be
equal to total households) in which the particular appliance or function will be utilized.
Items 2, 4, 6, and 7 from Table C–22; items 3, 5, and 14, arbitrary assumptions; item 8,
Table C–29; item 9, Table C–26; item 10, Table C–30, footnote b; item 11, Table C–14,
footnote d; items 12 and 13, Table C–22 and also discussion in Chapter 5, pp. 213–14.

TABLE C-38. HOUSEHOLD CONSUMPTION OF ELECTRICITY, 1975
PROJECTION

Household	Number of households[a] (1)	Consumption	
		Per average customer (kwh)[b] (2)	Total (million kwh) (3)
Family-type	56,162,000	6,448	362,133
Primary individual..	12,716,000	4,299	54,670
Total.............	68,878,000	6,051	416,803

[a] Appendix Table I–1.
[b] Family-type rate from Table C–37; primary individual households arbitrarily assumed
to use one-third less electricity.

TABLE C-39. SUMMARY: ENERGY CONSUMPTION IN HOUSEHOLDS, IN PHYSICAL UNITS, PROJECTION TO 1975

Item	Other than transportation and electricity			Transportation [c] (4)	Electricity [d] (5)	Grand total (6)
	Space heating [a] (1)	Other [b] (2)	Total (3)			
1. Coal (thous. tons):						
Bituminous..........	12,153		12,153		114,495	126,648
Anthracite..........	3,211		3,211			3,211
2. Oil (thous. bbl.):						
Gasoline...........				1,350,485		1,350,485
Kerosine...........	36,741	20,326	57,067			57,067
No. 1 heating oil.....	18,235	11,399	29,634			29,634
No. 2 heating oil.....	307,955	12,395	320,350			320,350
Residual...........					41,322	41,322
3. Gas (mill. cu. ft.)......	3,526,403	1,387,532	4,913,935		728,413	5,642,348
4. Natural gas liquids (thous. bbl.):						
LPG..............	65,445	53,532	118,977	47,700		166,677
Natural gasoline.....				184,157		184,157
5. Hydro (mill. kwh)......					72,603	72,603

[a] Tables C-14 and C-13.
[b] Tables C-18 and C-17.
[c] Appendix Tables D-40 and D-18.
[d] Appendix Table H-17.

TABLE C–40. SUMMARY: ENERGY CONSUMPTION IN HOUSEHOLDS, IN BTU'S, PROJECTION TO 1975

(Billions)

Item	Other than transportation and electricity			Transportation [c]	Electricity [d]	Grand total
	Space heating [a] (1)	Other [b] (2)	Total (3)	(4)	(5)	(6)
1. Coal:						
Bituminous.......	318,400		318,400		2,747,873	3,066,273
Anthracite.......	81,600		81,600			81,600
Total...........	400,000		400,000		2,747,873	3,147,873
2. Oil:						
Gasoline.........				7,033,326		7,033,326
Kerosine.........	208,321	115,249	323,570			323,570
No. 1 heating oil..	104,158	65,110	169,268			169,268
No. 2 heating oil..	1,791,375	72,103	1,863,478			1,863,478
Residual.........					260,330	260,330
Total...........	2,103,854	252,462	2,356,316	7,033,326	260,330	9,649,972
3. Gas.............	3,649,827	1,436,096	5,085,923		728,413	5,814,336
4. Natural gas liquids:						
LPG............	262,500	214,725	477,225	191,325		668,550
Natural gasoline..				959,090		959,090
Total...........	262,500	214,725	477,225	1,150,415		1,627,640
5. Hydro............					650,250	650,250
Grand total..........	6,416,181	1,903,283	8,319,464	8,183,741	4,386,866	20,890,071

[a] Tables C–14 and C–13.
[b] Tables C–18 and C–17.
[c] Appendix Tables D–40 and D–18.
[d] Appendix Table H–17.

Section D. Transportation

General Note

For easier understanding, Section D may be divided into six principal groups:

1) Energy consumption in highway transportation, by far the largest of the six groups, extending from Tables D–15 through D–43. The material is pre-sented under two different aspects: (a) type of vehicle, i.e., automobile, truck, etc., and (b) consuming sector, i.e., household, government, etc. Consumption by type of vehicle is developed in Tables D–15 through D–20 for 1955 and in Tables D–25 through D–38 for 1975. Consumption by consuming sector is covered in Tables D–18 through D–24 for 1955 and Tables D–39 through D–43 for 1975 (Tables D–18 and D–19 deal with both aspects, therefore appear in both subgroupings). Tables D–31 through D–37 which contain the basic assumptions leading to the 1975 projection of automobile fuel consumption (Table D–38) should be read in conjunction with the textual discussion on the same subject found in Chapter 5.

2) Intercity freight traffic, used for estimating 1975 size and division of freight volume: Tables D–1 through D–3.

3) Energy consumption by railroads: Tables D–4 through D–11, with Tables D–5 and D–6 deriving electricity use and Tables D–7 through D–10 supporting the 1975 projections.

4) Energy consumption in water transport: Tables D–12 through D–14.

5) Energy consumption in aviation: Tables D–46 through D–58.

6) Energy consumption in electric streetcars and railways: Tables D–44 and D–45.

Tables D–59 and D–60 summarize the results in all fields, in terms of physical units and Btu's.

Transportation Tables

D– 1. Estimated Volume and Percentage Distribution of Intercity Freight Traffic, Public and Private, by Kinds of Transport Media, 1939–56

D– 2. Relationship between Freight Traffic and Gross National Product, 1939–55

D– 3. Revenue Ton-Miles by Various Transportation Media, 1955 and Projection to 1975

D– 4. Energy Consumption in Railroads, 1955

D– 5. Electricity Consumption in Transportation, 1955

D– 6. Electricity Purchases and Production in Transportation, 1944–50

TABLE D-1. ESTIMATED VOLUME AND PERCENTAGE DISTRIBUTION OF INTERCITY FREIGHT TRAFFIC, PUBLIC AND PRIVATE, BY KINDS OF TRANSPORT MEDIA, 1939–56

Year	Railway revenue ton-miles, including electric railways, express, and mail		Motor vehicles		Inland waterways, including Great Lakes [a]		Pipe lines (oil)		Airways (domestic revenue service), including express, mail, and excess baggage		Total
	Million ton-miles	Per cent of total	Million ton-miles	Per cent of total	Million ton-miles	Per cent of total	Million ton-miles	Per cent of total	Million ton-miles	Per cent of total	Million ton-miles
1956	655,9—b	48.2%	253,8—b	18.7%	220,0—b	16.2%	230,0—b	16.9%	6—b	.04%	1,360,1—b
1955	631,385	49.41	226,188	17.70	216,508	16.94	203,244	15.91	481	.04	1,277,806
1954	556,557	49.50	214,626	19.09	173,679a	15.45	179,203	15.94	397	.04	1,124,462
1953	614,199	51.01	217,163	18.04	202,439a	16.81	169,884	14.11	413	.03	1,204,098
1952	623,373	54.48	194,607	17.01	168,367	14.71	157,502	13.76	415	.04	1,144,264
1951	655,353	55.63	188,012	15.96	182,216a	15.47	152,115	12.91	379	.03	1,178,075
1950	596,940	56.17	172,860	16.27	163,344	15.37	129,175	12.16	318	.03	1,062,637
1949	534,694	58.38	126,636	13.83	139,396	15.22	114,916	12.55	235	.03	915,877
1948	647,267	61.94	116,045	11.10	161,846a	15.49	119,597	11.44	223	.02	1,044,978
1947	664,523	65.24	102,095	10.02	146,714	14.40	105,161	10.32	158	.02	1,018,651
1946	602,069	66.61	81,992	9.07	123,973	13.72	95,727	10.59	93	.01	903,854
1945	690,809	67.26	66,948	6.52	142,737	13.90	126,530	12.32	91	.01	1,027,115
1944	746,912	68.63	58,264	5.35	150,155	13.80	132,864	12.21	71	.01	1,088,266
1943	734,829	71.26	56,784	5.51	141,652	13.74	97,867	9.49	53	.01	1,031,185
1942	645,422	69.47	59,896	6.45	148,565	15.99	75,087	8.08	34	c	929,004
1941	481,756	62.40	81,363	10.54	140,454	18.19	68,428	8.86	19	c	772,020
1940	379,201	61.30	62,043	10.03	118,057	19.08	59,277	9.58	14	c	618,592
1939	338,850	62.34	52,821	9.72	96,249	17.71	55,602	10.23	12	c	543,534

a Coverage expanded to include waterways previously in use but not covered. These changes in coverage increased the 1948 estimate by 2,600 millions of ton-miles; the 1951 by 4,300 millions; the 1953 by 6,400 millions, and the 1954 by 6,700 millions; each as related to the previous year (1947, 1950, 1952, and 1953, respectively). For details see Department of the Army, Corps of Engineers, *Waterborne Commerce of the United States*, various issues.

b Available data not carried to additional places.

c Less than 0.01 per cent.

SOURCE: ICC, Bureau of Transport Economics and Statistics: 1939–54 from *Intercity Ton-Miles, 1939–1954*, Statement No. 568, File No. 10–D–7, February 1956, p. 4; 1955–56 from *Transport Economics*, October 1957, p. 7.

TABLE D-2.   RELATIONSHIP BETWEEN FREIGHT TRAFFIC AND
GROSS NATIONAL PRODUCT, 1939–55

Year	Intercity ton-miles [a] (million) (1)	GNP (billion 1955 dollars) [b] (2)	Ton-miles per dollar of GNP (1) ÷ (2) (3)
1955....................	1,277,806	$390.7	3.271
1954....................	1,124,462	365.4	3.077
1953....................	1,204,098	374.3	3.217
1952....................	1,144,264	357.5	3.201
1951....................	1,178,075	345.4	3.411
1950....................	1,062,637	321.8	3.302
1949....................	915,877	294.9	3.106
1948....................	1,044,978	295.8	3.533
1947....................	1,018,651	282.7	3.603
1946....................	903,854	283.1	3.193
1945....................	1,027,115	317.5	3.235
1944....................	1,088,266	324.1	3.358
1943....................	1,031,185	301.2	3.424
1942....................	929,004	271.1	3.427
1941....................	772,020	240.3	3.213
1940....................	618,592	207.7	2.978
1939....................	543,534	190.4	2.855

[a] Table D-1.
[b] Economic Report of the President, January 1957.

TABLE D-3.   REVENUE TON-MILES BY VARIOUS TRANSPORTATION
MEDIA, 1955 AND PROJECTION TO 1975

(Millions)

Item	1955 [a] Ton-miles	1955 [a] Per cent of total	1975 Estimated per cent of total	1975 Estimated ton-miles	Percentage increase of 1975 over 1955
1. Total............	1,277,806	100.00%	100.00% [b]	2,799,830 [c]	
2. Railroads........	631,385	49.41%	35.0 %	979,940	55.20%
3. Trucks..........	226,188	17.70	30.0	839,949	271.35
4. Inland waterways.	216,508	16.94	17.0	475,971	119.81
5. Oil pipelines......	203,244	15.91	17.9	501,170	146.58
6. Airways..........	481	.04	.1	2,800	482.12

[a] Table D-1.
[b] Allocated on basis of interpretation of trends shown in Table D-1.
[c] Based on annual growth of 4 per cent (same as GNP) in accordance with the close relationship between the two rates shown in Table D-2.

TABLE D-4. ENERGY CONSUMPTION IN RAILROADS, 1955

Item	Coal (thous. tons)	Diesel oil (thous. bbl.)	Residual oil (thous. bbl.)	Gasoline (thous. bbl.)	Total	Electricity (mill. kwh)
I. Physical units						
1. All purposes:						
a. Purchased and produced[a]......	15,886	83,983	14,867	1,134		
b. Change in stocks[b].	−307	+298	−421	+1		
c. Total consumed...	16,194	83,685	15,288	1,133		2,583[c]
2. Motive purposes:[a]						
a. Yard switching...	1,569	8,635	908	2		61
b. Freight service....	8,594	53,428	6,442	1		813
c. Passenger service..	1,064	19,248	1,122	5		1,250
d. Total............	11,227	81,311	8,472	8		2,124
3. All other purposes:	4,967	2,374	6,816	(1,125)[d]		459[e]
a. Anthracite[f]......	457					
b. Bituminous[g]......	4,510					
II. Billion Btu, excl. electricity						
1. All purposes........	423,917	478,009	97,598	41[h]	999,565	
2. Motive purposes:						
a. Yard switching...	41,108	49,323	5,796	10	96,237	
b. Freight service....	225,163	305,181	41,126	5	571,475	
c. Passenger service..	27,876	109,945	7,163	26	145,010	
d. Total............	294,147	464,449	54,085	41	812,722	
3. All other purposes:	129,770	13,560	43,513	(5,859)[d]	186,843	
a. Anthracite.......	11,608					
b. Bituminous.......	118,162					

[a] ICC, Bureau of Transport Economics and Statistics, *Fuel and Power Statistics of Class I Railways in the United States; for twelve months ended with December 1956 and 1955*, Statement No. M–230 (OS–E).

[b] Difference between fuel stocks at beginning and end of 1955, from ICC, *69th Annual Report on Transport Statistics in the United States, for the Year Ended December 31, 1955*, p. 56, Table 70. Coverage is slightly smaller than Statement M–230, since latter includes also switching and terminal companies.

[c] Table D–5, item 3.

[d] Not included in total, as presumably going to motor vehicles which are covered in highway transportation.

[e] Table D–5, item 5. Includes 5 million kwh for worktrains (*69th Annual Report, op. cit.,* p. 57, Table 72).

[f] Mines, *Minerals Yearbook, 1955*, Vol. II, p. 123. This amount not used for motive purposes, according to *69th Annual Report, op. cit.,* p. 57, Table 72, footnote b.

[g] Derived as balance.

[h] Includes only Btu's for motive purposes. Not comparable with data in physical units in part I, item 1, above

TABLE D-5.   ELECTRICITY CONSUMPTION IN TRANSPORTATION, 1955

Item	Million kwh
1. Purchases by railways and railroads [a]	4,563
2. Transit system purchases [b]	1,980
3. Remainder for railroads	2,583
4. Railroad motive uses [c]	2,124
5. Railroad other uses (item 3 − item 4) [d]	459
6. Transit generation [b]	1,480
7. Total transit use (item 2 + item 6)	3,460
8. Total railroad and transit (item 3 + item 7)	6,043

[a] E.E.I., *Statistical Bulletin for the Year 1957*, p. 27, Table 18.

[b] ATA, *Transit Fact Book, 1957 Edition*, p. 11, Table 14. Purchases may include some small amounts which go to railroads.

[c] Table D-4, part I, item 2d.

[d] This is equivalent to the assumption that there is no electricity generation in the railroad industry. For material supporting this view, see Table D-6 which shows that at best only small amounts of electricity have been produced by railroads.

TABLE D-6.   ELECTRICITY PURCHASES AND PRODUCTION IN TRANSPORTATION, 1944-50 [a]

(Million kwh)

Year	Electricity purchased and produced by railroads [b] (1)	Sales to [c]		Transit purchases [d] (4)	Calculated production by railroads (1) − (3) (5)
		Street and interurban transportation (2)	Electrified steam railroads (3)		
1950	3,291	3,457	2,425	3,181	866
1949	3,310	3,685	2,427	3,589	883
1948	3,480	4,109	2,611	4,259	869
1947	3,072	4,487	2,617	4,803	455
1946	3,063	4,515	2,632	4,835	431
1945	3,127	4,683	2,671	4,903	456
1944	3,170	4,635	2,694	4,861	476

[a] The data in cols. 2 and 3 are not available after 1950.

[b] ICC, Bureau of Transport Economics and Statistics, *Fuel and Power Statistics of Class I Railways in the United States; for twelve months ended with December 1956 and 1955*, Statement No. M-230 (OS-E).

[c] E.E.I., *Statistical Bulletin, No. 19*, July 1952, p. 29.

[d] ATA, "Source and Distribution of Electrical Energy Consumed by the Transit Industry of the United States and Cost of Purchased Power—1920-1957, inclusive," mimeo. release by the Statistical Department, August 22, 1958.

TABLE D-7.   FUELS CONSUMED PER UNIT OF ACTIVITY IN RAILROAD TRANSPORTATION, 1955

Area	Fuel (used per unit of activity as shown in stub)			Total quantities used		Diesel oil which would be needed to replace:	
	Coal (pounds) (1)	Fuel oil (gallons) (2)	Diesel oil (gallons) (3)	Coal (tons) (4)	Fuel oil (gallons) (5)	Coal (gallons) [a] (6)	Fuel oil (gallons) [b] (7)
Eastern District:							
Yard switching (locomotive hour)	861	26.64	7.45	777,576	654,798	13,456,310	183,117
Freight (per thousand gross ton-miles)	110		1.62	3,232,140		95,201,215	
Passenger (per train-car mile)	20.7		.30	581,676		16,860,174	
Pocahontas Region:							
Yard switching (locomotive hour)	738		7.72	243,244		5,089,007	
Freight (per thousand gross ton-miles)	75		1.32	1,976,713		69,580,298	
Passenger (per train-car mile)	18.7		.33	232,920		8,220,706	
Southern Region:							
Yard switching (locomotive hour)	1,006	81.96	8.82	127,179	107,291	2,230,057	11,546
Freight (per thousand gross ton-miles)	102		1.70	1,531,983		51,066,100	
Passenger (per train-car mile)	14.3		.33	18,611		858,969	
Western District:							
Yard switching (locomotive hour)	991	60.80	7.61	421,345	37,387,726	6,471,111	4,679,615
Freight (per thousand gross ton-miles)	128	8.83	1.74	1,853,242	270,560,297	50,385,017	53,315,392
Passenger (per train-car mile)	39.1	.97	.33	230,568	47,126,799	3,891,941	16,032,828
National:							
Yard switching (locomotive hour)						27,246,485	4,874,278
Freight (per thousand gross ton-miles)						266,232,630	53,315,392
Passenger (per train-car mile)						29,831,790	16,032,828

[a] Computed on basis of substitution factors derived from cols. 1 and 3.
[b] Computed on basis of substitution factors derived from cols. 2 and 3.

NOTE: Freight tons include weight of locomotives and tender.

SOURCE: ICC, *Fuel and Power Statistics of Class I Railways in the United States; for twelve months ended with December 1956 and 1955*, Statement No. M-230 (OS-E). Regional figures used because of regional variations.

TABLE D-8. HYPOTHETICAL ENERGY CONSUMPTION IN RAILROADS,
ASSUMING COAL AND RESIDUAL OIL REPLACED BY DIESEL OIL IN
MOTIVE USES, 1955

Motive uses	Coal		Residual oil		Diesel oil actual (thous. bbl.) (5)	Diesel oil hypothetical (thous. bbl.) (2)+(4)+(5) (6)
	Actual (thous. tons) (1)	Diesel equivalent (thous. bbl.) (2)	Actual (thous. bbl.) (3)	Diesel equivalent (thous. bbl.) (4)		
Yard switching......	1,569	649	908	116	8,635	9,400
Freight service......	8,594	6,339	6,442	1,269	53,428	61,036
Passenger service....	1,064	710	1,122	382	19,248	20,340
Total..............	11,227	7,698	8,472	1,767	81,311	90,776

SOURCES: Actual figures from Table D-4; hypothetical replacement figures from Table
D-7, converted to barrels.

TABLE D-9. RELATIONSHIP OF YARD SERVICE TO FREIGHT
SERVICE, 1944-55

Year	Yard switching (thous. hours) [a] (1)	Freight ton-miles (million) [b] (2)	Ton-miles of freight per hour of yard switching (2) ÷ (1) (3)
1955...............	51,040	631,385	12,370
1954...............	47,602	556,557	11,692
1953...............	53,388	614,199	11,504
1952...............	53,994	623,373	11,545
1951...............	57,055	655,353	11,486
1950...............	54,948	596,940	10,864
1949...............	52,396	534,694	10,205
1948...............	60,311	647,267	10,732
1947...............	61,228	664,523	10,853
1946...............	57,845	602,069	10,408
1945...............	60,980	690,809	11,328
1944...............	62,434	746,912	11,963

[a] AAR, Bureau of Railway Economics, *Railroad Transportation, A Statistical Record,
1921-1955,* December 1956, p. 26.
[b] Table D-1.

TABLE D-10.   VOLUME OF REVENUE PASSENGER TRAFFIC, 1929-55

Year	Number of passengers (thousands)			Passenger-miles (millions) (4)
	Commuters (1)	Others (2)	Total[a] (3)	
1955................	247,759	184,209	431,999	28,526
1954................	249,069	189,539	439,356	29,286
1953................	255,829	200,941	456,817	31,655
1952................	260,463	209,018	469,537	34,010
1951................	269,464	214,302	483,833	34,614
1950................	277,102	209,094	486,194	31,760
1949................	308,512	245,994	554,430	35,095
1948................	332,196	310,736	642,781	41,179
1947................	344,604	359,726	703,280	45,921
1946................	340,670	451,975	790,130	64,673
1945................	322,734	571,225	891,128	91,717
1944................	317,918	595,299	910,295	95,549
1943................	312,246	572,494	881,965	87,820
1942................	286,225	383,299	667,287	53,659
1941................	232,456	254,126	485,399	29,350
1940................	229,266	224,626	452,921	23,762
1939................	231,126	219,897	450,373	22,651
1938................	227,412	212,515	452,731	21,629
1937................	245,824	251,476	497,288	24,655
1936................	259,199	230,892	490,091	22,421
1935................	259,099	186,321	445,872	18,476
1934................	262,825	187,082	449,775	18,033
1933................	271,984	160,618	432,980	16,341
1932................	315,462	161,572	478,800	16,971
1931................	386,349	209,741	596,391	21,894
1930................	438,688	264,134	703,598	26,815
1929................	457,617	321,449	780,468	31,074

[a] Discrepancies between sum of first two columns and total explained by fact that total is taken from annual returns, breakdown from monthly returns.

SOURCE: AAR, Bureau of Railway Economics, *Railroad Transportation, A Statistical Record, 1921-1955*, December 1956, p. 19.

TABLE D-11. ENERGY CONSUMPTION IN RAILROADS, PROJECTION TO 1975

Item	Diesel oil (thous. bbl.) (1)	Gasoline (thous. bbl.) (2)	Electricity (mill. kwh) (3)	Coal (thous. tons) Anthracite (4)	Coal (thous. tons) Bituminous (5)	Residual oil (thous. bbl.) (6)	Total (7)
1955 Hypothetical [a]— *Physical units*							
1. Motive purposes:							
a. Yard switching....	9,400	2	61				
b. Freight service....	61,036	1	813				
c. Passenger service..	20,340	5	1,250				
d. Total.............	90,776	8	2,124				
2. Nonmotive purposes..	2,374	(1,125) [b]	459	457	4,510	6,816	
3. All purposes.........	93,150	1,133	2,583	457	4,510	6,816	
1975—Physical units							
1. Motive purposes:							
a. Yard switching [c]...	12,401	3	80				
b. Freight service [d]...	94,731	2	1,262				
c. Passenger service [e].	15,255	4	938				
d. Total.............	122,387	9	2,280				
2. Nonmotive purposes [f].	2,374	(1,125) [b]	712	457	4,510	6,816	
3. All purposes.........	124,761	1,134	2,992	457	4,510	6,816	
1975—Billion Btu excl. electricity							
1. Motive purposes......	699,075	47					699,122
2. Nonmotive purposes..	13,560			11,608	118,162	43,513	186,843
3. All purposes.........	712,635	47		11,608	118,162	43,513	885,965

[a] Assuming use only of diesel oil in motive uses. From Table D–4 and Table D–8.

[b] Believed to be principally for automobiles and other uses covered in nonrailroad consuming sectors. Therefore, gasoline is excluded from the Btu calculations.

[c] Assumed to show 85 per cent of the 1975 projected level for freight service (i.e., .85 × 1.5520) (Table D–3), in accordance with the past tendency of switching-hours to decline relative to freight movements (Table D–9) and the anticipated reduction in passenger service (footnote e).

[d] 1955 quantities increased by growth in ton-miles calculated in Table D–3.

[e] Assumed to decline 25 per cent from the 1955 level (Table D–10).

[f] Fuels assumed to remain unchanged because 100 per cent diesel operation is likely to reduce maintenance and declining passenger service will eliminate many of the uses here covered; electricity use assumed to increase with ton-miles (Table D–3) because of spread of electronic controls and devices.

TABLE D-12. OIL CONSUMPTION IN SHIPPING COMPARED WITH GROSS NATIONAL PRODUCT, 1927-56

Year	Oil consumption (thousand barrels)									GNP (billion $ 1955) (10)	Barrel of oil per $1,000 GNP			Foreign trade as per cent of all shipping (14)	Distillates as per cent of total oil in—	
	All shipping			Vessels engaged in foreign trade			Vessels engaged in domestic trade [d]				Foreign trade (11)	Domestic trade (12)	Total (13)		Foreign trade (15)	Domestic trade (16)
	Total [a] (1)	Residual (2)	Distillates [b] (3)	Total [c] (4)	Residual (5)	Distillates (6)	Total (7)	Residual (8)	Distillates (9)							
1956	135,932	117,445	18,487	79,878	69,505	10,373	56,054	47,940	8,114	$403.8	.198	.139	.337	58.76%	12.99%	14.48%
1955	131,803	115,128	16,675	78,728	69,203	9,525	53,075	45,925	7,150	390.7	.202	.136	.337	59.73	12.10	13.47
1954	124,353	108,790	15,563	71,405	62,366	9,039	52,948	46,424	6,524	365.4	.195	.145	.340	57.42	12.66	12.32
1953	131,222	114,324	16,898	77,767	68,234	9,533	53,455	46,090	7,365	374.3	.208	.143	.351	59.26	12.26	13.78
1952	127,625	110,412	17,213	75,500	65,200	10,300	52,125	45,212	6,913	357.5	.211	.146	.357	59.16	13.64	13.26
1951	121,400	107,007	14,393	71,409	63,809	7,600	49,991	43,198	6,793	345.4	.207	.145	.351	58.82	10.64	13.59
1950	105,819	92,947	12,872	56,109	50,880	5,229	49,710	42,067	7,643	321.8	.174	.154	.329	53.02	9.32	15.38
1949	102,483	89,362	13,121	56,178	50,166	6,012	46,305	39,197	7,109	294.9	.190	.157	.348	54.82	10.70	15.35
1948	110,274	95,763	14,511	61,050	54,814	6,236	49,224	40,949	8,275	295.8	.206	.166	.373	55.36	10.21	16.81
1947	116,375	101,900	14,475	70,270	64,283	5,987	46,105	37,617	8,488	282.7	.249	.163	.412	60.38	8.52	18.41
1946	100,249	88,185	12,064	60,806	55,340	5,466	39,443	32,845	6,598	283.1	.215	.139	.354	60.65	8.99	16.73
1945	114,495	100,365	14,130	79,611			34,884			317.5	.251	.110	.361	69.53		
1944	105,256	92,069	13,187	70,061			35,195			324.1	.216	.109	.325	66.56		
1943	73,265	62,196	11,069	47,854			25,411			301.2	.159	.084	.243	65.32		
1942	46,717	37,817	8,900	25,148			21,569			271.1	.093	.080	.172	53.83		
1941	67,635	56,678	10,957	28,337			39,298			240.3	.118	.164	.281	41.90		
1940	74,803	61,554	13,249	32,943			41,860			207.7	.159	.202	.360	44.04		
1939	79,254	65,146	14,108	35,713			43,541			190.4	.188	.229	.416	45.06		
1938	74,266	61,178	13,088	34,849			39,417			176.5	.197	.223	.421	46.92		
1937	84,990	71,496	13,494	36,049			48,941			185.0	.195	.265	.459	42.42		
1936	80,324			31,643			48,681			174.2	.182	.279	.461	39.39		
1935	74,581			29,229			45,352			154.2	.190	.294	.484	39.19		
1934	69,262			28,994			40,268			139.5	.208	.289	.497	41.86		
1933	70,445			31,734			38,711			126.5	.251	.306	.557	45.05		
1932	72,531			37,395			35,136			129.8	.288	.271	.559	51.56		
1931	83,559			42,733			40,826			152.7	.280	.267	.547	51.14		
1930	94,152			49,912			44,240			164.7	.303	.269	.572	53.01		
1929	92,870			51,431			41,439			181.9	.283	.228	.511	55.38		
1928	89,942			50,392			39,550			170.5	.296	.232	.528	56.03		
1927	88,215			49,087			39,128			168.0	.292	.233	.525	55.64		

(Footnotes on next page.)

TABLE D-12 (continued)

[a] Years 1951–56, sum of cols. 2 and 3.

[b] Assumed to be all diesel oil.

[c] Sum of cols. 5 and 6, except for 1927–45 when only total is given.

[d] Obtained as difference between total and bunker consumption.

SOURCES: Mines, *Information Circular 7630*—col. 1, 1927–50, from p. 7, Table 3; col. 2, 1937–50, from p. 6, Table 2; col. 3, 1937–50, p. 5, Table 1; col. 4, 1927–45, p. 85, Table 64; col. 5, 1946–50, p. 84, Table 63; and col. 6, 1946–50, p. 83, Table 62.

Mines, *Minerals Yearbook, 1952*, Vol. II—col. 2, 1951–52, p. 414, Table 74; col. 3, 1951–52, p. 406, Table 70; col. 5, 1952, p. 412; and col. 6, 1951–52, p. 406. *Ibid., 1951*—col. 5, 1951, p. 1031.

Mines, *Mineral Market Report*, No. MMS 2800—col. 2, 1953–56, p. 3, Table 4; col. 3, 1953–56, p. 3, Table 1; col. 5, 1956, p. 2; and col. 6, 1956, p. 1. *Ibid.*, No. MMS 2412—1953: col. 5, p. 3, and col. 6, p. 1. *Ibid.*, No. MMS 2517—1954: col. 5, p. 2, and col. 6, p. 1. *Ibid.*, No. MMS 2681—1955: col. 5, p. 2, and col. 6, p. 1.

Column 10 figures—1927–28 from National Planning Association, *Productive Uses of Nuclear Energy, Report on Nuclear Energy and the U.S. Fuel Economy, 1955–1980*, Washington, 1958, pp. 118–19, Appendix 5, Table 2; 1929–54 from *Economic Report of the President, January 1956*, p. 166, Table D-2; 1955, prepublication figure since revised to $390.9; and 1956 from subsequent Commerce releases, adjusted to 1955 price level.

TABLE D–13. MARINE OIL CONSUMPTION, 1927–56 AND
PROJECTION TO 1975

| Period | Percentage change in ratio of oil consumption to GNP (GNP in constant $ 1955) | | | |
| | Foreign trade | | Domestic trade | |
	Total	Annual rate	Total	Annual rate
Actual				
1927–56.................	−32.2%	−1.3%	−40.3%	−1.8%
1927–38.................	−32.5	−3.5	− 4.3	−0.4
1938–56.................	+ 0.5	negl.	−37.7	−2.6
1948–56.................	− 3.9	−0.5	−16.3	−2.2
1949–56.................	+ 4.2	+0.6	−11.5	−1.7
1955–75 Projection				
Assumed growth in oil consumption per $ GNP.....		0 [a]		−2 [b]
Assumed growth rate in GNP...................		+4		+4
Assumed growth rate in oil consumption [c]..........	119.1	+4	48.6	+2

negl. Negligible.

[a] Based on negligible change since last full prewar year and in more recent periods.

[b] Based on continuing decline during entire period under review.

[c] Represents growth rate necessary to achieve assumed changes in oil consumption per $ GNP, given the GNP growth rate of 4 per cent.

SOURCE: Based on Table D–12, cols. 11 and 12.

TABLE D–14. MARINE FUEL CONSUMPTION, 1955 AND
PROJECTION TO 1975

| Item | 1955 | | 1975 | |
	Physical units [a] (1)	Billion Btu (2)	Physical units [a] (3)	Billion Btu (4)
1. Gasoline [b].....................	612	3,187	880	4,583
2. NGL [b].......................	84	437	120	625
3. Diesel plus residual [c]............	131,803	830,225	251,362	1,574,092
of which:				
a. Foreign trade...............	78,728		172,493	
b. Domestic trade..............	53,075		78,869	
c. Diesel.....................	16,675	95,248	45,541	260,124
d. Residual...................	115,128	734,977	205,821	1,313,968
4. Bituminous coal [d]..............	1,499	39,274		
5. Total......................		873,123		1,579,300

[a] Coal in thousand tons; all other in thousand barrels.

[b] 1955: Roads, *Highway Statistics, 1955*, p. 7, Table G–24; 1975: arbitrary assumption. Division between oil and natural gasoline according to Appendix Table I–10.

[c] 1955: Table D–12; 1975: 1955 quantities increased by rates developed in Table D–13; total (item 3) derived by adding items 3a and 3b. Total divided between diesel and residual by use of the following percentages derived from past trends appearing in Table D–12: foreign trade diesel—20 per cent, and domestic trade diesel—14 per cent, respectively, of total foreign trade and domestic trade.

[d] 1955: Mines, *Mineral Industry Surveys*, MMS No. 2830, p. 99. 1975: Coal use assumed to disappear by 1975.

TABLE D-15   CONSUMPTION OF MOTOR FUEL BY COMMERCIAL
BUSES, 1955

Fuel	Thousand barrels	Billion Btu
Motor fuel consumed by commercial buses[a] of which assumed to be:[b]		
Diesel..	7,750	44,268
Gasoline, total[c].............................	7,750	
Gasoline, from oil............................	6,820	35,519
Gasoline, natural............................	930	4,843
Total...	15,500	84,630

[a] Roads, *Highway Statistics, 1955*, p. 71, Table VM-1.

[b] Assumption based on following considerations: (1) Expenditure on fuels by transit system buses (as per ATA, *Transit Fact Book, 1956 Edition*, p. 3)—gasoline, $36,300,000, diesel, $15,000,000, making a total of $51,300,000. (2) Vehicle-miles—all commercial buses, including interurban, 3,256 million (from *Highway Statistics, 1955, op. cit.*), and transit buses only (urban), 1,710 million (from *Transit Fact Book, op. cit*). (3) Considering cost differences, it follows that transit buses use roughly equal amounts of diesel and gasoline. Transit buses account for about half of all vehicle-miles in this group. Their consumption pattern is assumed to be typical of all buses. In none of these calculations is account taken of the fact that some buses use LPG as fuel. Similar judgment is reached by Edwin M. Cope, John T. Lynch, and Clarence A. Steele, in "Estimate of User Taxes Paid by Vehicles in Different Type and Weight Groups," *Public Roads*, Vol. 28, No. 2 (June 1959).

[c] For distribution to gasoline from oil and natural gasoline see Appendix Table I-10.

TABLE D-16.   CONSUMPTION OF MOTOR FUELS BY TRUCKS AND
COMBINATIONS[a] (EXCLUDING MILITARY), 1955

Item	All trucks (1)	Publicly owned trucks (2)	All other trucks (3)
1. Number of vehicles (thous.)....	10,413[b]	443[c]	9,970
2. Fuel consumption (thous. bbl.):			
a. Total.....................	316,857[b]	13,480[d]	303,377
b. Diesel....................	16,550[e]	704	15,846
c. Gasoline, total............	300,307	12,776	287,531
d. Gasoline, from oil..........	264,270[f]	11,243	253,027
e. Gasoline, natural..........	36,037[f]	1,533	34,504
3. Fuel consumption (bill. Btu):			
a. Total.....................	1,658,533	70,558	1,587,975
b. Diesel....................	94,534	4,021	90,513
c. Gasoline, total............	1,563,999	66,537	1,497,462
d. Gasoline, from oil..........	1,376,318	58,553	1,317,765
e. Gasoline, natural..........	187,681	7,984	179,697

[a] Trailer trucks.

[b] Roads, *Highway Statistics, 1955*, p. 71, Table VM-1.

[c] *Ibid.*, p. 42, Table MV-1.

[d] Estimated on basis of proportion of publicly owned to total vehicles for entire column.

[e] Total diesel oil in road use (Mines, *Mineral Market Report*, No. MMS 2681, p. 14) minus diesel oil used by buses (Table D-15).

[f] For distribution to gasoline from oil and natural gasoline see Appendix Table I-10.

TABLE D-17.   CONSUMPTION OF MOTOR FUEL BY SCHOOL AND
NONREVENUE BUSES (EXCLUDING MILITARY), 1955

Item	Total (1)	Publicly owned (2)	Not publicly owned (1) − (2) (3)
1. Number of vehicles[a]...............	158,510	112,914	45,596
2. Fuel consumption (thous. bbl.):			
a. Total.........................	2,857[b]	2,035[c]	822
of which:[d]			
b. Gasoline (oil)..................	2,514	1,791	723
c. Natural gasoline................	343	244	99
3. Fuel consumption (bill. Btu):			
a. Total.........................	14,879	10,598	4,281
b. Gasoline (oil)..................	13,093	9,328	3,765
c. Natural gasoline................	1,786	1,271	516

[a] Roads, *Highway Statistics, 1955*, p. 45, Table MV-10.

[b] *Ibid.*, p. 71, Table VM-1.

[c] Fuel consumption estimated from col. 1 in proportion of publicly owned to total vehicles, as per item 1.

[d] For distribution to gasoline from oil and natural gasoline see Appendix Table I-10.

TABLE D-18. CONSUMPTION OF MOTOR FUEL BY MOTORCYCLES, 1955 AND (BY ASSUMPTION) 1975 [a]

Item	Number of vehicles[b] (1)	Percentage distribution of fuel[c] (2)	Physical units (thous. bbl.)			Billion Btu	
			Total (3)	Gasoline (oil)[d] (4)	Gasoline (natural)[d] (5)	Gasoline (oil) (6)	Gasoline (natural) (7)
1. Total	412,377	100.00%	2,466[e]	2,170	296	11,301	1,542
2. Government (excluding military)	10,987	3.52	87	77	10	401	52
3. Non-government	401,390	96.48	2,379	2,094	285	10,906	1,484
4. Household	200,695	32.16	793	698	95	3,635	495
5. General transportation[f]	200,695	64.32	1,586	1,396	190	7,270	990

[a] No change is assumed between 1955 and 1975, based on evidence presented in Table D-43.

[b] Roads, *Highway Statistics, 1955*, p. 42, Table MV-1. It is arbitrarily assumed that the non-government total consists of equal numbers of household and nonhousehold motorcycles.

[c] Derived from col. 1 on the assumption, suggested by trade opinion, that government and general transportation motorcycles consume twice as much gasoline per vehicle as do household motorcycles.

[d] For distribution to gasoline from oil and natural gasoline, see Appendix Table I-10.

[e] Derived as the difference between two tabulations, both published in *Highway Statistics, 1955, op. cit.*, p. 4, Table G-21, and p. 71, Table VM-1. The latter ". . . differs from Table G-21 because of adjustments to cover estimated amounts used for motorcycles." The difference between the two 1955 totals, amounting to 103,578,000 gallons, is therefore taken as motorcycle consumption.

[f] Includes all transportation other than that self-performed by government and households; consequently, includes all transportation services self-performed by industrial, agricultural, and commercial establishments, as well as those done by common carriers.

TABLE D-19. CONSUMPTION OF MOTOR FUELS BY GOVERNMENT
AUTOMOBILES, FEDERAL (EXCLUDING MILITARY),
STATE, COUNTY, AND MUNICIPAL, 1955

Item	Physical units
1. Highway consumption of fuels (thous. bbl.) [a]:	
a. Federal	1,959
b. State, county, and municipal	17,495
c. Total	19,454
2. Motor fuels to designated uses other than automobiles (thous. bbl.):	
a. Trucks and combinations [b]	13,480
b. School and nonrevenue buses [c]	2,035
c. Motorcycles [d]	87
3. Fuels for government automobiles (item 1c − item 2):	
a. Volume consumed—	
Barrels (thous.)	3,853
Gallons (thous.)	161,826
b. Number of government automobiles [e]	184,000
c. Motor fuel per government automobile (gal.) [f]	879

[a] Roads, *Highway Statistics, 1955*, p. 4, Table G-21.
[b] Table D-16, col. 2, item 2a.
[c] Table D-17, col. 2, item 2a.
[d] Table D-18, col. 3.
[e] *Highway Statistics, 1955, op. cit.*, p. 42, Table MV-1.
[f] This consumption per vehicle is shown merely to test the reasonableness of the estimated total fuel consumption. It compares with 668 gallons per vehicle for all automobiles (Table D-35).

TABLE D–20. CONSUMPTION OF AUTOMOBILE FUELS, BY CLASS OF USER AND TYPE OF FUEL, 1955

Item	Physical units (thous. bbl.) [a]				Billion Btu			
	Total automobile fuel (1)	Gasoline (oil) (2)	Gasoline (natural) (3)	LPG (4)	Gasoline (oil) (5)	Gasoline (natural) (6)	LPG (7)	Total (8)
1. Total passenger car (incl. taxicabs) fuels [b]	798,762	698,247	95,215	5,300	3,636,470	495,880	21,258	4,153,608
2. Household [c]	718,886	628,422	85,694	4,770	3,272,822	446,294	19,132	3,738,248
3. Nonhousehold [d]	79,876	69,825	9,522	530	363,649	49,591	2,126	415,366
a. Government (excl. military) [e]	3,853	3,368	459	26	17,541	2,390	104	20,035
b. General transportation (item 3a – item 3b) [f]	76,023	66,457	9,063	504	346,108	47,200	2,022	395,330

[a] Total gasoline distributed as follows: total special fuels for highway use (Roads, *Highway Statistics, 1955*, p. 8, Table G–25); 28.7 mill. bbl., of which diesel oil assumed to be 23.4 mill. bbl. (Mines, *Mineral Market Report*, No. MMS 2681, p. 14); balance assumed to be LPG, all going to automobiles. All other considered gasoline and allocated between oil and natural gasoline as explained in Appendix Table I–10.

[b] *Highway Statistics, 1955, op. cit.*, p. 71, Table VM–1.

[c] The distribution of automobiles between household and commercial use is tenuous on many counts, both in actual fact, and statistically. In fact, many vehicles are dual-purpose vehicles, and statistically the car registration figures themselves are the subject of uncertainty, depending on what source of data is preferred. A 9:1 distribution between household and commercial use was selected largely on the basis of recent University of Michigan survey materials as summarized in Table D–21. Actually, these survey materials yield a factor of 14.2 per cent for nonhousehold automobiles, but this percentage is regarded as too high for two reasons: (1) the fact that in many dual-use cases, commercial use is the less important of the two; and (2) use of Polk rather than Public Roads registration figures would drop the percentage to 8 per cent. Therefore, 10 per cent is used for nonhousehold and 90 per cent for household use of automobiles.

[d] Includes taxicabs.

[e] From Table D–19, item 3a; other columns estimated in proportion of government to total nonhousehold consumption, i.e., 4.8 per cent.

[f] See Table D–18, footnote f, for definition.

TABLE D-21. ESTIMATE OF NONHOUSEHOLD AUTOMOBILES, 1957

Item	Per cent of all spending units [a]	Number of cars per hundred spending units
1. Automobile ownership distribution:		
a. Spending units having 1 automobile...............	62.5%	62.5
b. Spending units having 2 automobiles.............	9.2	18.4
c. Spending units having 3 or more automobiles......	0.4	1.8 [a]
d. Spending units having automobiles..............	72.1	82.7
		(number in millions)
2. Number of spending units [b]......................................		56.3
3. Number of automobiles in spending units........................		46.6
4. Bureau of Public Roads automobile registration, Dec. 31, 1956........		54.3
5. Resulting number of commercial automobiles......................		7.7 (14.2%)

[a] Assuming 4.5 cars per unit having 3 cars or more.
[b] University of Michigan Survey Research Center Study No. 650, *Economic Behavior Program* (Ann Arbor), Table CO-4 entitled "Automobile Ownership Within Spending Units and Number of Persons in Spending Units, 1957."

TABLE D-22.   CONSUMPTION OF MOTOR FUELS IN HOUSEHOLD TRANSPORTATION, 1955

Item	Physical units (thous. bbl.)				Billion Btu			
	Total (1)	Gasoline (oil) (2)	Gasoline (natural) (3)	LPG (4)	Gasoline (oil) (5)	Gasoline (natural) (6)	LPG (7)	Total (8)
1. Automobiles [a]...	718,886	628,422	85,694	4,770	3,272,822	446,294	19,132	3,738,248
2. Motorcycles [b]...	793	698	95		3,635	495		4,130
3. Total..........	719,679	629,120	85,789	4,770	3,276,457	446,789	19,132	3,742,378

[a] Table D-20, item 2.
[b] Table D-18, item 4.

TABLE D-23. CONSUMPTION OF MOTOR FUELS IN GENERAL TRANSPORTATION,[a] 1955

Vehicle	Physical units (thous. bbl.)					Billion Btu				
	Total (1)	Gasoline (oil) (2)	Gasoline (natural) (3)	Diesel oil (4)	LPG (5)	Gasoline (oil) (6)	Gasoline (natural) (7)	Diesel oil (8)	LPG (9)	Total (10)
Automobiles[b]	76,023	66,457	9,063		504	346,108	47,200		2,022	395,330
Trucks and trailers[c]	303,377	253,027	34,504	15,846		1,317,765	179,697	90,513		1,587,975
Buses (commercial)[d]	15,500	6,820	930	7,750		35,519	4,843	44,268		84,630
School and nonrevenue buses[e]	822	723	99			3,765	516			4,281
Motorcycles[f]	1,586	1,396	190			7,270	990			8,260
Total	397,309	328,423	44,786	23,596	504	1,710,427	233,246	134,781	2,022	2,080,476

[a] See Table D-18, footnote f, for definition.
[b] Table D-20, item 3c.
[c] Table D-16, col. 3.
[d] Table D-15.
[e] Table D-17, col. 3.
[f] Table D-18, item 5.

TABLE D-24. CONSUMPTION OF MOTOR FUELS BY GOVERNMENT (EXCLUDING MILITARY), 1955

Vehicle	Physical units (thous. bbl.)					Billion Btu				
	Total (1)	Gasoline (oil) (2)	Gasoline (natural) (3)	Diesel oil (5)	LPG (5)	Gasoline (oil) (6)	Gasoline (natural) (7)	Diesel oil (8)	LPG (9)	Total (10)
Automobiles[a]	3,853	3,368	459		26	17,541	2,390		104	20,035
Trucks[b]	13,480	11,243	1,533	704		58,553	7,984	4,021		70,558
School and nonrevenue buses[c]	2,035	1,791	244			9,328	1,271			10,598
Motorcycles[d]	87	77	10			401	52			453
Total[e]	19,455	16,479	2,246	704	26	85,823	11,697	4,021	104	101,645

[a] Table D-20, item 3b.
[b] Table D-16, col. 2.
[c] Table D-17, col. 2.
[d] Table D-18, item 2.
[e] Totals may not check because of rounding.

TABLE D-25. TRUCK FREIGHT MOVEMENTS AND GASOLINE
CONSUMPTION, 1939-48 AND 1954-55

Date	Intercity ton-miles (thous.) [a] (1)	Gasoline consumed (mill. gal.) [b] (2)	Period	Annual rates of increase		
				Freight (3)	Gasoline consumption (4)	Excess of freight over gasoline consumption (5)
1955......	226,188	13,308				
1954......	214,626	12,541				
1948......	116,045	8,189	1948-55..	11.9%	7.2%	4.7%
1947......	102,095	7,243				
1946......	81,992	6,068				
1945......	66,948	5,055				
1944......	58,264	4,576	1939-55..	9.5	6.6	2.9
1943......	56,784	4,534				
1942......	59,896	4,889				
1941......	81,363	5,754				
1940......	62,043	5,156	1939-48..	7.7	6.1	1.6
1939......	52,821	4,807				

[a] Table D-1.
[b] Roads, *Highway Statistics Summary to 1955*, p. 40, Table VM-201-A. Includes small amount of diesel; for example, diesel was only 5 per cent of all fuel consumed by trucks in 1955 (Table D-16).

TABLE D-26. CHANGES IN AVERAGE LOAD CARRIED BY TRUCKS,
1936 AND 1940-55

(Tons)

Year	All trucks (1)	Single units (2)	All other (3)
1955..............	5.92	2.47	11.07
1954..............	5.74	2.40	10.91
1953..............	5.82	2.35	11.07
1952..............	5.56	2.34	10.93
1951..............	5.66	2.31	10.83
1950..............	5.64	2.31	10.62
1949..............	5.21	2.27	10.38
1948..............	5.03	2.33	10.10
1947..............	4.81	2.26	9.63
1946..............	4.84	2.31	9.70
1945..............	4.84	2.40	9.31
1944..............	4.63	2.36	8.96
1943..............	4.39	2.30	8.74
1942..............	4.13	2.24	8.47
1941..............	3.64	2.29	8.24
1940..............	3.32	2.13	7.41
1936..............	2.90	1.86	6.90

SOURCE: Roads, *Highway Statistics Summary to 1955*, p. 33, Table HT-2.

TABLE D-27. FUEL CONSUMPTION BY TRUCKS AND COMBINATIONS (EXCLUDING MILITARY), PROJECTION TO 1975

Consumption	Thousand barrels (1)	Per cent (2)	Billion Btu (3)
Fuel consumption, 1955 [a]	316,857		1,658,533
Assumed increase in freight volume [b]		271.35%	
Assumed increase in efficiency per year		1.5	
Adjusted increase in fuel consumption [c]		175.72	
Total fuel consumption, 1975	873,626 [d]		4,593,875
Diesel oil [e]	87,363		499,017
Gasoline [f]	786,263		4,094,858
From oil	691,911		3,603,473
Natural gasoline	94,352		491,385

[a] Table D-16.
[b] Table D-3.
[c] Increase in volume corrected for improvement in efficiency.
[d] Adjusted percentage increase applied to 1955 consumption.
[e] Assumed to increase from its share of approximately 5 per cent in 1955 (Table D-16) to 10 per cent, on basis of rising relative significance of diesel engine vs. gasoline engine trucks. This increased share was derived roughly in accordance with the growth rate of diesel fuel in road use shown in the years 1953–57.
[f] For breakdown between gasoline from oil and natural gasoline, see Appendix Table I-10.

TABLE D-28. COMMERCIAL BUSES: NUMBER, TRAVEL, AND FUEL CONSUMPTION, 1936-48 AND 1954-55

Year	Number (thous.) (1)	Vehicle-miles (mill.) (2)	Fuel consumption (mill. gal.) (3)
1955	96	3,256	651
1954	83	3,196	639
1948	92	3,548	709
1947	89	3,560	712
1946	80	3,401	680
1945	83	3,192	638
1944	80	3,193	639
1943	76	2,740	543
1942	69	2,492	484
1941	59	2,112	402
1940	54	1,944	367
1939	52	1,856	347
1938	51	1,854	343
1937	51	1,854	340
1936	49	1,764	320

SOURCE: Roads, *Highway Statistics Summary to 1955*, p. 40. Table VM-201-A.

TABLE D–29.   FUEL CONSUMPTION BY COMMERCIAL BUSES,
PROJECTION TO 1975

Year	Physical units (thous. bbl.)					Billion Btu				
	Total	Diesel oil	Gasoline[a]			Diesel oil	Gasoline			Total
			Total	Oil	Natural		Total	Oil	Natural	
	(1)	(2)	(3)	(4)	(5)	(6)	(7)	(8)	(9)	(10)
1955[b]...	15,500	7,750	7,750	6,820	930	44,268	40,362	35,519	4,843	84,630
1975[c]...	15,500	11,625	3,875	3,410	465	66,402	20,181	17,759	2,422	86,583

[a] Distributed between oil and natural gasoline on the basis of Appendix Table I–10.
[b] Table D–15.
[c] On basis of trend in last decade (Table D–28) and in the absence of specific indications as to future growth, no change is assumed. However, the current shift from gasoline to diesel engine buses is expected to continue. As compared to 50 per cent in 1955, 75 per cent of all fuel in 1975 is assumed to be diesel oil.

TABLE D–30.   FUEL CONSUMPTION BY SCHOOL AND NONREVENUE
BUSES (EXCLUDING MILITARY), PROJECTION TO 1975

Item	1955		1975	
1. Number of children aged 5–17[a]........	37,334,000		57,306,000	
2. 1975 as multiple of 1955..............			153.5	
3. Assumed percentage increase in participation of school children[b].............			10%	
4. 1975 as multiple of 1955 adjusted.......			168.8	
	(thous. bbl.)	(bill. Btu)	(thous. bbl.)	(bill. Btu)
5. Fuel consumption[c]				
a. Total..........................	2,857	14,879	4,823	25,116
b. Gasoline, from oil...............	2,514	13,093	4,244	22,102
c. Gasoline, natural...............	343	1,786	579	3,014

[a] Census, *Current Population Reports*, Series P–25, No. 123, p. 8, Table 1. The figures are from the AA estimate. Although the 1975 population estimate used in this study is different, the differences arise in the higher age groups and do not make use of the Census figures inappropriate.

[b] Based on recent faster increase in this category than justified by increase in school-age population.

[c] 1955 from Table D–17; 1975 projected on basis of percentage increase shown in item 4 above. Distributed between oil and natural gasoline on basis of Appendix Table I–10.

TABLE D-31. AUTOMOBILES AND POPULATION IN THE UNITED STATES, 1900–56

Year	Number of vehicles (thous.) (1)	Population 18 years and over (thous.) (2)	Total population (thous.) (3)	Vehicles per 10,000 of total population (4)	Total population per vehicle (5)	Vehicles per 10,000 population 18 years and over (6)	Population 18 years and over per vehicle (7)
1956...	54,249	110,656	168,091	3,227	3.099	4,902	2.040
1955...	52,092	109,623	165,271	3,152	3.173	4,752	2.104
1954...	48,413	108,617	162,417	2,981	3.355	4,457	2.244
1953...	46,460	107,604	159,636	2,910	3.436	4,318	2.316
1952...	43,818	106,676	157,028	2,790	3.584	4,108	2.435
1951...	42,683	105,719	154,360	2,765	3.616	4,307	2.477
1950...	40,334	104,633	151,683	2,659	3.761	3,855	2.594
1949...	36,453	103,361	149,188	2,443	4.093	3,527	2.835
1948...	33,394	102,063	146,631	2,277	4.391	3,272	3.056
1947...	30,872	100,759	144,126	2,142	4.669	3,064	3.264
1946...	28,209	99,567	141,389	1,995	5.012	2,833	3.530
1945...	25,789	98,435	139,928	1,842	5.426	2,619	3.817
1944...	25,562	97,209	138,397	1,847	5.414	2,630	3.803
1943...	26,005	95,873	136,739	1,902	5.258	2,712	3.687
1942...	27,970	94,478	134,860	2,074	4.822	2,960	3.378
1941...	29,691	93,104	133,402	2,226	4.493	3,189	3.136
1940...	27,488	91,588	131,954	2,083	4.800	3,001	3.332
1939...	26,252	90,311	130,880	2,006	4.986	2,907	3.440
1938...	25,272	89,073	129,825	1,947	5.137	2,837	3.525
1937...	25,490	87,877	128,825	1,978	5.054	2,901	3.449
1936...	24,201	86,792	128,053	1,890	5.291	2,788	3.586
1935...	22,568	85,698	127,250	1,773	5.639	2,633	3.797
1934...	21,544	84,553	126,374	1,705	5.866	2,548	3.925
1933...	20,657	83,392	125,579	1,645	6.079	2,477	4.036
1932...	20,901	82,295	124,840	1,674	5.973	2,540	3.937
1931...	22,396	81,209	124,040	1,806	5.538	2,758	3.626
1930...	23,035	80,069	123,077	1,872	5.343	2,877	3.476
1929...	23,121	78,618	121,770	1,899	5.267	2,941	3.400
1928...	21,362	77,319	120,501	1,773	5.641	2,763	3.619
1927...	20,193	75,981	119,038	1,696	5.895	2,658	3.763
1926...	19,268	74,615	117,399	1,641	6.093	2,582	3.872
1925...	17,481	73,330	115,832	1,509	6.626	2,384	4.195
1924...	15,436	72,037	114,113	1,353	7.393	2,142	4.667
1923...	13,253	70,464	111,950	1,184	8.448	1,881	5.317
1922...	10,704	69,103	110,055	973	10.282	1,549	6.456
1921...	9,212	68,153	108,541	849	11.782	1,352	7.398
1920...	8,132	66,841	106,466	764	13.092	1,217	8.220
1919...	6,679	65,969	105,063	636	15.730	1,012	9.877
1918...	5,555	65,474	104,550	531	18.820	848	11.786
1917...	4,727	64,792	103,414	457	21.877	730	13.701
1916...	3,368	63,813	101,966	330	30.274	528	18.947
1915...	2,332	62,866	100,549	232	43.117	371	26.958
1914...	1,664	61,909	99,118	168	59.566	269	37.205
1913...	1,190	60,655	97,227	122	81.703	196	50.971
1912...	902	59,384	95,331	95	105.688	152	65.835
1911...	619	58,374	93,868	66	151.644	106	94.303

TABLE D-31 (continued)

Year	Number of vehicles (thous.) (1)	Population 18 years and over (thous.) (2)	Total population (thous.) (3)	Vehicles per 10,000 of total population (4)	Total population per vehicle (5)	Vehicles per 10,000 population 18 years and over (6)	Population 18 years and over per vehicle (7)
1910...	458	57,347	92,407	50	201.762	80	125.211
1909...	306	55,973	90,492	34	295.725	55	182.918
1908...	194	54,659	88,709	22	457.262	35	281.747
1907...	140	53,391	87,000	16	621.428	26	381.364
1906...	106	52,216	85,437	12	806.009	20	492.603
1905...	77	51,010	83,820	9	1,088.570	15	662.468
1904...	55	49,794	82,165	7	1,493.909	11	905.345
1903...	33	48,660	80,632	4	2,443.394	7	1,474.545
1902...	23	47,576	79,160	3	3,441.739	5	2,068.522
1901...	15	46,446	77,585	2	5,172.333	3	3,096.400
1900...	8	45,382	76,094	1	9,511.750	2	5,672.750

SOURCES: Figures for automobiles from Roads. For 1956—*Highway Statistics, 1956*, p. 23, Table VM-1; for 1936-48 and 1954-55—*Highway Statistics Summary to 1955*, p. 40, Table MV-201-A; and for 1900-35 and 1949-53—*ibid.*, p. 28, Table MV-200.

Figures for population from Census, *Current Population Reports*, Series P-25. For 1950-56 from No. 146, pp. 7-10; for 1941-49—No. 98, p. 15; and for 1900-40—No. 114, pp. 3-5, Table 1.

TABLE D-32. INCREASE IN NUMBER OF AUTOMOBILES, 1925-55 AND PROJECTION TO 1975

Period	Average increase per year per 10,000 population 18 years and over [a] (1)	Total increase per 10,000 population 18 years and over [b] (2)
1925-29......................................	139.2	557
1925-40......................................	41.1	617
1930-40......................................	12.4	124
1920-40......................................	89.2	1,784
1940-55......................................	116.7	1,751
1950-55......................................	179.4	897
Average of 1940-55 and 1950-55 [c]...............	148.0	
Average increase [c] maintained for 20 years, 1955-75.		2,960

[a] Derived from col. 2.

[b] From Table D-31, except for last line which is derived from col. 1.

[c] It is assumed that future growth will follow an average between the long-term trend of 1940-55 and the more recent, accelerated, trend of 1950-55. For further implications of this assumption see Chapter 5, pp. 218-20, and Table D-33. Further use of this calculation is made in Table D-38, items 1 through 3.

TABLE D-33. ILLUSTRATIVE OWNERSHIP OF AUTOMOBILES,
BY AGE AND LOCATION OF POPULATION, 1975[a]

Age group	Population 18 years and over[b] (million) (1)	Cars per 10,000 population[c] (2)	Number of automobiles (million) (3)
18-65 years:			
In densely populated places.................	9	4,000	3.6
Other.....................................	116	8,500	98.6
65 years and over:			
In densely populated places.................	1	4,000	.4
Other.....................................	23	5,000	11.5
Total......................................	149	7,658[d]	114.1

[a] This is an example of how the 1975 projection might come about, taking into consideration age distribution and population density.

[b] Population based on Census projection AA of 1955 (Census, *Current Population Reports*, Series P-25, No. 123, 1955), adjusted upward especially in the 65-and-over age group, to reflect assumptions of lower mortality. Distribution between densely populated and other places assumes continuing suburban development, leaving less than 10 per cent of 18-65 population and 4 per cent of the older group in densely populated areas.

[c] Assumptions based partly on recent developments in the relation of densely populated areas to national average, Table D-34.

[d] Derived from cols. 1 and 3. This figure is very similar to that obtained by adding the increase of 2,960 (Table D-32) to the number existing in 1955 of 4,752 (Table D-31, col. 6), yielding a total of 7,712. It is the latter figure which forms the basis of further computations (Table D-38).

TABLE D-34. POPULATION PER AUTOMOBILE IN NEW YORK,
PHILADELPHIA, BOSTON, AND UNITED STATES, 1949, 1952, AND 1955

Location	1949		1952		1955	
	Persons per automobile (1)	City as per cent of national (2)	Persons per automobile (3)	City as per cent of national (4)	Persons per automobile (5)	City as per cent of national (6)
New York.................	8.654	190%	7.108	180%	6.139	175%
Philadelphia..............	7.445	163	5.704	144	4.974	142
Boston...................	7.353	161	6.166	156	4.762	136
National.................	4.556		3.952		3.500	

SOURCE: AMA—figures for 1949 from *Automobile Facts and Figures, 30th Edition, 1950*, pp. 26-27; 1952 from *33rd Edition, 1953*, pp. 26-27; and 1955 from *36th Edition, 1956*, pp. 70-71.

TABLE D–35.   VEHICLES AND FUEL CONSUMPTION, 1926–56

Year	Total motor fuel consumption for highway use (mill. gal.) (1)	Total number of vehicles (thous.) (2)	Gallons per vehicle (1) ÷ (2) (3)	Fuel consumption by automobiles (mill. gal.) (4)	Number of automobiles (thous.) (5)	Gallons per automobile (6)	Gallons per automobile as per cent of gallons per vehicle (7)	Adjusted gallons per automobile[a] (8)
1956....	50,106	65,241	768	35,326	54,249	651	84.8%	664
1955....	47,627	62,760	759	33,548	52,092	644	84.8	668
1954....	44,211	58,372	757	30,915	48,413	639	84.4	652
1953....	42,732	56,280	759	29,781	46,460	641	84.4	660
1952....	40,585	53,265	762	28,306	43,818	646	84.8	654
1951....	38,128	51,914	734	26,677	42,683	625	85.2	643
1950....	35,653	49,162	725	25,047	40,334	621	85.6	652
1949....	32,431	44,690	726	22,747	36,453	624	86.0	651
1948....	30,338	40,957	741	21,369	33,394	640	86.4	665
1947....	28,107	37,698	746	20,086	30,872	651	87.3	680
1946....	25,570	34,210	747	18,759	28,209	665	89.0	695
1945....	19,078	30,908	617	13,323	25,789	517	83.8	519
1944....	16,381	30,360	540	11,108	25,562	435	80.6	431
1943....	15,958	30,770	519	10,821	26,005	416	80.2	401
1942....	19,863	32,881	604	14,428	27,970	516	85.4	500
1941....	24,256	34,950	694	18,031	29,691	607	87.5	631
1940....	21,915	32,330	678	16,323	27,488	594	87.6	607
1939....	20,633	30,886	668	15,412	26,252	587	87.9	598
1938....	19,534	29,690	658	14,663	25,272	580	88.1	578
1937....	19,383	29,922	648	14,617	25,490	573	88.4	588
1936....	18,029	28,396	635	13,648	24,201	564	88.8	584
1935....	16,345	26,546	616	12,503	22,568	554	90.0	567
1934....	15,415	25,262	610	11,914	21,545	553	90.6	565
1933....	14,348	24,159	594	11,196	20,657	542	91.2	539
1932....	14,339	24,391	588	11,287	20,901	540	91.8	521
1931....	15,457	26,094	592	12,251	22,396	547	92.4	539
1930....	14,754	26,750	552	11,817	23,035	513	93.0	512
1929....	14,139	26,705	529	11,445	23,121	495	93.6	515
1928....	12,361	24,689	501	10,083	21,362	472	94.2	485
1927....	11,331	23,303	486	9,309	20,193	461	94.8	472
1926....	10,064	22,200	453	8,324	19,268	432	95.4	453

[a] Col. 6 corrected by substituting estimated mid-year for year-end registration figures.

SOURCES: Figures for 1936–48, 1954, and 1955, col. 1 through col. 6 are from Roads, *Highway Statistics Summary to 1955*, p. 40, Table VM–201–A; for 1956, col. 1 through col. 6 from Roads, *Highway Statistics, 1956*, p. 23, Table VM–1.

For 1949–53 and 1926–35 no data were available for fuel consumption by automobiles (col. 4), and, consequently, for cols. 6, 7, and 8. Data were available, however, for col. 1 from *Highway Statistics Summary to 1955, op. cit.*, Table G–221, p. 2 (total highway usage), and for col. 2 and 5 from p. 28, Table MV–200, of the same source.

The missing data were estimated as follows: Col. 7 was interpolated between 1948 and 1954 by inspection of the surrounding years. Similarly, extrapolation was used to estimate the percentage figures for the years preceding 1936. Here the reasoning was that the percentage must be rising as one goes back in time, as automobiles, with their lower per-vehicle consumption, formed an increasing proportion of total vehicles. With the missing years thus estimated for col. 7, col. 6 was completed by multiplying col. 3 by col. 7; col. 4 follows as a multiplication of col. 6 by col. 5.

TABLE D-36.   GROWTH RATES IN FUEL CONSUMPTION PER
AUTOMOBILE, SELECTED PERIODS, 1926-55

Year	Gallons per automobile [a]	Period	Growth rate, per cent per year
1926.......	453	1926-30......	3.11%
		1926-40......	2.11
1929.......	515	1926-55......	1.35
		1929-55......	1.00
1930.......	512		
		1930-40......	1.72
1940.......	607	1930-55......	1.07
1950.......	652	1940-50......	0.72
		1940-55......	0.64
1955.......	668		
		1950-55......	0.48

[a] Table D-35, col. 8.

TABLE D-37.   AUTOMOBILE-MILES PER GALLON OF FUEL, SELECTED
YEARS, 1940-56

Year	Vehicle-miles (million) [a] (1)	Fuel consumed (million gallons) [a] (2)	Miles per gallon	
			Bureau of Public Roads (1) ÷ (2) (3)	General Motors [b] (4)
1956...........	507,138	35,326	14.36	17.60
1955...........	487,540	33,548	14.53	18.20
1950...........	363,613	25,047	14.52	16.40
1945...........	200,398	13,323	15.04	16.40
1940...........	249,600	16,323	15.29	15.50

[a] Roads, *Highway Statistics*, various issues.
[b] John M. Campbell, General Motors Technical Center, "Looking Ahead in Fuels for Automotive Transportation," paper presented at Society of Automotive Engineers National Fuels and Lubricants Meeting, Cleveland, Ohio, November 7-8, 1957.

TABLE D-38. FUEL CONSUMPTION BY AUTOMOBILES, PROJECTION TO 1975

Item	1975
1. Automobiles per 10,000 population aged 18 and over, 1955[a]	4,752
2. Increase between 1955 and 1975[b]	2,960
3. Automobiles per 10,000 population aged 18 and over, 1975 (item 1 + item 2)	7,712
4. Populat'on 1975, aged 18 and over[c]	149,000,000
5. Number of automobiles, 1975 (thous.)[d]	114,909
6. Number of automobiles, 1955 (thous.)[a]	52,092
7. Percentage increase, 1955–75, in number of automobiles	120%

	1955[e] (bill. Btu)	(thous. bbl.)	1975 (bill. Btu)	(thous. bbl.)
8. Fuel consumption:				
a. Total motor fuels[f]	4,153,608	798,762	9,088,452	1,757,276
b. LPG[g]	21,258	5,300	212,583	53,000
c. Total gasoline[h]	4,132,350	793,462	8,875,869	1,704,276
d. Gasoline, from oil	3,636,470	698,247	7,810,766	1,499,763
e. Gasoline, natural	495,880	95,215	1,065,104	204,513

[a] Table D-31.

[b] Table D-32.

[c] Based on assumption of 233 million population in 1975.

[d] Item 3 × item 4 divided by 10,000.

[e] Table D-20, item 1.

[f] Estimated to increase as increase in number of automobiles (item 7), on assumption of constant fuel consumption per vehicle (Tables D-35 and D-36).

[g] Assumed to increase to ten times 1955 level in accord with recent rapid rise.

[h] Derived as difference between total motor fuel and LPG, and distributed to oil and natural gasoline on the basis of Appendix Table I-10.

TABLE D-39. PUBLICLY OWNED VEHICLES (EXCLUDING MILITARY)
AND THEIR FUEL CONSUMPTION IN RELATION TO ALL VEHICLES
AND TOTAL HIGHWAY FUEL CONSUMPTION, 1919-55

| Year | Publicly owned vehicles as per cent of total vehicles[a] | | | | Fuel consumption by publicly owned vehicles as per cent of total consumption by motor vehicles[b] (5) |
	Automobiles (1)	Trucks (2)	Buses (3)	Automobiles, trucks, and buses (4)	
1955....	0.35%	4.29%	44.24%	1.18%	1.71%
1954....	0.36	4.38	43.63	1.22	1.77
1953....	0.37	4.32	42.17	1.22	1.70
1952....	0.37	4.24	39.61	1.22	1.69
1951....	0.37	4.20	37.82	1.20	1.70
1950....	0.37	4.25	35.97	1.21	1.74
1949....	0.39	4.18	35.38	1.23	1.79
1948....	0.41	4.35	32.60	1.29	1.81
1947....	0.41	4.35	31.19	1.27	1.78
1946....	0.40	4.35	30.91	1.24	1.48
1945....	0.40	4.82	30.76	1.28	1.83
1944....	0.39	5.19	30.19	1.29	2.07
1943....	0.37	5.22	29.95	1.26	2.10
1942....	0.37	5.86	24.91	1.29	2.34
1941....	0.34	5.65	25.85	1.21	2.29
1940....	0.34	6.06	28.18	1.29	2.65
1939....	0.33	6.07	25.38	1.27	2.62
1938....	0.33	5.92	25.63	1.24	2.56
1937....	0.30	5.75	20.41	1.17	2.48
1936....	0.31	6.10		1.17	2.53
1935....	0.32	6.21		1.19	2.60
1934....	0.34	6.41		1.22	2.47
1933....	0.34	6.12		1.17	2.43
1932....	0.33	5.49		1.06	2.28
1931....	0.29	4.54		0.89	1.99
1930....	0.27	4.24		0.81	2.03
1929....	0.26	4.00		0.76	1.99
1928....	0.25	3.73		0.72	2.06
1927....	0.25	3.66		0.70	2.10
1926....	0.24	3.46		0.66	2.14
1925....	0.24	3.37		0.64	2.20
1924....					2.25
1923....					2.29
1922....					2.34
1921....					2.39
1920....					2.45
1919....					2.50

[a] Roads, *Highway Statistics Summary to 1955*, p. 28, Table MV-200.
[b] *Ibid.*, p. 2, Table G-221.

TABLE D-40. AUTOMOBILE AND TRUCK FUEL CONSUMPTION, BY TYPE OF CONSUMING SECTOR, PROJECTION TO 1975

| | Physical units (thous. bbl.) | | | | Billion Btu | | | |
| Consuming sector | Total (1) | LPG for automobiles; diesel for trucks (2) | Gasoline[a] | | Total (5) | LPG for automobiles; diesel for trucks (6) | Gasoline | |
			Oil (3)	Natural (4)			Oil (7)	Natural (8)
Automobiles								
All sectors[b]	1,757,276	53,000	1,499,763	204,513	9,088,452	212,583	7,810,766	1,065,104
Household[c]	1,581,548	47,700	1,349,787	184,062	8,179,611	191,325	7,029,691	958,595
Nonhousehold	175,728	5,300	149,976	20,451	908,842	21,258	781,075	106,509
Government[d] (excl. military)	8,477	256	7,235	987	43,847	1,027	37,680	5,140
General	167,251	5,044	142,741	19,464	864,995	20,231	743,395	101,369
Trucks								
All sectors[e]	873,626	87,363	691,911	94,352	4,593,875	499,017	3,603,472	491,385
Government[f] (excl. military)	26,209	2,621	20,757	2,831	137,817	14,971	108,102	14,744
General	847,417	84,742	671,154	91,521	4,456,057	484,046	3,495,370	476,641

[a] Distributed to oil and natural gasoline on the basis of Appendix Table I-10.

[b] Table D-38.

[c] Assumed to remain at 90 per cent of total as in 1955 (Table D-20).

[d] Assumed to have same share in nonhousehold as in 1955 (Table D-20), based on lack of trend (Table D-39, col. 1).

[e] Table D-27.

[f] Share assumed to be reduced to 3 per cent in view of long-run decline in government share (Table D-39) and light weight of government trucks relative to other trucks.

TABLE D-41. SCHOOL AND NONREVENUE BUS NUMBERS
(EXCLUDING MILITARY), 1946-56

Year	Total a (1)	Privately owned (2)	Government (3)	Government as per cent of total (4)
1956	166,800	55,659	112,125	67.2%
1955	158,510	46,640	112,914	71.2
1954	148,892	41,764	108,343	72.8
1953	142,147	40,472	102,996	72.5
1952	131,660	37,810	95,258	72.4
1951	123,038	37,283	87,171	70.8
1950	112,060	33,266	80,446	71.8
1949	97,611	26,295	73,927	75.7
1948	84,517	20,394	64,123	75.9
1947	84,656	26,182	58,474	69.1
1946	76,316	22,668	53,648	70.3

a For 1949 to 1956 components do not add to total since figures for publicly owned buses (col. 3) include besides federal buses other state, county, and municipal buses not included in the independently listed total school buses (col. 1). For 1946-48, col. 1 is a summation of col. 2 and col. 3.

SOURCE: Roads, *Highway Statistics*, various issues, Table MV-10.

TABLE D-42. SCHOOL AND NONREVENUE BUS FUEL CONSUMPTION
(EXCLUDING MILITARY), BY CONSUMING SECTOR, PROJECTION TO 1975

Consuming sector	Physical quantities (thous. bbl.)			Billion Btu		
	Total a (1)	Gasoline (oil) (2)	Natural gasoline (3)	Total (4)	Gasoline (oil) (5)	Natural gasoline (6)
All sectors b	4,823	4,244	579	25,116	22,103	3,015
Government c	3,434	3,022	412	17,884	15,739	2,146
Other	1,389	1,222	167	7,233	6,364	870

a Distributed to oil and natural gasoline on basis of Appendix Table I-10.
b Table D-30.
c Estimated, in absence of trend (Table D-41) to retain 1955 share of total, i.e., 71.2 per cent.

TABLE D-43. NUMBER OF MOTORCYCLES, BY CONSUMING SECTOR, 1947-56

Year	Total (1)	Public (excl. military) (2)	Household and commercial (3)	Public as per cent of total (4)
1956	431,494	11,662	419,832	2.7%
1955	412,377	10,987	401,390	2.7
1954	404,772	10,745	394,027	2.7
1953	411,835	10,288	401,547	2.5
1952	417,578	9,885	407,693	2.4
1951	429,699	9,571	420,128	2.2
1950	453,874	9,920	443,954	2.2
1949	478,851	8,979	469,872	1.9
1948	492,165	8,574	483,591	1.7
1947	434,741	7,947	426,794	1.8

SOURCE: Roads, *Highway Statistics*, various issues, Table MV-1.

TABLE D–44. SOURCE AND DISTRIBUTION OF ELECTRICAL ENERGY
CONSUMED BY THE TRANSIT INDUSTRY, 1920–55, AND PROJECTION TO 1975

(Million kwh)

Year	Total consumption				Source of supply	
	Rapid transit (1)	Surface railway (2)	Trolley coach (3)	Total (4)	Generated (5)	Purchased (6)
1975[a]	1,830	0	0	1,830	[b]	1,830[b]
1955	1,830	910	720	3,460	1,480	1,980
1954	1,780	1,080	790	3,650	1,510	2,140
1953	1,820	1,390	850	4,060	1,590	2,470
1952	1,860	1,640	859	4,359	1,770	2,589
1951	1,970	2,010	846	4,826	1,870	2,956
1950	2,000	2,410	841	5,251	2,070	3,181
1949	2,024	2,882	806	5,712	2,123	3,589
1948	2,019	3,621	732	6,372	2,113	4,259
1947	2,003	4,255	638	6,896	2,093	4,803
1946	1,964	4,380	568	6,912	2,077	4,835
1945	1,966	4,547	520	7,033	2,130	4,903
1944	1,940	4,667	492	7,099	2,238	4,861
1943	1,939	4,658	483	7,080	2,237	4,843
1942	1,964	4,082	425	6,471	2,227	4,244
1941	1,986	3,808	351	6,145	2,167	3,978
1940	1,977	4,050	307	6,334	2,255	4,079
1939	1,971	4,203	264	6,438	2,164	4,274
1938	1,921	4,399	234	6,554	2,114	4,440
1937	1,970	4,894	164	7,028	2,197	4,831
1936	1,934	5,087	87	7,108	2,271	4,837
1935	1,852	5,096	61	7,009	2,309	4,700
1934	1,793	5,265	47	7,105	2,352	4,753
1933	1,736	5,273	32	7,041	2,377	4,664
1932	1,715	5,629	29	7,373	2,433	4,940
1931	1,785	6,283	24	8,092	2,621	5,471
1930	1,842	6,816	18	8,676	2,770	5,906
1929	1,824	7,121	[c]	8,945	2,863	6,082
1928	1,760	7,410	[c]	9,170	2,935	6,235
1927	1,641	7,749		9,390	2,976	6,414
1926	1,592	8,021		9,613	3,108	6,505
1925	1,548	7,995		9,543	3,237	6,306
1924	1,488	7,951		9,439	3,356	6,083
1923	1,416	7,894		9,310	3,441	5,869
1922	1,314	7,887		9,201	3,506	5,695
1921	1,278	7,863		9,141	4,031	5,110
1920	1,256	8,066		9,322	4,313	5,009

[a] Based on data shown in this table and in Table D–45, the disappearance of surface railways and trolley coaches is projected by 1975, and it is assumed that rapid transit systems do not increase beyond their current level. The rapid transit fuel consumption figure is thus projected unchanged from 1955.

[b] In view of the small quantities involved in this entire segment of transportation, no attempt has been made to estimate the distribution of electricity consumption into generated and purchased. Instead, the simplifying assumption of considering the total as purchased was adopted.

[c] Included with surface railway.

SOURCE: ATA, "Source and Distribution of Electrical Energy Consumed by the Transit Industry of the United States and Cost of Purchased Power—1920–1957, Inclusive," mimeo. release by the Statistical Department, August 22, 1958.

TABLE D-45.   ELECTRIC RAILWAY TRACK, TROLLEY COACH ROUTE
MILEAGE, AND PASSENGER EQUI. MENT DELIVERIES, 1930-57

As of Dec. 31:	Railway track (miles) [a]		Trolley coach, negative overhead wire [a] (miles) (3)	New equipment delivered [b]		
	Surface (1)	Subway and elevated (2)		Surface cars (4)	Subway and elevated cars (5)	Trolley coaches (6)
1957...	3,774	1,245	3,007	n.a.	n.a.	n.a.
1956...	4,495	1,251	3,293	0	376	0
1955...	4,976	1,221	3,428	0	288	43
1954...	5,547	1,218	3,630	0	260	0
1953...	6,126	1,226	3,663	0	0	0
1952...	7,309	1,223	3,736	19	0	224
1951...	8,240	1,217	3,678	56	140	600
1950...	9,590	1,223	3,513	4	199	179
1949...	10,700	1,231	3,351	273	415	680
1948...	11,740	1,224	2,918	478	248	1,430
1947...	13,750	1,226	2,699	626	2	955
1946...	15,490	1,226	2,354	421	0	266
1945...	16,480	1,222	2,313	332	0	161
1944...	16,860	1,222	2,245	284	0	60
1943...	16,950	1,231	2,248	32	0	116
1942...	16,950	1,221	2,273	284	0	356
1941...	17,100	1,242	2,041	462	0	227
1940...	18,360	1,242	1,925	463	189	618
1939...	19,300	1,300	1,543			
1938...	20,500	1,300	1,398			
1937...	22,460	1,310	1,166			
1936...	24,040	1,260	859			
1935...	25,470	1,230	548			
1934...	27,270	1,230	423			
1933...	28,730	1,170	281			
1932...	30,370	1,130	251			
1931...	32,120	1,080	194			
1930...	34,420	1,080	146			

n.a. Not available.

[a] ATA, mimeo. release No. 58-75 MH, August 22, 1958.
[b] ATA, *Transit Fact Book, 1957 Edition*, p. 13, Table No. 18.

TABLE D–46. FUEL CONSUMPTION N AVIATION, 1955

Item	Thousand barrels	Billion Btu
1. Domestic demand for aviation gasoline [a]	70,141	
2. Military demand for aviation gasoline [b]	40,936	
3. Civilian demand for aviation gasoline (item 1 − item 2)	29,205	
4. Civilian demand for gasoline for aviation [c]	29,301	152,600
a. Of which natural gasoline	3,516	18,311
5. Civilian use of gasoline by classification of operation:		
a. General aviation [d]	4,524	
b. Scheduled operations of domestic combined operations [e]	21,498	
c. Domestic scheduled all-cargo [f]	359	
d. Nonscheduled and irregular cargo operations [g]	212	
e. Total domestic (items 5a through 5d)	26,593	
f. International (item 4 − item 5e) [h]	2,708	
6. Jet fuel [i]	44	249

[a] Mines, *Minerals Yearbook, 1956*, Vol. II, pp. 384–85, Table 47.

[b] Appendix Table E–8.

[c] Roads, *Highway Statistics, 1955*, p. 7, Table G–24. This is the sum of all the gasoline for aviation listed. Therefore, the Bureau of Public Roads figure for nonmilitary gasoline consumption for aviation purposes exceeds that indicated on the basis of the Bureau of Mines data. This difference of 96 thousand barrels is very small. However, the direction of the difference is reasonable because in general aviation some automobile gasoline is used.

[d] *CAA Statistical Handbook of Civil Aviation*, 1957 ed., p. 46. General aviation is defined by the CAA as including "all flying done by civil aircraft exclusive of air carrier operations." Fuels going to this classification did not, according to a communication from CAA, include fuel consumed by large irregular carriers, and nonscheduled operations of combination operations of all-cargo carriers listed on page 105 of the *Handbook*.

[e] *Ibid.*, p. 76. This is the gasoline consumed in the scheduled operations of scheduled carriers which carry both cargo and persons. Such carriers do, of course, have some all-cargo operations.

[f] See Table D–47, footnote b.

[g] See Table D–47, items 2, 3, and 4.

[h] This is gasoline purchased in the United States for international aviation. It differs from the purchases shown in the *CAA Handbook, op. cit.*, for scheduled international air operations in that the fuels so designated in the *Handbook* are purchases by U.S. lines in international traffic, irrespective of the place of purchase. In 1955, purchases by U.S. operators in international traffic totaled 5,748 thousand barrels consisting of 5,655 thousand barrels to scheduled international combination carriers (*Handbook*, p. 90), and 93 thousand barrels to international all-cargo carriers (communication to Resources for the Future from CAA). As a balancing item this must also include non-certificated (nonscheduled) passenger operations (Table D–48); these are declining and have been ignored in the projections. Since 1955 data cover all fuel used in civil aviation, this error does not affect the total.

[i] *CAA Statistical Handbook, op. cit.*, p. 76.

TABLE D-47.   AVIATION GASOLINE CONSUMED IN DOMESTIC
FREIGHT OPERATIONS, 1955

| Item | Ton-miles (thousand) | Fuels consumed | |
		Gallons (thousand)	Barrels (thousand)
1. Scheduled all-cargo carriers....................	88,802[a]	15,066[b]	359
2. Nonscheduled all-cargo carriers................	12,080[c]	2,049[d]	49
3. Large irregular carriers........................	40,056[e]	6,796[d]	162
4. Nonscheduled operations of scheduled combination carriers.................................	264[f]	45[d]	1
5. Scheduled operations of scheduled combination carriers.................................	334,830[g]	56,806[d]	1,353
6. Total (items 1 through 5).....................	476,032		1,924
7. Other......................................	4,968[h]	843[d]	20
8. Aggregate..................................	481,000[i]		1,944

[a] *CAA Statistical Handbook of Civil Aviation*, 1957 ed., p. 105, col. 5.

[b] Gasoline consumed by scheduled all-cargo carriers in domestic operations according to Mrs. Mary B. Thornton, editor of the 1957 *CAA Handbook, ibid.* The total fuel consumed by all-cargo scheduled carriers which is shown as 18,988,047 gallons in the first table on page 104 of the *Handbook*, adjusted to exclude fuels used in nondomestic operations.

[c] *Ibid.*, p. 105, col. 6.

[d] Derived on the assumption of the same ton-miles per gallon of gasoline as for scheduled all cargo carriers: 5.894 ton-miles per gallon (see item 1 above).

[e] Last column of page 105 of 1957 *CAA Handbook, ibid.*

[f] *Ibid.*, p. 105, col. 3. Nonscheduled ton-miles flown by scheduled combination carriers are not included in their ton-miles and the fuels used in such operations are not included in the fuel consumption of scheduled carriers.

[g] Revenue ton-miles of all domestic scheduled operations other than all-cargo carriers. The basis of the delineation between this group and the all-cargo carriers is that these lines also carry passengers. However, they may have all-cargo flights even though they also carry passengers. Data from 1957 *CAA Handbook, ibid.*, p. 85, and is the sum of "excess baggage" and "other" ton-miles.

[h] Difference between intercity ton-miles of 481 million and the sum of the groups shown. This difference is the net of a number of adjustments. It includes intrastate traffic by carriers not subject to federal jurisdiction. On the other hand, the ICC excludes tonnage between the United States and the territories in computing intercity ton-miles.

[i] Table D-1.

TABLE D-48.   AVIATION FUELS CONSUMED IN DOMESTIC
PASSENGER SERVICE, 1955

Item	Passenger-miles (thous.) (1)	Fuels consumed			
		Gasoline		Jet fuel	
		Gallons (thous.) (2)	Barrels (thous.) (3)	Gallons (thous.) (4)	Barrels (thous.) (5)
1. Scheduled carriers.........	19,819,221 ᵃ	846,130 ᵇ	20,146	1,827 ᶜ	44
2. Other:					
a. Nonscheduled domestic ᵈ .	857,000				
b. Business, government (nonmilitary), and pleasure ᵉ	2,143,000				
c. Total................	3,000,000	128,077 ᶠ	3,049		
3. Grand total.............	22,819,221		23,195		44

ᵃ Revenue passenger-miles, from *CAA Statistical Handbook of Civil Aviation*, 1957 ed., table at bottom of p. 86. Of this amount, 78 million appear to be helicopter and territorial (flights to and from the territories by domestic carriers) since domestic intercity (defined as passenger-miles of scheduled air carriers) are listed as 19,741 million revenue passenger-miles in the table on p. 79 of the *Handbook*.

ᵇ Total of 902,936 thousand gallons of gasoline to domestic regular airlines (*ibid.*, p. 76, middle table) minus 56,806 thousand gallons to freight service in Table D-47, item 5.

ᶜ Jet fuel for domestic consumption as listed, *ibid.*, on p. 76.

ᵈ ICC, *Intercity Passenger Miles, 1949-1959*, Statement No. 580, January 1958, p. 4, Table 2.

ᵉ The difference between the total shown, *ibid.*, in p. 2, Table 1, of 22,741 million and the 20,598 million "revenue intercity passenger-miles" shown in Table 2, p. 4. At page 6 of the Statement, the difference between Tables 1 and 2 is described as being due to pleasure and business travel. In accordance with CAA practice, this appears also to include government, nonmilitary travel.

ᶠ Derived from gasoline consumption per passenger-mile as calculated for scheduled carriers (item 1 above), on the assumption that the nonscheduled passenger-miles require the same amount of gasoline as scheduled.

TABLE D–49.   AVIATION FUELS CONSUMED IN DOMESTIC
REVENUE PASSENGER SERVICE, PROJECTION TO 1975

Item	Number and per cent
1. Domestic revenue passenger-miles (mill.), 1955[a]	19,819
2. Domestic revenue passenger-miles (mill.), 1970[b]	69,000
3. Annual rate of increase, 1955–70	8.7%
4. Domestic revenue passenger-miles (mill.), 1975, at 1955–70 rate	104,545
5. Fuels required (thous. bbl.), 1955[c]	21,498
6. Fuel per million revenue passenger-miles (thous. bbl.), 1955[d]	1.0847
7. Fuels required, 1975, if all gasoline-operated (thous. bbl.)[e]	113,404
a. Gasoline (thous. bbl.)	15,000
b. Other, if gasoline-operated (thous. bbl.)	98,404
c. Other as kerosine (jet fuel) (thous. bbl.)[g]	147,606

[a] *CAA Statistical Handbook of Civil Aviation*, 1957 ed., p. 78.

[b] Estimate made by Convair, a Division of General Dynamics Corporation, in "Post War Growth of Commercial Air Transportation in the Free World," Report SE #265-2, San Diego, Calif., July 23, 1958, p. 14. This exceeds by 1,000 million the top estimate made two years earlier by CAA in *1960–1965–1970 Civil Aviation and Federal Airways Forecasts*, December 1956, p. 16. This projection as well as the 1955 base refer only to scheduled operations. It is not believed that nonscheduled operations will be of a significant magnitude (see also Table D–46, footnote h).

[c] Table D–46, item 5b. This item refers essentially to passenger traffic, but also includes fuel consumed in the scheduled operations of scheduled carriers which carry both cargo and persons.

[d] Item 5 divided by item 1.

[e] Assumes no change from 1955 in unit fuel requirements and in proportion of cargo to total; therefore, figure derived by multiplying item 4 by item 6.

[f] Based on an estimate of 15,619,000 barrels for 1963 tapering off as follows from 1959 (in thousand barrels): 1959—31,429; 1960—27,333; 1961—20,857; 1962—16,286 (communication to author from Air Transport Association of America). It is assumed that consumption will stabilize around the 1963 level.

[g] It is here assumed that per passenger-mile and associated activities jets will require 1.5 times as much fuel as would piston-powered aircraft. This broad assumption is based upon a communication from Transworld Airlines, Inc., but can by no means be considered a firm ratio holding good for any plane, trip, or under any conditions. There is not as yet much agreement in the industry on this particular point, and the ratio used should be viewed as a first tentative approach to dealing with the problem. It is likely to be on the high side, especially when turbo-prop operations are taken into account.

TABLE D–50.   AVIATION GASOLINE CONSUMED IN DOMESTIC CARGO
SERVICE, PROJECTION TO 1975

Item	Number and per cent
1. Intercity cargo carried by domestic scheduled combination carriers (thous. ton-miles):	
a. 1955[a]	334,830
b. 1975[b]	1,766,228
2. Total intercity cargo, 1975 (thous. ton-miles)[c]	2,800,000
3. Intercity cargo carried by others, 1975 (thous. ton-miles) (item 2 − item 1b)	1,033,772
4. Intercity cargo carried by scheduled all-cargo carriers, 1955 (thous. ton-miles)	88,802[d]
5. 1975 cargo ton-miles as per cent of 1955 (item 3 ÷ item 4)	1,164%
6. Fuel consumption by scheduled all-cargo carriers, 1955 (thous. bbl.).	359[d]
7. Estimated fuel consumption by others (same as item 3), 1975 (thous. bbl.)[e]	4,176

[a] Table D–47, item 5.

[b] Assumed to increase at the same rate as revenue passenger-miles, since this cargo is carried on combined passenger-cargo lines. Therefore, based on Table D–49, item 4 ÷ item 1. Fuel consumed for this purpose estimated in figure derived in Table D–46.

[c] Table D–3, item 6.

[d] Table D–47, item 1.

[e] Since 1955 fuel consumption is known only for scheduled all-cargo carriers and all other types of flights are estimated to have the same unit-consumption (see Table D–47, footnote d); this projection is, for the sake of arithmetical simplicity, computed on the basis of scheduled all-cargo carriers.

TABLE D–51.   MILES PER GALLON IN PASSENGER SERVICE OF
DOMESTIC SCHEDULED AIR CARRIERS, 1937–55

Year	Revenue passenger-miles[a] (thous.) (1)	Gasoline consumed[b] (thous. gals.) (2)	Passenger-miles per gallon of gasoline (3)
1955	19,819,221	902,936,000[c]	21.950
1954	16,768,706	775,585,624	21.620
1953	14,760,309	691,903,326	21.333
1952	12,528,318	588,323,361	21.295
1951	10,566,182	491,483,855	21.499
1950	8,002,825	418,441,973	19.125
1949	6,752,622	375,283,794	17.993
1948	5,980,993	332,423,621	17.992
1947	6,109,508	294,196,130	20.767
1946	5,947,956	236,388,751	25.162
1945	3,362,455	134,824,120	24.940
1944	2,178,207	89,513,646	24.334
1943	1,634,135	65,025,412	25.131
1942	1,418,042	68,908,271	20.579
1941	1,384,733	81,657,020	16.958
1940	1,052,156	65,674,895	16.021
1939	682,904	47,196,559	14.469
1938	479,844	37,722,669	12.720
1937	411,545	33,961,273	12.118

[a] *CAA Statistical Handbook of Civil Aviation*, 1957 ed., p. 78.

[b] *Ibid.*, p. 76 for 1955; all other years, 1955 edition.

[c] Also 1,827 thousand gallons of jet fuel which is here ignored.

TABLE D–52. DISTRIBUTION OF REVENUE TON-MILES OF DOMESTIC
SCHEDULED AIR CARRIERS, 1940–56

Year	Revenue ton-miles (thousands)		Passenger as per cent of total (3)
	Passenger (1)	Total (2)	
1956	2,158,520	2,520,427	85.64%
1955	1,912,395	2,247,134	85.10
1954	1,616,754	1,903,180	84.95
1953	1,420,299	1,685,088	84.29
1952	1,205,283	1,447,174	83.29
1951	1,015,781	1,233,114	82.38
1950	769,725	976,457	78.83
1949	648,808	820,450	79.08
1948	571,173	717,239	79.63
1947	588,015	692,739	84.88
1946	576,802	654,595	88.12
1945	336,246	427,978	78.57
1944	217,821	289,885	75.14
1943	163,414	218,274	74.87
1942	141,804	177,099	80.07
1941	138,473	158,253	87.50
1940	105,216	119,766	87.85

SOURCE: *CAA Statistical Handbook of Civil Aviation*, 1957 ed., table at top of p. 85; 1942–47
excludes regular mail carried under special contract and foreign mail.

TABLE D–53. ESTIMATED HOURS FLOWN IN GENERAL AVIATION,
1965, 1970, 1975

(Thousand hours)

Type of aviation	Hours flown		Percentage increase, 1965–70 (3)	Hours flown, 1975[a] (4)
	1965 (1)	1970 (2)		
Business[b]	7,807	11,000	40.9%	15,499
Commercial[c]	3,215	4,200	30.6	5,485
Instruction[d]	1,531	1,900	24.1	2,358
Pleasure and miscellaneous[e]	2,755	3,600	30.7	4,705
Total	15,308	20,700	35.2%	28,047

[a] 1970 increased by percentage shown in col. 3.
[b] See CAA report cited as source, p. 43.
[c] *Ibid.*, p. 48.
[d] *Ibid.*, p. 52.
[e] *Ibid.*, p. 56.

SOURCE: CAA, *1960–1965–1970 Civil Aviation and Federal Airways Forecasts*. The 1970
estimate is in all instances the one designated as "high" by CAA. The 1975 estimates
are derived by extending the rates of change implicit in CAA's 1965 and 1970 projections.

TABLE D-54. FUELS CONSUMED IN GENERAL AVIATION,
PROJECTION TO 1975

Gallons per hour, 1955 [a]...	20
Hours of general aviation 1975 [b]....................................	28,047,000
Fuel consumed, 1975: [c]	
Gallons (thousand)..	560,940
Barrels (thousand)..	13,356
Of which assumed to be: [d]	
Gasoline (90 per cent)...	12,020
Jet fuel, gasoline equivalent....................................	1,336
Jet fuel, kerosine...	2,004

[a] Table D-56.

[b] Table D-53.

[c] Fuel per hour assumed to be unchanged from 1955, despite the rising trend shown in Table D-56. This assumption based on aircraft types which CAA anticipates will expand in business flying (CAA, *1960-1965-1970 Civil Aviation and Federal Airways Forecasts*, p. 41). Emphasis is placed on shift to twin-engine aircraft which "are smaller and less costly than other multi-engine equipment which had previously been available . . . such as the Super Beech 18 . . ." The Beech 18 consumes 40.6 gallons per hour as contrasted with 18 to 19 gallons per hour for the Beech Twin-Bonanza and the Piper Apache.

[d] It is assumed that an amount of flying equivalent to 10 per cent of the total will be done with jets and that jets will consume 1.5 times the gasoline quantities which they displace (cf., Table D-49, footnote g).

TABLE D-55. CHANGES IN COMPOSITION OF GENERAL AVIATION, 1946-55 [a]

(Thousand miles flown)

Year	Business and commercial (1)	Instructional [a] (2)	Pleasure (3)	Total [b] (4)
1955.............	873,500	120,650	221,850	1,216,000
1954.............	778,850	124,290	209,980	1,119,295
1953.............	709,107	120,700	196,174	1,045,346
1952.............	637,570	144,035	165,795	972,055
1951.............	570,325	190,195	200,265	975,480
1950.............	520,200	286,600	244,100	1,061,500
1949.............	475,200	378,660	269,892	1,128,992
1948.............	441,585	754,740	255,150	1,469,540
1947.............	378,385	848,670	262,060	1,502,420
1946.............	229,465	478,825	156,555	874,740

[a] Through 1952, includes military flight instruction by civilian contractors.

[b] Includes, in addition, testing, experimental, ferrying, Civil Air Patrol, and miscellaneous types of flying, amounting to 1 to 3 per cent of total.

SOURCE: *CAA Statistical Handbook of Civil Aviation*, 1957 ed., p. 45.

TABLE D-56. GENERAL AVIATION: MILES, HOURS, AND
FUEL CONSUMPTION, 1931–55

Year	Miles flown [a] (thous.) (1)	Gasoline consumed [a] (thous. gal.) (2)	Hours flown [b] (thous.) (3)	Gallons per hour (4)	Miles per hour (5)	Miles per gallon (6)
1955.......	1,216,000	190,000	9,500	20.0	128	6.4
1954.......	1,119,295	176,649	8,963	19.7	125	6.3
1953.......	1,045,346	168,948	8,527	19.8	123	6.2
1952.......	972,055	137,846	8,186	16.8	119	7.1
1951.......	975,480	131,833	8,451	15.6	115	7.4
1950.......	1,061,500	131,200	9,650	13.6	110	8.1
1949.......	1,128,992	131,766	11,031	11.9	102	8.6
1948.......	1,469,540	179,368	15,130	11.9	97	8.2
1947.......	1,502,420	156,668	16,334	9.6	92	9.6
1946.......	874,740	98,576	9,788	10.1	89	8.9
1942.......	293,593	24,900	3,786	6.6	78	11.8
1941.......	346,303	29,300	4,460	6.6	78	11.8
1940.......	264,000	22,400	3,200	7.0	83	11.8
1939.......	177,868	16,394	1,922	8.5	92	10.8
1938.......	129,359	10,201	1,478	6.9	88	12.7
1937.......	103,196	10,618	1,173	9.1	88	9.7
1936.......	93,320	10,451	1,059	9.9	90	9.1
1935.......	84,756	11,104	954	11.6	89	7.6
1934.......	75,602	9,631	846	11.4	89	7.8
1933.......	71,223	8,861	795	11.1	89	8.0
1932.......	78,179	10,294	877	11.7	89	7.6
1931.......	94,343	11,658	1,083	10.8	87	8.1

[a] *CAA Statistical Handbook of Civil Aviation*, 1957 ed., p. 46.
[b] *Ibid.*, p. 44.

TABLE D-57. FUEL CONSUMPTION IN INTERNATIONAL AVIATION, 1955 AND PROJECTION TO 1975

International revenue passenger-miles by U.S. carriers (bill.):	
1955..	4.4
1965..	15.5
1970..	20.0
1975 [b]..	25.8
Fuel consumed (thous. gal.):	
1955..	2,708 [c]
1975, on all-gasoline assumption......................................	15,879 [d]
1975, on all-jet assumption [e].......................................	23,818

[a] CAA, *1960–1965–1970 Civil Aviation and Federal Airways Forecasts*, p. 30; 1965 and 1970 are the estimates designated as "high" by CAA.

[b] Derived on the assumption that the growth rate for 1970–75 will be the same as for 1965–70.

[c] Table D–46, item 5f.

[d] Increased by the percentage by which passenger-miles flown are increasing. This implies the assumption that there is no net change between 1955 and 1975 in the relationship between total passenger-miles by U.S. planes in international traffic and fuel purchased in the United States for international aviation irrespective of the ownership of the airplane. This assumption, not a critical one, is in correspondence with that suggested on p. 27 of the CAA *1960–1965–1970* forecast, *op. cit.*

[e] On replacement basis of 1.5 gallons of jet fuel per 1 gallon of gasoline (cf., Table D–49, footnote g).

TABLE D-58. SUMMARY: FUEL CONSUMPTION IN AVIATION, 1975 PROJECTIONS

Fuel	Kerosine (1)	Gasoline Total (2)	Gasoline From oil (3)	Gasoline Natural (4)
Physical units (thous. bbl.):				
Domestic passenger and cargo service..	147,606 [a]	19,176 [b]		
General aviation [c]...................	2,004	12,020		
International aviation [d].............	23,818			
Total...............................	173,428	31,196	27,452 [e]	3,744 [e]
Billion Btu.........................	983,337	162,469	142,970	19,499

[a] Table D–49, item 7c.

[b] From Tables D–49, item 7a, plus D–50, item 7.

[c] Table D–54.

[d] Table D–57.

[e] Allocated to gasoline from oil and natural gasoline on basis of Appendix Table I–10.

TABLE D–59. ENERGY CONSUMPTION IN TRANSPORTATION, BY ENERGY SOURCE AND MAJOR CONSUMER SECTOR, IN PHYSICAL UNITS, 1955 AND 1975

Physical units	Railroads (other than electric)ᵃ		Railroads and railways (electric)ᵇ		Marineᶜ		Automotiveᵈ		Aviationᵉ	
	1955 (1)	1975 (2)	1955 (3)	1975 (4)	1955 (5)	1975 (6)	1955 (7)	1975 (8)	1955 (9)	1975 (10)
Coal (thous. tons)	11,227		2,252	1,231						
Gasoline (thous. bbl.)	8	9			1,499	880	974,021	2,201,498	25,785	27,452
Kerosine (thous. bbl.)					612				44	173,428
Distillates (thous. bbl.)	81,311	122,387			16,675	45,541	24,300	98,988		
Residual (thous. bbl.)	8,472		812	444	115,128	205,821				
LPG (thous. bbl.)							5,300	53,000		
Natural gasoline (thous. bbl.)					84	120	132,821	300,205	3,516	3,744
Gas (mill. cu. ft.)			12,350	7,832						
Hydro (mill. kwh.)			1,214	781						

Physical units	Gas pipelines		Totalʰ		Transportation self-performed					
					Householdsⁱ		Gov't (excl. mil.)ʲ		All other	
	1955ᶠ (11)	1975ᵍ (12)	1955 (13)	1975 (14)	1955 (15)	1975 (16)	1955 (17)	1975 (18)	1955 (19)	1975 (20)
Coal (thous. tons)			14,978	1,231					14,978	1,231
Gasoline (thous. bbl.)			1,000,426	2,229,839	629,120	1,350,485	16,479	31,091	354,826	848,264
Kerosine (thous. bbl.)			44	173,428					44	173,428
Distillates (thous. bbl.)			122,286	266,916			704	2,621	121,582	264,295
Residual (thous. bbl.)			124,412	206,265					124,412	206,265
LPG (thous. bbl.)			5,300	53,000				256	504	5,044
Natural gasoline (thous. bbl.)			136,421	304,069	4,770	47,700	26	4,240	48,386	115,672
Gas (mill. cu. ft.)	245,246	515,017	257,596	522,849	85,789	184,157	2,246		257,596	522,849
Hydro (mill. kwh.)			1,214	781					1,214	781

ᵃ Tables D–4 and D–11; excludes fuel consumption for nonmotive purposes.
ᵇ Appendix Tables H–9 and H–17; includes small amount of nonmotive electricity use by nonelectric railroads.
ᶜ Table D–14.
ᵈ 1955: Tables D–15, D–16, D–17, D–18, D–20; 1975: Tables D–18, D–27, D–29, D–30, D–38.
ᵉ Tables D–46 and D–58.
ᶠ Mines, *Minerals Yearbook, 1956*, Vol. II, pp. 294–95, Table 11.
ᵍ Assumed to increase same as natural gas demand, i.e., 110 per cent.
ʰ Does not include energy consumed by oil pipelines due to lack of data. See text, Chapter 5, p. 221.
ⁱ Derived from Tables D–22, D–40, and D–18.
ʲ Derived from Tables D–24, D–40, D–42, and D–18.

TABLE D-60. ENERGY CONSUMPTION IN TRANSPORTATION, BY ENERGY SOURCE AND MAJOR CONSUMER SECTOR, IN BTU'S, 1955 AND 1975

(Billions)

Billion BTU	Railroads (other than electric)[a]		Railroads and railways (electric)[b]		Marine[c]		Automotive[d]		Aviation[e]	
	1955 (1)	1975 (2)	1955 (3)	1975 (4)	1955 (5)	1975 (6)	1955 (7)	1975 (8)	1955 (9)	1975 (10)
Coal	294,147		54,194	29,547	39,274					
Gasoline	41	47			3,187	4,583	5,072,701	11,465,401	134,289	142,970
Kerosine									249	983,337
Distillates	464,449	699,075			95,248	260,124	138,802	565,419		
Residual	54,085		5,131	2,799	734,977	1,313,968				
LPG							21,258	212,583		
Natural gasoline					437	625	691,732	1,563,468	18,311	19,499
Gas			12,423	7,832						
Hydro			14,274	6,992						
Total	812,722	699,122	86,022	47,170	873,123	1,579,300	5,924,493	13,806,869	152,849	1,145,806

Billion BTU	Gas pipelines		Total[h]		Transportation self-performed				All other	
					Households[i]		Gov't (excl. mil.)[j]			
	1955[f] (11)	1975[g] (12)	1955 (13)	1975 (14)	1955 (15)	1975 (16)	1955 (17)	1975 (18)	1955 (19)	1975 (20)
Coal			387,615	29,547	3,276,457	7,033,326			387,615	29,547
Gasoline			5,210,224	11,613,006			85,823	161,922	1,847,944	4,417,758
Kerosine			249	983,337					249	983,337
Distillates			698,499	1,524,618	19,132	191,325	4,021	14,971	694,478	1,509,647
Residual			794,193	1,316,767					794,193	1,316,767
LPG			21,258	212,583			104	1,027	2,022	20,231
Natural gasoline			710,480	1,583,588			11,697	22,082	251,994	602,416
Gas	253,830	533,043	266,253	540,875	446,789	959,090			266,253	540,875
Hydro			14,274	6,992					14,274	6,992
Total	253,830	533,043	8,103,045	17,811,313	3,742,378	8,183,741	101,645	200,002	4,259,022	9,427,570

[a] Tables D-4 and D-11; excludes fuel consumption for nonmotive purposes.
[b] Appendix Tables H-9 and H-17; includes small amount of nonmotive electricity use by nonelectric railroads.
[c] Table D-14.
[d] 1955: Tables D-15, D-16, D-17, D-18, D-20; 1975: Tables D-18, D-27, D-29, D-30, D-38.
[e] Tables D-46 and D-58.
[f] Mines, *Minerals Yearbook, 1956*, Vol. II, pp. 294-95, Table 11.
[g] Assumed to increase same as natural gas demand, i.e., 110 per cent.
[h] Does not include energy consumed by oil pipelines due to lack of data.   See text, Chapter 5, p. 221.
[i] Derived from Tables D-22, D-40, and D-18.
[j] Derived from Tables D-24, D-40, D-42, and D-18.

Section E. Government

General Note

Tables E–1 through E–5 and E–10 through E–12 deal with nonmilitary activities of government.

The 1975 projections for nonmilitary consumption are presented in Table E–1 together with the 1955 base, followed by four tables which support the projection methods used. Tables E–10 through E–12 present the derivation of gas consumption estimates in government. Table E–8 presents the estimate of 1955 military petroleum consumption as well as the projection for 1975. The latter is based on data shown in Tables E–6 and E–7. Table E–9 is supplied merely as an illustrative example of types of Army utilization of petroleum. It does not enter into the calculations, either in 1955 or 1975. Table E–13 summarizes the results for both 1955 and 1975.

Government Tables

TABLE E-1. ELECTRICITY AND NONMOTIVE GASOLINE
CONSUMPTION BY GOVERNMENT, EXCLUDING MILITARY, 1955
AND PROJECTION TO 1975

Fuel	1955	1975
Electricity:	(mill. kwh)	(mill. kwh)
AEC		
From utilities......................	47,199 [a]	55,000
Generated and retained...............	2,906 [a]	
Total............................	50,105	55,000 [b]
Street and highway lighting............	4,373 [c]	16,922 [d]
Other public authorities...............	10,151 [c]	35,768 [e]

Gasoline, nonmotive uses:	(thous. bbl.)	(bill. Btu)	(thous. bbl.)	(bill. Btu)
Total..............................	5,519 [f]		16,103 [g]	
Oil [h]..............................	4,857	25,295	14,171	73,803
Natural gasoline [h]..................	662	3,448	1,932	10,062

[a] Appendix Table A-27.

[b] Assumed to remain at 1957-58 levels as suggested by recent leveling off.

[c] Appendix Table H-1.

[d] Assumed to increase at 7 per cent per year, based upon past experience shown in Table E-2. At this rate, 1968 consumption would be 10.538 billion kwh. This is quite similar to a General Electric forecast for 1968 of 10 billion kwh. (Conference on Street and Highway Lighting, *Electrical World*, November 3, 1958, p. 63.)

[e] Assumed to increase at 6.5 per cent per year, based upon past experience shown in Table E-2. The resulting consumption figure represents 13.3 per cent of projected commercial consumption, as compared with 12.6 per cent in 1955, and well in line with past experience, see Table E-4.

[f] Table E-5.

[g] Assumed to increase at 5.5 per cent per year, on the basis of growth shown in recent years in Table E-5. The record is obviously badly disturbed by the war years, and, therefore, it has been ignored prior to 1949.

[h] Distributed in accordance with Appendix Table I-10.

TABLE E-2. ELECTRICITY CONSUMPTION BY PUBLIC AUTHORITIES OTHER THAN AEC AND MILITARY, 1926–57

Year	Other public authorities		Street and highway lighting		Total	
	Consumption (mill. kwh)	Year-to-year percentage change	Consumption (mill. kwh)	Year-to-year percentage change	Consumption (mill. kwh) (1) + (2)	Year-to-year percentage change [a]
	(1)	(2)	(3)	(4)	(5)	(6)
1957.........	11,774	6.8%	5,090	7.4%	16,864	7.0%
1956.........	11,026	8.6	4,738	8.3	15,764	8.5
1955.........	10,151	7.7	4,373	8.2	14,524	7.9
1954.........	9,423	4.6	4,042	6.9	13,465	5.3
1953.........	9,011	6.8	3,780	7.3	12,791	7.0
1952.........	8,435	5.6	3,522	7.2	11,957	6.1
1951.........	7,987	11.5	3,285	10.4	11,272	11.2
1950.........	7,163	8.8	2,976	9.2	10,139	8.9
1949.........	6,583	5.2	2,725	7.9	9,308	6.0
1948.........	6,255	5.7	2,525	6.8	8,780	6.0
1947.........	5,916	1.1	2,365	4.1	8,281	1.9
1946.........	5,854	−22.9	2,272	4.0	8,126	−16.9
1945.........	7,589	−10.3	2,184	1.0	9,773	−8.0
1944.........	8,463	−7.4	2,163	4.2	10,626	−5.3
1943.........	9,139	117.3	2,075	0.7	11,214	78.9
1942.........	4,206	36.0	2,061	−2.3	6,267	20.4
1941.........	3,093	13.7	2,110	3.0	5,203	9.1
1940.........	2,720	7.2	2,048	2.3	4,768	5.0
1939.........	2,538	3.5	2,002	3.8	4,540	3.6
1938.........	2,451	2.0	1,929	3.6	4,380	2.7
1937.........	2,403		1,862		4,265	36.3
1936.........	908		2,222		3,130	7.2
1935.........	842		2,078		2,920	2.8
1934.........	945		1,896		2,841	0.8
1933.........	926		1,893		2,819	−4.7
1932.........	926		2,033		2,959	−1.2
1931.........	664		2,330		2,994	9.5
1930.........	508		2,227		2,735	11.7
1929.........	412		2,037		2,449	10.2
1928.........	311		1,911		2,222	10.9
1927.........	262		1,741		2,003	12.2
1926.........	196		1,589		1,785	

[a] Combined up to and including 1937, because the 1937 change in classification is especially important in the case of street and highway lighting and other public authorities.

SOURCE: E.E.I., *Statistical Bulletin* for various years: 1945–57 from *1957* edition, p. 27, Table 18; for 1942–44, *1951* edition, p. 29; and 1926–41, *1941* edition, p. 21.

TABLE E-3. ANNUAL GROWTH RATES IN ELECTRICITY
CONSUMPTION BY GOVERNMENT OTHER THAN AEC AND MILITARY,
SELECTED PERIODS 1926-57

Period	Other public authorities (1)	Street and highway lighting (2)	Total (3)
1926-57.............................	a	a	7.5%
1926-36.............................	16.6%	3.4%	5.8
1936-57.............................	a	a	8.3
1937-57.............................	8.3	5.1	7.1
1937-47.............................	9.4	2.4	6.9
1947-57.............................	7.1	8.0	7.3
1952-57.............................	6.9	7.6	7.1

ᵃ No separate rates computed because of changes in classification in 1937.

SOURCE: Based on Table E-2.

TABLE E-4. ELECTRICITY CONSUMPTION BY OTHER PUBLIC
AUTHORITIES AS PER CENT OF "SMALL LIGHT AND POWER
PURCHASES," 1940-56 AND ESTIMATED 1975

(Million kwh)

Year	Other public authorities ᵃ (1)	Small light and power purchases ᵇ (2)	Other public authorities as per cent of small light and power purchases (3)
1975..............................	35,768	269,055	13.29%
1956..............................	11,026	87,743	12.57
1955..............................	10,151	80,759	12.57
1954..............................	9,423	73,373	12.84
1953..............................	9,011	69,208	13.02
1952..............................	8,435	62,080	13.59
1951..............................	7,987	57,278	13.94
1950..............................	7,163	50,446	14.20
1949..............................	6,583	46,262	14.23
1948..............................	6,255	43,193	14.48
1947..............................	5,916	38,379	15.41
1946..............................	5,854	33,016	17.73
1945..............................	7,589	30,438	24.93
1944..............................	8,463	29,837	28.36
1943..............................	9,139	28,192	32.42
1942..............................	4,206	27,233	15.44
1941..............................	3,093	24,628	12.56
1940..............................	2,720	22,373	12.16

ᵃ 1940-56 from Table E-2; 1975 from Table E-1.

ᵇ 1975 from Appendix Table B-7, item 7; others from E.E.I., *Statistical Bulletin* for
various years: 1945-56 from *1957* edition, p. 27, Table 18; 1940-44 from *1951* edition,
pp. 28-29, Table 14.

TABLE E-5.   NON-ROAD USE OF GASOLINE BY GOVERNMENT, 1934-55

Year	Thousand barrels[a]	Year-to-year percentage change
1955	5,519	4.1%
1954	5,300	8.8
1953	4,870	5.1
1952	4,632	5.3
1951	4,398	3.5
1950	4,251	5.7
1949	4,020	4.4
1948	3,849	8.1
1947	3,559	30.0
1946	2,731	−4.6
1945	2,862	4.8
1944	2,732	3.6
1943	2,638	−21.4
1942	3,356	−13.1
1941	3,861	159.3
1940	1,449	17.2
1939	1,270	8.7
1938	1,168	17.0
1937	998	2.3
1936	976	14.0
1935	856	69.5
1934	505	

[a] Roads, *Highway Statistics Summary to 1955*, p. 2, Table G–221 (none shown for federal use in 1955).

TABLE E-6. U.S. DEPARTMENT OF DEFENSE PROJECTED
PURCHASES OF PETROLEUM FUELS, 1957-63

(Thousand barrels per fiscal year)

Fuel	1957	1958	1959	1960	1961	1962	1963
Aviation gasoline 115/145....	31,390	24,455	33,580	27,375	24,090	21,900	19,345
Aviation gasoline 100/130....	8,030	6,935	7,300	7,300	6,205	5,110	4,015
Aviation gasoline, all other...	1,825	1,825	1,825	1,825	1,825	1,825	1,825
Total, aviation gasoline......	41,245	33,215	42,705	36,500	32,120	28,835	25,185
Jet fuel JP-5..............	2,190	1,825	4,015	4,380	5,110	6,205	6,935
Jet fuel, other.............	93,075	92,710	120,815	127,020	131,035	133,955	136,510
Total, jet fuel.............	95,265	94,535	124,830	131,400	136,145	140,160	143,445
Motor gasoline.............	18,615	15,330	14,600	13,870	13,140	13,140	13,140
Distillates................	24,455	22,995	22,265	21,170	19,710	18,615	18,250
Navy-grade residual........	45,990	39,055	49,640	45,625	44,530	43,800	43,070
Other residual.............	14,965	13,140	13,140	13,140	13,140	13,140	13,140
Total, residual............	60,955	52,195	62,780	58,765	57,670	56,940	56,210
All other products..........	4,015	3,650	4,015	4,015	4,015	4,015	4,015

SOURCE: U.S. Department of Defense, Office of Petroleum Logistics of the Assistant
Secretary of Defense for Supply and Logistics, as reported in the *Oil and Gas Journal*,
October 6, 1958, p. 103.

TABLE E-7. MILITARY OIL: DEMAND AND OVERSEAS PURCHASES,
FISCAL 1957, AND ASSUMED PERCENTAGE OF OVERSEAS PURCHASES
FOR 1975

(Thousand barrels per day)

Fuel	Total demand 1957 [a] (1)	Overseas purchases 1957 [b] (2)	Overseas purchases as per cent of total demand	
			Actual 1957 (3)	Assumed 1975 (4)
Aviation gasoline.........	114	7	6.1%	5.0% [c]
Jet fuel................	261	33	12.6	12.5 [d]
Motor gasoline..........	51	23	45.1	45.0
Distillates..............	67	22	32.8	30.0 [e]
Residual................	167	62	37.1	34.0 [e]

[a] *Oil and Gas Journal*, October 7, 1957, p. 95.

[b] Except for the amount listed for aviation gasoline the overseas purchases are those
given in the *Oil and Gas Journal*, October 7, 1957, p. 97. The amount listed for aviation
gasoline is the difference between the total overseas purchases of about 147,000 barrels per
day and the 140,000 barrels for jet fuel, motor gasoline, distillates, and residual oil.

[c] A slight reduction is assumed in the proportion of aviation gasoline purchased overseas.

[d] Rounded from 1957.

[e] For both distillates and residual oil the proportion purchased overseas is expected to
decrease because of the effect of nuclear-powered vessels.

TABLE E-8. PETROLEUM FUEL CONSUMPTION BY MILITARY, 1955 AND PROJECTION TO 1975

Fuel	1955		1975			
	Thousand barrels	Billion Btu	Total (thous. bbl.)	Domestic		Billion Btu
				Per cent[a]	Thousand barrels	
	(1)	(2)	(3)	(4)	(5)	(6)
Aviation gasoline........	40,936[b]		13,870[c]	95.0%	13,176	
Jet fuel:						
JP-5................	365[d]		9,490[c]	87.5	8,304	
JP-4................	52,221[e]		146,000[c]	87.5	127,750	
Gasoline...........	39,881				97,563	
Kerosine..........	9,113				22,292	
Distillate..........	3,227				7,895	
Motor gasoline.........	10,635[b]		13,140[f]	55.0	7,227	
Diesel oil.............	7,794[g]					
Other light distillates.....	3,151[g]					
Total distillates.....	10,945		13,687[h]	70.0	9,581	
Navy-grade residual.....	16,204[g]		25,000[i]			
Other residual..........	12,164[g]		13,140[e]			
Total residual.......	28,368		38,140	66.0	25,172	
Summary by principal fuels:						
Gasoline[j]..............	91,452	476,282			117,966	614,366
From oil.............	80,478	419,129			103,810	540,642
From natural gasoline..	10,974	57,153			14,156	73,724
Kerosine (incl. JP-5).....	9,478	53,740			30,596	173,479
Distillate..............	14,172	80,950			17,476	99,823
Residual...............	28,368	181,101			25,172	160,698
Total.................	143,470	792,073			191,210	1,048,366

[a] Table E-7.

[b] From U.S. Army Statistical Report 531, as furnished by Petroleum Logistics Division of the Office of the Assistant Secretary of Defense for Supply and Logistics.

[c] Aviation gasoline and jet fuels are each projected as changing in absolute quantities between 1963 and 1975 by the same amounts as the changes projected by the Office of Petroleum Logistics for the three-year period fiscal years 1960-63 (Table E-6). This represents a considerable retardation in the growth of jet fuel and in the reduction of regular aviation gasoline. This projection is regarded as conforming generally to statements of the Aeronautics Division, Directorate of Research and Development, U.S. Air Force which characterizes jet fuel as gradually increasing to 1970 and then declining and aviation gasoline declining as turbines replace pistons (reported in Oil and Gas Journal, October 6, 1958, p. 105).

[d] Oil and Gas Journal, October 7, 1957, based on 1,000 barrels per day for fiscal 1956 as shown on p. 95.

[e] Derived as total jet fuel sales of 52,673,000 barrels (Mines, Mineral Market Report, No. MMS 2681, p. 13, Table 15), reduced by assumed civilian consumption of 87,000 barrels and JP-5 consumption. The amount attributed to civilian consumption is double the civilian consumption of jet fuel listed for civilian aviation in 1955 in CAA Statistical Handbook of Civil Aviation, 1957 ed., p. 76. The doubling is to take into account increases in storage which must have accompanied the rapid increase in use. The fuels in JP-4 are based on their relative shares in jet fuel production as shown in Mines, Annual Petroleum Statement, No. 410, December 27, 1956, p. 3: 76.37 per cent gasoline; 17.45 per cent kerosine; and 6.18 per cent distillates.

TABLE E–8 (continued)

  [f] Continuation of 1963 level as shown in Table E–6.
  [g] *Mineral Market Report, op. cit.*, p. 13.
  [h] The absolute reduction between fiscal years 1962 and 1963, as projected by Office of Petroleum Logistics (Table E–6) is continued for twelve and a half years from 1963 to estimate consumption in calendar year 1975.
  [i] Assumed to drop to about half of the highest total reached in the 1957–63 period. The level of consumption shown for 1963 in Table E–6 would correspond approximately to a nuclear fleet having 19 submarines, 1 carrier, and 1 cruiser, compared to 119, 23, and 17 total active units in the same categories in the 1957 active fleet (*Oil and Gas Journal*, October 7, 1957, p. 97).
  [j] For distribution to oil and natural gasoline see Appendix Table I–10.

TABLE E–9. CONSUMPTION OF MAJOR PETROLEUM PRODUCTS BY PRINCIPAL ARMY FUNCTION IN CONTINENTAL UNITED STATES, FISCAL 1956

(Thousand barrels)

Projects	Gasoline (1)	Diesel oil (2)	Fuel oil (3)	Miscellaneous[a] (4)	Total (5)
Operation of administrative motor pools................	610.7	5.0	12.8	21.0	649.5
Operation of rail equipment....	3.3	14.0	.6	.6	18.5
Operation of floating equipment.	7.8	10.6	31.7	.4	50.5
Repairs and utilities............	69.2	125.0	2,053.8	19.2	2,267.2
Depot receipt, storage, and issue functions.................	82.1	15.0	7.7	12.3	117.1
Operation of forces (organizational elements)............	1,279.0	56.1	11.6	69.7	1,416.4
Other[b].....................	753.7	109.5	1,003.1	71.2	1,937.5
Total......................	2,805.8	335.2	3,121.3	194.4	6,456.7

  [a] Includes kerosine, solvent, greases, and lubricants.
  [b] Includes balance of Army activities, some of which are training, special exercises, reserve components, and manufacturing.

SOURCE: Communication to author from U.S. Department of the Army, Office of the Quartermaster General, August 27, 1957.

TABLE E–10. GAS CONSUMPTION IN GOVERNMENT, 1955

Item	Billion Btu	Million cu. ft.
1. Total "other" sales[a]....................................	314,840	
2. For generation of AEC electricity[b].......................	21,944	
3. Net of AEC..	292,896	282,991

  [a] This category is "other" than residential, commercial, and industrial, and defined by A.G.A. as sales to government and interdepartmental sales in *1957 Gas Facts*, p. 98, Table 82.
  [b] Gas consumed at Oak Ridge and accounted for in Appendix Table H–4.

TABLE E-11. FACTORS IN DERIVATION OF GAS CONSUMPTION IN GOVERNMENT IN 1975

(Million therms, or 100 billion Btu's)

Year	Commercial sales			Other sales [a]			Other sales as per cent of commercial sales	
	U.S. (1)	5-state[b] component (2)	Rest of U.S. (3)	U.S. (4)	5-state[b] component (5)	Rest of U.S. (6)	5-state[b] component (5) ÷ (2) (7)	Rest of U.S. (6) ÷ (3) (8)
1957.......	6,988.9	1,925.6	5,063.3	3,949.6	2,773.0	1,176.6	144.0%	23.2%
1956.......	6,557.7	1,849.8	4,707.9	3,035.6	2,003.6	1,032.0	108.3	21.9
1955.......	6,029.3	1,802.8	4,226.5	3,148.4	2,277.8	870.6	126.3	20.6
1954.......	5,404.9	1,613.9	3,791.0	2,896.8	2,139.0	757.8	132.5	20.0
1953.......	4,980.2	1,512.7	3,467.5	3,057.9	2,281.0	776.9	150.8	22.4
1952.......	4,929.1	1,600.6	3,328.5	2,437.3	1,725.6	711.7	107.8	21.4
1951.......	4,559.4	1,457.5	3,101.9	1,936.0	1,331.5	604.5	91.4	19.5
1950.......	4,103.8	1,365.8	2,738.0	1,260.5	786.5	474.0	57.6	17.3
1949.......	3,724.2	1,412.7	2,311.5	1,259.6	822.5	437.1	58.2	18.9
1948.......	3,535.3	1,313.4	2,221.9	1,216.2	810.6	405.6	61.7	18.3
1947.......	3,106.7	1,126.0	1,908.7	897.4	591.3	306.1	52.5	16.0
1946.......	2,629.9	1,023.6	1,606.3	664.7	336.7	328.0	32.9	20.4
1945.......	2,497.3	988.7	1,508.6	1,097.8	520.1	577.7	52.6	38.3

[a] Defined by A.G.A. as sales to governmental customers and interdepartmental sales (unless on a rate basis as regular sales).

[b] Kansas, Tennessee, Texas, New Mexico, California. Reasons for setting up this category are discussed in Chapter 5, pp. 222-23.

SOURCE: A.G.A., 1954 and preceding years: *Historical Statistics of the Gas Industry* (1956), pp. 160–64, Table 93. 1955–57 are from *Gas Facts*—the *1956* edition, p. 99; *1957* edition, p. 100; and *1958* edition, p. 98.

TABLE E-12. GAS CONSUMPTION IN GOVERNMENT, PROJECTION TO 1975

Item	Billion Btu	Million cu. ft.
1. Commercial sales, U. S., 1975[a]	1,271,481	1,228,484
2. Estimated "other" sales, excluding special element in 5-state component, 1975[b]	317,870	307,121
3. Commercial sales in 5-state component, 1955[c]	180,280	
4. "Other" sales in 5-state component, 1955: a. Expected, if based on 1955 ratio of "other" to commercial sales in rest of country[d]	37,140	
b. Actual[e]	227,780	
c. Excess of actual over expected	190,640	
5. 1955 sales to AEC in 5-state component[f]	21,940	
6. Unidentified excess in 5-state area, 1955[g]	168,700	162,995
7. Total estimated "other" or government sales, 1975, excluding AEC (item 2 + item 6)	486,570	470,116

[a] Appendix Table B-3.

[b] Assumed to be 25 per cent of commercial consumption, based on past relationships shown in Table E-11, col. 8. This relationship excludes the states of Kansas, Tennessee, Texas, New Mexico, and California, which, by inspection of figures are judged to have, more than others, a special consumption element consisting partly of military, possibly also irrigation consumption and other unidentified sales (Table E-11, col. 5; see also text, Chapter 5, pp. 222-23).

[c] Table E-11, col. 2.

[d] Item 3 multiplied by 20.6 per cent (Table E-11, col. 8, for 1955).

[e] Table E-11, col. 5.

[f] Gas consumption by Oak Ridge, Tennessee, plant, Appendix Table H-4, col. 2 (rounded.)

[g] Assumed to remain unchanged to 1975.

TABLE E-13. SUMMARY: ENERGY CONSUMPTION IN GOVERNMENT, 1955 AND 1975

Fuel	Other than via electricity or nonmilitary transportation		Via electricity		Via transportation		Total	
	1955 (1)	1975 (2)	1955 (3)	1975 (4)	1955 (5)	1975 (6)	1955 (7)	1975 (8)
Physical units								
Coal (thous. tons):								
Bituminous			24,173	34,244			24,173	34,244
Anthracite								
Total			24,173	34,244			24,173	34,244
Oil (thous. bbl.):								
Gasoline	85,335	117,981			16,479	31,091	101,814	149,072
Kerosine	9,478	30,596					9,478	30,596
Distillates	14,172	17,476			704	2,621	14,876	20,097
Residual	28,368	25,172	2,584	5,184			30,952	30,356
Total	137,353	191,225	2,584	5,184	17,183	33,712	157,120	230,121
Natural gas (mill. cu. ft.)	282,991	470,116	56,996	115,072			339,987	585,188
Natural gas liquids (thous. bbl.):								
LPG					26	256	26	256
Natural gasoline	11,636	16,088			2,246	4,240	13,882	20,328
Total	11,636	16,088			2,272	4,496	13,908	20,584
Hydro (mill. kwh)			5,890	11,107			5,890	11,107

Billion Btu

	(1)	(3)	(5)	Total	(2)	(4)	(6)	Total
Coal:								
Bituminous.........		580,606		580,606		821,854		821,854
Anthracite.........								
Total............		580,606		580,606		821,854		821,854
Oil:								
Gasoline..........	444,424		85,823	530,247	614,445		161,922	776,367
Kerosine..........	53,740			53,740	173,479			173,479
Distillates........	80,950		4,021	84,971	99,823		14,971	114,794
Residual..........	181,101	16,333		197,434	160,698	32,658		193,356
Total............	760,215	16,333	89,844	866,392	1,048,445	32,658	176,893	1,257,996
Natural gas........	292,896	57,229		350,125	486,570	115,072		601,642
Natural gas liquids:								
LPG..............			104	104			1,027	1,027
Natural gasoline......	60,601		11,697	72,298	83,786		22,082	105,868
Total............	60,601		11,801	72,402	83,786		23,109	106,895
Hydro............		69,228		69,228		99,480		99,480
Grand total.......	1,113,712	723,396	101,645	1,938,753	1,618,801	1,069,064	200,002	2,887,867

SOURCES: Col. 1—Tables E-1, E-8, and E-10; col. 2—Tables E-1, E-8, and E-12; col. 3—Appendix Table H-9; col. 4—Appendix Table H-17; col. 5—Appendix Table D-24; and col. 6—Appendix Tables D-40, D-42, and D-24 (for motorcycles which remain at 1955 level on past trend shown in Appendix Table D-43).

Section F. Agriculture

General Note

This section of the Appendix consists of only four tables: after deriving estimates for the different petroleum products and listing the electricity consumption for 1955 and that expected for 1975, the major categories of both the oil and electricity data are summarized in Table F–4.

Agriculture Tables

TABLE F-1. DERIVATION OF FUEL CONSUMPTION IN AGRICULTURE, EXCLUDING ELECTRICITY, 1955

Fuel	Thousand gallons (1)	Thousand barrels (2)
Consumption for machinery		
Gasoline (including natural):		
Tractors...................................	3,490,831	83,115
Other engines..............................	174,866	4,163
Tractor fuel (so designated)...................	217,284	5,173
Kerosine for other machines (usually sold under designation of tractor fuel).....................	10,944	261
Total tractor fuel, comparable in scope to Bureau of Mines designation [a].................	228,228	5,434
Of which:		
Kerosine,[b] for tractors and other machines..........		2,804
Distillates [c]..................................		2,630
Diesel for other machinery......................	309,363	7,366
LPG for other machinery.......................	398,990	9,500
Consumption for other uses [d]		
Kerosine....................................	184,002	4,381
LPG.......................................	91,203	2,172
Distillates..................................	127,471	3,035

[a] Despite inconsistency over the years, between tractor fuel sales reported by the Bureau of Mines, and special surveys by the USDA, the Mines series was resorted to as the most direct short-cut for separating tractor fuel into its most likely components.

688

TABLE F–1 (continued)

b Mines, *Mineral Market Report*, No. MMS 2517, p. 4, Table 5.

c This balancing quantity is in all likelihood an understatement, especially in the light of a special USDA survey (see Chapter 5, p. 226, footnote 35). Different practices in trade names and fuel designation thoroughly confuse the picture. No further fuel type division is here made because it would be entirely arbitrary and would not affect the Btu values.

d Brooding, drying and curing of crops, weed and brush control, orchard heating, water heating in milk houses, space heating of farm buildings (other than dwellings), and other lesser uses.

SOURCE: Unless otherwise noted, data are from Census, *U.S. Census of Agriculture: 1954*, Vol. III, Special Reports, Part 11, Farmers' Expenditures, pp. 19–20.

TABLE F–2. ELECTRICITY CONSUMPTION IN AGRICULTURE, 1955 AND ESTIMATED 1975

Uses[a]	Million kwh
Irrigation and pumping, 1955	8,000
Irrigation and pumping, 1975	12,100

a The uses shown are the only instances of electricity consumption in agriculture that can be statistically identified. All other uses are merged in residential consumption and, possibly for large consumers, in commercial consumption.

SOURCE: FPC, *Estimated Future Power Requirements in the United States*, Publication P–29, October 1955, p. 12, Table D. The FPC estimate is made for 1980, but is here used for 1975 for lack of a better method.

TABLE F–3. FUEL CONSUMPTION IN AGRICULTURE BY TYPE OF FUEL, EXCLUDING ELECTRICITY, 1955 AND PROJECTION TO 1975

Fuel	1975[a] Physical unit (thous. bbl.) (1)	1975[a] Billion Btu (2)	1955[b] Physical unit (thous. bbl.) (3)	1955[b] Billion Btu (4)
Tractor fuel:				
Gasoline[c]	108,683	566,020	73,140	380,915
Kerosine	3,779	21,426	2,543	14,419
Distillates	3,908	22,323	2,630	15,023
Natural gasoline[c]	14,820	77,184	9,974	51,943
Total		686,953		462,300
Other machinery:				
Gasoline[c]	5,445	28,358	3,664	19,085
Kerosine	388	2,199	261	1,480
Diesel	10,945	62,521	7,366	42,075
LPG	14,117	56,622	9,500	38,105
Natural gasoline[c]	743	3,867	500	2,602
Total		153,567		103,347

(*Table continued on next page.*)

TABLE F-3 (continued)

Fuel	1975[a]		1955[b]	
	Physical unit (thous. bbl.) (1)	Billion Btu (2)	Physical unit (thous. bbl.) (3)	Billion Btu (4)
Other uses:[d]				
Kerosine	6,510	36,911	4,381	24,840
LPG	3,227	12,946	2,172	8,712
Distillates	4,510	25,760	3,035	17,336
Total		75,617		50,888
Grand total		916,137		616,535
Summary, by fuels [e]				
Oil:				
Gasoline [c]	114,127	594,378	76,804	400,000
Kerosine	10,677	60,536	7,185	40,739
Diesel	10,945	62,521	7,366	42,075
Other distillates	8,418	48,083	5,665	32,359
Total		765,518		515,173
NGL:				
Natural gasoline [c]	15,563	81,051	10,474	54,545
LPG	17,344	69,568	11,672	46,817
Total		150,619		101,362
Grand total		916,137		616,535

[a] Based upon annual growth since 1955 of 2 per cent for each fuel in each use; for implications of this assumption, see discussion in Chapter 5, pp. 225-26.

[b] Derived from Table F-1.

[c] For gasoline allocation between gasoline from oil and natural gasoline, see Appendix Table I-10.

[d] For definition, see Table F-1, footnote d.

[e] Represents summary, under each designation, of figures shown in upper part of this table.

TABLE F-4. SUMMARY: ENERGY CONSUMPTION IN AGRICULTURE, 1955 AND 1975

(Billion Btu)

Fuel	1975	1955
Coal via electric power generation	78,792	56,428
Oil:		
Via electric power generation	7,465	8,997
Nonelectric uses	765,518	515,173
Gas via electric power generation	20,886	21,780
NGL	150,619	101,362
Hydro	18,645	25,026
Total:		
Electric	125,788	112,231
Nonelectric	916,137	616,535
Grand total	1,041,925	728,766

SOURCE: Electricity data from Appendix Tables H-9 and H-17; oil and NGL data from Table F-3.

Section G. Miscellaneous

General Note

This section contains one summary table, G–1, and nineteen supporting tables explaining the projection to 1975 for each of the separate entries. The reason for having the summary table precede rather than follow the explanatory tables is the loosely defined character of this section. Footnotes to Table G–1 refer the reader to the pertinent supporting table in each instance.

In most instances, one table covers one or more commodities, but for miscellaneous oils and gas waste there are two each, Tables G–6 and G–7, and G–8 and G–9, respectively; asphalt and road oil are sufficiently complex to require a set of five, Tables G–11 to G–15, and consumption of gas and oil for carbon black manufacture is developed and projected in five tables: G–16 through G–20. Table G–21 derives the estimates of miscellaneous gasoline consumption and of losses. Both are small categories, but are required to provide complete coverage.

Miscellaneous Tables

TABLE G-1. SUMMARY: CONSUMPTION OF OIL, GAS, AND NATURAL
GASOLINE FOR MISCELLANEOUS PURPOSES, INCLUDING LOSSES,
1955 AND PROJECTION TO 1975

Fuel	Physical unit		Billion Btu	
	1955	1975	1955	1975
Kerosine [a]	28,745	16,708	162,984	94,734
Diesel oil [b]	13,403	35,562	}118,358	244,931
Other distillates [c]	7,318	7,318		
Residual: Carbon black only [d]	5,264	17,319	33,605	110,564
Miscellaneous uses [e]	4,540	10,000	28,983	63,840
Lubricants [f]	42,477	59,430	257,623	360,443
Petroleum wax [g]	4,056	7,706	22,572	42,884
Petroleum coke:				
In primary aluminum production [h]	3,914	16,250	} 72,918	228,666
In other uses, excl. petrol. ref. [i]	8,239	21,861		
Naphtha [j]	24,152	45,889	125,784	238,990
Miscellaneous oils [k]	13,062	87,868	75,707	509,283
Gasoline, incl. NGL, misc. uses [l]	5,536	11,681	28,831	60,835
Of which: oil [m]	4,872	10,279	25,373	53,533
NGL [m]	664	1,402	3,458	7,302
Gasoline, losses in handling, etc. [n]	13,123	28,535	68,345	148,610
Of which: oil [m]	11,548	25,111	60,142	130,778
NGL [m]	1,575	3,424	8,203	17,832
Miscellaneous LPG [o]	760	7,600	3,048	30,484
NGL: For chemical uses [p]	35,552	239,158	142,599	959,263
For synthetic rubber [q]	9,672	19,245	38,794	77,192
Natural gas, wasted and vented [r]	773,639	1,107,521	800,716	1,146,284
Asphalt and road oil [s]	17,140	20,984	613,636	748,372
Natural gas for carbon black [t]	244,794	142,287	253,362	147,267
Summary by fuels:				
Oil			1,597,685	2,827,018
Gas			1,054,078	1,293,551
NGL			196,102	1,092,073
Grand total			2,847,865	5,212,642

NOTE: Physical units are in thousand barrels except natural gas (million cubic feet), and
asphalt and road oil (thousand tons).

[a] 1955: Mines, *Mineral Market Report*, No. MMS 2800, p. 4, Table 5. 1975: assumed to
decrease at 2.75 per cent per year, which is roughly the rate at which use has been declining
between 1948 and 1956, see Table G-2.

[b] 1955: Table G-2, col. 3; 1975: assumed to increase at 5 per cent per year, which is less
than the rate during the past four years, but takes into account the slow growth in the most
recent past.

[c] 1955: Table G-2, col. 4; 1975: left unchanged in view of constancy in last three years.
[d] From Table G-20, item 5.

[e] 1955: difference between total (Table G-2, col. 5) and use in carbon black production;
1975: assumed roughly doubled in view of last three years, notwithstanding large increase
after 1954 (Table G-2). Converted to Btu's at 6,384,000 Btu's per barrel.

[f] 1955: Mines, *Minerals Yearbook, 1956*, Vol. II, p. 374; 1975: estimated at 2 per cent of
total automotive fuel demand, based on Table G-3. Total fuel demand from Roads,
Highway Statistics, various issues. While Table G-3 is based on all motor fuel rather than
gasoline only, the resulting difference is of no quantitative consequence. The 2 per cent
relationship, derived in view of the declining trend from the 3 per cent appearing in the
table is based on a communication to the author from W. M. Drout, Jr., Manager of
Marketing Economics of the Standard Oil Co. of New Jersey (October 28, 1958). Converted
on basis of 6,065,000 Btu's per barrel.

TABLE G-1 (continued)

ᵍ 1955: *Minerals Yearbook, 1956, op. cit.;* 1975: estimated on basis of Table G-4, to increase at same rate as runs-to-stills. These were estimated at a preliminary stage of this study to rise by 90 per cent in 1975. Converted at 5,565,000 Btu's per barrel.

ʰ 1955: from Table G-5; 1975: based on assumption of 0.5 barrels of petroleum coke per pound of aluminum, output of which, according to Appendix Table A-35, is projected at 6.5 million tons in 1975. Converted at 6 million Btu's per barrel.

ⁱ 1955: from Table G-5; 1975: assumed to increase at 5 per cent per year, based on growth shown in same table (1948-56 rate equals 4.5 per cent). Converted at 6 million Btu's per barrel.

ʲ 1955: Mines, *Minerals Yearbook, 1955,* Vol. II, p. 382; 1975: for lack of other evidence assumed to increase at estimated rate of growth in runs-to-stills, which approximates 90 per cent between 1955 and 1975. Converted to Btu's at rate for gasoline.

ᵏ 1955: *Minerals Yearbook, 1956, op. cit.,* p. 375; 1975: in absence of definite indications, but in view of rapid growth in the past, especially in categories comprising oils used in the petrochemicals industry (Tables G-6 and G-7), an annual growth rate of 10 per cent has been arbitrarily assumed. Converted at 5,796,000 Btu's per barrel.

ˡ 1955: derived as difference between domestic demand for gasoline excluding naphtha, and consumption for all purposes here identified excluding gasoline component of jet fuel (Table G-21).

ᵐ Allocated on basis of data shown in Appendix Table I-10.

ⁿ 1955: from Roads, *Highway Statistics Summary to 1955,* p. 2, Table G-221. (These are losses legally allowed for, not actually incurred.) 1975: assumed at 1 per cent of total gasoline consumption excluding military consumption, which is also excluded from data in Table G-10, from which the 1 per cent rate is derived, and including diesel oil and LPG used in highway transportation. The relevant calculations for 1975 follow:

Total, excluding losses	2,807,846	(Table G-21)
Plus miscellaneous	11,681	(Table G-21)
Plus diesel oil for trucks	87,363	(Appendix Table D-27)
Plus diesel oil for commercial buses	11,625	(Appendix Table D-29)
Plus LPG for automobiles	53,000	(Appendix Table D-38)
Net motor fuel	2,971,515	
Minus military consumption	117,966	(Table G-21)
Net civilian motor fuel	2,853,549	
1 per cent loss	28,535	

ᵒ 1955: *Minerals Yearbook, 1956, op. cit.,* p. 311; 1975: assumed to be tenfold that of 1955, based on data shown in Table G-2.

ᵖ 1955: from Table G-2; 1975: on basis of data shown in same table and to allow for heavy growth, assumed to rise at 10 per cent per year. Converted at 4,011,000 Btu's per barrel.

ᑫ 1955: from Table G-2; 1975: on basis of data shown in same table and in recognition of slowdown in growth rate assumed to grow at rate of 3.5 per cent per year. Converted at 4,011,000 Btu's per barrel.

ʳ 1955: from Table G-8; 1975: estimated at 4.5 per cent of gross amount of gas withdrawn, which in turn is estimated from the demand projection of this study (though at a preliminary stage of it) as 210 per cent of 1955 withdrawals. The 4.5 per cent figure is lower than the 1955 waste rate, as shown in Table G-8. However, it was judged that the states now having low waste rates have the larger reserves and that the over-all rate would tend to drop further (Table G-9).

ˢ Tables G-11 and G-12.

ᵗ Table G-20.

TABLE G-2. MISCELLANEOUS USES OF KEROSINE, DISTILLATES, RESIDUAL, LPG, AND NATURAL GAS LIQUIDS, 1937-57

(Thousand barrels)

Year	Kerosine[a] (1)	Distillates[b]			Residual[c] (5)	LPG[d] (6)	Natural gas liquids[e]	
		Diesel oil		Other distillates (4)			Chemicals (7)	Synthetic rubber (8)
		Road use (2)	Other (3)					
1957...	24,306	26,817	22,867	9,828	9,984			
1956...	28,319	26,501	22,369	9,908	10,331	1,161	37,409	9,955
1955...	28,745	23,446	20,769 [f]	9,948 [g]	9,804	760	35,552	9,672
1954...	29,568	22,728	16,081	10,257	7,035	631	25,006	7,327
1953...	28,500	20,908	14,072	12,087	6,326	612	23,034	9,298
1952...	32,194				5,745	333	20,738	8,833
1951...	32,580				5,280	174	20,108	8,925
1950...	34,285				4,898	204	14,868	5,440
1949...	31,577				4,574	165	12,974	4,235
1948...	35,682				6,623	58	12,485	5,372
1947...	32,012				6,859		9,863	4,798
1946...	28,441				5,028		7,417	6,998
1945...	24,689				5,200		5,340	4,971
1944...	24,054				4,484		3,619	3,859
1943...	23,725				6,420		1,318	
1942...	23,608				6,019		1,263	
1941...	22,868				5,568		1,053	
1940...	22,264				5,313		825	
1939...	21,580				4,990		640	
1938...	20,810				4,939		769	
1937...	20,785				6,911		639	

[a] Data from Mines. 1953-57: *Mineral Market Report*, No. MMS 2800, p. 4, Table 5; 1951-52: *ibid.*, No MMS 2412, p. 3, Table 5; and 1937-50: *Information Circular 7630*, p. 81, Table 60.

[b] *Mineral Market Report, op. cit.*, No. MMS 2681, p. 14, Table 16; No. MMS 2412, p. 12, Table 16; and No. MMS 2800, p. 13, Table 16.

[c] Mines. 1957: *Mineral Market Report*, No. MMS 2800, Table 4; 1952-56: *Minerals Yearbook, 1956*, Vol. II, p. 412; 1950-51: *ibid.*, *1952*, Vol. II, p. 414; and 1937-49: *Information Circular 7630, op. cit.*, p. 6.

[d] Mines. 1952-56: *Minerals Yearbook, 1956, op. cit.*, p. 311, Table 11; and 1948-51: *ibid.*, *1952*, Vol. II, p. 311, Table 10.

[e] Mines. 1952-56: *ibid.*, *1956*, p. 311, Table 11; 1949-51: *ibid.*, *1953*, Vol. II, p. 344, Table 10; and 1937-48: *Information Circular 7684*, p. 6, Table 5.

[f] Of which 7,366 used in agriculture (Appendix Table F-1) and therefore excluded in carrying this figure to Table G-1.

[g] Of which 2,630 used in agriculture (Appendix Table F-1) and therefore excluded in carrying this figure to Table G-1. Actually, the figure in Appendix Table F-1 is simply designated "distillates," but in the context of the data on agriculture is assumed to be wholly other than diesel oil.

TABLE G–3. DEMAND FOR LUBRICANTS COMPARED WITH
GASOLINE, 1945–57

Year	Lubricants (thous. bbl.)	Gasoline (thous. bbl.)	Lubricants as per cent of gasoline
1957...............	41,215	1,392,953	3.0%
1956...............	43,933	1,373,079	3.2
1955...............	42,477	1,334,205	3.2
1954...............	38,537	1,230,595	3.1
1953...............	40,497	1,205,775	3.4
1952...............	38,165	1,142,987	3.3
1951...............	42,292	1,089,566	3.9
1950...............	38,853	994,290	3.9
1949...............	33,101	913,713	3.6
1948...............	35,983	871,200	4.1
1947...............	36,481	795,015	4.6
1946...............	34,891	735,417	4.7
1945...............	35,334	696,333	5.1

SOURCE: Mines, *Minerals Yearbook, 1948*, p. 961; *ibid., 1950*, p. 878; *ibid., 1952*, Vol. II, pp. 320–21; *ibid., 1954*, Vol. II, p. 316; *ibid., 1953*, Vol. II, p. 324; and *Annual Petroleum Statement*, No. 434, November 14, 1958.

TABLE G–4. PRODUCTION OF PETROLEUM WAX AND CRUDE OIL
RUNS-TO-STILLS, 1931–56

Year	Runs-to-stills (thous. bbl.) (1)	Wax production (thous. bbl.) (2)	Wax production as per cent of runs-to-stills (3)
1956...............	2,905,106	5,367	0.185%
1955...............	2,730,218	5,293	0.194
1954...............	2,539,564	5,290	0.208
1953...............	2,554,865	4,978	0.195
1952...............	2,441,259	4,331	0.177
1951...............	2,370,404	4,814	0.203
1950...............	2,094,867	4,462	0.213
1949...............	1,944,221	3,208	0.165
1948...............	2,048,349	3,515	0.172
1947...............	1,852,246	3,624	0.196
1946...............	1,730,197	3,003	0.174
1945...............	1,719,534	2,921	0.170
1944...............	1,665,684	2,883	0.173
1943...............	1,429,738	2,697	0.189
1942...............	1,333,769	2,502	0.188
1941...............	1,409,192	2,393	0.170
1940...............	1,294,283	1,833	0.142
1939...............	1,237,840	1,659	0.134
1938...............	1,165,015	1,555	0.133
1937...............	1,183,440	1,863	0.157
1936...............	1,068,570	1,689	0.158
1935...............	965,790	1,608	0.166
1934...............	895,636	1,674	0.187
1933...............	861,254	1,677	0.195
1932...............	819,997	1,639	0.200
1931...............	894,608	1,705	0.191

SOURCES: Wax production—1931–48, A.P.I., *Petroleum Facts and Figures, 1950*, 9th edition, p. 217 (at 280 lbs. per bbl.); 1949–54, *ibid., 1956*, p. 211; and 1955–56, Mines, *Minerals Yearbook, 1956*, Vol. II, p. 374. Crude oil runs-to-stills—1931–48, *Petroleum Facts and Figures, 1950, op. cit.*, p. 222; 1949–54, *ibid., 1956*, p. 200; and 1955–56, *Minerals Yearbook, 1956, op. cit.*, p. 380.

TABLE G-5. CONSUMPTION OF PETROLEUM COKE, 1931-55

(Thousand barrels, at 5 barrels per ton)

Year	All uses[a] (1)	Refinery use[b] (2)	Primary aluminum production[c] (3)	Other uses (1)−(2)−(3) (4)
1955	24,403	12,250	3,914	8,239
1954	19,776	9,475	3,651	6,650
1953	17,599	9,030	3,130	5,439
1952	13,924	7,330	2,343	4,251
1951	14,481	7,290	2,092	5,099
1950	15,021	7,275	1,797	5,949
1949	14,427	6,270	1,509	6,648
1948	11,670	4,625	1,559	5,486
1947	10,082	3,605	1,429	5,048
1946	9,029	2,610	1,024	5,395
1945	9,214	2,980	1,238	4,996
1944	8,327	1,910	1,941	4,476
1943	5,250	570	2,300	2,380
1942	5,036	265	1,303	3,468
1941	8,143	365	773	7,005
1940	7,034	565	516	5,953
1939	7,108	615	409	6,084
1938	5,589	375	359	4,855
1937	5,765	420	366	4,979
1936	6,266	615	281	5,370
1935	6,703	585	149	5,969
1934	7,540	970	93	6,477
1933	9,962	1,315	106	8,541
1932	9,592	1,665	131	7,796
1931	7,820	2,645	222	4,953

[a] Mines, 1952-55, *Minerals Yearbook, 1956*, Vol. II, p. 374; 1948-51, *ibid., 1952*, Vol. II, p. 373; and 1931-47 from A.P.I., *Petroleum Facts and Figures, 1950*, 9th edition, pp. 1-2.
[b] From Appendix Table A-14 at 5 barrels per ton.
[c] On the assumption of one-half pound of petroleum coke per pound of primary aluminum production. *Metal Statistics, 1958* (New York: *American Metal Market*), p. 605.

TABLE G-6. DOMESTIC DEMAND FOR MISCELLANEOUS OILS, 1948-57

(Thousand barrels)

Year	Domestic demand for miscellaneous oils	Transfers from gasoline plants	Net demand (miscellaneous minus transfers)
1957	16,876	1,664	15,212
1956	14,385	2,347	12,038
1955	13,062	2,677	10,385
1954	10,486		
1953	8,882		
1952	7,098		
1951	6,565		
1950	4,394		
1949	3,995		
1948	6,506		

SOURCE: Mines. 1957, *Annual Petroleum Statement*; No. 434, November 14, 1958; 1952-56, *Minerals Yearbook, 1956*, Vol. II, p. 375; and 1948-51, *ibid., 1952*, Vol. II, p. 373.

TABLE G-7.   PRODUCTION OF MISCELLANEOUS OILS, SELECTED
YEARS, 1948–56

(Thousand barrels)

Year	Petrolatum (1)	Medicinal oils (2)	Absorption oils (3)	Specialties (4)	Solvents (5)	Other (6)	Total (7)
1956.....	758	89	2,528	5,627	394	5,444	14,840
1955.....	953	79	2,951	5,397	748	3,355	13,483
1952.....	838	71	2,020	2,804	253	1,272	7,258
1950.....	866	64	1,071	1,909	268	539	4,717
1948.....	952	128	574	1,849	232	2,453	6,188

SOURCE: Mines. 1956, *Minerals Yearbook, 1956*, Vol. II, p. 421 (includes production at
natural gasoline and cycling plants); 1955, *ibid., 1955*, Vol. II, p. 412 (includes transfers
from natural gasoline plants; 1952, *ibid., 1956*, p. 424; 1950, *ibid., 1950*, p. 989; and
1948, *ibid., 1948*, p. 1013.

TABLE G-8.   GAS WASTED AND VENTED AS PERCENTAGE OF GAS
WITHDRAWN, 1936–56

(Million cubic feet)

Year	Gross withdrawal (1)	Vented and wasted (2)	Vented and wasted as per cent of gross withdrawal (3)
1956..............	12,372,905	864,334	6.99%
1955..............	11,719,794	773,639	6.60
1954..............	10,984,850	723,567	6.59
1953..............	10,645,798	810,276	7.61
1952..............	10,272,566	848,608	8.26
1951..............	9,689,372	793,186	8.19
1950..............	8,479,650	801,044	9.45
1949..............	7,546,825	853,884	11.31
1948..............	7,178,777	810,178	11.29
1947..............	6,733,230	1,067,938	15.86
1946..............	6,190,200	1,102,033	17.80
1945..............	5,902,180	896,208	15.18
1944..............	5,614,220	1,010,285	18.00
1943..............	4,942,560	684,115	13.84
1942..............	4,453,900	626,782	14.07
1941..............	4,103,500	630,212	15.36
1940..............	3,694,100	655,967	17.76
1939..............	3,333,500	677,311	20.32
1938..............	3,061,200	649,106	21.20
1937..............	3,032,410	526,159	17.35
1936..............	2,644,835	392,528	14.84

SOURCE: Mines. 1955–56, *Minerals Yearbook, 1956*, Vol. II, p. 284; 1953–54, *ibid., 1954*,
Vol. II, p. 280; 1951–52, *ibid., 1952*, Vol. II, p. 280; and 1936–50, *Information Circular
7644*, p. 3.

TABLE G-9. REGIONAL DIFFERENCES IN GAS VENTED AND WASTED, 1955

(Million cubic feet)

Location	Gross withdrawal (1)	Vented and wasted (2)	Vented and wasted as per cent of gross withdrawal (3)
States with high ratio:			
Colorado..........	97,000	19,711	20.32%
Illinois.............	40,400	31,730	78.54
Indiana............	4,500	3,237	71.93
Mississippi.........	266,000	40,235	15.13
Nebraska...........	18,000	5,130	28.50
North Dakota.......	15,500	10,244	66.09
Oklahoma..........	955,000	214,079	22.42
Wyoming...........	100,000	15,313	15.31
All other..........	510	123	24.12
Total..............	1,496,910	339,802	22.70%
States with low ratio:			
Arkansas...........	55,000	6,228	11.32%
California..........	802,000	8,326	1.04
Kansas.............	525,000	51,785	9.86
Kentucky..........	76,000	2,707	3.56
Louisiana...........	1,948,000	66,204	3.40
Maryland...........	3,116		
Michigan...........	12,100	1,630	13.47
Montana...........	29,000	618	2.13
New Mexico........	565,000	21,563	3.82
New York..........	4,000	363	9.08
Ohio...............	35,000	1,189	3.40
Pennsylvania........	99,800	481	0.48
Texas..............	5,836,000	270,525	4.64
Utah..............	17,900	737	4.12
Virginia............	968		
West Virginia.......	214,000	1,481	0.69
Total..............	10,222,884	433,837	4.24%
U.S. Total........	11,719,794	773,639	6.60%

SOURCE: Mines, *Minerals Yearbook, 1956*, Vol. II, p. 284.

TABLE G-10. MOTOR FUELS: LOSSES ALLOWED FOR EVAPORATION, HANDLING, ETC., AS PER CENT OF TOTAL CONSUMED DOMESTICALLY (EXCLUDING MILITARY), 1935-55

Year	Percentage	Year	Percentage
1955......................	1.04%	1944.....................	1.19%
1954......................	1.04	1943.....................	1.21
1953......................	1.06	1942.....................	1.12
1952......................	1.07	1941.....................	1.09
1951......................	1.11	1940.....................	1.50
1950......................	1.11	1939.....................	1.50
1949......................	1.07	1938.....................	1.50
1948......................	1.09	1937.....................	1.21
1947......................	1.11	1936.....................	1.20
1946......................	1.11	1935.....................	1.21
1945......................	1.15		

SOURCE: Roads, *Highway Statistics Summary to 1955*, p. 2, Table G-221. Total consumption includes losses allowed for. Motor fuel includes diesel and any other fuel used solely for propulsion of motor vehicles on public highways.

TABLE G–11. CONSUMPTION OF ASPHALT AND ROAD OIL, 1955

Item	Sold		
	Thousand tons (1)	Thousand barrels (2)	Billion Btu (3)
1. Paving:			
a. Asphalt[a]	10,766		
Of which:			
New construction	6,210		
Maintenance and other uses	4,556		
b. Road oil	1,460[b]	8,356[c]	54,314[d]
c. Total	12,226		
2. Roofing (all asphalt)	3,502[a]		
3. Miscellaneous (all asphalt)	1,412[a]		
4. Total asphalt	15,680[a]	84,286[e]	559,322[f]
5. Asphalt and road oil (item 4 + item 1b)	17,140		613,636

[a] Table G–14.

[b] Mines, *Minerals Yearbook, 1956*, Vol. II, p. 265.

[c] Table G–13, col. 4.

[d] 6,500,000 Btu per barrel.

[e] The barrelage shown is not derived by conversion of sales figure, but is the domestic demand at the refinery level (Table G–13, col. 1), which does not correspond precisely to the sales figure because of reporting differences (see Table G–13, cols. 1 and 3). Even under ideal conditions, there would be differences because of the addition of water and other liquids to make emulsified asphalts (*Minerals Yearbook, 1956, op. cit.*, p. 260).

[f] 6,636,000 Btu per barrel.

TABLE G–12. CONSUMPTION OF ASPHALT AND ROAD OIL, PROJECTION TO 1975

Item	Total annual expenditure (billion)[a] (1)	Construction expenditure (billion) (2)	Tons of bituminous material per million $ of construction (3)	Total tonnage of material		
				Thousand tons (4)	Thousand barrels[b] (5)	Billion Btu (6)
1. Paving:						
a. Asphalt, of which:						
New construction of highways	$5.72	$4.86[c]	1,567[d]	7,619	41,904	
Maintenance of highways	2.44	2.44	1,827[e]	4,458	24,519	
Other				381[f]	2,096	
Total				12,458	68,519	
b. Road oil				1,273[g]	7,000	
2. Roofing				5,253[h]	28,892	
3. Miscellaneous				2,000[i]	11,000	
4. All uses:						
a. Asphalt, as estimated				19,711	108,411	
b. Asphalt, as adjusted[j]					105,918	702,872
c. Road oil				1,273	7,000	45,500
d. Asphalt and road oil				20,984	112,918	748,372

(Footnotes on next page.)

TABLE G–12 (continued)

ᵃ Average annual expenditure derived from twenty-year (1965–84) estimates contained in *Needs of the Highway System, 1955–1984*, 84th Congress, 1st Session, House Doc. No. 120, March 28, 1955, Tables 4 and 5, respectively. As the first three years' actual consumption shows (Table G–15), these figures may be on the high side when translated into material requirements. It is assumed that these data, as those of the Bureau of Mines, refer to petroleum asphalt. In any event, other sources of asphalt are of negligible importance in the categories of road-building with which these data are concerned.

ᵇ At 5.5 barrels per ton.

ᶜ Assumed to be 85 per cent of total, with remainder representing payments for preliminary organizing, etc., and right-of-way. This assumption checks closely with the data contained in a preliminary estimate for 1962 costs, released by the U.S. Bureau of Public Roads on August 18, 1958, p. 2.

ᵈ From Roads, *Highway Construction Usage Factors for Cement, Bituminous, Concrete Pipe and Clay Pipe*, October 1958; weighted averages of 1955, 1956, and 1957.

ᵉ Derived from *Needs of the Highway System, 1955–1984, op. cit.*, on following reasoning:
(1) surface costs as per cent of maintenance costs: 48 (p. 24);
(2) surface costs as per cent of total highway construction costs: 35 (Table 3);
(3) assumed that 15 per cent of highway costs are not construction (footnote c above);
(4) surface costs as per cent of new construction costs: 41.18 (0.35 ÷ 0.85);
(5) ratio of surface costs in maintenance to new construction: 48 ÷ 41.18 = 1.166;
(6) tons of bituminous per million dollars of new construction: 1,567 (col. 3, item 1a); and
(7) tons of bituminous per million dollars of maintenance: 1,567 × 1.166 = 1,827.

ᶠ Assumed as 5 per cent of new highway construction, mainly as reminder of existence of this item. No information is available that would permit more factual projection.

ᵍ Arbitrarily assumed at this figure to stay at 1955 level (Table G–11, col. 1) but yield rounded number when converted to barrels.

ʰ Assumed at 50 per cent above the 1955 level (Table G–11), in accordance with projected increase over present level of households. Household numbers are projected to increase by 44.1 per cent (Appendix Table I–1). For the sake of simplicity, here a 50 per cent increase is assumed instead. This is done partly to reflect the long-run reduction in the role of wood shingles (BLS, *New Housing and Its Maintenance, 1940–1956*, Bulletin 1231, especially p. 29, Table 1), which is assumed to continue and would boost asphalt use per household. It is assumed that between 1955 and 1975 no material (such as coal tar) will be substituted for asphalt or vice versa.

ⁱ Assumed to increase modestly from 1955 (Table G–11). Round figure reflects arbitrary nature of this assumption.

ʲ Represents 97.7 per cent of the amount of asphalt shown, in order to allow for water and other materials included in the estimates as they are based on "bituminous material" rather than pure asphalt at the refinery level.

TABLE G–13. DEMAND FOR AND SALES OF ASPHALT AND
ROAD OIL, 1931–57

Year	Domestic demand at refinery level (thous. bbl.) a (1)	Asphalt Sales Thousand tons b (2)	Thousand barrels c (3)	Demand for road oil (thous. bbl.) a (4)
1957....................	88,973	16,373	90,052	7,123
1956....................	91,347	17,257	94,914	8,086
1955....................	84,286	15,680	86,240	8,356
1954....................	76,577	14,681	80,746	7,216
1953....................	72,208	14,042	77,231	6,610
1952....................	71,007	12,529	68,910	6,947
1951....................	66,179	11,701	64,356	6,095
1950....................	58,677	10,528	57,904	6,897
1949....................	49,362	8,921	49,066	7,826
1948....................	49,962	9,178	50,479	8,027
1947....................	47,023	8,735	48,043	7,067
1946....................	43,253	7,614	41,877	5,939
1945....................	38,350	6,851	37,681	2,505
1944....................	38,129	6,735	37,043	1,560
1943....................	36,404	6,898	37,939	2,450
1942....................	35,733	6,841	37,626	8,484
1941....................	35,485	6,229	34,260	8,980
1940....................	28,182	4,942	27,181	7,849
1939....................	27,093	4,826	26,543	7,846
1938....................	24,155	4,477	24,624	7,847
1937....................	21,876	4,032	22,176	7,954
1936....................	20,595	4,075	22,413	7,279
1935....................	15,652	3,143	17,287	5,962
1934....................	13,924	2,727	14,999	6,378
1933....................	11,808	2,424	13,338	5,266
1932....................	12,652	2,409	13,250	6,648
1931....................	14,729	2,873	15,802	5,078

a 1956–57: Mines, *Annual Petroleum Statement*, No. 434; 1952–55: Mines, *Minerals Yearbook, 1956*, Vol. II, p. 375; 1949–51: A.P.I., *Petroleum Facts and Figures, 1956*, p. 5; and 1931–48: *ibid., 1950*, pp. 1–2.

b 1956–57: Mines, *Mineral Market Report*, No. MMS 2779; 1955: *Minerals Yearbook, 1956, op. cit.*, p. 265; 1954: *ibid., 1955*, Vol. II, p. 265; 1953: *ibid., 1954*, Vol. II, p. 447; 1951–52: *ibid., 1952*, Vol. II, p. 262; and 1950: *ibid., 1951*, p. 179. 1931–49: *Petroleum Facts and Figures, 1950, op. cit.*, p. 79.

c Converted at 5.5 barrels per ton.

TABLE G-14. ASPHALT SALES BY TYPE OF USE, 1948-57

(Thousand tons)

Year	All uses[a]				Paving	
	Paving (1)	Roofing (2)	Other (3)	Total (4)	New construction[b] (5)	Maintenance and non-highway (1)−(5) (6)
1957.......	11,936	2,819	1,620	16,373	7,750	4,185
1956.......	12,208	3,411	1,639	17,257	6,760	5,448
1955.......	10,766	3,502	1,412	15,680	6,210	4,556
1954.......	9,968	3,250	1,462	14,681	5,090	4,878
1953.......	9,158	3,459	1,424	14,042	4,420	4,738
1952.......	8,808				4,300	4,508
1951.......	7,535				3,470	4,065
1950.......	6,540				3,010	3,530
1949.......	5,722				2,540	3,182
1948.......	5,569				2,780	2,789

[a] Mines. Figures for 1957 from *Mineral Market Report*, No. MMS 2779; 1955-56: *Minerals Yearbook, 1956*, Vol. II, pp. 261-63, 265; 1954: *ibid., 1955*, Vol. II, pp. 261-63, 265; 1953: *ibid., 1954*, Vol. II, pp. 444-47; 1952, *ibid., 1952*, Vol, II. p. 262; 1951: *ibid., 1951*, p. 179 (asphalt for paving, flux for paving, and rapid and medium curing cut-back asphalt); 1950: *ibid., 1950*, p. 151; 1949: *ibid., 1949*, p. 151; and 1948: *ibid., 1948*, p. 158.

[b] Roads, communication to the author.

TABLE G-15. REQUIREMENTS FOR BITUMINOUS MATERIALS IN HIGHWAY CONSTRUCTION, ESTIMATED 1955-69 AND ACTUAL 1955-57

(Million tons)

Year	Estimated[a]	Year	Estimated[a]
1969...................	8.77	1963...................	10.18
1968...................	9.34	1962...................	10.18
1967...................	10.18	1961...................	10.18
1966...................	10.18	1960...................	10.18
1965...................	10.18	1959...................	9.90
1964...................	10.18	1958...................	9.49

	Estimated[a]		Actual[b]
1957...................	8.73	1957...................	7.75
1956...................	7.15	1956...................	6.76
1955...................	5.85	1955...................	6.21

[a] Roads, Press release Comm.-DC-10077, July 25, 1956.

[b] Roads, Office of Engineering Construction and Maintenance Division, communication to the author, November 18, 1958.

TABLE G–16. RAW MATERIAL CONSUMPTION IN PRODUCTION OF CARBON BLACK, 1955

Raw material	Physical unit[a]	Billion Btu[b]
Natural gas (million cu. ft.)..................................	244,794	253,362
Liquid hydrocarbons (thous. bbl.).........................	5,264	33,605
Total..		286,967

[a] Mines, *Minerals Yearbook, 1956*, Vol. II, p. 273.

[b] Natural gas at 1,035 Btu per cu. ft. and liquid hydrocarbons at 6,384,000 Btu per barrel (the "residual No. 6" value). The category within which the oil sold for this purpose appears in the data is not clear. For the sake of simplicity, it has been assumed to be in the miscellaneous use of residual, but there is strong evidence that this is not a satisfactory resolution of the question.

TABLE G–17. CARBON BLACK PRODUCTION FROM NATURAL GAS AND LIQUID HYDROCARBONS, 1948–56

Year	Production from gas (tons) (1)	Production from liquid hydrocarbons (tons) (2)	Production from liquid hydrocarbons as per cent of production from gas (3)
1956..............	431,824	488,448	113.11%
1955..............	438,181	433,360	98.90
1954..............	408,161	296,670	72.68
1953..............	460,441	344,461	74.81
1952..............	528,652	273,682	51.77
1951..............	569,275	269,868	47.41
1950..............	527,945	162,638	30.81
1949..............	509,191	103,513	20.33
1948..............	579,178	69,277	11.96

NOTE: Derived by the application of yield factors and materials in Table G–18, as follows: col. 1 here = col. 1 × col. 3 of Table G–18 converted to tons; similarly, col. 2 here = col. 2 × col. 4 of Table G–18 converted to tons.

TABLE G–18. RAW MATERIALS USED IN PRODUCTION OF CARBON BLACK, 1948–56

Year	Gas used (mill. cu. ft.) (1)	Liquid hydro- carbons used (thous. gal.) (2)	Yield per thousand cubic feet of gas (lb.) (3)	Yield per gallon of liquid hydrocarbon (lb.) (4)
1956........	242,598	242,406	3.56	4.03
1955........	244,794	221,102	3.58	3.92
1954........	251,176	154,919	3.25	3.83
1953........	300,942	187,207	3.06	3.68
1952........	368,399	163,392	2.87	3.35
1951........	426,423	182,343	2.67	2.96
1950........	410,852	107,707	2.57	3.02
1949........	427,892	72,387	2.38	2.86
1948........	480,646	44,551	2.41	3.11

SOURCE: Mines. 1952–56—*Minerals Yearbook, 1956*, Vol. II, p. 273, Table 5; 1948–51— *ibid., 1952*, Vol. II, p. 272, Table 5.

TABLE G-19. SALES AND PRODUCTION OF CARBON BLACK, 1943-56

(Thousand pounds)

Year	Domestic sales[a] to						Exports[b] (7)	Total shipments[b] (8)	Total production[b] (9)
	Rubber (1)	Ink (2)	Paint (3)	Miscellaneous (4)	Other than rubber (2)+(3)+(4) (5)	Total (6)			
1956	1,244,651	42,047	13,231	3,100	58,378	1,303,029	425,328	1,728,357	1,839,968
1955	1,286,861	55,313	13,661	17,942	86,916	1,373,777	454,181	1,827,958	1,743,512
1954	1,023,626	48,797	7,681	15,152	71,630	1,095,256	402,777	1,498,033	1,409,547
1953	1,133,594	45,801	8,464	13,012	67,277	1,200,871	358,620	1,559,491	1,610,437
1952	1,074,545	44,116	10,628	24,985	79,729	1,154,274	292,908	1,447,182	1,604,102
1951	1,061,229	45,496	11,366	11,554	68,416	1,129,645	433,493	1,563,138	1,677,363
1950	1,030,368	50,903	11,139	16,661	78,703	1,109,071	399,568	1,508,639	1,381,990
1949	767,131	32,054	7,005	15,976	55,035	822,166	303,244	1,125,410	1,233,636
1948	870,564	32,436	6,799	22,634	61,869	932,433	321,915	1,254,348	1,297,729
1947	943,580	32,260	8,137	16,707		1,000,684	319,076	1,319,760	
1946	941,464	29,561	9,312	18,318		998,655	271,085	1,269,740	
1945	804,386	22,824	7,421	11,631		846,262	173,773	1,020,035	
1944	738,029	24,479	5,315	12,616		780,439	156,991	937,430	
1943	473,473	23,530	3,945	23,440		524,388	104,912	629,300	

[a] Mines. Figures for 1952–56: *Minerals Yearbook, 1956,* Vol. II, p. 275, Table 7; 1948–51: *ibid., 1952,* Vol. II, p. 273, Table 7; 1944–47: *ibid., 1948,* p. 207; and 1943: *ibid., 1947,* p. 194

[b] 1952–56: *ibid., 1956,* Vol. II, p. 269, Table 1; 1945–51: *ibid., 1952,* Vol. II, p. 268, Table 1; 1944–47: *ibid., 1948,* p. 200; and 1943: *ibid., 1947,* p. 194.

TABLE G–20. CONSUMPTION OF GAS AND LIQUID HYDROCARBONS
IN CARBON BLACK PRODUCTION, PROJECTION TO 1975

Item	1955	1975
Carbon black consumption by type of use (thous. tons) [a]		
1. Domestic:		
a. Rubber	643,430	1,409,834 [b]
b. Other uses	43,458	43,458 [c]
c. Total domestic	686,888	1,453,292
2. Exports	227,091	227,091 [d]
3. Total	913,979	1,680,383
Raw material consumption [e]		
4. Natural gas (mill. cu. ft.)	244,794	142,287 [f]
5. Liquid hydrocarbons (thous. bbl.)	5,264	17,319 [g]
Carbon black consumption by type of raw material (tons)		
6. From natural gas		254,694 [h]
7. From liquid hydrocarbons		1,425,689 [i]
Btu equivalent (*bill.*)		
9. Natural gas		147,267
10. Liquid hydrocarbons		110,564

[a] 1955: from Table G–19.

[b] Assumed to grow at 4 per cent per year, which is the approximate growth rate of recent years following 1950, see Table G–19, col. 1.

[c] Variations are too wide from year to year to ascertain a trend (Table G–19, col. 5).

[d] The expected quantity is taken to be unchanged because of the wide periodic variations which have taken place in the recent past. In part this is due to the postwar tendency for major importing countries to become carbon black producers. For example, carbon black production in the United Kingdom in 1951 was about 35 million pounds (Mines, *Minerals Yearbook, 1951*, p. 241), and its imports from the United States were about 101 million pounds (*ibid.*, p. 240). In 1955, its production was 170 million pounds (*ibid., 1956*, Vol. II, p. 279, Table 12) and its imports from the United States were less than 33 million pounds (*ibid.*, p. 278).

[e] 1955: from Table G–16.

[f] On the assumption that natural gas going to carbon black production will continue to decline, but at a lower rate than in the past (Table G–17). The recent rate is on the order of 5.5 per cent. Here it is assumed that the decline rate for the two decades will be 2.75 per cent per year.

[g] Item 7 divided by 1955 yield factor (Table G–18, col. 4).

[h] Item 4 multiplied by 1955 yield factor (Table G–18, col. 3) converted to tons.

[i] Difference between projected total (item 3) and amount derived from natural gas (item 6).

TABLE G-21.   DERIVATION OF MISCELLANEOUS GASOLINE
CONSUMPTION, 1955 AND PROJECTION TO 1975

Consumer	1955	1975
	(thousand barrels)	
Automobiles[a]	793,462	1,704,276
Trucks[b]	300,307	786,263
Buses, commercial[c]	7,750	3,875
Buses, other[d]	2,857	4,823
Motorcycles[e]	2,466	2,466
Aviation[f]	29,301	31,196
Marine[g]	696	1,000
Railroads[h]	8	9
Military[i]	91,452	117,966
Other government[j]	5,519	16,103
Agriculture[k]	87,278	129,690
Industrial, commercial, and construction[l]	10,179	10,179
Losses[m]	13,123	28,535
Total	1,344,398	2,836,381
Gasoline in jet fuel[n]	39,881	
Total gasoline, comparable with Bureau of Mines figure	1,304,517	
Bureau of Mines total, excluding naphtha[o]	1,310,053	
Difference between two totals:		
Miscellaneous	5,536	11,681[p]
Oil[q]	4,872	10,279
Natural gasoline[q]	664	1,402
	(billion Btu)	
Miscellaneous	28,831	60,835
Oil	25,373	53,533
Natural gasoline	3,458	7,302

[a] Appendix Tables D-20 and D-38.
[b] Appendix Tables D-16 and D-27.
[c] Appendix Tables D-15 and D-29.
[d] Appendix Tables D-17 and D-30.
[e] Appendix Table D-18.
[f] Appendix Tables D-46 and D-58.
[g] Appendix Table D-14.
[h] Appendix Tables D-4 and D-11.
[i] Appendix Table E-8.
[j] Appendix Table E-1.
[k] Appendix Table F-3.
[l] Roads, *Highway Statistics, 1955,* p. 7, Table G-24; assumed to be unchanged in 1975.
[m] Table G-1.
[n] Appendix Table E-8.
[o] Mines, *Minerals Yearbook, 1956,* Vol. II, p. 374; *ibid., 1955,* Vol. II, p. 382.

[p] Assumed to increase as total gasoline consumption, before calculating losses (which are based on total consumption, including miscellaneous, see Table G-1, footnote n).

[q] For allocation factor, see Appendix Table I-10.

Section H. Electricity

General Note

This section, dealing with electricity generation, its translation into energy sources, and their allocation to consuming sectors, has several distinct strands.

The backbone consists of sales by utilities to the various consuming sectors, in 1955 (Table H–1) and 1975 (Table H–11). Utility sales are related to power generation in Table H–2 for 1955 and H–16 for 1975. Finally, these amounts are translated into fuels, in Table H–8 for 1955 and in Table H–16 for 1975, the latter on the basis of assumptions contained and discussed in Tables H–15 and H–24 through H–26.

Power consumption of the Atomic Energy Commission in 1955 is treated separately in Tables H–3 and H–4. The simplifying assumption of no power generation by AEC in 1975 permits dispensing with a separate tabulation for that year; AEC is dealt with in a footnote to Table H–17.

The generation and disposition of non-utility power in 1955 is contained in Tables H–5 and H–6, and is supported by Table H–7 which develops the applicable fuel pattern and thermal efficiency. Tables H–12, H–13, and H–18 deal with non-utility generation in 1975; H–12 develops the projection rationale, H–13 contains the actual projection, and H–18 converts the results into fuels, on the basis of assumptions formulated in the table's footnotes.

All but two of the remaining tables are devoted to estimating electricity consumption, in terms of fuels, in that segment of industry which forms one of the groups in the industry sector: iron and steel, petroleum refining, and cement. Table H–10 does so for 1955, and Tables H–19 through H–23 for 1975.

Tables H–9 and H–17 present the summary, in terms of energy sources and consuming sectors for 1955 and 1975 respectively. It is these tables which provide the allocation, in the summary tables for consuming sectors, of fuels via electricity to the different activities.

Electricity Tables

H– 1. Electricity Sales by Utilities, 1955
H– 2. Electricity Entering Utility Systems, 1955 (Including Losses)
H– 3. Atomic Energy Commission Purchases from Utilities, 1955
H– 4. Amount and Disposition of Electricity Generated by AEC, 1955
H– 5. Non-Utility Generation and Disposition of Electricity, 1955
H– 6. Non-Utility Generation and Disposition of Electricity Other Than AEC, by Source of Energy, 1955
H– 7. Fuel Pattern and Heat Rates in Utility Systems, 1949

707

TABLE H–1. ELECTRICITY SALES BY UTILITIES, 1955 [a]

Item	Quantity sold (million kwh)	Per cent of total, excluding AEC
1. Households [b].	123,275	28.46%
2. Agriculture [c].	8,000	1.85
3. Commercial [d].	80,759	18.65
4. Industrial, [e] excl. AEC.	202,007	46.64
5. AEC [f].	47,199	
6. Street and highway lighting.	4,373	1.01
7. Other public authorities.	10,151	2.34
8. Railways [g].	4,563	1.05
9. Total.	480,327	
10. Total, excl. AEC.	433,128	100.00

[a] Data from E.E.I., *Statistical Bulletin for the Year 1957*, p. 21, or as otherwise indicated.
[b] Appendix Table C–19.
[c] Appendix Table F–2
[d] "Small light and power sales," see Appendix Table B–8.
[e] "Large light and power sales," see Appendix Table B–8.
[f] Appendix Table A–27.
[g] Appendix Table D–5, item 1.

TABLE H-2. ELECTRICITY ENTERING UTILITY SYSTEMS, 1955 (INCLUDING LOSSES)

Item	Total entering utility systems (mill. kwh) (1)	Fuels used in generation, in physical units				Btu input (billions)				
		Coal (thous. tons) (2)	Gas (mill. cu. ft.) (3)	Oil (thous. bbl.) (4)	From hydro-electric stations (mill. kwh) (5)	Coal (6)	Gas (7)	Oil (8)	Hydro (9)	Total (10)
1. Utility generation	547,038 a	143,759 b	1,153,280 b	75,274 b	112,975 b	3,464,017 c	1,160,200 c	475,889 c	1,327,421 d	6,427,527
2. Purchases by utilities										
a. From industrial generation e	5,622	2,249	14,738	1,777	238	53,977	14,738	11,197	3,526	83,438
b. From AEC generation f	415	23	4,257			543	4,257			4,800
c. Net imports g	4,068				4,068				47,798 d	47,798
3. Total	557,143	146,031	1,172,275	77,051	117,281	3,518,537	1,179,195	487,086	1,378,745	6,563,563
4. Sales to AEC in terms of equivalent generated electricity h	49,559	19,311			2,025	463,457			23,793	487,250
5. Total, excluding AEC purchases	507,584	126,720	1,172,275	77,051	115,256	3,055,080	1,179,195	487,086	1,354,952	6,076,313

a E.E.I., *Statistical Bulletin for the Year 1957*, p. 14. Includes 277 million kwh generated with wood and wood waste which are here ignored.

b *Ibid.*, p. 47, Table 40.

c Obtained by applying the Btu factors listed for 1955 in *ibid.*, p. 48; Table 41: 24,096,000 Btu per ton of coal; 1,006 Btu per cubic foot of gas; and 6,322,092 Btu per barrel of oil. These differ from the factors in Appendix Table I-11; they are the Btu values given by E.E.I. for fuel actually consumed at central stations.

d Equivalent Btu per kwh assumed to be those of total thermal utility generation (ignoring wood and wood waste item), i.e., Btu's consumed in thermal generation (cols. 6 + 7 + 8) divided by thermal generation (cols. 1 − 5), or 5,100,106 million kwh, equal to 11,750 Btu per kwh.

e Table H-6.

f Table H-4.

g *Statistical Bulletin for the Year 1957, op. cit.*, p. 13.

h Table H-3.

TABLE H-3. ATOMIC ENERGY COMMISSION PURCHASES FROM UTILITIES, 1955

Item	Amount and per cent
1. Total purchases (mill. kwh) [a]	47,199
2. Of which: hydro purchased by Hanford (mill. kwh) [a]	1,328
3. Of which: hydro purchased by other AEC installations (mill. kwh) [b]	600
4. Remainder: thermal (mill. kwh)	45,271
5. Thermal: transmission and other losses [c]	5%
6. Thermal: generation required (mill. kwh) (item 4 $\times$ 1.05)	47,534
7. Assumed heat rate (Btu per kwh) [d]	9,750
8. Btu's required for thermal generation (bill.)	463,457
9. Coal equivalent (thous. tons)	19,311
10. Hydro purchases (mill. kwh) (item 2 + item 3)	1,928
11. Hydro: transmission and other losses [c]	5%
12. Hydro: generation required (mill. kwh) (item 11 $\times$ 1.05)	2,025
13. Hydro: assumed equivalent heat rate [e]	11,750
14. Equivalent Btu's required for hydro generation (bill.)	23,793
15. Total generation required (mill. kwh) (item 6 + item 12)	49,559
16. Total generation required (bill. Btu) (item 8 + item 14)	487,250

[a] Appendix Table A-27.

[b] Derived from data furnished by AEC.

[c] Assumed on basis of practical absence of distribution losses.

[d] All generation assumed to be coal, on basis of stations listed in Appendix Table A-27. Heat rate estimated similarly, which for these stations is better than average.

[e] Equivalent heat rate assumed is that of over-all utility generation in 1955, see Table H-2, footnote d.

TABLE H-4. AMOUNT AND DISPOSITION OF ELECTRICITY GENERATED BY AEC, 1955

Item	Generated			Sold Oak Ridge only (4)	Retained Savannah River and Oak Ridge (5)
	Savannah River (1)	Oak Ridge (2)	Savannah River and Oak Ridge (3)		
1. Kilowatt hours (mill.)	1,183	2,138	3,321	415	2,906
2. Coal consumed (thous. tons)	518	116	634	23	613
3. Coal consumed (bill. Btu)	12,451	2,797	15,248	543	14,705
4. Gas consumed (mill. cu. ft.)		21,944	21,944	4,257	17,687
5. Gas consumed (bill. Btu)		21,944	21,944	4,257	17,687
6. Total Btu consumed (bill.)	12,451	24,741	37,192	4,800	32,392
7. Btu per kwh, total	10,525	11,570	11,198		

SOURCE: Communication from Atomic Energy Commission.

TABLE H–5. NON-UTILITY GENERATION AND DISPOSITION
OF ELECTRICITY, 1955

(Million kwh)

Item	Generated (1)	Sold to utilities (2)	Retained or sold within same consumer category (3)
1. Total..............................	81,972 [a]		
2. Transit system [b].....................	1,480		1,480
3. Total, excl. transit.................	80,492	6,037 [c]	74,455
4. AEC [d].............................	3,321	415	2,906
5. Total, excl. transit and AEC.........	77,171	5,622	71,549

[a] E.E.I., *Statistical Bulletin for the Year 1957*, p. 13.
[b] ATA, *Transit Fact Book, 1957 Edition*, p. 11, Table 14.
[c] Sales assumed to be 7.5 per cent of industrial generation, exclusive of transit generation. Total sales by industrial generators are larger than here shown, but include sales to non-utility consumers. It is here assumed that all such sales are within industry. For derivation of 7.5 per cent assumption see Appendix Table B–8, footnote d.
[d] Table H–4, item 1.

TABLE H–6. NON-UTILITY GENERATION AND DISPOSITION OF
ELECTRICITY OTHER THAN AEC, BY SOURCE OF ENERGY, 1955 [a]

Item	Total (1)	Hydro (2)	Thermal (3)	Coal (4)	Gas (5)	Oil (6)
1. Transit generation, all retained						
Million kwh [b].....	1,480		1,480	1,480		
Btu per kwh [c].....	14,871.1		14,871.1	14,871.1		
Billion Btu.......	22,009		22,009	22,009		
Physical units.....				917		
2. All other, generation						
Million kwh [d].....	77,171	3,261	73,910	49,823	13,607	10,480
Btu per kwh [c].....			14,841.4	14,871.1	14,868.1	14,665.8
Billion Btu.......	1,145,329	48,398	1,096,931	740,923	202,310	153,698
Physical units.....				30,872	202,310	24,397
3. All other, sales to utilities [e]						
Million kwh......	5,622	238				
Billion Btu.......	83,438	3,526	79,906	53,977	14,738	11,197
Physical units.....				2,249	14,738	1,777
4. All other, generated and retained [f]						
Million kwh......	71,549	3,023				
Billion Btu.......	1,061,891	44,866	1,017,025	686,941	187,576	142,508
Physical units.....				28,623	187,576	22,620
5. Iron and steel, petroleum refining, and cement, generated [g]						
Million kwh......	21,395		21,395	14,422	3,938	3,033
Btu per kwh......			14,841.4	14,871.1	14,868.1	14,665.8
Billion Btu.......	317,532		317,532	214,477	58,560	44,493
Physical units.....				8,937	58,560	7,060
6. General industrial group, generated [h]						
Million kwh......	55,776	3,261	52,515	35,400	9,668	7,446
Billion Btu.......	827,797	48,398	779,399	526,446	143,740	109,205
Physical units.....				21,935	143,740	17,330

(Footnotes on next page.)

TABLE H–6 (continued)

ᵃ Physical units as follows: coal, thousands of tons; gas, millions of cubic feet; and oil, thousands of barrels.

Btu conversions as follows: coal, 24 million per ton; gas, 1,000 per cubic foot; and oil, 6,300,000 per barrel.

ᵇ Table H–5, item 2.

ᶜ Heat rate (Btu per kwh) assumed to exceed that of utility systems by 25 per cent; this is about the improvement in fuel efficiency in utility generation between 1949 and 1955, so that the 1949 utility pattern may be used to estimate the 1955 non-utility fuel quantity and composition. The average 1949 thermal rate was used to convert hydro-generated electricity to Btu's (Table H–7, col. 5).

ᵈ Total from Table H–5, item 5, col. 1; hydro generation from Commerce, *Statistical Abstract of the United States, 1957*, p. 527, Table No. 656; fuel distribution based on working assumption that it lagged the equivalent of six years behind that of utilities. Thus, the 1949 utility pattern, as developed in Table H–7, col. 1, was applied to col. 3 of this table to obtain cols. 4, 5, and 6.

ᵉ Total kwh from Table H–5. All Btu and quantity allocations to energy sources in same proportions as for total generation (item 2, above).

ᶠ Derived as difference between generation and sales.

ᵍ Total kwh from Table H–10; attributed to different fuels in same proportion and at same heat rates as prevail in item 2, but assuming no hydro generation. See discussion of industry estimates—other than electricity consumption—in Chapter 5, pp. 205–06 for reasons for separating out specific industries.

ʰ Obtained as difference between items 2 and 5.

NOTE: Parts do not necessarily add to totals because of rounding.

TABLE H–7.   FUEL PATTERN AND HEAT RATES IN UTILITY SYSTEMS, 1949

Fuel	Relative share in generation (per cent) (1)	Physical units ᵃ (2)	Equivalent Btu's (billion) (3)	Electricity generated (billion kwh) (4)	Heat rate (Btu per kwh) (5)
Coal...............	67.41%	83.96	2,015,040	135.5	14,871.1
Gas...............	18.41	550,120	550,120	37.0	14,868.1
Oil...............	14.18	66.30	417,690	28.5	14,665.8
Total.............	100.00%		2,982,850	201.0	14,841.4

ᵃ Coal: million tons; gas: million cubic feet; oil: million barrels.

SOURCE: *Electrical World*, January 28, 1957, p. 137.

TABLE H-8. SHARES OF CONSUMING SECTORS IN DISTRIBUTION OF UTILITY ELECTRICITY, 1955 [a]

Consuming sector	Utility generation (mill. kwh) (1)	Physical units				Energy source				
		Coal (thous. tons) (2)	Gas (mill. cu. ft.) (3)	Oil (thous. bbl.) (4)	Hydro (mill. kwh) (5)	Coal (6)	Gas (7)	Oil (8)	Hydro (9)	Total (10)
							Billion Btu			
1. Total[b]	557,143	146,031	1,172,275	77,051	117,281	3,518,537	1,179,195	487,086	1,378,745	6,563,563
2. AEC[c]	49,559	19,311			2,025	463,457			23,793	487,250
3. Total, excluding AEC[d]	507,584	126,720	1,172,275	77,051	115,256	3,055,080	1,179,195	487,086	1,354,952	6,076,313
4. Households	144,466	36,066	333,648	21,930	32,804	869,523	335,627	138,632	385,640	1,729,413
5. Agriculture	9,375	2,341	21,652	1,423	2,129	56,428	21,780	8,997	25,026	112,231
6. Commercial	94,642	23,628	218,577	14,367	21,490	569,636	219,867	90,820	252,638	1,132,961
7. Industrial	236,733	59,101	546,739	35,936	53,754	1,424,862	549,966	227,173	631,937	2,833,938
8. Street and highway lighting	5,125	1,279	11,836	778	1,164	30,845	11,906	4,918	13,680	61,348
9. Other public authorities	11,896	2,970	27,473	1,806	2,701	71,599	27,636	11,415	31,755	142,404
10. Railroads and railways	5,347	1,335	12,350	812	1,214	32,185	12,423	5,131	14,274	64,014

a Kilowatt hours, fuel, and Btu allocation to item 4 through item 10 are based upon the relative share of each consuming sector, other than AEC, in total electricity sales by utilities excluding AEC; consequently the percentages of Table H-1 are applied to item 3 to yield item 4 through item 10.

b Table H-2, item 3.

c Table H-3.

d Table H-2, item 5.

TABLE H-9. SHARES OF CONSUMING SECTORS IN DISTRIBUTION OF UTILITY AND NON-UTILITY ELECTRICITY, 1955

Consuming sector	Utility and non-utility generation		Energy sources							
			Coal		Gas		Oil		Hydro	
	Million kwh (1)	Billion Btu (2)	Thousand tons (3)	Billion Btu (4)	Million cu. ft. (5)	Billion Btu (6)	Thousand barrels (7)	Billion Btu (8)	Million kwh (9)	Billion Btu (10)
1. Households[a]	144,466	1,729,413	36,066	869,523	333,648	335,617	21,930	138,632	32,804	385,640
2. Agriculture (irrigating and pumping)[a]	9,375	112,231	2,341	56,428	21,652	21,780	1,423	8,997	2,129	25,026
3. Commercial[a]	94,642	1,132,961	23,628	569,636	218,577	219,867	14,367	90,820	21,490	252,638
4. Industry:										
a. From utilities[a]	236,733	2,833,938	59,101	1,424,862	546,739	549,966	35,936	227,173	53,754	631,937
b. Generated and retained[b]	71,549	1,061,891	28,623	686,941	187,576	187,576	22,620	142,508	3,023	44,866
5. AEC:										
a. From utilities[a]	49,559	487,250	19,311	463,457					2,025	23,793
b. Generated and retained[c]	2,906	32,392	613	14,705	17,687	17,687				
6. Railroad and street transportation:										
a. From utilities[a]	5,347	64,014	1,335	32,185	12,350	12,423	812	5,131	1,214	14,274
b. Generated and retained[b]	1,480	22,009	917	22,009						
7. Street and highway lighting[a]	5,125	61,348	1,279	30,845	11,836	11,906	778	4,918	1,164	13,680
8. Other public authorities[a]	11,896	142,404	2,970	71,599	27,473	27,636	1,806	11,415	2,701	31,755
9. Total	633,078	7,679,855	176,184	4,242,192	1,377,538	1,384,458	99,671	629,594	120,304	1,423,611

[a] From Table H-8.
[b] From Table H-6.
[c] From Table H-4.

TABLE H–10. DERIVATION OF ELECTRICITY GENERATION IN IRON AND STEEL, PETROLEUM REFINING, AND CEMENT INDUSTRIES, 1955

Item	Amount
Iron and steel	
1. Generated and used, American Iron and Steel Institue,[a] 1955	11,610 million kwh
2. Generated and used, American Iron and Steel Institute,[a] 1954	10,280 million kwh
3. Generated, blast furnaces and steel mills, 1954 Census[b]	12,997 million kwh
4. Generated, iron and steel foundries, 1954 Census[b]	69 million kwh
5. Total generated, 1954 Census	13,066 million kwh
6. Sales, 1954 Census[b]	3,301 million kwh
7. Generated and used, 1954 Census	9,765 million kwh
8. Generation (item 5) as per cent of generation used (item 2)	About 125%
9. 1955 American Iron and Steel Institute figure adjusted to reflect sales (item 1 × item 8)	14,592 million kwh
Petroleum refining	
10. Runs-to-stills[c]	2,730,218 thousand bbl.
11. Ratio between electricity generated and runs-to-stills[d]	1.6 kwh per bbl.
12. Estimated 1955 generated electricity	4,368 million kwh
Cement	
13. Electricity generated[e]	2,435 million kwh
14. Total, three industries	21,395 million kwh

[a] AISI, *Annual Statistical Report, 1956*, p. 23.

[b] Census, *Census of Manufactures, 1954*, Vol. I, *Summary Statistics*, p. 208–15.

[c] Mines, *Minerals Yearbook, 1956*, Vol. II, p. 322.

[d] Assumed on basis of 1954 Census and trend considerations. See Table H–21.

[e] *Minerals Yearbook, 1956, op. cit.*, Vol. I, p. 308. No correction made for inclusion of Puerto Rico in this figure.

TABLE H–11. ELECTRICITY PURCHASES FROM UTILITIES BY CONSUMING SECTORS AND UTILITY INPUT BY SUPPLIER CATEGORIES, PROJECTION TO 1975

Item	1975 purchases from utility system	
	Million kwh	Per cent of total
1. Households[a]...................................	416,803	27.9%
2. Agriculture[b]..................................	12,100	.8
3. Commercial[c].................................	269,055	18.0
4. Industry, excl. AEC[d].........................	738,869	49.5
5. Transportation[e]..............................	4,822	.3
6. Street and highway lighting[f]....................	16,922	1.1
7. Other public authorities[f].......................	35,768	2.4
8. Total, excl. AEC..............................	1,494,339	100.0
9. AEC[f].......................................	55,000	
10. Total, incl. AEC..............................	1,549,339	
11. Losses and unaccounted for[g]....................	259,776	
12. Utility input required (item 10 + item 11).........	1,809,115	
a. From industry[h]...........................	12,682	
b. From imports[i]............................	5,000	
c. Balance from utility generation...............	1,791,433	

[a] Appendix Table C–38.

[b] Appendix Table F–2.

[c] Appendix Table B–7.

[d] Total consumption from Appendix Tables A–32, A–35, and A–36, minus electricity generated and retained from Table H–13.

[e] Appendix Table D–11, col. 3, plus Appendix Table D–44.

[f] Appendix Table E–1.

[g] Assumed to be same as in 1955, i.e., 17.2 per cent (derived from Table H–1, item 10, and Table H–2, item 5) for total utility sales and total utility input, both net of AEC, and 5 per cent of consumption for AEC.

[h] Table H–13.

[i] Arbitrarily assumed to have increased from approximately 4,000 in 1955.

TABLE H-12. RELATIONSHIP BETWEEN NON-UTILITY GENERATION OF ELECTRICITY AND THE FEDERAL RESERVE BOARD INDEX OF INDUSTRIAL PRODUCTION, 1926–56

Year	Generation (million kwh)		AEC[b] (3)	Industrial generation net of transit and AEC (1) − (2) − (3) (4)	FRB index of industrial production (1947–49 = 100)[c] (5)	Million kwh per point of index (4) ÷ (5) (6)	Electricity generated in aluminum production[d] (mill. kwh) (7)	Non-utility generation net of transit, AEC, and aluminum self-generation (4) − (7) (8)	Million kwh per point of index, adjusted for generation in aluminum industry (8) ÷ (9) (9)
	Industrial[a] (1)	Transit[a] (2)							
1956	84,136	1,450	2,921	79,815	143	558			
1955	81,972	1,480	3,321	77,171	139	555			
1954	72,959	1,510	3,218	68,231	125	546	9,241	58,990	472
1953	71,504	1,590	2,543	67,371	134	503			
1952	63,831	1,770	2,065	59,996	124	484			
1951	62,685	1,870	2,158	58,657	120	489			
1950	59,533	2,070	1,689	55,774	112	498			
1949	53,966	2,123	1,326	50,517	97	521			
1948	54,110	2,113	1,541	50,456	104	485			
1947	51,661	2,093	1,478	48,090	100	481	1,074	47,016	470
1946	46,431	2,077	1,319	43,035	90	478			
1945	48,769	2,130	1,072	45,567	107	426			
1944	51,336	2,238	408	48,690	125	390			
1943	49,781	2,237		47,544	127	374			
1942	47,167	2,227		44,940	106	424			
1941	43,518	2,167		41,351	87	475			
1940	38,070	2,255		35,815	67	535			
1939	33,666	2,164		31,502	58	543			
1938	28,143	2,114		26,029	48	542			
1937	27,563	2,197		25,366	61	416			
1936	26,690	2,271		24,419	56	436	2,241	22,178	396

(*Table continued on next page.*)

TABLE H-12 (continued)

Year	Generation (million kwh) Industrial[a] (1)	Transit[a] (2)	AEC[b] (3)	Industrial generation net of transit and AEC (1) − (2) − (3) (4)	FRB index of industrial production (1947–49 = 100)[c] (5)	Million kwh per point of index (4) ÷ (5) (6)	Electricity generated in aluminum production[d] (mill. kwh) (7)	Non-utility generation net of transit, AEC, and aluminum self-generation (4) − (7) (8)	Million kwh per point of index, adjusted for generation in aluminum industry (8) ÷ (5) (9)
1935...	23,648	2,309		21,339	47	454	1,565	19,774	421
1934...	23,146	2,352		20,794	40	520	1,351	19,443	486
1933...	20,915	2,377		18,538	37	501	1,334	17,204	465
1932...	19,966	2,433		17,533	31	566	1,239	16,294	526
1931...	22,023	2,621		19,402	40	485	1,570	17,832	446
1930...	23,525	2,770		20,755	49	424	1,824	18,931	386
1929...	24,567	2,863		21,704	59	368	1,943	19,761	335
1928...	25,275	2,935		22,340	53	422	1,715	20,625	389
1927...	25,972	2,976		22,996	51	451	1,282	21,714	426
1926...	24,869	3,108		21,761	51	427	1,190	20,571	403

[a] Appendix Table B–8.

[b] Appendix Table A–27.

[c] Federal Reserve Bulletin, August 1958, p. 972.

[d] Census, Census of Manufactures, 1954, Vol. I, Summary Statistics, p. 208–15; Census of Manufactures, 1947, General Summary, p. 213 (includes primary zinc); and 1926–36—Nathanael Engle, Homer E. Gregory, and Robert Mossé, Aluminum (Chicago: Richard D. Irwin, Inc., 1945), p. 94.

TABLE H-13. GENERATION OF ELECTRICITY BY INDUSTRY AND
ITS DISPOSITION, PROJECTION TO 1975

(Million kilowatt hours)

Electricity	Total	Hydro
1955 generation, net of AEC and transit [a]	77,171	3,261
1975 generation, at assumed growth of 4 per cent per year [b]	169,091	3,000 [c]
Iron and steel, petroleum refining, and cement [d]	42,838	
General industrial group	126,253	3,000 [e]
Sales to utilities [f]	12,682	225
Retained for own use	156,409	2,775

[a] Table H-6.

[b] On basis of parallel movements shown in Table H-12; this holds true even when a component that has shown recent rapid growth—aluminum—is eliminated (cols. 8 and 9).

[c] Assumed to decline from 1955 level, in accordance with recent experience (Commerce, *Statistical Abstract of the United States, 1957*, p. 527, Table 656).

[d] Table H-19.

[e] Assumed to be generated only in general industrial group as in 1955 (Table H-6).

[f] Assumed to remain at 1955 ratio of 7.5 per cent of generation as used in Appendix Table B-8 and Table H-5.

TABLE H-14. UTILIZATION OF HYDRO POWER, 1930, 1935, AND 1940-56

Year	Kwh generated		Hydro generation as per cent of total generation [c] (3)
	Per kw installed [a] (1)	As plant capacity factor [b] (2)	
1956	4,818	55.0%	20.3%
1955	4,686	53.5	20.6
1954	4,732	54.0	22.7
1953	4,956	56.6	23.8
1952	5,350	61.1	26.3
1951	5,459	62.3	26.9
1950	5,589	63.8	29.1
1949	5,556	63.4	30.8
1948	5,386	61.5	29.2
1947	5,260	60.0	30.7
1946	5,269	60.1	35.1
1945	5,422	61.9	35.9
1944	5,195	59.3	32.4
1943	5,510	62.9	33.8
1942	5,180	59.1	34.3
1941	4,415	50.4	30.9
1940	4,258	48.6	33.4
1935	4,094	46.7	40.3
1930	3,804	43.4	34.2

[a] E.E.I., 1945-56, *Statistical Summary for the Year 1957*, p. 16, Table 10; remaining years from *ibid.*, *1954*, p. 16, Table 10.

[b] Col. 1 as percentage of 8,760 kwh (100 per cent operation).

[c] *Statistical Summary for the Year 1957*, *op. cit.*, p. 17, Table 11; and *ibid.*, *1954*, p. 17, Table 11.

TABLE H-15. SHARE OF FUELS IN UTILITY THERMAL GENERATION OF ELECTRICITY, 1922-56[a] AND PROJECTIONS TO 1975

Year	Per cent of thermal			
	Coal (1)	Gas (2)	Oil (3)	Nuclear (4)
1975:				
RFF[b]	74.0%	20.0%	6.0%	
PMPC[c]	72.7	13.6	13.6	
Sporn[d]	74.3	11.4	5.7	8.6%
Black[e]	76.3	14.7	4.8	4.2
Elec. World[f]	75.5	14.1	6.5	3.8
1956	70.8	21.7	7.5	
1955	69.5	21.9	8.6	
1954	65.6	25.7	8.7	
1953	65.0	23.6	11.4	
1952	66.6	23.3	10.1	
1951	68.5	20.9	10.6	
1950	66.4	19.2	14.4	
1949	67.5	18.3	14.2	
1948	76.6	15.1	8.3	
1947	77.5	13.0	9.5	
1946	77.3	13.0	9.7	
1945	80.6	13.9	5.5	
1944	80.8	14.0	5.2	
1943	82.9	12.4	4.7	
1942	83.8	11.6	4.6	
1941	82.8	10.6	6.6	
1940	81.8	11.6	6.6	
1937	80.3	13.2	6.5	
1932	81.2	13.2	5.6	
1927	90.0	6.1	3.9	
1922	87.8	2.9	9.3	

[a] *E.E.I. Pocketbook of Electric Industry Statistics,* 1957 edition, p. 25.

[b] The shares assumed in this study are based broadly on past trends and on a study of other projections. Since there is no provision for nuclear power generation, as in other studies, the percentage shares necessarily differ. The principal difference in emphasis is a judgment that the share of gas will not substantially diminish in the next two decades.

[c] PMPC, *Resources for Freedom,* Vol. III, "The Outlook for Energy Sources," June 1952, p. 36.

[d] Philip Sporn, "Electric Power in Peace and in Defense," exhibits in connection with a talk before the Industrial College of the Armed Forces, Washington, D. C., February 7, 1957, figure (d)-5.

[e] Fischer S. Black, "The Outlook for Electric Utilities," address to the New York Society of Security Analysts, New York City, February 5, 1958.

[f] *Electrical World,* June 9, 1958, p. 108.

TABLE H–16.   ENERGY SOURCES OF ELECTRICITY GENERATED
BY UTILITIES AND PURCHASED BY UTILITIES FROM NON-UTILITY
GENERATION AND IMPORTS, ESTIMATED 1975

Energy sources	Million kwh (1)	Billion Btu[a] (2)	Physical units[a] (3)
All fuels and hydro:[b]			
From non-utilities....................	12,682	146,792	
From utilities........................	1,791,433	16,050,710	
Net imports.........................	5,000	44,770	
Total.............................	1,809,115	16,242,272	
Hydro generation:[c]			
From non-utilities....................	225	2,604	
From utilities........................	257,000	2,301,178	
Net imports.........................	5,000	44,770	
Total.............................	262,225	2,348,552	
Coal (thous. tons):			
From non-utilities[d]..................	8,346	96,606	4,025
From utilities........................	1,135,480[e]	10,229,539	426,231
Total.............................	1,143,826	10,326,145	430,256
Gas (mill. cu. ft.):			
From non-utilities[d]..................	2,242	25,953	25,953
From utilities........................	306,887[e]	2,608,540	2,608,540
Total.............................	309,129	2,634,493	2,634,493
Oil (thous. bbl.):			
From non-utilities[d]..................	1,869	21,629	3,433
From utilities........................	92,066[e]	911,453	144,675
Total.............................	93,935	933,082	148,108

[a] For non-utilities from Table H–18; for utilities and imports computed on basis of Btu's per kwh and Btu's per physical unit as per Table H–24.

[b] Kilowatt hours from Table H–11; Btu's and physical quantities summed from individual energy source portions below.

[c] Utility kwh based upon installed capacity of 65 million kw by 1975 (see Chapter 11), operating at 45 per cent plant capacity factor, or somewhat lower than in recent years, in view of the declining trend (Table H–14), the expectation that perhaps 10 per cent of capacity will be pump-storage capacity, and that hydro capacity will be increasingly developed for peaking rather than for base-load generation. The resulting generation was rounded to 260 billion kwh, including industrial generation of 3 billion kwh (Table H–13). On this assumption, utility hydro generation will drop from 20.6 per cent in 1955 (Table H–14) to 14.3 per cent of all utility generation in 1975. Imports from Table H–11 and non-utility purchases from Table H–18. Non-utility: Table H–13. Imports assumed to rise 25 per cent above 1955.

[d] From Table H–18.

[e] Derived from total utility above minus hydro portion, in proportion to assumed fuel shares shown in Table H–15 for 1975.

TABLE H-17. SHARES IN ELECTRICITY CONSUMPTION, INCLUDING LOSSES, OF CONSUMING SECTORS, BY TYPE OF ENERGY SOURCE, 1975ᵃ

Item	Percentage distribution of purchase from utilitiesᵇ (1)	Million kwh (2)	Coal		Gas		Oil		Hydro	
			Thousand tons (3)	Billion Btu (4)	Million cu. ft. (5)	Billion Btu (6)	Thousand bbl. (7)	Billion Btu (8)	Million kwh (9)	Billion Btu (10)
1. Total utility sales (incl. losses)ᶜ		1,809,115	430,256	10,326,145	2,634,493	2,634,493	148,108	933,082	262,225	2,348,552
2. AECᵈ		57,750	19,881	477,139	23,694	23,694			2,000	17,908
3. Total utility sales (incl. losses), excl. AEC	100.0%	1,751,365	410,375	9,849,006	2,610,799	2,610,799	148,108	933,082	260,225	2,330,644
4. Households	27.9	488,631	114,495	2,747,873	728,413	728,413	41,322	260,330	72,603	650,250
5. Agriculture	.8	14,011	3,283	78,792	20,886	20,886	1,185	7,465	2,082	18,645
6. Commercial	18.0	315,246	73,868	1,772,821	469,944	469,944	26,659	167,955	46,840	419,516
7. Industry	49.5	866,926	203,136	4,875,258	1,292,346	1,292,346	73,313	461,876	128,811	1,153,669
8. Transportation	.3	5,254	1,231	29,547	7,832	7,832	444	2,799	781	6,992
9. Street and highway lighting	1.1	19,265	4,514	108,339	28,719	28,719	1,629	10,264	2,862	25,637
10. Other public authorities	2.4	42,033	9,849	236,376	62,659	62,659	3,555	22,394	6,245	55,935
11. Industry consumption, purchased and self-generated:										
a. Generated and retainedᵉ		156,409	49,645	1,191,471	320,093	320,093	42,342	266,751	2,775	32,121
b. From utilities		866,926	203,136	4,875,258	1,292,346	1,292,346	73,313	461,876	128,811	1,153,669
c. Total industry		1,023,335	252,781	6,066,729	1,612,439	1,612,439	115,655	728,627	131,586	1,185,790
12. Grand total, utility and non-utility		1,965,524	479,901	11,517,616	2,954,586	2,954,586	190,450	1,199,833	265,000	2,380,673

ᵃ Figures for individual consuming sectors, other than AEC (see footnote d) are derived by applying the percentage distribution shown in col. 1 to item 3.

ᵇ Table H-11.

ᶜ Table H-16.

ᵈ 1975 consumption and losses as per Table H-11. Distributed to energy sources on assumption that hydro generation will stay around 2 billion kwh, that there will be no oil-fired steam generation and that, of the balance, 95 per cent will be coal and 5 per cent gas-fired. These relationships are simply rounded figures derived from the 1955 fuel pattern of AEC utility purchases (Table H-3). Heat rates are assumed to be those of the utility system as a whole (Table H-24).

ᵉ Table H-18.

TABLE H-18. GENERATION OF ELECTRICITY BY INDUSTRY AND ITS DISPOSITION, BY SOURCE OF ENERGY, PROJECTION TO 1975

Item	All energy sources (1)	Hydro (2)	Thermal (3)	Coal (4)	Gas (5)	Oil (6)
1. Fuel composition of thermal generation (per cent)[a]			100	67	18	15
2. Btu per kwh[b]	11,575	11,575	11,575	11,575	11,575	11,575
3. All industry:						
a. Generation (mill. kwh)[c]	169,091	3,000	166,091	111,281	29,896	24,914
b. Billion Btu	1,957,228	34,725	1,922,503	1,288,077	346,046	288,380
c. Physical units		3,000		53,670	346,046	45,775
4. Iron and steel, petroleum refining and cement:[d]						
a. Generation (mill. kwh)	42,838		42,838	28,701	7,711	6,426
b. Billion Btu	495,850		495,850	332,214	89,255	74,381
c. Physical units				13,842	89,255	11,807
5. General industrial group:[e]						
a. Generation (mill. kwh)	126,253	3,000	123,253	82,580	22,185	18,488
b. Billion Btu	1,461,378	34,725	1,426,653	955,863	256,791	213,999
c. Physical units		3,000		39,828	256,791	33,968
6. Sales to utilities:[f]						
a. Million kwh	12,682	225	12,457	8,346	2,242	1,869
b. Billion Btu	146,792	2,604	144,188	96,606	25,953	21,629
c. Physical units		225		4,025	25,953	3,433
7. Retained for use within industry:[g]						
a. Million kwh	156,409	2,775	153,634	102,935	27,654	23,045
b. Billion Btu	1,810,436	32,121	1,778,315	1,191,471	320,093	266,751
c. Physical units		2,775		49,645	320,093	42,342

[a] No essential change assumed in fuel composition between 1955 and 1975. Therefore the percentages are those developed in Table H-7, rounded to give slightly increased emphasis to oil.

[b] For sake of simplicity, identical efficiencies are assumed for all fuels. The 1975 heat rate is estimated by assuming an annual improvement of 1.25 per cent in fuel efficiency over the 1955 rate for industry, excluding transit, of 14,871 Btu per kwh, as found in Table H-6.

[c] Total and hydro generation from Table H-13. All other figures derived on basis of items 1 and 2 and Btu content of fuels.

[d] Total generation from Table H-19.

[e] Derived as difference between preceding two groups.

[f] 7.5 per cent of generation, as per Appendix Table B-8 and Table H-5.

[g] Obtained as difference between "all industry" and "sales to utilities."

NOTE: Physical units are: coal, thousand tons; gas, million cubic feet; oil, thousand barrels; hydro, million kilowatthour.

TABLE H-19. GENERATION OF ELECTRICITY IN THE IRON AND STEEL, PETROLEUM REFINING, AND CEMENT INDUSTRIES, 1955 AND PROJECTION TO 1975

(Million kwh)

Industry	Generation of electricity		
	1955[a]	Assumed increase	1975
Iron and steel.....................	14,592	105.58%[b]	29,998
Petroleum refining.................	4,368	143.58[c]	10,640
Cement...........................	2,435		2,200[d]
Total...........................	21,395		42,838

[a] Table H-10.

[b] Equals increase in steel production (Appendix Table A-11). As shown in Table H-20, electricity generated and used—assumed to represent adequately electricity generated—shows no trend compared to production. On this basis, no change has been assumed in the period through 1975. As a 1.25 per cent increase in fuel efficiency in the industry has been assumed in Appendix Table A-11, no adjustment on this score is here required.

[c] Table H-21 shows a rapidly declining trend in the growth of electricity generated per barrel of runs-to-stills. It is assumed that growth will cease altogether, and that generation will therefore be in step with runs-to-stills, or rise by 90 per cent above the 1955 level (see Appendix Table A-16, footnote a). However, since no improvement has been assumed in thermal efficiency of fuels used for all purposes in refineries (see Appendix Table A-16, footnote a), there must be provision here for the general assumption that thermal efficiency of fuel used in electricity generation will increase by 1.25 per cent per year between 1955 and 1975—or 28.24 per cent in twenty years (Table H-18, footnote b), and that electricity generation will therefore exceed by this factor the increase in runs-to-stills. Thus the increase will be: $(190 \times 128.2) - 100 = 143.58$.

[d] Based upon the almost stationary level of generation in recent years (Table H-22, col. 1). As brought out in Table H-23, the industry is composed of units generating all their power, those purchasing all their power, and those generating and purchasing. It is presumed that the recent lack of growth in generation is due to concentration of output in that portion of the industry which purchases its power, and that this development will continue.

TABLE H-20. ELECTRICITY GENERATION IN THE IRON AND
STEEL INDUSTRY, 1946-56

Year	Total steel production[a] (tons)	Electricity generated and used[b] (million kwh)	Kwh generated and used per ton of steel	Kwh generated per ton of steel in Census years[c]
1956......	115,216,149	11,540	100.16	
1955......	117,036,085	11,610	99.20	
1954......	88,311,652	10,280	116.40	148.77
1953......	111,609,719	10,630	95.24	
1952......	93,168,039	8,686	93.23	
1951......	105,199,848	9,241	87.84	
1950......	96,836,075	8,976	92.69	
1949......	77,978,176	8,124	104.18	
1948......	88,640,470	9,766	110.18	
1947......	84,894,071	9,204	108.42	120.35
1946......	66,602,724	8,030	120.56	

[a] AISI, *Annual Statistical Report, 1956*, p. 51.

[b] *Ibid.*, p. 23, for 1947-56. For 1946, *Annual Statistical Report, 1955*, p. 23. This series excludes electricity generated and sold, but in the absence of data relating to sales it has been assumed that the series is representative of total generation. The Census data for 1947 and 1954 show a relative increase of "generated" versus "generated and used," but not sufficiently to make the use of the latter series misleading.

[c] Census, *Census of Manufactures, 1954*, Vol. I, p. 208-15 (electricity generated in industries 331, 332, and 339 per ton of steel as shown in column 1); and *Census of Manufactures, 1947*, Vol. I, p. 213 (electricity generated in industries 331, 332, and 339 per ton of steel as shown in column 1).

TABLE H-21. ELECTRICITY GENERATION IN PETROLEUM
REFINING, 1939, 1947, AND 1954

Year	Runs-to-stills[a] (million bbls.) (1)	Electricity generated[b] (million kwh) (2)	Electricity generated per barrel of runs to stills (kwh) (3)	Percentage increase over previous Census year (4)
1954..............	2,540	4,023	1.5839	6%
1947..............	1,852	2,765	1.4930	38
1939..............	1,238	1,339	1.0816	

[a] Mines, *Minerals Yearbook, 1955*, Vol. II, p. 315; *ibid., 1949*, p. 864; and *ibid., 1941*, p. 1023.

[b] Census, *Census of Manufactures, 1954*, Vol. I, *Summary Statistics*, p. 208-13; *ibid., 1947*, Vol. I, *General Summary*, p. 211; and *ibid., 1939*, Vol. I, *General Summary*, p. 307.

TABLE H-22. ELECTRICITY GENERATION IN THE CEMENT INDUSTRY, 1934-57

Year	Electricity generated [a] (million kwh) (1)	Portland cement produced [b] (thousand bbls.) (2)	Kwh generated per barrel (3)
1957	2,243	298,424	7.516
1956	2,326	316,438	7.351
1955	2,435	297,453	8.186
1954	2,209	272,353	8.111
1953	2,202	264,180	8.335
1952	2,125	249,256	8.525
1951	2,198	246,022	8.934
1950	2,115	226,026	9.357
1949	1,987	209,727	9.474
1948	1,981	205,448	9.642
1947	1,894	186,519	10.154
1946	1,886	164,064	11.496
1945	1,119	102,805	10.885
1944	1,027	90,906	11.297
1943	1,473	133,424	11.040
1942	1,885	182,781	10.313
1941	1,720	164,031	10.486
1940	1,460	130,217	11.212
1939	1,386	122,259	11.337
1938	1,233	105,357	11.703
1937	1,424	116,175	12.257
1936	1,349	112,650	11.975
1935	888	76,742	11.571
1934	941	77,748	12.103

[a] Mines, *Minerals Yearbook* for following years: *1957*, Vol. I, p. 314, Table 13; *1955*, Vol. I, p. 287, Table 14; *1953*, Vol. I, p. 294, Table 13; *1951*, p. 257, Table 16; *1949*, p. 218, Table 16; *1947*, p. 219; *1945*, p. 1239; *1943*, p. 1263; *1941*, p. 1211; *1940*, p. 1124; *1939*, p. 1109; *1938*, p. 1005; and *1937*, p. 1157.

[b] *Ibid.*, for following years: *1956*, Vol. I, p. 296, Table 1; *1951*, p. 244, Table 1; *1946*, p. 208; *1941*, p. 1192; and *1938*, p. 990.

TABLE H–23. ELECTRICITY GENERATION AND USE IN CEMENT
PRODUCTION BY TYPE OF MILL, 1955

Item	Mills with all self-generated electricity	Mills generating and purchasing electricity	Mills not generating electricity	Total
1. Per cent of cement production	9.66%	32.36%	57.98%	
2. Number of plants...........	13	49	95	
3. Production (thous. bbl.).....	28,741	96,261	172,451	297,455
4. Electricity (thous. kwh):				
a. Purchased.............	0	468,349	3,553,720	4,022,069
b. Generated.............	660,045	1,775,195	0	2,435,241
c. Total................	660,045	2,243,544	3,553,720	6,457,310
d. Used per bbl. of production..........	22.965	23.307	20.607	21.709
e. Generated per bbl. of production........	22.965	18.442	0	8.186

SOURCE: Based on special tabulation of Mines.

TABLE H–24. ESTIMATED HEAT RATE, 1975[a]

Source	Billion kwh generated (1)	Quantity of fuel (2)	Btu per unit of fuel (3)	Billion Btu (4)	Btu per kwh (5)
Coal....	1,300	488 million tons	24 million per ton	11,712,000	9,009
Gas....	200	1,700 billion cu. ft.	1,000 per cu. ft.	1,700,000	8,500
Oil.....	91	143 million bbls.	6.3 million per bbl.	900,900	9,900
Hydro[b].					8,954

[a] Basic data (kwh and fuel quantities) from Philip Sporn, "Electric Power in Peace and in Defense," exhibits presented in connection with a talk given before the Industrial College of the Armed Forces, Washington, D. C., February 7, 1957, figure (d)–5. (Note: The Btu values in col. 3 are those applied also for 1955 generation in Table H–2, footnote c, but rounded.)

[b] Computed on the basis of Sporn's material as the weighted average of the above, using the fuel composition assumed in this study as given in Table H–15. This rate thus is the over-all heat rate.

TABLE H-25. OVER-ALL HEAT RATE IN UTILITY GENERATION, 1925-56

Year	Btu input per net kwh output	Year	Btu input per net kwh output
1956	11,456	1940	16,400
1955	11,699	1939	16,700
1954	12,180	1938	17,450
1953	12,889	1937	17,850
1952	13,361	1936	17,800
1951	13,641		
		1935	17,850
1950	14,030	1934	17,950
1949	15,033	1933	18,150
1948	15,738	1932	18,450
1947	15,600	1931	18,800
1946	15,700		
		1930	19,800
1945	15,800	1929	20,550
1944	15,850	1928	21,500
1943	16,000	1927	22,600
1942	16,100	1926	23,600
1941	16,550	1925	25,175

SOURCE: E.E.I., 1926-53: *Statistical Bulletin for the Year 1954*, p. 41, Table 33; 1925 and 1954-56, *ibid., 1957*, p. 47, Table 40.

TABLE H-26. RATES OF INCREASE IN THERMAL EFFICIENCY OF ELECTRICITY GENERATION, 1925-55[a] AND PROJECTION TO 1955-75[b]

Period	Approximate annual rates of increase (per cent)
1955-75	1.35%
1950-55	3.5
1945-50	2.25
1940-55	2.25
1940-45	0.75
1935-55	2.0
1935-40	1.75
1930-55	2.0
1930-35	2.0
1925-30	5.0

[a] Based on Table H-25.
[b] Based on comparison of rates implied in Table H-2 for 1955—11,750 Btu per kwh—(*cf.* footnote d) and Table H-24 for 1975—8,954 Btu per kwh.

Section I. General data and summary tables

General Note

Table I–1 is a summary of the basic economic assumptions. Population, number of households, and gross national product are used as such in various projections. Table I–2 provides background material for the population projection. Tables I–3 to I–6 do the same for households, and Tables I–7 to I–9 for labor force and hours of work.

With Table I–10, there begins a group of miscellaneous tables that are germane to more than one of the sections of Part II. Table I–10 provides the calculation on which the division of gasoline into that part derived from oil and that coming from natural gas production is based. Table I–11 shows the conversion rates used. Table I–12 gives historical data on bituminous coal markets, and Table I–13 presents a comprehensive comparison of expected changes in markets for principal petroleum products.

General Data and Summary Tables

729

TABLE I-1. PROJECTION OF BASIC ECONOMIC PARAMETERS TO 1975

Item	Number 1955 (1)	Number 1975 (2)	Percentage increase (3)	Approximate annual rate of growth (per cent) (4)
Population [a]	165,271,000	233,000,000	41.2%	1.7%
Households [b]	47,788,000	68,878,000	44.1	1.9
Family	41,713,000	56,162,000	34.6	1.5
Primary individual	6,075,000	12,716,000	109.3	3.8
Labor force [c]	67,784,000	94,700,000	39.9	1.6
Labor force employed [d]	63,193,000	88,700,000	40.4	1.7
Hours of work per year [e]	2,080	1,872	−10.0	−0.5
Labor input (bill. man-hours)	131.4	166.0	26.3	1.2
Output per man-hour				2.8 [f]
GNP (billion 1955 $) [g]	$390.7	$857	119.1	4.0

[a] 1955: Table I-2; 1975: see Chapter 5, pp. 195–98.

[b] 1955: Tables I-3 through I-6; 1975: see Chapter 5, pp. 198–99.

[c] 1955: Tables I-7 and I-8; 1975: see Chapter 5, pp. 199–200.

[d] 1955: Table I-9; 1975: assuming armed force of 2.2 million and 4 per cent unemployment.

[e] 1955: Table I-9; 1975: assuming 10 per cent decline from 1955 (see Chapter 5, p. 200).

[f] Implicit in 4 per cent GNP growth rate combined with 1.2 per cent rate of increase in labor input, see Chapter 5, *ibid.*

[g] 1955: Appendix Table D-12; 1975: assuming 4 per cent growth rate, see Chapter 5, pp. 194-95.

TABLE I-2. SOME ACTUAL AND PROJECTED POPULATION LEVELS, 1950–75

(Thousands)

Source and date	1950 (1)	1955 (2)	1960 (3)	1965 (4)	1970 (5)	1975 (6)
Actual (July 1)	151,683	165,271				
National Resources Committee (1937–38): [a]						
Highest	146,829	153,605	160,246	166,923	173,657	180,325
Preference range—						
High	141,645	145,508	149,372	152,421	154,969	156,977
Low	137,084	138,721	139,457	139,372	138,455	136,680
Whelpton (June 1947): [b]						
Generally used	145,460	149,840	153,375	156,692	159,847	162,337
Highest	147,986	155,126	162,011	169,270	177,118	185,071
Lowest	144,922	147,990	149,827	151,047	151,627	151,090
Census Bureau:						
February 1949 [c]	149,886	155,745				
	149,386	154,669				
August 1950 [d]						
Series I		166,179	180,276			
Series II		161,748	169,371			
Series III		158,176	161,679			
Recent Census projections: [e]						
Series AA			179,358	193,346	209,380	228,463
Series A		164,782	177,840	190,296	204,620	221,522
Series B		164,782	177,840	190,296	202,984	214,580
Series C		164,644	176,452	186,291	196,370	206,907
Series D		164,403	173,847	180,927	189,110	198,632

TABLE I-2 (continued)

ᵃ"Highest": High fertility, low mortality, and net immigration of 200,000 per year (National Resources Committee, *Population Statistics,* 1. *National Data,* October 1937, p. 21).

"Preference range": (designated by Committee) High-medium mortality, medium fertility, and 100,000 net immigration; low-medium mortality, low fertility, and no net immigration (NRC, *The Problems of a Changing Population,* May 1938, p. 24).

ᵇ P. K. Whelpton, *Forecasts of the Population of the United States, 1945–1975,* Commerce, 1947, p. 41, Table 28. Note: "Generally used" selected for "special" attention in Table 27 of his text, for example; and "highest" devised to take into account the "spectacular rise" in the birth rate from June to December 1946. His assumptions are: generally used—medium fertility, medium mortality and no net immigration; highest—highest fertility, lowest mortality, 15,000,000 births in 1945–50, and 200,000 annual net immigration; and lowest—lowest fertility, highest mortality, no immigration.

ᶜ Census, *Current Population Reports,* Series P-25, No. 18, designed as revision of Whelpton projection. Links actual number of births for the year ending June 1947 with the Whelpton medium number of births projected for the year ending June 1955. High projection includes net immigration of 1,000,000 (July 1, 1948 to 1955).

ᵈ *Ibid.,* No. 43. Series I: low mortality; high fertility (1948 rate, except for 1949–50); net immigration at 450,000 per year for 1949–50; 400,000 per year during 1950–55; and 350,000 per year during 1955–60. Series II: medium mortality; medium fertility; and net immigration of 350,000 per year during 1949–50 and 200,000 per year to 1960. Series III: high mortality; low fertility; no net immigration.

ᵉ AA through C for 1960 through 1975 are from *ibid.,* No. 123, October 20, 1955. Series A through C for 1955 and all of Series D are from *ibid.,* No. 78, August 1953. Assumptions are as follows:

Census designation	Fertility	Mortality	Immigration
AA	Continuation through 1975 of 1954–55 specific age fertility rates.	Reduction in rates up to 1955–60. No change thereafter.	July 1955 to July 1960: 1.4 million; thereafter 240,000 per year.
A	Continuation through 1975 of 1950–53 specific age fertility rates.	Same as AA	Same as AA
B	Continuation through 1965 of 1950–53 specific age fertility rates; thereafter linear decline to the 1940–42 rates by 1975.	Same as AA	Same as AA
C	Linear decrease in specific age fertility rates from 1950–53 levels to 1940–42 level, beginning immediately, ending in 1975.	Same as AA	Same as AA
D	Decrease from 1950–53 specific age fertility rates beginning immediately, to be reached in 1960; no change thereafter.	Same as AA	Same as AA

TABLE I-3. NUMBER AND TYPES OF HOUSEHOLD UNITS,
APRIL 1955 AND PROJECTION TO JULY 1975

(Thousands)

Type of household	Actual	Projection					
	April 1955 (1)	Series I (2)	Series II (3)	Series III (4)	Series IV (5)	Difference between Series I and Series IV (6)	Percentage of difference attributable to each category (7)
Primary families:							
Husband-wife.....	36,266	49,545	48,391	47,584	46,462	3,083	
Other male head...	1,303	1,295	1,169	1,329	1,497	−202	
Female head......	4,144	4,822	5,191	5,373	5,476	−654	
Total...........	41,713	55,662	54,751	54,286	53,435	2,227	38.44%
Primary individuals:							
Male...........	2,019	3,012	2,833	2,555	2,376	636	
Female..........	4,056	8,704	8,896	7,471	5,773	2,931	
Total...........	6,075	11,716	11,729	10,026	8,149	3,567	61.56
Total households....	47,788	67,378	66,480	64,312	61,584	5,794	100.00%

SOURCE: Derived from Census, *Current Population Reports*, Series P–20, No. 69, p. 4, Table 3.

TABLE I-4. HOUSEHOLDS, BY PRIMARY FAMILIES AND PRIMARY
INDIVIDUALS, ACTUAL AND PROJECTED, SELECTED YEARS 1940–75

(Thousands)

Years	All households (1)	Primary family households (2)	Primary individual households (3)	Primary individual households as per cent of total households (4)
Actual:[a]				
April 1940......	34,949	31,491	3,458	9.89%
April 1947......	39,107	34,964	4,143	10.59
April 1951......	44,656	39,487	5,169	11.58
April 1955......	47,788	41,713	6,075	12.71
March 1956.....	48,785	42,548	6,237	12.78
Projected:[b]				
July 1960.......	51,838	44,556	7,282	14.05
July 1965.......	56,145	47,585	8,560	15.25
July 1970.......	61,378	51,325	10,053	16.38
July 1975.......	67,378	55,662	11,716	17.39

[a] Census, *Current Population Reports*, Series P–20, No. 68, p. 4.
[b] *Ibid.*, No. 69, p. 4, series I.

TABLE I-5. PRIMARY AND SECONDARY UNRELATED INDIVIDUALS, ACTUAL AND PROJECTED, SELECTED YEARS 1940-75

(Thousands)

Year	Total unrelated individuals [a] (1)	Primary individuals (households) [b] (2)	Secondary individuals [c] (3)	Primary individuals (households) as per cent of total (4)
1940..........	9,277	3,458	5,819	37.27%
1947..........	8,491	4,143	4,348	48.79
1951..........	9,510	5,169	4,341	54.35
1955..........	9,790	6,075	3,715	62.05
1956..........	9,897	6,237	3,660	63.02
1960..........	10,912	7,282	3,630	66.73
1965..........	12,202	8,560	3,642	70.15
1970..........	13,898	10,053	3,845	72.33
1975..........	15,733	11,716	4,017	74.47

[a] The Census projection gives unrelated individuals fourteen years of age and over rather than all unrelated individuals. Total unrelated individuals fourteen years of age and over in the years through 1975 was increased by the same relationship which total unrelated individuals had to unrelated individuals fourteen years of age and over in 1955. The factor was 1.017+.

[b] Households formed by household heads living alone or only with persons who are not related.

[c] Lodgers, guests, or resident employees who are not related to any person in the household.

SOURCE: 1940-56 (actual)—Census, *Current Population Reports*, Series P-20, No. 68, p. 4; 1960-75 (projected)—*ibid.*, No. 69, p. 4, series I.

TABLE I-6. SECONDARY AND TOTAL FAMILIES, ACTUAL AND PROJECTED, SELECTED YEARS 1940-75

(Thousands)

Year	Total (1)	Secondary (2)	Secondary as per cent of total (3)
1940..............	32,166	675	2.10%
1947..............	35,794	830	2.32
1951..............	39,929	442	1.11
1955..............	41,934	221	0.53
1956..............	42,843	295	0.69
1960..............	44,723	167	0.37
1965..............	47,728	143	0.30
1970..............	51,476	151	0.29
1975..............	55,819	157	0.28

SOURCE: 1940-56 (actual)—Census, *Current Population Reports*, Series P-20, No. 68, p. 4; 1960-75 (projected)—*ibid.*, No. 69, p. 4, series I. Secondary families obtained as the difference between all families and primary families.

TABLE I-7. ACTUAL VERSUS PROJECTED 1955 LABOR FORCE
PARTICIPATION RATES

Age and sex	Labor force (thousands)		Actual as per cent of projected (3)	Participation rates (per cent)		Actual as per cent of projected (6)
	Actual[a] (1)	Projected[b] (2)		Actual[a] (4)	Projected[b] (5)	
Both sexes, 14 years and over..	67,784	62,860	107.8%	57.2%	54.5%	105.0%
Male:						
14 years and over..	47,593	44,800	106.2	81.7	78.8	103.7
14 to 19 years.....	3,036	1,940	156.6	44.1	27.4	161.0
20 to 24 years.....	4,832	4,840	99.8	88.7	88.3	100.5
25 to 34 years.....	11,487	11,520	99.7	96.5	96.6	99.9
35 to 44 years.....	10,782	10,280	104.9	96.6	97.0	99.6
45 to 54 years.....	8,876	8,390	105.8	95.4	93.5	102.0
55 to 64 years.....	6,087	5,860	103.9	86.0	84.8	101.4
65 years and over..	2,490	1,970	126.4	38.2	33.6	113.7
Female:						
14 years and over..	20,191	18,060	111.8	33.5	30.9	108.4
14 to 19 years.....	1,611	910	177.0	24.2	13.3	182.0
20 to 24 years.....	2,358	2,870	82.2	43.9	54.2	81.0
25 to 34 years.....	4,227	4,860	87.0	34.5	41.0	84.1
34 to 44 years.....	4,745	3,990	118.9	40.9	35.6	114.9
45 to 54 years.....	4,051	3,240	125.0	42.6	34.6	123.1
55 to 64 years.....	2,382	1,760	135.3	32.2	24.2	133.1
65 years and over..	814	430	189.3	10.9	6.5	167.7

[a] Census, *Current Population Reports*, Series P-57, No. 154, p. 4.
[b] Projections adjusted for effect of World War II, from John D. Durand, *The Labor Force in the United States, 1890–1960* (New York: Social Science Research Council, 1948), p. 257.

TABLE I-8. ESTIMATES OF THE ANNUAL AVERAGE TOTAL
LABOR FORCE AND LABOR FORCE PARTICIPATION RATES,
PROJECTED FOR 1975 BY AGE AND SEX

Age and sex	Total labor force (millions)				Labor force participation rates (per cent)			
	I	II	III	IV	I	II	III	IV
Both sexes, 14 years and over.	93.4	93.7	91.4	89.8	58.8	59.0	57.5	56.5
Male, 14 years and over......	60.9	60.1	60.1	62.2	78.9	77.9	77.9	80.7
14 to 19 years.............	5.0	4.6	4.6	5.7	43.4	40.3	40.3	49.5
20 to 24 years.............	8.7	8.3	8.3	8.7	88.7	84.5	84.5	89.5
25 to 34 years.............	15.1	15.2	15.1	15.1	96.6	97.5	96.6	96.5
35 to 44 years.............	10.7	10.9	10.7	10.7	97.0	98.3	97.0	96.9
45 to 54 years.............	10.8	10.9	10.8	10.7	95.6	97.1	95.6	95.1
55 to 64 years.............	7.9	8.3	7.9	8.0	86.0	90.0	86.0	86.4
65 years and over..........	2.7	1.9	2.7	3.3	31.1	21.8	31.1	38.5
Female, 14 years and over....	32.5	33.6	31.3	27.6	39.8	41.1	38.3	33.7
14 to 19 years.............	3.1	3.0	3.0	3.3	27.9	27.1	27.1	30.2
20 to 24 years.............	5.0	4.4	4.4	4.4	52.5	46.4	46.4	45.8
25 to 34 years.............	6.6	6.0	6.0	5.4	42.7	39.1	39.1	34.8
35 to 44 years.............	5.8	5.7	5.8	4.6	51.7	50.9	51.7	41.4
45 to 54 years.............	6.4	7.6	6.4	5.2	53.3	62.8	53.3	43.5
55 to 64 years.............	4.3	5.3	4.3	3.4	40.8	50.1	40.8	32.2
65 years and over..........	1.4	1.6	1.4	1.2	11.4	13.4	11.4	10.3

NOTE: I: Projection of average annual rates of change in labor force participation rates
between 1920 and average of April 1954, 1955, and 1956. II: Projection of average
annual rates of change between 1950 and 1955. III: Use of Projection II rates for men
14 to 24 years and women 14 to 34 years, use of Projection I rates for other age groups.
IV: Continuation of 1955 labor force rates to 1975.

SOURCE: Census, *Current Population Reports*, Series P-50, No. 69, p. 5.

TABLE I-9. HOURS OF WORK, 1955 AND 1975

Item	Number
1955:	
1. Employed civilian labor force.....................................	63,193,000[a]
2. Annual average number employed but not at work during survey week.	2,932,000[b]
3. Average hours worked during survey week by those at work.........	41.9[c]
4. Approximate weekly hours worked by all employed $\frac{(\text{item 1} - \text{item 2}) \times (\text{item 3})}{(\text{item 1})}$	40.0
5. Approximate annual hours worked by all employed (item 4 × 52)....	2,080
1975:	
6. Weekly hours of work at 90 per cent of 1955.....................	1,872

[a] Census, *Current Population Reports*, Series P-50, No. 67, p. 3.
[b] *Ibid.*, p. 29, Table 14.
[c] *Ibid.*, No. 63, p. 1.

TABLE I–10. DERIVATION OF ALLOCATION BETWEEN CRUDE OIL
AND NATURAL GASOLINE OF TOTAL GASOLINE PRODUCTION, 1955

Item	Thous. bbl. and per cent
1. Production of finished gasoline and naphtha from crude oil[a]	1,204,481
Of which:	
a. Naphtha[b]	24,152
b. Finished gasoline	1,180,329
2. Gasoline admixture in jet fuel production[c]	43,262
3. Production of finished gasoline + jet fuel gasoline	1,223,591
4. Natural gas liquids used with gasoline	168,804
5. Total production of gasoline, including jet fuel, but excluding naphtha	1,392,395
6. NGL as per cent of total	12.12%
7. Allocation factor used	12%

[a] Mines, *Minerals Yearbook, 1956,* Vol. II, p. 389; excludes gasoline portion of jet fuel.
[b] *Ibid., 1955,* Vol. II, p. 382.
[c] *Ibid., 1956,* Vol. II, p. 374.

TABLE I–11. CONVERSION FACTORS

Fuel	Physical unit	Btu per unit
Bituminous coal	ton	26,200,000
Anthracite	ton	25,400,000
Gasoline (incl. natural)	barrel	5,208,000
Kerosine	barrel	5,670,000
Diesel oil and light distillates (No. 1 and No. 2 heating oil)	barrel	5,712,000
Heating oil:		
No. 3	barrel	5,880,000
No. 4	barrel	6,090,000
No. 5	barrel	6,237,000
No. 6	barrel	6,384,000
Residual (unclassified)	barrel	6,384,000
Petroleum coke	ton	30,000,000
Acid sludge	barrel	4,494,000
Refinery (or still) gas	cubic foot	1,500
Natural gas	cubic foot	1,035
Natural gas liquids (other than natural gasoline)	barrel	4,011,000

NOTE: Exceptions noted in Appendix Tables A–15, H–2, and H–24.

TABLE I-12. CONSUMPTION OF BITUMINOUS COAL, BY CLASS OF USER, 1933–56

Year	Electric power utilities [a] (1)	Bunker, foreign and lake vessel [b] (2)	Railroads (class I) [c] (3)	Beehive coke plants (4)	Oven coke plants (5)	Steel and rolling mills [d] (6)	Cement mills (7)	Other manufacturing and mining industries [e] (8)	Retail deliveries to other consumers [f] (9)	Total of classes shown [g] (10)
Part I (thous. net tons)										
1956	154,983	1,470	12,308	4,043	101,870	7,189	9,026	93,302	48,667	432,858
1955	140,550	1,499	15,473	2,869	104,508	7,353	8,529	89,611	53,020	423,412
1954	115,235	1,244	17,370	980	84,411	6,983	7,924	77,115	51,798	363,060
1953	112,283	1,839	27,735	8,226	104,648	8,764	8,167	95,160	59,976	426,798
1952	103,309	1,839	37,962	6,912	90,702	9,632	7,903	93,637	66,861	418,757
1951	101,898	2,220	54,005	11,418	102,030	11,260	8,507	103,188	74,378	468,904
1950	88,262	2,042	60,969	9,088	94,757	10,877	7,923	95,862	84,422	454,202
1949	80,610	2,056	68,123	5,354	85,882	10,529	7,966	96,629	88,389	445,538
1948	95,620	2,552	94,838	10,322	96,984	14,193	8,546	110,060	86,794	519,909
1947	86,009	3,087	109,296	10,475	94,325	14,195	7,919	123,928	96,657	545,891
1946	68,743	2,632	110,166	7,167	76,121	12,151	6,990	117,732	98,684	500,386
1945	71,603	3,192	125,120	8,135	87,214	14,241	4,203	126,562	119,297	559,567
1944	76,656	3,069	132,049	10,858	94,438	15,152	3,767	131,498	122,112	589,599
1943	74,036	3,042	130,283	12,441	90,019	15,864	5,842	142,149	120,121	593,797
1942	63,472	3,226	115,410	12,876	87,974	14,722	7,462	132,767	102,141	540,050
1941	59,888	3,304	97,384	10,529	82,609	15,384	6,735	121,880	94,402	492,115
1940	49,126	2,989	85,130	4,803	76,583	14,169	5,559	107,864	84,687	430,910
1939	42,304	2,764	79,072	2,298	61,216	13,843	5,194	100,637	68,770	376,098
1938	36,440	2,310	73,921	1,360	45,266	11,877	4,413	94,196	66,498	336,281
1937	41,045	3,433	88,080	4,927	69,575	18,148	5,182	124,056	76,331	430,777
1936	38,104	3,052	86,391	2,698	63,244	19,019	4,711	111,030	80,044	408,293
1935	30,936	2,683	77,109	1,469	49,046	16,585	3,456	94,598	80,444	356,326
1934	29,707	2,423	76,037	1,635	44,343	15,391	3,457	87,314	83,507	343,814
1933	27,088	2,298	72,548	1,408	38,681	14,129	2,760	81,377	77,396	317,685

(*Table continued on next page.*)

TABLE I-12 (continued)

Part II (per cent of total)

Year	Electric power utilities a (1)	Bunker, foreign and lake vessel b (2)	Railroads (class I) c (3)	Beehive coke plants (4)	Oven coke plants (5)	Steel and rolling mills d (6)	Cement mills (7)	Other manufacturing and mining industries e (8)	Retail deliveries to other consumers f (9)	Total of classes shown g (10)
					Manufacturing and mining industries					
1956	35.8%	.3%	2.8%	.9%	23.5%	1.7%	2.1%	21.6%	11.2%	100.0%
1955	33.2	.4	3.7	.7	24.7	1.7	2.0	21.2	12.5	100.0
1954	31.7	.4	4.8	.3	23.2	1.9	2.2	21.2	14.3	100.0
1953	26.3	.4	6.5	1.9	24.5	2.1	1.9	22.2	14.1	100.0
1952	24.7	.4	9.1	1.7	21.7	2.3	1.9	22.4	16.0	100.0
1951	21.7	.5	11.5	2.4	21.8	2.4	1.8	22.0	15.9	100.0
1950	19.4	.4	13.4	2.0	20.9	2.4	1.7	21.1	18.6	100.0
1949	18.1	.5	15.3	1.2	19.3	2.4	1.8	21.7	19.8	100.0
1948	18.4	.5	18.2	2.0	18.7	2.7	1.8	21.2	16.7	100.0
1947	15.8	.6	20.0	1.9	17.3	2.6	1.6	22.7	17.7	100.0
1946	13.7	.6	22.0	1.4	15.2	2.4	1.5	23.5	19.7	100.0
1945	12.8	.6	22.4	1.5	15.7	2.5	1.4	22.6	21.3	100.0
1944	13.0	.6	22.4	1.8	16.0	2.6	.8	22.3	20.7	100.0
1943	12.5	.5	21.9	2.1	15.2	2.7	.6	24.0	20.2	100.0
1942	11.8	.6	21.4	2.4	16.3	2.7	1.0	24.6	18.9	100.0
1941	12.2	.7	19.8	2.1	16.8	3.1	1.4	24.8	19.2	100.0
1940	11.4	.7	19.8	1.1	17.8	3.3	1.3	25.0	19.7	100.0
1939	11.2	.8	21.0	.6	16.3	3.3	1.4	26.8	18.3	100.0
1938	10.8	.7	22.0	.4	13.5	3.7	1.3	28.0	19.8	100.0
1937	9.5	.8	20.4	1.1	16.2	3.5	1.2	28.8	17.7	100.0
1936	9.3	.7	21.2	.7	15.5	4.2	1.2	27.2	19.6	100.0
1935	8.7	.8	21.6	.4	13.8	4.7	1.0	26.5	22.6	100.0
1934	8.6	.7	22.1	.5	12.9	4.7	1.0	25.4	24.3	100.0
1933	8.5	.7	22.8	.4	12.2	4.4	.9	25.6	24.4	100.0

a FPC.

b Given by Census as "ore and coal exchange."

c AAR. Represents consumption of bituminous coal and lignite for all uses, including locomotive, powerhouse, shop, and station fuel.

d Estimates based upon reports collected from a selected list of representative steel and rolling mills.

e Estimates based upon reports collected from a selected list of representative manufacturing plants.   Includes some coal shipped by truck from mine to final destination.

f Estimates based upon reports collected from a selected list of representative retailers.

g The total of classes shown approximates total consumption. The calculation of consumption from production, imports, exports, and changes in stocks is not as accurate as the "total of classes shown" because certain significant items of stocks are not included in year-end stocks. These items are: stocks on Lake and Tidewater docks; stocks at other intermediate storage piles between mine and consumer; and coal in transit.

SOURCE: Mines, *Mineral Industry Surveys*, MMS 2830, p. 99, Table 52.

TABLE I–13.   CONSUMPTION BY SECTORS OF PRINCIPAL PETROLEUM PRODUCTS, 1955 AND 1975

(Billion Btu)

Item	Total 1955 (1)	Total 1975 (2)	Gasoline 1955 (3)	Gasoline 1975 (4)	Diesel and all other distillates 1955 (5)	Diesel and all other distillates 1975 (6)	Kerosine 1955 (7)	Kerosine 1975 (8)	Residual 1955 (9)	Residual 1975 (10)
1. Industry[a]	2,666,390	4,621,319	46,651	46,651	316,322	526,510			1,333,253	1,996,188
a. Iron and steel, petroleum refining, and cement	1,715,547	3,124,478			49,106	95,015			696,277	977,493
b. Special industrial group	57,073	57,073			13,560	13,560			43,513	43,513
c. General industrial group	893,770	1,439,768	46,651	46,651	253,656	417,935			593,463	975,182
d. Via electricity									369,681[b]	728,627[b]
2. Commercial[c]	736,917	1,321,274			190,534	341,623			546,383	979,651
a. Via electricity									90,820[b]	167,955[b]
3. Households[d]	2,316,304	2,356,316			1,862,988	2,032,746	453,316	323,570	138,632[b]	260,330[b]
4. Transportation:										
a. Railroads[e]	518,575	699,122	41	47	464,449	699,075			59,216[f]	2,799[b]
b. Marine[e]	833,412	1,578,675	3,187	4,583	95,248	260,124			734,977	1,313,968
c. Automotive—										
Automobiles[g]	3,636,470	7,810,766	3,636,470	7,810,766						
Household[h]	3,272,822	7,029,691	3,272,822	7,029,691						
Government[h]	17,541	37,680	17,541	37,680						
General	346,108	743,395	346,108	743,395						
Trucks[i]	1,470,852	4,102,489	1,376,318	3,603,472	94,534	499,017				
Government[h]	62,574	123,073	58,553	108,102	4,021	14,971				
General	1,408,278	3,979,416	1,317,765	3,495,370	90,513	484,046				
Commercial buses, general[j]	79,787	84,161	35,519	17,759	44,268	66,402				
School and nonrevenue buses[k]	13,093	22,103	13,093	22,103						
Government[b]	9,328	15,739	9,328	15,739						
General	3,765	6,364	3,765	6,364						

(Table continued on next page.)

TABLE I-13 (continued)

Item	Total 1955 (1)	Total 1975 (2)	Gasoline 1955 (3)	Gasoline 1975 (4)	Diesel and all other distillates 1955 (5)	Diesel and all other distillates 1975 (6)	Kerosine 1955 (7)	Kerosine 1975 (8)	Residual 1955 (9)	Residual 1975 (10)
Motorcycles [l]	11,306	11,306	11,306	11,306						
Household	3,635	3,635	3,635	3,635						
Government [h]	401	401	401	401						
General	7,270	7,270	7,270	7,270						
d. Aviation [e]	134,538	1,126,307	134,289	142,970			249	983,337		
5. Government, civilian, excl. transportation [m]	25,295	73,803	25,295	73,803					16,333 [b]	32,658 [b]
a. Military	734,920	974,642	419,129	540,642	80,950	99,823	53,740	173,479	181,101	160,698
6. Agriculture [n]	515,173	765,518	400,000	594,378	74,434	110,604	40,739	60,536	8,997 [b]	7,465 [b]
7. Electricity [o]	629,594	1,199,833							629,594	1,199,833
8. Miscellaneous [p]	371,979	568,568	25,373	53,533	118,358	244,931	162,984	94,734	62,588	174,404
9. Losses [p]	60,142	130,778	60,142	130,778						
10. Total			6,186,813	13,052,791	3,342,085	4,880,855	711,028	1,635,656	3,541,981	5,824,742

[a] Total as shown includes in addition, petroleum coke, refinery gas, and acid sludge, as per Appendix Tables A-9 and A-23.
[b] Electricity generation. Included in total only in item 7; data from Appendix Tables H-9 and H-17.
[c] Appendix Tables B-1, B-4, H-9 and H-17.
[d] Appendix Tables C-6 and C-40.
[e] Appendix Table D-60.
[f] Including 5,131 for electricity generation, totaled only in item 7.
[g] Appendix Tables D-20 and D-40.
[h] Excluding military.
[i] Appendix Tables D-16 and D-40.
[j] Appendix Table D-29.
[k] Appendix Tables D-17 and D-42.
[l] Appendix Table D-18; totals differ slightly from Appendix Table D-18 because of rounding and conversion.
[m] Appendix Tables E-1 and E-8.
[n] Appendix Table F-3.
[o] Appendix Tables H-9 and H-17.
[p] Appendix Table G-1.

Section J. Comparative data, 1929-47

General Note

The six tables constituting this section describe the changes that we made in a Bureau of Mines study, *Production, Consumption, and Use of Fuels and Electric Energy in the United States in 1929, 1939, and 1947*, to construct consumption categories comparable to those constructed in this study for 1955 and 1975.

The principal changes consist of reworking the transportation sector to exclude losses in the transmission of electric energy, and of applying higher heat rates for electricity generation than used by the authors of the Bureau of Mines study. Finally, industrial consumption is derived as a residual after the two major corrections above and some minor ones have been made.

Comparative Data Tables, 1929, 1939, 1947

J-1. Energy Consumption in 1929, 1939, 1947, as Adjusted
J-2. Derivation of Btu's, Electric and Other
J-3. Consumption of Electricity by Sectors, Purchased and Generated
J-4. Consumption of Btu's, Excluding Electricity, by Sectors
J-5. Adjustment of Energy Consumption in Transportation Sector
J-6. Adjustment of Energy Consumption, All Other Sectors

TABLE J-1. ENERGY CONSUMPTION IN 1929, 1939, 1947, AS ADJUSTED

(Billion Btu)

Item	1947	1939	1929
1. Commercial and households (excl. transportation):			
a. Electric	1,764,767	968,861	669,023
b. Nonelectric	8,745,390	6,274,630	6,386,520
c. Total	10,510,157	7,243,491	7,055,543
d. Per cent of aggregate	30.17%	31.40%	28.26%
2. Transportation:			
a. Electric	173,515	169,221	253,735
b. Nonelectric	7,981,975	5,640,097	6,299,671
c. Total	8,155,490	5,809,318	6,553,406
d. Per cent of aggregate	23.41%	25.19%	26.25%
3. Industry:			
a. Electric	2,780,465	1,542,118	1,516,000
b. Nonelectric	9,671,315	6,252,353	7,798,489
c. Total	12,451,780	7,794,471	9,314,489
d. Per cent of aggregate	35.74%	33.79%	37.30%
4. All other:			
a. Electric	183,069	102,278	19,562
b. Nonelectric	3,538,990	2,116,300	2,026,020
c. Total	3,722,059	2,218,578	2,045,582
d. Per cent of aggregate	10.68%	9.62%	8.19%
5. Grand total:			
a. Electric	4,901,816	2,782,478	2,458,320
b. Nonelectric	29,937,670	20,283,380	22,510,700
c. Aggregate	34,839,486	23,065,858	24,969,020

SOURCES: Grand total from Table J-2; nonelectric data from Table J-4; and electric data from Table J-3.

TABLE J-2. DERIVATION OF BTU'S, ELECTRIC AND OTHER

(Billions)

Item	1947 [a]	1939 [b]	1929 [c]
1. Domestic production:			
a. Bituminous coal..............	16,522,350	10,298,300	14,016,710
b. Anthracite...................	1,452,630	1,307,770	1,875,230
c. Crude petroleum.............	10,770,520	7,336,780	5,842,470
d. Natural gas..................	6,345,300	3,513,660	2,847,370
e. Hydropower..................	1,418,050	874,670	806,880
f. Wood and wood waste.........	846,790	814,610	855,630
g. Total......................	37,355,640	24,145,790	26,244,290
2. Foreign trade and stock changes:			
a. Imports.....................	997,790	407,880	695,780
b. Exports.....................	3,007,370	1,471,770	1,510,840
c. Stock change adjustment.......	−128,890	+196,570	−347,860
d. Apparent disappearance (incl. waste)................	35,217,170	23,278,470	25,081,370
3. Electric and other energy:			
a. Utility electricity..............	4,399,440	2,377,630	2,036,340
b. Total, excl. utility electricity.....	30,817,730	20,900,840	23,045,030
c. Revised utility electricity [d].......	4,021,756	2,165,018	1,923,990
d. Revised apparent disappearance (incl. waste)................	34,839,486	23,065,858	24,969,020
e. Non-utility electricity..........	880,060	617,460	534,330
f. Total electricity (item 3c + item 3e)..........	4,901,816	2,782,478	2,458,320
g. Total nonelectric (item 3d − item 3f)..........	29,937,670	20,283,380	22,510,700

[a] Mines, Wm. H. Lyon and D. Colby, *Production, Consumption, and Use of Fuel and Electric Energy in the United States in 1929, 1939, and 1947*, Report of Investigations 4805, October 1951, p. 12, Table 4.

[b] *Ibid.*, p. 14, Table 5.

[c] *Ibid.*, p. 16, Table 6.

[d] Lyon and Colby use the following Btu per kwh (*ibid.*, p. 24, line 32): 1947, 17,065; 1939, 18,340; 1929, 21,750. According to E.E.I., Btu per kwh were 15,600 in 1947; 16,700 in 1939; and 20,550 in 1929. The Btu necessary to generate utility electricity, and therefore total Btu, were accordingly reduced.

TABLE J-3.   CONSUMPTION OF ELECTRICITY BY SECTORS,
PURCHASED AND GENERATED [a]   (Billion Btu)

Sector	1947	1939	1929
Transportation:			
Purchased............................	130,075	122,181	182,765
Generated............................	43,480	47,040	70,970
Total................................	173,515	169,221	253,735
Households and commercial (excl. transportation):			
Purchased............................	1,764,767	968,861	669,023
Industry:			
Purchased............................	1,943,845	971,698	1,052,640
Generated............................	836,580	570,420	463,360
Total................................	2,780,465	1,542,118	1,516,000
All other:			
Purchased............................	183,069	102,278	19,562
Grand total:			
Generated............................	880,060	617,460	534,330
Purchased............................	4,021,756	2,165,018	1,923,990
Total................................	4,901,816	2,782,478	2,458,320

[a] Btu's allocated to sectors at the revised central power station rates and the Btu's distributed in proportion to purchases as determined in the respective tables for each of the years. Therefore, transmission losses, etc., were distributed to purchases on a proportionate basis. The following is the set of percentages derived:

	1947	*1939*	*1929*
Transportation.................	3.23%	5.64%	9.50%
Domestic and commercial........	43.88	44.75	34.77
Miscellaneous and other.........	4.55	4.72	1.02
Industrial......................	48.33	44.88	54.71

No adjustments were made in the Btu requirements for non-utility generation and the amounts generated in each sector were assumed to be used in the sector; no allowance is made for sales of non-utility generation to utilities.

TABLE J-4.   CONSUMPTION OF BTU'S, EXCLUDING ELECTRICITY,
BY SECTORS

(Billions)

Item	1947	1939	1929
1. Total [a].......................	29,937,670	20,283,380	22,510,700
2. Transportation [b].............	7,981,975	5,640,097	6,299,671
3. Miscellaneous and losses [c]......	3,538,990	2,116,300	2,026,020
4. Households and commercial (excl. transportation)........	8,745,390 [d]	6,274,630 [e]	6,386,520 [f]
5. Item 2 through item 4.........	20,266,355	14,031,027	14,712,211
6. Remainder (industrial).........	9,671,315	6,252,353	7,798,489

[a] Table J-2, item 3g.

[b] Table J-5, item 5.

[c] Table J-6, item 11.

[d] Mines, Wm. H. Lyon and D. Colby, *Production, Consumption, and Use of Fuel and Electric Energy in the United States in 1929, 1939, and 1947*, Report of Investigations 4805, October 1951, p. 13, Table 4 (total minus electricity).

[e] *Ibid.*, p. 15, Table 5 (total minus electricity).

[f] *Ibid.*, p. 17, Table 6 (total minus electricity).

TABLE J-5. ADJUSTMENT OF ENERGY CONSUMPTION IN
TRANSPORTATION SECTOR

(Billion Btu)

Item	1947	1939	1929
1. Initial level, incl. electric[a].................	9,507,190	6,705,230	7,473,930
2. Electricity[b].............................	164,710	158,580	229,520
3. Nonelectric..............................	9,342,480	6,546,650	7,244,410
4. Reductions:			
a. Aggregate electricity transmission......	651,170[c]	401,170	367,270
b. Military aviation....................	37,050[d]		
c. Gasoline evaporation and handling loss..	64,890[e]	57,850	52,750
d. Two-thirds of non-highway gasoline.....	201,620[f]	163,840	90,260
e. Ten per cent of railroad fuel...........	373,715[g]	266,113	423,789
f. Nonrefinery use by oil companies[h]......	32,060	17,580	10,670
g. Item 4a through item 4f...............	1,360,505	906,553	944,739
5. Net nonelectric (item 3 − item 4g).........	7,981,975	5,640,097	6,299,671

[a] From Mines, Wm. H. Lyon and D. Colby, *Production, Consumption, and Use of Fuel and Electric Energy in the United States in 1929, 1939, and 1947*, Report of Investigations 4805, October 1951, Table on p. 4.

[b] *Ibid.*, Tables 4, 5, and 6, sums of Btu's in self-generated and purchased electricity as shown for transportation.

[c] *Ibid.*, Table 4, line 32; Table 5, line 32; Table 6, line 32, column headed "Pipeline and utility system usage and losses."

[d] *Ibid.*, Table 4, line 19, column headed "Army, Navy and Coast Guard."

[e] *Ibid.*, Table 4, line 19; Table 5, line 19; Table 6, line 19, column headed "Pipeline and utility system usage and losses."

[f] *Ibid.*, Table 4, line 19; Table 5, line 19; and Table 6, line 19. Assumed that two-thirds of "Non-highway, other" is not transportation.

[g] *Ibid.*, represents 10 per cent of total Btu's to railroads reduced by Btu's of purchased electricity: Table on p. 4 minus Table 4, line 32 (railroad column), for 1947; minus Table 5, line 32 (railroad column), for 1939; minus Table 6, line 32 (railroad column), for 1929.

[h] *Ibid.*, Table 4, line 23; Table 5, line 3 plus line 23; Table 6, line 3, column headed "Pipeline and utility system usage and losses."

TABLE J-6. ADJUSTMENT OF ENERGY CONSUMPTION,
ALL OTHER SECTORS

(Billion Btu)

Item	1947	1939	1929
1. Army, Navy, and Coast Guard[a]........	231,620	77,880	39,200
2. Nonfuel use[a].........................	1,345,340	829,670	659,270
3. Miscellaneous[a].......................	707,760	428,060	676,510
4. Row 1 through row 3..................	2,284,720	1,335,610	1,374,980
5. Electricity in row 4 above[a]............	170,620	93,370	16,970
6. Net of electricity.....................	2,114,100	1,242,240	1,358,010
7. Military aviation[b].....................	37,050		
8. Gasoline losses[b]......................	64,890	57,850	52,750
9. Portion of non-highway gasoline[b].......	201,620	163,840	90,260
10. Natural gas wasted and vented[c]........	1,121,330	652,370	525,000
11. Total (row 6 plus row 7 through row 10)..	3,538,990	2,116,300	2,026,020

[a] Under these designations in Tables 4, 5, and 6—less aviation. Mines, Wm. H. Lyon and D. Colby, *Production, Consumption, and Use of Fuel and Electric Energy in the United States in 1929, 1939, and 1947*, Report of Investigations 4805, October 1951.

[b] Subtracted from transportation in Table J-5.

[c] Designated as natural gas "self-consumed products (loss)" in Tables 4, 5, and 6 of Lyons and Colby, *op. cit.*

Index

NOTE: A large part of this index is grouped under the following key headings, representing the energy sources and commodities: Anthracite, Bituminous coal, Coal, Crude oil, Electricity, Fuel wood, Hydropower, Natural gas, and Natural gas liquids.

745